"COMMONWEALTH"
FIVE REIGNS
POSTAGE STAMP
CATALOGUE

14th EDITION

1980

©

Published by

Bridger & Kay, Limited

1980

ISBN   0/902 784/02/1

Printed in Univers 689 by
R. Ward & Sons Ltd., Printers and Stationers,
Dunston Industrial Estate, Gateshead, Tyne and Wear, England.

FOREWORD

Thanks to the unstinted devotion of our colleagues — Neil Donaldson, John Dixey, Steve Papworth and Donald Smith — we are at last able to publish this long awaited catalogue. To these gentlemen who persevered through the long hot summer and deep snows at our Suffolk retreat, and also Cyril McBrine, the harassed printer, my gratitude.

We would also like to thank the many collectors and professional stamp dealers who have helped us to put so much new information into this edition. It is difficult to mention all of those who have helped, but we would particularly thank those who have been very generous with their time — K. Baker, H. F. Deakin, G. C. Horsman, W. Frazer, S. Goldblatt, F. M. Johnson, Miss K. Lamble, Dr. J. M. Lockie, M. H. Ludington, J. B. Marriott, J. L. Messenger, J. N. Michael amongst many others. Without the extensive listings and cataloguing which we were able to obtain from the work prepared by the late Mr. P. E. Gravenor of Messrs. Ewens, a lot of the finer detail of printings and shades would not have been possible. Perhaps most especially we would like to thank Mr. B. P. Purcell for his superb listing of Samoa and we do hope that although this listing is purposely not, as specialised as some would wish, the final result will be helpful to those starting this interesting country.

We must apologise for the delay in producing this fourteenth edition of the Commonwealth Catalogue, but a lot of new work has had to be included and this has taken longer than we anticipated. But more than this, repricing which we have had to do, even now as late as mid May 1979 to keep in touch with the present stamp market has held things up considerably. But judging by the recent auction realisations both in this country and in Europe, it is obvious that there is a new and growing demand for British Colonials, mainly in the section of George V and perhaps the more popular sets such as the Centenaries. We have endeavoured to reflect the present market trend although doubtless these prices will soon be out of date.

It is our intention over the course of the next few years to add further countries to make the listing virtually complete. We hope to add a simplified listing of Australian states, and although at present there is no intention to prepare Indian Native States or the Japanese Occupation issues, it may be possible that these could be included if a suitable volunteer were to offer his services.

May we ask those collectors who find this volume interesting and of help in forming their collection to kindly let us have their names and addresses so that we can inform them when further additions and countries are added to the present listing.

We include a new feature in this catalogue, the listing of G.B. stamps used abroad, departing from the normal procedure in so far as they are listed in front of the countries to which they refer, rather than complete listing at the end of G.B.

It is hoped that the repricing of the GKVI section will be helpful to collectors of this particular group. The scarcity of the rare stamps is at last beginning to be reflected in auction, but even the straightforward sets to the top value are becoming difficult to find and we confidently expect that the present level will increase as a result of this new pricing. It will be noted that in the King George V high value tablet type we have listed a number of the plate flaws. In this connection we strongly recommend reading the re-issue of the Ludington Bermuda book, as the illustrations and write up which has been included in this revised edition cover the subject very fully. The size and clarity of the illustrations make the collecting of these particularly straightforward.

If you collect Q.E.II issues we very strongly recommend the companion volume to this catalogue which is published by Urch Harris of Bristol. Over the years we have jointly made a particular point of ensuring that the catalogue numbers coincide, one catalogue running naturally into the other. In some cases there is overlapping, but we feel that the two catalogues taken together should make a complete pricing and catalogue listing of the whole British Commonwealth, second to none.

May, 1979.   A.L.

INDEX

Terms of Business

We regret we are no longer able to undertake to supply stamps on approval against want lists. If you have a firm order to place for stamps listed in this catalogue — please write and advise details — we will then let you know our stock situation and price required for any stamps available.

We prepare frequent lists of special offers of British Commonwealth issues and we would be pleased to send a sample selection of these offers — stamped addressed envelope would be appreciated. Overseas air mail postage is normally charged to client. We will gladly send quotations for stamps not listed in our catalogue. It would be appreciated if a duplicate list of your wants could be sent to enable us to keep a record of our quotations.

GUARANTEE. All stamps sold by us are fully guaranteed to be genuine in every respect. We are perfectly willing to grant an extension of two months for any rare item for which the buyer may require an Expert Certificate, but arrangements have to be fully agreed at the time of purchase, and it is normal practice for us to expect the full payment to be held by us as a deposit pending the Expert Committee decision.

EXAMINATION OF STAMPS

We are willing to give opinions on stamps listed in this catalogue, providing the Owner submits stamps by registered post, together with a fee of £4 per stamp, plus return postage, all responsibility and insurance for the stamp whilst in our possession being at Owner's risk.

We recognise certificates given by certain Expert Committees. The main British Expert Committees are:—**B.P.A. Expertising Ltd.,** No. 1, Whitehall Place, London SW1A 2HE and the **Royal Philatelic Society,** 41 Devonshire Place, London W1N 1PE.

INSURANCE

All sendings we make are covered by our transit insurance policy up to the time they are received by the client, but unless special arrangements are made, stamps are not insured whilst in the client's possession. All material on approval being returned to us is covered in transit if sent by registered post (and by Air Mail from overseas).

We regret that we are unable to undertake the work of numbering stamps according to our, or any other, catalogue

---

PRICES

Unless otherwise indicated the prices in the first column are for unused stamps and those in the second column are for postally used stamps. Prices are for good copies in well-centred condition. Pricing of unmounted mint stamps cannot be entertained, as we consider this quite impracticable.

SETS. These normally contain cheapest varieties of perf. or shade, and as a general rule there is no individual catalogue number given for each stamp in the set. For the convenience of collectors the OMNIBUS sets are listed and priced at the end of this catalogue.

INTRODUCTION

PAID FRANKS. In order to avoid frequent repetition in the text we illustrate the three typical types of PAID Franks.

Crowned Double Circle	Crowned Single Circle	Uncrowned Single Circle
(to June 1852)	(from June 1852)	(from 1858)

It should be noted that, as these Franks were hand cut, there are many variations in the shape of the Crown and in the size of the letters.

PRE GEORGE VI STAMPS

In order to retain the old K.G. VI numbers, we have allotted prefixed numbers to the issues of earlier reigns:—

V — Queen Victoria issues.
E — King Edward VII issues.
G — King George V issues.

We have not continued the practice of giving special and commemorative issues an 'S' prefix, but have listed these in chronological order.

ABBREVIATIONS. With the object of making lists not only complete but as concise as possible, where necessary the following abbreviations have been made: **Colours.** Bright—bt, Deep—dp, Black—blk, Brown—brn, Carmine—car, Green—grn, Grey—gr, Magenta —mag, Purple—pur, Scarlet—scar, Ultramarine—ult, Violet—vio, Yellow—yel, Fluorescent Aniline—F.A. **Printing.** Later Printings—L.P., Line-engraved (*recess*), Photogravure (*photo*), Rotogravure (*roto*), Typographed (*typo*). **Paper.** Ordinary—**O,** Chalk-surfaced— (ch) or **C,** Substitute—(Sub). **Perforation.** Comb—(C), Line—(L), **Format.** Horizontal— H, Vertical—V.

SHADES. It will facilitate the identification of catalogued shades if it is borne in mind that shade designations are fixed in relation to stamps in the same set. For instance, a stamp may be listed as yellow-green but it may differ from a stamp in another set also classified thus, but it will be yellow-green compared with the other stamp in the same set, of which it is a shade variation. Another point to remember is that the following scale of density is always followed: Pale, Light, Normal, Deep, Dark.

Where stamps are printed on coloured paper the list indicates—e.g.—'black/green'. 'Black and green' indicates a stamp printed in those colours on white paper.

PAPER. Collectors now realise how important it is, from a philatelic standpoint, to differentiate between the various kinds of papers which were used for K.G. V and K.G. VI stamps. Some issues are to be found with various coloured papers and also in certain cases the back of the paper varies quite considerably from yellow to white and even pale green to bright emerald. These differences are mainly due to the shortages of paper during the first and second world wars. Different coloured papers are also sometimes used for security reasons—to stop cleaning and re-use. During the war certain Postage Due stamps were printed on a rough paper which can readily be distinguished by touch. Chalk coated paper (*ch*) (if rubbed with silver, a lead-pencil like mark remains) was replaced for a period by a substitute paper (*sub*) which was uncoated, and on which no mark is left by silver. **A piece of clean rubber will remove a mark made by the silver test.**

GUM. It is normal for the late issues of Queen Victoria and most K.E. VII and K.G. V issues to have a clear whitish gum but this is sometimes toned as a result of climatic conditions. However, some stamps, especially K.G. V high value key type issues, have a thicker brown gum; this also applies to the early printings of K.G. VI which usually have a more yellowish thick gum than the post-war issues, which have a clear shiny gum, Of course the climatic effect on gums in hot or humid countries must be allowed for— some of the high value issues made during the difficult war years have a streaky yellow gum, which was made up specially from glue when the more normal Arabic gum was not available.

WATERMARKS. All Watermarks are illustrated as they appear from the **front** of the stamp. The following Watermarks are common to most Crown Colonies and other Territories and are illustrated here for convenience. Unless otherwise indicated, all K.G. VI Colonial issues are on Multiple Script C.A. watermark.

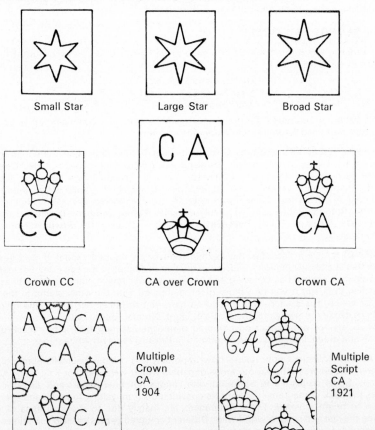

Small Star   Large Star   Broad Star

Crown CC   CA over Crown   Crown CA

Multiple Crown CA 1904   Multiple Script CA 1921

Certain stamps printed in 1950-52 showed variations in the Multiple Script CA watermark. These arose from damage to two of the Dandy Rolls used for impressing the watermark into the paper; on one a Crown 'bit' was lost from a Crown only row (Type A), whereas on the other the Crown 'bit' was lost from a Crown CA row (Type B). In both cases the missing Imperial Crown 'bit' was subsequently replaced by a Crown of different shape, the St. Edward's Crown (reduced size illustrations).

Type A

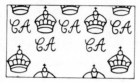 

Crown Missing   St. Edward's Crown

Postage stamps of Johore and Seychelles. Postage Due stamps of Barbados, Basutoland, British Guiana, Gold Coast, Grenada, Northern Rhodesia, St. Lucia, Swaziland and Trinidad & Tobago.

Type B

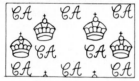 

Crown Missing   St. Edward's Crown

Postage stamps of Bahamas, British Guiana, St. Kitts-Nevis and Singapore.

The position in the sheet of the stamp affected varies as between Types A and B and also according to the size of the stamps and sheet layout; but, in the case of the Type A variety on Postage Due Stamps, this will invariably be found within the fifth and sixth vertical rows of the sheet (6 x 10).

PERFORATION. In detailing the perforations the first figure refers to the horizontal and the second figure to the vertical: thus, 'Perf 15 x 14' means that the perforations measure 15 at top and bottom and 14 at both sides. Mixed perforations are indicated in the order—top, right, bottom and left.

SHEETS. In describing the make-up of sheets the first figure gives the number of **vertical columns** and the second figure the number of **horizontal rows**—e.g. 12 x 20 means the sheet is made up of 20 horizontal rows each of 12 stamps.

SHEET POSITIONS. The position of the sheet of a stamp with a listed variety is indicated as for instance Row 1/2. The 1 signifies the first horizontal row and the 2 the second stamp on that row, and so on.

DE LA RUE COLONIAL KEYPLATE DIES

In the interests of economy many Colonial territories used a common Head and frame design, the individual territory name and the denomination being printed at a separate operation.

The common 'Keyplate' was re-drawn when new plates were made and, in order to elucidate references to Die I and Die II in the text, they are here illustrated.

A*

Die I
(Plates 1 and 2)

Die II
(Plates 3 and 4)

(1) The diadem jewel immediately above and behind the left eye is heavily shaded.

(1) The jewel is virtually unshaded and shows almost white.

(2) The front lower lock of hair on the bun is shaded.

(2) The lock appears almost entirely white.

(3) The vertical outline of the throat traverse six lines of shading below the chin.

(3) The outline is extended downwards to the eighth line of shading.

There are many other minor differences between the two Dies.

Die I

Die II

Lines of shading appear to the right of the jewel in the band of the coronet.

There is no shading to the right of the jewel.

There are many other minor differences between the two Dies.

Die I **Die II**

(1) The break in the thick line either side of the crown conforms to the shape of the crown extending somewhat similarly to the shape of the bow of a sailing ship.

(2) There is a bud in each side of the filigree work lower left and right corners.

(3) The side panels inscribed POSTAGE AND REVENUE are square at top.

(1) The thick line either side of the crown finishes in a vertical cut.

(2) There is no bud either side in the filigree work lower left and right corners.

(3) The side panels inscribed POSTAGE AND REVENUE are thickened at top to taper inwards towards the centre.

With very few exceptions, as indicated in the text, Die I appears on Multiple Crown CA issues and Die II on Multiple Script CA issues.

SYMBOLS USED. The following sybmols have been used in this catalogue:—

† — Does not (or cannot) exist.
— — Pricing is impracticable.
* — Used in a heading drawing attention to a general foot-note.

SPECIMENS. Not all Specimens listed were for UPU distribution. Full details of specimen stamps are contained in "Specimen Stamps of the Crown Colonies 1857-1948" by Marcus Samuel, published by The Royal Philatelic Society 1976 and available from Bridger & Kay Ltd.

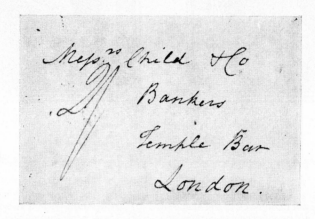

GREAT BRITAIN

Apart from their principal use in the British Isles, many of the stamps of Great Britain were used from 1854 onwards in a variety of overseas territories. A wide range of colonies including Ascension, Cyprus, Gibraltar, Malta and the West Indian possessions used them prior to the issue of their own stamps; and such use may be recognised by the type of postal cancellation.

Additionally they were used in a number of British Post Offices established in foreign territories which did not then have their own Postal Services. These included the old Turkish Empire, Egypt (see under British Levant), South and Central American Republics and Morocco Agencies (q.v.). They were also, and still are, used by British Forces engaged in overseas operations. In all these cases the postal cancellation or marking is the only proof of such use.

1840 (May 6-8)-**41** (*Recess*) **Perkins Bacon. Wmk. Small Crown. Imperf. Sheets 12 x 20. Each stamp in the sheet bears a different combination of Check letters in the lower corners.**

**Row   1 A-A : A-B etc. to A-L
        2 B-A : B-B etc. to B-L
       20 T-A : T-B etc. to T-L**

V1	1d.	**black**	.. .. ..	£2000	£175
V2	1d.	**grey-black** (worn plate)	£2200	£195
V3	2d.	**blue** (May 8) ..	£3250	£185
V4	2d.	**pale blue**	£3250	£200

The 1d. stamp was printed from Plates 1–11. Plate 1 being known in its original (1a) and repaired (1b) states.

Plate			Plate		
1a	£3000	£275	6	£2000	£185
1b	£2000	£185	7	£2200	£200
2	£2000	£185	8	£2200	£200
3	£2250	£200	9	£2750	£225
4	£2000	£185	10	£3000	£300
5	£2000	£200	11	£3000	£1850

The 2d. stamp was printed from Plates 1 and 2.

Plate			Plate		
1	£3250	£185	2	£3750	£225

The 1d. stamp with letters "VR" in the upper corners was an Official Stamp prepared for use but not issued. Used copies are nevertheless known but are very rare (See VR 1 under OFFICIAL STAMPS).

1841 (Feb. 10th-March 13th)-**54 As before but the 2d. has white lines added below POSTAGE and above TWO PENCE.**

V5	1d.	**red-brown**	.. ..	£75	2·00
	a	"A" omitted ..	..	—	£5000

V6	1d.	**pl red-brown** (worn plate)	£95	4·50
V7	1d.	**lake-red** ..	£250	£45
V8	1d.	**orange-brown** ..	£150	£20
V9	2d.	**pale blue**	£850	£30
V10	2d.	**blue**	£675	£24
V11	2d.	**blue** (lavender head) ..	£4000	£240

V5*a* The Check letter "A" was omitted on stamp "BA" (Row 2/1) on Plate 77.

V11 This stamp was printed from Plate 4 and has become generally known as "violet-blue". In fact it is printed in a pale blue on paper with a lavender tint, most noticeable on the back.

The 1d. stamp was originally printed from the 1d. Black Plates Nos. 1b, 2, 5, 8, 9, 10 and 11; and, subsequently from Plates 12–175.

Plate			Plate		
1b	£1750	£80	9	£285	£25
2	£1000	£55	10	£285	£25
5	£300	£30	11	£285	£25
8	£285	£35			

An unissued trial printing of 8 sheets was made from Plate 11 in April 1841 on Dickinson silk-thread paper. Unused £850 (no gum).

The 2d. stamp was printed from Plates 3 and 4.

Plate			Plate		
3	£700	£30	4	£800	£24

See Note after V41 regarding the styles of lettering (the 'Alphabets') used for the corner Check letters on the recess printed stamps from 1840 to 1862.

1847-54 (*Embossed*) **Somerset House (from Die engraved at Royal Mint). Wmk. "VR" (6d. only). 10d. and 1/– on Dickinson silk-thread paper. Imperf. Sheets 6d. 40-two panes, each 5 x 4: 10d. 6 x 4: 1/– 5 x 4.**

V12	6d.	**mauve** (1/3/54) ..	£1450	£100
V13	6d.	**purple**	£1450	£100
V14	6d.	**violet**	£1650	£110
V15	10d.	**brown** (6/11/48) ..	£1350	£185
V16	1/–	**pl green** (11/9/47) ..	£1800	£95
V17	1/–	**deep green**	£2000	£120

These stamps were printed one at a time on the sheet and impressions are frequently badly spaced, causing overlapping. Double impressions of all values exist. In later printings of the 6d. the gum was green tinted.

The wmk. on the 6d. stamp may be found upright, inverted, reversed and inverted reversed.

The 6d. stamp was printed from Die 1 only.

The 10d. stamp was printed Dies 1–4 (and, possibly, 5).

Die 1 £1500 £200 Die 3 £1350 £185
2 £1350 £185 4 £1500 £200

The 1/– stamp was printed from Dies 1 and 2.
Die 1 £1800 £95 Die 2 £2200 £95

The Die Number is indicated (e.g. '1 WW') on the base of the bust.

1848-53 A series of experiments was made, initially by Henry Archer and subsequently by the Post Office, to find a satisfactory method of separating the hitherto imperforate stamps. Sheets of stamps (V5) used in these experiments were subsequently issued for sale through Post Offices.

(a) Rouletted 12 by Henry Archer (1848).

V18 1d. **red-brown** (Pl. 70,
71) .. .. £1850 —

(b) Perf. 16 by Henry Archer (1850).

V19 1d. **red-brown** (Pl. 8,
71, 79, 90–101, 105) £350 £95

(c) Perf. by Post Office (1853).

V20 1d. **red-brown** (perf. 16)
(on dated cover) .. ‡ £3000
V21 1d. **red-brown** (perf. 14) £2250 —

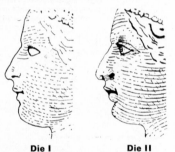

Die I **Die II**

After 15 years of use the original Die I was recut by William Humphrys. The resulting Die II shows the following easily discernible differences:

(i) Eye deeply shaded.
(ii) Lips made thicker.
(iii) Nostril more deeply defined.
(iv) Deep indentation below lower lip and at corner of mouth.

1854 (Feb)-62 As V5/11 but perf. Paper blued. Sheets 12 x 20.

(a) Wmk. Small Crown. Perf. 16.

V22	1d.	**red-brown** (Die I) ..	£75	1·50
V23	1d.	**yel-brown** (Die I) ..	£75	2·00
V24	1d.	**red-brown** (Die II)		
		(1/3/55)	£95	4·50
		a imperf.	—	—
V25	2d.	**dp blue** (13/3/54) ..	£700	£14
V26	2d.	**pale blue** (Pl. 4) ..	£850	£25
V26A	2d.	**blue** (Pl. 5)	£1000	£60

(b) Wmk Small Crown Perf. 14.

V27	1d.	**red-brown** (Die I)		
		(1/55)	£150	£12

V28	1d.	**red-brown** (Die II)		
		(28/2/55)	£110	£12
V29	1d.	**or-brown** (Die II) ..	£275	£20
V30	2d.	**blue** (Pl. 4) (4/3/55)	£1000	£48
V30A	2d.	**blue** (Pl. 5) (18/8/55)	£1000	£48
		a imperf. (Pl. 5) ..	—	—

(c) Wmk. Large Crown. Perf. 16. Die II (1d.).

V31	1d.	**red-brn** (15/5/55) ..	£270	£18
		a imperf. (Pl. 7) ..	—	—
V32	2d.	**blue** (20/7/55) ..	£1250	£65
		a imperf. (Pl. 5) ..	—	—

(d) Wmk. Large Crown. Perf. 14. Die II (1d.).

V33	1d.	**red-brn** (18/8/55) ..	£70	80
		a imperf.	£400	£385
V34	1d.	**plum** (2/57)	£450	£60
V35	1d.	**orange-brown** (3/57)	£150	£10
V36	2d.	**blue** (Pl. 5) (20/7/55)	£700	£18
V36A	2d.	**blue** (Pl. 6) (2/7/57)	£700	£18

1856 (Nov.)-58 As before but paper no longer blued.

(a) Wmk. Large Crown. Perf. 14. Die II.

V37	1d.	**red-brown**	£115	£14
V38	1d.	**pale red** (9/4/57) ..	£45	2·00
		a imperf.	£300	£250
V39	1d.	**rose-red** (9/57) ..	£20	40
		a imperf.	£300	£250

(b) Wmk. Large Crown. Perf. 16. Die II (1d.).

V40	1d.	**rose-red** (29/12/57)	£400	£20
V41	2d.	**blue** (1/2/58) ..	£1600	£65

The 1d. stamp (Die I) was printed from Plates 176–204 and R 1–14 and subsequently (Die II) from a new numbered series 1–68 and R 15–17 and R 50–51. (R—Reserve Plates).

The 2d. stamp was printed from Plates 4–6. On Plate 6 the white lines are thinner than before.

Four main types of corner check letters were used during the period 1840 to 1862 briefly summarised as follows:

Alphabet I. Small letters.

Alphabet II. Slightly larger and generally of thicker appearance.

Alphabet III. Considerably larger and more elegant appearance.

Alphabet IV. Large hand engraved letters all having individual characteristics.

The following list of Plates indicates the Alphabet type used:

1d. Die I. Plates 1 to 131 — Alphabet I.
2d. Plates 1, 2, 3 and 4 — Alphabet I.
1d. Die I. Plates 132–204 incl. R 1–14 — Alphabet II.

1d. Die II.   Plates 1 to 21 and R 15 and 16 — Alphabet II.
2d.   Plate 5 — Alphabet II.
1d. Die II.   Plates 22 to 68 and R 17 — Alphabet III.
2d.   Plate 6 — Alphabet III.
1d. Die II.   Plates 50 and 51 — Alphabet IV.

Reserve Plates 15, 16 and 17, Plates 50 and 51 were issued during the later 1d. rose-red period of issue (1861–4) and command considerably higher prices than the basic V39.

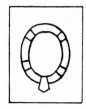
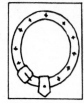
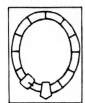

Prices for surface printed stamps between V42 and V196 are for good average copies, both mint and used. Very fine unused and lightly cancelled copies command a good premium.

1855 (July 31st)-1857 (Jan.) Surface printed De La Rue. Various frames. Perf. 14. Sheets 240 – four panes, each 6 x 10.
(a) Wmk. Small Garter. Deeply blued paper. Plates 1 and 2.

V42	4d. **carmine**	.. ..	£1850	£80
	a on white paper	..	£2250	£175

(b) Wmk. Medium Garter. Thick blued, glazed paper. Plate 1.

V43	4d. **carmine** (25/2/56) ..	£2000	£95
	a on thin unglazed white paper (9/56)	£850	£70

(c) Wmk. Large Garter. Ordinary paper. Plates 1 and 2.

V44	4d. **rose-car** (1/57)	£400	£14
	a on thick glazed paper	£850	£40

(d) Wmk. Emblems. Sheets 240 – twelve panes, each 4 x 5.

V45	6d. **dp lilac** (21/10/56) (**Pl. 1**)	.. ..	£325	£25
V46	6d. **pale lilac** (**Pl. 1**)	..	£285	£18
	a on azure paper		—	—
	b wmk. Rose in place of Thistle	.. ..	—	—
V47	1/– **dp green** (1/11/56) (**Pl. 1**)	.. ..	£800	£80
V48	1/– **pl green** (**Pl. 1**)	..	£425	£35
	a on azure paper		—	£300

V46*b* This occurred on stamp 'TA' on which a third rose, instead of a thistle, appears in the watermark at lower left.

1858 (July)-64 As V40/41 but with Check letters in all four corners, those at the upper corners being the reverse of those in the lowers corners; and Plate Nos. incorporated in the design. Perf. 14.

V49	1d. **rose-red** (1/4/64) ..		3·00	40
	a imperf. (Pl. 116 and others)	.. ..	£700	£400
V50	1d. **lake-red**	..	5·00	40
V51	2d. **blue** (thick lines) (7/58)	£65	3·00
	a imperf. (Pl. 9)	..	—	£1850
V52	2d. **dp blue** (thin lines) ..	£65	4·00
	a imperf. (Pl. 13)	..	£800	—

V49*a* comes from a number of Plates between 79 and 191: the only known mint imperforate stamps are from Plate 116, a sheet having been issued at Cardiff on 18/1/70.

Stamps of this and subsequent issues may be found overprinted or underprinted (under the gum) with names or initials of various firms or organisations e.g. "O.U.S." (Oxford Union Society), "W. H. Smith and Son, 186 Strand", "Copestake, Moore, Crampton and Co". Such security identifications were the forerunners of present day PERFINS.

The 1d. stamp was printed from Plates 71–225 (less 75, 126 and 128 which were defective and not used). Plate 77 was also rejected but a few copies printed from it are known.

The 2d. stamp V51 was printed from Plates 7, 8, 9 and 12 and V52 from Plates 13, 14 and 15.

1d

Plate			Plate		
71	£14	40	150	6·00	40
72	£12	40	151	£11	40
73	£12	40	152	8·00	40
74	£12	40	153	£40	4·00
76	£14	40	154	9·00	40
77	£20000	£14000	155	9·00	1·00
78	8·00	40	156	9·00	40
79	8·00	40	157	9·00	40
80	£12	40	158	6·00	40
81	£20	40	159	7·00	40
82	£75	2·00	160	7·00	40
83	£125	3·00	161	£20	2·00
84	8·00	40	162	£10	40
85	£10	40	163	£10	40
86	£20	40	164	£10	40
87	8·00	40	165	7·00	40
88	£95	5·00	166	9·00	40
89	£10	40	167	6·00	40
90	7·00	40	168	7·00	40
91	7·00	40	169	£10	2·00
92	£10	40	170	8·00	40

Plate			Plate		
93	£10	60	171	5·00	40
94	£12	40	172	7·00	40
95	9·00	40	173	5·00	40
96	£18	40	174	5·00	40
97	£10	40	175	5·00	40
98	£10	40	176	£10	1·00
99	£12	40	177	5·00	40
100	£10	40	178	£10	1·00
101	£18	40	179	£10	1·00
102	£10	40	180	£10	1·00
103	£12	40	181	£10	40
104	£17	2·00	182	£10	2·00
105	£40	3·00	183	8·00	40
106	9·00	40	184	5·00	40
107	£18	40	185	£10	1·00
108	£20	1·00	186	£10	1·00
109	£65	1·00	187	8·00	40
110	£12	40	188	£10	40
111	£10	40	189	£10	40
112	£20	1·00	190	5·00	1·00
113	9·00	40	191	5·00	40
114	£60	40	192	5·00	40
115	£60	1·00	193	5·00	40
116	£22	40	194	£10	40
117	£10	40	195	£10	40
118	4·00	40	196	6·00	40
119	7·00	40	197	£10	40
120	4·00	40	198	6·00	40
121	6·00	40	199	6·00	40
122	6·00	40	200	7·00	40
123	6·00	60	201	5·00	40
124	5·00	40	202	7·00	40
125	9·00	40	203	6·00	40
127	8·00	40	204	8·00	40
129	8·00	40	205	8·00	40
130	8·00	40	206	8·00	40
131	8·00	40	207	6·00	40
132	£80	6·00	208	8·00	40
133	£75	6·00	209	9·00	40
134	5·00	40	210	£10	40
135	7·00	40	211	£28	3·00
136	8·00	40	212	8·00	40
137	8·00	40	213	7·00	40
138	6·00	40	214	£10	40
139	7·00	40	215	9·00	40
140	5·00	40	216	8·00	40
141	£25	1·50	217	£10	3·00
142	9·00	40	218	8·00	2·00
143	£12	40	219	£20	£14
144	£18	40	220	6·00	2·00
145	5·00	40	221	£22	5·00
146	7·00	40	222	£18	£10
147	7·00	40	223	£24	£10
148	5·00	40	224	£40	£18
149	9·00	40	225	£775	£125

All above prices are for good copies ,reasonably centred, *not* oxidized.

2d

Plate			Plate		
7	£200	£10	13	£65	4·00
8	£200	£10	14	£90	4·00
9	£65	3·00	15	£90	4·00
12	£375	£15			

All stamps from V53 to V196 (with the exception of V108/112) were surface printed by De La Rue and are Perf. 14 unless otherwise indicated.

With very few exceptions the stamps each have the Plate Number incorporated in the design, and the majority have Check letters in all four corners, those at the top being the reverse of those at the bottom of the stamp. The arrangement of these Check letters is *by the sheet* regardless of whether it is made up of separate panes or not.

A number of these stamps may be found with "Wing Margins", a term used to describe an additional 5mm. of unprinted paper between a vertical side and the neighbouring perforation. These varieties were caused by the manner of perforating sheets which were printed in panes, horizontal pairs of panes being separated only by a single line of vertical perforations through the centre of the unprinted 'gutter' between them.

V56, 66, 69, 69a, 76b, 85, 91, 99, 116, 117, 125, 129, 132, 134 are generally known as the "Abnormals", and are exceedingly rare. Their existence is due to the practice of printing six sheets of stamps from each Plate *as it was made* one being kept for record at Somerset House and the others perforated and *usually* issued. If such Plates were not subsequently used or were used to print stamps in a different colour or on different watermarked paper, then the five sheets referred to would either constitute the total issue or would differ from the later issued stamp.

1862 (May 1st)-64 Various frames. Small uncoloured Check letters. Sheets 240 — twelve panes, each 4 x 5. Wmk. Emblems (except 4d — four panes, each 6 x 10. Wmk. Large Garter).

V53	3d. **deep carmine-rose (Pl. 2)**	£500	£60
V54	3d. **br carmine-rose (Pl. 2)**	£355	£40
V55	3d. **pl carmine-rose (Pl. 2)**	£355	£40
V56	3d. **rose (Pl. 3)** (8/62)	£1250	£1250
V57	4d. **bright red (Pl. 3)** (15/1/62)	£500	£30
V58	4d. **pale red (Pl. 3)**	£300	£20
V59	4d. **bright red (Pl. 4)** (16/10/63)	£325	£24
V60	4d. **pale red (Pl. 4)**	£300	£18
	a imperf.	£525	—
V61	6d. **deep lilac (Pl. 3)** (1/12/62)	£400	£30
V62	6d. **lilac (Pl. 3)**	£325	£15
	a on azure paper	—	£175
	b wmk. Rose in place of Shamrock	—	—
V63	6d. **lilac (Pl. 4)** (20/4/64)	£450	£35
	a imperf.	£600	—
V64	9d. **bistre (Pl. 2)** (15/1/62)	£600	£55
V65	9d. **straw (Pl. 2)**	£600	£55
	a on azure paper	—	—
V66	9d. **bistre (Pl. 9)** ((5/62)	£4500	£950
V67	1/- **deep green (Pl. 2)** (1/12/62)	£450	£24

V68   1/– **green (Pl. 2)** £425   £20
    a "K" circled £2500   £375
    b "K" normal ..   ..   —   —
    c on azure paper   ..   —   —
V69   1/– **deep green (Pl. 3)** ..   £8000   —
    a imperf.   ..   ..   £700   —

V56 Plate 3 (an Abnormal) different from Plate 2 in that two white dots appeared on the scroll before and after the word "POSTAGE".

V62*b* This occurred on stamp "TF" on which a third Rose, instead of a Shamrock, appears in the watermark at lower right.

V59, 60, 60*a*, 63, 63*a*, 66, 69, 69*a* On all these stamps white Hair Lines appear diagonally across the outer corners of the Check letter squares, but only V66 and V69 are Abnormals.

V67, 68, 68*a*, 68*b* Although the Plate is No. 2 the stamps are numbered 1.

V68*a* On stamp "KD" the "K" plug was not flush with the plate and a white circle surrounds the Check letter.

V69, 69*a* Although the Plate is No. 3 the stamps are numbered 2 (an Abnormal).

The 6d. Plate No. 2 was never registered.

1865 (Feb.) As Nos. V53/69 but with large uncoloured Check letters.

V70   3d. **rose (Pl. 4)** (1/3/65)   £300   £18
    a wmk. Rose in place of Thistle £550   £185
V71   4d. **dl verm** (4/7/65)   ..   £150   £12
V72   4d. **vermilion** £120   £12
    a imperf. (Pl. 11, 12)   £200   —
V73   4d. **deep vermilion**   ..   £160   £12
V74   6d. **deep lilac** (1/4/65)..   £275   £20
V75   6d. **lilac** £250   £15
    a stamp doubly printed (Pl. 6)   ..   —   £2250
    b wmk. Rose in place of Thistle (Pl. 5, 6)   —   £275
V76   9d. **straw (Pl. 4)** (1/12/65)   £600   £100
    a wmk. Rose in place of Thistle   ..   —   £400
V76B 9d. **straw (Pl. 5)** ..   £8500   —
V77   1/– **green (Pl. 4)** (2/65)   £400   £18
    a wmk. Rose in place of Thistle ..   ..   —   £225
    b imperf. between (vert pair)   ..   —   £2000

V70*a*, 75*b*, 76*a*, 77*a* See note under V46*b*.

V76B This stamp (an Abnormal) was never issued, but a few unused copies are known. They are believed to have been taken from the Imprimatur sheets and perforated for use in the Souvenir Albums presented to the Stamp Committee in 1884. The perforations are invariably guillotined.

The 4d. stamp was printed from Plates 7 to 14.

Plate			Plate		
7	£180	£18	11	£180	£12
8	£180	£18	12	£160	£12
9	£180	£12	13	£180	£12
10	£210	£20	14	£225	£18

The 6d. stamp was printed from Plates 5 and 6.

Plate			Plate		
5	£250	£15	6	£750	£40

The 10d. red-brown with Emblems wmk. will be found under V88*a*.

1867 (June 21st)-80 As before but wmk. Rose Spray.

V78   3d. **deep rose** (12/7/67)   £150   £12
    a imperf. (Pl. 6, 8) ..   £300   —
V78A 3d. **rose**   ..   ..   —   —
V79   6d. **lilac (Pl. 6)** (21/6/67)   ..   £325   £18
V80   6d. **dp lilac (Pl. 6)**   ..   £325   £18
V81   6d. **purple (Pl. 6)**   ..   £325   £18
V82   6d. **brn violet (Pl. 6)** (22/7/68)   ..   £325   £18
V83   6d. **dull violet** (no hyphen (13/3/69)   £225   £20
V84   6d. **mauve** (no hyphen)   £225   £15
    a imperf. (Pl. 8, 9) ..   £425   £275
V85   6d. **mauve (Pl. 10)** (1869)   ..   —   £7500
V86   9d. **straw (Pl. 44)** (3/10/67)   ..   £425   £42
V87   9d. **pl straw (Pl. 4)**   ..   £425   £42
    a imperf. (Pl. 4)   ..   £850   —
V88   10d. **red-brown (Pl. 1)** (1/7/67)   ..   £800   £55
    a wmk. Emblems (Pl. 1) (11/11/67)   —   £8000
V89   10d. **pale red-brown (Pl. 1)**   ..   £850   £60
V90   10d. **deep red-brown (Pl. 1)**   ..   £950   £75
    a imperf. (Pl. 1)   ..   £950   —
V91   10d. **pale red-brown (Pl. 2)** (1867)   ..   £8500   £2000
V92   1/– **deep green**   ..   £250   5·00
V93   1/– **pale green**   ..   £225   3·00
    a imperf. between (pair) (Pl. 7) ..   —   —
    b imperf. (Pl. 4)   ..   £500   £300
V94   2/– **dull blue (Pl. 1)** (1/7/67)   ..   £650   £30
V95   2/– **deep blue (Pl. 1)** ..   £650   £30
V96   2/– **pale blue (Pl. 1)** ..   £800   £40
    a imperf. (Pl. 1)   ..   £750   —
V97   2/– **cobalt (Pl. 1)**   ..   £3000   £350
V98   2/– **milky-blue (Pl. 1)** ..   £1500   £125
V99   2/– **pale blue (Pl. 3)** (1868)   ..   —   £2000
V100 2/– **brown (Pl. 1)** (27/2/80)   ..   £3000   £425
    a imperf.   ..   ..   £2000   —

V79/82 (Plate 6) have a hyphen between "SIX" and "PENCE".

V83/85 (Plates 8–10, the latter being an Abnormal) have no hyphen.
The 6d. Plate 7 was never registered.

V88*a* The known examples of this error are all used.

V91 Stamps printed from Plate 2 are Abnormals, and there are no stamps with Wing Margins. Only one unused copy is known.

V99 Stamps printed from Plate 3 are Abnormals. Plate 2 was never registered.

The 3d. stamp was printed from Plates 4–10.

Plate			Plate		
4	£240	£20	8	£200	£12
5	£150	£12	9	£200	£14
6	£150	£12	10	£220	£20
7	£200	£12			

The 1/– stamps were printed from Plates 4–7.

Plate			Plate		
4	£225	3·00	6	£325	5·00
5	£250	4·00	7	£325	£12

The well-known "Stock Exchange Forgeries" were of stamps from Plates 5 and 6, some of them bearing impossible combinations of Check letters.

They are typographed without watermark; and and were used 1872-3, postmarked "STOCK EX-CHANGE E.C.".

Price (Normal Check letters) Plate 5 £275, Plate 6 £1350.

(Impossible Check letters) Plate 5 £400, Plate 6 £1750.

1867 (July 1st)-83 Various frames. Large uncoloured Check letters, the £5 having Check letters in the lower corners only.

(a) Wmk. Maltese Cross. Perf. 15½ x 15. Sheets 80, four panes, each 5 x 4.

V101	5/–	**rose** **(Pl. 1, 2)**			
		(1/7/67) ..	..	£2000	£125
		a imperf. (Pl. 1)	..	£1850	—
V102	10/–	**grn-grey** **(Pl. 1)**			
		(26/9/78)	..	£10000	£750
V103	£1	**brn-lilac** **(Pl. 1)**			
		(26/9/78)	..	£14000	£1000

(b) Wmk Large Anchor (two on £5 stamp). Blued Paper. Perf. 14. Sheets 5/– to £1, 8 x 7; £5, 56 – two panes, each 4 x 7 (with Check letters arranged downwards instead of across the sheet – Row 1 across A-A to D-A: Row 14 across A-N to D-N).

V104	5/–	**rose (Pl. 4)**			
		(25/11/82)	..	£3250	£425
		a on white paper	..	£3250	£425
V105	10/–	**grn-grey** **(Pl. 1)**			
		(2/83) ..	..	£12000	£900
		a on white paper	..	£12000	£900
V106	£1	**brn-lilac** **(Pl. 1)**			
		(12/82) ..	..	£15000	£1500
		a on white paper	..	£15000	£1500
V107	£5	**orange** **(Pl. 1)**			
		(21/3/82)	..	£9500	£2750
		a on white paper	..	£4500	£2000

The 5/– Plate 3 was never registered.

1870 (Oct. 1st) (*Recess*) **Perkins Bacon. Perf. 14. Plate Numbers incorporated in the design. Wmk. ¼d., "half penny" extending across three stamps: 1½d., Large Crown. Sheets ¼d., 24 x 20 (Check letters A-A to A-X etc. to T-X): 1½d., 12 x 20. Check letters in all four corners as V49/52.**

V108	½d.	**rose-red**	..	..	£24	2·00
V109	½d.	**rose** ..	..	..	£24	2·00
		a imperf. (Pl. 1, 4–6				
		8, 14)	..	..	£600	£325
V110	1½d.	**rose-red (Pl. 1, 3)**	..		£90	9·00
		a "OP-PC" (Pl. 1)	..		£2250	£325
V111	1½d.	**lake-red (Pl. 1, 3)**	..		£90	9·00
		a imperf. (Pl. 1, 3)	..		£800	—

(1860) Prepared for use but not issued. Blued paper.

| V112 | 1½d. | **rosy-mauve (Pl. 1)** | £1250 | — |
| | | *a* "OP-PC" | .. | — | — |

The method of perforating the sheets of ½d. stamps was such that the outer stamps in both vertical marginal rows are imperf. between the stamp and sheet margin.

V110*a*/V112*a* On Plate 1 the CP-PC stamp (Row 16/3) was incorrectly lettered OP-PC; the error was never corrected.

The ½d. stamp was printed from Plates 1–15 (less 2 and 7) and 19–20.

Plate			Plate		
1	£50	£20	11	£25	2·00
3	£30	3·50	12	£25	2·00
4	£28	2·00	13	£28	2·00
5	£28	2·00	14	£28	2·00
6	£28	2·00	15	£28	3·50
8	£50	£20	19	£40	3·50
9	£650	£100	20	£32	5·00
10	£24	2·00			

The 1½d. stamp was printed from Plates 1 (*not* incorporated in the design) and 3.

V112/V112*a* The 1½d. stamp was originally printed in this colour in anticipation of a change in postal rate that did not then materialise. Most of this printing was subsequently destroyed. Only one copy of V112*a* is known, in the Royal Collection.

1872 (April 12th)-73 Large uncoloured Check letters. Wmk. Rose Spray. Sheets 240 – twelve panes, each 4 x 5. No hyphen.

V113	6d.	**dp chest (Pl. 11)**	..	£240	£10
V114	6d.	**chestnut (Pl. 11)**			
		(23/5/72)	..	£185	£10
V115	6d.	**pale buff (Pl. 11)**			
		(26/10/72)	..	£220	£18
V116	6d.	**pl chest (Pl. 12)**	..	—	£800
V117	6d.	**chestnut (Pl. 12)**	..	—	£800
V118	6d.	**pale buff (Pl. 12)**			
		(30/10/72)	..	£485	£35
V119	6d.	**grey (Pl. 12)**			
		(24/4/73)	..	£225	£14
		a imperf.	..	£600	—

V116/117 Stamps printed in these shades from Plate 12 are Abnormals, and postmarked copies show considerable range of shades from yellowish brown to chestnut.

1873 (March 15th)-80 Various frames. Large coloured Check letters.

(a) Wmk. Anchor. Sheets 192 – two panes, each 12 x 8. (Check letters A-A to A-L etc. to P-L).

V120	2½d.	**rosy-mauve** (blued			
		paper) (1/7/75)	..	£220	£20
V121	2½d.	**rosy-mauve** (white			
		paper)	..	£175	£10
		a LH-FL (Pl. 2)	..	£4000	£300

V121*a* On Plate 2 (blued or white paper) the LH-HL stamp (Row 8/12) was incorrectly lettered LH-FL. These stamps were printed from Plates 1–3.

Plate	Blued Paper		White Paper	
1	£220	£20	£175	£10
2	£1750	£225	£175	£10
3	—	£800	£200	£18

(b) Wmk. Orb. Sheets as before.

V122	2½d.	**rosy-mauve**			
		(16/5/76)	..	..	£135	7·00
V123	2½d.	**blue** (5/2/80)	..	£90	4·00

V122 was printed from Plates 3–17 and V123 from Plates 17–20.

Rosy-mauve

Plate			Plate		
3	£250	£20	11	£135	£8
4	£135	£8	12	£135	£10
5	£135	£8	13	£135	£10
6	£135	£8	14	£135	£8
7	£135	£8	15	£135	£8
8	£135	£8	16	£135	£9
9	£135	£8	17	£300	£35
10	£175	£10			

Blue

Plate			Plate		
17	£90	£8	19	£95	£4
18	£125	£6	20	£95	£4

(c) Wmk. Rose Spray. Sheets 240 – twelve panes, each 4 x 5.

V124	3d.	**rose** (5/7/73)	..	£140	£6
V125	6d.	**pale buff (Pl. 13)**	..	—	£2000
V126	6d.	**grey** (31/3/74)	..	£120	£8
V127	1/–	**dp green** (1/9/73)	..	£185	£12
V128	1/–	**pale green**	..	..	£140	£10

V129   1/–   **green (Pl. 14)**   ..   —   £7500
V130   1/–   **orange-brn (Pl. 13)**
     (14/10/80)   ..   £600   £60

The 3d. stamp was printed from Plates 11–20 (less 13 which was never registered).

Plate			Plate	
11	£150	£6	17	£175	£8
12	£165	£8	18	£185	£8
14	£200	£8	19	£150	£8
15	£160	£8	20	£175	£20
16	£160	£8			

The 6d. (V125) is an Abnormal, the issued stamps having been printed in grey from Plates 13–17.

Plate			Plate		
13	£120	£9	16	£120	£9
14	£120	£9	17	£185	£18
15	£120	£8			

The 1/– stamp (V127/8) was printed from Plates 8–13, the green printing on Plate 14 (V129) being an Abnormal.

Plate			Plate		
8	£200	£12	11	£175	£12
9	£200	£12	12	£140	£10
10	£175	£12	13	£140	£10

(d) Wmk. Large Garter. Sheets 240 – four panes, each 6 x 10.

V131   4d.   **vermilion (Pl. 15)**
     (1/3/76)   ..   £325   £45
V132   4d.   **vermilion (Pl. 16)** ..   —   £5500
V133   4d.   **sage-green (Pl. 15, 16)** (12/3/77) ..   £200   £28
V134   4d.   **sage-green (Pl. 17)**   —   £4250
V135   4d.   **grey-brn (Pl. 17)**
     (15/8/80)   ..   £325   £45
     a imperf. (Pl. 17)   ..   —   —
V136   8d.   **or (Pl. 1)** (11/9/76)   £350   £40

V132, V134 are Abnormals.

1876 (July) Prepared for use but not issued.

V138   8d.   **pur-brn (Pl. 1)**   ..   £2450   —

1880 (Jan. 1st)-83 As before but wmk. Imperial Crown, and new value (1d.). Sheets 240 – two panes, each 12 x 10.

V138   1d.   **venetian-red**   ..   3·50   40
     a imperf.   ..   ..   £140   —
V139   2½d.   **blue** (23/3/81) ..   £95   3·00
V140   3d.   **rose** (2/81) ..   ..   £120   6·00
V141   4d.   **grey-brown**   ..   £110   6·00
V142   6d.   **grey** (1/1/81)   ..   £110   7·00
V143   1/–   **or-brn** (29/5/81) ..   £120   £12

V143 in purple was not issued. It was an official reprint made in 1884 for Souvenir Albums presented to the Stamp Committee. Price £2000.

The 2½d. stamps were printed from Plates 21–23; 3d., Plates 20–21; 4d., Plates 17, 18; 6d., Plates 17, 18; 1/–, Plates 13–14.

(b) Nos. V140 and V142 in altered colours and surcharged with large figures in carmine (1/1/83).

V144   3d. on 6d.   **lilac (Pl. 21)**   ..   £120   £35
V145   6d. on 6d.   **lilac (Pl. 18)**   ..   £175   £35
     a slanting dots
     from   ..   £220   £45

V145*a* The two dots below the "d" are slanting instead of horizontal on stamps lettered AF, DC, MG, MH, MI, OI, PH, PJ and SJ.

1880 (Oct. 14th)-84 (April 1st) Various frames. No Check letters. Wmk. Imperial Crown. Sheets 240 – two panes, each 12 x 10.

V146   ½d.   **dp grn** (14/10/80)..   8·00   1·50
     a imperf.   ..   £140   —
V147   ½d.   **pale green** ..   ..   8·00   1·50
V148   ½d.   **sl blue** (1/4/84)   ..   6·00   60
V149   1d.   **lilac   (Die   I)**
     (12/7/81)   ..   £42   4·50
V150   1d.   **pl lilac (Die I)**   ..   £42   4·50
V151   1d.   **lilac   (Die   II)**
     (12/12/81)   ..   50   10
V152   1d.   **bluish-lilac (Die II)**   £100   £18
V153   1d.   **dp purple (Die II)** ..   50   10
     a printed both sides   £280   —
     b ditto, but reverse
     impression in-
     verted   ..   ..   £250   —
     c printed on gummed
     side   ..   ..   £250   —
     d imperf. (3 sides),
     pair   ..   ..   £1150   —
V154   1d.   **mauve (Die II)**   ..   50   10
     a imperf. (pair)   ..   £400   —
V155   1½d.   **venetian-red**   ..   £35   £10
V156   2d.   **pl rose** (8/12/80) ..   £42   £10
V157   2d.   **deep rose**   ..   £42   £10
V158   5d.   **indigo** (15/3/81)   ..   £240   £20
     a imperf.   ..   ..   £300   —

V149/154 Die I has 14 pearls in each corner; Die II has 16 pearls.

V151/154 The Die II printing may be found with "PEAR'S SOAP" printed on the back in orange blue or mauve. Price: £175 unused.

1883 (July 2nd)-84 Various frames. Large coloured Check letters.

(a) Wmk. Imperial Crown (sideways on horizontal stamps). Sheets 240 – two panes,

each 12 x 10 or 10 x 12. (V166 1/8/83: rest 1/4/84).

V159	1½d.	**lilac**	..	..	..	£40	5·00
V160	2d.	**lilac**	..	..	..	£50	8·00
V161	2½d.	**lilac**	..	..	..	£30	2·00
V162	3d.	**lilac**	..	..	..	£85	£14
V163	4d.	**dull green**	..	..	£150	£30
V164	5d.	**dull green**	..	..	£150	£30
	a	line under d	..		—	—
V165	6d.	**dull green**	..	..	£160	£35
V166	9d.	**dull green**	..	..	£385	£95
V167	1/-	**dull green**	..	..	£385	£75

V164*a* The first two Plates made had a line under the d instead of a dot. The stamps printed from these plates were not issued but a few unused copies are known.

Prices of V163/167 are for fine dull green copies. Stamps which have been immersed in water, thus causing the colour to run, have little value.

(b) Wmk. Anchor. Blued paper. Sheets 112 – two panes, each 7 x 8.

V168	2/6	**lilac**	..	..	..	£1000	£135
	a	on white	paper			
		('84)	..	..	£500	£35
V169	5/-	**rose** (1/4/84)	..	£2200	£375
	a	on white	paper			
		('84)	..	..	£650	£60
V170	5/-	**crimson/white**	..	£650	£60
V171	10/-	**ult** (1/4/84) ..	..	£7500	£950
	a	on white	paper			
		('84)	..	..	£1250	£225
V172	10/-	**cobalt** (5/84)	..	£8000	£1850
	a	on white	paper			
		('84)	..	..	£8000	£1850

1884-91 Large uncoloured Check letters. Sheets 80 – two panes, each 4 x 10.

(a) Wmk. Three Imperial Crowns (1/4/84).

| V173 | £1 | **brown-lilac** | .. | £6500 | £850 |
| | *a* | broken frame | .. | — | £1000 |

(b) Wmk. Three Orbs (1/2/88).

| V174 | £1 | **brown-lilac** | .. | £12000 | £1250 |
| | *a* | broken frame | .. | — | £1500 |

(c) Wmk. Three Imperial Crowns (27/1/91).

| V175 | £1 | **green** | .. | .. | £2500 | £475 |
| | *a* | broken frame | .. | — | £650 |

V173*a*/175*a* On stamps lettered "JC" and "TA" on Plate 2 the lower frame line is broken.

1887 (Jan. 1st)-1900 Jubilee issue. Various

frames. Wmk. Imperial Crown. Sheets ½d. to 3d., 5d., 6d. and 1/- 240 – two panes, each 12 x 10: others 80 – four panes, each 5 x 4.

V176	½d.	**vermilion**	..	..	75	10
	a	printed on gummed			
		side	..	..	£300	—
	b	printed both sides	..	—	—
	c	doubly printed	..	£900	—
	d	imperf.	..	£150	—
V177	½d.	**blue-grn** (17/4/00)	..	60	15
	a	printed on gummed			
		side	..	..	—	—
	b	imperf.	..	..	£425	—
V178	1½d.	**dl pur and grn**	..	£12	—
	a	pur print double ..		—	—
V179	2d.	**green and verm**	..	£250	£60
V180	2d.	**green and car**	..	£25	2·50
V181	2½d.	**purple/blue**	..	£15	20
	a	printed on gummed			
		side	..	..	—	—
V182	3d.	**purple/yellow**	..	£25	75
	a	imperf.	..	..	—	—
V183	3d.	**dp purple/orange**			
		('91)	..	..	£300	£45
V184	4d.	**green and brown** ..	£32	3·00
V185	4d.	**grn and dp brown**	£32	3·00
V186	4½d.	**green and car**			
		(15/9/92)	..	3·00	9·00
V187	4½d.	**grn and aniline-carmine**	..	£200	£40
V188	5d.	**dp purple and blue (Die I)**	..	£300	£25
V189	5d.	**dl purple and blue (Die II)**	..	£35	2·50
V190	6d.	**purple/rose-red** ..	£35	2·50
V191	6d.	**dp pur/rose-red** ..	£35	2·50
V192	9d.	**dl purple and blue**	£90	8·00
V193	10d.	**dp pur and car**			
		(24/2/90)	..	£100	8·00
	a	imperf.	..	..	—	—
V194	10d.	**dl pur and aniline-carmine**	..	£275	£30
V195	1/-	**green** ..	..	£185	£18
V196	1/-	**green and car**			
		(11/7/00)	..	£70	£22
V176/196		**set** (14v)	..	£500	£60

V188, V189 Die I has square dots to the right of "d" in value tablets. Die II has vertical lines to the right of "d" in value tablets, and the figure "5" is separate from the lower frame line.

V176 may be found with "PEAR'S SOAP" printed on the back in orange, blue or mauve. Price: £175 unused.

1902 (Jan. 1st)-13 Surface printed. Various frames. Wmk. Imperial Crown (½d.–1/–), Anchor (2/6–10/–), 3 Imperial Crowns (£1). Sheets – ½d.–7d. and 1/–, 240 – two panes, each 12 x 10: 9d., 160 – eight panes, each 5 x 4: 10d, 192 – four panes, each 12 x 4.

(I) Printed by De La Rue (1902-10) Perf. 14.

E1	½d.	**blue-green** O	..	60	30
E2	½d.	**yellow-green** O	..	60	30
		a double print..	..	£1750	—
		b in pair with Cross	..	£90	£80
E3	1d.	**scarlet** O	..	30	10
		a imperf.	..	£1400	—
E4	1½d.	**dl purple and green** O		£20	1·50
E5	1½d.	**slate-pur and grn** C		£20	1·50
E6	2d.	**grey-grn and car** O..		£20	1·50
E7	2d.	**blue-grn and car** C..		£20	1·50
E8	2d.	**grey-grn and scar** C		£20	1·50
E9	2½d.	**ultramarine** O	..	8·00	1·00
E10	3d.	**dl pur/or-yel** O	..	£20	1·50
E11	3d.	**dp pur/or-yel** O	..	£20	1·50
E12	3d.	**dl pur/or-yel** C	..	£90	8·00
E13	3d.	**dl reddish purple/yel** (lemon back) C		£85	8·00
E14	3d.	**purple/lemon** C	..	£18	1·50
E15	4d.	**green and grey-brn** O		£32	7·00
E16	4d.	**grn and choc-brn** OC		£32	7·00
E17	4d.	**brn-orange** O (11/09)		£115	£40
E18	4d.	**orange-red** O (12/09)		£18	5·00
E19	5d.	**dl pur and ultra** O	..	£25	4·00
E20	5d.	**slate-pur and ultra** C		£25	4·00
E21	6d.	**pale dull purple** OC..		£20	2·00
E22	6d.	**slate-purple** O	..	£20	2·00
E23	7d.	**grey-black** O..		2·00	2·50
E24	7d.	**deep grey-black** O ..		£80	£35
E25	9d.	**dl pur and ultra** OC..		£50	£12
E26	9d.	**slate-pur and ultra** OC		£50	£12
E27	10d.	**dl purple and car** O..		£50	8·00
		a no Cross on Crown		£110	£30
E28	10d.	**slate-pur and car** C		£50	8·00
		a no Cross on Crown		£110	£30
E29	10d.	**dl pur and scarlet** C		£50	8·00
		a no Cross on Crown		£110	£30
E30	1/–	**dl grn and carmine** OC		£55	3·00
E31	1/–	**dl grn and scar** C	..	£55	3·00
E32	2/6d	**lilac** O ..	..	£400	£25
E33	2/6d	**dull purple** C ..	..	£400	£25
E34	5/–	**carmine** O	..	£525	£45
E35	10/–	**blue** O ..	..	£1100	£225
E36	£1	**green** O	..	£2000	£500
E1/31		**set** (14v)	..	£310	£45

E2*a* Only 13 copies existed from the bottom two rows of one sheet (Control H9).

E2*b* Comes from Booklets containing 12 stamps at 1d. and 23 stamps at ½d. A St. Andrew's Cross in green took the place of the 24th ½d. stamp, thereby enabling the Post Office to charge a half-penny premium on the cost of the Booklet.

E27*a*/29*a* The Cross at the apex of the Crown is missing at various positions in the sheet.

1910 (May) Prepared for use, but not issued.

E37	2d.	**tyrian-plum** ..	..	£10000	—

Only one used copy of this stamp is known, in the Royal Collection.

(II) Printed by Harrison & Sons (1911).

(a) Ordinary paper. Perf. 14.

E38	½d.	**dull green** ..	..	1·00	25
E39	½d.	**pale bluish green**	..	£17	£12
		a in pair with Cross	..	£95	£80
		b wmk. sideways	..	—	—
		c imperf. (pair)		—	—
E40	½d.	**bright green** ..		£220	£50
E41	1d.	**rose-red** ..	..	2·00	80
		a no wmk.	..	£75	£75
E42	1d.	**rose-carmine**	..	£28	5·00
E43	1d.	**aniline pink** ..	..	£220	£55
E44	1d.	**aniline rose** ..	..	£100	£40
E45	2½d.	**bright blue** ..	..	£18	5·00
E46	3d.	**purple/lemon** ..	..	£35	£20
E47	3d.	**grey/lemon** ..		—	—
E48	4d.	**bright orange** ..	..	£35	£18

E39*a* See Note after E2*b*.

E40 comes from a fine impression printing of June 1911.

(b) Ordinary paper. Perf. 15 x 14.

E49	½d.	**dull green** ..	..	£12	6·00
E50	1d.	**rose-red** ..	..	£15	4·00
E51	1d.	**rose-carmine** ..	..	4·00	1·00
E52	2½d.	**blue**	..	£18	1·50
E53	3d.	**purple/lemon** ..		£22	60
E54	3d.	**grey/lemon** ..	..	—	—
E55	4d.	**bright orange** ..		£24	£18

(III) Printed at Somerset House (1911-13) Perf. 14.

Ordinary paper, except E62 and E65.

E56	1½d.	**dull purple and green**	£14	4·00
E57	1½d.	**slate-pur and green**	4·00	3·00
E58	2d.	**green and red** ..	£12	2·00
E59	2d.	**green and carmine**..	£12	2·00
E60	5d.	**dull reddish purple and bright blue** ..	£14	3·00
E61	6d.	**Royal purple**..	£25	£22
E62	6d.	**bright magenta** C ..	£1500	—
E63	6d.	**dull purple** ..	£22	3·00
		a no Cross on Crown	£80	£70
E64	6d.	**dull purple** (coated paper)	£135	£35
E65	6d.	**deep plum** C ..	£22	£14
		a no Cross on Crown	£80	£70
E66	7d.	**slate-grey** ..	4·00	4·00
E67	9d.	**reddish purple and blue** ..	£48	£14
E68	9d.	**deep plum and blue**	£40	£14
E69	9d.	**slate-pur and blue**..	£40	£14
E70	10d.	**dull pur and scarlet**	£50	£20
E71	10d.	**dl purple and aniline pink**	£185	£60
E72	10d.	**dl purple and carmine**	£40	£10
		a no Cross on Crown	£125	£100
E73	1/–	**dark green and scar**	£40	£12
E74	1/–	**dark green and car**..	£40	4·00
E75	2/6d.	**dull purple** ..	£400	£30
E75*a*	2/6d.	**dull grey purple** (FA)	£550	£125
E76	2/6d.	**dark purple**	£400	£30
E77	5/–	**carmine**	£575	£45

E78 10/– **blue** £1100 £225
E79 £1 **deep green** £2000 £500

E63*a*/65*a*/72*a* See Note after E29*a*.

E64 was an experimental printing on Dickinson Coated (not Chalky) paper, made in March 1913.

The LOWDEN forgery of the £1 (E79) in the Somerset House deep green shade was produced by *photo-litho* and is slightly coarser than the genuine stamp. The forgery has a watermark impressed in the paper and is usually found affixed to brown paper and tied with a forged Channel Islands postmark. Price: £850 used.

HALF PENNY

Die A

The three upper scales on the dolphin at right form a triangle.

Die B

The topmost scale is incomplete.

Die A

The jewel in the middle of the lower central cross in the Crown is shaped like a comma.

Die B

The jewel is crescent shaped, with points to North West.

ONE PENNY

Die A

Two complete lines cross the ribbon near the "R" of "REVENUE".

Die B

Only one line crosses the ribbon.

Die A

On the central leaf below the ribbon to the right of the Head a fine vertical line appears to the left of the mid-rib.

Die B

There is a dot in place of the fine line.

In each case Die B was a deepening of Die A in an effort to improve the appearance of the stamps.

1911 (June 22nd)-12 (*Typo*) Harrison and Sons (certain preliminary printings having been made at Somerset House). Perf. 15 x 14. Sheets 240 – two panes, each 12 x 10.

(i) Wmk. Imperial Crown. Die A.

G1	½d.	**green** (22/6/11)	..	2·50	1·00
G2	½d.	**bluish-green**	..	£200	£30
		a perf. 14	..	£2000	£200
G3	1d.	**car-red** (22/6/11)	..	2·50	50
		a perf. 14	..	£3000	—
		b wmk. sideways	..	—	—
G4	1d.	**pale carmine**	..	4·00	60
		a no cross on crown	..	£190	£40

(ii) Die B.

(a) Wmk. Imperial Crown.

G5	½d.	**yellow-green**	..	3·00	45
G5A	½d.	**bright green** ..	..	2·50	40
		a wmk. sideways	..	—	£1000
G6	½d.	**bluish-green**	..	£125	£30
G7	1d.	**pale carmine**	..	2·00	75
		a no cross on crown	..	£200	£40
G7A	1d.	**rose-pink**	..	£22	8·00
G8	1d.	**scarlet** (6/12)	..	£18	6·00
G8A	1d.	**aniline scarlet**	..	£90	£35

(b) Wmk. Single Cypher GVR (Booklet Stamps.

G9	½d.	**green** ..	.. ..	8·00	6·00
G10	1d.	**scarlet**	.. ..	6·00	6·00

REDRAWN TYPES
HALF PENNY

Original	Redrawn

Ornament between dol- | The ornament has one
phin's heads has two | thick line.
thin lines left of centre.

PENNY

The body of the lion is | The body is shaded all
unshaded. | over.

1912 (Jan. 1st-Oct.) (*Typo*) **Harrison and Sons. Perf. 15 x 14. Sheets as before.**

(a) Wmk. Imperial Crown. (1/1/12).

G11	½d.	**deep green** ..	.. ..	8·00	2·50
G12	½d.	**yellow-green**	.. ..	1·50	1·00
	a	no cross on crown..		£60	£12
G13	1d.	**bright scarlet**	..	1·00	20
	a	no cross on crown..		£40	£10
G14	1d.	**scarlet**	.. ..	1·00	20
G14A	1d.	**aniline scarlet**	..	£100	£30
	a	no cross on crown..		£425	—

(b) Wmk. Single Cypher GVR (Aug. 1912).

G15	½d.	**green** ..	.. ..	85	30
	a	no cross on crown..		£45	£12
G16	1d.	**scarlet**	.. ..	80	20
	a	no cross on crown..		£45	£12

(c) Wmk. Mult. Cypher GVR (October 1912).

G17	½d.	**green** ..	.. ..	85	85
	a	no cross on crown..		£60	£20
	aa	yellow green	..	3·00	2·50
	b	imperf.	.. ..	£75	—
	c	wmk. sideways	..	—	£700

G18	1d.	**scarlet**	.. ..	2·80	1·60
	a	no cross on crown..		£60	£20
	aa	bright red ..		3·00	1·50
	b	imperf.	.. ..	£60	—
	c	wmk. sideways	..	£75	£45
	d	wmk. side no cross		£350	—

1912-22 (*Typo*) **Harrison and Sons (except 6d. which, together with certain printings of other values, came from Somerset House). Wmk. Single Cypher. Perf. 15 x 14. Sheets 240 – two panes, each 12 x 10.**

2d. Die I Four lines of shading between top of head and oval frame. Die II Three lines of shading between top of head and oval frame.

G19	½d.	**green** (1/13)..	..	15	15
	a	doubly printed (1915)	.. ..	£1750	—
G20	½d.	**yellow-green**		6·00	1·00
G21	1d.	**br scarlet** (10/12) ..		15	10
	a	"Q" for "O"	..	£120	£120
G22	1d.	**carmine**	.. ..	8·00	20
G23	1½d.	**red-brown** (10/12)		25	20
	a	"PENCF" ..	..	£130	£120
G24	1½d.	**chestnut**	.. ..	1·00	25
	a	"PENCF" ..	..	£130	£120
G25	2d.	**orange-yel** (Die I) (8/12)	.. ..	6·00	1·00
G26	2d.	**reddish-or** (Die I) (11/13)	.. ..	1·50	25
G27	2d.	**orange** (Die II) (9/21)	.. ..	2·00	80
G28	2½d.	**cobalt-blue** (10/12)		5·00	1·00
G29	2½d.	**blue** ..	.. ..	3·50	1·00
G30	3d.	**dull reddish-violet** (10/12)	.. ..	8·00	1·00
G31	3d.	**pale violet**	..	2·25	35
G32	4d.	**dp grey** (1/13)	..	4·00	1·50
G33	4d.	**pale grey-green**		3·00	1·00
G34	5d.	**brown** (6/13)	..	4·00	1·50
G35	5d.	**bistre brown**	..	£35	£10
G36	6d.	**reddish-purple**	..	3·50	60
	a	perf. 14	.. ..	£60	£30
G37	6d.	**plum** ..	.. ..	5·00	1·00
G38	7d.	**olive** (8/13) ..	..	£10	3·00
G39	7d.	**sage-green** ('17) ..		£15	4·00
G40	8d.	**black/yellow** (8/13)	..	£28	6·00
G41	8d.	**blk/yel buff-granite** (5/17)	.. ..	£32	7·00
G42	9d.	**pale agate** (6/13) ..		8·00	2·00
G43	9d.	**deep agate** ..	..	8·00	2·50
G44	9d.	**pl or-grn** (9/22) ..		£95	£16
G45	9d.	**deep olive-green** ..		£95	£16
G46	10d.	**tur-blue** (8/13) ..		£11	8·00
G47	10d.	**pl greenish-blue** ..		£15	9·00
G48	1/–	**bistre-brn** (8/13) ..		9·00	50
G49	1/–	**olive-brown** ('20) ..		£24	1·50
G19/48		**set** (15v)	.. ..	£170	£40

The above is a simplified listing of a large variety of shades. The 6d. value may be found on Chalky as well as Ordinary paper.

G19a comes from the bottom of a sheet with Control G15 (6 copies known).

G21a This variety was caused by a scratch on Row 1/4 which turns the "O" of "ONE" into a "Q" (Control E14).

G23a, 24a Occurred and was corrected on Row 15/12 of Plates 12 and 29 (Controls L18, M19, O19 and Q21).

The 1½d. in chocolate-brown and the 5d. in yellow-brown exist without wmk.

All values, except 10d., exist with inverted watermark.

For G25, 26, 27 bisected, see Channel Islands.

1913 (Aug.) As before but wmk. Multiple Cypher. Perf. 15 x 14. Originally issued in vertical rolls of 480; but subsequently a part sheet was found, giving horizontal pairs and blocks.

G50	½d.	**bright green**	£80	£50
G51	1d.	**dull scarlet**	£225	£75

1913-34 (Recess) Wmk. Large Single Cypher. Perf. 11 x 12. Sheets 4 x 10.
(i) Portrait medallion background horizontal lines only.

(a) Waterlow Bros. and Layton (July 1913). Height 22mm.

G52	2/6	**sepia-brown**	£250	£25
G52A	2/6	**deep sepia-brown**	£250	£30
G53	5/-	**rose-carmine**	£500	£55
G54	10/-	**indigo-blue**	£1150	£125
G55	£1	**green**	£3500	£950
G55A	£1	**blue green**	£3500	£950
G55B	£1	**bright green**	£4000	£1200
G52/55		**set** (4v)	£5000	£1100

(b) De La Rue and Co. (Dec. 1915-18). Height 22mm.

G56	2/6	**yellow-brown**	£450	£35
G57	2/6	**seal-brown**	£400	£35
G58	5/-	**bright carmine**	£750	£60
G59	5/-	**pale carmine**	£750	£60
G60	10/-	**deep blue**	£3000	£275
G61	10/-	**pale blue**	£3000	£275
G61A	10/-	**deep bright blue**	£5000	£1000
G61B	10/-	**Cambridge blue**	£6000	£1200

(c) Bradbury Wilkinson and Co. (Dec. 1918). Height 22¾-23mm.

G62	2/6	**olive-brown**	£150	£12
G63	2/6	**reddish-brown**	£150	£12
G64	5/-	**rose-red**	£300	£12
G65	10/-	**dull grey-blue**	£750	£30

Re-entries are known as follows :—

Waterlow 2/6—Row 1/2—Row 2/1.
De La Rue 2/6—Row 2/1—Row 10/4.
Bradbury 2/6—Row 1—Nos. 1, 2, 3 and 4.
Row 2/4—Row 3, Nos. 2 and 4.
Row 5/1—Row 7/1.
10/- Row 1/1—Row 6/1.
Prices from £400 unused, £175 used.

(ii) Portrait medallion background horizontal and diagonal lines.

Waterlow (Re-engraved Die). Oct. 1934.

G66	2/6	**chocolate-brown**		£125	5·00
G67	2/6	**reddish-brown**		£150	5·00
G68	5/-	**rose-red**		£285	8·00
G69	10/-	**indigo**		£500	£14

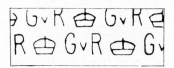

1924 (April)-26 As G19/49 but wmk. Multiple Block GVR. Waterlow and Sons (except 6d. printed as Somerset House and Harrison and Sons (1934-5). Sheets 12 x 20.

G70	¾d.	**green**		15	15
	a	wmk. sideways		9·00	3·50
	b	doubly printed		£800	—
G71	1d.	**scarlet**		60	20
	a	inverted "Q" for "O"		£300	—
	b	wmk. sideways		£18	8·00
	c	experimental paper		£30	—
G72	1½d.	**red-brown**		35	15
	a	wmk. sideways		4·00	2·00
	b	tete beche (pair)		£200	£175
	c	printed on gummed side		£240	—
	d	experimental paper		£25	—
	e	booklet pane (4 stamps and 2 labels)		£25	—
G73	2d.	**orange (Die II)**		1·25	35
	a	wmk. sideways		£155	£40
	b	double print		£2000	—
	c	no wmk.		£250	—
G74	2½d.	**blue**		3·25	1·00
	a	no wmk		£275	—
G75	3d.	**violet**		5·00	60
G76	4d.	**grey-green**		9·50	1·00
	a	printed on gummed side		£625	—
G77	5d.	**brown**		£13	1·75
G78	6d.	**purple (C)**		8·00	1·00
	a	ordinary paper (6/26)		4·00	20
G79	9d.	**olive-green**		£12	1·50
G80	10d.	**turquoise-blue**		£22	8·00
G81	1/-	**bistre-brown**		£24	1·00
G70/81		**set** (12v)		£85	£15

G70b came from the upper and left side of a sheet with Control U34.

G71a consists of a thick tail projecting from the top left of the "O" of "ONE" (Row 20/3). A diagonal cut is invariably found in the Jubilee Line below the stamp showing this variety.

71c, G72d The watermark on this paper is shorter, rounder and thicker.
G73 and G74 exist without wmk.
For G73 bisected, see Channel Islands.

1924-25 British Empire Exhibition. (Recess) **Waterlow and Sons. Wmk. Multiple Block GVR. Perf. 14. Sheets 6 x 10. Designer, H. Nelson.**

(a) Dated 1924. (April 23rd 1924).

G82	1d. **scarlet**	.. ..	8·00	£10
	a imperf. between stamp and margin		—	—
G83	1½d. **brown**..	.. ..	£13	£12
	a imperf. between stamp and left margin ..	..	—	—

(b) Dated 1925 (May 9th 1925).

G84	1d. **scarlet**	.. ..	£18	£17
G85	1½d. **brown**..	.. ..	£70	£40

G82a is known imperf. on lower margin and also on left margin.
Total Printed—(G82/5), 17,000,000.

1929 (May 10th) 9th U.P.U. Congress

(London). Designers, G86 and G89 J. Farleigh: G87, G88, E. Linzell: G90 H. Nelson.

(a) (Typo) **Waterlow and Sons. Wmk. Multiple Block GVR. Perf. 15 x 14. Sheets 12 x 20.**

G86	½d. **green**	..	..	2·50	10
	a wmk. sideways	..		£65	£30
	b wmk. invt.	..	..	£10	6·00
G87	1d. **scarlet**		..	1·75	80
	a wmk. sideways		..	£60	£35
	b wmk. invt.	..	..	£10	6·00
G88	1½d. **purple-brown**		..	1·25	30
	a wmk. sideways		..	£60	£18
	b wmk. invt.	..	..	£10	6·00
G89	2½d. **blue**	..	..	£12	4·00
	a wmk. invt.	..	..	£225	—

G86/89 were also sold in 2,'– and 3/– booklets.

(b) (Recess) **Bradbury Wilkinson. Wmk. Large Single Cypher. Perf. 12. Sheets 5 x 4.**

G90	£1 **black**	..	..	£1250	£850

Numbers Issued—G86, 677.500,000; G87, 341,000,000; G88, 751,250,000; G89, 26,750,000; G90, 61,000.

All stamps from G91 onwards are (photo) **Harrison and Sons Ltd. on Multiple Block GVR paper, perf. 15 x 14 – unless otherwise indicated.**

1934 (Aug. 20th)-36 Designs as Nos. G70/81 but with dark background in portrait medallion. Sheets 12 x 20.

(a) Large Format. 18¼ x 22¼ mm.

G91	1d. **scarlet** (24/9/34)	..		25	10
	a printed on gummed side		.. ..	£300	—
G92	1½d. **red-brn** (20/8/34)	..		25	10

(b) Intermediate Format. 18 x 22mm.

G93	½d. **green** (19/11/34)	..		15	10
G94	1d. **scarlet** ('34)	..		25	10
G95	1½d. **red-brown** ('34)	..		50	20
	a imperf. (pair)	..		£160	—
	b imperf. three sides (pair)	..	..	£200	—
G96	2d. **orange** (21/1/35)	..		40	15

(c) Small Format. 17¼ x 21½mm.

G97	½d. **green** ('35)	..	..	15	1C
	a wmk. sideways	..		6·00	75
	b Devil's Horns	..		—	—
	c wmk. invt...		..	6·00	3·00
G98	1d. **scarlet** ('35)		..	15	10
	a wmk. sideways	..		8·00	4·00
	b imperf. (pair)	..		£525	—
	c imperf. three sides (pair)	..		—	—
	d wmk. invt.		..	6·00	3·00

G99	1½d.	**red-brown**	15	10
	a	wmk. sideways ..	8·00	3·00
	b	booklet pane (4 stamps and 2 labels)	£15	—
G100	2d.	**orange**	35	15
	a	wmk. sideways ..	£125	£45
	b	imperf. (pair) ..	£650	—
	c	wmk. invt...	2·00	1·50
G101	2½d.	**blue** (18/3/35) ..	1·50	75
G102	3d.	**violet** (18/3/35) ..	1·50	50
G103	4d.	**deep grey-green** (2/12/35).. ..	1·50	60
G104	5d.	**yel-brn** (17/2/36)..	3·50	60
G105	9d.	**deep olive-green** (2/12/35).. ..	£13	1·25
G106	10d.	**tur-blue** (24/2/36)	£13	4·00
G107	1/-	**bistre-brown** (24/2/36).. ..	£22	75
G97/107		**set** (11v)	£55	9·00

G97*b* The combination of a plate flaw in conjunction with the nick at the outer end of the "POSTAGE" scroll gives the appearance of Satanic Horns (Row 1/12, Cyl. 36, Control X 35).

The reduction in size of these stamps was on account of the need for wider gutters for high speed perforating.

For G96, G100 bisected, see Channel Islands.

1935 (May 7th) Silver Jubilee, Designer, Barnett Freedman. Sheets 6 x 20. There are three different types of the ½d., 1d. and 1½d. Type I (Sheet Printing): Type II (Booklet Printing — wmk. inverted): Type III (Booklet Printing — wmk. upright).

G108	½d.	**green**	05	10
G109	1d.	**scarlet**	80	80
G110	1½d.	**red-brown**	50	10
G111	2½d.	**blue**	6·50	5·00
G112	2½d.	**prussian blue** ..	£3650	£2250
G108/111		**set** (4v)	7·00	5·50

G112 was a Colour Trial of which three sheets were perforated and issued in error to a Post Office in Edmonton (London), 319 copies were bought by a local collector.

Numbers Issued—G108, 353m; G109, 150m; G110, 490m; G111, 14m; G112, 360.

G108/111 were also sold in 2/- and 3/- booklets.

1936 (Sept. 1st) Design suggested by H. J.

Brown. Wmk. Multiple Block E8R. Sheets 12 x 20.

E113	½d.	**green**..	10	05
	a	falling pearl ..	—	—
E114	1d.	**scarlet** (Sept. 14) ..	10	05
E115	1½d.	**red-brown**	15	05
E116	2½d.	**bright blue**	35	40
E113/116		**set** (4v)	60	50

E113*a* A superfluous pearl appears to the right of the crown Row 20/2 (Cyls. 7, 10 and 12—all with stop, Control A/36).

As before but wmk. invert. (ex booklets).

E113b	½d.	**green**	3·50	3·50
E114a	1d.	**scarlet**	2·25	2·25
E115a	1½d.	**red-brown**	60	60

Complete Booklet Panes.
(Unused) Wmk.

				Upright	Invert
E113c	½d.	pane of 6		1·00	£20
E114b	1d.	pane of 6		1·00	£14
E115b	1½d.	pane of 6		1·50	4·00
E115c	1½d.	pane of 4 plus 2 labels		6·00	8·00
E115d	1½d.	pane of 2		1·50	1·50

The following stamps were printed on "Multiple Block GVIR" paper and perf. 14¾ x 14 (C), unless otherwise indicated. Sheets 12 x 20.

1937-47 Designs, King's Head with National Emblems in corners. Designers, E. Gill (*frames*) and E. Dulac (*portrait*), but 7d. to 1/- designed entirely by the latter.

1	½d.	**dp green** (10/5/37) ..	10	05
2	1d.	**dp scarlet** (10/5/37)..	10	05
3	1½d.	**dp red-brn** (30/7/37) ..	10	05
	a	damaged crown ..	—	—
	aa	pair imperf three sides	—	—
4	2d.	**dp orange** (31/1/38)..	50	10
5	2½d.	**dp ult** (10/5/37) ..	20	10
	aa	tete beche pair ..	—	—
6	3d.	**violet** (31/1/38) ..	1·25	30
7	4d.	**grn-grey** (21/11/38)..	40	25
	a	imperf pair	£320	—
	aa	pair imperf three sides	£300	—
	b	dp greenish-grey (/44)	60	30

8	5d.	**pale brown** (21/11/38)		1·00	25
	a	imperf pair	..	£375	—
	aa	pair imperf three sides		£300	—
	b	dull chestnut (/46)		1·75	35
9	6d.	**pale purple** (30/1/39)		1·40	15
	a	reddish-purple (/42)		1·50	15
10	7d.	**emerald grn** (27/2/39)		3·00	35
	a	imperf pair	..	£350	—
	b	imperf pair (3 sides)		£300	—
11	8d.	**dp rose** (27/2/39)	..	4·75	45
12	9d.	**dp olive** (1/5/39)	..	3·75	30
13	10d.	**dp grey-blue** (1/5/39)		3·20	30
	a	imperf pair	..	—	£400
14	11d.	**dp plum** (29/12/47)	..	2·80	80
15	1/–	**bistre-brown** (1/5/39)		3·50	10
	a	broken barb..	..	£80	£35
	b	broken cross	..	£80	£35
1–15		**set** (15) ..	..	£25	3·00

As before but wmk. invert (ex booklets)

1a	½d.	**dp green** (8/37)	..	1·00	75
2a	1d.	**dp scarlet** (8/37)	..	£20	3·00
3b	1½d.	**dp red-brn** (8/37)	..	1·00	75
4a	2d.	**dp orange** (7/40)	..	£32	4·00
5a	2½d.	**dp ult** (7/40)	..	£18	3·00
1a–5a		**set** (5) ..	..	£65	£10

Complete Booklet Panes
(Unused)

				Wmk. Upright	Invert
1c	½d.	pane of 6..	..	1·00	8·00
1e	½d.	pane of 2..	..	50	—
2c	1d.	pane of 6..	..	5·00	£100
2e	1d.	pane of 2..	..	50	—
3d	1½d.	pane of 6..	..	£10	£15
3e	1½d.	pane of 4 plus 2 labels..		£15	£18
3f	1½d.	pane of 2..	..	75	—
4c	2d.	pane of 6..	..	£20	£135
5c	2½d.	pane of 6..	..	£15	£85

As before but wmk. sideways

1b	½d.	**dp green** (1/38)	..	35	35
1d		pane of 4..	..	£18	—
2b	1d.	**dp scarlet** (2/38)	..	6·00	3·00
2d		pane of 4..	..	£25	—
3c	1½d.	**dp red-brn** (2/38)	..	1·00	70
4b	2d.	**dp orange** (2/38)	..	£24	£12
5b	2½d.	**dp ult** (10/37) ..	..	£28	£16
1b–5b		**set** (5) ..	..	£90	£30

Stamps with wmk. sideways are from coils (½d. and 1d values exist also in panes from booklets), and those with wmk. inverted from booklets, and the dates given (*supplied officially*) refer to when they were issued to postmasters for use by the public.

Perforated or imperforate stamps with thick bars cancelling the stamps are "School Stamps" or experimental material not issued for postal purposes.

3*a* The left cross at the base of the crown is broken. Row 19/7.

8*a* A sheet of stamps purchased at a Stockport P.O. had perforation missing on the first three rows.

13*a* Used block (3 x 2) with partial vertical perfs on top row is known with Belfast postmark.

15*a* The sepal (*heraldic term barb*) at right side of rose is broken short. Row 7/12, Control S/46, Cyl. 16.

15*b* Base of cross at right side of crown is missing. Row 18/2 (*same sheet as variety* 15*a*).

1939-48 Design and Designers, 2/6 and 5/– (King's Head above Royal Arms, by E. Dulac) ; 10/– and £1 (King's Head with Frame of National Emblems, by Hon. G. R. Bellew). Printers (*recess*) **Waterlow & Sons. Wmk. "Crown on GVIR"** (*single*)**. Perf. 14 (C). Sheets 8 x 5.**

16	2/6	**brown** (4/9/39)	..	£65	£10
	a	dp brn	..	£75	£10
	aa	re-entry	..	£125	£40
17	2/6	**green** (9/3/42)	..	£10	40
	a	re-entry	..	£85	£30
18	5/–	**red** (21/8/39) ..		£25	1·00
	a	re-entry	..	£200	£35
	b	"T" Guide line	..	—	—
19	10/–	**blue-black** (3/10/39)		£165	£12
	a	steel blue-black (/42)		£200	£15
	b	retouched frame	..	£300	£35
20	10/–	**ultramarine** (30/11/42)		£30	2·00
21	£1	**dp brown** (1/10/48)..		£50	£15
16/21		**set** (6) ..	..	£325	£35

16*aa* This re-entry shows on fore leg and under unicorn and in shield Row 4/3.

17*a* These re-entries show strong doubling of the harp and lower right quarter of shield (Row 5/2) ; and ragged left frame and extra vertical line between upper quarters of shield (Row 1/7).

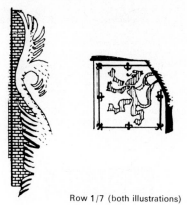

Row 1/7 (both illustrations)

18a This re-entry shows as doubling of the lions in the shield, Row 4/2.

Row 2/7

18b The "T" Guide Lines are found on Rows 2/3. 2/7 and 5/4.

19b This retouch is to be found at the lower left side of oval frame, Row 2/6.

Number issued—2/6 (16), 8,660,000; 2/6 (17), 56,000,000; 5/–, 27,380,000; 10/– (19 and 19a), 1,960,000; 10/– (20), 7,350,000; £1, 920,000.

Specimen overprints exist on 2/6 brn; 2/6 grn; 5/– red; 10/– blue-black; 10/– ult; £1 brn. All are scarce.

1941-51 As Nos. 1 to 6 but backgrounds in lighter shades (a wartime measure).

22	½d.	**green** (1/9/41) ..	10	05
	a	tete-beche horiz. pr	£400	—
	c	imperf pair (9/43) ..	£325	—
	d	dull green (/48) ..	25	05
23	1d.	**scarlet** (1st state) (11/8/41)	20	05
	a	scar left cheek ..	£40	—
	b	imperf pair	£325	—
	ba	pair imperf three sides	£275	—
	bb	vert pair imperf between	£450	—
	d	thick paper (/42) ..	2·00	1·00
	f	scarlet (2nd state) (/48)	20	10
	g	thick paper (/51) ..	2·00	80

24	1½d.	**red-brown** (28/9/42)	40	1‡
25	2d.	**dull orange** (6/10/41)	50	05
	c	tete-beche horiz. pr.	£650	—
	d	imperf pair (8/43) ..	£700	—
26	2½d.	**ultramarine** (21/7/41)	20	05
	a	tete-beche horiz. pr.	£700	—
	d	imperf pair ..	£325	—
	e	b for D var. (/48) ..	£15	£10
	f	thick paper (/47) ..	2·00	50
27	3d.	**purple-violet** (3/11/41)	80	20
	a	major retouch ..	£20	£12
22/27		**set** (6)	2·00	50

As before but wmk. invert (ex booklets).

22b	½d.	**green** (3/42)	1·50	1·00
25a	2d.	**dull orange** (3/42) ..	3·00	1·50
	da	imperf (/49) ..	£600	—
26b	2½d.	**ult** (3/42)	2·50	1·75
22b/26b		**set** (3)	6·00	4·00

Complete Booklet Panes

		(Unused)		Wmk. Upright	Invert
22e	½d.	pane of 6	.. ..	2·00	£10
22f	½d.	pane of 4		5·00	—
22g	½d.	pane of 2		1·00	—
23h	1d.	pane of 4		5·00	—
23l	1d.	pane of 2		1·00	—
24a	1½d.	pane of 4		5·00	—
24b	1½d.	pane of 2		1·00	—
25e	2d.	pane of 6		£10	£20
25g	2½d.	pane of 6		£10	£18

As before but wmk. sideways (ex coils).

23c	1d.	**scarlet** (1st state) (9/42)	3·50	2·00
	e	ditto (thick paper) (/51)	£12	6·00
25b	2d.	**dull orange** (6/42) ..	7·00	6·00
26c	2½d.	**ult** (8/42)	5·00	3·00
23c/26c		**set** (3)	£15	£11

22a/25c/26a These tete-beche varieties came from faulty made booklets (with an extra row of stamps doubled back).

22c Only one used block of four and a mint vertical pair are known, ex a booklet bought in Huddersfield in 1943.

23a A small oval-shaped flaw on the left cheek has the appearance of a scar. Row 3/4, U/47, Cyl. 149.

23 1st State—At the back of the King's head an unshaded lock crosses the dark patch of hair. The upper lip is straight and a white mark is to be found alongside the front upper edge of the ear. All overprinted stamps (1d. Scarlet) are 1st State, except Eritrea No. 15, Morocco Agencies No. B2 and Tripolitania No. 15.

2nd State—The lock and white mark have been eliminated by retouching and the upper lip now curves inwards.

23d/23g/26f In mint copies the gum has an enamelled appearance and the wmk. is barely visible.

25d A block of five ex a booklet, is known, with wmk. normal.

25da A block of six (ex a booklet with wmk. inverted) was bought at a Cardiff P.O. in 1949. Three used copies (on cover) and a mint pair are also known.

26*d* A block of six (*ex a booklet*), a block of four and pairs are known.

26*e* What would normally be a D after the 2½ has been converted into a b through small defect on the plate Row 18/3, Cyl. 238 (*see illustration*).

(26*e*)

27*a* Considerable retouching had been undertaken on the background and hair of the King. Row 9/10, Cyl. 34.

1951 (May 3rd) As No. 22, etc., but colours changed (*to conform with "U.P.U." regulations*).

28	½d.	**dull orange**	..	10	10
	b	imperf pair	..	£500	—
	c	tete-beche pair	..	£1200	—
29	1d.	**ultramarine** (2nd state)		10	10
	c	imperf. pair	..	£375	—
	d	pair imperf 3 sides	..	£160	—
30	1½d.	**green**	..	40	15
31	2d.	**red-brown**	..	60	20
	aa	tete-beche pair	..	£1100	—
	ab	pair imperf 3 sides	..	£180	—
	e	dp red-brown (/51)		50	20
32	2½d.	**scarlet**	..	25	10
	aa	tete-beche pair	..	£1000	—
33	4d.	**light blue**	..	1·00	50
	a	double print..	..	—	—
28/33		**set** (6)	..	2·40	1·00

For No. 29 overprinted "POSTAGE DUE" see PD13*a*.

As before but wmk. invert (ex booklets).

28a	½d.	**dull orange**	..	30	20
29b	1d.	**ult** (2nd state) (3/52)		2·00	1·50
30b	1½d.	**green** (3/52)	..	1·20	80
31a	2d.	**red-brown**	..	3·00	1·50
	f	dp red-brn (/51)	..	4·50	2·00
32a	2½d.	**scarlet** (/51)	..	80	60
28a/32a		**set** (5)	..	7·00	4·50

Complete Booklet Panes
(**Unused**)

				Wmk.	
				Upright	Invert
28d	½d.	pane of 6	..	3·00	8·00
28e	½d.	pane of 4	..	2·00	5·00
28f	½d.	pane of 2	..	50	—
29e	1d.	pane of 6	..	3·00	£14
29f	1d.	pane of 4	..	2·00	£10
29g	1d.	pane of 2	..	75	—
29h	1d.	pane of 3 plus 3 labels	£10	£10
30c	1½d.	pane of 6	..	3·00	8·00
30d	1½d.	pane of 4	..	2·50	6·00
30e	1½d.	pane of 2	..	2·00	—
31h	2d.	pane of 6	..	3·00	£20
31i	2d.	pane of 6 (31f)	..	5·00	£14
32d	2½d.	pane of 6	..	3·00	6·00

As before but wmk. sideways (ex coils).

29a	1d.	**ult** (1st state) (3/51)	..	15	25
30a	1½d.	**green** (3/51)	..	55	45
31b	2d.	**red-brown** (/51)	..	60	60
	c	swan neck variety	..	£12	£12
	d	ditto (retouched)	..	£10	£10
	g	bt red-brn	..	70	70

32b	2½d.	**scarlet** (/51)	..	60	60
	c	long serif to S	..	£10	£10
29a/32b		**set** (4)	..	1·85	1·75

28*b* An imperf booklet pane (perf at bottom) and a strip of three imperf exist.

31*c*/31*d* A flaw on the 2, and visible to the naked eye earned by its appearance the designation of "swan neck" variety. There are two types of the flaw (both are listed under No. 31*c*), the second showing also a vertical smudge. A subsequent retouch left a dark speck where the flaw had been (*see illustration*).

32*c* The serif of S in postage is to be found lengthened on every 25th stamp of certain coils with wmk. sideways (*see illustration*).

1951 (May 3rd) Designs and Designers, 2/6 "H.M.S. Victory"; 5/– "The Cliffs of Dover" by Miss Adshead; 10/– "St. George and Dragon"; £1 "Royal Arms" by Percy Metcalfe. Printers (*recess*) **Waterlow & Sons. Wmk. "Crown on GVIR"** (*single*)**, Perf. 11 x 11¾ (C). Sheets 4 x 10.**

34	2/6	**green**	..	£15	30
35	5/–	**red**	..	£30	1·00
36	10/–	**ultramarine**	..	£20	5·50
37	£1	**dp brown**	..	£65	8·00
	a	brown	..	£60	7·50
	b	re-entry	..	£150	£25
34/37		**set** (4)	..	£120	£14

37*b* "DIEU" is doubled on Row 7/1.

Number issued—2/6, 40,723,102; 5/– 22,141,445; 10/–, 10,122,720; £1, 2,383,720.

SPECIAL ISSUES

1937 (May 13th) Coronation. Designer, E. Dulac. Sheets 6 x 20.

S1	1½d.	**dark maroon**	..	10	10
	a	colon variety	..	2·50	1·50

S1a Two dots (vertical) appear between 12 and May. Row 10/1, Cyl. 7 (see illustration).

Number issued—388,731,480.

1940 (May 6th) Centenary of First Postage Stamps. Designer, H. L. Palmer. Perf. 14½ x 14 (C). Sheets 8 x 20.

S2	½d. **dp green**	10	10
S3	1d. **dp scarlet**	10	10
S4	1½d. **dp red-brown**	35	40
S5	2d. **dp orange**	30	25
S6	2½d. **dp blue**	70	20
	a neck flaw	—	—
	b flaw retouched	£25	£10
S7	3d. **violet**	6·00	4·00
S2/7	**set** (6)	7·50	5·00

S6a Small oval flaw on lower part of Queen's neck. Row 20/2, G40, Cyl. 2.

S6b Above flaw retouched by three short lines.

Number issued—½d., 82,896,960; 1d., 232,903,680; 1½d., 40,412,880; 2d., 121,065,120; 2½d., 312,957,440; 3d. 22,128,000.

1946 (June 11th) Victory. Designs and Designers, 2½d. (King's Head, with Emblems of State and Commerce, by H. L. Palmer); 3d. (Dove and Olive Branch, by R. Stone). Sheets 6 x 20.

S8	2½d. **ultramarine**	10	10
	a extra hawse-pipe	£30	£10
S9	3d. **violet**	10	10
	a seven berries	£12	2·00
	b glossy surface	35	20

S8a A white dot in line with and abaft the two hawse-pipes in bows of ship (commonly known as three port holes variety). Row 16/1, S46, Cyl. 11.

S9a An extra olive on the lower leaf (right hand side of branch). Row 12/5, Cyl. 4, Row 20/1, Cyl. 4.

S9b Final releases (on slightly thicker paper) presented a shiny appearance.

Number issued—2½d., 307,832,520; 3d. 43,185,720.

1948 (April 26th) Silver Wedding. Designs (from photographs by Dorothy Wilding) Portraits of King and Queen. Designers, 2½d. (G. T Knipe). Sheets 6 x 20; £1 (Joan Hassall). Sheets 5 x 4.

S10	2½d. **ultramarine**	10	10
S11	£1 **dp blue**	£80	£50

Number issued—2½d., 147,500,000; £1, 419,628.

1948 (May 10th) Third Anniversary of Liberation. Designs and Designers, 1d. (Gathering Seaweed, by J. R. Stobie); 2½d. (Gathering Seaweed, from painting by E. Blampied). Sheets 6 x 20.

CIS1	1d. **scarlet**	10	10
	a rose red	50	15

CIS2 2½d. **dp ultramrine** .. 15 15
　　　　a wheel flaw.. .. 6·00 6·00

CIS2*a* A white blotch breaks rim of cartwheel, Row 20/5. This variety was present on the sheet from very first printing and never retouched as far as we know.

Number issued—1d., 5,934,000; 2d., 5,398,000.

These stamps were only on general sale at Post Offices in the Channel Islands, but they were available at certain Head Post Offices and were valid for use throughout Great Britain.

1948 (July 29th) London Olympic Games. Designs, King's Head and various Olympic symbols. Designers, 2½d. (P. Metcalfe); 3d. (A. Games); 6d. (S. D. Scott); 1/– (E. Dulac). Sheets 6 x 20.

S12	2½d.	**ultramarine** ..	10	10
S13	3d.	**violet** ..	20	20
		a crown flaw ..	£10	4·00
		b flaw retouched	£20	8·00
S14	6d.	**reddish-purple**	30	40
		a "HLP"	£125	—
		b retouch	£20	—
S15	1/–	**bistre-brown**	50	60
S12/15		**set** (4) ..	1·00	1·20

S13*a*/*b* A white blotch at the left base of the crown, which was later retouched, leaving a small blotch, Row 20/2, Cyl. 1.

S14*a*/*b* The initials H.L.P. (H. L. Palmer) exist on Cyl. 9 stop in the Jubilee lines below stamps Nos. 118, 119, 120. Later printings have these letters erased.

Number issued—2½d., 155,350,000; 3d., 32,554,000; 6d., 24,397,000 (*air letters with* 6d *stamps*, 4,060,000); 1/–, 32,187,000.

1949 (Oct. 10th) U.P.U. Designs and Designers, 2½d. (Globes by Mary Adshead); 3d. (U.P.U. Statue at Berne, by P. Metcalfe); 6d. (Goddess Concordia, by H. Fleury); 1/– (Globe and Horn, by Hon. G. Bellew). Sheets 6 x 20.

S16	2½d.	**ultramarine** ..	10	10
		a Indian lake ..	£15	8·00
		b Indian lake ..	£30	£12
		c flaw retouched	£50	£20
		d America retouch	—	—
S17	3d.	**pale violet**	20	30
S18	6d.	**reddish-mauve**	50	55
S19	1/–	**bistre-brown**	85	1·00
S16/19		**set** (4) ..	1·50	1·85

S16*a*　　　　　　　S16*b*

S16*a* A white blotch appears on India, resembling a lake, Row 14/1, Cyl. 3 (stop).

S16*b*/*c* A similar "lake" is also known in a slightly lower position Row 8/2, Cyl. 2 (no stop). This flaw was subsequently retouched.

S16*d* Extensive retouching of Central and South America, etc. Hawaii and Galapagos Islands are missing. Island in wrong position, etc. Row 18/2, Cyl. 5.

Number issued—2½d., 135,150,000; 3d., 16,400,000; 6d., 11,450,000; 1/–, 11,400,000.

1951 (May 3rd) Festival of Britain. Designs and Designers, 2½d. "Cornucopia and Mercury" by E. Dulac; 4d. "Festival Symbols" by A. Games. Sheets 6 x 20.

| S20 | 2½d. | dp scarlet | .. | .. | 10 | 10 |
| S21 | 4d. | dp ultramarine | .. | | 25 | 25 |

Number issued—2½d., 260,142,000; 4d., 22,197,000.

POSTAGE DUE STAMPS

All Postage Due Stamps were (*Typo*) in sheets 20 x 12 with wmk. sideways (normally pointing to left of stamp). Perf. 14 x 15.

1914 (April 20th)-23 Wmk. Single Cypher. Printed by Harrison and Sons (except 1/– value and certain printings of other values).

GD1	½d.	emerald	..	..	50	20
GD2	1d.	carmine	..	..	60	10
GD3	1½d.	chestnut ('23)	..	£25	£12
GD4	2d.	agate ..	..	..	1·00	20
GD5	3d.	violet ('18)	..	..	2·50	75
GD6	4d.	dl grey-grn ('21)	..	5·00	75
GD7	5d.	bistre-brown	..	..	6·00	1·00
GD8	1/–	bright blue (7/15)..	£15	2·50
GD1/8		set (8v)	..	..	£55	£16

GD2 is known bisected for use as a ½d. value to make up 1½d. rate on letters from Ceylon (1921).

1924 As GD2 but printed on thick chalk surfaced paper by Waterlow and Sons.

| GD9 | 1d. | carmine | .. | .. | 4·50 | 3·00 |

1924-31 As before but wmk. Multiple Block GVR. Printed by Waterlow and Sons and, from 1934, Harrison and Sons.

GD10	½d.	emerald	..	..	60	15
GD11	1d.	carmine	..	..	70	10
GD12	1½d.	chestnut	..	..	£18	£11
GD13	2d.	agate	..	..	1·25	20
GD14	3d.	violet	..	..	2·25	20
		a printed on gummed				
		side	..	..	£50	—
		b experimental paper		£30	£15
GD15	4d.	dull grey-green	..	5·00	75
GD16	5d.	bistre-brn ('31)	..	£15	£11
GD17	1/–	deep blue	..	..	7·00	50
GD18	2/6	pur/yellow	..	..	£22	1·50
GD10/18		set (9v)	..	..	£70	£23

GD14*b* See note below G71*b* and G72*d*.

1936 (Nov.)-37 As before but wmk. Multiple Block E8R. Printed by Harrison and Sons.

ED1	½d.	emerald (6/37)	..	1·00	1·00
ED2	1d.	carmine (5/37)	..	1·00	1·00
ED3	2d.	agate (5/37)..	..	2·50	1·75
ED4	3d.	violet (3/37)..	..	1·50	1·00
ED5	4d.	dull grey-green			
		(12/36)	..	..	6·00	5·50
ED6	5d.	bistre-brn (11/36)..	£15	£10
ED7	5d.	yel-brown ('37)	..	£10	£10
ED8	1/–	deep blue (12/36)	..	7·00	5·50
ED9	2/6	purple-yellow (5/37)	£75	£16
E1/9		set (8v)	..	..	£100	£40

1937-51 As before but Wmk. Multiple Block GVIR.

PD1	½d.	emerald-grn (5/38)	1·00	80
PD2	1d.	rose-red (5/38)	..	1·00	30
		a scarlet (/51)	..	1·25	50
PD3	2d.	agate (6/38)..	..	1·50	30
PD4	3d.	violet (12/37)	..	1·50	30
PD5	4d.	grey-green (9/37) ..	7·00	6·00
		a dull gr-green (/51)	7·00	6·00
PD6	5d.	light brown (11/38)	2·50	40
		a yellow-brown	..	3·00	75
PD7	1/–	blue (10/37)..	..	£10	75
PD8	2/6	dp pur/pale yel	..		
		(9/38)	..	..	£40	1·50
		a purple/yellow (/50)	£40	2·00
PD1/8		set (8v)	..	..	£65	9·00

The dates given (*supplied officially*) refer to when the postage due stamps were issued to postmasters for general release.

1951-2 As Nos. PD1, etc., but colours changed.

PD9	½d.	dull orange (10/51)	80	1·25
		a orange (/53?)	..	£10	5·00
PD10	1d.	cobalt (6/51)	..	1·50	50
PD11	1½d.	green (4/2/52)	..	2·50	1·25
		a stop after "three"		
		(Rows 1/7 8, 9)	£15	3·00
PD12	4d.	light blue (9/8/51)	9·00	3·50
PD13	1/–	bistre-brown		
		(29/11/51)	..	£15	1·50
PD9/13		set (5)	..	..	£28	7·00

1952 (June 7th) No. 29 handstamped POSTAGE DUE horizontally or diagonally in black at Bury St. Edmunds.

| PD13a | 1d. | ultramarine | .. | — | — |

On the authority of the local Postmaster a half sheet was handstamped when supplies of No. PD10 ran out. Initially, two separate handstamps were used and the two words were spaced approximately 3mm apart: the two handstamps were then fixed together with 5mm between the two lines.

100 copies were used and 20 survived mint.

OFFICIAL STAMPS

1840 Prepared for use but not issued. As V1 but with letters VR in upper corners.

| VR1 | 1d. | black .. | .. | .. | £5500 | £7500 |
| | | *a* on cover | .. | .. | ‡ £12500 |

Overprinted in black, as indicated, by De La Rue for use within the Government Departments named. Initially these stamps could be purchased by the public at Somerset House but it consequently became illegal to deal in unused copies until after their use ceased on May 12th, 1904.

1 ADMIRALTY

Overprinted "ADMIRALTY OFFICIAL" in two lines on stamps identified by their Catalogue Numbers after the prefix "AD".

1903 (March 3rd) Stamps of King Edward VII. The mid point of the "M" of ADMIRALTY extends fully to the base of the letter.

ADE1	½d. **blue-green**	6·00	2·00
ADE3	1d. **scarlet**	4·00	2·00
ADE4	1½d. **purple and green** ..	£40	£20
ADE6	2d. **green and car** ..	£60	£24
ADE9	2½d. **ultramarine** ..	£40	£22
ADE10	3d. **purple/yellow** ..	£60	£22

1903 (Sept.)-04 As before but overprinted from a new plate with thicker type in a narrower setting. The mid point of the "M" of ADMIRALTY does not extend to the base of the letter.

ADE1a	½d. **blue-green** ..	6·00	2·50
ADE3a	1d. **scarlet**	5·00	2·00
ADE4a	1½d. **purple and grn** ..	£95	f32
ADE6a	2d. **green and car** ..	£185	£70
ADE9a	2½d. **ultramarine** ..	£350	£170
ADE10a	3d. **purple/yellow** ..	£185	£25

2 ARMY

Overprinted "ARMY OFFICIAL" in two lines on stamps as indicated.

1896 (Sept. 1st)-1901 Stamps of Queen Victoria (1881 and 1887-1900 issues).

ARV176	½d. **vermilion** ..	1·00	25
	a "OFFICIAI" ..	£18	£10
ARV177	½d. **blue-grn** (4/00)	1·00	25
ARV151	1d. **lilac (Die II)** ..	1·00	25
	a "OFFICIAI" ..	£18	£10
ARV181	2½d. **purple/blue** ..	3·00	1·00
ARV190	6d. **pur/rose-red** (7/11/01) ..	£10	5·00

1902-03 Stamps of King Edward VII (1902 issue).

ARE1	½d. **blue-grn** (11/2/02)	1·50	40
ARE3	1d. **scarlet** (11/2/02)..	1·00	40
	a "ARMY" omitted	—	—
	b "OFFICIAI" ..	—	—
ARE21	6d. **dl pur** (23/8/02) ..	£35	£20
	a short "M"..	£650	£185

The mid point of the "M" of "ARMY" on ARE21 extends fully to the base of the letter, whilst that of the "M" on ARE21a only extends downwards half way to the base.

3 BOARD OF EDUCATION

Overprinted "BOARD OF EDUCATION" in three lines on stamps as indicated.

1902 (Feb. 19th) Stamps of Queen Victoria (1887-1900 issue).

BEV189	5d. **dl pur and blue** (Die II) ..	£250	£45
BEV196	1/- **green and car** ..	£600	£275

Numbers sold (figure in brackets indicate numbers printed)—BEV189, 4,800 (60,000) ; BEV196, 2,000 (30,000).

1902-04 Stamps of King Edward VII (1902 issue).

BEE1	½d. **blue green** (19/2/02) ..	£14	3·50
BEE3	1d. **scar** (19/2/02) ..	£14	3·50
BEE9	2½d. **ult** (19/2/02) ..	£250	£45
BEE19	5d. **purple and blue** (6/2/04).. ..	£675	£275
BEE30	1/- **green and car** (23/12/02) ..	£14000	£7000

Numbers issued—BEE1, 6,000 ; BEE3, 240,000 ; BEE9, 6,000.

4 GOVERNMENT PARCELS

Overprinted "GOVT PARCELS" in two lines on stamps as indicated.

1883 (July 1st)-1900 Stamps of Queen Victoria.

(a) from 1881-1884 issues.

GPV151	1d. **lilac (Die II)** (6/97) ..	4·00	50
	a no dot under "T"	£10	3·00
	b overprint invtd.	£500	£275
GPV159	1½d. **lilac** (30/4/86) ..	£50	£10
	a no dot under "T"	—	£20
GPV165	6d. **dull green** (30/4/86) ..	£200	£40
GPV166	9d. **dl grn** (1/8/83)..	£375	£100
GPV143	1/- **brn (Pl. 13, 14)**..	£225	£40
	a no dot under "T"	£300	£55

(b) from 1887-1900 (Jubilee) issue.

GPV178	1½d. **dl pur and grn** (29/10/87) ..	£10	2·00
	a no dot under "T"	£15	4·00
GPV180	2d. **green and car** (24/10/91) ..	£34	3·00
	a no dot under "T'	£40	4·00
GPV186	4½d. **green and car** (9/92)	£38	£40
GPV190	6d. **pur/rose-red** (19/12/87) ..	£18	8·00
	a no dot under "T"	£24	£10
GPV192	9d. **pur and blue** (21/8/88) ..	£40	£10
GPV195	1/- **pur** (25/3/90) ..	£80	£40
	a no dot under "T"	£90	£50
	b overprint in blue-black ..	—	—
GPV196	1/- **green and car** (11/00) ..	£100	£35
	a overprint invtd	—	£2850

1902 Stamps of King Edward VII (1902 issue).

GPE3	1d. **scar** (30/10/02) ..	7·00	5·00
GPE6	2d. **green and car** (29/4/02) ..	£50	£12
GPE21	6d. **dl pur** (19/2/02) ..	£85	£14
GPE25	9d. **purple and ult** (28/8/02) ..	£210	£35
GPE30	1/- **green and car** (17/12/02) ..	£325	£60

5 INLAND REVENUE

Overprinted "I. R. OFFICIAL" in two lines on stamps as indicated.

1882-1901 Stamps of Queen Victoria. (a) from 1880-1891 issues.

IRV146	½d.	**green** (28/10/82)	6·00	2·00
IRV148	½d.	**sl-blue** (8/5/85)	8·00	2·00
IRV151	1d.	**lilac (Die II)**		
		(27/9/82) ..	1·00	60
	a	"OFFICIAL"		
		omitted ..	£600	—
	b	lines transposed	—	—
	c	overprint in		
		blue-black ..	£60	£18
IRV161	2½d.	**lilac** (12/3/85)..	£38	£14
IRV142	6d.	**grey** (30/10/82)	£42	£14
IRV167	1/–	**green** (12/3/85)	£1750	£285
IRV169	5/–	**rose** (blued paper		
		(12/3/85) ..	£1800	£285
IRV169a	5/–	**rose** (white paper		
		(12/3/85) ..	£1100	£225
	a	raised stop after		
		"R"	£1200	£250
	b	overprint in		
		blue-black ..	£1450	£325
IRV171	10/–	**ult** (blued paper)	£3250	£950
IRV171a	10/–	**ult** (white paper)		
		(12/3/85) ..	£1250	£475
	a	raised stop after		
		"R"	£1750	£450
	b	overprint in		
		blue-black ..	£2000	£500
IRV172	10/–	**cobalt** (white		
		paper) (12/3/85)	£3500	£750
IRV173	£1	**brown-lilac**		
		(12/3/85) ..	£9500	£2000
IRV174	£1	**brn-lilac** ('90)	£9000	£2000
IRV175	£1	**green** (13/4/92)	£3000	£400
	a	no stop after		
		"R"	—	£800

(b) from 1887-1900 (Jubilee) issue.

IRV176	½d.	**verm** (21/1/88)	1·00	35
	a	"I.R." omitted	—	—
	b	imperf... ..	£300	—
	c	imperf. over-		
		print double	£450	—
IRV177	½d.	**blue-grn** (4/01)	3·00	80
IRV181	2½d.	**purple/blue**		
		(20/10/91) ..	£30	2·50
IRV190	6d.	**pur/rose-red**		
		(14/6/01) ..	£65	£10
IRV195	1/–	**green** (15/3/89)	£95	£18
IRV196	1/–	**green and car**		
		(12/01) ..	£325	£55

1902-1904 Stamps of King Edward VII (1902 issue).

IRE1	½d.	**blue-grn** (4/2/02)	4·50	1·00
IRE3	1d.	**scarlet**	3·00	80
IRE9	2½d.	**ult** (19/2/02) ..	£325	£45
IRE21	6d.	**dl pur** (14/3/04) ..	£35000	—
IRE30	1/–	**green and car**		
		(29/4/02) ..	£300	£55
IRE34	5/–	**car** (29/4/02) ..	£3000	£750
	a	raised stop after		
		"R"	£4000	£1000
IRE35	10/–	**blue** (29/4/02) ..	£12000	£7500
	a	raised stop after		
		"R"	£1400	£8500
IRE36	£1	**green** (29/4/02) ..	£9500	£2250

IRE35 Unused copies without gum are known. Price £7500.

6 OFFICE OF WORKS

Overprinted "O.W. OFFICIAL" in two lines on stamps as indicated.

1896-1902 Stamps of Queen Victoria (1881 and 1887-1900 issues).

OWV176	½d.	**verm** (24/3/96)	£30	8·00
OWV177	½d.	**blue-green**		
		(5/11/01) ..	£30	£14
OWV151	1d.	**lilac (Die II)**		
		(24/3/96) ..	£30	8·00
OWV189	5d.	**dl pur and blue**		
		(Die II)		
		(29/4/02) ..	£325	£75
OWV193	10d.	**dl pur and car**		
		(28/5/02) ..	£675	£150

Numbers sold (figures in brackets indicate numbers printed)—OWV177, 6,000; OWV189, 949 (12,000); OWV193, 480 (8,000).

1902-03 Stamps of King Edward VII (1902 issue).

OWE1	½d.	**blue-green**		
		(11/2/02) ..	£50	£13
OWE3	1d.	**scarlet** (11/2/02)	£50	£13
OWE6	2d.	**green and car**		
		(29/3/02) ..	£185	£45
OWE9	2½d.	**ult** (29/3/02) ..	£300	£60
OWE27	10d.	**purple and car**		
		(18/5/03) ..	£1550	£425

Numbers sold—OWE27, 134 (printed 1,440).

7 ROYAL HOUSEHOLD

Overprinted "R. H. OFFICIAL" in two lines on stamps as indicated.

1902 Stamps of King Edward VII.

RHE1	½d.	**blue-green** (April		
		29th)	£90	£55
RHE3	1d.	**scarlet** (Feb 19th)	£80	£50

TEST LABELS

These labels are printed in green or grey on watermarked paper with normal perforations and are used for testing stamp vending machines. They have no postal validity, but are occasionally found used.

They also exist in horizontal pairs, imperf. between printed in magenta. These were used to test automatic machines dispensing the 1957 Scout Jamboree issue.

GERMAN PROPAGANDA LABELS

During 1944 the Germans prepared imitations of the G.B. 1935 Silver Jubilee ½d., 1937 Coronation 1½d. and 1937 Definitives ½d. to 3d. Their purpose was, apparently, to circulate these in neutral countries with the intention of discrediting Great Britain.

They were printed on poor quality paper with a wavy line watermark and were perforated 11½ (Line).

The definitives were less altered than the two 'commemoratives'; The Cross on the Crown was replaced by the Star of David, which also appears in the thistle, and a Hammer and Sickle was substituted for "D" in the value circle and also appears within the rose. The colours were generally well matched to Nos. 1–6.

The definitives also appeared with a variety of propaganda overprints ("Liquidation of Empire/Hong Kong" etc.) within thick rectangular frames or within a star-shaped device or in a straight line. They were also circulated stuck on a card headed with the G.P.O. symbol and a Hammer and Sickle and inscribed "SPECIAL STAMP IN MEMORY OF THE FIRST DAY OF INVASION" (in English and Russian), the 'stamps' being cancelled with a c.d.s. "LONDON/AAAO/6 JUN 44/SPECIAL STAMP".

Prices:—

1935 ½d. green	..	..	..	£50
1937 1½d. maroon	..	..	..	£50
1937 ½d.–3d. (set of 6)		..	..	£150

CHANNEL ISLANDS

Stamps issued and used during the German Occupation, 1940-5.

GUERNSEY

The K.G. VI definitive 1d. was overprinted with a small swastika and the Postal Centenary 2d. with two swastikas when the Germans occupied Guernsey in 1940. They were not issued, and very few copies are known.

1940 (Dec. 27th) Stamps of Great Britain (Nos. 4 and S5) bisected diagonally and used as 1d. stamps for Inter-Island Postage.

G1	2d. (*half*) G.B. No. 4 used on piece or cover	.. ..	£12
G2	2d. (*half*) G.B. No. S5, used on piece or cover	.. ..	£10

Covers with 2d. stamps of 1912, 1924 and 1934 Issues simiiarly bisected were used by Philatelists.

The use of bisected stamps was authorised up to Feb. 24, 1941.

1941-4 Design, Guernsey Coat of Arms. Designer, E. W. Vaudin. Printers (*typo*) Guernsey Press Co. Roul. 14 and/or 7. No wmk. Sheets 6 x 10.

G3	½d.	**emerald** (7/4/41) ..	3·00	1·50
	a	dp blue-grn (11/41)	£18	£11
	b	imp. between horiz. pair	£275	—
	bb	ditto, vert. pair ..	£325	—
	c	pea-green (2/42) ..	8·00	2·00
	d	sage-green (9/42)	3·00	2·00
	e	olive-green (2/43)	£18	£10
	f	dp yel-green (7/43)	2·00	1·50
	ff	printed gummed side	£60	—
	g	pale yel-grn (11/44)	2·00	—
G4	1d.	**car-red** (*thin paper*) (18/2/41)	2·00	50
	a	carmine-red (/41)	3·00	1·25
	b	imperf pair ..	£60	£40
	bb	imp. between horiz. pair	£275	—
	c	imp. between vert. pr.	£315	—
	d	golden-red (7/43)	7·00	3·00
	e	dull scarlet (12/43)	8·00	3·00
	f	double printing ..	£75	—
G5	2½d.	**dp ult** (12/4/44) ..	3·50	3·00
	a	imperf. pair ..	£100	£100
G3/5		**set** (3)	7·50	5·00

G4 The design can be seen clearly through the back of the stamp, owing to the thinness of the paper.

1942 Design as before but Stamps printed on coloured French Bank Note Paper. Wmk. Loops. Roul. 14 and/or 7.

G6	½d.	**green/blue** (11/3/42)	£10	£10
	a	green/grey-blue ..	£10	£10
G7	1d.	**dp red/blue** (7/4/42)	7·00	7·00
	a	red/grey-blue ..	7·00	7·00

Most of the stamps are to be found roul. 7 or 14 (*the latter has the appearance of pin perf.*) or a combination of both (*same valuation*).

Both types occur in the same sheet.

JERSEY

On entering Jersey the Germans ordered all current stamps found to be overprinted Jersey 1940, and with swastika. Small quantities of KG VI definitive stamps from ½d. to 10/- (less 1d. and 11d.) and Postal Centenary issue (less 1d.) were treated, but none was officially issued owing to strong protests. Copies are scarce, as very few escaped destruction.

A local printing of 1d. stamps depicting Arms of Jersey was made, but never issued. Imperf. copies exist with and without swastika overprint.

1941-3 Design, Jersey Coat of Arms. Designer Major Rybot. Printers (*typo*) Jersey Evening Post. Perf. 11 (L). No wmk. Sheets 6 x 10.

J1	½d.	**emerald-grn** (29/1/42)	2·00	1·00
	a	ring flaw	£20	£20
	b	emerald green (thin paper) (8/42) ..	2·00	2·00
	c	ring flaw	£20	£20
	d	imp. between vert. pair	£350	—
	dd	ditto horiz. pair ..	£300	—
	e	on news print (/43)	3·00	3·00
	f	imperf. pair ..	£50	—
	g	ring flaw ..	£15	£15
J2	1d.	**scar** (thin paper) (1/4/41)	2·00	1·25
	a	small ring flaw ..	£20	£20
	b	scarlet (/41) ..	1·30	1·00
	c	small ring flaw ..	£20	£20
	d	imperf between vertical pair ..	£325	—
	dd	ditto horiz. pair ..	£275	—
	e	chalky paper (/41)	£30	£30
	f	on newsprint (1/43)	2·50	2·50
	g	small ring flaw ..	£20	£20

J1a/1c/1g	An irregularly shaped ring near Y in JERSEY Row 8/6 (*see illustration*).
J1b/2	The design is visible through the back of the stamps of the thin paper varieties.
J1e/2f	This paper is somewhat coarse and greyish.
J2a/2c/2g	A smaller ring is to be found on right side between Coar of Arms and 1d. Row 7/6 (*see illustration*).
J2d	This variety is not known mint.
J2e	The heavily chalk coated paper has a strong glaze.

J1a/c/g

J2a/c/g

1943-4 Designs, Views of Jersey. Designer, Ed. Blampied. Engraver, H. Cortot. Printers (*typo*) French Govt. Printing Works, Paris. Perf. 13½ x 13¼ (C). No wmk. Sheets 120— four panes, each 3 x 10.

J3	½d.	**green** (1/6/43)	4·25	1·50
	a	on newsprint (7/10/43)	£10	—
J4	1d.	**scarlet** (1/6/43)	40	15
	a	on newsprint (28/2/44)		
J5	1½d.	**brown** (8/6/43)	3·00	—
J6	2d.	**orange** (8/6/43)	1·25	1·75
J7	2½d.	**blue** (29/6/43)	1·25	1·75
	a	on newsprint (25/2/44)	3·00	1·25
J8	3d.	**pur-violet** (29/6/43)	4·00	
J3/8		**set** (6)	2·00	2·50

J3a/4a/7a   The dates given after these stamps refer to when printed; actually they were placed on sale, unnoticed, later on in the year.

SPECIAL ISSUES

1948 (May 10th) Third Anniversary of Liberation. Designs and Designers, 1d. (Gathering Seaweed, by J. R. Stobie); 2½d. (Gathering Seaweed, from painting by E. Blampied). Printers (*photo*) Harrison & Sons. Wmk. as Great Britain. Perf. 14¾ x 14 (C). Sheets 6 x 20.

CIS1	1d.	**scarlet**		10	10
	a	rose red		50	15
CIS2	2½d.	**dp ultramarine**		15	15
	a	wheel flaw		6·00	6·00

CIS2*a* A white blotch breaks rim of cartwheel, Row 20/5. This variety was present on the sheet from very first printing and never retouched as far as we know. (See page 32 for illustration).

Numbers issued—

1d, 5,934,000; 2½d., 5,398,000.

These two stamps were valid for postage throughout Great Britain.

BRITISH LEVANT

The first British Post Office was opened to the public in Constantinople in July 1857. Contemporary G.B. stamps were used; and they were cancelled initially by "C" in a transverse, or upright, oval of horizontal bars, and later by date stamp inscribed "British Post Office, Constantinople". This office was closed from 1914 to 1918, when it reopened until 1923.

Other British Post Offices were opened, using cancellations as shown:

Alexandria 1860-1879 "B01".

Suez 1860-1879 "B02".

Smyrna 1872-1923 "F87".

Beirut (Beyrout) 1873-1913 "G06".

Stamboul 1884–1914 "S".

(All these offices subsequently used named date stamps).

Salonica 1900–1914 "British Post Office, Salonica".

1857-1923 Stamps of Great Britain identified by their Catalogue Nos. after prefixes 'C·' 'EA', 'ES', 'SM' 'B', 'ST' or 'SA'.

(I) Used at Constantinople: 'C' in transverse, or upright, oval of horizontal bars or named circular date-stamp.

(i) Stamps of Queen Victoria

(a) 1857-1883

CV108	½d.	**rose-red**
		(Various Plates)
CV22	1d.	**red-brown**
CV28	1d.	**red-brown**
CV33	1d.	**red-brown**
CV39	1d.	**rose-red**
	a	Plates 50.51
		(Alph. IV)
CV49.	1d.	**rose-red**
		(Various Plates)
CV138	1d.	**venetian red**
CV110	1½d.	**rose-red**
CV36	2d.	**blue**
CV51	2d.	**blue**
CV52	2d.	**blue**
CV120	2½d.	**rosy-mauve**
CV121	2½d.	**rosy-mauve**
CV121a	2½d.	**rosy-mauve**
		(LH-FL)
CV122	2½d.	**rosy-mauve**
CV123	2½d.	**blue**
CV139	2½d.	**blue**
CV53	3d.	**carmine rose**
CV70	3d.	**rose**
CV78	3d.	**rose**
CV124	3d.	**rose**
CV140	3d.	**rose**
CV144	3d. on 3d.	**lilac**
CV44	4d.	**rose-carmine**
CV59	4d.	**bright red**
CV72	4d.	**vermilion**
CV131	4d.	**vermilion**
CV133	4d.	**sage-green**
CV135	4d.	**grey-brown**
CV141	4d.	**grey-brown**
CV45	6d.	**lilac**
CV62	6d.	**lilac**
CV75	6d.	**lilac**
CV79	6d.	**lilac**
CV82	6d.	**bright violet**
		(Hyphen)
CV83	6d.	**dull violet**
		(No Hyphen)
CV114	6d.	**chestnut**

CV115	6d.	**buff**
CV119	6d.	**grey**
CV126	6d.	**grey**
CV142	6d	**grey**
CV145	6d. on 6d.	**lilac**
CV145a	*a*	slanting dots
CV136	8d.	**orange**
CV88	10d.	**red-brown**
CV88a	*a*	wmk emblems
CV47	1/-	**green**
CV68	1/-	**green**
CV68a	*a*	'k' circled
CV77	1/-	**green**
CV92	1/-	**green**
CV127	1/-	**green**
CV130	1/-	**orange-brown**
CV143	1/-	**orange-brown**
CV95	2/-	**blue**
CV101	5/-	**rose**
CV104	5/-	**rose**
CV104a	5/-	**rose**

(b) 1880-84

CV146	½d.	**deep green**
CV147	½d.	**pale green**
CV148	½d.	**slate-blue**
CV149	1d.	**lilac** (14 pearls)
CV151	1d.	**lilac** (16 pearls)
CV156	2d.	**pale rose**
CV157	2d.	**deep rose**
CV158	5d.	**indigo**

(c) 1883-84

CV159	1½d.	**lilac**
CV160	2d.	**lilac**
CV161	2½d.	**lilac**
CV162	3d.	**lilac**
CV163	4d.	**dull green**
CV164	5d.	**dull green**
CV165	6d.	**dull green**
CV166	9d.	**dull green**
CV167	1/-	**dull green**
CV168	2/6	**lilac**
CV168a	2/6	**lilac**
CV169	5/-	**rose**
CV169a	5/-	**rose**

(d) 1887-1900

CV176	½d.	**vermilion**
CV177	½d.	**blue-green**
CV178	1½d.	**dull pur. & grn**
CV179	2d.	**grn and car**
CV181	2½d.	**purple/blue**
CV182	3d.	**purple/yellow**
CV184	4d.	**grn and brown**
CV186	4½d.	**grn and car**
CV189	5d	**dull pur & blue**
CV190	6d.	**pur/rose red**

CV192	9d.	**dull pur & blue**
CV193	10d.	**dull pur & car**
CV195	1/-	**green**
CV196	1/-	**grn and car**

(ii) Stamps of King Edward VII (1902) (Catalogue Nos. refer only to the first listed shade of the De la Rue printings. The later Harrison and Somerset House printings were also used at Constantinople).

CE1	½d.	**blue-green**
CE3	1d.	**scarlet**
CE4	1½d.	**dull pr and grn**
CE6	2d.	**grey-grn & car**
CE9	2½d.	**ultramarine**
CE10	3d.	**dull purple/or-yellow**
CE15	4d.	**grn & grey-brn**
CE17	4d.	**brown-orange**
CE19	5d.	**dull pur & brn**
CE21	6d.	**pale dull-purple**
CE23	7d.	**grey-black**
CE25	9d.	**dull pur & ult**
CE27	10d.	**dull pur & car**
CE30	1/-	**dull grn & car**
CE32	2/6	**lilac**
CE34	5/-	**carmine**

(iii) Stamps of King George V (1911-23).

CG11	½d.	**deep green**
CG19	½d.	**green**
CG7	1d.	**pale carmine**
CG14A	1d.	**aniline scarlet**
CG21	1d.	**bright scarlet**
CG23	1½d.	**red-brown**
CG26	2d.	**reddish orange**
CG29	2½d.	**blue**
CG31	3d.	**pale violet**
CG33	4d.	**pale grey-grn**
CG34	5d.	**brown**
CG36	6d.	**reddish purple**
CG42	9d.	**agate**
CG44	9d.	**pale olive-grn**
CG48	1/-	**bistre-brown**
CG62	2/6	**olive-brown**
CG64	5/-	**rose-red**
CG65	10/-	**dull grey-blue**

(II) Used at Alexandria (1860-79) : 'BO1' in traverse, or upright, oval of horizontal bars; and 'BO1' in duplex with named circular date-stamp.

EAV108 ½d. **rose-red**
(Various Plates)
EAV39 1d. **rose-red**
Plates 50.51
(Alph IV)
EAV49 1d. **rose-red**
(Various Plates)
EAV51 2d. **blue**
EAV52 2d. **blue**
EAV120 2½d. **rosy-mauve**
EAV121 2½d. **rosy-mauve**
EAV121a 2½d. **rosy-mauve**
(LH-FL)
EAV122 2½d. **rosy-mauve**
EAV53 3d. **carmine-rose**
EAV70 3d. **rose**
EAV78 3d. **rose**
EAV124 3d. **rose**
EAV140 3d. **rose**
EAV44 4d. **rose-carmine**
EAV59 4d. **bright red**
EAV72 4d. **vermilion**
EAV131 4d. **vermilion**
EAV133 4d. **sage-green**
EAV45 6d. **lilac**
EAV62 6d. **lilac**
EAV75 6d. **lilac**
EAV79 6d. **lilac**
EAV82 6d. **bright violet**
(Hyphen)
EAV83 6d. **dull violet**
(No Hyphen)
EAV114 6d. **chestnut**
EAV115 6d. **buff**
EAV119 6d. **grey**
EAV126 6d. **grey**
EAV64 9d. **bistre**
EAV65 9d. **straw**
EAV76 9d. **straw**
EAV86 9d. **straw**
EAV88 10d. **red-brown**
EAV47 1/- **green**
EAV68 1/- **green**
EAV68a a 'k' circled
EAV77 1/- **green**
EAV92 1/- **green**
EAV127 1/- **green**
EAV95 2/- **blue**
EAV101 5/- **rose**

**(III) Used at Suez (1860-79);
'BO2' in transverse, or upright, oval of horizontal bars
and 'BO2'· in duplex with
named circular date-stamp.**

ESV108 ½d. **rose-red**
(Various Plates)
ESV39 1d. **rose-red**
ESV49 1d. **rose-red**
(Various Plates)
ESV51 2d. **blue**
ESV52 2d. **blue**
ESV120 2½d. **rosy-mauve**
ESV121 2½d. **rosy-mauve**
ESV121a 2½d. **rosy-mauve**
(LH-FL)
ESV122 2½d. **rosy-mauve**
ESV53 3d. **carmine-rose**
ESV70 3d. **rose**
ESV78 3d. **rose**
ESV124 3d. **rose**
ESV44 4d. **rose-carmine**

ESV59 4d. **bright red**
ESV72 4d. **vermilion**
ESV131 4d. **vermilion**
ESV133 4d. **sage-green**
ESV45 6d. **lilac**
ESV62 6d. **lilac**
ESV75 6d. **lilac**
ESV79 6d. **lilac**
ESV82 6d. **bright violet**
(Hyphen)
ESV83 6d. **dull violet**
(No Hyphen)
ESV114 6d. **chestnut**
ESV115 6d. **buff**
ESV116 6d. **pale chestnut**
(Pl. 12)
ESV119 6d. **grey**
ESV126 6d. **grey**
ESV136 8d. **orange**
ESV64 9d. **bistre**
ESV65 9d. **straw**
ESV86 9d. **straw**
ESV88 10d. **red-brown**
ESV47 1/- **green**
ESV68 1/- **green**
ESV68a a 'k' circled
ESV77 1/- **green**
ESV92 1/- **green**
ESV127 1/- **green**
ESV95 2/- **blue**
ESV101 5/- **rose**

**(IV) Used at Smyrna: 'F87·
in transverse, or upright,
oval of horizontal bars or
named circular date-stamp.**

**(i) Stamps of Queen Vic-
toria**

(a) 1872-1883
SMV108 ½d. **rose-red**
SMV49 1d. **rose-red**
(Various Plates)
SMV138 1d. **venetian red**
SMV110 1½d. **rose-red**
SMV41 2d. **blue**
SMV52 2d. **blue**
SMV120 2½d. **rosy-mauve**
SMV121 2½d. **rosy-mauve**
SMV121a 2½d. **rosy-mauve**
(LH-FL)
SMV122 2½d. **rosy-mauve**
SMV123 2½d. **blue**
SMV139 2½d. **blue**
SMV78 3d. **rose**
SMV124 3d. **rose**
SMV72 4d. **vermilion**
SMV131 4d. **vermilion**
SMV133 4d. **sage-green**
SMV135 4d. **grey-brown**
SMV141 4d. **grey-brown**
SMV114 6d. **chestnut**
SMV115 6d. **buff**
SMV119 6d. **grey**
SMV126 6d. **grey**
SMV142 6d. **grey**
SMV145 6d. on 6d. **lilac**
SMV145a a slanting dots
SMV136 8d. **orange**
SMV86 9d. **straw**
SMV88 10d. **red-brown**
SMV92 1/— **green**
SMV127 1/— **green**

SMV130 1/- **orange-brown**
SMV143 1/- **orange-brown**
SMV101 5/- **rose**

(b) 1880-84.
SMV146 ½d. **deep green**
SMV147 ½d. **pale green**
SMV148 ½d. **slate blue**
SMV151 1d. **lilac** (16pearls)
SMV155 1½d. **venetian red**
SMV156 2d. **pale rose**
SMV157 2d. **deep rose**
SMV158 5d. **indigo**

(c) 1883-84.
SMV160 2d. **lilac**
SMV161 2½d. **lilac**
SMV163 4d. **dull green**
SMV164 5d. **dull green**
SMV167 1/- **dull green**

(d) 1887-1900.
SMV176 ½d. **vermilion**
SMV177 ½d. **blue-green**
SMV178 1½d. **dull pur & grn**
SMV179 2d. **grn and car**
SMV181 2½d. **purple/blue**
SMV182 3d. **purple/yellow**
SMV184 4d. **grn & brown**
SMV189 5d. **dull pur & blue**
SMV190 6d. **pur/rose-red**
SMV195 1/- **green**
SMV196 1/- **grn and car**

**(ii) Stamps of King Edward
VII (1902) (Catalogue Nos.
refer only to the first listed
shade of the De la Rue
printings. The later Harrison
and Somerset House print-
ings were also used at
Smyrna).**

SME1 ½d. **blue-green**
SME3 1d. **scarlet**
SME4 1½d. **dull pur & grn**
SME6 2d. **grey-grn & car**
SME9 2½d. **ultramarine**
SME10 3d. **dull pur/or-yel**
SME15 4d. **grn & gry-brn**
SME19 5d. **dull pur & ult**
SME21 6d. **pale dull pur**
SME23 7d. **grey-black**
SME25 9d. **dull pur & ult**
SME27 10d. **dull pur & car**
SME30 1/- **dull grn & car**
SME32 2/6 **lilac**

**(iii) Stamps of King George
V (1911-23).**
SMG19 ½d. **green**
SMG21 1d. **bright scarlet**
SMG23 1½d. **red-brown**
SMG26 2d. **reddish or**
SMG29 2½d. **blue**
SMG31 3d. **pale violet**
SMG33 4d. **pale grey-grn**
SMG34 5d. **brown**
SMG36 6d. **reddish pur**
SMG38 7d. **olive**
SMG40 8d. **black/yellow**
SMG42 9d. **agate**
SMG44 9d. **pale olive-grn**

SMG46 10d. **tur blue**
SMG48 1/- **bistre-brown**
SMG52 2/6 **sepia brown**

(V) Used at Beirut: 'G06' in upright oval of horizontal bars, or named circular date-stamp.

(i) Stamps of Queen Victoria

(a) 1873-83.

BV108 ½d. **rose-red**
BV49 1d. **rose-red**
  (Various Plates)
BV138 1d. **venetian red**
BV110 1½d. **rose-red**
BV52 2d. **blue**
BV120 2½d. **rosy mauve**
BV121 2½d. **rosy mauve**
BV122 2½d. **rosy mauve**
BV123 2½d. **blue**
BV139 2½d. **blue**
BV78 3d. **rose**
BV124 3d. **rose**
BV140 3d. **rose**
BV72 4d. **vermilion**
BV131 4d. **vermilion**
BV133 4d. **sage-green**
BV135 4d. **grey-brown**
BV141 4d. **grey-brown**
BV84 6d. **mauve**
  (No Hyphen)
BV114 6d. **chestnut**
BV115 6d. **buff**
BV119 6d. **grey**
BV126 6d. **grey**
BV136 8d. **orange**
BV88 10d. **red-brown**
BV92 1/- **green**
BV127 1/- **green**
BV130 1/- **orange-brown**
BV143 1/- **orange-brown**
BV95 2/- **blue**
BV101 5/- **rose**

(b) 1880-84

BV146 ½d. **deep green**
BV147 ½d. **pale green**
BV148 ½d. **slate-blue**
BV149 1d. **lilac** (14 pearls)
BV151 1d. **lilac** (16 pearls)
BV155 1½d. **venetian red**
BV156 2d. **pale rose**
BV157 2d. **deep rose**
BV158 5d. **indigo**

(c) 1883-84.

BV159 1½d. **lilac**
BV160 2d. **lilac**
BV161 2½d. **lilac**
BV163 4d. **dull green**
BV164 5d. **dull green**
BV167 1/- **dull green**

(d) 1887-1900.

BV176 ½d. **vermilion**
BV177 ½d. **blue-green**
BV178 1½d. **dull pur & grn**
BV179 2d. **grn and car**
BV181 2½d. **purple/blue**
BV182 3d. **purple/yellow**
BV186 4½d. **grn and car**

BV189 5d. **dull pur & blue**
BV190 6d. **pur/rose-red**
BV195 1/- **green**
BV196 1/- **green and car**

(ii) Stamps of King Edward VII (1902).

BE1 ½d. **blue-green**
BE3 1d. **scarlet**
BE9 2½d. **ultramarine**
BE19 5d. **dull pur & ult**
BE27 10d. **dull pur & car**
BE30 1/- **dull grn & car**

(iii) Stamps of King George V (1912-13).

BG19 ½d. **green**
BG21 1d. **bright scarlet**

(VI) Used at Stamboul: 'S' (with or without stop) in upright oval of horizontal bars, or named circular date-stamp.

(i) Stamps of Queen Victoria.

(a) 1884.

STV148 ½d. **slate-blue**
STV151 1d. **lilac** (16 pearls)
STV160 2d. **lilac**
STV161 2½d. **lilac**
STV164 5d. **dull green**

(b) 1887-1900.

STV176 ½d. **vermilion**
STV177 ½d. **blue-green**
STV178 1½d. **dull pur & grn**
STV179 2d. **grn and car**
STV181 2½d. **pur/blue**
STV182 3d. **pur/yellow**
STV184 4d. **grn and brn**
STV186 4½d. **grn and car**
STV189 5d. **dull pur & blue**
STV190 6d. **pur/rose-red**
STV192 9d. **dull pur & blue**
STV193 10d. **dull pur & car**
STV195 1/- **green**
STV196 1/- **grn and car**

(ii) Stamps of King Edward VII (1902) (Catalogue Nos. refer only to the first listed shade of the De la Rue printings. The later Harrison and Somerset House printings were also used at Stamboul.

STE1 ½d. **blue-green**
STE3 1d. **scarlet**
STE4 1½d. **dull pur & grn**
STE6 2d. **gry-grn & car**
STE9 2½d. **ultramarine**
STE10 3d. **dull pur/or yel**
STE15 4d. **grn & gry-brn**
STE17 4d. **brown-orange**
STE19 5d. **dull pur & ult**
STE21 6d. **pale dull pur**
STE23 7d. **grey-black**
STE25 9d. **dull pur & ult**
STE27 10d. **dull pur & car**
STE30 1/- **dull grn & car**
STE32 2/6d. **lilac**
STE34 5/– **carmine**

(iii) Stamps of King George V (1911-14).

STG1 ½d. **green**
STG11 ½d. **deep green**
STG19 ½d. **green**
STG3 1d. **carmine-red**
STG21 1d. **bright scarlet**
STG23 1½d. **red-brown**
STG26 2d. **reddish or.**
STG29 2½d. **blue**
STG31 3d. **pale violet**
STG33 4d. **pale grey-grn**
STG34 5d. **brown**
STG36 6d. **reddish pur**
STG38 7d. **olive**
STG40 8d. **black/yellow**
STG42 9d. **agate**
STG46 10d. **tur-blue**
STG48 1/- **bistre-brown**
STG52 2/6 **sepia-brown**
STG53 5/- **rose-carmine**

(VII) Used at Salonica (1900 -14): named circular date-stamp.

(i) Stamps of Queen Victoria (1887-1900).

SAV176 ½d. **vermilion**
SAV177 ½d. **blue-green**
SAV151 1d. **lilac**
SAV190 6d. **pur/rose-red**
SAV196 1/- **grn and car**

(ii) Stamps of King Edward VII (1902).

SAE1 ½d. **blue-green**
SAE3 1d. **scarlet**
SAE9 2½d. **ultramarine**
SAE30 1/- **dull grn & car**

(iii) Stamps of King George V (1911-14).

SAG1 ½d. **green**
SAG19 ½d. **green**
SAG3 1d. **carmine-red**
SAG14 1d. **scarlet**
SAG21 1d. **bright scarlet**

CRIMEA

1854-57 Stamps of Great Britain (Queen Victoria) identified by their Catalogue Nos. after either 'CC' or 'CS', used at Army Post Offices during the Crimean Campaign. (See also under Malta.)

(i) Cancelled: Crown between stars within transverse oval of horizontal bars.

CC5 1d. **red-brown**
CC22 1d. **red-brown**
CC24 1d. **red-brown**
CC27 1d. **red-brown**
CC28 1d. **red-brown**
CC10 2d. **blue**
CC26 2d. **pale blue**
CC16 1/- **green**

(ii) Cancelled: Star between Circles (OXO) within transverse oval of horizontal bars.

		CS24	1d. **red-brown**		CS30	2d. **blue**	
		CS27	1d. **red-brown**		CS32	2d. **blue**	
		CS28	1d. **red-brown**		CS36	2d. **blue**	
		CS31	1d. **red-brown**		CS44	4d. **rose-carmine**	
CS5	1d. **red-brown**	CS33	1d. **red-brown**		CS14	6d. **violet**	
CS22	1d. **red-brown**	CS10	2d. **blue**		CS16	1/- **green**	
		CS26	2d. **pale blue**				

In 1885 devaluation of the Turkish piastre from 2½d. to 2d. resulted in G.B. stamps being issued with surcharges in Turkish currency.

I TURKISH CURRENCY ISSUES

1885 (April 1st) Stamps of Great Britain (QV) surcharged in black.

VT1	40 pa. on 2½d. **lilac**	..	8·00	1·75
VT2	80 pa. on 5d. **green**	..	£65	4·00
VT3	12 pi. on 2/6 **lilac**	..	£80	£35
	a on deeply blue paper		£90	8·00
	b on white paper	..	£15	6·50

All values exist overprinted "Specimen".

1887-96 Stamps of Great Britain (QV) similarly surcharged.

VT4	40 pa. on 2½d. **purple/blue**	..	75	25
	a surcharge double		£700	£875
VT5	80 pa. on 5d. **purple and blue**	..	2·00	50
	a small "o" in "80"		£20	£15
VT6	4 pi. on 10d. **purple and car**	..	6·00	4·00
	a wide "4" ..		£12	£10
VT4/6	**set (3v)**	.. ..	8·00	4·00

All values exist overprinted "Specimen".

1893 (Feb. 25th) Stamp of Great Britain (QV) roughly hand-stamped in black at Constantinople.

VT7	40 pa. on ½d. **vermilion** ..	£65	£35

This provisional was in use for only five days and as fraudulent copies were subsequently produced with the original handstamp, it should only be purchased with a certificate. Being a handstamp, the surcharge may be found in a variety of positions horizontally or diagonally.

1902-5 Stamps of Great Britain (KE 7 D.L.R. printings) surcharged in black.

ET1	40 pa. on 2½d. **br blue**	.. ..	60	25
ET2	80 pa. on 5d. **purple and blue** ..		90	75
	a small "0" in "80"		£20	£10
ET3	4 pi. on 10d. **purple and car (O)**		3·00	1·50
	a no cross on crown		£40	—
ET4	4 pi. on 10d. **purple and car (C)**		3·50	3·00
	a no cross on crown		£40	—
ET5	12 pi. on 2/6 **dl purple (O)**	..	£15	£17
ET6	12 pi. on 2/6 **red-purple (C)**	..	£15	£18

ET7	24 pi. on 5/— **carmine** (1905)	..	£28	£30
ET1/7	**set (5v)**	.. ..	£48	£50

All values exist overprinted "Specimen".

1906-10 Stamps of Great Britain, as before, surcharged.

ET8	30 pa. on 1½d. **dl pur and grn (C)**		50	50
ET9	1 pi. on 2½d. **br blue**	..	90	15
ET10	1 pi. 10 pa. on 3d. **pur/yel (C)**	..	3·00	4·25
ET11	1¼ pi. on 3d. **pur/yel (C)**	..	30	75
ET12	1 pi. 30 pa. on 4d. **grn and choc brn (C)**	.. ..	3·25	4·00
ET13	1 pi. 30 pa. on 4d. **orange**	..	3·50	4·25
ET14	1¾ pi. on 4d. **orange**	..	40	75
	a thin pointed "4" in fraction	..	£15	£15
ET15	2 pi. on 5d. **pur and blu (OC)**		2·50	1·00
ET16	2 pi. 20 pa. on 6d. **red-purple (C)**	..	7·00	8·00
ET17	2½ pi. on 6d. **red-purple (C)**	..	90	75
ET18	5 pi. on 1/— **grn and car (C)**	..	2·75	3·50
ET8/18	**set (11v)**	.. ..	£22	£25

The 5 pi./1/— (ET18) exists overprinted "Specimen".

1911 Stamps of Great Britain (KE 7 Harrison and Somerset House printings) surcharged in black.

ET19	30 pa. on 1½d. **dl red-pur and yel-grn**	.. ..	1·00	40
	a surcharge double. one albino	..	—	—
ET20	30 pa. on 1½d. **slate-pur and grn**		1·00	1·25
ET21	1 pi. on 2½d. (p. 14) **br blue Type I**		1·50	75
	a surcharge double one albino	..	—	—
ET22	1 pi. on 2½d. (p. 15x14) **br blue Type I**		2·75	90
ET23	1 pi. on 2½d. (p. 15x1 4) **br blue Type II** ..		5·00	1·50
ET24	1 pi. on 2½d. (p. 15x14) **br blue Type III** ..		8·00	1·25
ET25	2 pi. on 5d. **pur and br blue** ..		90	1·00
ET26	4 pi. on 10d. **dl pur and scar** ..		3·50	5·00
ET27	4 pi. on 10d. **dl pur and car** ..		4·50	6·00

ET28	5 pi. on 1/–			
	grn and car	..	4·25	4·00
ET29	12 pi. on 2/6			
	dp red-pur	..	£35	£30
ET30	12 pi. on 2/6			
	dull purple	..	£15	£18
ET31	12 pi. on 2/6d.			
	pale red-pur	..	£15	£18
ET32	24 pi. on 5/–			
	carmine	..	£28	£30
ET19/32	set (7v)	..	£50	£55

Type I. Letters tall and narrow. Space enclosed above bar of "A" small.

Type II. Letters shorter and broader.

Type III. Letters shorter and broader. Space enclosed above bar of "A" large.

1913-14 Stamps of Great Britain (KG V). Wmk. Royal Cypher. Surcharged in black.

GT1	30 pa. on 1½d.			
	red-brown	..	1·00	1·25
GT2	1 pi. on 2½d.			
	bright blue	..	20	15
GT3	1¼ pi. on 3d.			
	violet	..	60	1·75
GT4	1¾ pi. on 4d.			
	grey-green	..	75	2·00
	a thin pointed "4" in			
	fraction	..	£25	£25
GT5	4 pi. on 10d.			
	turquoise-blue	..	3·50	3·50
GT6	5 pi. on 1/–			
	brown	..	8·00	£10
GT1/6	set (6v)	..	£12·50	£17·50

British Post Offices in the Turkish Empire were closed during the 1914-18 War. The issues from 1921 were made during the subsequent British Occupation.

1921 Stamps of Great Britain, as before, surcharged. Nos. GT14–16 are surcharged on Bradbury Wilkinson printings.

GT7	30 pa. on ½d.			
	green	..	10	30
	a surcharge inverted		—	—
GT8	1½ pi. on 1d.			
	scarlet	..	10	15
GT9	3¾ pi. on 2½d.			
	blue ..	..	20	40
GT10	4½ pi. on 3d.			
	blue-violet	..	40	75
GT11	7½ pi. on 5d.			
	yellow-brown	..	25	20
GT12	15 pi. on 10d.			
	turquoise ..	..	35	20
GT13	18¾ pi. on 1/–			
	bistre-brown	..	2·25	1·50
	a raised "3" in			
	fraction	..	—	—
GT14	45 pi. on 2/6			
	chocolate-brown		£10	£14
GT15	90 pi. on 5/–			
	rose-red	.. :	£22	£12
GT16	180 pi. on 10/–			
	dull grey blue	..	£55	£30
GT7/16	set (10v)	..	£85	£55

13a The "3" in the fraction is ¼mm higher above the fraction bar on No. 11 in Rows 2, 4, 6, 8 and 10.

The 18¾–180 piastres (GT13–16) exist overprinted "Specimen".

II BRITISH CURRENCY ISSUES

1905 Stamps of Great Britain (KE 7 D.L.R. printings) overprinted "LEVANT".

EB1	½d.	pl yel-grn	..	30	20
EB2	1d.	scarlet	.. ..	30	20
EB3	1½d.	dl pur and yel-grn			
		(OC)	..	2·50	2 00
EB4	2d.	grn and car (O)		2·50	2·50
		a grn and car (C)		1·50	2·00
EB5	2½d.	br blue	..	3·75	3·50
EB6	3d.	purple/yellow	..	3·25	3·25
EB7	4d.	grn and choc-brn		3·00	3·25
EB8	5d.	purple and blue ..		6·50	7·00
EB9	6d.	dl purple	.. ..	5·50	6·00
EB10	1/–	grn and car (OC)		9·00	8·50
EB1/10		set (10v)	..	£35	£36

1906 (July 2nd) No. EB 4. Surcharged at Beirut.

EB11	1 pi on 2d.	grn and		
		car (O)	£550	£250

Only 480 copies were surcharged and collectors are warned that clever forgeries of this stamp exist. It should be purchased only with Certificate.

1911 Stamp of Great Britain (KE 7 Harrison printing) overprinted in black.

EB12	½d.	green	..	1·50	3·50

1911 (Sept.) Stamps of Great Britain (KG V – Die A) similarly overprinted. Wmk. Crown.

GB1	½d.	yellow-green	..	60	80
GB2	1d.	deep rose-red	..	70	90
		a no cross on crown		—	—

1912 (March) Re-drawn types (KG V) similarly overprinted.

GB3	½d.	green	.. ..	20	10
GB4	1d.	scarlet	.. ..	20	10
		a overprint treble,			
		(two albino)	..	—	—

1913 (July) New types (KG V). Wmk. Royal Cypher. Similarly overprinted.

GB5	½d.	green	.. ..	20	25
GB6	1d.	scarlet	.. ..	25	70

See note below GT6.

1921 Stamps of Great Britain (KG V) overprinted as before.

GB7	2d.	red-or (Die I)	..	75	1·00
GB8	3d.	blue-violet	..	1·50	80
GB9	4d.	grey-green	..	175	1·50
GB10	5d.	yellow-brown	..	2·50	3·00
GB11	6d.	reddish purple(C)		3·00	3·00
GB12	1/–	bistre brown	..	2·00	1·50
GB13	2/6	choc-brn (B.W.)		£25	£30
GB7/13		set (7v)	.. ..	£32	£38

III SPECIAL ISSUE FOR SALONICA

1916 (Feb.-Mar.) Stamps of Great Britain (KG V) overprinted "Levant".

GS1	½d.	green (3000)	..	£15	£20
		a overprint double			
		(12)	..	£75	£90
		b overprint omitted			
		vert pair with nor-			
		mal (36)	.. ..	£50	£65

GS2	1d.	**scarlet** (2880)	..	£15	£20
		a overprint double		£95	£100
		(18)	.. ..	£25	£30
GS3	2d.	**red-or (Die I)** (480)		£35	£40
GS4	3d.	**blue-violet** (720)	..	—	—
		a overprint double	..	£45	£50
GS5	4d.	**grey-green** (480)	..	£25	£30
GS6	6d.	**reddish pur** (1440)			
		a overprint omitted in vert pair with normal (24)	..	£75	£90
GS7	9d.	**agate** (360) ..	..	£60	£85
		a overprint double(6)		£450	£500
GS8	1/–	**bistre-brown** (360)		£60	£85
GS1/8		**set** (8v)	.. ..	£275	£350

These stamps were overprinted at the Army Printing Office in a setting of twelve covering one horizontal row, on the authority of Lieut.-Comd. H. Pirie-Gordon, D.S.C. who had been appointed Resident-Elect for Mount Athos. The intended invasion was called off and the stamps were never sold over the counter at the Salonica Field Post Office.

Following a subsequent Court of Enquiry held aboard H.M.S. Edgar on May 19th, 1916 a statement was made that "the stamps . . . were unauthorised and the Post Office has never recognised such stamps as valid for the prepayment of postage".

Nevertheless, although only parcels required stamps (letters for Servicemen were postage free), a number of these stamps did pass through the Army Mails, being cancelled "Field Post Office GX" (or "S.X."). There was therefore genuine, if unauthorised, usage. Numbers printed are shown in brackets, but the following unsold were withdrawn and destroyed:

GS1 1648 (Net Sales — 1352)
GS2 1434 „ „ — 1446
GS4 100 „ „ — 620
GS6 600 „ „ — 840

The overprint has been extensively forged and examples of this issue should be purchased only with Certificate.

MIDDLE EAST FORCES

ADDIS ABABA

1941 (April 5th) British Forces occupied Addis Ababa on April 5th, 1941 and until March 23rd, 1942, administered the Postal Services. Current G.B. stamps without overprint were used. No stamps were sold over the counter, mail being paid for and all letters both local and foreign were franked by the Post Office Staff. The Anglo Ethiopian Treaty was signed Jan. 21st, 1942, but British stamps were used until March 23rd, 1942, when Ethiopian stamps were available. The following G.B. Stamps not overprinted exist cancelled with a circular cancellation "ADDIS ABABA" in upper portion date across centre and "ETHIOPIA" inside upper circle. Also native characters for Addis Ababa in lower part of circle.

Price from £40 per cover.

½d. **deep green** .. .. .. —
¼d. **pale green** .. .. .. —

1d.	**deep scarlet**	.. .. ..	—
1d.	**scarlet**	.. .. ..	—
1½d.	**deep red-brown**	.. .. ..	—
1½d.	**red-brown**	. .. ..	—
2d.	**deep orange**	.. .. ..	—
2d.	**dull orange**	.. .. ..	—
2½d.	**deep ultramarine**	.. ..	—
2½d.	**ultramarine**	.. ..	—
3d.	**violet**	.. .. ..	—
3d.	**pale violet**	.. .. ..	—
4d.	**green-grey**	.. .. ..	—
5d.	**pale brown**	.. .. ..	—
6d.	**pale purple**	.. .. ..	—
7d.	**emerald**	.. .. ..	—
8d.	**deep rose**	.. .. ..	—
9d.	**deep olive**	.. .. ..	—
10d.	**grey-blue**	.. .. ..	—
1/–	**bistre brown**	.. .. ..	—

M.E.F.

1942 (Mar. 2nd) Stamps of Great Britain overprinted M.E.F. by Army Printing Services, Cairo, for use in Eritrea.

1	1d.	**dp scarlet**	..	6·00	4·00
		a round stops	..	6·00	4·00
		se-tenant pair	..	£15	£12
2	2d.	**dp orange**	..	£15	£12
		a round stops	..	£15	£12
		b se-tenant pair		£35	£35
3	2½d.	**dp ultramarine**	..	8·00	6·00
		a round stops	..	8·00	6·00
		b se-tenant pair		£20	£20
4	3d.	**violet**	..	£10	£10
		a round stops	..	£10	£9
		b se-tenant pair	..	£25	£25
5	5d.	**pale brown**	..	£60	£25
		a round stops	..	£60	£30
		b se-tenant pair	..	£160	£100

1-5 Overprint 13½ mm and letters somewhat uneven at edges.

1*a*-5*a* Overprint 13½ mm but end of letters and stops rounded.

Both round and square stops occur on the same sheets.

The complete setting consists of 10 rows of 6 stamps, the square stops being rows, 2, 3 and 7 only.

1942 (Mar. 2nd) As before but overprinted in London by Harrison & Sons, for use in Eritrea and Italian Somaliland.

6	1d.	**dp scarlet**	..	10	20
7	2d.	**dp orange**	..	10	20
8	2½d.	**dp ultramarine**	..	15	25
9	3d.	**violet**	..	15	25
		a ovpt double	..	—	—
10	5d.	**pale brown**	..	15	25

Overprint 14 mm. letters and stops clear cut and straight, and in general the Harrison "overprints" are sharper. Both printings were released at the same time in Eritrea.

1943 (Jan. 1st) -47 Stamps of Great Britain overprinted M. E. F. in blue-black or black (2/6, 5/- and 10/-) by Harrison & Sons, for use in Cyrenaica, Dodecanese Islands, Eritrea, and Tripolitania.

11	1d.	**scarlet**	.. .. ..	5	5
12	2d.	**dull orange**	.. ..	10	5
13	2½d.	**ultramarine**	.. ..	10	10
14	3d.	**purple-violet**	..	10	10
15	5d.	**pale brown**	.. ..	10	10
16	6d.	**pale purple**	..	15	15
17	9d.	**deep olive**	.. ..	20	25
18	1/-	**bistre-brown**	..	20	25
	a	broken barb	..	£45	—
	b	broken cross	..	£45	—
19	2/6	**green**	.. .. ..	1·00	75
20	5/-	**red** (27/1/47)	..	3·00	3·00
21	10/-	**ultramarine** (27/1/47)		8·00	8·00
11/21		**set** (11)	.. ..	£12	£11
SP18/21		**specimen set** (4)	..	£140	‡

15 This overprint measures 13½ mm. and can be distinguished from that on No. 10 by its glossy blue-black surface, as against the matt black of the previous overprint (*most noticeable when light shines across the overprint*). Also the stop between M and E is slightly nearer M than E in the case of No. 15, whereas it is exactly in the centre on No. 10.

M. E. F. overprints on ½d. and 1½d. 1941 colours exist. These may be proofs, but their status is not known at present.

18a/b See G.B., Nos. 15a and 15b.

Number issued—

1d., 2,338,263;   2d., 2,387,731;
2½d., 3,006,679;   3d., 1,929,050;
5d., 2,240,604;   6d., 1,318,924;
9d., 1,030,036;   1/-, 2,060,434;
2/6, 271,850;   5/-, 101,830;
10/-, 130,986.

POSTAGE DUE STAMPS

1942 (Mar. 2nd) Postage Due Stamps of Great

Britain overprinted M. E. F. in dark blue by Harrison & Sons for use as Nos. 11/21.

PD1	½d.	**emerald-green**	..	10	10
PD2	1d.	**rose-red**	.. ..	10	10
PD3	2d.	**agate**	.. .. ..	20	20
PD4	3d.	**violet**	.. ..	30	30
PD5	1/-	**blue**	.. .. ..	50	65
PD1/5		**set** (5)	.. ..	1·00	1·30
SP PD5		**overprint specimen** (1)	£25	‡

Number issued—½d., 336,613; 1d., 243,941; 2d., 242,887; 3d., 294,394; 1/-, 260,344.

The use in the United Kingdom of stamps overprinted "M.E.F." was permitted from 1950. Our prices for used stamps are for copies with postmarks of the territories in which the stamps were issued; and copies with U.K. postmarks are occasionally available at two-thirds of these prices.

ERITREA

1948 (May 27th) -49 Stamps of Great Britain surcharged and overprinted B. M. A. ERITREA etc., by Harrison & Sons, London, for civilian use and to replace M. E. F. overprinted stamps.

1	5c./½d.	**green**	.. ..	10	10
2	10c./1d.	**scarlet**	.. ..	10	15
3	20c./2d.	**dull orange**	..	20	35
4	25c./2½d.	**ultramarine**	..	15	20
5	30c./3d.	**purple-violet**	..	15	20
6	40c./5d.	**pale brown**	..	15	20
7	50c./6d.	**pale purple**	..	15	20
8	65c./8d.	**dp rose** (1/2/49)		35	55
9	75c./9d.	**dp olive**	..	20	30
10	1s./1s.	**bistre-brown**	..	20	25
11	2.50/2/6	**green**	..	2·50	2·50
	a	misplaced stop		£15	£15
12	5s./5s.	**red**	.. ..	4·00	5·00
	a	re-entry	..	00	00
13	10s./10s.	**ultramarine**	..	8·00	8·00
1/13		**set** (13)	..	£16	£15

11a The stop after SH is smaller and near the 50 of the surcharge. Row 4/7.

12a See G.B., 18a (Row 4/2).

Number issued—5c., 171,441; 10c., 232,179; 20c., 327,677; 25c., 434,917; 30c., 218,741; 40c., 319,432; 50c., 338,946; 65c., 316 958; 75c., 173,926; 1s., 213,267; 2.50c., 71,608; 5s., 70,864; 10s., 89,912.

1950 (Feb. 6th) As before but overprint altered to B. A.

14	5c./½d.	**green**	10	15
15	10c./1d.	**scarlet** (2nd state)	10	15
16	20c./2d.	**dull orange** ..	15	20
17	25c./2½d.	**ultramarine** ..	15	20
18	30c./3d.	**purple-violet** ..	15	20
19	40c./5d.	**pale brown** ..	15	25
20	50c./6d.	**pale purple** ..	20	25
21	65c./8d.	**dp rose**	35	30
22	75c./9d.	**dp olive**	30	35
23	1s./1s.	**bistre-brown** ..	35	20
24	2.50/2/6	**green**	2·50	2·50
		a re-entry ..	£50	£50
25	5s./5s.	**red**	6·00	5·00
26	10s./10s.	**ultramarine** ..	£10	7·00
14/26		**set** (13) ..	£20	£16

24*a* see G.B. 17*a* (Row 1/7)

Number issued—5c., 116,664; 10c., 169,469; 20c., 313,389; 25c., 248,558; 30c., 310,202; 40c., 198,134; 50c., 536,347; 65c., 715,228; 75c., 277,165; 1s., 394,870.

1951 (May 3rd) As No. 14, etc., but colours changed (Nos. 31—3 as Nos. 34—6 of G.B.).

27	5c./½d.	**dull orange** ..	10	35
28	10c./1d.	**ultramarine** ..	10	30
29	20c./2d.	**red-brown** ..	10	25
30	25c./2½d.	**scarlet**	10	25
31	2.50/2/6	**green**	1·50	3·00
32	5s./5s.	**red**	4·00	5·50
33	10s./10s.	**ultramarine** ..	£10	6·00
27/33		**set**	£15	£14

Number issued—5c., 131,716; 10c., 174,181; 20c., 261,294; 25c., 261,712.

POSTAGE DUE STAMPS

1948 (May 27th) Postage Due Stamps of Great Britain overprinted.

PD1	5c./½d.	**emerald-green** .	2·00	4·00
PD2	10c./1d.	**rose-red** ..	2·00	4·00
PD3	20c./2d.	**agate**	2·00	5·00
		a no stop after A ..	£10	£10
		b no stop after B	£10	£10
PD4	30c./3d.	**violet**	3·00	5·00
PD5	1s./1s.	**blue**	6·50	8·00
PD1/5		**set**	£14	£25

PD3*a* The stop after A in B.M.A. is missing. (*Various positions*).

PD3*b* The stop after B in B.M.A. is missing. Row 1/9.

Number issued—5c., 22,991; 10c., 26,164; 20c., 40,436; 30c., 52,000; 1s., 22,264.

1950 (Feb. 6th) As before but overprint altered to B. A.

PD6	5c./½d.	**emerald-green** .	3·00	4·25
PD7	10c./1d.	**rose-red** ..	3·00	4·25
		a 10 ents ..	£350	—
		b no stop after A	£10	£10
PD8	20c./2d.	**agate**	3·00	3·50
		a no stop after A	8·00	8·00
PD9	30c./3d.	**violet**	4·00	4·00
PD10	1s./1s.	**blue**	6·00	5·00
		a no stop after A	£10	£10
PD6/10		**set** (5)	£17	£18

PD7*a* The C in CENTS of surcharge was omitted in first releases (Row 7/20) but almost immediately the omission was rectified.

PD7*b*/8*a*/10*a* The stop after A in B.A. is missing. (*Various positions*).

Number issued—5c., 19,917; 10c., 32,761; 20c., 40,349; 30c., 39,267; 1s., 26,234.

SOMALIA

All stamps were overprinted by Harrison & Sons.

1943 (Jan. 1st) -46 Stamps of Great Britain, overprinted E.A.F. (blue), for use in Somalia

1	1d.	**scarlet**	10	20
2	2d.	**dull orange**	10	20
3	2½d.	**ultramarine**	10	20
4	3d.	**purple-violet** ..	10	20
5	5d.	**pale brown**	15	25
6	6d.	**pale purple**	15	25
7	9d.	**dp olive**	20	75
8	1/–	**bistre-brown** ..	20	20
9	2/6	**green** (14/1/46) ..	1·00	1·75
1/9		**set**	2·00	3·50
SP8/9		**specimen pair** ..	£60	‡

Number issued—1d., 160,091; 2d., 204,321; 2½d.. 150.505; 3d., 310,111; 5d., 178,410; 6d., 132,386; 9d., 157,081; 1/–, 323,781; 2/6, 84,127.

The use in the United Kingdom of stamps overprinted "E.A.F." was permitted from 1950. Our prices for used stamps are for copies with postmarks of the territories in which the stamps were issued; and copies with U.K. postmarks are occasionally available at two-thirds of these prices.

1948 (May 27th) Stamps of Great Britain surcharged and overprinted to replace the E.A.F. issue.

10	5c./½d.	green	..	..	10	20
11	15c./1½d.	red-brown		..	40	90
12	20c./2d.	dull orange		..	10	50
13	25c./2½d.	ultramarine		..	10	25
14	30c./3d.	purple-violet		..	40	90
15	40c./5d.	light brown		..	10	60
16	50c./6d.	pale purple		..	15	75
17	75c./9d.	dp olive	..	..	60	1·75
18	1s./1–	bistre-brown		..	30	75
19	2.50/2/6	green	..	..	2·00	4·00
		a misplaced stop			£35	£35
20	5s./5s.	red	..	..	4·00	8·00
10/20		set (11)	..	..	7·50	£17

19a See No. 11a Entries for details of this variety.

Number issued—5c., 123,200; 15c., 35,924; 20c., 80,033; 25c., 277,790; 30c., 42,107; 40c., 88,235; 50c., 102,984; 75c., 31,500; 1s., 140,873; 2.50c., 29,057; 5s., 20,082.

1950 (Jan. 2nd) As before but overprint altered to B. A. SOMALIA, etc.

21	5c./½d.	green	..	..	10	10
22	15c./1½d.	red-brown		..	20	75
23	20c./2d.	dull orange		..	20	50
24	25c./2½d.	ultramarine		..	10	40
25	30c./3d.	purple-violet		..	30	90
26	40c./5d.	pale brown		..	25	50
27	50c./6d.	pale purple		..	25	45
28	75c./9d.	dp olive	..	..	35	1·00
29	1s./1–	bistre-brown		..	30	60
30	2.50/2/6	green	..	..	2·50	5·00
		a re-entry			—	—
31	5s./5s.	red	..	..	4·00	6·00
21/31		set (11)	..	..	7·50	£15

30a. See G.B. 17a (Row 1/7).

Number issued—5c., 45,811; 15c., 28,094; 20c., 34,522; 25c., 109,461; 30c., 29,236; 40c., 36,748; 50c., 56,418; 75c., 26,145; 1s., 58,170; 2.50c., 20,884; 5s., 19,310.

TRIPOLITANIA

1948 (July 1st) Stamps of Great Britain surcharged and overprinted to replace the M.E.F. issue.

1	1l./½d.	green	..	..	10	30
2	2l./1d.	scarlet	..	..	10	20
3	3l./1½d.	red-brown		..	10	30
4	4l./2d.	dull orange		..	10	30
5	5l./2½d.	ultramarine		..	10	30
6	6l./3d.	purple-violet		..	10	30
7	10l./5d.	pale brown		..	10	30
8	12l./6d.	pale purple		..	10	30
9	18l./9d.	dp olive	..	..	20	75
10	24l./1s.	bistre-brown		..	30	90
11	60l./2/6	green	..	..	80	2·50
12	120l./5s.	red	..	..	3·00	5·00
13	240l./10s.	ultramarine		..	4·50	7·00
1/13		set (13)	..	..	9·00	£17

Number issued—1l., 91,405; 2l., 396,555; 3l., 115,888; 4l., 221,453; 5l., 303,580; 6l., 194,095; 10l., 380,896; 12l., 151,505; 18l., 90,208; 24l., 77,993; 60l., 31,048; 120l., 19,127; 240l., 14,793.

1950 (Feb. 6th) As No. 1, etc., but overprint altered to B. A.

14	1l./½d.	green	..	..	10	30
15	2l./1d.	scar (2nd state)		..	10	30
16	3l./1½d.	red-brown		..	10	30
17	4l./2d.	dull orange		..	10	30
18	5l./2½d.	ultramarine		..	10	30
19	6l./3d.	purple-violet		..	10	30
20	10l./5d.	pale brown		..	10	30
21	12l./6d.	pale purple		..	10	30
22	18l./9d.	dp olive	..	..	20	50
23	24l./1s.	bistre-brown		..	20	50
24	60l./2/6	green	..	..	2·50	4·00
25	120l./5s.	red	..	..	3·25	6·50
26	240l./10s.	ultramarine		..	5·50	8·00
14/26		set (13)	..	..	£11	£20

Number issued—1l., 71,248; 2l., 285,458; 3l., 97,615; 4l., 212,377; 5l., 434,138; 6l., 302,874; 10l. 622,901; 12l., 233,534; 18l., 118,337; 24l., 91,583; 60l., 25,303; 120l., 18,020, 240l., 13,417.

1951 (May 3rd) As No. 14, etc., but colours changed (Nos. 32—4 as Nos. 34—6 of G.B.).

27	1l./½d.	dull orange		..	10	30
28	2l./1d.	ultramarine		..	10	30
29	3l./1½d.	green	..	..	15	30
30	4l./2d.	red-brown		..	15	30
31	5l./2½d.	scarlet	..	..	15	30
32	60l./2/6	green	..	..	2·50	3·50
33	120l./5s.	red	..	..	3·25	5·50
34	240l./10s.	ultramarine		..	£10	6·00
27/34		set (8)	..	..	£15	£15

Number issued—1l., 74,590; 2l., 200,530; 3l., 72,077; 4l., 126,803; 5l., 222,817; 60l., 19,148; 120l., 17,037; 240l., 12.858.

POSTAGE DUE STAMPS

1948 (July 1st) Postage Due Stamps of Great Britain, overprinted. As No. 1, etc.

| PD1 | 1l./½d. | emerald-green | . | 1·50 | 2·50 |
| | | a no stop after A | | £10 | £10 |

PD2	2l./1d. **rose-red**	..	1·50	2·50
	a no stop after A		£10	£10
PD3	4l./2d. **agate**	.. ..	1·50	3·00
	a no stop after A		£10	£10
	b no stop after M		£10	£10
PD4	6l./3d. **violet**	.. ..	2·50	4·00
	a no stop after A		£12	£12
PD5	24l./1s. **blue**		5·00	6·00
	a no stop after A		£15	£15
PD1/5	**set** (5)	.. ..	£10	£16

Number issued—1l., 20,863; 2l., 22,742; 4l., 19,649; 6l., 17,702; 24l., 10,640.

1950 (Feb. 6th) As before but overprint altered to B. A.

PD6	1l./½d. **emerald-green** .		1·50	2·50
	a no stop after B		£10	£10
PD7	2l./1d. **rose red**	..	1·50	2·50
	a no stop after B		£10	£10
PD8	4l./2d. **agate**		1·50	3·00
	no stop after B		£10	£10
PD9	6l./3d. **violet**	.. ..	2·50	4·00
	a no stop after B		£12	£12
PD10	24l./1s. **blue**	.. ..	5·00	6·00
	a no stop after B		£15	£15
	b no stop after A		£15	£15
PD6/10	**set** (5)	.. ..	£10	£16

PD1*a*-4*a* The stop after A in B.M.A. is missing.

PD3*b* The stop after M in B.M.A. is missing.

PD6*a*-10*a* The stop after B in B.A. is missing.

PD10*b* The stop after B in B.A. is missing.

Number issued—1l., 16,404; 2l., 20,312; 4l., 19,008; 6l., 24,137; 24l., 10,682.

Numbers issued from MEF 11 to Tripolitania No. PD10 are subject to revision in the light of research at present in hand.

CYRENAICA

1950 (Jan. 16th) Design, Mounted Mujahid. Printers (*recess*) **Waterlow & Sons. No Wmk. Perf. 12¼ (L.).**

1	1m. **sepia**	..	.. ..	10	10
2	2m. **rose-red**		..	10	10
3	3m. **orange-yellow**		..	10	10
4	4m. **dull myrtle-green**	..		10	10
5	5m. **brownish-grey**		..	15	15
6	8m. **orange**		..	15	15
7	10m. **violet**		.. ..	15	15
8	12m. **scarlet**		.. ..	25	25
9	20m. **deep blue**		.. ..	50	25
10	50m. **ult and dp brown**	..		1·25	1·00
11	100m. **carmine and black**	..		2·75	1·50
12	200m. **violet and violet-blue**			4·00	3·00
13	500m. **orange-yel and grn**			£10	8·00
1/13	**set** (13)	.. ..		£18	£14

POSTAGE DUE STAMPS

1950 (Jan. 16th). Design POSTAGE DUE in Ornamental Frame. Printers (*recess*) **Waterlow & Sons. No Wmk. Perf. 12¼ (L.)**

PD1	2m. **sepia**	.. ..	65	65
PD2	4m. **green**	.. ..	75	75
PD3	8m. **carmine-red**	..	1·00	1·00
PD4	10m. **dull scarlet**	..	3·00	3·00
PD5	20m. **yellow-orange**	..	6·00	6·00
PD6	40m. **slate-blue**	..	£10	£10
PD7	100m. **slate-black**	..	£20	£20
PD1/7	**set** (7)	.. ..	£40	£40

MOROCCO AGENCIES

The first British Post Office was opened in Tangier on April 1st, 1857: no stamps were sold, but G.B. stamps were used and were cancelled with "A26" obliterator on arrival at Gibraltar.

From 1872 to 1885 G.B. stamps were used and were cancelled either "A26" in small oval of horizontal bars or with "A26" in duplex with a small single lined circle Gibraltar datestamp: at the same time a single-lined circle "Tangier" datestamp appeared on the cover (not cancelling the stamp). Until 1875 the "N" in "TANGIER" was reversed.

On January 1st, 1886 the Colonial Office took over from the Postmaster General the administration of the Gibraltar and Tangier Post Offices and from then until 1898 all the contemporary Gibraltar stamps were used without overprint in Casablanca, Fez, Larache, Mazagan, Mogador, Rabat, Safi, Tangier and Tetuan Post Offices. These offices remained under the control of the Gibraltar Post Office until 1907; and all used their own c.d.s. in duplex with "A26", or oval registered cancellations.

The "short I in CENTIMOS" variety of the 1889 (July) issue of Gibraltar (V18*a*) is recorded used from Mogador in July 1889.

The following bisected stamps of the 1889 (Nov.) issue of Gibraltar (q.v.) were only used in Tangier.

V23*a*	10c. bisect (5c.) on cover 1891 (15/1, 15/2, 6/4, 13/5) ..	‡	£600
V28*a*	40c. bisect (20c.) on cover 1892 (17/5, 17/9)	‡	£850
V29*a*	50c. bisect (25c.) on cover 1892 (24/3, 12/4, 19/4, 2/8, 13/9)	‡	£700

On February 22nd, 1891, during a temporary shortage of stamps at Tangier, covers were franked in manuscript "Postage prepaid in cash" and initialled "R.L." by the Postmaster (Roque Lyons).

In 1898 Gibraltar reverted to Sterling currency: such a change was not possible in Morocco, hence the overprinting of stamps valued in Spanish currency which were no longer usable in Gibraltar.

I COLONIAL OFFICE ISSUES

for use in all British Post Offices in Morocco.

Type I

Type II	Type III
Morocco	Morocco
Agencies	Agencies

1898-9 Gibraltar Issues of 1889-1895. Wmk Crown CA. Perf. 14 overprinted in half sheets of 120 (two panes, each 6 x 10).

A. With Type I at "Gibraltar Chronicle" office (Wide "M" and ear of "g" projecting upwards).

(a) In black.

V1	5c.	green	.. ..	20	15
V2	10c.	carmine	.. ..	20	15
		b overprint double	..	£200	—
V3	20c.	olive-green	..	80	80
		b overprint double	..	£150	—
V4	20c.	olive-grn and brn	..	80	50
V5	25c.	ultramarine	..	40	30
V6	40c.	orange-brown	..	1·25	1·25
V7	50c.	bright lilac	..	6·50	£10
V8	1p.	bistre and ult	..	4·00	7·50
V9	2p.	black and carmine	..	2·00	5·50
V1/9		set (9v)	.. ..	£13	£20

2b occurred on the right hand pane (of 60) on one sheet.

3b occurred on one complete sheet (of 120).

A variety — Inverted "V" for "A" in "Agencies" occurred on No. 36 (1st setting) of the right hand pane (of 60) on all values. This variety has been forged; and the genuine stamp has a small dot in the lower loop of the "g" of "Agencies".

V1a	5c.	..	..	..	£10	£20
V2a	10c.	..	..	..	£120	£145
V3a	20c.	..	..	..	8·00	£10
V4a	20c.	..	..	..	8·00	£10
V5a	25c.	..	..	..	£45	£50
V6a	40c.	..	..	..	£80	£90
V7a	50c.	..	..	..	£100	£120

V8a	1p.	..	..	..	£80	£90
V9a	2p.	..	..	..	£100	£120

(b) In blue-black (2nd setting).

V10	40c.	orange-brown	..	£10	£12
V11	50c.	bright lilac..	..	3·00	4·00
V12	1p.	bistre and ult	..	£40	£45

B. With Type II in London (Narrow "M" and ear of "g" projecting horizontally) in black.

V13	5c.	green	.. ..	10	10
V14	10c.	carmine (4/99)	..	15	10
		c bisect(5c.)on cover		—	£400
V15	20c.	olive-green	..	45	30
V16	25c.	ultramarine	..	1·50	50
V17	40c.	or-brn (4/99)	..	3·00	3·50
V18	50c.	bright lilac..	..	2·50	1·50
V19	1p.	bistre and ult (4/99)	..	6·50	7·50
V20	2p.	blk and carmine	..	8·00	£10
V13/20		set (8v)	.. ..	£20	£22

14c This bisect was authorised at Casablanca on July 30th, 1901.

The 40c. and 50c. are also reported to have been bisected and used from Tangier and Rabat.

All values exist overprinted "Specimen" in black sans-serif capitals 14½ x 2½ mm.

Numbers Printed—V13-122,160; V14-122,400; V15-60,840; V16-120,720; V17-36,480; V18-36,000; V19-36,240, V20-36,000.

plus 750 Specimen sets.

Varieties:

(a) Broad top to "M". No. 39 left hand pane (Type III).

(b) Hyphen between "n-c". No. 17 Right hand pane.

		(a)		(b)	
V13	5c. ..	2·00	2·25	2·00	2·25
V14	10c. ..	2·00	2·25	2·00	2·25
V15	20c. ..	5·00	6·00	5·00	6·00
V16	25c. ..	5·00	6·00	5·00	6·00
V17	40c. ..	£25	£30	£25	£30
V18	50c. ..	£35	£40	£35	£40
V19	1p. ..	£40	£45	£40	£45
V20	2p. ..	£125	£140	£125	£140

1903-5 Stamps of Gibraltar (KE VII) but with values expressed in Spanish currency. Wmk. Crown CA. Perf. 14 overprinted by De La Rue in black (Type II) in half sheets of 120—two panes, each 6 x 10.

E1	5c.	grey-grn and grn (1/04)		1·00	30
E2	10c.	dl-pur/red (8/03) ..		1·00	40
		c bisect diag (5c.) on cover		—	—
E3	20c.	grey-grn and car (9/04)		2·50	7·00
E4	25c.	pur and blk/blu (7/03)		75	30
E5	50c.	pur and vio (7/05)..		£35	£40
E6	1p.	blk and car (11/05)		£30	£35
E7	2p.	blk and blu (11/05)		£38	£35
E1/7		set (7v)	.. ..	£100	£110

2c The 10c. is known bisected and used with two 10c. making the 25c. rate, on covers from Rabat May 17th and October 24th, 1905.

All values exist overprinted "Specimen" in black sans-serif capitals 14½ x 2½ mm.

Numbers Printed—50c. 3,120; 2p. 3,000.

Varieties:

(*a*) Broad top to "M". No. 39 left hand pane (Type III).

(*b*) Hyphen between "n-c". No. 17 right hand pane.

		(a)		(b)	
E1	5c.	8·00	9·00	8·00	9·00
E2	10c	8·00	9·00	8·00	9·00
E3	20c.	£12	£15	£12	£15
E4	25c.	£12	£15	£12	£15
E5	50c.	£125	£140	£125	£140
E6	1p.	£115	£125	£115	£125
E7	2p.	£125	£140	£125	£140

1905-6 As before, but wmk. Mult. Crown CA

E8	5c.	grey-grn and grn (OC)	30	25
E9	10c.	dl purple/red (OC)	40	20
E10	20c.	grey-grn and car (O)	1·00	2·50
E11	25c.	pur and blk/blu (C)	£10	5·00
E12	50c.	pur and vio (C)	4·50	4·50
E13	1p.	blk and car (C)	£17·50	£22
E14	2p.	blk and blu (C)	£12·50	£10
E8/14		set (7v)	£42	£40

All values except 20c. (E10) exist overprinted "Specimen" in black sans-serif capitals 15 x 2 mm (**Not** by De La Rue).

The 10c. on **O** paper is known with wmk. inverted.

Varieties:

(*a*) Broad top to "M". No. 39 left hand pane (Type III).

(*b*) Hyphen between "n-c". No. 17 right hand pane.

		(a)		(b)	
E8	5c.	7·00	8·00	£100	£120
E9	10c.	8·00	9·00	—	—
E10	20c.	£30	£32	—	—
E11	25c.	5·00	6·00	—	—
E12	50c.	£75	£85	—	—
E13	1p.	£90	£100	—	—
E14	2p.	£125	£140	—	—

All the foregoing Colonial Office issues were withdrawn on December 31st, 1906 and ceased to be valid on February 12th, 1907. The withdrawn stamps were destroyed on March 6th, 1907.

On January 1st, 1907 the British P.M.G. again assumed control of the British Post Offices in Morocco (including additional offices at Alcazar and Mequinez).

II. G.P.O. ISSUES

for use in all British Post Offices in Morocco.

1. BRITISH CURRENCY

1907–1937 and 1949–1956.

1907-13 Stamps of Great Britain (KE VII) overprinted "MOROCCO AGENCIES".

(a) De La Rue printings. Perf. 14.

EB1	½d.	pale green	30	50
EB2	1d.	scarlet	75	1·00
EB3	2d.	grn and car (C)	75	2·25
EB4	4d.	grn and pur-brn (C)	8·50	1·75
EB5	4d.	pale orange	1·25	1·25
EB6	6d.	dl purple (C)	2·50	1·25
EB7	1/–	grn and car (C)	7·50	6·00
EB8	2/6	lilac (C)	£40	£38
EB9	2/6	purple (C)	£40	£38
EB1/9		set (9v)	£90	£80

(b) Harrison printings. Perf. 15 x 14.

EB10	4d.	bright orange	5·50	6·00

(c) Somerset House printings.

EB11	2/6	dull purple	£42	£45

All values except 4d. (EB5 and EB10) exist overprinted "Specimen" in block capitals 3mm. high arranged in a semi-circle.

1914-31 Stamps of Great Britain (KG V) overprinted "MOROCCO AGENCIES". Wmk. Royal Cypher. Perf. 15 x 14.

GB1	½d.	green	15	30
GB2	1d.	scarlet	15	15
GB3	1½d.	red-brown	75	80
GB4	2d.	orange (Die I)	60	30
		a overprint double (one albino)	—	—
GB5	3d.	blue-violet	80	40
GB6	4d.	grey-green	1·10	50
GB7	6d.	reddish-purple	3·25	3·25
GB8	1/–	bistre	7·50	1·50
		a overprint treble (two albino)	—	—
GB9	2/6	dp brn (Water-low)	£65	£45
		a overprint double (one albino)	—	—
		b re-entry	—	—
GB10	2/6	chestnut (D.L.R.	£65	£45
		a overprint double	—	—
		b overprint treble (two albino)	—	—
GB11	2/6	grey-brn (D.L.R.	£65	£45
GB12	2/6	choc-brn (B.W.)	£80	£30
		a overprint double (one albino)	—	—
GB13	5/–	rose-red (1931) (B.W.)	£85	£50
		a overprint treble (two albino)	—	—
GB1/13		set (10v)	£160	£85

The 1/– (GB8) and 2/6 (GB9) and (GB12) are recorded with "Specimen" overprint 10 x 1½ mm. in sloping sans-serif capitals: the 5/– (GB13) exists with the overprint 10½ x 2 mm. in upright sans-serif capitals.

1925-36 Stamps of Great Britain (KG V). Wmk. Multiple Block GVR overprinted "MOROCCO AGENCIES".

(*a*) 14 mm. overprint. Ends of "S" cut diagonally.

(*b*) 15½ mm. overprint. Ends of "S" cut horizontally.

		(a)	(b)
GB14	½d.		
	green	50 25	30

GB15 1½d.
chestnut
('31) .. 5·00 6·00 — —
GB16 2d.
orange .. 1·00 75 — —
GB17 2½d
blue .. 1·50 75 £40 £25
GB18 4d.
grey-grn
(1/36) — — 3·00 8·00
GB19 6d.
pur ('31) 1·50 2·00 60 75
GB20 1/–
bistre .. 5·00 3·50 £20 £15
GB14/20
set (7v) cheapest £15 £17

The 1/– (GB20) exists overprinted "Specimen" 10 x 1¼ mm. in sloping sans-serif capitals.

1935 (May 8th) Silver Jubilee stamps of Great Britain overprinted "MOROCCO AGENCIES" vertically up and down.

GB21 ½d. **green (Bl)** .. 25 40
GB22 1d. **scarlet (Bl)** .. 40 90
GB23 1½d. **red- brown(Bl)** 1·50 2·50
GB24 2½d. **blue (R)** .. 2·00 2·25
GB21/24 **set** (4v) . 3·50 4·75

All values exist overprinted "AGENCIFS" for "AGENCIES" (No. 46).

Numbers Printed—½d., 107,813; 1d., 46,875; 1½d., 153,125; 2½d., 62,500.

1935-37 Stamps of Great Britain (KG V. Harrison (*Photo*) **and Waterlow** (*Re-engraved*)**) overprinted "MOROCCO AGENCIES".**

GB25 1d. **scarlet** 25 30
GB26 1½d. **red-brown** .. 75 2·00
GB27 2d. **orange** 15 10
GB28 2½d. **ultramarine** .. 1·00 1·00
GB29 3d. **violet** 25 10
GB30 4d. **dp grey-green**
GB31 1/– **bistre-brown** .. 80 60
GB32 2/6 **chocolate** .. £35 £25
GB33 5/– **br rose-red**
(3/37) .. £45 £30
GB25/33 **set** (9v) .. £80 £55

The 1/– (GB31) exists overprinted "Specimen" 11 x 2 mm. in upright sans serif capitals; and the 2/6 (GB32) in sloping capitals the same size.

1936 Stamps of Great Britain (KE 8) overprinted "MOROCCO AGENCIES", vertically up and down.

(*a*) "MOROCCO" 14¼ mm. long.
(*b*) "MOROCCO" 15¼ mm. long.

(*a*) (*b*)
EB34 1d.
scarlet .. 10 10 50 90
EB35 2½d. 15 15 50 90
ultramarine
EB34/35
set (2v) .. 20 20 80 1·50

In 1937 unoverprinted stamps of Great Britain gradually replaced the Morocco Agencies issues. (See Section IV). In 1949, however, overprinted issues re-appeared for use at Tetuan (in the Spanish zone), the only remaining British Post Office, apart from Tangier, in Morocco. They were finally withdrawn on December 31st, 1956.

1949 (Aug. 16th) Stamps of Great Britain, overprinted "MOROCCO AGENCIES", for use at Tetuan (Spanish Zone).

B1 ½d. **green** 10 15
B2 1d. **scarlet** (2nd state) .. 10 15
B3 1½d. **red-brown** .. 10 15
B4 2d. **dull orange** .. 15 20
B5 2½d. **ultramarine** .. 15 20
B6 3d. **purple-violet** .. 15 20
B7 4d. **greenish-grey** .. 15 20
B8 5d. **pale brown** .. 20 25
B9 6d. **pale purple** .. 20 25
B10 7d. **emerald-green** .. 25 30
B11 8d. **dp rose** 25 40
B12 9d. **dp olive** .. 30 50
B13 10d. **dp grey-blue** .. 40 50
B14 11d. **dp plum** 50 60
B15 1/– **bistre-brown** .. 1·00 1·00
B16 2/6 **green** .. .. 4·00 6·00
a re-entry .. .. —
B17 5/– **red** .. .. 9·00 £12
B1/17 **set** (17) £17 £22

B16*a*—See G.B. 17*a* (Row 1/7).

Number issued—½d., 43,483; 1d., 36,829; 1½d., 27,637; 2d., 28,644; 2½d., 30,422; 3d., 51,954; 4d., 42,203; 5d., 25,267; 6d., 42,910; 7d., 29,474; 8d., 24,548; 9d., 33,038; 10d., 28,864; 11d., 29,345; 1/–, 30,910; 2/6, 15,560; 5/–, 13,751.

1951 (May 3rd) As No. B1, etc., but colours changed (Nos. 24—5 as Nos. 34—5 of G.B.), similarly overprinted.

B18 ½d. **dull orange** .. 10 10
B19 1d. **ultramarine** .. 10 15
B20 1½d. **green** 15 15
B21 2d. **red-brown** .. 15 15
B22 2½d. **scarlet** 15 15
B24 2/6 **green** .. .. 3·00 3·50
B25 5/– **red** .. .. 5·00 7·00
B18/25 **set** (7) .. .. 8·50 £11

Number issued—½d., 52,227; 1d., 43,557; 1½d., 34,563; 2d., 33,363; 2½d., 50,136; 2/6, 21,033; 5/–, 18,066.

Note:

The use in the United Kingdom of stamps overprinted "Morocco Agencies" (without currency surcharge) was permitted from 1950. Our prices for used stamps are for copies with Morocco Agencies postmarks; and stamps with U.K. postmarks are occasionally available at 2/3 of these prices.

2 SPANISH CURRENCY
1907–1956 (December 31st)

1907-13 Stamps of Great Britain (KE VII) overprinted "MOROCCO AGENCIES" and surcharged.

(a) De La Rue printings. Perf. 14.

ES1 5c. on ½d. **pl grn** .. 15 10

ES2	10c. on 1d.	**scarlet** ..	15	10
ES3	15c. on 1½d.	**pur and grn**		
		(C) ..	25	15
		a "1" of "15		
		omitted..	£750	£900
ES4	20c. on 2d.	**grn and car**		
		(C) ..	30	15
ES5	25c. on 2½d.	**br blue** ..	60	15
ES6	40c. on 4d.	**grn and**		
		pur - brn		
		(C) ..	1·00	2·25
ES7	40c. on 4d.	**orange** ..	30	45
ES8	50c. on 5d.	**pur and blu**		
		(C) ..	1·25	40
ES9	1p. on 10d.	**pur and car**		
		(C) ..	2·75	3·50
ES10	3p. on 2/6	**lilac (C)** ..	£15	£12
ES11	6p. on 5/−	**carmine** ..	£30	£35
ES12	12p. on 10/−	**ult**	£45	£35
ES1/12		**set** (12v) ..	£85	£80

(b) Harrison printings. Perf. 15 x 14.

ES13	25c. on 2½d.	**br blue** ..	5·00	6·00

(c) Somerset House printings.

ES14	12p. on 10/−	**br blue** ..	£80	£90

3*a* Only 12 copies are known, from the first vertical row.

All values except 40c./4d. (ES7) exist overprinted "Specimen" in block capitals 3 mm. high arranged in a semi-circle.

1912 Stamps of Great Britain (KG V) similarly overprinted and surcharged. Wmk. Crown. Perf. 15 x 14.

GS1	5c. on ½d.	**green** ..	50	5
GS2	10c. on 1d.	**scarlet** ..	75	5
		a no cross on		
		crown ..	£30	£25

1914-26 Stamps of Great Britain (KG V) similarly overprinted and surcharged. Wmk. Royal Cypher. Perf. 15 x 14.

GS3	3c. on ½d.	**grn** ..	10	80
GS4	5c. on ½d.	**grn** ..	30	10
GS5	10c. on 1d.	**scar** ..	20	10
GS6	15c. on 1½d.	**brn** ..	20	10
GS7	20c. on 2d.	**or (Die I)**	25	45
		a opt double		
		(one		
		albino)	—	—
		b bisect		
		(10c.)		
		on cover	—	—
GS8	25c. on 2½d.	**ult** ..	25	10
GS9	40c. on 4d.	**grey-grn**	2·00	3·00
GS10	1p. on 10d.	**tur** ..	90	1·50
GS11	3p. on 2/6	**grey-brn**		
		(D.L.R.)	£50	£40
		a opt double		
		(one		
		albino)	—	—
GS12	3p. on 2/6	**chestnut**		
		(D.L.R.) ..	£50	£40
		a opt double		
		(one		
		albino)	—	—
GS13	3p. on 2/6	**choc-brn**		
		(B.W.)	£35	£30
GS13a	3p. on 2/6	**reddish- brn**		
		(B.W.)	£35	£30

GS14	6p. on 5/−	**rose-car**		
		(Water- low) ..	£65	£50
		a opt double		
		(one		
		albino)	—	—
GS15	6p. on 5/−	**pl rose- car**		
		(Water- low) ..	£200	£175
GS16	12p.(R) on 10/−	**dp blu**		
		(Water- low) ..	£200	£200
		a opt double		
		(one		
		albino)	—	—
GS17	12p.(R) on 10/−	**blu**		
		(D.L.R.)	£150	£150
		a opt double		
		(one		
		albino)	—	—
GS6/17		**set** (11v)	£250	£250

GS7*b* This bisect was authorised at Tetuan on October 21st, 1919.

The 10c./1d. is known with wmk. inverted and reversed.

The 25c./2½d. is known with wmk inverted.

The 5c./½d. and 6p./5/− (GS4 and GS14) exist overprinted "Specimen" 10 x 1½ mm. in sloping sans serif capitals. The 12p./10/− (GS16) is similarly overprinted in 13 x 2 mm. upright capitals.

From 1917 stamps surcharged in Spanish Currency ceased to be used in the French Zone of Morocco.

From 1927 they also ceased to be used in Tangier.

1925-31 Stamps of Great Britain (KG V). Wmk. Multiple Block GVR overprinted and surcharged as before.

GS18	5c. on ½d.	**grn** ..	15	60
GS19	10c. on 1d.	**scar** ..	2·00	3·75
GS20	15c. on 1½d.	**red-brn** ..	7·00	6·00
GS21	20c. on 2d.	**orange** ..	1·25	1·50
GS22	25c. on 2½d.	**blue** ..	30	50
GS23	40c. on 4d.	**grey-grn**	30	30
GS18/23		**set** (6v)	£10	£12

1935 (May 8th) Silver Jubilee stamps of Great Britain overprinted "MOROCCO AGENCIES" and surcharged.

GS24	5c. on ½d.	**grn (Bl)**	10	25
GS25	10c. on 1d.	**scar (Bl)**	1·50	1·75
		a "CEN- TIMES"		
		for		
		"CEN- TIMOS"	£950	£1050
GS26	15c. on 1½d.	**red-brn**		
		(Bl) ..	30	1·50
GS27	25c. on 2½d.	**blu (R)** ..	3·00	2·00
GS24/27		**set** (4v)	4·50	5·00

GS25*a* occurred on Row 5/4 (No. 28) when a French currency cliche was wrongly used in a small second printing made in June, 1935. It must, of course, be collected at least in pair with normal. Only about 25 copies are known to have survived and, as this variety has been forged, it should be purchased with Certificate.

All values exist overprinted "AGENCIFS" for "AGENCIES" (No. 46).

Numbers Printed—5c., 107,813; 10c., 46,875; 15c., 153,125; 25c., 62,500.

1935-37 Stamps of Great Britain (KG V Harrison (*photo*) overprinted and surcharged.

GS28	5c. on ½d.	**green** ..		10	25
GS29	10c. on 1d.	**scarlet** ..		25	50
GS30	15c. on 1¼d.	**red-brn.** .		3·00	2·00
GS31	20c. on 2d.	**orange** ..		25	30
GS32	25c. on 2½d.	**ult** ..		1·00	1·00
GS33	40c. on 4d.	**dp grey-grn** ..		20	50
GS34	1p. on 10d.	**tur** ..		20	20
GS28/34		**set** (7v)		4·50	4·00

1936 Stamps of Great Britain (KE 8) over-printed and surcharged.

(*a*) "MOROCCO" 14¼ mm. long.

(*b*) "MOROCCO" 15¼ mm. long.

		(*a*)		(*b*)	
ES35	5c. on ½d. **green** ..	5	5	—	—
ES36	10c. on 1d. **scarlet**	5	5	15	20
ES37	15c. on 1½d. **red-brn**	5	5	—	—
ES38	25c. on 2½d. **ult** ..	5	5	—	—
ES35/38	**set** (4v)	10	10	—	—

1937-40 Stamps of Great Britain, overprinted (in black or blue) "MOROCCO AGENCIES" and surcharged.

S1	5c./½d.	**dp green (blue)** (10/6/37) ..	10	10
S2	10c./1d.	**dp scarlet** (10/6/37)	10	10
S3	15c./1½d.	**dp red-brown (blue)** (4/8/37)	10	10
S4	25c./2½d.	**dp ult** (10/6/37)	10	10
S5	40c./4d.	**greenish-grey** (3/9/40) ..	30	30
S6	70c./7d.	**emerald-green** (3/9/40) ..	25	25

Number issued—5c., 507,142; 10c., 332,503; 15c., 316,234; 25c., 319,884; 40c., 95,866; 70c., 120,769.

1951 (May 3rd) -52. As No. S1, etc., but colours changed, and new value similarly overprinted and surcharged.

S7	5c./½d.	**dull orange** ..	10	10
S8	10c./1d.	**ultramarine** ..	10	10

S9	15c./1½d.	**green**	10	35
S10	25c./2½d.	**scarlet** ..	15	30
S11	40c./4d.	**light blue** (26/5/52) ..	15	30
S12	1p./10d.	**dp blue-grey** (16/6/52) ..	20	35
S1/12		**set** (12) ..	1·50	2·00

A single copy of the 1p./10d. (S12) has been recorded with the two lines of the overprint spaced 15 mm instead of the normal 13 mm. MOROCCO AGENCIES is further to the left in relation to 1 PESETA than on the normal.

Numbers issued—5c., 207,309; 10c., 124,321; 15c., 93,356; 25c., 81,786; 40c., 63,799; 1p., 99,384.

SPECIAL ISSUES

1937 (May 13th) Coronation Issue of Great Britain, overprinted "MOROCCO AGENCIES" and surcharged.

SS1	15c./1½d.	**dk maroon (blue)**	10	10

Number issued—1,766,723.

1940 (May 6th) Centenary of First Postage Stamp issue of Great Britain, overprinted "MOROCCO AGENCIES" and surcharged.

SS2	5c./½d.	**dp green (blue)**	10	15
SS3	10c./1d.	**dp scarlet** ..	10	15
SS4	15c./1½d.	**dp red-brn (blue)**	10	15
SS5	25c./2½d.	**dp ultramarine** .	10	15
		a flaw retouch ..	£14	£14
SS2/5		**set** (4)	40	60

SS5*a* See Great Britain S6*b* for details of this variety.

Number issued—5c., 543,155; 10c., 289,467; 15c., 242,027; 25c., 195,947.

1948 (April 26th) Silver Wedding Issue of Great Britain, overprinted "MOROCCO AGENCIES" and surcharged.

SS6	25c./2½d.	**ultramarine** ..	10	10
SS7	45p./£1	**dp blue** ..	£25	£25

Number issued—25c., 411,439; 45p., 26,033.

1948 (July 29th) Olympic Games Issue of Great Britain, overprinted "MOROCCO AGENCIES" and surcharged.

SS8	25c./2½d.	**ultramarine** ..	10	10
SS9	30c./3d.	**violet** ..	10	10
		a crown flaw ..	£18	£20
SS10	60c./6d.	**reddish-purple**	15	15
SS11	1.20/1/–	**bistre-brown** .	30	30
		a surcharge double ..	£175	£300
SS8/11		**set** (4) ..	60	60

SS9*a*—For details of this variety see Great Britain No. S13*a*. (Row 20/2).

SS11*a*–A sheet of 120 copies with the double surcharge was released in London. One copy is known used from Tetuan 24.9.48.

Number issued—25c., 107,309; 30c., 100,020; 60c., 94,278; 1.20c., 93,304.

III. G.P.O. ISSUES

for use in certain British P.O's only.

1 FRENCH CURRENCY

1917–1938 (January 8th)

1917-32 Stamps of Great Britain (KG V) overprinted "MOROCCO AGENCIES" and surcharged. Wmk. Royal Cypher. Perf. 15x14.

GF1	3c.(R) on ½d.	green..	5	50
GF2	5c. on ½d.	green..	5	5
GF3	10c. on 1d.	scar ..	10	15
GF4	15c. on 1½d.	brn ..	80	20
GF5	25c. on 2½d.	blue ..	20	10
GF6	40c. on 4d.	grey-		
		grn ..	70	25
GF7	50c. on 5d.	yel-brn	90	90
GF8	75c. on 9d.	ol-grn	40	50
GF9	1f. on 10d.	tur ..	40	50
GF10	3f. on 2/6	choc-		
		brn		
		(B.W.)	£20	£10
		a re-entry		
		(shield)	—	—
GF11	6f. on 5/–	rose-		
		red		
		(B.W.)	£60	£50
GF1/11		set		
		(11v)	£80	£60

GF10*a* The re-entry affects the shield and right vertical frame line on R1/4.

The 3f. and 6f. (GF 10 and 11) exist overprinted "Specimen" 11 mm. x 2 mm. in sloping and upright sans-serif capitals respectively.

1925-34 Stamps of Great Britain (KG V). Wmk. Multiple Block GVR overprinted and surcharged as before.

GF12	5c. on ½d.	green..	10	30
GF13	10c. on 1d.	scarlet	10	10
GF14	15c. on 1½d.	red-brn	75	80
GF15	25c. on 2½d.	blue ..	10	10
GF16	40c. on 4d.	grey-		
		grn ..	40	25
		a overprint		
		double		
		(one		
		albino)	—	—
GF17	50c. on 5d.	yel-brn	40	10
		a wmk.		
		inverted	£25	—
GF18	75c. on 9d.	ol-grn	1·00	—
GF19	90c. on 9d.	ol-grn	60	1·00
GF20	1f. on 10d.	tur ..	30	20
GF21	1f.50c. on 1/–	bistre	1·00	1·25
GF12/21		set		
		(10v)	4·50	4·00

GF17*a* comes from a sheet with Control C.25.

The 1f. 50c. (GF21) exists overprinted "Specimen" 11 x 2 mm. in upright sans-serif capitals.

1935 (May 8th) Silver Jubilee stamps of Great Britain overprinted "MOROCCO AGENCIES" and surcharged.

GF22	5c. on ½d.	grn (Bl)	5	5
GF23	10c. on 1d.	scar (Bl)	60	90
GF24	15c. on 1½d.	red-brn		
		(Bl) ..	15	25
		a misplaced		
		sur-		
		charge	—	—
GF25	25c. on 2½d.	blu (R) ..	25	25
GF22/25		set (4v)..	1·00	1·25

GF24*a* Only one copy is known where "15 Centimes" appeared above instead of on top of the Sterling denomination (Row 20/2).

The 5c., 10c., and 15c. exist overprinted 'AGENCIFS" for "AGENCIES" (No. 46).

Numbers Printed—5c., 107,813; 10c., 46,875; 15c., 153,125; 25c., 42,500.

1935-37 Stamps of Great Britain (KG V Harrison (*photo*) and Waterlow (*re-engraved*) overprinted and surcharged.

GF26	5c. on ½d.	green ..	10	10
GF27	10c. on 1d.	scarlet	10	10
GF28	15c. on 1½d.	red-brn	30	20
GF29	25c. on 2½d.	ult ..	15	10
GF30	40c. on 4d.	dp grey-		
		grn ..	15	10
GF31	50c. on 5d.	yel-brn	15	10
GF32	90c. on 9d.	dpolive-		
		grn ..	30	25
GF33	1f. on 10d.	tur-blue	20	20
GF34	1f. 50c. on 1/–	bistre-		
		brn ..	25	25
GF35	3f. on 2/6	choc ..	£20	£20
GF36	6f. on 5/–	br rose-		
		red		
		(7/37)	£50	£40
GF26/36		set(11v)	£70	£60

The 1f. 50c. and 6f. (GF34 and GF36) exist overprinted "Specimen ' 11 x 2 mm. in upright sans serif capitals. The 3f. (GF35) exists with 10 x 1¼ mm. sloping capital overprint.

1936 Stamps of Great Britain (KE 8) overprinted and surcharged.

EF37	5c. on ½d.	green ..	5	5
		a bar		
		through		
		"POST-		
		AGE" ..	£60	—
EF38	15c. on 1½d.	red-brn	10	10
EF37/38		set (2v)..	15	15

EF37*a* A length of printer's rule gives the appearance of cancelling the word "POSTAGE" on the last three stamps of the third row from the bottom of the sheet (Nos. 214, 215, 216). Only eight sheets were affected.

One sheet is also known on which a similar bar appears on the first six stamps in this row.

1937 (June 11th) Stamp of Great Britain overprinted "MOROCCO AGENCIES" and surcharged.

F1 5c./½d. **dp green (blue)** .. 10 10

Number issued—806,782.

SPECIAL ISSUES

1937 (May 13th) Coronation Issue of Great Britain overprinted "MOROCCO AGENCIES" and surcharged.

FS1 15c./1½d. **dk maroon (blue)** 10 10

Number issued—2,203,087.

2. TANGIER
1927–1957 (April 30th)

1927 Stamps of Great Britain (KG V). Wmk. Multiple Block GVR overprinted "TANGIER".

GT1	½d.	**green**	.. ..	50	5
		a overprint double (one albino) ..		—	—
GT2	1d.	**scarlet**	.. ..	35	5
GT3	1½d.	**chestnut**	.. ..	2·00	1·00
GT4	2d.	**orange**	.. ..	60	10
		a overprint double (one albino) ..		—	—
GT1/4		**set** (4v)	.. ..	2·75	1·00

1934-5 Stamps of Great Britain (KG V Harrison (*photo*)) similarly overprinted.

GT5	½d.	**green**	.. ..	50	25
GT6	1d.	**scarlet**	.. ..	90	25
GT7	1½d.	**red-brown**	.. ..	15	10
GT5/7		**set** (3v)	.. ..	1·25	50

1935 (May 8th) Silver Jubilee stamps of Great Britain overprinted "TANGIER" (vertically up and down).

GT8	½d.	**green (Bl)**	.. ..	25	30
GT9	1d.	**scarlet**	.. ..	75	75
GT10	1½d.	**red-brown (Bl)**		20	20
GT8/10		**set** (3v)	.. ..	1·15	1·15

Numbers Printed—½d., 107,812; 1d., 46,875; 1½d., 153,125.

1936 Stamps of Great Britain (KE 8) overprinted "TANGIER".

ET11	½d.	**green**	..	5	5
ET12	1d.	**scarlet**	..	5	5
ET13	1½d.	**red-brown**		10	10
ET11/13		**set** (3v)	.. ..	20	20

1937 Stamps of Great Britain, overprinted "TANGIER" in blue or black.

T1	½d.	**dp green (blue)** (11/6/37)	10	10
T2	1d.	**dp scarlet** (11/6/37)	10	10
T3	1½d.	**dp red-brown (blue)** (4/8/37)	10	10

Number issued—½d., 807,805; 1d., 838,219; 1½d., 398,723.

1944-49 (Jan. 1st) Stamps of Great Britain, similarly overprinted in blue or black.

T4	½d.	**green (blue)** (3/5/44)		10	10
T5	1d.	**scarlet** (1/10/45)	..	15	15
T6	2d.	**dull orange**	..	15	15
T7	2½d.	**ultramarine**	..	15	15
T8	3d.	**purple-violet**	..	15	15
T9	4d.	**greyish-green**	..	20	20
T10	5d.	**pale brown**	..	20	25
T11	6d.	**pale purple**	..	20	25
T12	7d.	**emerald-green**	..	20	30
T13	8d.	**dp rose**	..	20	35
T14	9d.	**dp olive**	..	20	35
T15	10d.	**dp grey-blue**		25	35
T16	11d.	**dp plum**	..	25	40
T17	1/–	**bistre-brown**	..	30	45
T18	2/6	**green**	..	2·00	3·00
T19	5/–	**red**	.. ..	4·00	6·00
T20	10/–	**ultramarine**	..	£10	£11
T4/20		**set** (17)	.. ..	£17	£22

Number issued—½d., 734,338; 1d., 282,605; 2d., 51,517; 2½d., 103,521; 3d., 294,853; 4d., 33,149; 5d., 35,622; 6d., 464,149; 7d., 46,050; 8d., 31,327; 9d., 56,439; 10d., 36,291; 11d., 26,609; 1/–, 214,672; 2/6, 24,629; 5/–, 16,122; 10/–, 11,359.

1950-1 (May 3rd) As No. T4, etc., but colours changed (Nos. 27—29 as Nos. 34—6 of G.B.), similarly overprinted.

T21	½d.	**dull orange**	..	10	10
T22	1d.	**ultramarine**	..	10	10
T23	1½d.	**green**	.. ..	15	15
T24	2d.	**red-brown**	..	15	15
T25	2½d.	**scarlet**	..	15	15
T26	4d.	**light blue** (2/10/50)		25	25
T27	2/6	**green**	.. ..	2·00	3·00
T28	5/–	**red**	.. ..	3·00	4·00
T29	10/–	**ultramarine**	..	6·00	7·00
T21/29		**set** (9)	.. ..	£11	£14

Number issued—½d., 506,283; 1d., 101,853; 1½d., 73,350; 2d., 63,309; 2½d., 132,419; 4d., 73,178; 2/6, 62,259; 5/–, 38,699; 10/–, 30,305.

SPECIAL ISSUES

1937 (May 13th) Coronation Issue of Great Britain, overprinted "TANGIER".

TS1 1½d. **dark maroon (blue)** 10 10

Number issued—1,397,799.

1940 (May 6th) Centenary of First Postage Stamp Issue of Great Britain, overprinted "TANGIER" in black or blue.

TS2	½d. dp green (blue) ..	15	15
TS3	1d. dp scarlet	15	15
TS4	1½d. dp red-brown (blue)	25	25
TS2/4	set (3)	50	50

Number issued—½d., 192,427; 1d., 174,507; 1½d., 139,627.

1946 (June 11th) Victory Issue of Great Britain, overprinted "TANGIER".

TS5	2½d. ultramarine ..	10	10
TS6	3d. violet	15	15

Number issued—2½d., 545,540; 3d., 547,640.

1948 (April 26th) Silver Wedding Issue of Britain, overprinted "TANGIER".

TS7	2½d. ultramarine ..	10	10
	a overprint omitted in pr. with normal ..	£400	—
	b overprint at top ..	£35	£35
TS8	£1 dp blue ..	£22	£25
	a overprint misplaced up and to left. (£1 value not overprinted)	£200	—

TS7a—A sheet of stamps was discovered with overprint (normally at the bottom) misplaced, which resulted in the first row missing the overprint entirely, and the rest of the sheet with the overprint near the tops of the stamps and overprints appearing on the lower sheet margin. Forgeries exist of No. TS7a.

Number issued—2½d., 192,513; £1, 24,102.

1948 (July 29th) Olympic Games Issue of Great Britain, overprinted "TANGIER".

TS9	2½d. ultramarine ..	10	10
TS10	3d. violet ..	15	15
	a crown flaw ..	£50	—
TS11	6d. reddish-purple ..	20	20
	a 'HLP'	£225	—
	b retouch	£40	—
TS12	1/– bistre-brown ..	40	40
TS9/12	set (4)	75	75

TS10a—For details of this variety see Great Britain No. S13a (Row 20/2).

TS11a/b was overprinted on sheets from Cylinder 9 Stop; and the 'H.L.P.' variety (See Great Britain S14a/b), in its original and erased states, exists in the Jubilee Lines below Nos. 118/9/20.

Number issued—2½d., 101,965; 3d., 101,638; 6d., 101,175; 1/–, 96,190.

1949 (Oct. 10th) U.P.U. Issue of Great Britain, overprinted "TANGIER".

TS13	2½d. ultramarine ..	10	10
	a Indian lake ..	£30	£30
TS14	3d. pale violet ..	15	15
TS15	6d. reddish-mauve ..	25	25
TS16	1/– bistre-brown ..	40	40
TS13/16	set (4)	80	80

TS13a—For details of this variety see Great Britain, No. S16b (Row 8/2).

Number issued—2½d., 81,873; 3d., 74,103; 6d., 77,198; 1/–, 72,404.

Note:

The use in the United Kingdom of stamps overprinted "TANGIER" was permitted from 1950. Our prices for used stamps are for copies with Tangier postmarks; and stamps with U.K. postmarks are occasionally available at 2/3 of these prices.

IV STAMPS OF GREAT BRITAIN

WITHOUT OVERPRINT

Officially sold and used at certain Post Offices in Morocco. 1937–1949.

1. TANGIER

				Used
1937-47 Issue.				
PO1	½d. dp green	..	..	50
PO2	1d. dp scarlet	..	..	50
PO3	1½d. dp red-brown	..	..	60
PO4	2d. dp orange	..	..	70
PO5	2½d. dp ultramarine	..	..	70
PO6	3d. violet	..	..	70
PO7	4d. greenish-grey	..	..	90
PO8	5d. pale brown	..	..	90
PO9	6d. pale purple	..	..	1·00
PO10	7d. emerald-green	..	..	1·00
PO11	8d. dp rose	..	..	1·25
PO12	9d. dp olive	..	..	1·25
PO13	10d. dp grey-blue	..	..	1·25
PO15	1/– bistre-brown	..	..	1·50
PO16	2/6 brown	..	..	£30
PO17	2/6 green	..	..	£10
PO18	5/– red	..	..	£15
PO19	10/– blue-black	..	..	£30

1941-51 Issue.				
PO22	½d. green	..	..	40
PO23	1d. scarlet	..	..	50
PO25	2d. dull orange	..	..	50
PO26	2½d. ultramarine	..	..	60

1946 Victory Issue.				
POS8	2½d. ultramarine	..	..	80
POS9	3d. violet	..	..	80

2. TETUAN

				Used
1937-47 Issue.				
POT4	2d. dp orange	..	..	70
POT5	2½d. dp ultramarine	..	..	70
POT6	3d. violet	..	..	70
POT7	4d. greenish-grey	..	..	90
POT9	6d. pale purple	..	..	90
POT12	9d. dp olive	..	..	1·00
POT15	1/– bistre-brown	..	..	1·00
POT16	2/6 brown	..	..	£30
POT17	2/6 green	..	..	£10
POT18	5/– red	..	..	£15

1941-51 Issue.				
POT22	½d. green	..	..	40
POT25	2d. dull orange	..	..	50
POT26	2½d. ultramarine	..	..	60

Prices are for stamps on piece or cover with clear Agency postmark. The numbers are those of the Great Britain stamps with appropriate letter prefix.

ADEN

Following annexation by Great Britain in 1839, Aden was administered as part of the Bombay Presidency until 1932, when it came under the Governor-General of India. It became a Crown Colony on April 1, 1937.

The first Post Office was opened in 1839 at Crater, which became a sub-officewhen the G.P .O. was opened at Steamer Point in 1868.

Throughout the period 1854–1937 unoverprinted contemporary stamps of India were in use, and may be recognised by the cancellation "124", "125" or "B–22", with or without datestamp, during the 19th Century; and later by named datestamps "Aden", "Aden Camp", "Aden–Cantonment", "Aden–Steamer Point", "Kamaran", "Khormaksar", "Ma'alla", "Perim", "Sheikh Othman"; also "D'thali" (various spellings) and "Experimental P.O. B-84" and "Experimental P.O. B-523" (1922).

1937 (April 1st) Printers (recess) **De La Rue.** Perf. 13 x 11¾ (C). Sheets 5 x 10.

1	¼a.	light green	.. ..	25	30
2	9p.	dp grey-green	..	35	40
3	1a.	sepia	.. ..	30	30
4	2a.	scarlet	.. ..	00	60
5	2½a.	light blue	..	80	1·00
6	3a.	carmine-rose	..	1·00	1·50
7	3½a.	dull grey-blue	..	1·00	1·50
8	8a.	pale reddish-purple	..	2·00	2·00
9	1r.	brown	.. ..	3·00	3·00
10	2r.	orange-yellow	..	£10	£12
11	5r.	purple	.. ..	£40	£40
		a bt aniline purple	..	£50	£40
12	10r.	pale olive green	..	£90	£100
1/12		set (12)	.. ..	£135	£150

SP 1/12 **specimen set** (perf) .. £100 ‡

1939 (Jan. 1st) -46 Designs, ¼a., 2a (Aidrus

Mosque, Crater); ¾a., 5r. (Adenese Camel Corps); 1a., 2r. (Aden Harbour); 1½a., 1r. (Adenese Dhow, "Al-Nars"); 2½a., 8a. (Mukalla); 3a., 14a., 10r. (Capture of Aden, 1839, H.M.S. "Volage"). Printers (recess) Waterlow & Sons. Perf. 12½ (L). Sheets ¼a. to 2½a. and 8a., 5 x 16; 3a., 8 x 10; Rupee values, 5 x 12.

13	½a.	yellow-green	..	15	15
		a green (7/42)	..	10	10
		b blue-green	.. ..	30	40
14	¾a.	chocolate-brown	..	15	20
		a red-brown (24/4/46)		10	10
15	1a.	light blue	..	15	10
		a bright blue	.. ..	10	10
16	1½a.	scarlet-red	.. ..	25	25
17	2a.	sepia	.. ..	25	20
		a deep sepia (24/4/46)		15	15
18	2½a.	dp ultramarine	..	15	15
19	3a.	sepia and rose-carmine		25	20
20	8a.	orange		30	15
		a red-orange	.. ..	40	15
21	14a.	sepia and pale blue (15/1/45)	.. ..	60	70
22	1r.	emerald-green	..	30	35
		a bright green	.. ..	25	30
23	2r.	indigo and magenta .		1·50	1·00
		a blue-black and deep magenta (1/44)	..	1·25	1·00
24	5r.	lake-brn and olive-grn		2·75	2·75
		a lake-brown and deep olive (1/44)	..	2·00	2·00
25	10r.	sepia and violet	..	4·00	4·50
		a bt. sepia, bt. violet ..		3·50	4·00
13/25		set (13)	.. ..	9·00	9·00

SP 13/25 **specimen set** perf (12) £45 ‡

1951 (Oct. 1st) -52. Nos. 15, etc., surcharged in black or red to bring in line with changed currency.

26	5c./1a.	light blue	..	10	15
		a bright light blue		15	15
27	10c./2a.	sepia	.. ..	10	10
		a brown-sepia	..	30	30
		b dp sepia (18/3/52)		15	15
28	15c./2½a.	dp ultramarine ..		25	30
		a surcharge double		£125	—
29	20c./3a.	sepia and rose-car		15	25
		a dark sepia and car rose (18/3/52)		25	35
30	30c./8a.	orange (red)	..	25	30
31	50c./8a.	orange	.. ..	25	30
32	70c./14a.	sepia and pale blue		30	35
		a dk sepia and bt pale blue (18/3/52) ..		40	40
33	1s./1r.	emerald-green ..		50	30
34	2s./2r.	greyish-indigo and bt magenta		1·25	1·00
		a surcharge omitted (albino)		£80	—
		b blue-blk and mag		1·00	1·00
35	5s./5r.	lake-brn and olive-green	.. ..	2·25	2·00
		a lake-brn and sage-green ..		2·00	2·00
36	10s./10r.	sepia and violet .		5·00	6·00
26/36		set (11)	.. ..	£10	£10

28*a* One sheet of the 15c. surcharge exists double overprint. The variety varies over the sheet and the price quoted is for a well separated double— lesser doubles are usually available at lower prices.

34/34*a* A printing of the surcharged stamps exists in which Flourescent aniline ink was used for the frames, and the under the quartz lamp they show up as fluorescent salmon-pink and the centres appear as greenish-black, whereas the centres of all other printings are in varying shades of blue-black.

SPECIAL ISSUES

1937 (May 12th) Coronation. Printers (*recess*) De La Rue. Perf. 13¾ x 14 (**C**). Sheets 5 x 16.

S1	1a.	sepia	.. .. ..	10	10
S2	2½a.	light blue	.. ..	15	15
S3	3½a.	blue-grey	.. ..	40	40
SP S1/S3	**specimen set** perf (3)	£12			‡

1946 (Oct. 15th) Victory. Printers (*recess*) De La Rue. Perf. 13¾ x 14 (**C**). Sheets 6 x 10.

S4	1½a.	carmine-red	.. ..	10	10
S5	2½a.	dp blue	.. ..	20	20
	a	wmk inv.	.. ..	£50	—
SP S4/5	**specimen set** perf (2)	£14			‡

1949 (Jan. 17th) Silver Wedding. Printers

(*Low Value*) **Waterlow & Sons** (*photo*) and **Perf. 14 x 14¾** (**C**). (*Top Value*) **Bradbury, Wilkinson** (*Design recess, name typo*) **and Perf. 11½ x 10¾** (**C**). **10r. V. Sheets 10 x 6** (*Low Values*), **6 x 10** (*High Values*).

S6	1½a.	**scarlet**	15	15
S7	10r.	**dull purple**	£10	£10

1949 (Oct. 10th) U.P.U. Designs (*Low Value*) Hermes, Globe and Transport. (*Second Value*) Hemisphere, Plane and Steamer. (*Third Value*) Hermes on Globe. (*Top Value*) "U.P.U." Monument at Berne. Printers (*High and Low Values*) **Waterlow & Sons** (*recess*) **and Perf. 13½ x 13¾** (**C**). (*Middle Values*) **Bradbury, Wilkinson** (*Design recess, name typo*) **and Perf. 10¾ x 11½** (**C**). **Sheets 5 x 12.**

S8	2½a./20c.	**dull violet-blue** .	20	30
S9	3a./30c.	**carmine**	30	35
S10	8a./50c.	**orange**	70	80
S11	1r./1s.	**azure**	1·25	1·50
S8/11		**set (4)**	2·26	3·00

The "U.P.U." stamps printed by Waterlow & Sons exist in two different perforations vertically, either 13.7 or 13.9, but the difference is too small to merit more than a general note. The surcharging of the Aden, Aden States and Somaliland sets was occasioned by an unexpected delay in the change of currency.

KATHIRI STATE OF SEIYUN

1942 (July 1st) -50 Designs, ½a., ¾a., 1a. (Portrait of Sultan Jafar bin Mansar); 1½a. (Sultan's Palace, Seiyun); 2a. (Mosque, Tarim); 2½a. (Mosque, Seiyun); 3a. (Palace, Tarim); 8a. (Mosque, Seiyun); 1r. (South Gate, Tarim); 2r. (Kathiri House); 5r. (Mosque

Door, Tarim). Printers (*recess*) **De La Rue. Designs, 1½a., 3a., 8a., 2r. H. Sheets 6 x 10.**

(a) Perf. 14 (L).

1	½a.	**dp green**	.. ..	30	30
1A	¾a.	**chestnut**	.. ..	40	40
1B	1a.	**deep blue**	.. ..	40	40

(b) Perf. 13¾ x 14 (C).

2	½a.	**green** (8/3/48)	..	10	15
3	¾a.	**chestnut**	.. ..	10	15
4	1a.	**dp blue** ..	.. ..	10	15

(c) Perf. 11¾ x 13 (C).

5	1½a.	**dp carmine (F.A.)**	..	20	20
		a carmine (8/3/48)	..	10	10
6	2a.	**sepia**	..	30	30
		a sepia-brown (8/3/48)		15	15
7	2½a.	**dp blue**	.. ..	15	30
8	3a.	**sepia and dp carmine**		15	30
		a sepia-brn and car (8/3/49)	..	30	30
9	8a.	**vermilion-red**	..	30	30
10	1r.	**green**	.. ..	30	40
11	2r.	**dk blue and dp purple**		1·50	1·50
		a indigo and reddish-pur (8/3/48)	..	80	90
12	5r.	**chestnut and green** (1/10/42)	..	1·25	2·00
1/12		**set** (11)		3·00	4·00
SP 1/12		**specimen set** perf (11)		£22	‡

1951 (Oct. 1st) Nos. 4, etc., surcharged in black or red to bring in line with changed currency.

13	5c./1a.	**dp blue (red)**	..	10	20
14	10c./2a.	**sepia**	.. ..	10	20
		a sepia-brown	..	20	30
15	15c./2½a.	**dp blue**	..	10	20
16	20c./3a.	**sepia and carmine**		10	25
		a sepia-brn and dp car	..	20	30
17	50c./8a.	**vermilion-red**	..	15	30
18	1s./1r.	**green**	.. ..	30	60
19	2s./2r.	**indigo and reddish-pur**	.. ..	60	1·20
		a dk blue and dp pur	..	3·00	3·00
20	5s./5r.	**chestnut and grn**		1·50	2·25
13/20		**set** (8)		2·80	£5

The 1r. (No. 10) exists with surcharge '5' in black, the original value tablets being overprinted with black circles.

This was a bogus production, made in Bombay.

SPECIAL ISSUES

1946 (Oct. 15th) Victory. Nos. 5 and 7 overprinted VICTORY ISSUE 8th JUNE 1946, in black or red.

S1	1½a.	**dp carmine**	.. ..	5	5
S2	2½a.	**dp blue (red)**	..	10	10
		a overprint inverted	..	£200	—
SP S1/2		**specimen set** perf (2)		£22	‡

S2*a* One sheet of 60 was purchased from Crown Agents. Distributed unnoticed, a number of copies have not been traced.

1949 (Jan. 17th) Silver Wedding. As Aden.

S3	1½a.	**scarlet** ..	.. ..	10	10
S4	5r.	**grey-green**	.. ..	2·00	2·50

1949 (Oct. 10th) U.P.U. As Aden.

S5	2½a./20c.	**dull violet blue** ..		10	20
S6	3a./30c.	**carmine**	..	10	25
S7	8a./50c.	**orange**	..	40	80
S8	1r./1s.	**azure**	.. ..	70	1·20
S5/8		**set** (4)	.. ..	1·30	2·45

QU'AITI STATE OF SHIHR AND MUKALLA

There is some evidence to suggest that, in 1927, a local stamp was used in the State.

It is printed in blue and inscribed, in Arabic, 'POST /QU'AITI STATE/½ HARF/1346'.

1942 (July 1st) -50 Designs, ½a., ¾a., 1a. (Portrait of Sultan Salih bin Ghalib); 1½a. (Harbour, Mukalla); 2a. (Gateway of Shihr); 2½a. (Shibam, Qu'aiti Capital); 3a. (Outpost Fortress, Mukalla); 8a. ('Einat, City of Seiyids); 1r. (Du'an); 2r. (Mosque, Hureidha, at time of pilgrimage feast); 5r. (Meshhed, Du'an Province). Printers (*recess*) **De La Rue. Designs, 2½a., 8a., 2r., 5r. H. Sheets 6 x 10.**

(a) Perf. 14 (L).

1	½a.	**dp green**	.. ..	25	25
1A	¾a.	**chestnut**	.. ..	30	30
1B	1a.	**deep blue**	.. ..	30	30

(b) Perf. 13¾ x 14 (C).

2	½a.	**olive-green** (18/12/46)		2·00	3·00
		a dp olive-green (6/3/50)		30	30
3	¾a.	**chestnut**	.. ..	10	15
4	1a.	**blue**	.. ..	20	25
		a dark blue (12/8/48) .		10	15

(c) Perf. 11¾ x 13 (C).

5	1½a.	**carmine (F.A.)**	..	15	15
		a dp carmine (6/3/50)		10	10
6	2a.	**sepia**	.. ..	15	15
		a yellowish-brown (18/12/46)		4·00	4·00
		b sepia-brn (12/8/48) .		10	10
7	2½a.	**dp blue**	.. ..	10	15
8	3a.	**sepia and carmine**	..	10	15
		a sepia and dp carmine (6/3/50)	..	20	25

9	8a.	vermilion-red	..	30	50
10	1r.	green		25	25
11	2r.	dp blue and dp purple		2·00	2·25
		a greenish-blue and red-			
		purple (6/3/50) ..		1·00	1·25
12	5r.	light chestnut and			
		green (1/10/42) ..		1·50	2·00
1/12		set (11)		3·50	4·70
SP 1/12 specimen set perf (11)				£20	‡

1951 (Oct. 1st) Nos. 4, etc., surcharged in black or red to bring into line with changed currency.

13	5c./1s.	dp blue (red) ..	10	15
		a dark blue (red) .	15	20
14	10c./2a.	sepia	10	15
		a yellowish-brown	2·50	3·00
		b sepia-brown ..	10	15
15	15c./2½a.	dp blue	10	15
16	20c./3a.	sepia and carmine	15	15
		a sepia and dp car	15	15
		b surcharge double		
		one albino ..	£40	—
17	50c./8a.	vermilion-red ..	25	25
		a scarlet-red		
		(18/8/54) ..	20	20
18	1s./1r.	green	25	25
19	2s./2r.	greenish-blue and		
		red-purple ..	60	1·00
20	5s./5r.	lt chestnut and		
		green	1·25	2·00
13/20		set (8)	2·60	4·00

SPECIAL ISSUES

1946 (Oct. 15th) Victory. Nos. 5 and 7 over-printed VICTORY ISSUE 8th JUNE 1946, in red or black.

S1	1½a.	carmine	10	10
S2	2½a.	dp blue (red) ..	10	10
SP S1/2 specimen set perf (2)			£22	‡

1949 (Jan. 17th) Silver Wedding. As Aden.

| S3 | 1½a. | scarlet .. .. .. | 10 | 10 |
| S4 | 5r. | grey-green .. .. | 2·50 | 3·00 |

1949 (Oct. 10th) U.P.U., As Aden.

S5	2½a./20c.	dull viot-blue ..	15	25
S6	3a./30c.	carmine	50	60
S7	8a./50c.	orange	80	100
S8	1r./1s.	azure	1·25	1·50
		a surcharge missing	£325	—
S5/8		set (4)	2·50	3·00

ANTIGUA

The island was first settled from England in 1632, and was later granted to Lord Willoughby by King Charles II.

Following the use of other handstamps or manu-script marks Crowned Circle PAID Franks were registered at the G.P.O. in London on March 9th, 1850 (Antigua) and December 10th, 1857 (English Harbour); and were thereafter struck in red to indicate prepayment of postage on overseas letters (See Introduction).

From May, 1858 to March, 1860 contemporary G.B. stamps were in use and were cancelled with "AO 2" (St. John's) or "A 18" (English Harbour) in transverse ovals of horizontal bars.

The Crowned Circle Franks were again used from April 1st, 1860 until the first Antigua stamps were issued.

See also under Leeward Islands.

1850-1862 PAID Franks   *on Cover*
| VF 1 | Antigua | £300 |
| VF 2 | English Harbour | £350 |

1858-60 Stamps of Great Britain identified by their Catalogue Nos. after prefix 'SJ' or 'EH'.

(I) Used at St. John's: 'A 02'
SJ V39	1d.	rose-red	..
SJ V36A	2d.	blue	..
SJ V51	2d.	blue	..
SJ V44	4d.	rose	..
SJ V45	6d.	lilac	..
SJ V47	1/-	green	..

(II) Used at English Harbour: 'A 18'
| EH V45 | 6d. | lilac | .. |
| EH V47 | 1/- | green | .. |

1862 (Aug.) *(recess)* **Perkins, Bacon and Co. No wmk. Sheets 12 x 10.**

(a) Rough Perf. 14-16.
| V1 | 6d. | blue-green | .. | £400 | £200 |

(b) Perf. 11-13.
| V2 | 6d. | blue-green | .. | £1400 | — |

(c) Perf. 14-16 x 11-13.
| V3 | 6d. | blue-green | .. | £1000 | — |

Three copies are known Perf 11-13 compound with 14-16 at base. Neither these nor Nos. V2 and V3 are known used; and they may all have come from a trial perforation sheet.

Total printing 16,000.

1863 (Jan.)—87. As before but Wmk. Small Star.

(a) Rough Perf. 14-16.
V4	1d.	rosy mauve	£40	£18
		a imperf between (pair)	—	—
V5	1d.	dull rose('64) ..	£30	£18
V6	1d.	vermilion ('67) ..	£20	£16
		a imperf between (pair)	—	—

V7 6d. **green** £80 £20
   a imperf between (pair) — —
V8 6d. **dark green** £70 £20
V9 6d. **yellow-green** .. £900 £30
   a imperf between (pair) — —

(b) Compound Perf. 11, 12 and 14-16.

V10 1d. **rosy mauve** .. .. £350 —

Total printing—1d. 480,000; 6d. 178,120.

The last printing of each value was made in July, 1871; and in November the Dies, Rollers and Plates were handed to De La Rue.

1872-76. As before but printed (*recess*) **by De La Rue from the same Plates. Wmk. Crown CC.**

(a) Perf. 12½. (1872).

V11 1d. **lake** £30 £18
V12 1d. **scarlet** £38 £18
V13 6d. **blue-green** £220 £10

Numbers printed—1d. 550 sheets; 6d. 250 sheets.

(b) Perf. 14. (1876).

V14 1d. **lake** £20 £10
   a bisect vert. (½d.) on
    cover .. .. .. ‡ £450
V15 1d. **lake-rose** £20 £10
V16 1d. **rose** £30 £15
   a bisect vert. (½d.) on
    cover .. .. .. ‡ £600
V17 6d. **blue-green** £120 £10

1884-86. As before but Wmk. Crown CA.

(a) Perf. 12. (1884).

V18 1d. **carmine-red** £12 £10
V18 in deep brown is a Colour Trial

(b) Perf. 14.

V19 1d. **carmine-red** .. .. 2·00 5·00
V20 1d. **rose** £20 £12
V21 6d. **deep green** £22 £30

V19 and V20 may be found used in St. Christopher (**A12**). *See St. Christopher V30.*
V19 and V21 exist Comb as well as Line perf.

See Introduction for details of Dies I and II.

1879-87. (*typo*) **De La Rue. (Die I) Perf. 14. Sheets 6 x 10.**
(a) Wmk. Crown CC. (1879).

V22 2½d. **red-brown** £225 £70
   a large slanting '2' .. £1750 £700
V23 4d. **blue** £150 £25

(b) Wmk. Crown CA. (1882-87).

V24 ½d. **dull green** .. .. 3·00 7·00
   a imperf (pair) .. .. — —
V25 2½d. **red-brown** £45 £20
   a large slanting '2' .. £400 £300
V26 2½d. **ultramarine** ('87) .. £10 £10
   a large slanting '2' .. £90 £100
V27 4d. **blue** £110 £20
V28 4d. **chestnut** ('87) .. 5·00 6·00

V29 1/- **mauve** ('86) £120 £80
SPE V25,
27,29 **ovpt specimen** (3) £60 ‡

V22a/25a/26a. The '2' is larger than normal and has a slanting foot on Row 3/1 (right hand pane) and Row 7/1 (both panes).

From November 1890 until 1903 the stamps of Leeward Islands were used in Antigua.

The following issues were in concurrent use with Leeward Islands stamps until June, 1956.

All stamps from E1 to G54 are (*typo*) **De La Rue. Perf. 14.**

1903 (June)-09. Wmk. Crown CC. Sheets 12 x 5.

E1 ½d. **grey-blk & grey-grn** 1·00 2·00
   a on blue paper (7/09) £30 £30
E2 1d. **grey-blk and rose-red** 2·00 6·00
   a on blue paper (7/09) £30 £30
E3 2d. **dull pur and brown** 5·00 8·00
E4 2½d. **gr-blk and blue OC** 5·00 9·00
E5 3d. **gr-grn and or-brn** .. 7·00 9·00
E6 6d. **purple and black** .. £15 £15
E7 1/- **bl and dull pur OC** .. £15 £15
E8 2/- **gr-grn and pale vio** £20 £24
E9 2/6 **gr-blk and purple** .. £16 £20
E10 5/- **gr-grn and vio OC** .. £70 £80
E1/10 **set** (10v) £150 £175
SPE1/10 **specimen set** (10v) £65 ‡

E4/7/10 on **C** paper were issued in Jan. 1906, imperf Colour Trials of E1 exist in the issued colour, and also in the colour of E5.

Numbers issued—**O** E1 120,120: E2 243,720: E3 24,840: E4 30,360: E5 18,840: E6 12,720: E7 6,240: E8/9 6,360 each: E10 2,640.
    C E4 6,000: E7/10 3,000 each.

1907. (Feb.)-20. As before but Wmk. Multiple Crown CA. Printed in error on thick paper normally used for recess printing.

E11 ½d. **dull green** .. .. 60 1·00
   a on thin paper (7/09) 2·00 2·50
E12 ½d. **blue-green** (5/17) .. 80 1·20
E13 ½d. **dark green** (10/20) .. 1·00 1·40
E14 1d. **red** .. .. .. 2·00 80
E15 1d. **bright scarlet** (thin
    paper '15) .. .. 3·00 2·00
E16 1d. **deep scarlet** (5/17) .. 3·00 2·00
E17 1d. **dark red** (29.9.19) .. 2·00 2·00
E18 2d. **dull pur and brown**
    C ('12) .. .. 2·50 2·50
     3·00 3·75
E19 2d. **dull pur and red-brn**
    C ('15) .. .. 3·50 4·00
E20 2½d. **ultramarine** .. .. 3·00 4·00
E21 2½d. **blue** (thin paper (11/
    09) .. .. .. 4·50 4·50
E22 2½d. **deep blue** (8/18) .. 8·00 8·00

E23	3d.	**grey-grn and or-brn C** ('12)	5·00	7·00
E24	3d.	**deep green and or** (8/18)	6·00 8·00	8·00 9·00
E25	6d.	**pur and blk C** (7/11)		
E26	6d.	**mag and gr-blk C** ('15)	9·00 £10	£10 £12
E27	1/–	**bl and dull purple C**		
E28	1/–	**deep blue and dark purple C** ('15) ..	£12	£14
E29	2/–	**grey-green and violet C** ('12)	£27 £57	£34 £68
E11/29		**set** (8v)	£20	—
SPE11, 14,20		**specimen set** (3v)	£20	‡

E13 is on extra thick paper.

Numbers printed—E11/13 33,300 : E14/17 30,040 : E20/22 21,420 : E25/26 6,000 : E27/28 7,940

1913-14. As E10 but head of King George V.

G1	5/–	**grey-green and violet C** (7/13)	£45	£50
G2	5/–	**bright green and dull violet C** (2/14) .	£50	£55
SPG1/2		**specimen** (1v)	£30	‡

1916-18. War Tax. Nos. E12, E13 and previously unissued 1½d. value overprinted WAR STAMP in sans serif capitals in London.

(a) In black (Sept 1916).

G3	½d.	**deep blue-green** ..	25	50
		a on extra thick paper	2·00	—

(b) In dull red (Oct. 1st, 1917).

G4	½d.	**dull green**	25	50
		a on extra thick paper	2·00	—
		b on thin paper ..	2·00	—

(c) In deep red. (July 1918).

G5	½d.	**deep green**	50	1·00
		a on extra thick paper..	4·00	—
		b on thin paper ..	4·00	—

(d) In black (June/July 1918).

G6	1½d.	**brown-orange** ..	25	50
G7	1½d.	**yellow and orange** (9/19)	50	1·00
G8	1½d.	**dp yel and dp or** (3/20)	50	1·00
G3/8		**set** (3v)	70	1·50
SPG3/8		**specimen set** (3v) ..	£30	‡

G6/8. Although this value was first issued in the reign of King George V the seal was still inscribed "EDWARDUS VII".

1921 (June)-29. Sheets 120—two panes, each 6 x 10.

(a) Wmk. Multiple Crown CA on Chalky paper.

G9	3d.	**purple/pale yellow**..	2·00	4·00
G10	3d.	**purple/deep yellow**	3·00	4.50
G11	4d.	**grey-black and red /pale yellow** (1/22)	2·50	4·00
		a on yellow	3·50	5·00

G12	4d.	**black and red/yel** ..	5·00	6·00
		a on pale buff	7·00	8·00
G13	1/–	**black/emerald** ..	3·00	5·00
G14	1/–	**grey-black/emerald**	5·00	6·00
G15	2/–	**pur and bl/bl** ..	5·00	9·00
G16	2/6	**black and red/blue**	6·00	£10
G17	2/6	**grey-black and red /blue-green**	8·00	£12
G18	5/–	**green and red/pale yellow** (1/22) ..	£11	£15
G19	£1	**purple and black/red** ('22)	£225	£250
G9/19		**set** (7v)	£250	£300
SPG9/19		**specimen set** (7v)	£120	‡

(b) Wmk. Multiple Script CA. G20/43 O: G44/54 C.

G20	½d.	**dull green**	25	30
G21	½d.	**green**	40	50
G22	½d.	**deep green**	50	60
G23	1d.	**carmine**	60	25
G24	1d.	**dull rose**	80	30
G25	1d.	**rose-red**	80	30
G26	1d.	**scarlet** ('29) ..	40	40
G27	1d.	**bright violet** ..	2·00	2·00
G28	1d.	**reddish violet** ..	1·50	2·00
G29	1d.	**reddish lilac** ..	80	1·00
G30	1½d.	**orange-yellow** ('22)	3·00	6·00
G31	1½d.	**yellow-orange** ..	4·00	6·00
G32	1½d.	**carmine** ('26) ..	50	80
G33	1½d.	**rosine**	70	1·00
G34	1½d.	**scarlet**	1·00	1·50
G35	1½d.	**pale red-brown** ('29)	1·25	2·00
G36	2d.	**grey**	80	1·00
G37	2d.	**pale grey**	1·00	1·50
		a wmk. sideways ..	£200	—
G38	2d.	**dark slate**	1·25	2·00
G39	2d.	**greenish slate** ..	1·50	2·00
G40	2½d.	**bright blue** ..	3·00	5·00
G41	2½d.	**ultramarine** ('27) ..	3·00	4·00
G42	2½d.	**orange-yellow** ..	1·00	4·00
G43	2½d.	**yellow-orange** ..	1·50	5·00
G44	3d.	**pale purple/yellow** ('25)	2·00	4·00
G45	3d.	**pur brn/yellow** ..	2·50	5·00
G46	6d.	**dull and bright pur**..	1·50	3·00
G47	6d.	**pale dull pur and pur**	2·00	3·00
G48	1/–	**black/emerald** ('29)	4·00	8·00
G49	1/–	**grey-black/green** ..	5·00	9·00
G50	2/–	**purple and blue/blue** ('27)	7·50	£10
G51	2/–	**slate purple and blue /blue**	8·50	£11
G52	2/6	**black and red/blue** ('27)	8·00	£12
G53	3/–	**green and violet** ('22)	£12	£15
G54	4/–	**grey-black and red** ('22)	£14	£17
G20/54		**set** (16v)	£60	£70
SPG20/54		**specimen set** (16v)	£90	‡

1932 (Jan. 27). Tercentenary of British Settlement. (*recess*) **Waterlow and Sons. Designer (5/- value) Mrs. J. Goodwin. Wmk. Multiple Script CA. Perf. 12½. Sheets 6 x 10.**

G55	½d. **green**	60	70
G56	1d. **scarlet**..	80	1·00
G57	1½d. **brown**	1·50	2·00
G58	2d. **grey**	4·00	5·00
G59	2½d. **deep blue**	3·00	5·00
G60	3d. **orange**..	5·00	£10
G61	6d. **violet**	£12	£14
G62	1/- **olive-green**	£16	£20
G63	2/6 **claret**	£35	£40
G64	5/- **black and chocolate**	£110	£130
G55/64	**set (10v)**	£180	£225
SPG55/64 **specimen set (10v)**	£125	‡

All values exist on thick and on thin paper.

1935 (May 6). Silver Jubilee. (*recess*) **De La Rue. Designer, H. Fleury. Wmk. Multiple Script CA. Perf. 13¼ x 14. Sheets 6 x 10.**

G65	1d. **indigo and carmine**	1·00	1·00
G66	1½d. **ultramarine and grey**	1·50	1·50
G67	2½d. **brown and deep blue**	3·50	4·50
G68	1/- **slate and purple** ..	9·00	£10
G65/68	**set (4v)**	£14	£16
SPG65/68 **specimen set (4v)**	£20	‡

Remainders were withdrawn on December 31st 1935.

1938 (Nov. 15th) -51 Designs, ½d., 2d. (English Harbour); 1d., 1½d., 2½d., 10/- (Nelson's Dockyard); 3d., 2/6, £1 (Fort James); 6d., 1/-, 5/- (St. John's Harbour). Printers (*recess*) **Waterlow & Sons. Perf. 12½ (L). Designs, 1d., 1½d., 2½d., 3d., 2/6, 10/-, £1, H. Sheets 12 x 10 or 10 x 12.**

1	½d. **yellow-green** ..	10	10
	a green (7/42) ..	15	10
2	1d. **dp scarlet**	15	10
	a red	20	15
3	1½d. **chocolate brown** ..	15	10
	a lake-brown (7/7/49)	7·00	8·00
	b red-brown (23/1/50)	60	10
4	2d. **grey**	20	10
	a slate-grey (14/6/51)	30	10
5	2½d. **dp ultramarine** ..	20	15
	a ultramarine (12/43) .	25	20
6	3d. **orange**	30	15
	a pale orange (26/6/44)	20	15
7	6d. **violet**	30	20

8	1/- **black and chocolate** .	30	30
	a black and lake-brown (7/7/49) ..	3·00	3·00
9	2/6 **purple-claret** ..	1·00	1·25
	a dull purple (7/42) ..	1·50	1·70
10	5/- **olive**	3·00	3·50
	a grey-olive (26/6/44)	4·00	4·50
11	10/- **dp magenta** (1/4/48)		
12	£1 **greenish-slate** (1/4/48)	8·00	£10
		£16	£20
1/12	**set (12)**	£28	£35
SP 1/12 **specimen set** perf	£50	‡

3a/3b There is a somewhat purple tinge in the colour of 3a which is lacking in 3b, though the two are often confused.

SPECIAL ISSUES

1937 (May 12th) Coronation. As Aden, but printers, Bradbury, Wilkinson. Perf. 11 x 11¾ (C). Sheets 6 x 10.

S1	1d. **carmine-red**	20	20
S2	1½d. **light brown**	25	25
S3	2½d. **blue**	7p	70
SP S1/3 **specimen set** perf (3)	£15	‡

1946 (Oct. 12th) Victory. As Aden.

S4	1½d. **chocolate-brown** ..	10	10
S5	3d. **reddish-orange** ..	15	15
SP S4/5 **specimen set** perf (2)	£15	‡

1949 (Jan. 3rd) Silver Wedding. As Aden.

S6	2½d. **ultramarine**	10	10
S7	5/- **olive-green**	4·00	4·50

1949 (Oct. 10th) U.P.U. As Aden.

S8	2½d. **dull violet-blue** ..	25	25
S9	3d. **dp orange**	60	60
S10	6d. **purple**	1·25	1·25
S11	1/- **beech-brown**	2·00	2·00
S8/11	**set (4)**	4·00	4·00

1951 (Feb. 16th) West Indies University College. Designs, 3c. (Arms of College); 12c. (Portrait of Princess Alice. Chancellor). (*recess*) **Waterlow & Sons. Perf. 14 x 14¾ (C). Sheets 10 x 6.**

S12	3c. **black and brown** ..	20	30
S13	12c. **black and violet** ..	50	60

Fourteen colonies participated in the issue, and they contributed to the University College funds the portion realised for the sales of the stamps over and above normal receipts.

ASCENSION

Originally occupied by Great Britain on October 22nd, 1815, to prevent its possible use as a base to rescue Napoleon from St. Helena, the island was commissioned as a Naval Establishment in 1816. It remained under the administration of the Royal Navy until October 20th, 1922, when it was transferred to the Colonial Office as a dependency of St. Helena.

From March 3rd, 1867, contemporary stamps of Great Britain up to 1/- value were sold; and, up to 1887, were cancelled on arrival at British ports. Thereafter, until 1922, G.B. stamps were cancelled with a named "Ascension" date stamp.

By an anomalous provision of the Post Office Act of 1922, the first G.B. stamps overprinted for use in Ireland were authorised for use in Ascension. This provision was quickly rescinded and examples of Irish stamps used in Ascension are extremely rare.

1887-1922 Stamps of Great Britain identified by their Catalogue Nos. after prefix 'AS'.

Used at Georgetown; Circular or oval (Registered) named date-stamps.

(I) Stamps of Queen Victoria

(a) 1887

AS V33	1d.	**red-brown**	..
AS V49	1d.	**rose-red**	
		(Various Plates)	
AS V151	1d.	**lilac**	.. ..
AS V75	6d.	**lilac** (Pl. 5)	..
AS V142	6d.	**grey** (Pl. 17)	..
AS V77	1/-	**green** (Pl. 4)	..
AS V92	1/-	**green** (Pl. 7)	..

(b) 1887-1900

AS V176	½d.	**vermilion**	
AS V177	½d.	**blue-green**	..
AS V178	1½d.	**dull purple and green**	..
AS V180	2d.	**green and carmine**	
AS V181	2½d.	**purple/blue**	..
AS V182	3d.	**prrple/yellow**	
AS V184	4d.	**green and brown**	
AS V186	4½d.	**green and carmine**	
AS V188	5d.	**dull purple and blue**	..
AS V190	6d.	**purple/rose-red**	
AS V192	9d.	**dull purple and blue**	..
AS V195	1/-	**green**	.. ..
AS V196	1/-	**green and carmine**	

(II) Stamps of King Edward VII (1902)

(Catalogue Nos. refer only to the first listed shade of the De La Rue printings. The later Harrison and Somerset House printings were also used on Ascension).

AS E1	½d.	**green**	.. ..
AS E3	1d.	**scarlet**	.. ..
AS E4	1½d.	**purple and green**	
AS E6	2d.	**green and carmine**	..
AS E9	2½d.	**blue**	.. ..
AS E10	3d.	**purple/orange-yellow**	..
AS E15	4d.	**green and brown**	
AS E17	4d.	**orange**	..
AS E19	5d.	**purple and blue**	
AS E21	6d.	**purple**	.. ..
AS E23	7d.	**grey-black**	..
AS E25	9d.	**purple and blue**	
AS E27	10d.	**purple and carmine**	..
AS E30	1/-	**green and carmine**	..

AS E23 and AS E27 were not sold on Ascension but are known postmarked, together with 2/6d. – £1, for collectors.

(III) Stamps of King George V (1911-22).

AS G5	½d.	**yellow-green**	..
AS G11	½d.	**green**	.. ..
AS G14	1d.	**scarlet**	..
AS G20	1½d.	**yellow-green**	
AS G22	1d.	**carmine**	..
AS G23	1½d.	**red-brown**	..
AS G25	2d.	**orange**	..
AS G29	2½d.	**blue**	.. ..
AS G31	3d.	**violet**	.. ..
AS G33	4d.	**grey-green**	..
AS G34	5d.	**brown**	.. ..
AS G36	6d.	**purple**	.. ..
AS G38	7d.	**olive**	.. ..
AS G40	8d.	**black/yellow**	..
AS G42	9d.	**agate**	.. ..
AS G44	9d.	**olive-green**	..
AS G46	10d.	**turquoise blue**	
AS G48	1/-	**bistre-brown**	

AS G38/G40/G46 were not sold on Ascension but are known postmarked, together with 2/6d – 10/-, for collectors.

1922 (Nov. 2) Printers (*typo*) **De La Rue & Co. overprinted in black or red (1/- value) on 1912-22 issues of St. Helena. Perf. 14. Sheets 12 x 5.**

(a) Wmk Mult Script CA

G1	½d.	**black and green**	..	1·00	2·50
G2	1d.	**green**	.. ..	1·50	2·50
G3	1½d.	**rose-scarlet**	..	4·00	£10
G4	2d.	**black and grey**	..	4·00	7·00
		a wmk reversed		—	—
G5	3d.	**bright blue**	..	5·00	£10
G6	8d.	**black and dull purple**	£14	£15
G7	2/–	**black and blue/blue**	.	£65	£75
G8	3/–	**black and violet**	..	£100	£120

(b) Wmk Mult Crown CA

G9	1/–	**black on green**	..	£15	£18
G1/9		**set** (9)	.. ..	£200	£250
SP G1/9		**specimen set** (9)	..	£140	‡

1924-33 Printers (*typo*) **De La Rue & Co. Wmk. Mult Script CA. Perf. 14. Chalky paper. Sheets 12 x 5.**

G10	½d. **grey-black and black**	75	1·00
	a cleft rock	£30	—
	b torn flag	£30	—
	c split mast	£30	—
G11	1d. **grey- black and dp blue-green**	1·00	1·50
	aa grey-black and brt blue-green	£22	£30
	a cleft rock	£30	—
	b torn flag	£30	—
	c split mast	£30	—
G12	1½d. **rose-red**	2·00	4·00
	a cleft rock	£40	—
	b torn flag	£40	—
	c split mast	£40	—
	d line through C of Ascension	£95	—
	e damaged scroll	£75	—
G13	2d. **grey-black and grey**	2·00	3·00
	a cleft rock	£40	—
	b torn flag	£40	—
	c split mast	£40	—
G14	3d. **blue**	1·50	2·50
	a cleft rock	£45	—
	b torn flag	£45	—
	c split mast	£45	—
G15	4d. **gry-blk, blk/pale-yel**	£15	£17
	aa gry-blk, blk/lemon	£15	£17
	a cleft rock	£110	—
	b torn flag	£110	—
	c split mast	£110	—
G16	5d. **reddish-purple and ol-green** (1927)	7·00	£10
	a cleft rock	£80	—
	c split mast	£80	—
G17	6d. **gry-blk and br-purple**	£27	£35
	a cleft rock	£140	—
	b torn flag	£140	—
	c split mast	£140	—
G18	8d. **gry-blk and br-violet**	7·00	£10
	a cleft rock	£75	—
	b torn flag	£75	—
	c split mast	£75	—
G19	1/– **gry-blk and brown**	£12	£15
	a cleft rock	£75	—
	b torn flag	£75	—
	c split mast	£75	—
G20	2/– **gry-blk and blu/blu**	£45	£55
	a cleft rock	£200	—
	b torn flag	£200	—
	c split mast	£200	—
G21	3/– **gry-blk and blk/blu**	£65	£75
	a cleft rock	£300	—
	b torn flag	£300	—
	c split mast	£300	—
G10/21	**set** (12)	£175	£225

SP G10/21 **specimen set** (12) . £100   ‡

Prices for the Vignette varieties are for unused copies. Fine used examples are less frequently found and a substantial premium can be expected for such items. The torn flag does not occur on G11aa.

Varieties (a) Cleft rock (Row 5/1).
(b) Torn Flag (Row 4/6)
This was probably corrected early in 1927 as it does not occur on the 5d. value which was issued in that year.
(c) Split mast (Row 2/1).

G12d Line through C of ASCENSION Row 1/6. Occurs only on 1½d. value.

G12e Damaged scroll below 'PO' of 'POSTAGE' Row 1/4. Occurs only on 1½d. value.

1934 Various Pictorial Designs. Printers (*recess*) **De La Rue & Co. Wmk. Mult Script CA. Perf. 14. Sheets 6 x 10 or 10 x 6.**

G22	½d. **black and violet**	15	35
G23	1d. **black and emerald**	70	70
G24	1½d. **black and scarlet**	70	80
G25	2d. **black and orange**	70	70
G26	3d. **black and ult**	90	1·20
G27	5d. **black and blue**	1·75	2·50

G28	8d. **black and sepia** ..	5·00	6·00
G29	1/– **black and carmine** .	£13	£15
G30	2/6 **black and bt-purple**	£30	£35
G31	5/– **black and brown** ..	£40	£50
G22/31	**set** (10	£85	£100
SP G22/31 **specimen set** perf			
(10)	£75	‡	

1935 (May 6th) Silver Jubilee. Printers (*recess*)
**Waterlow. Wmk. Mult Script CA. Perf.
11 x 12. Sheets 6 x 10.**

G32	1½d. **dp blue and scarlet** .	2·50	2·50
G33	2d. **ult and grey** ..	3·00	4·00
G34	5d. **green and indigo** ..	8·00	£10
G35	1/– **slate and purple** ..	£19	£25
G32/35	**set** (4)	£30	£40
SP G32/35 **specimen set** perf			
(4)	£25	‡	

Numbers sold—G32, 50,800; G33, 31,300;
G34, 42,700; G35, 38,500.

1938 (May 12th) -40 Designs, ½d., 1/- (Georgetown Clarence Bay); 1d., 6d., 10/- ("Three
Sisters" Hills); 1½d., 2/6 (The Pier, Georgetown); 1d., 2d., 4d. (Green Mountain); 3d.,
5/- (Long Beach, opposite Georgetown).
Printers (*recess*) **De La Rue. Perf. 13½ (C).
Centres black. Sheets 6 x 10.**

1	½d. **violet**	10	15
	a re-entry ..	4·00	4·00
	b long E ..	4·00	4·00
2	1d. **grn** (Green Mountain) .	5·00	3·00
3	1d. **oran-yellow** (8/7/40)	1·50	2·50
4	1½d. **scarlet**	50	50
	a davit flaw ..	£10	£10
5	2d. **dp orange**	15	25
6	3d. **ultramarine**	£15	£15
7	3d. **grey** ((8/7/40) ..	30	40
8	4d. **ultramarine** (8/7/40)	25	40
9	6d. **grey-blue**	35	40
10	1/– **sepia**	60	70
	a re-entry ..	£14	£14
11	2/6 **carmine**	2·50	3·00
	a davit flaw ..	£20	£20
12	5/– **pale brown**	4·00	3·00
13	10/– **bright red-purple** ..	£10	£11
1/13	**set** (13)	£40	£40
SP 1/13 **specimen set** perf(13)	£50	‡	

As before but Perf. 13 x 12¾ (C). (*Issued
17/5/44 unless otherwise indicated*).

14	½d. **pale violet**	5	10
	a re-entry ..	4·00	4·00
	b long E ..	4·00	4·00

15	1d. **orange-yellow** (5/42)	10	20
16	1d. **green** ("Three Sisters")		
	(1/6/49)	10	20
	a re-entry	8·00	8·00
17	1½d. **scarlet**	10	15
	aa davit flaw ..	£10	£10
17a	1½d. **rose-carmine** (25/2/53)	10	15
	b davit flaw ..	£10	£10
18	2d. **dp orange**	15	20
19	3d. **dark grey**	15	25
	a grey-black and dp grey		
	(6/12/50) ..	25	30
	b major retouch ..	£12	£12
20	4d. **ultramarine**	25	30
21	6d. **grey-blue**	60	70
22	1/– **sepia**	40	50
	a re-entry	£14	£14
23	2/6 **carmine**	2·50	3·00
	a davit flaw ..	£20	£20
24	5/– **light brown**	3·50	5·00
25	10/– **bright red-purple**	9·00	9·00
	a grey-black and red-		
	pur (14/2/45) ..	7·50	8·50
14/25	**set** (13)	£15	£19

**As before, but Perf. 14 (L) and colours
changed (1½d. and 2d.).**

26	1d. **orange-yel** (17/2/49)	25	40
27	1½d. **dp scarlet** (17/2/49) .	80	1·00
	a davit flaw ..	£25	£25
28	1½d. **rose-carmine** (1/6/49)	15	20
	aa davit flaw ..	£15	£15
	a dull rose-car (1/6/49)	70	90
	b davit flaw ..	£20	£20
29	2d. **dp orange** (17/2/49) .	2·00	3·00
30	2d. **dp scarlet** (1/6/49) ..	20	20
26/30	**set** (5)	3·25	4·50

19b A major retouch is to be found above central
mountain on Row 10/2.

25 The frame is fluorescent-aniline.

4a/11a/17aa/17b/23a/27a/28aa/28b There is a
small davit-like object at top left of the pier, Row
5/1.

10a/22a Doubling of right vertical frame lines and
value tablet (Row 6/4).

1a/14a Right frame line doubled (Row 2/2).

1b/14b Long centre bar to second E in GEORGE-
TOWN (Row 2/3).

16a Left vertical frame lines doubled (Row 4/6).

SPECIAL ISSUES

**1937 (May 19th) Coronation. Perf. 13¾ x 14
(C). As Aden. Sheets 6 x 10.**

S1	1d. **green**	15	20
S2	2d. **orange**	20	25
S3	3d. **dp blue**	80	90
SP S1/3 **specimen set** perf (3)	£12	‡	

1946 (Oct. 21st) Victory. As Aden.

S4	2d. **reddish-orange** ..	10	20
S5	4d. **dp blue**	10	20
SP S4/5 **specimen set** perf (2)	£12	‡	

1948 (Oct. 20th) Silver Wedding. As Aden.

S6	3d. **black**	15	15
S7	10/– **red-purple**	9·00	£14

1949 (Oct. 10th) U.P.U. As Aden.

S8	3d. **carmine-rose** ..	25	25
S9	4d. **indigo**	60	70
S10	6d. **dull olive**	1·00	1·25
S11	1/– **slate-black**	1·75	2·00
S8/11	**set** (4)	3·50	4·00

AUSTRALIA

Prior to federation, individual States used their own stamps, but control of all Postal Services was taken over by the Commonwealth on March 1st, 1901.

State stamps continued in use only in their respective territories until October 13th, 1910 when all were made valid throughout the Commonwealth of Australia.

FIRST SINGLE　　　　SECOND SINGLE

THIRD SINGLE　　　　FIRST MULTIPLE

SECOND MULTIPLE　　THIRD MULTIPLE

In order to ensure clarity from the philatelic standpoint the King George V definitives are not listed here in strict order of issue.

The entire range of the Kangaroo type is listed under G1–83, whilst the Georgian type is listed under G89–208. Within these two groups the stamps have been listed in such a way as to illustrate the progression from the First Single wmk. to the Third (C of A) multiple wmk.

The line-engraved definitives are listed under G84–88 whilst the listing of other and later issues follows a strict chronological order (G209 onwards).

1912-1947 THE KANGAROO TYPE ISSUES

Designed by B. Young and engraved by J. Reading. The first two issues (G1–G28b) typographed by J. B. Cooke, and the third series (G29–G62) by J. B. Cooke (1915–1918), T. S. Harrison (1918–1926), A. J. Mullett (1926–1927) and John Ash (1927). Of the fourth series (G63–G65) numbers G63 and G64 were printed by T. S.

Harrison (1923), A. J. Mullett (1926) and John Ash (1927) whilst G65 was only printed by T. S. Harrison (1923). The fifth and sixth issues (G66–G81) were only printed by John Ash whilst the final 2/–d. (G82–G83) was produced by W. E. G. McCracken.

1912-13 First Kangaroo Issue. First Single Crown over "A" wmk. Perf. 12. The dates given are those of the first deliveries from the Stamp Printing Office to the Post Office. Sheets 120—two panes, each 6 x 10.

G1	½d.	**grn** (4/1/13)	..	3·00	50
		a wmk inverted	..	£15	4·00
		b printed on the gummed side ..		—	—
G2	1d.	**red** (31/12/12)	..	3·00	25
		a wmk sideways	..	£10	6·00
		b thin paper	..	£200	£100
		c thick paper	..		
G3	1d.	**deep scarlet**	..		
		a wmk inverted	..	5·00	3·00
G4	2d.	**grey** (11/1/13)	..	£12	8·00
		a wmk inverted	..	£10	1·00
G5	2½d.	**indigo** (17/1/13)	..	£30	£15
		a wmk inverted	..	£10	3·00
		b thin paper	..	£15	5·00
		c thick paper	..	£15	5·00
		d printed on the gummed side ..		—	—
G6	3d.	**brn-olive to olive** (22/1/13)	..	£15	2·00
		a wmk inverted	..	£40	5·00
		b thin paper	..		
G7	3d.	**yel-ol to ol-grn**	..	£17	2·00
		a wmk inverted	..	£40	£10
		b thin paper	..		
G8	4d.	**br or to or-yel** (12/2/13)	..	£35	7·00
		a thin paper	..		
G9	4d.	**dp or-yel** ..	..	£100	£20
G10	5d.	**pl chestnut to br chestnut** (16/1/13)	..		
		a thin paper	..	£35	£10
G11	5d.	**dl or dp chestnut**		£38	£12
G12	6d.	**ult blu** (14/1/13)	..	£27	5·00
		a wmk. inverted	..	£55	£25
G13	9d.	**vio** (29/1/13)	..	£27	5·00
G14	1/–	**emerald** (21/1/13)	..	£27	5·00
		a wmk inverted	..	£60	£25
G15	1/–	**aniline emerald**		£35	6·00
G16	2/–	**dk brn** (25/1/13)	..	£85	£20
G17	5/–	**grey and yellow** (20/3/13)	..	£175	£100
G18	10/–	**grey and pink** (20/3/13)	..	£380	£250
G19	£1	**brown and blue** (20/3/13)	..	£1100	£550
G20	£2	**black and rose** (8/4/13)	..	£2400	£950

G1/17 **basic series, one of each value, (12)** £420 £150
SPG18/20 **specimen set** (3).. £650 ‡
"Cancelled" overprints £1, £2 .. — —

G1 The ½d. value was issued in both sheets and coils. The coils stamps may be collected in the form of coil join pairs.

G20 The colour of the black in the £2 value may vary from pale grey black to intense black. The original plans for the First Kangaroo issue made provision for a 2/6 denomination, but by error the £2 value was produced instead. The £2 denomination has been dangerously forged by Sperati.

1914 The Second (Provisional) Kangaroo issue. Printed on white wove surfaced paper having the Second Single Crown over "A" wmk. intended for the production of the First Typographed Georgian Issue. Perf. 12. The dates of issue are unrecorded, the dates given being those of the actual printing. Sheets as before.

G21 2d. **grey** (–/12/14) .. £28 3·00
G22 2½d. **indigo** (–/7/15) .. — £100
    a wmk. inverted .. £30 7·00
G23 6d. **ult blu to dp ult blu** (–/2/15) .. £85 7·00
    a wmk. inverted .. — £100
G24 6d. **br ult** (–/2/15) .. £150 £35
G25 9d. **violet** (–/6/15) .. £100 £10
    a wmk. inverted .. £500 £250
G26 1/– **blu-grn** (–/6/15).. £100 £10
G27 2/– **dk brn** (–/4/15) .. £350 £50
G28 5/– **grey and yellow** (–/8/14) .. £600 £100
    a wmk. inverted .. £675 £150
    b yel printed double £2500 —
G21/8 **basic series, one of each value** (7) £1250 £175

Numbers Issued — 2d., 6,120,000; 2½d, 1,416,000; 6d., 4,800,000; 9d., 8,619,000; 1/–, 7,200,000; 2/–, 960,000; 5/–, 720,000.

1915-28 The Third Kangaroo Issue. Third Single Crown over "A" wmk. Perf. 12.

(i) On ordinary wove paper. Sheets as before.

G29 2d. **grey** (–/11/15) .. £12 1·00
    a wmk. inverted .. £25 3·00
G30 2d. **ol-grey** .. .. £30 6·00
G31 2½d. **indigo** (22/3/17) £12 2·00
    a wmk. inverted .. £40 £20
    b very thin paper.. £50 £25
G32 2½d. **blue to dp blue**.. £25 2·00
    a wmk. inverted .. £50 £25
G33 3d. **bistre olive** (–/11/15) .. £12 1·50
    a wmk. inverted .. £25 4·00
G34 3d. **yellow-olive** .. £12 2·00
    a wmk. inverted .. £25 £10
G35 3d. **olive-green** .. £12 2·00
    a wmk. inverted .. £25 4·00
G36 6d. **ult** (–/12/15) .. £24 3·00
    a wmk. inverted .. £50 8·00
G37 6d. **dull blue** .. .. £24 3·00
    a wmk. inverted .. £50 8·00
G38 6d. **vio milky blue** .. £24 3·00

G39 9d. **violet, pl to dp** (–/6/16) .. £18 2·00
    a wmk. inverted .. £50 £15
G40 9d. **red-vio to indigo-vio** .. .. £18 2·00
    a wmk. inverted .. £50 £15
G41 1/– **blu-grn, br to dl** (–/6/16) £18 1·50
    a wmk. inverted .. £40 8·00
    b wmk. sideways £35 £35
G42 2/– **brn** (–/1/16) .. £110 £12
    a very thin paper £140 £16
G43 5/– **grey and yellow** (1916) .. £175 £30
    a wmk. inverted .. £260 £80
G44 5/– **grey and or-yel** (1916) .. £175 £30
G45 5/– **grey and chrome** (1917) .. £175 £30
G46 5/– **grey and pl yel** (1928) .. £175 £30
G47 5/– **grey and br ch-ye** £175 £30
    a yellow printed double .. £400 —
G48 10/– **grey and pink** (29/3/16) .. £300 £125
    a wmk. inverted .. £450 £200
G49 10/– **grey and br pink** (1917) .. £300 £125
G50 10/– **grey and br anl pink** (1918) .. £300 £125
    a wmk. sideways £2500 £1000
G51 10/– **grey and pl pink** (1920) .. £300 £125
G52 10/– **grey and pl rose-pink** (1922) .. £300 £125
G53 £1 **brown and blue** (28/3/16) .. £1000 £450
G54 £1 **chestnut and blu to br blu** £1000 £450
    a wmk. inverted .. £2000 £800
    b wmk. sideways £4000 £2000
G55 £1 **brn and pl blu** .. £1000 £450
G56 £2 **blk and rose** (1918) £2250 £1100
G57 £2 **grey-blk and crm** (1920) £2250 £1100
G58 £2 **pur-blk and rose** (1924) £2250 £1100
SPG48/G53/G55 **specimen set** (3) £700 ‡

(ii) On highly surfaced shiny paper.

G59 2d. **sil-grey** (1918) .. £16 3·00
G60 6d. **dull blue** (1918) £35 6·00

(iii) On "Milk white" paper.

G61 2d. **grey** (–/9/20) .. £16 3·00
G62 3d. **pl olive** (1920) .. £25 7·00
G29/43 **basic series, one of each value** (8) £380 £50

G30 The rare olive-grey shade is probably due to accidental mixing with the ink employed in the production of the 3d. value.

G31/32/41 A vast range of shades may be found as war time shortages prevented the colour of the original printing being matched with any accuracy.

G41*b* Were available in Sydney for a short period at the end of 1927.

G42 A bright red-brown shade is known to have been produced in 1917, but the bulk of the printing was overprinted for use in New Guinea. The overprinted mint stamp is almost unique.

1923 (Dec. 6th)-1924 The Fourth Kangaroo Issue, having the third Single Crown over "A" wmk, but with the colours of the stamps changed to conform with U.P.U. custom. Perf. 12. Sheets as before.

G63	6d.	chestnut (6/12/23)	£10	1·50
G64	2/–	maroon to red-cl		
		(1/5/24)	£24	5·00
		a wmk. inverted ..	£100	£20
G65	£1	grey (1/5/24) ..	£325	£150
G63/5		basic series (3) ..	£350	£150
SPG65		specimen ovpt (1)	£100	‡

1929 (Feb.)-1930 The Fifth Kangaroo Issue, having the Second Multiple Crown over "A" wmk. Perf. 12. Sheets as before.

G66	6d.	chest (25/9/29) ..	£12	1·50
G67	9d.	violet (–/2/29) ..	£15	1·50
G68	1/–	emerald (–/6/29)		
		a wmk. inverted ..	£17	2·00
G69	2/–	maroon to red-maroon (–/3/29)	£250	£200
G70	5/–	grey and or-yel (30/11/29) ..	£25	4·00
G71	10/–	grey and lt pink (–/2/29)	£170	£40
G72	£2	grey and rose to rose-crimson (–/11/30) ..	£1800	£250
G66/70		basic series (5) ..	£230	£47
SPG71/72		specimen pair ..	£300	‡

1932 (April 28th)-1935 The Sixth Kangaroo Issue, having the third Multiple (C of A over Crown) wmk. Perf. 11¾ to 12. Sheets as before.

G73	6d.	chest to br chest (28/4/32) ..	£12	8·00
G74	9d.	vio to dp vio (2/5/32) ..	£14	1·50
G75	2/–	maroon to brn-pur (–/10/35)..	4·00	75
G76	5/–	grey and or-yel (–/12/32) ..	£160	£20
G77	5/–	grey and yel-buff	£160	£20
G78	10/–	grey and pl pink (–/7/32) ..	£240	£80
G79	10/–	grey and aniline-pink	£260	£80
G80	£1	bluish-grey (–/10/35) ..	£375	£150
G81	£2	grey and crimson (–/6/34) ..	£1700	£235
G73/77		basic series, one of each value (4)	£180	£28
SPG78/G80		specimen pair ..	£140	‡

G73 Only one printing was ever produced, the stamp being replaced in June, 1932 by the 6d. Kookaburra typographed, G225.

Dies I and II   Die III

1946 (Jan. 3rd) The Seventh and last Kangaroo Issue. The 2/– value from redrawn Die III. The third die may be distinguished from Dies I and II employed in the production of the earlier 2/– values inasmuch as the new die has one coloured background line between the value circle and the "SH" of Shillings, whilst stamps produced from Dies I and II show two coloured lines at the same position. Wmk. as before. Sheets as before.

G82	(Ex 41)	2/– mar (3/1/46)	2·50	50
G83	(Ex 41a)	2/– pale maroon (1947)	2·50	50

THE K.G. V RECESS DEFINITIVES

1913 (Dec. 8th)-1932 Engraved and (*recess*) printed by T. S. Harrison, the Australian Commonwealth Note Printer, at the Treasury, Melbourne, (1d. and 6d.) or under J. Ash (3d. and 1/–) on white wove unwmk. paper. Perf. 11 Line. Designs, 1d., King George V; 3d. and 6d., Kookaburra; 1/–, Lyre–bird. Sheets 12 x 10.

G84	1d.	pale rose-red (8/12/13)	4·00	3·50
		a imperf. between pair	£1000	—
G85	1d.	dep red (20/3/14) ..	3·00	2·50
		a imperf. between pair	£1000	—
G86	3d.	blue (21/11/28) ..	4·00	3·50
		a sheet of four (29/10/28) ..	£230	£240
G87	6d.	brn-cl (26/8/14) ..	£80	£50
G88	1/–	green to yel-green (15/2/32)	£40	1·00

G84 From Plate No. 1, a lightly engraved plate producing a pale shade.

G85 From Plates No. 2, 3 and 4, being heavily engraved in comparison with Plate No. 1, and thereby producing a deep rich colour.

G84*a*/85*a* Prices are for vertical or horizontal pairs.

G84/85 Many flaws, retouches and re-entries are to be found on the 1d. *(Recess)* Georgian issue, re-entries being especially prominent on the first nine positions of the second vertical column on Plate 4. Prices vary according to prominence and significance. For full details specialists are referred to the leading handbooks.

G86/G86*a* Based on the design of the 6d. brownish claret of 1914, the lettering, background and detail of the Kookaburra being redrawn. Although the 3d. blue is a definitive design the issue was in fact made to mark the International Philatelic Exhibition held in October, 1928 at Melbourne. Special sheets were printed for the Exhibition each being divided into fifteen blocks of four with wide gutters between each block, thereby producing a special pane of four stamps, listed as G86*a*. Some of these special format sheets were actually printed and perforated in the Australian Post Office Stand at the Exhibition. The first two sheets printed at the Exhibition were not perforated, one each of the same being presented to King George V and the Australian Postmaster General. Imperforate blocks of four, are known. Price £6000.

G86*a* A general issue in the form of standard format sheets was made throughout Australia in November, 1928 in order to prevent speculation on the Exhibition issue.

G87 The date of issue given is that of the first release in Brisbane, Queensland. From plates numbered 1, 2, 3 and 4. The 1d. and 6d. values of 1913–1914 were part of a projected line-engraved definitive series, the 2d. and 1/– values being under consideration at the time of issue. As only 8,000 sheets were printed, stocks soon became exhausted, further production being discontinued owing to a re-orientation of stamp issuing policy that resulted from a change of Government. In accordance with instructions given by the new administration, most of the 6d. brownish-claret issue were used on telegrams, and it is thought that upwards of 70% of the total issue were used in this fashion. The new Government abandoned the projected line-engraved definitive series. This stamp imperf. is a plate proof.

G88 The Lyre-Bird type represents the commencement of a later programme to introduce line-engraved definitives, but as in 1914 the project was abandoned as the result of a change of Government.

THE K.G. V TYPOGRAPHED DEFINITIVES

1914 (July)-1918 The First *(typo)* Georgian Issue. Dies engraved by Perkins Bacon & Co. and printed by J. B. Cooke (1914/1918) and T. S. Harrison (1918 onwards) on paper having the Second Single Crown over "A" wmk. Sheets 120 – two panes each 6 x 10.

(i) Perf. 14 (Line). Wove paper.

G89	½d.	br green (–/2/15)	£150	£100
G90	1d.	car-red (17/7/14)	8·00	1·00
G91	1d.	rose-carmine	£10	1·00
G92	5d.	brn to pl brn (–/2/15)	£15	2·00
		a wmk. inverted ..	£50	£15

(ii) Perf. 14 Comb. Wove paper.

G93	½d.	bright green ..	2·00	50
		a wmk. inverted ..	4·00	2·50
G94	½d.	br yellow-green ..	2·00	50
		a wmk. inverted ..	4·00	2·50
G95	½d.	emerald-green ..	2·00	50
		a wmk. inverted ..	4·00	2·00
G96	½d.	olive-green ..	3·00	1·00
		a wmk. inverted ..	6·00	3·00
G97	1d.	dp dk car-red ..	4·00	50
		a wmk. inverted ..	£10	2·00
G98	1d.	car-red ..	4·00	50
		a wmk. inverted ..	£10	2·00
G99	1d.	pl car-red ..	4·00	50
		a wmk. inverted ..	£10	2·00
G100	1d.	car-pink ..	£50	7·00
		a wmk. inverted ..	£125	£25
G101	1d.	rose-carmine ..	£20	5·00
		a wmk. inverted ..	£50	£12
G102	1d.	pl scarlet-red ..	£30	6·00
		a wmk. inverted ..	£70	£15
G103	1d.	pale rose-red ..	£10	4·00
		a wmk. invered ..	£35	£10
G104	1d.	aniline salmon-red (1914) ..	£25	8·00
G105	1d.	dp aniline-carmine (1917/8) ..	£25	8·00
G106	4d.	orange (–/1/15) ..	£10	2·50
		a wmk. inverted ..	£25	6·00
G107	4d.	pl yellow-orange ..	£10	2·50
G108	4d.	yellow-orange ..	£10	2·50
		a wmk. inverted ..	£25	6·00
G109	4d.	lemon-or (1916)	£150	£18
G110	4d.	pl dl orange ..	£20	4·00
		a thick paper ..	£40	£10
G111	5d.	brn to dp red-brn (12/9/17) ..	£12	2·00
		a wmk. inverted ..	£40	£12
G112	5d.	chestnut (shades)	£15	2·00
		a wmk. inverted ..	£50	£14

(iii) Perf. 14 Comb. On inferior rough un-surfaced paper of variable texture. Gummed locally.

G113	1d.	dp scar (–/12/16)	8·00	50

G114	1d.	**dp red** (–/1/17) ..	8·00	50
G115	1d.	**reddish-or to brn** (–/8/17) ..	8·00	50
G116	1d.	**pink, rose-pink to salmon** (–/3/18)	£15	2·00
G117	1d.	**dp rosine to lilac-rose** (–/4/18) ..	£30	8·00
G118	1d.	**car-red to crim-lk** (–/5/18) ..	£30	8·00
G119	1d.	**brn venetian-red to russet-brown** (–/6/18) ..	£30	8·00

(iv) Perf. 14 Comb. Printed by J. B. Cooke from a new plate manufactured from a new die (Die III) which may be distinguished from the first two dies used for the 1d. value by the small horizontal white line cutting through the vertical shading lines at the left of the King's neck. Printed on paper originally intended for War Savings Stamps.

G120	1d.	**rose-car to red** (–/6/18) ..	£40	£10
	a	wmk. inverted ..	£100	£25
	b	printed on both sides	£250	—

G97-G105 A vast range of shades exists on the 1d. carmine of the 1914 series. Those listed above are to be regarded as distinctive stages in the overall colour spectrum, and not as a complete listing of the thirty or forty shades recognised by specialists.

Die I   **Die II**

G98-G100 The so-called Die II on the 1d. carmine shades is in fact a flaw occasioned by the use of a defective roller die, the flaw itself consists of a spur on the inside of the lower left value tablet, as illustrated above. Prices from £300.

G105 Fluorescent "cosin" dye was used in the production of a number of printings during the period 1916-1918. The use of this dye produces a fluorescent effect under U.V. lamp, similar to that obtained from modern stamps coated with luminescent materials.

G109/G110/G113/G119 These shade variations were caused by war time shortages which became increasingly difficult during the period late-1916 to mid-1918.

G111 Earliest recorded date of use.

1918 (Jan. 8th)-1924 The Second (*typo*) **Georgian Issue. On paper having the first mult. wmk. Perf. 14. Printed by J. B. Cooke (G121–G125) or T. S. Harrison (G122–G122***c* **and G127–G130***a***). Sheets as before.**

G121	½d.	**yel-grn to br yel-grn** (8/1/18) ..	2·00	30
	a	wmk. inverted ..	4·00	1·50

G122	½d.	**dl to blue-grn** ..	2·00	30
	a	wmk. inverted ..	4·00	1·50
	b	wmk. sideways	—	£2000
	c	thin (semi pelure) paper ..	—	—
G123	1d.	**carmine-pink** (28/1/18) ..	£75	£10
G124	1d.	**pl rose-pink** ..	£75	£10
	a	wmk. inverted ..	£400	£200
G125	1d.	**dp dk red** ..	£150	£30
G126	1d.	**pl to dp carmine** (–/12/19) ..	£12	3·00
	a	wmk. inverted ..	£100	£500
G127	1d.	**sage-green** (20/5/24) ..	3·00	2·00
	a	wmk. inverted ..	—	£200
	b	very thin "semi pelure" paper	£20	8·00
G128	1½d.	**dp blackish-brn** (–/1/19) ..	2·00	40
	a	wmk. inverted ..	5·00	1·50
	b	very thin, "semi pelure" paper	£12	8·00
G129	1½d.	**red-brn to pur-brn** ..	4·00	1·00
	a	wmk. inverted ..	£10	2·50
G130	1½d.	**choc-brown** ..	2·50	50
	a	wmk. inverted ..	5·00	2·00

G122 The bluish-green shade of the ½d. appeared in 1919. All examples of G122*c*, the thin "semi pelure" paper, are of this shade.

G122*b* Only one copy of the ½d. wmk. sideways, has been recorded. This example was used somewhere in Western Australia.

G123/G124/G125 A small experimental printing by J. B. Cooke, said to have been of only 1,250 sheets, i.e. 150,000 stamps. The printing falls into three shade groups as indicated. G123 produces a gold fluorescent under a U.V. lamp owing to the use of cosin dye (see note re G105). G124 is a very strong rose-red, whilst G125 is an unusually deep red and the scarcest of the three groups. This printing was replaced by G126 printed by T. S. Harrison.

G127 The 1d. sage green was on sale concurrently with numbers G135 and G167 during mid-1924.

G128*b* was issued in very small quantities in Sydney and Melbourne during the first quarter of 1919.

G129 and G130 represent a distinct change in colour in relation to G128, and were used alongside numbers G139 and G140.

1918 (Nov. 9th)-1926 The Third (*typo*) **Georgian Issue. Printed on medium wove paper, having the Second Single Crown over "A" wmk. by T. S. Harrison (131–135***a***, G138–G144***d***, G146–G155 and G157–G165) or by A. J. Mullett (G136–7, G145, G156, G162–G163***a* **and G166). Perf. 14 Comb. Sheets as before.**

G131	½d.	**orange** (8/11/23) ..	1·00	50
	a	wmk. inverted ..	3·00	1·50
G132	1d.	**dp purple-violet** (13/2/22) ..	3·00	60

G133	1d.	**violet**	3·00	60
G134	1d.	**reddish-violet** ..	3·00	60
G135	1d.	**pl to dp sage-green** (1/5/24)	2·00	30
		a wmk. inverted ..	4·00	2·00
G136	1d.	**yellowish-green** (1926) ..	2·00	30
G137	1d.	**moss-green** ..	2·00	30
G138	1½d.	**blackish-brown** (9/11/18)	2·00	40
		a wmk. inverted ..	4·00	1·50
G139	1½d.	**choc-brn** (1919)	3·00	50
		a wmk. inverted ..	5·00	2·00
G140	1½d.	**deep red-brown** (–/6/19) ..	4·00	50
G141	1½d.	**lt reddish-brown** (–/12/21) ..	4·00	50
G142	1½d.	**dl to pl green** (8/3/23) ..	2·00	50
		a wmk. inverted ..	—	£300
		b rough,unsurf-paper, b green (–/–/23) ..	£50	£25
G143	1½d.	**bluish-grn, dp to pale**	2·00	50
		a wmk. inverted ..	—	£300
G144	1½d.	**dp scar to lt scar** (–/5/24) ..	2·00	30
		a wmk. inverted ..	£10	3·00
		b rough unsurfaced paper ..	£25	£10
		c thin pelure paper	£25	£15
		d orange-red ..	£15	6·00
G145	1½d.	**pl rose to dullish-red**	2·00	30
		a wmk. inverted ..	£10	3·00
G146	2d.	**dl orange to pl orange** (–/9/20)	5·00	50
		a wmk. inverted ..	£250	£100
G147	2d.	**reddish orange to brown orange**	5·00	50
		a wmk. inverted ..	£250	£100
G148	2d.	**dl buff or (on thin paper)** (–/–/21)	£10	4·00
G149	2d.	**scar to scar-ver** (17/2/22) ..	5·00	30
G150	2d.	**dp rose-scarlet**	6·00	30
G151	2d.	**dp red-brown to brown** (1/5/24)	5·00	2·00
G152	2d.	**pale red-brown**	5·00	2·00
G153	2d.	**dp red aniline-brown** ..	£10	3·00
G154	3d.	**dl to dk blue** (1/5/24) ..	£10	75
		a imperf. three sides, perf. at top ..	£3000	—
G155	3d.	**dp br blue** ..	£10	1·00
G156	3d.	**dp to br ult** ..	£10	1·00
G157	4d.	**dp to dp br vio** (–/6/21) ..	£15	6·00
G158	4d.	**bright to dull ult** (12/4/22) ..	£30	5·00
		a wmk. inverted ..	£40	£32
G159	4d.	**deep ult** ..	£30	6·00
G160	4d.	**pl milky blue** ..	£30	5·00
G161	4d.	**greenish-olive** ..	£12	2·00
		a wmk. inverted ..	—	£300
G162	4d.	**yel'ish to brn'ish-olive** (1926) ..	£14	2·00
		a wmk. inverted ..	—	£300
G163	4½d.	**violet**	£15	3·00
G164	1/4	**pl blue** (6/12/20)	£60	£10

G165	1/4	**dp turquoise** ..	£180	£80
G166	1/4	**pl dl blue to grey-blue**	£60	£10

G136/7 The A. J. Mullett printings of the 1d. green are of a rough and somewhat mottled appearance in comparison with the Harrison productions. Dry prints abound.

G141 represents a distinct change of colour in relation to numbers G138–140.

G142b A rare emergency printing made early in 1923 on thick, coarse grained paper. Mint examples are especially scarce and may be found with either yellowish or white gum – the former having been applied by hand and the latter by machine.

G144/G145 The T. S. Harrison and A. J. Mullett printings of the 1½d. red respectively. The Harrison printings are of a fairly uniform scarlet colour with occasional inclination towards scarlet-vermilion, whilst the A. J. Mullett productions vary considerably in shade from pale rose through rose-pink to dullish-red. Refer also to number G144d.

G144c represents a small printing on very thin paper that appeared during 1925.

G144d A very scarce T. S. Harrison printing.

G148 The 2d. orange on thin paper is from a late printing and appeared just prior to the introduction of the 2d. scarlet (G149).

G154a The 3d. imperf. on three sides is from part sheets found at Prahran, Sea Lake and Bairnsdale (Victoria) during the mid 1920s. A little over thirty copies are thought to exist.

G154–5 represent the T. S. Harrison printings of the 3d., whilst the single A. J. Mullett printing is listed under number G156. The Mullett productions all have shiny gum and are scarce, as they were on sale for only a few weeks.

G158–G160 The colour of the 4d. ultramarine varies considerably in brightness and depth.

G162 A distinctive brown-olive shade appeared some months after A. J. Mullett took over the production of the 4d. olive from T. S. Harrison.

G164 The T. S. Harrison printings of the 1/4d. were usually in the pale shade, whilst the A. J. Mullett printings have a characteristic dull, greyish-muddy appearance (G166).

G165 represents a very scarce and distinctive T. S. Harrison printing of 1922 and is best described as a deep bright (greenish) turquoise-blue.

1924 (Aug.) Fourth (*typo*) Georgian Issue. Perf. 14. No wmk. Produced during a temporary shortage of watermarked paper in mid-1924.

G167	1d.	**sage-green** (18/8/24) ..	2·50	1·50
G168	1½d.	**scarlet** (14/8/24)	3·00	2·00
G167/8		**the pair**	5·00	3·00

Only two weeks supply was produced, 150,000 sheets of the 1d. and 110,000 sheets of the 1½d. value.

G168 Date issued in Melbourne, Victoria.

The 2d. golden-scarlet no wmk. is an error listed under number G194a.

1926 (Oct. 23rd)-28 The Fifth (*typo*) **Georgian Issue. Printed on medium wove paper having the Second Multiple Crown over "A" wmk. by A. J. Mullett (G169–G171, G173–G175a, G177–G178 and G181/a), or J. Ash (G171/ G172a, G176 and G179–G180). Perf. 14 Comb. Sheets as before.**

G169	½d.	**yel-or** (10/3/27)	3·00	1·50
		a wmk. inver. ..	£10	4·00
G170	1d.	**sage-green** (23/10/26) ..	2·00	25
		a wmk. inverted ..	5·00	2·00
G171	1d.	**dull green** ..	3·00	50
		a wmk. inverted ..	7·00	3·00
G172	1d.	**yellow-green** ..	2·00	75
		a wmk. inverted ..	5·00	2·00
G173	1½d.	**reddish-pink** (5/11/26) ..	5·00	2·00
G174	1½d.	**scarlet to dp red** (shades) ..	4·00	25
		a wmk. inverted ..	8·00	2·00
G175	1½d.	**verm to pl pink**	4·00	75
		a wmk. inverted ..	5·00	2·00
G176	1½d.	**golden-scar** ..	8·00	1·00
G177	2d.	**red-brn** (17/8/27)	£10	4·00
G178	3d.	**dull to deep ult** (−/12/26) ..	£10	2·00
G179	4d.	**greenish-olive** (17/1/28) ..	£20	4·00
G180	4½d.	**bright violet** (26/10/27) ..	£12	1·50
G181	1/4	**pl greenish-blue** (6/9/27) ..	£140	£40
		a wmk. inverted ..	—	£400
G169/181		**basic series, one of each value** (8)	£190	£48

G169a is very scarce, only one sheet having been discovered.

G173–5 A considerable range of shades are to be found in the A. J. Mullett printings of the 1½d. value. Those listed represent major groupings of shades, the reddish pink being the first to appear.

G176 The golden-scarlet colour is characteristic of the John Ash printings of the 1½d. and 2d. Georgian type. See also numbers G188, G193– G194b and G204/a.

G179 Date of appearance in Sydney, New South Wales.

1926-30 The Sixth (*typo*) **Georgian Issue. Wmk. as previous set and printed by A. J. Mullett (G183, G187, G189 and G190) or J. Ash (G182, G184–6, G188 and G191–G200) but with Perf. changed to 13½ x 12½ Comb. Sheets as before.**

G182	½d.	**or-yel** (28/11/28)	1·00	50
G183	1d.	**sage-grn** (1926) (**Die I**) ..	1·00	25
G184	1d.	**dl green** (1928) (**Die I**) ..	1·00	25

G185	1d.	**yel-grn** (−/2/28) (**Die I**) ..	1·00	25
		a wmk. inverted ..	2·00	1·00
G186	1d.	**yel-grn** (−/6/28) (**Die II**) ..	£28	£20
		a wmk. inverted ..	£150	£80
G187	1½d.	**dl red to pl red-pink** (14/1/27)	1·00	25
G188	1½d.	**golden-scar** ..	1·00	25
G189	1½d.	**dl rose-red** ..	1·00	25
G190	1½d.	**dp rose-red** ..	1·00	25
G191	1½d.	**reddish-brown** (16/9/30) ..	3·00	1·00
G192	2d.	**chocolate-brown**	4·00	1·50
G193	2d.	**golden-scarlet** (2/8/30) (**Die II**)	3·00	25
G194	2d.	**golden-scarlet** (9/9/30) (**Die III**) ..	2·50	25
		a no wmk. ..	4·00	1·00
		b wmk. inverted ..	£22	—
		c tete beche pair	£22000	—
G195	3d.	**dullish ult** (26/1/28) (**Die II**) ..	£14	1·00
		a wmk. inverted ..	£300	£150
G196	3d.	**deep ultramarine** (28/9/29) (**Die III**) ..	£12	1·00
		a wmk. inverted ..	—	£200
G197	4d.	**yel-olive** (−/4/29)	£12	1·00
		a wmk. inverted ..	—	£300
G198	4½d.	**violet** (−/11/28)	£25	2·00
		a Die II ..	£1000	£28
G199	5d.	**pl brown** (4/8/30)	£10	1·00
G200	1/4	**pl tur** (−/9/32) ..	£55	6·00
		a wmk. inverted ..	—	£400
G182/200		**basic series (11)**	£125	£14

G182 Produced by J. Ash during December 1927 but not released until almost a year later.

G183–G186 All the A. J. Mullett printings of the 1d. are of a deep sage-green shade, whilst the J. Ash are mainly yellow-green in colour.

G186 The "Second Die" on the 1d. shows the variation described and illustrated after G120.

G187/189/190 The A. J. Mullett printings of the 1½d. vary greatly in shade.

G188 The 1½d. Perf. 13½ x 12½ Comb first appeared in Booklets during October 1928 and was subsequently released in sheet form. See note re G176.

G193/4 Die III represents a re-engraving of Die II; with the following main differences. (See note re G176.

Die II	**Die III**
22 x 25½ mm	21¾ x 25 mm
Numerals thin and uneven. Words of value uneven.	Numerals thick and even. Words of value even.

G194a Only two sheets are thought to exist, the first having been sold at Brunswick, Victoria, July 1931.

G194c Booklet sheets were printed early in 1931 by Ash from a plate specially laid down. Only one pair of this variety is known, bought at Malvern P.O.: the top left pair of a normal sheet of stamps

*C

had been damaged, and the printers substituted this tete beche pair to complete the sheet by gumming strips to hold it in place.

G195–196 Die II   Die III

Figures of value thin and uneven. Words of value uneven.

Figures thick and even. Words thicker and even.

G198*a* A second Die was produced but not issued, The stamps employed in the 1930 provisional issue were from this second Die. Copies exist C.T.O. as well as mint. See G215*a*.

1931 (Oct. 2nd)-1936 The Seventh (*typo*) **Georgian Issue. Printed by John Ash on medium white wove paper,· having the Third Mult. (C of A) wmk. Perf. 13½ x 12½ comb. Sheets as before.**

G201	½d.	**orange** (11/7/32)	2·00	50
G202	1d.	**green** (2/10/31)	1·00	25
		a wmk. inverted	6·00	4·00
		b wmk. reversed	£60	£40
		c wmk. inverted and reversed	£70	£50
G203	1½d.	**red-brn** (–/10/36)	2·50	1·00
G204	2d.	**golden-scarlet** (18/12/31)	1·50	25
		a wmk. inverted (from booklets)	3·00	1·00
G205	3d.	**ult** (–/9/32)	£12	1·00
		a wmk. inverted	£150	£120
G206	4d.	**yellowish-olive** (–/2/33)	£12	1·00
		a wmk. inverted	—	£250
G207	5d.	**or-brn** (25/2/32)	£12	1·00
		a wmk. inverted	—	£150
G208	1/4	**tur** (18/8/32)	£55	6·00
		a wmk. inverted	—	£300
G201/8		**complete set** (8v)	£90	9·00

We understand that the reversed wmk. variations only occur on the 1d. value and are very scarce.

Forgeries of G204 without wmk and Perf. 11 were made to defraud the Post Office and were used on covers postmarked on or about March 24th, 1932.

1927 (May 9th) Opening of the Federal Parliament House, Canberra. Designed by R. A. Harrison of Elwood, Victoria. Dies engraved by Waterlow and Sons, London. Printed by J. Ash from plates made by A. J. Mullett. Perf. 11. No wmk. Sheets 10 x 8.

G209	1½d.	**brown-lake**	50	30
		a imperf. between pair	£1650	—

Three sheets are known to have been issued, each with one horizontal line of perforation missing.

Number Issued—32,213,680

1929 (May 20th) First Airmail issue. Engraved and (*recess*) **printed by John Ash on unwmk'd. paper. Perf. 11 line. The East–West airmail service came into operation on July 2nd 1929. After 1930 this issue was used on ordinary as well as airmail posts. Sheets 10 x 8.**

G210	3d.	**yel to dp grn**	5·00	3·50

Although the bulk of this issue was produced in ordinary sheets, a special plate was manufactured to facilitate the binding of panes into booklets. The stamps produced from this booklet plate may be distinguished by a small guide dot to be found midway between each stamp above the "R" of Australia. In many instances, however, the guide dot is absent, having been removed by the perforating process.

1929 (Sept. 28th) Centenary of the State of Western Australia. Designed by Pitt Morrison and (*recess*) **printed by John Ash. White wove unwmk'd. paper. Perf. 11 (L). Sheets 10 x 8.**

G211	1½d.	**carmine-red**	70	40
		a major re-entry	£30	£20

The colour used in the production of G211 was officially described as deep vermilion.

G211*a* is a clear transfer roller shift showing a marked doubling of the "TR" in Australia and around the curve in the swan's neck.

Printed from twelve plates numbered 1 to 12, 21,281,040 copies produced, less 12,000 copies punctured "OS" and handed to members of Parliament.

1930 (June 2nd) Centenary of the exploration of the River Murray by Captain Charles Sturt. Printed by John Ash on white wove unwmk'd paper. Perf. 11 (L). Sheets 10 x 8.

G212	1½d.	**scarlet**	60	30
G213	3d.	**blue**	4·00	3·00

The colours were officially described as deep vermilion and oriental blue.

The 1½d. was printed from eight plates numbered 1 to 8, total number issued 20,366,400 less 12,000 copies punctured "OS", whilst the 3d. value was printed from two plates numbered 1 and 2, the total number issued being 2,052,000 less 9,000 copies punctured "OS".

G212 exists with manuscript surcharge "2d. Paid. P.M., L.H.I.". See under Lord Howe Island.

1930 (July 31st) Provisional surcharges on the Georgian definitives. Overprinted by John Ash. Second Mult. Wmk. paper. Perf. 13½ x 12½ (C).

G214	2d. on 1½d.	**golden-scar**	50	30
		a dull scarlet	—	—
G215	5d. on 4½d.	**violet** ..	3·00	2·50
		a surcharge omitted	—	—

G214 exists with manuscript surcharge "2d. Paid. P.M., L.H.I." See under Lord Howe Island.

G214a Overprinted in error on stamps produced by A. J. Mullet and very scarce.

G215a The basic stamp used for the Surcharge overprinting was from a die not employed for the normal production of the unoverprinted stamp, although a number of unoverprinted examples are known. See G198a.

Number Surcharged—2d. on 1½d., 18,000,000; 5d. on 4½d., 480,000.

1931 (March 19th) Commemorative series to honour the pioneer flights of Captain (and later Air-Commodore) Sir Charles Kingsford-Smith. The design includes a representation of Kingsford-Smith's aeroplane, the Southern Cross. On unwmk'd. white wove paper. Perf. 11 (L). (Recess) **printed by John Ash. Inscribed "Postage – Postage" (2d. and 3d.) or "Air Mail – Service" at the sides (6d.). Sheets 10 x 8.**

G216	2d.	**red**	50	30
G217	3d.	**blue**	4·00	3·00
G218	6d.	**violet**	8·00	7·00
		a re-entry, ST, FO and LD in centre strongly doubled (No. 65 on sheet) ..	£40	£35
G216/8		**set** (3)	£12	£10

The 2d. was produced from eight plates numbered 1 to 8, the 3d. from three plates numbered 1 to 3 and the 6d. from a single unnumbered plate.

Numbers Issued—2d., 20,298,000; 3d., 2,180,000; 6d., 503,200.

Less 7,000 and 5,000 of the 2d. and 3d. respectively overprinted "O.S".

1931 (Nov. 4th) The Kingsford-Smith commemorative design adapted for general use as an air-mail stamp. (Recess) **printed by John Ash on white wove unwmk'd. paper. Perf.11 (L). Sheets 5 x 8.**

G219	6d.	**dl sepia brown** ..	£12	9·00
G220	6d.	**dark grey-brown** (1934)	£12	9·00

Printed from a single unnumbered plate.

1932 (March 14th) Special issue to mark the opening of the Sydney Harbour Bridge, Sydney. New South Wales. Sheets 2d. and 3d., 10 x 8; 5/–, 80 – four panes, each 5 x 4.

(i) (Recess) **printed by John Ash on unwmk'd. paper. Perf. 11 (L).**

G221	2d.	**red**	1·00	60
G222	3d.	**blue (br to dp)** ..	4·00	3·50
G223	5/–	**dark green** ..	£650	£330

The 2d. was produced from four plates, unnumbered but distinguishable by marginal markings, the 3d. was printed from four plates numbered 1 to 4 whilst the 5/– was printed from a single plate.

Numbers Issued—2d., 9,749,680; 3d., 3,128,800; 5/–, 72,800.

(ii) (Typo) **by John Ash on paper having the third (C of A) mult. wmk. Perf. 10½ x 11 (C). Sheets 88 – two panes, each 11 x 4.**

G224	2d.	**golden-scarlet** ..	1·00	50

Number Issued—27,280,616.

Forgeries of G.224 without wmk. and perf. 11 were made to defraud the Post Office. These forgeries were never used, but a few cancelled copies are known.

1932 (June 1st) (Typo) **Kookaburra definitive. The third mult. (C of A over Crown) wmk.**

Perf. 13½ x 12½. Sheets 120 – two panes, each 6 x 10.

G225 6d. **red-brown**.. .. £12 30
    a wmk. inverted .. — £140

1934 (July 2nd) Centenary of the State of Victoria. Design, an aborigine of the now extinct Yarra Yarra tribe looking across the River Yarra towards modern Melbourne. (*Recess*) printed by John Ash on Cowan or Wiggins Teape paper having the third mult. C of A over Crown) wmk. Sheets 80 – two panes, each 4 x 10.

(i) Perf. 10½ (C). (2/7/34).

G226 2d. **dull orange** .. 70 30
G227 3d. **blue** .. .. .. 4·00 3·00
G228 1/– **black** £35 £15
G226/8 **set (3)** .. .. £38 £17·50

(ii) Perf. 11½ (C). (6/8/34).

G229 2d. **dull orange** .. 80 30
G230 3d. **blue** .. .. .. 4·50 3·50
G231 1/– **black** £38 £15
G229/231 **set (3)** £42 £18

Numbers Issued—2d., (i) 70,000,000; (ii) 45,000,000; 3d., (i) 5,000,000; (ii) 1,000,000; 1/–, (i) 2,000,000; (ii) 1,500,000.

1934 (Nov. 1st) Centenary of the death of Captain John Macarthur, the first man to bring Merino sheep to Australia and founder of the Australian wool industry. Dies engraved and (*recess*) printed by John Ash. On white wove paper with the mult. (C of A over Crown) wmk. Perf. 11½ (C). Sheets 80 – two panes, each 4 x 10.

(i) Die I.

G232 2d. **carmine-lake** .. 1·50 50
G233 3d. **deep blue** .. .. 6·00 4·50
G234 9d. **violet** £30 £14
G232/4 **set (3)** .. .. £35 £17·50

(ii) Die II.

G235 2d. **car-lk** (26/11/34) £17 1·00

Die II was a reworked version of Die I. There are many differences, the most noticeable being the darker shading on the hillside in Die II.

Numbers Issued—2d. (both), 57,432,000; 3d. 2,896,000; 9d., 1,216,000.

1934 (Dec. 1st)-1948 Design, Hermes between the two hemispheres. Originally intended for the combined postage and air fee rate to Great Britain.

(i) (*Recess*) printed by John Ash on unwmk'd., chalk-surfaced paper. Perf. 11 (L). Sheets 80 – two panes, each 4 x 10.

G236 1/6 **purple** (1/12/34).. £25 1·50

(ii) (*Recess*) printed by John Ash or W. C. G. McCracken on chalk-surfaced paper having the third mult (C of A over Crown) wmk. Sheets 80 – two panes, each 8 x 5.

G237 (Ex 14) 1/6 **brn'sh-claret**
    (22/10/37) 6·00 1·30
(Ex *14a*) *a* **dl purple**
    (1946) 6·00 1·00

(iii) As (ii) above but on uncoated paper.

G238 (Ex *14b*) 1/6 **dull purple**
    (–/2/48) 6·00 1·00

Imperf. copies of G237 were not officially issued.

1935 (March 18th) A.N.Z.A.C. Commemoration and 25th Anniversary of the Gallipoli landings. Design, the Cenotaph, Whitehall, London. Dies engraved and (*recess*) printed by John Ash. On white wove paper (2d.) or white wove chalky paper (1/–) with the mult. (C of A over Crown) wmk. Perf. 13½ x 12½ (C). (2d.) or 11 (L) (1/–).Sheets, 2d 96 – two panes, each 6 x 8; 1/– 120 – two panes, each 6 x 10.

G239 2d. **scarlet** 60 30
G240 1/– **greyish-black** .. £40 £18

The sheets of the 1/– value were usually divided vertically and as a result complete imprint blocks are scarce.

Numbers Printed—2d., 47,814,240; 1/–, 996,600.

1935 (May 2nd) Silver Jubilee. (*Recess*)

printed by John Ash on chalk-surfaced paper having the third (C of A) mult. wmk. sideways. Perf. 11½ (C). Sheets 80 – two panes, each 10 x 4.

G241	2d.	dull carmine to carmine	60	30
		a br scarlet	—	—
G242	3d.	dark blue	5·00	3·00
		a pl br blue	—	—
G243	2/–	purple	£32	£22
G241/3		set	£35	£24

Many retouches are to be found on all values of this series, especially the 2d. and 3d. denominations.

G241a and G242a represent the very first printings of the 2d. and 3d. values. Both are in distinctive bright shades and are very scarce. The bright shades were considered unsatisfactory, hence the change to the darker colours.

G243 The colour of the value was officially described as "royal purple". The colour remained uniform throughout the printing and consequently the first experimental sheets cannot be distinguished from the rest of the printing.

Numbers Issued—2d. from six plates numbered 1–6 96,044,000; 3d., 2,879,920; 2/–, 499,920 each from a single numbered plate.

1936 (April 1st) Opening of submarine cable to Tasmania. (Recess) John Ash. Wmk. Mult. C of A. Perf. 11½ (C). Sheets 80 – two panes, each 4 x 10.

G244	2d.	scarlet (Die I)	50	30
		a (Die II)	50	30
G245	3d.	blue	4·00	3·00

Die I has a short line joining the inner and outer frame lines at left of the inscription tablet. Die II has no such line.

Numbers Issued—G244/244a, 89,116,000; G245, 3,902,000.

1936 (Aug. 3rd) Centenary of South Australia. (Recess) John Ash. Wmk. Mult. C of A. Perf. 11½. Sheets 80 – two panes, each 4 x 10.

G246	2d.	carmine	50	30
G247	3d.	blue	4·00	3·00
G248	1/–	green	£16	8·00
G246/8		set (3)	£19	£10

Numbers Issued—G246, 78,088,000; G247 5,448,000; G248, 2,888 000.

All stamps hereafter were printed (recess) at the Australian Note and Stamp Printing Works, Melbourne, on Third Multiple (C of A) wmk. paper, unless otherwise mentioned.

1937-45 Designs. Portraits of King and Queen 1d. to 3d. and 1/4); Australian Fauna (Other Values). Perf. 13½ x 14 (C). Wmk. sideways (5d. and 9d.), upright (Other Values). Designs, 5d., 9d., H. Sheets 160–two panes, each 8 x 10 or 10 x 8.

1	½d.	orange (Kangaroo) (3/10/38)	40	20
2	1d.	emerald-green (Queen) (10/5/37)	30	20
3	1½d.	lake-brown (King) (20/4/38)	2·50	1·00
4	2d.	scarlet (King) (10/5/37)	30	20
		a pale scarlet (/38)	40	20
5	3d.	dp blue (ch) (Die 1, 1st printing) (2/8/37)	£50	£30
		a dull blue (ch) (Die 1, 2nd printing (2/8/37)	£12	2·00
6	3d.	dull blue (ch) (Die 1a) (/38)	£20	2·00
7	3d.	dull blue (ch) (Die 1b) (3/38)	£12	·002
		a blue (Die 1b) (uncoated) (21/12/38)	£12	1·00
8	4d.	green (Koala) (1/2/38)	2·00	40
9	5d.	dull pur (Ram) (1/12/38)	2·80	50
10	6d.	reddish-brown (Kookaburra) (2/8/37)	2·80	50
11	9d.	sepia-brn (Platypus) (1/9/38)	2·80	50
12	1/–	dull green (Lyre Bird) (2/8/37)	£12·50	1·00
13	1/4	mag (King) (31/10/38)	1·30	80
		a rose-magenta (/45)	1·30	80
1/13		set (12)	£35	4·00

No. 5 has letters TA (at right) well joined at base. The wattles and King's face have a whitish appearance, lacking much of the detail to be found in subsequent printings. The stamps are of a relatively deep blue shade, quite distinct from the paler chalky blue of later printings. Nos. 5 and 5a exist in the same sheet of early printings and is the effect of ink stripping during the printing run.

No. 5a normally shows more detail on wattles and King's face, and the joining of letters TA is not so pronounced. The shade is pale chalky blue, but as the same plates were used for the printings of Nos. 5 and 5a only the shades are invariably different.

No. 6 is as No. 5a but the letters TA have been clearly separated by the individual retouching of each stamp on the plate.

No. 7 is as No. 6 but a firm line has been added around the King's chin. No. 7a is as No. 7, but is printed on thinner paper, and the shade is of a deeper blue.

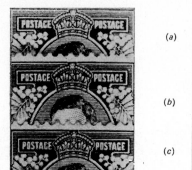

(a)

(b)

(c)

Imperf. copies of Nos. 8, 10, 11 and 12 were not officially issued.

1937-48 Designs, 1/6 (Hermes and Globes); Other Values (King and Queen in State Robes). Perf. 13¾ x 13¼ (C). (*Wmk. sideways 5/– and 10/–; wmk. upright other values*). **Sheets 80–two panes, each 10 x 4 or 4 x 10.**

14		1/6 (See G237–238)		
14a				
14b				
15	5/–	**red-claret** (*ch*) (1/4/38)	9·00	1·50
		a uncoated tinted paper (12/47)	£10	2·00
		b uncoated white paper (6/48)	£10	2·00
16	10/–	**dull purple** (*ch*) (1/4/38)	£30	£12
		a uncoated paper (11/48)	£32	£15
17	£1	**bluish-slate** (*ch*) (1/11/38)	£60	£18
		a uncoated paper (/48)	£100	£50
15/17		**set** (3) ..	£95	£30

Specimen overprint—10/– at £25, £1 at £320.

Though Nos. 7a, 15b, 16a, 17a have been described as being of thin paper, they are actually similar in this respect to other Australian stamps not on chalk-coated paper. The difference arises from the latter being thicker than normal.

> Care should be exercised in purchasing imperforate or tete beche varieties issued between 1942–1950, some of which were unofficial leakages.

1938-51 As No. 1, etc., but Perf. 14¾ x 14 (C) (*Nos. 19 to 24 have solid background, similar to No. 3*).

18	½d.	**orange** (28/1/42) ..	15	10
		a coil pair, varied perf ..	4·00	3·00
		b no watermark (9/9/49)	20	10
		c retouch (2/51) ..	4·00	3·00
		d coil pair, varied perf. (no wmk) ..	1·50	1·00
		e retouch (/51) ..	5·00	4·00
19	1d.	**emerald-grn** (11/7/38)	30	15
		a thin paper (11/38) ..	5·00	1·50
20	1d.	**pur-brn** (10/12/41) ..	30	15
		a coil pair, varied perf. .	4·00	4·00
21	1½d.	**lake-brown** (11/41) .	2·00	2·00
22	1½d.	**emerald-grn** (10/12/41)	30	15
23	2d.	**scarlet** (11/7/38) ..	30	15
		a wmk. inverted ..	60	30
		aa booklet pane of six	3·00	2·00
		b medallion flaw ..	£20	£10
		c thin paper (/39) ..	3·00	2·00
		c booklet pane of six .	£20	£10
		d coil pair, varied perf.	£180	£120
24	2d.	**pur-mauve** (10/12/41)	20	15
		a medallion flaw ..	6·00	4·00
		b coil pair, varied perf.	6·00	5·00
		c ditto (wmk inverted)	£40	£30
25	3d.	**blue** (Die 2) (11/40)	£12	50
26	3d.	**pur-brn** (10/12/41) ..	20	15
		a thin paper ..	3·00	1·00
27	4d.	**green** (10/42) ..	50	20
28	5d.	**dull purple** (12/45) ..	80	20
29	6d.	**reddish-brown** (6/42)	60	15
		a red-chocolate (/44) .	1·00	25
		b greyish-brown (/51)	50	15
30	9d.	**sepia-brown** (/42) ..	80	20
		a thin paper ..	2·00	1·00
31	1/–	**dull green** (3/41) ..	70	20
		a wmk. inverted ..	—	—
18/31		**set** (15) ..	£17	3·50

For note on coil perf. varieties see after 55.

18c/e The sky just above hill (normally unshaded) has been clearly lined in No. 6/8, right pane.

23b/24a A flaw obliterates the medallion which is normally below the end medal at left, on the King's right breast (No. 2/5 right pane).

25 Notable differences between this die and the one in use previously (*for Nos. 5—7a*) is that more of epaulette on the left shoulder shows and the King's left eyebrow is shaded from left to right (*downwards*) instead of the reverse as previously.

26 The "AUSTRALIA" panel is noticeably paler on No. 8/15 (*ex* sheets originally made up for booklets).

1941 (Dec. 10th) Nos. 23, 25 and 9 surcharged in violet (2½d. and 5½d.) and yellow on black (3½d.).

32	2½d./2d. **scarlet**	.. ..	30	20
	a	medallion flaw ..	£50	£25
	b	surcharge omitted		
		in pair with		
		normal ..	£1000	—
33	3½d./3d. **blue** ..	.. ..	40	30
34	5½d./5d. **dull purple**		2·00	1·80
32/34		**set** (3)	2·50	2·00

32a See after 31.

32b Two copies of this error are known.

Number surcharged—2½d., 32,366,400; 3½d., 2,946,080; 5½d., 3,820,500.

1942-51 Designs, King and Queen's Portraits and Emu (5½d.), framed by designs incorporating Australian Flora and Fauna. Perf. 14¾ x 14 (C).

35	1d. **plum** (Queen) (1/1/43)		20	15
	a	coil pair, varied perf.	3·50	3·00
	b	dp plum (/47)	40	15
36	1½d. **grn** (as No. 35) (1/12/42)		20	15
	a	deep green (/47) ..	40	15
	b	ditto no wmk. (8/8/49)	20	15
37	2d. **mauve-purple** (King)			
		(4/12/44)	20	15
	a	coil pair, varied perf.	£40	£30
	aa	ditto no wmk. ..	3·50	2·50
	b	bt mauve-purple (/47)	20	15
	c	no wmk. (12/48) ..	20	15
	d	coil pair, varied perf.		
		(no wmk.) ..	3·50	2·50
38	2½d. **scarlet** (King) (7/1/42)		20	10
	a	wmk. inverted ..	40	30
	aa	booklet pane of six .	4·00	3·00
	b	imperf. strip ..	£500	—
	c	right side imperf		
		vertically ..	£100	—
39	3½d. **blue** King (3/42) ..		20	15
	a	dp violet-blue (8/51)	1·00	40
	b	thin paper (/51) ..	2·00	1·00
40	5½d. **slate** (Emu) (2/42) ..		50	15
	a	bluish-slate (/47) ..	30	15
35/40		**set** (8)	1·20	60

38b A quarter sheet (*top right*) bought at St. Kilda P.O. had the end and vertical strip of five imperf.

For coil perf. varieties see note after 55.

1946-47 Design, Kangaroo with Map Background (*re-engraved*). **Perf. 11¾ (C).** *Typo.*

41	2/– (see G82–83)	3·50	1·00

1947-48 Design, Portrait of Queen Elizabeth II. Perf. 14 x 14¾ (C). Wmk. sideways. Sheets 160—two panes, 10 x 8.

43	1d. **dull purple** (20/11/47)		15	10
	a	dp dull purple (/48)	15	10
	b	dark purple (no wmk)		
		(8/48)	15	10
	c	coil pair, varied perf.	3·00	2·00

Imperf. varieties of No. 43 were not officially issued. See also note after 55.

1948-52 Designs, Portraits of Royal Family 1½d., 2d., 2½d., 3d. and 7½d.); 8½d. Aborigine; 1/3 Bull; 1/6 Hermes and Globe; 2/- Aboriginal Art. Perf. 14¾ x 14 (C) (1½d. to 8½d.). Perf. 14½ x 14¾ (C) (Other Values).

44	1½d. **dp green** (no wmk.)			
		(Queen) (19/6/50) ..	20	10
46	2d. **yel-green** (as No. 44)			
		(no wmk.) (28/3/51)	20	10
	a	varied perf. vert. pair	3·00	2·00
	b	green (1956) ..	20	10
47	2½d. **scarlet** (King) (12/4/50)		20	10
48	2½d. **pur-brown** (as No. 47)			
		(no wmk.) (23/5/51)	20	15
49	3d. **scarlet** (as No. 47)			
		(28/2/51)	20	15
	a	coil pair, varied perf.		
		(5/51)	6·00	5·00
	b	thin paper	5·00	2·00
	c	weak entry ..	4·00	3·00
	d	strip of three ex book-		
		let printing with		
		margin each side		
		(vertical strip) ..	3·00	2·00
50	3d. **myrtle-grn** (as No. 47)			
		(no wmk.) (14/11/51)	25	15
	a	coil pair, varied perf.	£12	£10
51	7½d. **blue** (King) (31/10/51)	40	30
	a	thin paper	4·00	2·00

b imperf three sides vert,
pair .. .. £500 —
52 8½d. **brown** (Aborigine)
(14/8/50) 40 30
53 1/3 **purple-brown** (Bull)
(16/2/48) .. .. 1·00 30
a dp pur-brown (/52) 1·00 30
54 1/6 **sepia-black** (Hermes)
(1/9/49) .. .. 1·20 20
a black .. .. 1·50 30
55 2/– **dp choc** (Crocodile)
(16/2/48) .. .. 1·50 30
a blk-brn (thin paper)
(/51) .. .. 5·00 2·00
43/55 **set (13)** .. .. 5·00 1·60

The horizontal perforation of these stamps for
coils consist of larger holes in the centre, with
smaller at each side. This is said to facilitate the
separation of the stamps. Nos. 18d, 37a, 43c were
released, also in sheet form. No. 46a was issued
only in sheet form.

**1949-51 Design, Commonwealth Coat of
Arms. Perf. 14¼ x 13¾ (C). Sheets 8 x 10.**

59 5/– **red-claret** (11/4/49) 7·00 30
a thin paper (/51) .. £14 2·00
60 10/– **pur-violet** (3/10/49) . £20 1·00
a thin paper .. .. £30 3·00
61 £1 **dp blue** (28/11/49) .. £40 2·50
a thin paper .. .. £50 4·00
62 £2 **reseda-grn** (16/1/50) £175 £12
a roller flaw .. £200 £40
b thin paper £175 £15
59/62 **set (4)** £240 £14
SP60/62 **specimen set** (3) .. £180 ‡

62a The flaw appears on Row 5/1 and Row 6/1
as a smudge under E.

**1951-52 Designs, King's Head. Perf. 14¾ x 14
(C) No. 67, wmk. sideways. Perf. 14¾ x 14½
(C).**

63 3½d. **pur-brown** (28/11/51) 15 10
a booklet pane of six .. 3·00 2·00
b booklet pane, imperf.
between (vert.) £1000 —
64 4½d. **scarlet** (20/2/52) .. 30 25
65 6½d. **dp brown** (20/2/52).. 30 25
a re-entry .. .. 3·00 2·00
66 6½d. **emerald-grn** (9/4/52) 30 15
a re-entry .. .. 3·00 2·00
67 1/0½ **slate-black** (19/3/52) 1·00 30
63/67 **set (5)** .. .. .. 1·80 80

63b was found in Wollongong Post Office.

65a—66a Re-entries occur—

Row 1/No. 7 left vertical frame re-cut.
Row 2/No. 8 right lower frame lines doubled.
Row 10/No. 4 All letters of Australia re-
entered or doubled. Also left
and right corner frame lines
doubled.

SPECIAL ISSUES

**1937 (Oct. 1st) 150th Anniversary of Founda-
tion of N.S.W. Design, Gov. Phillip and
Companions at Sydney Cove. Perf. 13¼ x 13¾
(C). Sheets 80—two panes, each 8 x 5.**

S1 2d. **scarlet** 60 20
a tail variety £120 £45
S2 3d. **blue** .. .. .. 3·50 2·50
S3 9d. **dull purple** £17 £10
S1/3 **set (3)** £20 £12

S1a A short curved line extending from the right
figure has the appearance of a tail (No. 7/1)
(left pane).

Number issued—
2d., 71,668,000; 3d., 2,454,000; 9d., 512,000.

**1940 (July 15th) War Effort. Design from
drawing by Virgil Reilly. Perf. 13¾ x 13¼ (C).
Sheets 80—two panes, each 8 x 5.**

S4 1d. **green** 60 20
a rifle flaw .. .. £15 6·00

S5	2d. **scarlet**	..	..	..	60	20
S6	3d. **blue**	..	..	..	3·50	2·50
S7	6d. **brownish-purple**		..		£17	£10
S5/7	**set** (3)	..	..	..	£20	£12

S4a A flaw on the butt of the soldier's rifle appears on No. 2/2.

Number issued—
1d., 61,244,000; 2d., 85,782,800; 3d., 3,078,240; 6d., 1,808,400.

1945 (Feb. 19th) Swearing-in of Governor-General Duke of Gloucester. Perf. 14¾ x 14½ (C). Sheets 60—two panes, each 5 x 6.

S8	2½d. **carmine-lake**	..	15	10
S9	3½d. **dp ultramarine**	..	25	25
S10	5½d. **dp slate-blue**	..	45	40
S8/10	**set** (3) ..	..	80	70

Number issued—
2½d., 88,290,000; 3½d., 4,048,320; 5½d., 5,886,900.

1946 (Feb. 18th) Peace. Perf. 14½ x 14¾ (C). Design, 5½d., V. Sheets 6 x 5 or 5 x 6.

S11	2½d. **carmine-red**	..	15	10
S12	3½d. **grey-blue**	..	25	25
S13	5½d. **dp emerald-green**	..	45	40
S11/13	**set** (3) ..		80	70

Number issued—
2½d., 93,585,500; 3½d., 5,448,600; 5½d., 7,840,500.

Copies exist of No. S11 without watermark, but they were never issued thus.

1946 (Oct. 14th) Centenary of Discovery of Pastoral Lands in Central Queensland. Design Portrait of Sir T. Mitchell. Perf. 14¾ x 14½ (C). Sheets 60—two panes, each 5 x 6.

S14	2½d. **carmine-red** ..	..	15	10
S15	3½d. **blue**	..	..	25	25

S16	1/– **grey-green**	..	..	60	50
S14/16	**set** (3)..	..	..	90	75

Number issued—
2½d., 104,492,160; 3½d., 4,640,940; 1/–, 9,401,160.

1947 (Sept. 8th) 150th Anniversary of Foundation of Newcastle, N.S.W. Designs, 2½d. (Portrait of Lt. John Shortland); 3½d. (Steel Foundry); 5½d. (Coal Cranes). Perf. 14¾ x 14 (C) (2½d.) and Perf. 14½ x 14¾ (C). (Other Values). (S18–S19 surfaced paper). Design, 5½d., H. Sheets, 2½d., 160—two panes, each 8 x 10; others, 60—two panes, each 6 x 5.

S17	2½d. **carmine-lake**	..	15	10
S18	3½d. **blue**	..	..	25	25
S19	5½d. **green** ..	..	45	40
S17/19	**set** (3) ..	..	80	70

The portrait on No. S17 is that of the father of the actual discoverer of the Hunter River whom it was intended to portray.

Number issued—
2½d. 105,840,000; 3½d. 4,531,500; 5½d. 7,516,380.

Imperf. copies of No. S17 were not officially issued. Also shades of dull blue S18.

1948 (July 12th) William J. Farrer. (An Englishman who, in Australia, greatly improved wheat breeds). Perf. 14¾ x 14 (C). Sheets 160—two panes, each 8 x 10.

S20	2½d. **scarlet**	..	..	15	10

Number issued—74,168,000.

1948 (Sept. 13th) Sir F. von Mueller (Botanist

and Explorer). Perf. 14¾ x 14 (C). Sheets 160—
two panes, each 8 x 10.
S21 2½d. lake-carmine   ..   15   10

      Number issued—73,754,880.

1948 (Nov.15th) Pan-Pacific Scout Jamboree
Perf. 14 x 14¾ (C). Wmk. sideways. Sheets
160—two panes, each 10 x 8.
S22 2½d. lake-carmine   ..   15   10

      Number issued—90,307,200.

1949 (June 17th) Anniversary of Birth of
Henry Lawson (Poet and Author). Perf. 14¾ x
14 (C). No wmk. Sheets 160—two panes, each
8 x 10.
S23 2½d. dp lake-maroon   ..   15   10
     Number issued—109,252,000.

1949 (Oct. 10th) U.P.U. Design, Mounted
Postman. No wmk. Perf. 14¾ x 14 (C). Sheets
6 x 14.
S24 3½d. bright ultramarine .   20   20
      Number issued—5,084,688.

1949 (Nov. 28th) Lord Forrest of Bunbury
(Explorer and Politician). Design, Portrait of
Forrest. Perf. 14¾ x 14 (C). Sheets 160—two
panes, each 8 x 10.
S25 2½d. lake-carmine   ..   15   10
      Number issued—90,602,880.

1950 (Sept. 27th) Dual Centenary of Postage
Stamps for N.S.W. and Victoria. Designs,
Adaptations of Original Stamps (se tenant).
No wmk. Perf. 14¾ x 14 (C). Sheets 160—two
panes, each 8 x 10.
S26 2½d. maroon (N.S.W.) ..   15   10
S27 2½d. maroon (Victoria) ..   15   10
     a both values se tenant
       pair   50   40
    Number issued—47,040,000 each value.

1951 (May 1st) Golden Jubilee of Common-
wealth of Australia. Designs, 3d. (se tenant)
Portraits of Sir Henry Parkes and Sir Edmund
Barton; 5½d., Opening First Parliament by
Duke of York (later KG 5th); 1/6, Parliament
House, Canberra. No wmk. Perf. 14¾ x 14 (C).
Sheets, 3d., 160—two panes, each 8 x 10;
others 6 x 14.
S28   3d. lake-carmine (Barton)   15   10
S29   3d. lake-carmine (Parkes)   15   10
     a both values se tenant
       pair   50   40
S30 5½d. dark blue   50   50
S31   1/6 red-brown   ..   ..   1·00   80
S28/31   set (4)..   ..   ..   1·80   1·40
    Number issued—3d. (each), 52,709,920; 5½d.,
2,137,716; 1/5, 6,351,576.

1951 (July 2nd) Gold Centenary and Victoria
Government Centenary. Designs (se tenant),
Portrait of Ed. H. Hargraves (closely associated
with the event) and Chas. J. Latrobe, First
Gov. of Victoria. No wmk. Perf. 14¾ x 14 (C).
Sheets 160—two panes, each 8 x 10.
S32 3d. lake-maroon (Hargraves)   15   10
S33 3d. lake-maroon (Latrobe)   15   10
     a both values se tenant
       pair   50   40
    Number issued—32,023,360 (pairs).

POSTAGE DUE STAMPS

1902 (July)-04 Design similar to the New South Wales 1891 Postage Due series, but without N.S.W. at foot leaving a blank area below the value inscription. (*Typo*) by the Government Printing Office, Sydney, on Chalk-surfaced paper having an Imperial Crown over N.S.W.wmk. Almost all values can be found with wmk. inverted.

		(a) P.12		(b) P.12 x 11½		(c) P.11½		(d) P.11 x 11½		(e) P.11	
D1	½d. **em-grn**	1·00	75	1·00	75	1·00	75	*		*	
D2	½d. **dull green** (1904)	*		2·50	1·75	*		*		*	
D3	1d. **em-grn**	2·50	1·75	2·50	1·75	*		2·50	1·75	£30	£10
D4	2d. **em-grn**	3·00	2·00	3·00	2·00	*		3·00	2·00	*	
D5	3d. **em-grn**	4·50	3·00	4·50	3·00	*		*		*	
D6	4d. **em-grn**	*		5·00	3·00	*		*		*	
D7	6d. **em-grn**	8·00	4·00	8·00	4·00	*		*		*	
D8	6d. **dull green** (1904)	*		£10	5·00	*		*		*	
D9	8d. **em-grn**	*		£20	£15	*		*		*	
D10	8d. **dull green** (1904)	*		£30	£15	*		*		*	
D11	5/- **em-grn**	*		£65	£15	*		*		*	

*Denotes that a perforation variation is not known to exist.

D7   The 6d. value can be found with the old "NSW" inscription only partly removed, the "SW" being clearly present. Lesser traces of the same inscription can be found on other values.

1902 (Nov.)-04 New redrawn design. On paper having the Imperial Crown over NSW wmk. The dull green shades all appeared during 1904. Inverted wmks. are common.

		(a) P.12		(b) P.12 x 11½		(c) P.12 x 11	
D12	½d. **emerald-green**	*		*		1·75	50
D13	½d. **dull green**	*		*		1·75	75
D14	1d. **emerald-green**	*		*		2·00	1·00
D15	1d. **dull green**	*		*		*	
D16	2d. **emerald-green**	£30	£10	*		2·50	1·00
D17	2d. **dull green**	*		*		3·00	1·00
D18	3d. **emerald-green**	£40	£10	*		£15	8·00
D19	3d. **dull green**	*		*		4·00	2·00
D20	4d. **emerald-green**	*		*		6·00	2·00
D21	4d. **dull green**	*		*		6·00	2·00
D22	5d. **emerald-green**	*		2·50	2·00	7·50	2·00
D23	5d. **dull green**	*		*		8·00	2·00
D24	6d. **emerald-green**	*		*		9·00	2·50
D25	8d. **emerald-green**	*		*		£14	7·00
D26	10d. **emerald-green**	*		8·00	1·50	£15	7·00
D27	10d. **dull green**	*		*		£20	7·00
D28	1/- **emerald-green**	8·00	2·00	9·00	3·00	£15	7·00
D29	2/- **emerald-green**	£12	5·00	£15	5·00	£30	£10
D30	5/- **emerald-green**	*		*		£60	£15
D31	5/- **dull green**	*		*		£65	£15
D32	10/- **dull green**	*		*		*	
D33	20/- **dull green**	*		*		*	

		(d) P.11½ x 12		(e) P.11½		(f) 11½ x 11	
D12	½d. emerald-green	*		*		*	
D13	½d. dull green	*		*		*	
D14	1d. emerald-green	*		6·00	2·00	*	
D15	1d. dull green	*		*		*	
D16	2d. emerald-green	*		*		*	
D17	2d. dull green	*		*		*	
D18	3d. emerald-green	*		*		*	
D19	3d. dull green	*		*		*	
D20	4d. emerald-green	*		*		£10	1·75
D21	4d. dull green	*		*		*	
D22	5d. emerald-green	£25	£10	*		£15	2·00
D23	5d. dull green	*		*		*	
D24	6d. emerald-green	*		*		*	
D25	8d. emerald-green	*		*		£15	3·00
D26	10d. emerald-green	*		*		*	
D27	10d. dull green	*		*		*	
D28	1/– emerald-green	*		*		*	
D29	2/– emerald-green	*		*		£30	£10
D30	5/– emerald-green	*		*		*	
D31	5/– dull green	*		*		*	
D32	10/– dull green	*		*		*	
D33	20/– dull green	*		*		*	

		(g) P.11 x 12		(h) P.11 x 11½		(i) P.11	
D12	½d. emerald-green	£15	8·00	6·00	2·00	7·00	3·50
D13	½d. dull green	*		*		7·00	3·50
D14	1d. emerald-green	*		3·00	1·00	4·00	2·00
D15	1d. dull green	£20	£10	*		4·00	2·00
D16	2d. emerald-green	£20	£10	4·00	1·00	4·50	1·75
D17	2d. dull green	£20	£10	*		4·50	1·75
D18	3d. emerald-green	*		*		5·00	2·00
D19	3d. dull green	*		*		*	
D20	4d. emerald-green	*		8·00	3·00	7·00	3·00
D21	4d. dull green	*		*		7·00	3·00
D22	5d. emerald-green	*		*		£18	5·00
D23	5d. dull green	*		*		*	
D24	6d. emerald-green	*		*		£10	3·00
D25	8d. emerald-green	*		*		*	
D26	10d. emerald-green	*		*		*	
D27	10d. dull green	*		*		*	
D28	1/– emerald-green	*		*		£20	5·00
D29	2/– emerald-green	*		*		*	
D30	5/– emerald-green	*		*		£75	£12
D31	5/– dull green	*		*		*	
D32	10/– dull green	*		*		£500	£300
D33	20/– dull green	*		*		£900	£600

*Denotes that a perforation variation is not known to exist.

1906-08 Redrawn design as numbers D12-D33, but with Tudor Crown over single line A wmk.

		(a) P.12 x 11		(b) P.11½ x 11		(c) P.11 x 11½		(d) P.11	
D34	½d. dull green	1·50	25	1·50	25	*		*	
D35	1d. bright green	1·50	25	*		*		*	
D36	1d. dull green	1·50	25	1·50	25	*		£15	5·00
D37	2d. bright green	2·50	50	*		*		*	
D38	2d. dull green	2·50	50	2·50	50	2·50	50	*	
D39	3d. bright green	*		£12	5·00	*		*	
D40	3d. dull green	*		£15	7·00	*		*	
D41	4d. dull green	7·50	4·00	£15	8·00	*		£30	£10
D42	6d. bright green	*		£15	9·00	*		*	
D43	6d. dull green	*		£17	£10	*		*	

*Denotes that a perforation variation is not known to exist.

D37 The 2d. Green also exists in a bright aniline emerald-green shade and is scarce. Perf. 12 x 11 only.

1907 Provisional printing on paper from the Victorian Government. Wmk., (Tudor) Crown over double lined "A". The watermarks in this paper did not register at all well with the subjects on the plate and all values in the series may be found without watermark and also with marginal watermarks. Perf. 11½ x 11. Chalk-surfaced paper.

D44	½d.	emerald green	3·00	1·50
D45	1d.	emerald green	3·00	1·50
D46	2d.	emerald green	5·00	3·00
D47	4d.	emerald green	£15	8·00
D48	6d.	emerald green	£15	8·00

1908 (Aug.)-09 Redrawn High Values. On Chalk-surfaced paper having the Imperial Crown over NSW wmk. Various perforations.

D49	1/–	green (P. 11½x11)	£15	6·00
D50	2/–	green (P.11)	£200	£150
D51	5/–	green (P. 11½x 11)	£75	£20
D52	10/–	green (P.11)	£500	£300
D53	20/–	green (P. 11)	£1400	£700

The above issues (numbers D1 to D53) were issued in all States except Victoria, whilst the subsequent issues were used throughout the entire Australian Commonwealth.

1909 (July to Dec.) First general Commonwealth Postage Due series. Printed by J. B. Cooke, wmk. as the 1907 Provisional issue.
(i) Perf. 12 x 12½ (C).

D54	½d.	rose-carmine and yellow-green	1·00	1·00
D55	1d.	rose-carmine and yellow-green	2·00	1·00
D56	2d.	rose-carmine and yellow-green	3·00	2·00
D57	3d.	rose-carmine and yellow-green	4·00	2·00
D58	4d.	rose-carmine and yellow-green	3·00	1·50
D59	6d.	rose-carmine and yellow-green	4·00	2·00
D60	1/–	rose-carmine and yellow-green	6·00	2·00
D61	2/–	rose-carmine and yellow-green	£17	6·00
D62	5/–	rose-carmine and yellow-green	£30	8·00
D63	10/–	rose-carmine and yellow-green	£100	£50
D64	£1	rose-carmine and yellow-green	£200	£100
D54/64		complete set (11v)	—	—

(ii) Perf. 12½ (L).

D65	1d.	rose-carmine and yellow-green	3·00	1·00
D66	2d.	rose-carmine and yellow-green	3·00	1·00
D67	4d.	rose-carmine and yellow-green	5·00	2·00

(iii) Perf. 11.

D68	1d.	rose-carmine and yellow-green	£70	£60
D69	6d.	rose-carmine and yellow-green	£350	£250

1911 As the 1909 issue listed above but from retouched Dies and redrawn value tablets. Wmk. as before.
(i) Perf. 12½ x 12.

D70	1d.	rose-carmine and yel-green	2·00	50
D71	2d.	rose-carmine and yel-green	3·00	60

(ii) Perf. 12½.

D72	1d.	rose-carmine and yellow-green	3·00	1·00

With numbers D70 and D72 there is a break of between ¾mm. and 1mm. in the outer octagon framing the figure "1", whereas with the original Die there was no such break.

On the second Die of the 2d. the tip of the tail of the "2" is separate from the shaded curve. With the original Die the tip of "2" merges into the shading.

All subsequent 1d. and 2d. issues of this design were produced from the second Dies.

1912 (Dec.)-23 As the 1909 Series. Thinnish paper, white gum.
(i) Perf. 12½ (L).

D73	½d.	pl scar and pl pea grn (–/12/12)	3·00	2·00

(ii) Perf. 11 (L).

D74	½d.	rose-car and apple green (1914)	1·00	50
	a	wmk. sideways	1·00	50
D75	1d.	rose-carmine and apple-grn (1913)	60	30
	a	wmk. sideways	60	30

(iii) Perf. 14 (L).

D76	½d.	rose-carmine and apple grn (1916)	4·00	2·00
D77	1d.	rose-carmine and apple-grn (1915)	3·00	2·00
D78	2d.	rose-carmine and apple-grn (1915)	1·50	1·00
D79	3d.	rose-carmine and apple-grn (1916)	5·00	5·00
	a	wmk. sideways	£100	£75
D80	4d.	rose-carmine and apple-grn (1916)	7·00	7·00
	a	wmk. sideways	£80	£50
D81	1/–	pl scar and pl pea-green (1923)	3·00	2·00
D82	10/–	pl scar and pl pea-green (1921)	£100	£65
D83	£1	pl scar and pl pea-green (1921)	£200	£100

1918 (May) -21 As above, but different shades and printed by T. S. Harrison. Perf. 14 (L).

D84	½d.	rose and olive-grn	1·00	50
D85	1d.	rose and olive-grn	1·00	1·00
D86	2d.	rose and olive-grn	1·50	1·00
D87	4d.	rose and olive-grn (26/4/21)	2·50	2·00
	a	wmk. sideways	£100	£75

1921-30 As above but on paper having the third single Crown over A wmk. (*Typo*) by T. S. Harrison, A. J. Mullett and John Ash. The wmks. of this issue are often found badly misplaced.

(i) Perf. 14 (L).

D88	½d.	car and yel-grn ..	60	60
D89	1d.	car and yel-grn ..	60	30
D90	1½d.	car and yel-grn ..	5·00	4·00
D91	2d.	car and yel-grn ..	1·50	1·00
D92	3d.	car and yel-grn ..	2·00	1·50
D93	4d.	car and yel-grn ..	5·00	1·50
D94	6d.	car and yel-grn ..	5·00	2·00

(ii) Perf. 11 (L.).

D95	4d.	car and yel-grn ..	1·00	60

1932-37 As above but on paper having the third mult. (C of A) wmk. (*Typo*) by John Ash

(i) Perf. 14 (L) (1932).

D96	1d.	car and yel-grn ..	2·00	50
D97	2d.	car and yel-grn ..	2·00	50

(ii) Perf. 11 (L).

D98	½d.	car and yel-green (1934)	1·50	50
D99	1d.	car and yel-green (–/1/33) ..	60	20
D100	2d.	car and yel-green (–/3/33) ..	60	20
D101	3d.	car and yel-green (–/4/37) ..	£40	£28
D102	4d.	car and yel-green (1934)	2·00	1·00
D103	6d.	car and yel-green (–/8/36)	£150	£50
D104	1/-	car and yel-green (1934)	£10	3·50

1938 (June) Design, Value (*typo*) **with ornamental frame** (*recess*). **Perf. 14¾ x 14 (C). Centres carmine.**

PD1	½d.	yellow-green ..	40	20
PD2	1d.	yellow-green ..	40	20
PD3	2d.	yellow-green ..	40	20
PD4	3d.	yellow-green ..	1·00	80
PD5	4d.	yellow-green ..	70	40
PD6	6d.	yellow-green ..	3·00	2·00
PD7	1/-	yellow-green ..	8·00	2·00
PD1/7		set (7)	£13	5·00

The coloured portion of the centre of the D in the Pence Values differs in shape from the stamps they precede. The hyphen on the 1/- value contains three dots.

1946-8 As before, but with slight variations in designs. Centres carmine. (*See below for details*).

PD8	1d.	yel-green (3/47) ..	30	20
PD9	2d.	yel-green (3/47) ..	80	20
PD10	3d.	yel-green (4/47) ..	80	20
PD12	5d.	yel-green (2/12/48)	1·00	50
PD13	6d.	yel-green (6/47) ..	1·00	50
PD16	1/-	yel-green (7/46) ..	5·00	1·00
PD8/16		set (6)	8·00	2·00

The coloured portion of the centre of the D is half-moon shaped. The 1 of the 1/- is larger than No. PD7 and there are three lines between the top of the figure and the frame.

OFFICIAL STAMPS

I FEDERAL PERFORATED ISSUES

Only a basic listing of the perforated initials (OS) stamps is given below, and no attempt has been made to list all the various shades that exist on certain values.

1913-31 THE KANGAROO TYPE

1913 (Jan.) First Kangaroo Issue (G1-20) with large "OS" puncture measuring 14 mm x 14 mm. First Single Crown over A wmk.

O1	½d.	green ..	..	..	5·00	1·00
O2	1d.	red	..	..	5·00	50
O3	2d.	grey	..	..	£15	1·00
O4	2½d.	indigo	..	..	£15	6·00
O5	3d.	olive	..	..	£20	3·00
O6	4d.	orange	..	..	£50	£12
O7	5d.	chestnut	..	..	£50	£12
O8	6d.	ultramarine-blue			£25	5·00
O9	9d.	violet ..	..	..	£25	5·00
O10	1/-	emerald	..	..	£25	5·00
O11	2/-	dark brown		..	£150	£15
O12	5/-	grey and yellow	..		£200	£50
O13	10/-	grey and pink	..		£350	£200
O14	£1	brown and blue	..		£850	£450
O15	£2	black and rose	..		£1400	£750
O1/15		complete set (15)			—	—

1913 (June) First Kangaroo Issue (G1-20) with small "OS" puncture measuring 8¼mm x 15½mm. First Single Crown over A wmk.

O16	½d.	green ..	..	..	5·00	1·00
O17	1d.	red ..	..	..	5·00	50
O18	2d.	grey	..	..	£15	1·00
O19	2½d.	indigo	..	..	£15	5·00
O20	3d.	olive ..	..	..	£20	3·00
O21	4d.	orange	..	..	£50	£12
O22	5d.	chestnut ..		..	£50	£12
O23	6d.	ultramarine blue		..	£25	5·00
O24	9d.	violet ..	..	..	£25	5·00
O25	1/-	emerald	..	..	£25	5·00
O26	2/-	dark brown		..	£150	£15

O27	5/-	**grey and yellow**	£200	£50
O28	10/-	**grey and pink** ..	£350	£200
O29	£1	**brown and blue**	£850	£450
O16/29		**complete set** (14)	—	—

All subsequent perforated "OS." issues are of the small (8½mm x 15½mm) puncture category.

1915 On the Second (Provisional) Kangaroo Issue (G21-28). Second Single Crown over A wmk.

O30	2d.	**grey**	£30	5·00
O31	2½d.	**indigo**	£1000	£500
O32	6d.	**ultramarine-blue**	£100	£15
O33	9d.	**violet**	£120	£20
O34	1/-	**bluish-green** ..	£120	£20
O35	2/-	**dark brown** ..	£400	£70
O36	5/-	**grey and yellow**	£700	£100
O30/6		**complete set** (7)	—	—

1915-28 On the Third Kangaroo Issue (G29–58). Third Single Crown over A wmk.

O37	2d.	**grey**	8·00	1·00
O38	2½d.	**indigo**	£10	3·00
O39	3d.	**olive**	£12	2·00
O40	6d.	**blue**	£20	3·00
O41	9d.	**violet**	£20	3·00
O42	1/-	**blue-green** ..	£20	3·00
O43	2/-	**brown**	£100	8·00
O44	5/-	**grey and yellow**	£120	£25
O45	10/-	**grey and pink** ..	£300	£60
O46	£1	**brown and blue**	£1000	£400
O47	£2	**black and rose** ..	£1800	£750
O37/47		**complete set** (11)	—	—

1924 On the Fourth Kangaroo Issue (G63-5) (U.P.U. colour changes) Third Single Crown over A wmk.

O48	6d.	**chestnut**	£15	2·00
O49	2/-	**maroon**	£15	3·00
O50	£1	**grey**	£400	£250
O48/50		**complete set** (3)	—	—

1929-31 On the Fifth Kangaroo Issue (G66-72). Second Mult. Crown over A wmk.

O51	6d.	**chestnut**	£15	2·00
O52	9d.	**violet**	£18	3·00
O53	1/-	**emerald**	£18	3·00
O54	2/-	**maroon**	£30	5·00
O55	5/-	**grey and or-yellow**	£200	£50
O56	10/-	**grey and lt pink** ..	£300	£200
O57	£2	**grey and rose** ..	£2000	£400
O51/7		**complete set** (7)	—	—

1914-31 THE (*Typo*) GEORGIAN TYPE

1914 First (*Typo*) Georgian Issue

(i) On Wove paper (refer to numbers G93–112).

O58	½d.	**green**	1·50	30
O59	1d.	**carmine**	5·00	15
O60	4d.	**orange-yellow** ..	£20	1·50
O61	5d.	**chestnut**	£15	1·00

(ii) Wmk. as (i) above, but on inferior unsurfaced paper of variable texture. Gummed locally. (Refer to numbers G113 etc.).

O62	1d.	**car (shades)** ..	6·00	30
O63	5d.	**br chest** (1918) ..	£1000	£100

The so-called Die II on the 1d. carmine (refer to note after G120) also exists on O59 and O62.

O63 only exists perforated "OS".

1918-24 Second (*Typo*) Georgian Isue, having the First Multiple wmk. (Refer to numbers G121, etc.).

O64	½d.	**green**	1·50	40
O65	1d.	**car (shades)** ..	£10	3·00
O66	1½d.	**dp blackish-brn** ..	2·00	30
O67	1½d.	**red-brown** ..	2·00	30

1918-26 Third (*Typo*) Georgian Issue, having the Second Single Crown over A wmk. (Refer to numbers G131, etc.).

O68	½d.	**green**	2·00	50
O69	½d.	**orange**	1·50	30
O70	1d.	**red**	5·00	15
O71	1d.	**purple**	3·00	40
O72	1d.	**green**	1·50	20
O73	1½d.	**black-brown** ..	2·00	30
O74	1½d.	**red-brown** ..	2·00	30
O75	1½d.	**green**	3·00	30
O76	1½d.	**red**	1·50	20
O77	2d.	**orange**	5·00	30
O78	2d.	**red**	2·50	20
O79	2d.	**brown**	7·00	1·00
O80	3d.	**blue**	8·00	1·00
O81	4d.	**orange**	£15	2·50
O82	4d.	**purple**	£15	5·00
O83	4d.	**blue**	£20	3·00
O84	4d.	**olive**	£10	1·50
O85	4½d.	**violet**	£12	2·00
O86	5d.	**pale brown** ..	£10	1·50
O87	1/4	**turquoise**	£40	£10

1924 (Aug.) No wmk. (Refer to numbers G167 & G168).

O88	1d.	**sage-green** ..	2·50	2·00
O89	1½d.	**scarlet**	3·50	2·00

1926-28 The Fifth (*Typo*) Issue having the Second Crown over A mult. wmk. (Refer to number G169, etc.).

(i) Perf. 14.

O90	½d.	**yellow-orange** ..	2·00	40
O91	1d.	**green**	1·50	30
O92	1½d.	**scarlet**	2·00	30
O93	2d.	**red-brown** ..	6·00	1·50
O94	3d.	**ult (shades)** ..	£10	2·00
O95	4d.	**greenish-olive** ..	£15	3·00
O96	4½d.	**bright violet** ..	£15	3·00
O97	1/4	**pl greenish-blue**	£100	£4

(ii) Perf. 13½ x 12½.

O98	½d.	**orange-yellow** ..	1·00	25
O99	1d.	**green (Dies I&II)**	£25	£15
O100	1½d.	**red**	1·00	25
O101	1½d.	**reddish-brown**	3·00	50
O102	2d.	**chocolate** ..	5·00	1·50
O103	2d.	**golden-scar(Dies II & III)** ..	2·00	50
O104	3d.	**dullish ult** ..	£10	1·50
O105	3d.	**dp ultramarine** ..	£10	1·50
O106	4d.	**yellow-olive** ..	£12	1·50
O107	4½d.	**violet**	£15	2·00
O108	5d.	**pale brown** ..	£15	2·00
O109	1/4	**turquoise** ..	£40	8·00

1927-1930 Commemorative Issues, perforated "OS". Mainly only issued in mint condition to members of the Federal Parliament. (Refer to numbers G86, G209, G211 and G212–3.

O113	1½d.	**Canberra** (1927)	£15	9·00

O114	3d.	**Kookaburra**		
		(1928)	£15	9·00
O115	1½d.	**West. Aust.Cent.**		
		(1929)	£15	9·00
O116	1½d.	**Sturt** (1930) ..	7·00	4·00
O117	3d.	**Sturt** (1930) ..	£15	9·00

Numbers Issued—O113, 18,800; O114, 15,000; O115–6 12,000(each) O117, 9,000.

1929 Airmail Issue. (Refer to number G210).

| O118 | 3d. | **green** | .. .. | £18 | £10 |

Number Issued—probably 18,000.

II STATE PERFORATED ISSUES

A number of Commonwealth issues exist punctured V.G. (Victoria), O.S., N.S.W., O.S.and G., N.S.W. (New South Wales), T. (Tasmania) and W.A. (Western Australia). These issues do not fall within the scope of Federal Australian stamps. Queensland and South Australia did not produce such issues.

III FEDERAL OVERPRINTED ISSUES

1931-33 Various stamps, as indicated, overprinted "O.S." in large double-lined letters, blue-black unless otherwise noted.
(a) Kangaroo G66 and G73.

| O119 | 6d. | **chestnut** (3/32) .. | £70 | £25 |
| O120 | 6d. | **chestnut** (5/32) .. | £25 | £18 |

Number Issued—O119/120, 250,000, the former being the scarcer.

(b) Georgian G193 and G197.

O121	2d.	**golden-scar** (2/32)	7·00	1·00
		a wmk. inverted ..	—	£100
O122	4d.	**yel-olive** (1/32) ..	£35	6·00
		a overprint in blue	£50	7·00

Number Issued—O122, 515,280.

(c) Georgian G201, 202, 204, 205, 207.

O123	½d.	**orange** (7/32) ..	5·00	1·50
		a overprint inverted	£1500	£600
O124	1d.	**green** (2/32) ..	2·00	1·00
		a overprint in blue	£15	5·00
O125	2d.	**golden-scar** (2/32)	4·00	1·00
		a overprint inverted	—	—
O126	3d.	**deep blue** (3/33)..	£12	8·00
O127	5d.	**yel-brn** (7/32) ..	£45	£25
		a overprint in blue	£60	£40

Number Issued—O123, 66,000; O126, 48,000; O127, 160,680.

(d) Lyre Bird G88.

| O128 | 1/- | **green** (3/32) .. | £65 | £25 |

Number Issued—120,000.

(e) Kingsford Smith. Overprint in black. (May 1st 1931) G216/7.

| O129 | 2d. | **rose-red** .. .. | £35 | £15 |
| O130 | 3d. | **bright blue** .. | £150 | £42 |

Numbers Issued—O129, 7,000; O130, 5,000 (to M.Ps. only).

(f) Air Mail Stamp. (Nov. 17th 1931) G219.

| O131 | 6d. .. .. | £40 | £22 |

This "Official" Stamp was sold to the public (40,000 copies).

(g) Sydney Harbour Bridge (March 1932) G21/2.

| O132 | 2d. | **red** .. .. .. | 5·00 | 3·00 |
| O133 | 3d. | **blue** .. .. .. | £17 | £12 |

Numbers Issued—O132, 246,000; O133, 102,000

SEMI POSTAL ISSUES

(Reduced size illustration)

1920 (Feb. 26th) Ross Smith England-Australia Flight. (*Typo*) **Commonweath Printing Office. Wmk. Second Single Crown over A. Perf. 12 (Line). Printed singly in miniature sheets with margins all round.**

GSP1	**dark blue**		
	mint with margins ..	—	£5000
	mint without margins..	—	£1200
	used on cover	—	£1600
	used	—	£800

The Vickers Vimy Biplane G-EAOU left Hounslow on November 12th and reached Darwin on December 10th, 1919. On its arrival at Melbourne on February 25th, 1920, one of these stamps (which express no value) was affixed to each cover carried from England – the margins being first removed – and was cancelled with a special oval postmark "FIRST AERIAL MAIL—GREAT BRITAIN TO AUSTRALIA—RECEIVED 26 FEB 1920".

Number printed—576.
Number destroyed (on 6/9/21)—126.
Number used—320.
Number Mint—130 *.

*Only some 40 copies are now known to have survived, a number of them lacking the margins or in other ways defective. A reproduction exists on yellowish unwatermarked paper.

LORD HOWE ISLAND

Postal rates were increased from 1½d. to 2d. in July 1930 (hence the provisional surcharge G214). The Postmaster at Lord Howe Island, 500 miles from Sydney and a dependency of New South Wales, had no stock of 2d. stamps and asked Sydney G.P.O. for instructions.

The reply was intended to convey an instruction to use 1½d. stamps and to endorse *the cover* "2d. Paid P.M., L.H.I." but it was ambiguously worded and was understood to require such an endorsement on *the stamps*.

Accordingly, the Postmaster surcharged in manuscript his entire stock of the Sturt 1½d; the handwritten surcharge in black ink in four lines reads "2d./Paid/P.M./L.H.I.". They were issued in the early part of August 1930 and a copy is known used as late as September 1931.

He had also prepared a small number of Georgian 1½d. stamps with similar surcharge, but these were not placed on sale until after the arrival of a new stock of 2d. stamps – by which time there was no longer any need of this provisional.

1930 (Aug.) Provisionals made in manuscript by the Postmaster, Lord Howe Island.

LH1	2d. on 1½d. **scar** (G212)..	£150	£180
LH2	2d. on 1½d. **golden-scar** (G188) ..	£150	£180

Numbers Issued—LH1, 260.

COMMONWEALTH OCCUPATION FORCE IN JAPAN

1946 (Oct. 11th) -48 Australian stamps overprinted B.C.O.F. JAPAN 1946, in black, at Hiroshima Printing Works, for use of Australian Occupation Force.

J1	½d. **orange** (No. 18)	..	1·00	1·00
	a narrow N	..	4·00	4·00
	b narrow B and A		4·00	4·00
	c 4 different fount	.	4·00	4·00
J2	1d. **dp plum** (No. 35)	..	60	60
	a purple	..	60	30
	b dp blue overprint (/48)		£40	£40
J3	3d. **purple-brown** (No. 26)		1·00	1·00
	a double overprint	..	—	—
J4	6d. **reddish-brn** (No. 29) (8/5/47)	..	3·00	3·00
	a narrow N	..	7·00	7·00
	b narrow B and A	..	7·00	7·00
	c 4 different fount		7·00	7·00
J5	1/– **dull green** (No. 31) (8/5/47)	..	5·00	5·00
	a narrow N	..	£15	£15
	b narrow B and A	..	£15	£15
	c 4 different fount	..	£15	£15

J6	2/– **maroon** (No. G82) (8/5/47)	..	£20	£20
	a narrow 4	..	£20	£20
	b narrow B	..	£20	£20
	c pale maroon (No. G83)		£20	£20
	d narrow 4	..	£30	£30
	e narrow B	..	£30	£30
J7	5/– **red-claret** (No. 15) (8/5/47)	..	£125	£125
	a thin paper (No. 15*b*) (8/48)	..	£125	£125
J1/7	**set** (7)..	..	£155	£155

1d. and 3d. values are overprinted in thick condensed type; other values as ½d. illustrated.

Numerous small varieties exist amongst the overprints, but only those due to use of different founts have been listed; however, in the overprinting of the 5/– the A is in two founts but as these have been used indiscriminately they have been ignored.

J1*a*/J4*a*/J5*a* No. 1/8 (right pane) (*see illustration*).
J1*b*/J4*b*/J5*b* No. 4/5 (left pane) (*see illustration*).
J1*c*/J4*c*/J5*c* No. 2/7 (left pane) (*see illustration*).
No. J2*a* (a lighter shade) does not appear to exist without overprint.
J6*a*/*d* No. 2/7 (left pane).
J6*b*/*e* No. 5/2 (right pane).

Narrow 'N'

Narrow 'B' and 'A'

Different Fount

Number issued—½d., 189,670; 1d., 378,750; 3d., 891,643; 6d., 136,133; 1/–, 131,055; 2/–, 62,651; 5/–, 32,508 (approx. 6,000 thin paper No. J7*a*).

Australian stamps supplied to the Army were charged at full face value, and it was consequently necessary for the Army to account for trial overprints submitted for approval.

One sheet of 160 of each of the following rejected proofs was placed on sale with the normal stamps, this being an easier alternative to writing them off.

½d. thin overprint in red.
1d. thin overprint in black or red.
3d. thin overprint in black, red or gold.

They are mostly found used with A.P.O. cancellations (£60 each).

BAHAMAS

The Bahamas were originally settled from England and Bermuda in 1649, although claimed by Spain until the Treaty of Versailles in 1783, when they were finally ceded to Great Britain.

From 1802 to 1846 various straight line "BAHAMAS" and other handstamps were used at the Packet Station on Crooked Island and at Nassau. The first Frank was the original straight line 'BAHAMAS' struck in red between 1843 and 1846. This was followed by the Crowned Circle, registered at the G.P.O., London, on May 22nd 1846 and a 'NASSAU PAID' dated Frank registered on November 29th 1860. Both of these, struck in red, were used until 1865. The Crowned Circle then became an Official Paid Frank, and remained in use, in black, until the 1930s. The 'NASSAU PAID' is known as a regular datestamp in black and late examples are with 'PAID' removed. (See Introduction).

Contemporary British adhesive stamps (1d, 2d, 4d and 6d) were valid from May 1858 to March 1860 to pay overseas postage and were cancelled 'AO5' in a transverse oval of horizontal bars. The 1s. is also known similarly cancelled, though intended only for making small payments to England, as no money orders were available until 1865.

The Bahamas 1d adhesives (V1/3) were only valid for postage within the Colony until May 1st 1860, when the Bahamas took control of its postal affairs, after which the stamps could be used also on overseas mail.

1843-65 PAID Franks On Cover

VF1	in red (1843-46)	..	—
VF2	in red (1846-65)	..	—
VF3	in red (1860-65)	..	—

1858-60 Stamps of Great Britain identified by their Catalogue Nos. after prefix 'BS'.

Used at Nassau: 'A 05'

BS V39	1d.	rose-red	..
BS V51	2d.	blue	.. ..
BS V44	4d.	rose	.. ..
BS V45	6d.	lilac	.. ..
BS V47	1/-	green	.. ..

All stamps from VI to V9 are recess, Perkins, Bacon and Co. on unwatermarked paper.

1859-60 Imperf. Sheets. 10 x 6.

(a) Thick Wove paper (10.6.59)

V1	1d.	reddish lake (shades)	..	.. £1100	£400

(b) Medium Wove paper (11/59).

V2	1d.	brown-lake(shades)	£1100	£400

(c) Thin Wove paper (4/60).

V3	1d.	dull lake (shades) ..	£500	£200

The papermaker's watermark in the sheet margins was normally trimmed off, but sheets are known showing part of the "Stacey Wise" watermark.

Used copies from the out-islands were sometimes pen-cancelled with a cross or other mark, but these can only be proved to have been postally used when on cover with other postal markings or overstamped with the "27" in bars canceller. Otherwise, only those with the "27" canceller or the manuscript name of the P.O. can be recognised as postally used. The great majority of pen cancellations are fiscal.

However, a heavy diagonal line on V1, or a heavy horizontal ink line on V3, are believed to be a form of "Specimen" mark put on by the printers, but in both cases the stamps must have the original gum.

Die and Plate proofs exist in black on India paper and on white card. Plate Proofs are also known in the issued colours.

Numbers printed—V1 1,000 : V2 1,000 : V3 2,000.

Between 1887 and 1900 a large remainder of imperforate stamps from later printings came on to the philatelic market; but, due to similarity of paper and colour, it is not possible to distinguish them with certainty from the original V3 issue.

1860 (Oct.)-61 (Feb.). As before (Thin Wove paper) but Perf 14-16 (Clean Cut).

V4	1d.	lake	.. .. £500	£200

Six copies of V4 were overprinted CANCELLED between bars for presentation; the whereabouts of only three copies, including one in the Royal Collection, are now known.

Number issued 2,020.

1861 (June)-62 (May). As before but Perf. 14-16 (Rough).

V5	1d.	lake	.. ..	£400	£100
V6	4d.	dull rose (12/61)	..	£600	£150
V7	6d.	grey-lilac (12/61)	..	£750	£175
V8	6d.	pale dull lilac (5/62)		£800	£175

V5—A pair is known with part of the Stacey Wise watermark appearing in the margin.

V6—is recorded imperf between; but this variety was possibly not sold in the Post Office. It also exists with double horizontal perforation at the top.

V6 and V8—exist with "Specimen" diagonally in manuscript.

V5/V8—were perforated on the same machine as V4 but the pin recesses had become clogged with previously punched paper.

Die Proofs exist in black of the 4d. on India paper. and of the 6d. on thin white wove paper

Plate Proofs exist in black of the 4d. and 6d. on white wove paper and on India paper.

Numbers printed—V5 11,880 : V6 7,140 : V7 2,640 : V8 2,280.

1862 (May). Prepared but not issued. Trial Perf. 11-12.

V9	1d.	lake	.. .. .. £800	—

This stamp was perforated on a machine which was commissioned only after the last despatch of stamps printed by Perkins, Bacon. Supplies were not sent to the Colony and it is believed that the stamps so perforated were remainders used for experiments on the new machine. Multiples are known imperf between, in both directions, and also imperf.

1862 (Aug)-63 (May). As before but printed (*recess*) by De La Rue from the same plates. No Wmk.

(a) Perf. 11½-12.

V10	1d.	carmine-lake	£200	£50
V11	1d.	lake	£200	£60
V12	4d.	dull-rose	£700	£100
V13	6d.	lavender grey	£750	£100

V10/11—Imperforate copies are known, but they were probably not sold in the Post Office.

(b) Compound Perf. 11½-12 and 11.

V14	1d.	carmine-lake	£500	£200
V15	1d.	lake	£500	£200
V16	4d.	dull-rose	£2750	£500
V17	6d.	lavender grey	£3500	£400

V14/V17—are from sheets of V10/V13 which were imperfectly perforated and were subsequently re-perforated on a different machine.

(c) Perf. 13.

V18	1d.	lake	£200	£50
V19	1d.	brown-lake	£200	£50
V20	4d.	dull rose	£650	£100
V21	6d.	lavender grey	£650	£100
V22	6d.	lilac	£650	£150

Parts of the papermaker's watermark (T. H. SAUNDERS 1860) may be found on all values.

V20—exists with double horizontal perforation at the bottom.

V19 and V20—exist with Specimen overprint in small block letters in black.

Proofs exist of all values in the issued colours on thick glazed card.

Numbers printed—1d. 18,180 : 4d. 13,320 : 6d. 10,020.

1863 (July)-81 (June). As before but Wmk. Crown CC.

(a) Perf. 12½ (1863).

V23	1d.	brown-lake	£45	£45
		a wmk inverted	—	—
V24	1d.	lake	£45	£50
		a wmk inverted	—	—
V25	1d.	carmine-lake (aniline)	£45	£50
V26	1d.	deep-rose	£30	£30
V27	1d.	rose-red	£30	£30
		a wmk reversed	—	—
V28	1d.	red	£30	£30
V29	1d.	scarlet	£35	£40
V30	1d.	vermilion	£30	£30
		a wmk. inverted	—	—
		b wmk. reversed	—	—
V31	4d.	rose	£100	£45
V32	4d.	lilac-rose	£60	£35
		a wmk. reversed	—	—
V33	4d.	rose-lake	£100	£45
		a wmk. reversed	£1500	—
V34	6d.	rose-lilac	£100	£35
V35	6d.	lilac	—	—
		a wmk. inverted	£120	£50
V36	6d.	bright lilac	£65	£35
V37	6d.	violet	£65	£35
V38	6d.	deep violet	£65	£35
V39	6d.	violet (aniline)	£80	£45

(b) Perf. 14 (1877).

V40	1d.	scarlet	£25	£15
V41	1d.	scarlet-vermilion	£25	£15
		a wmk. reversed	—	—

V42	1d.	scarlet (aniline)	£550	†
V43	1d.	carmine-lake	£30	£20
V44	4d.	bright rose	£275	£30
V45	4d.	dull rose	£550	£30
V46	4d.	rose-lake	£250	£30
V47	4d.	lilac-rose	£300	£45

V41 may be found on both thick and thin papers.

The following exist overprinted Specimen.

In black	V25, V28, V38.
In blue	V31, V38.
Handstamped	V41, V44.

All three values, each in several shades, are known imperforate with full gum. They were probably from Plate Proofs. The 6d. is known imperforate and overprinted CANCELLED.

Numbers printed—V30 82,200 : V34 4,800.

1863 (Aug.)-80 (May) (*typo*) De La Rue. Wmk. Crown CC. Sheets 240 – four panes, each 6 x 10.

(a) Perf. 14. ('63).

V48	1/–	dark green	£40	£20

(b) Perf. 12½. ('65).

V49	1/–	green	£600	£100

(c) Perf. 14. (Thick paper) ('80)

V50	1/–	pale green	5·00	5·00

Die Proofs exist on white enamelled card in black, dark green, brown and blue. Cut down progress Die Proofs exist, in a set of ten, on white enamelled card, some with different Head Dies.

1881 (Dec.)-83 As before but Wmk Crown CA.

(a) Perf. 11¾.

V51	1d.	scarlet vermilion	£22	£15
		a wmk. reversed	—	—
V52	4d.	rose	£200	£35

(b) Perf. 14.

V53	1d.	scarlet vermilion	£90	£30
V54	4d.	rose	£275	£30
V55	1/–	green	£18	£15

V55 may be found with clear and with yellow gum.

The order in which the two different perforations was used is not known; but Perf. 11¾ is assumed to have been the first in view of the existence of the following colour trials of No. V55 with that perforation.

Carmine-rose, Deep yellow, Mauve, Sage-green, Venetian red, Slate-grey, Brown and Blue.

The 1/– value exists (perf or imperf) overprinted 'Specimen' in small black or blue or large black letters; and (imperf) overprinted CANCELLED.

The Royal Collection contains a Proof of the 1d. in olive-brown.

1883 No. V38 surcharged FOURPENCE in black serif capitals.

(a) Horizontally

V56	4d. on 6d.	deep violet	£225	£100

a surcharge inverted ..   £650   —
b surcharge double ..   —   —

(b) Diagonally

V57 4d. on 6d. **deep violet** .. £300   £150
      a surcharge inverted ..   —   —

The surcharge is also recorded on V39 but this is believed to have been done at a later date with the original handstamp.

V56*b*—The horizontal surcharge is faint, and there is also a heavier vertical surcharge.

1884 (June 28th)-98. (*typo*) **De La Rue. Wmk. Crown CA. Perf. 14. Sheets 6 x 10 (except V70: 240 – four panes, each 6 x 10).**

V58 1d. **pale rose** (7/84) ..   8·00   5·00
V59 1d. **deep rose** ..   ..   4·00   2·00
V60 1d. **carmine** ..   ..   4·00   2·00
V61 1d. **carmine** (aniline) ..   3·00   5·00
V62 2½d. **dull blue** (2/88) ..   £10   8·00
V63 2½d. **blue** ..   ..   £12   6·00
V64 2½d. **ultramarine** ..   ..   4·50   3·00
      a wmk. inverted ..   ..   —   —
V65 2½d. **dp ultramarine** ..   6·00   4·00
V66 4d. **yellow** ..   ..   5·00   3·00
V67 4d. **orange** (7/84) ..   7·00   5·00
V68 6d. **mauve** (8/90) ..   6·00   5·00
      a malformed E ..   £60   —
V69 6d. **dull mauve** ..   ..   8·00   6·00
      a malformed E ..   £80   ‡
V70 1/– **blue-green** ('98) ..   £22   £15
V71 5/– **sage-green** ..   £30   £30
V72 5/– **deep sage green** ..   £35   £30
V73 £1   **light brown** £200   £125
V74 £1   **chestnut** £250   £150
V58/74   **set** (7v)   ..   ..   £270   —
SPV62/V68 **specimen pair** ..   £40   ‡

V68/69—Although the printing plate had been prepared in 1884 no printings were made from it until 1890.

V68*a*/69*a* The second 'E' in 'PENCE' is malformed on No. 36.

V70/71/72/73/74 may be found with clear and with yellow gum.

All values except 6d. exist locally handstamped SPECIMEN diagonally in black (also in violet on 1/-).

The original order for the 2½d. value called for an inscription '37 2½d. '87 in honour of Queen Victoria's Golden Jubilee.

Imperforate Colour Trials of the 1d. value exist in many colours on white, yellow and red paper.

A Die Proof of V55 in blue on white enamelled card and with the value tablet scratched out was submitted by De La Rue as an Essay for this issue in September, 1883.

A Die Proof from the undenominated Master Die (for all values except 1/–) exists in black on white enamelled card.

1901 (Sept. 23)-08 (Oct.) (*recess*) **De La Rue. Wmk. Crown CC. Perf. 14. Sheets 12 x 5.**

E1 1d. **black and red** ..   2·00   3·00
E2 1d. **grey-black and**
         carmine-red ..   4·00   5·00
      a wmk inverted ..   —   —
E3 1d. **black and carmine-**
         red (thinner paper)
         (10/08) .. ..   3·00   4·00
E4 5d. **blk and or** (1/03) ..   £14   £15
E5 5d. **grey-blk and bt or**
         (thinner paper)
         (10/08) £18   £15
E6 2/– **blk and blue** (1/03)..   £14   £18
E7 2/– **grey-blk and dl blue**
         (thinner paper)
         10/08 .. ..   £20   £18
E8 3/– **blk and dp grn** (1/03)   £18   £20
E9 3/– **grey-blk and grn**
         (thinner paper)
         10/08 .. ..   £22   £20
      a wmk. inverted and
         reversed .. ..   —   —
E1/9   **set** (4v) £45   £55
SPE1/9   **specimen set** (4v) ..   £40   ‡

Constant varieties occur on all values printed from Centre Plates 1 – 5.

Half extra tree trunk   Row 1/12.
Whole extra tree trunk   Row 5/8.

Normal stamp   Row 1/12   Row 5/8

These varieties are not re-entries on the working plates but arose from the method employed in making Centre Plates 1 – 5 from a Master Plate and not directly from the original Die. Fresh entries on the Master Plate were repeated on each of the first five working plates.

All values exist locally hand-stamped SPECIMEN in black (also in purple on 5d.).

Die Proofs of the vignette exist in black on white wove paper.

Die Proofs of the frame exist in black on thick paper (1d.); and in blue on thin paper (undenominated).

Plate Proofs of the vignette in blue and of the frame in blue and in black are recorded. There is also a Plate Proof of Centre Plate 6 (retouched die) in blue (See G66/67).

Perforated Colour Trials of the 1d and 5d. values exist in several colour combinations.

Numbers printed—E1/4 46,900: E4/5 29,520: E6/7 11,460: E8/9 12,120.

See also G1/14 and G63/71.

1902 (Dec. 18)-11. (*typo*) **De La Rue. Perf. 14. Sheets 6 x 10.**

(a) Wmk. Crown CA.

E10	1d.	**carmine**	2·00	1·00
E11	1d.	**carmine-rose**	3·00	2·00
E12	2½d.	**ultramarine**	7·00	4·00
E13	2½d.	**bt ultramarine**	£10	6·00
E14	4d.	**orange**	£10	£12
E15	4d.	**deep yellow** (3/10)	£10	£14
E16	6d.	**bistre-brown**	9·00	£10
		a malformed E	£90	—
E17	6d.	**deep bistre brown**	£12	£12
		a malformed E	—	—
E18	1/–	**gr-blk and car**	£100	—
E19	1/–	**brownish-grey and**	£10	£12
		carmine (6/07)	£10	£12
E20	5/–	**purple and blue**	£40	£35
E21	5/–	**dull purple and blue**	£45	£40
E22	£1	**bt green and black**	£335	£375
E23	£1	**dull green and black**	£335	£350
E10/23		**set** (7v)	£425	£425
SPE10/23		**specimen set** (7v)	£120	‡

(b) Wmk. Multiple Crown CA

E24	½d.	**g een** (5/06)	3·00	60
E25	½d.	**yellow-green**	5·00	1·25
E26	1d.	**carmine-rose** (4/06)	3·00	50
E27	2½d.	**ultramarine** (4/07)	£12	£12
		a wmk. inverted	—	—
E28	6d.	**bistre-brown** (8/11)	£50	£90
		a malformed E	—	—
E24/28		**set** (4v)	£70	£100
SPE24/28		**specimen set** (4v)	£30	‡

E16*a*/17*a*/28*a* See Note under V74.

All values exist locally hand-stamped SPECIMEN in black (in purple on 2½d.).

Die Proofs exist (without value) on card; also Die Proofs of values only.

Imperforate Colour Trials of the 1d. and 1/– values exist, on Crown CA paper, in many colours.

Numbers printed—E10/11 425,820: E12/13 410,400: E14 21,240: E16/17 30,540: E18 36,540: E20/21 11,340: E22/23 9,240. E24/25 241,800: E26 1,206,660: E27 485,100: E28 6,240 (E28 had a very short life, as it was replaced by G28 within one year).

1911 (Feb.)-20. As Nos. E1/9 but Wmk. Multiple Crown CA.

G1	1d.	**black and red**	4·00	3·00
G2	1d.	**gr-blk and car-red**	4·00	3·50
G3	1d.	**blk and scar** (greyish paper) ('16)	6·00	4·50
G4	1d.	**gr-blk and dp car red** ('19)	3·00	3·50
G5	1d.	**blk and sal-red** ('20)	5·00	4·00
G6	3d.	**purple/bright lemon** (thin paper) (18.5.17)	7·00	6·00
		a on yellow-orange (thick greyish (1/19)	2·00	3·00
		b on dull orange (thick paper) 1/19	4·00	3·75
G7	3d.	**blk and brn** (21.3.19)	1·00	3·00
		a imperf (pair)	—	—
G8	3d.	**black and dp brown**	2·00	3·00
G9	3d.	**gr-bl and pl brn**	4·00	4·50
G10	5d.	**blk and mve** (18.5.17)	2·00	5·00
G11	5d.	**gr-blk and dp mauve**	4·00	6·00
G12	2/–	**blk and bl** (11/16)	£14	£20
G13	3/-	**bl and br grn** (8/17)	£25	£28
G14	3/-	**gr-blk and dl grn**	£30	£30
		a wmk. inverted	—	—
		b wmk. inverted and reversed	—	—
G1/14		**set** (6v)	£45	£60
SPG1/14		**specimen set** (6v)	£60	‡

G7*a*—The Royal Collection contains ⊞ taken from the Colour Trial sheet.

G12—May be found in differing shades on a variety of thick papers.

See Note after SPE1/9 for details of constant varieties Rows 1/12 and 5/8.

1912-19. (*typo*) **De La Rue. Wmk. Multiple Crown CA. Perf. 14. Sheets 120 – two panes, each 6 x 10. G15/28 O: G29/35 C.**

G15	½d.	**green**	50	50
G16	½d.	**yellow-green**	1·00	70
G17	½d.	**deep green**	1·50	90
G18	1d.	**rose-carmine**	3·50	1·75
G19	1d.	**dp carmine** (aniline)	40	40
G20	1d.	**carmine** (bluish paper)	1·00	50
G21	1d.	**scarlet**	2·00	1·25
G22	2d.	**grey** ('19)	1·50	1·75
G23	2d.	**slate**	2·00	2·25
G24	2½d.	**ultramarine**	3·50	4·50
G25	2½d.	**deep dull blue**	5·00	6·50
G26	4d.	**orange**	3·00	5·50
G27	4d.	**yellow-orange**	1·50	3·50
G28	6d.	**bistre-brown**	2·00	4·50
		a malformed E	—	—
G29	1/–	**jet blk and car**	£25	—
G30	1/–	**gr-blk and carmine**	5·00	7·50
G31	1/–	**black and carmine** (bluish paper)	2·50	4·50
			7·50	6·50

G32 5/–	**dl pur and dp bl** ..	£25	£20
G33 5/–	**pur and bt blue** ..	£20	£20
G34 £1	**lt green and black** ..	£200	£225
G35 £1	**dl green and black** ..	£200	£225
G15/35	**set** (9v)	£230	£255
SPG15/35	**specimen set** (9v)	£120	‡

G28a See Note under V74.

Die Proofs exist (without value) on card; also Die Proofs of values only.

Typel   Type II

1917-19 War Charity. No. G1 overprinted in red by De La Rue.

(a) With Type I (18.5.17).

G36 1d.	**black and red** ..	35	65
	a long '7'	£20	£24
SPG36	**specimen** (1) ..	£20	‡

G36a—The stroke of '7' is elongated downwards Row 4/6.

Delays in shipment caused postponement of the issue date from 1.1.17.

Number issued—240,000.

(b) With Type II (1.1.19).

G37 1d.	**black and red** (shades)	30	1·00
	a overprint double ..	£425	—
	b wmk. inverted. ..	—	—
SPG37	**specimen** (1) ..	£20	‡

The shades come, respectively, from Centre Plates 3 and 4.

G37a—A half sheet of 30 exists and is believed to be from a trial sheet on which the first overprint was too faint and which was overprinted a second time.

G36/37 are both known imperforate, but these varieties were not issued and probably came from Plate Proofs.

Delays in shipment caused postponement of the issue date from 3.6.18. The stamp had also been intended to commemorate the bicentenary of the arrival in 1718 of the first Governor appointed by the Crown, Woods Rogers.

Number issued—240,000.

G36 and G37 were overprinted on special printings of G1. They were sold at face value, but half the proceeds was given to the British Red Cross Society.

See Note after SPE1/9 for details of constant varieties Rows 1/12 and 5/8.

WAR TAX

1918 War Tax. Overprinted in black at the Office of the Nassau Guardian.

(a) On Nos. G15, G18, G6 and G30 (Feb. 21). (Setting 6 x 5).

G38 ½d.	**green**	2·75	3·25
	a overprint double ..	£175	£175
	b overprint inverted ..	£175	—
G39 1d.	**carmine**	1·00	1·00
	a overprint double ..	£175	£175
	b overprint inverted ..	£175	—
G40 3d.	**purple/yellow** ..	3·00	3·00
	a overprint double ..	£175	£175
	b overprint inverted ..	£175	£175
	c "TAX" omitted ..	—	—
G41 1/–	**gr-blk and car** ..	£35	£40
	a overprint double ..	£500	—

(b) On No. G1 (July 10). (Setting 6 x 5).

G42 1d.	**black and red** ..	2·50	3·50
	a overprint double ..	£225	—
	b overprint inverted ..	£250	£300
	c overprint double, one inverted	£250	—

G40b—30 copies exist.

G42c—On one half sheet the top row showed a normal overprint and the other four rows (24 copies) were all this variety. Two other half sheets are known with this variety, making a total of 84 copies.

See note after SPE1/9 for details of constant varieties on Rows 1/12 and 5/8.

Numbers printed—G40 42,000: G42 48,000 (On sale for only ten days).

1918-19. Nos. G15/17, G18, G6, G7 (in black) and G30/31 (in red) overprinted WAR TAX in sans serif capitals by De La Rue.

(a) In one line (1.6.18).

G43 ½d.	**green**	25	60
G44 ½d.	**deep green**	50	1·00
G45 1d.	**deep carmine** ..	80	1·25
G46 1d.	**carmine**	30	70
	a wmk. sideways ..	£275	—
	b wmk. inverted ..	—	—
G47 3d.	**pur/yel** (20/7) ..	50	1·50
	a on deep yellow ..	1·00	2·25
	b on orange	2·00	3·75
G48 3d.	**blk and brn** (21.3.19)	50	2·50
	a imperf (pair).. ..	—	—
G49 1/–	**black and carmine**..	1·80	2·50
G50 1/–	**gr-black and car** ..	80	2·00
G43/50	**set** (5v)	2·25	7·00
SPG43/50	**specimen set** (5v)	£60	‡

(b) In two lines (14.7.19).

G51 ½d.	**green**	30	70
G52 ½d.	**yellow-green**	60	1·00
G53 1d.	**rose-carmine**	30	70
G54 1d.	**red**	60	1·00
G55 3d.	**black and brown** ..	70	2·50
	a wmk. inverted ..	—	—
	b wmk. reversed ..	—	—
G56 1/–	**black and carmine** ..	4·50	5·00
G57 1/–	**gr-bl and car** ..	3·00	4·50
G51/57	**set** (4v)	4·00	8·00
SPG51/57	**specimen set** (4v)	£40	‡

G47/48/55—See Note after SPE1/9 for details of constant varieties on Rows 1/12 and 5/8.

G48a—The Royal Collection contains ⊞ taken from the Colour Trial sheet.

The ½d., 1d. and 1/– are all known imperforate, but these varieties were not issued and probably came from Plate Proofs.

1920 (Mar. 1). **Peace Celebrations.** (*recess*) **De La Rue. Wmk. Multiple Crown CA** (sideways). **Perf. 14. Sheets 5 x 12.**

G58	½d.	**green**	30	80
G59	1d.	**carmine**	1·50	1·25
	a	wmk. reversed ..	—	—
G60	2d.	**slate-grey**	2·75	4·00
G61	3d.	**deep brown** ..	2·75	5·00
G62	1/–	**deep myrtle-green**..	£15	£20
G58/62		**set** (5v)	£20	£30
SPG58/62		**specimen set** (5v)	£60	‡

Remainders withdrawn in May, 1921 and destroyed

Die Proofs of the Master Die (undenominated) exist in black and in blue on wove paper.

Colour Trials of G58 are known in olive-brown, bistre and myrtle-green (all imperforate).

G58/62 are all known imperforate, but these varieties were not issued and probably came from Plate Proofs.

1921 (Mar. 29)-29. **As Nos. G1/14 but Wmk. Multiple Script CA.**

G63	1d.	**black and rose-red**	2·00	2·50
G64	1d.	**gr-blk and rose-red**	1·50	2·50
G65	1d.	**black and deep aniline red**('26?) ..	4·00	3·50
G66	1d.	**grey-black and carmine red** (8/29) ..	5·00	6·00
G67	5d.	**gr-blk and mauve** (8/29)	4·00	5·50
G68	2/–	**blk and bt bl** (11/22)	£14	£15
G69	2/–	**gr-blk and bt blue**..	£18	£16
G70	3/–	**blk and dpgrn** (9/24)	£24	£25
G71	3/–	**g'-bl and dp grn** ..	£28	£30
G63/71		**set** (4v)	£40	£45
SPG63/71		**specimen set** (4v)	£45	‡

Except in the case of G66/67 (which were printed from Centre Plate 6) see Note after SPE1/9 for details of constant varieties on Rows 1/12 and 5/8.

Centre Plate 6 was laid down directly from the original Die after it had been retouched and deepened.

Number issued : G66 6,000.

1921 (Sept. 8th)-37. **As Nos. G15/35 but Wmk. Multiple Script CA G72/87 O : G88/93 C.**

G72	½d.	**green** ('24)	15	30
G73	½d.	**bt green** ('27) ..	30	45
G74	1d.	**carmine-red** (8.9.21)	35	35
G75	1d.	**deep carmine** ('27)	1·00	1·25
G76	1½d.	**red-brown** ('34) ..	70	80
G77	2d.	**grey** ('27)	60	1·00
G78	2d.	**slate-grey**	1·00	1·50
G79	2½d.	**dl ultramarine** ('21)	70	1·25

G80	2½d.	**ultramarine** ('22) ..	1·00	1·50
G81	2½d.	**bt ultramarine** ('31)	2·00	2·25
G82	3d.	**pur/pl yel C** ('31) ..	4·00	6·50
	a	on deep yellow C ('37)	4·00	6·50
G83	4d.	**pale yellow** ('21) ..	1·00	3·00
G84	4d.	**yellow-orange** ('27)	2·00	3·25
G85	4d.	**yellow** (value in brn)	3·50	4·00
G86	6d.	**bistre-brown** ('21)..	80	3·00
	a	malformed E ..	£10	—
G87	6d.	**dp bistre-brn** ('31)..	1·25	3·75
	a	malformed E ..	£15	—
G88	1/–	**gr-blk and car** ('26)	4·00	6·50
G89	1/–	**blk and car** ('28) ..	2·50	5·00
G90	1/–	**jet blk and car** ('29)	4·00	6·50
G91	5/–	**dl pur and blue** ('24)	£20	£25
G92	5/–	**pur and bt blue** ..	£25	£30
G93	£1	**grn and blk** ('26) ..	£200	£225
G72/93		**set** (11v)	£230	£265
SPG72/93		**specimen**v) **set** (11	£125	‡

G86a/87a See Note under V74.

Printers' samples of the ½d exist in purple on heavy paper. The value is in red, black or blue, and the stamps are machine overprinted or handstamped SPECIMEN. Similar samples are known in red and black, and in red and blue.

1930 (Jan. 2nd) **Tercentenary of Settlement** (in 1629) **and bicentenary of the Representative Assembly** (in 1729). (*recess*) **Bradbury Wilkinson. Wmk. Multiple Script CA. Perf. 12. Sheets 12 x 5.**

G94	1d.	**black and scarlet** ..	1·75	2·50
G95	3d.	**black and dp brown**	3·50	4·50
G96	5d.	**black and dp purple**	6·50	9·00
G97	2/–	**black and dp blue** ..	£18	£24
G98	3/–	**black and green** ..	£25	£30
G94/98		**set** (5v)	£50	£65
SPG94/98		**specimen set** (5v)	£50	‡

Numbers sold—G94 167,446 : G95 34,556 : G96 27,155 : G97 11,689 : G98 10,303

Remainders were withdrawn on May 1st, 1931 and destroyed on May 26th.

1931. As before but with commemorative dates omitted. Thick paper with yellowish gum.

G99	2/–	**gr-blk and blue** ..	1·00	50
G100	2/–	**sep-blk and bt blue**	4·00	2·50
G101	2/–	**sep-blk and dl blue**	2·00	1·50
G102	2/–	**slate-black and dp blue**	£12	£10
G103	3/–	**black and green** ..	1·00	50
G104	3/–	**gr-blk and green** ..	2·00	1·00
G105	3/–	**slate-blk and grn**..	9·00	9·50
G106	3/–	**gr-blk and dp yelgreen**	3·00	1·75
SPG99/106		**specimen** (pair) ..	£20	‡

For similar stamps on thin white paper with clear gum see Nos. 22/23 (1943-46).

1935 (May 6th). Silver Jubilee (*recess*) **De La Rue. Wmk. Multiple Script CA. Perf. 13½ x 14. Sheets 6 x 10.**

G107	1½d.	**dp bl and carmine** ..	50	50
G108	2½d.	**brn and dp blue** ..	1·50	1·50
G109	6d.	**lt bl and olive-grn** ..	3·50	4·50
G110	1/–	**slate and purple** ..	5·50	6·50
G107/110	**set** (4v)	.. ..	£10	£12
SPG107/110	**specimen set** (4v)		£18	‡

Die Proofs of the frames of all values exist in black.

Numbers printed—G107 226,920: G108 150,020: G109 55,200: G110 48,600.

Remainders were withdrawn on December 31st 1935.

1935 (June) (*recess*) **Waterlow and Sons. Wmk. Multiple Script CA. Perf. 12½. Sheets 5 x 12.**

G111	8d.	**ultra and scar** ..	6·00	4·50
SPG111		**specimen** (1v) ..	£15	‡

1938-52 Printers (*typo*) **De La Rue. Perf. 13¾ x 14 (C). Sheets 120—two panes, each 6 x 10.**

1	½d.	**green** (11/3/38) ..	10	10
	a	**blue-green** (9/42) ..	15	15
	b	**dp green** (11/12/46)	15	15
2	½d.	**claret** (18/2/52) ..	10	15
3	1d.	**rose-carmine** (11/3/38)	1·25	1·25
	a	**white ear**.. ..	—	—
4	1d.	**pale grey** (17/9/41) ..	10	10
	a	**pearl-grey** (27/6/50)	15	15
5	1½d.	**red-brown** (19/4/38)	20	10
	a	**pale red-brn** (19/4/48)	15	10
6	2d.	**pale grey** (19/4/38) ..	£10	£10
	a	**short T**	£120	—
7	2d.	**rose-car** (17/9/41) ..	15	10
	a	**short T**	£35	£35
	b	**dull scarlet** (19/4/48)	20	20
	c	**value tablet doubly printed**	—	—
8	2d.	**yellow-green** (1/5/51)	20	30

	a	**green and yel-green** .	20	30
9	2½d.	**blue** (11/3/38) ..	50	50
10	2½d.	**pale violet** (1/7/43) ..	1·00	1·00
	a	**violet**	15	15
11	3d.	**pale violet** (19/4/38)	10	15
12	3d.	**blue** (1/7/43) ..	1·00	2·00
	a	**bright blue** (19/4/48)	15	20
13	3d.	**rose-carmine** (1/2/52)	40	50
14	10d.	**orange** (18/11/46) ..	25	30
15	1/–	**black and carmine** (*ch*) (15/9/38) ..	75	75
	a	**grey and scarlet** (thin paper (*ch*) (/42)	£15	£10
	b	**blk and car** (sub) (9/42)	75	75
	c	**grey and scarlet** (sub) (6/3/44)	60	60
	d	**dull grey and dp crimson** (*ch*) (19/4/48)	40	40
16	5/–	**pale lilac and blue** (*ch*) (19/4/38)	£21	£10
	aa	**lilac and blue** (thin paper) (*ch*) (/42)	£45	£30
	a	**pur-lilac and blue** (sub) (9/42) ..	4·00	2·00
	b	**dp purple and dp blue** (*ch*) (19/4/48) ..	4·00	2·00
	c	**red-purple and bt blue** (*ch*) (/51)	4·00	2·00
17	£1	**green and black** (*ch*) (15/9/38)	£15	£15
	a	**green and black** (sub) (13/4/43) ..	£11	£12
1/17		**set** (17)	£30	£30
SP 1/17		**specimen set** perf (14)	£90	‡

6a/7a—The stem of the T in TWO was cut short (*the letters* WO *were also misshapen*) Row 3/6 (right pane) but retouches on subsequent printings partly rectified the faults, though the retouches themselves were always evident, particularly on No. 8. On Nos. 7b and 8 the stem of the T is practically normal in length.

Nos. 15a and 16aa were placed on sale shortly before the release of the "Landfall" set and most were used up for the commemorative issues (Nos. S13 and S16).

16—The 5/- later printings is known faded or chemically changed in the pale grey colour of the 1/–.

No. 16c was released in London 15/8/51.

Watermark Variety (Type B)
(See Introduction for details)

2a	½d.	**Crown missing**	£750	—
2b	½d.	**St. Edward's Crown** ..	£275	—

1938 (July 1st) Designs, 4d. (Sea Gardens,

Nassau); 6d. (Fort Charlotte, New Providence); 8d. (Flamingoes in Flight). Printers (*recess*) Waterlow & Sons. Perf. 12½ (L). Sheets 5 x 12.

18	4d. lt blue and orange-red	30	30
19	6d. olive-green and lt blue	20	20
20	8d. ultramarine and red .	35	35
18/20	set (3)	85	85
SP18/20	specimen set (3) ..	£18	‡

1940 (Nov. 28th) No. 9 surcharged 3d., by the City Press, Nassau.

21	3d./2½d. blue	15	30

1942-46 As Nos. G99/106 (1931) but on thin white paper with clear gum.

22	2/– pur-slate and indigo-blue (9/42) ..	£12	£10
	a black and dp blue (13/4/43) ..	1·00	1·25
	b black and steel-blue (1/10/46) ..	60	75
23	3/– pur-slate and myrtle-green (9/42) ..	9·00	9·50
	a black and dp yellow-green (13/4/43) ..	1·50	1·50
	b black and dull myrtle-green (1/10/46) ..	75	80
SP22/23	specimen (pair) ..	£20	‡

Nos. 22 and 23 were released in the Colony late in 1942, but most of the printing was used for the "Landfall' issue.

For similar stamps on thick paper with yellowish gum see G99/106 (1931).

SPECIAL ISSUES

1937 (May 12th) Coronation. As Aden.

S1	½d. green	20	20
S2	1½d. light brown	80	80
S3	2½d. blue	1·00	1·00
SP S1/3	specimen set perf (3)	£12	‡

1942 (Oct. 12th) -43 450th Anniversary of Landfall of America. No. 1 etc. locally overprinted in black at the office of the Nassau Guardian.

S4	¼d. green	10	15
	a overprint double ..	£60	—
	b blue-green ..	10	15
S5	1d. pale grey	10	15
S6	1½d. red-brown	10	15
S7	2d. rose-carmine ..	10	15
	a short T ..	£25	£25
S8	2½d. blue	10	15
S9	3d. blue	15	20
	a overprint double ..	—	—
S10	4d. lt blue and orange-red	20	30
	a COIUMBUS ..	£100	£100
S11	6d. ol-green and lt blue	20	30
	a COIUMBUS ..	£100	£100

S12	8d. ultramarine and red	30	40
	a COIUMBUS ..	£150	£150
S13	1/– grey and scarlet (thin paper) (*ch*) ..	30	35
	a black and car (sub) (/43) ..	30	35
	b black and crimson ..	—	—
S14	2/– black and dp blue ..	2·00	3·00
	a pur-slate and indigo-blue (/42) ..	1·75	2·25
	b stop after COLUMBUS ..	£12	£12
S15	3/– black and green ..	6·00	6·00
	a pur-slate and myrtle-green (/42) ..	1·50	2·00
	b stop after COLUMBUS ..	£14	£14
S16	5/– lilac and blue (thin paper) (*ch*) ..	3·00	3·50
	a pu-lilac and blue (sub) ..	2·00	3·00
S17	£1 green and black (*ch*)	£12	£10
	a green and black (sub)	£10	£12
S4/17	set (14) ..	£16	£20
SPS4/17	specimen set (14) ..	£80	‡

S7a See Note under Nos. 6a/7a.

S9a is only known on stamps perforated SPECIMEN.

S10a/11a/12a—The L lacking the foot has been converted into I, Row 5/2 (*on one overprinting only*). Copies of No. S12 have been noted with this variety and have been passed by B.P.A. Expert Committee.

S14b/15b. Row 2/12.

S17 has brown gum generally whereas the gum of No. S17a is clear.

The overprint on Nos. 2, 3, 4 and 5 of the bottom row of all values (small head type) in first releases have the C of Columbus directly beneath first L of Landfall, instead of to the left as is normal.

1946 (Nov. 11th) Victory. As Aden.

S18	1½d. sepia-brown ..	10	10
S19	3d. dp blue	10	10
SP S18/19	specimen set perf (2)	£12	‡

1948 (Oct. 11th) Tercentenary of Eleutheran Settlement. Designs, ½d., 4d., 8d., 10d., £1 (Buildings and Scenes); 1d., 1½d., 2d., 2½d., 3d., 6d., 3/-, 10/- (Island Pursuits); 1/-, 2/- (Sports); 5/- (Transport). Printers (*recess*) Canadian Bank Note Co. No wmk. Perf. 12 (L). Sheets 120—two panes, each 5 x 12.

S20	½d. orange	10	15
S21	1d. sage	10	15
S22	1½d. greenish-bistre ..	15	20
S23	2d. dull scarlet ..	15	20
S24	2½d. dull Indian-red ..	50	40
S25	3d. bright ultramarine .	25	30
S26	4d. grey-black ..	25	40
S27	6d. emerald	1·00	1·00

S28	8d. **bright violet**	..	40	40
S29	10d. **dp rose-carmine**	..	50	50
S30	1/– **sepia**	..	80	60
S31	2/– **reddish-purple**	..	4·00	4·00
S32	3/– **dp blue**	..	4·00	4·00
S33	5/– **dp lilac**	..	3·00	3·00
S34	10/– **dp grey**	..	5·00	5·00
S35	£1 **vermilion-red**	..	8·00	8·00
S20/35	**set** (16)	..	£26	£26
SP S20/35 **specimen set** (16)..			£100	‡

Die Proofs of the undenominated frame exist in black.

1948 (Dec. 1st) Silver Wedding. As Aden.

S36	1½d. **chestnut-brown**	..	10	10
S37	£1 **greenish-slate**	..	£20	£22

1949 (Oct. 10th) U.P.U. As Aden.

S38	2½d. **dull violet**	.. ..	15	15
S39	3d. **indigo**	.. ..	25	25
S40	6d. **slate-blue**	.. ..	50	50
S41	1/– **rose-pink**	.. ..	1·00	1·00
S38/41	**set** (4)	.. ..	1·25	1·75

SPECIAL DELIVERY STAMPS

1916-17 Nos. E4 and E5 overprinted in black at the Office of the Nassau Guardian. Setting 6 x 5.

GS1 5d.	**black and orange** (1st & 2nd printings)		—	—
GS2 5d.	**gr-blk and bt orange** (3rd printing)	..	7·00	8·00
	a overprint double	..	£425	£475
	b overprint inverted	..	£425	£475
	c overprint double,one inverted	..	£475	£525
	d overprint omitted in horizontal pair with normal	..	£2000	£2400

GS2*a*/*b*/*c*—It is believed that two full sheets (120 stamps) of each error were printed.

GS2*d*—On one sheet the second overprinting intended for the right half of the sheet, was applied one stamp's width to the left. This resulted in the five right hand marginal stamps being without overprint and the sixth vertical row bearing double overprints.

The purpose of these stamps was to facilitate the exchange of Special Delivery mail between Canada and Bahamas. The Bahamas stamp was available (at 10c) for such mail from Canada to Bahamas, and Canadian 10c stamps were available in Bahamas for mail to Canada.

There were three printings—

1st May 1st, 1916. 600 stamps (GS 1 only) all of which were sent to Canada where they were available at Ottawa, Toronto, Westmount and Winnipeg. Copies genuinely used under the special arrangements were affixed by P.O. counter clerks and were cancelled with Canadian datestamps; and 430 copies had been sold when the agreement was terminated by the Canadian Post Office in December, 1916. The remaining 170 copies were then put on general sale and those subsequently used philatelically were cancelled in Nassau.

2nd December, 1916. Quantity unknown (GS1 and GS2). Sold only at Nassau and all known used copies were cancelled there.

3rd March 1st, 1917. 6,000 stamps (GS1 and GS2). Sold only at Nassau and all known used copies were cancelled there.

As the 2nd and 3rd printings were made after the Canadian Post Office had cancelled the agreement they were apparently intended to satisfy philatelic demand.

Although the same type was used for all three printings it was re-set and it is necessary to plate both the basic stamp and the overprint in order to identify the several printings.

The listed errors, all of which have been extensively forged, are believed to have come from the 3rd printing.

Type I	Type II

1917 (July 2nd). As No. E4 (but Wmk. Multiple Crown CA) overprinted with Type I in black by De La Rue.

GS3 5d.	**blk and pl orange**	..	1·50	2·50
SPGS3	**specimen** (1v)	..	£25	‡

1918 No. G10 overprinted with Type II in red by De La Rue.

GS4 5d.	**black and mauve**	..	60	1·25
SPGS4	**specimen** (1v)	..	£25	‡

GS3/4 are both known imperforate, but these varieties were not issued and probably came from Plate Proofs.

The 5d. black and mauve, imperforate, with Type I overprint in red and in black was an Essay for GS4.

GS3/4 were sold only at Nassau.

GERMAN PROPAGANDA LABELS

The 1944 German imitations of the G.B. 1937 Definitives ½d to 3d (see after Great Britain for details) were also overprinted in black "LIQUIDA-TION/OF EMPIRE/BAHAMA 1s" within a vertical rectangular frame. £150

BAHRAIN

An Indian Postal Agency was opened on August 1, 1884, and contemporary Indian stamps were used without overprint until 1933. Their use during this period may only be recognised by the named BAHRAIN cancellation.

1933 (Aug. 10th) 1937. Stamps of India (1926-33 and 1932-36 Issues), all inscribed INDIA POSTAGE except Nos. G2, 5, 8, 15 which are "POSTAGE AND REVENUE". Wmk. Mult. Star, overprinted BAHRAIN at the Nasik Security Press. The overprint measures 13 mm. (low values); 19 mm. (Rupee values).

G1	3p. **slate** (12/33)	..	30	30
G2	½a. **green**	.. ..	75	60
G3	½a. **green** ('35)	..	30	5
G4	9p. **dp green** Offset litho			
	('33) ..	.. ..	75	50
	a Typo ('34) ..	..	90	80
G5	1a. **chocolate**	..	45	45
G6	1a. **chocolate** ('35)	..	75	10
G7	1¼a. **mauve** (Die I)	..	50	30
G8	2a. **vermilion**	..	90	80
G9	2a. **vermilion** ('35)	..	3 50	1·25
G10	2a. **vermilion** ('37) small			
	die ..	.. ..	5·00	40
G11	3a. **blue** ..	.. ..	4·00	4·00
G12	3a. **carmine** ('34)	..	1·50	15
G13	3½a. **deep blue**	..	50	40
G14	3½a. **grey-blue**	.. ..	2·50	2·50
G15	4a. **sage green**	..	4·50	5·00
G16	4a. **sage green** ('35)	..	1·00	20
G17	8a. **purple**	.. ..	50	30
G18	12a. **claret**	.. ..	75	50
G19	R1 **chocolate and green**		4·00	1·00
G20	Rs2 **carmine and orange**		£10	4·00
G21	Rs5 **ultramarine and pur**		£25	£20
G1/21	**set** (20v.)	.. ..	£60	£40

G4/4a Apart from differences in the basic stamps (See India G52), the overprint on the Typo stamps is slightly thicker, longer and taller than the cleaner overprint on the Offset litho stamps.

G6 was initially issued only in booklets, as India Booklet B19 with BAHRAIN overprinted on front cover in red sans serif capitals 21¼ x 3 mm. Price £65.

G7 For details of Die I see Note after INDIA G55.

G10 For details of small die see Note after INDIA G61.

The following values are known with inverted watermark:—G3, 5, 7. 8, 13 and 21.

1938-41 Stamps of India (1937–46 issue) overprinted BAHRAIN. The overprint measures 13 mm. (low value); 19 mm. (Rupee values).

1		3p. **slate** (5/38)	..	50	40
2		½a. **red-brown** (5/38)	..	10	10
3		9p. **dp green** (5/38)	..	15	10
4		1a. **carmine** (5/38)	..	10	5
5		2a. **vermilion** (/39)	..	40	15
6		3a. **yellow-green** (/41)	.	3·00	15
7		3½a. **blue** (7/38)	..	60	80
8		4a. **deep brown** (/41)	..	£12	£12
9		8a. **violet-slate** (/40)	..	£30	£30
10		12a. **dp crimson** (/40)	..	£27	£27
11	R1	**vio-grey and lt brn**			
		(/40)	.. ..	50	40
12	Rs2	**vio-pur and brn** (/40)		3·00	1·00
		a dp purple and brown		5·00	1·50
13	Rs5	**dp grn and dp blue**			
		(/40)	.. ..	8·00	4·00
14	Rs10	**vio-pur and red-**			
		claret (/41)	..	£18	6·00
15	Rs15	**choc and dp grn** (/41)		£15	£12
		a wmk. inverted	..	£20	£14
16	Rs25	**slate-vio and pur-vio**			
		(/41)	.. ..	£23	£12
1/16		**set** (16v)	.. ..	£140	£95

1942-5 Stamps of India (1941-3 Issue) overprinted BAHRAIN.

17		3p. **slate** (/43)	.. ..	5	5
18		½a. **purple** (/45)	..	5	5
		a defective 'H'	..	£20	—
19		9p. **green** (/43)	..	5	5
20		1a. **rose-carmine** (/44)	.	5	20
21	1a.	3p. **bistre** (/43)	.. ..	20	40
22		1½a. **slate-purple** (/44)	..	20	10
23		2a. **vermilion** (/42)	..	20	10
24		3a. **bright violet** (/45)	..	25	10
25		3½a. **blue** (/42)	..	60	50
26		4a. **brown** (/42)	..	40	10
27		6a. **greenish-blue** (/42)	.	2·50	1·25
28		8a. **violet-slate** (/42)	..	35	30
29		12a. **dp crimson** (/42)	..	1·00	40
17/29		**set** (13)	.. ..	6·00	5·00

18a The 'H' in the overprint lacks the cross-bar (Row 20/14).

Crude, and easily recognised, forged and bogus overprints exist on several values of the foregoing three issues. They were handstamped on used Indian stamps.

Although Indian stamps without overprint were not officially used in Bahrain at the time, such stamps (India KGVI 1941/43 and 1937 Rupee values) are known with forged Bahrain cancellations dated 26th January, 1942.

An American A.P.O. 816 operated at Muharraq Airport from June 1944 to the end of 1945. Mail from American Servicemen was carried free; but Contractors' employees working on the erection of Refinery installations in Bahrain were permitted the use of the A.P.O. as they were employed on a U.S. Government project. and postage on their mail was paid with U.S. stamps.

The Indian Victory stamps (S1-4) were issued (without overprint) in Bahrain in 1946, but are very scarce with Bahrain postmarks.

Casual carriage resulted in very occasional use in Bahrain in early 1948 of Indian stamps with Nasik "PAKISTAN" overprints. Such use was not intended and examples are extremely rare.

1951 (May 3rd) -55 As No. 30, etc., but colours changed (Nos. 48–50 as Nos. 34–6 of G.B.), similarly overprinted and surcharged.

42	½a./½d.	dull orange	..	5	5
43	1a./1d.	ultramarine	..	5	5
44	1½a./1½d.	green	..	10	10
45	2a./2d.	red-brown	..	10	5
46	2½a./2½d.	scarlet	..	10	15
47	4a./4d.	light blue (2/10/50)		15	15
48	Rs2/2/6	green Type I	..	2·00	1·00
		a Type II ('53)		£15	£10
		b Type III ('55)		£100	£20
		ba raised 'I'		£350	£100
49	Rs5/5/-	red	..	3·00	2·00
		a extra bar in over-print	..	£50	£50
50	Rs10/10/-	ultramarine	..	5·00	3·50
42/50		set (9)	..	£10	7·00

BAHRAIN

2 RUPEES

48   'BAHRAIN" in sharp letters.
Type I   "2" and "RUPEES" in line, overall measurement 16mm.
The surcharge is *slightly* to the left of "BAHRAIN" in certain sheet positions.

BAHRAIN

2 RUPEES

48a   "BAHRAIN" in heavier, worn type.
Type II   '2" raised in relation to "RUPEES" overall measurement 15½mm.
The surcharge is *imperceptibly* to the left of "BAHRAIN" in certain sheet positions.

48b   As Type II, but vertical distance between
Type III   "BAHRAIN" and "2 RUPEES" is 15¾–16½ instead of 15mm. and the surcharge is set ¾ to 1½mm. to the left of "BAHRAIN".

This Type did *not* occur on sheets of the Type II printing.

48ba The 'I' in BAHRAIN, is higher than the other letters. Row 2/1.

1948 (April 1st) -49 Stamps of Great Britain overprinted BAHRAIN and surcharged by Harrison & Sons. The change from Indian to G.B. stamps coincided with change of Administration.

30	½a./½d.	green	..	..	5	10
31	1a./1d.	scarlet	..	..	5	10
32	1½a./1½d.	red-brown	..	5	15
33	2a./2d.	dull orange	..	5	5
34	2½a./2½d.	ultramarine	..	15	20
35	3a./3d.	purple-violet	..	5	5
37	6a./6d.	pale purple	..	5	10
38	R1/1/-	bistre-brown	..	40	20
39	Rs2/2/6	green	..	..	80	1·00
40	Rs5/5/-	red	..	3·00	3·00
		a re-entry	..	—	—
		b 'T' Guide line		—	—
41	Rs10/10/-	ult (4/7/49)	..	£15	£12
30/41		set (11)	..	£19	£16

40a Row 4/2 (See G.B. 18a).

40b Row 2/7 (See G.B. 18b).

Number issued—½a., 481,713; 1a., 465,689; 1½a., 213,418; 2a., 484,939; 2½a., 198,928; 3a., 1,138,523 6a., 2,152,034; 1r., 423,706; 2r., 46,709; 5r., 43,379; 10r., 16,460.

From 1948 British Forces in Bahrain used stamps of the foregoing and following issues, which were cancelled with British F.P.O. date-stamps (No. 756 and, later, No. 518).

49a—Row 6 No. 1 has a third (thinner) bar below the normal two bars on part of the printing only.

Number issued—½a., 407,547; 1a., 347,155; 1½a., 155,944; 2a., 374,277; 2½a., 171,900; 4a., 304,323; 2r., 58,184; 5r., 38,937; 10r., 28,994.

SPECIAL ISSUES

1948 (May 1st) Silver Wedding Issue of Great Britain surcharged and overprinted BAHRAIN.

S1	2½a./2½d.	**ultramarine** ..	10	10
S2	Rs15/£1	**dp blue** ..	£22	£25

Number issued—2½a., 186,095; 15r., 21,984.

1948 (July 29th) Olympic Games Issue of Great Britain, surcharged and overprinted BAHRAIN.

S3	2½a./2½d.	**ultramarine** ..	10	10
		a surcharge dble	£175	£300
S4	3a./3d.	**violet**	15	15
S5	6a./6d.	**reddish-purple** .	20	20
S6	R1/1/–	**bistre-brown** ..	30	40
S3/6		**set** (4)	70	80

S3a—The balance of a sheet of 120 was purchased by a serviceman in Muharraq Post Office after a number had been sold and used. Most of the 12 known used copies were cancelled "EXPERIMENTAL P.O. K–121" at this Post Office.

Number issued—2½a., 99,304; 3a., 112,515; 6a., 112,919; 1r., 87,858.

1949 (Oct. 10th) U.P.U. Issue of Great Britain, surcharged and overprinted BAHRAIN.

S7	2½a./2½d.	**ultramarine** ..	10	10
		a Indian lake	£35	£35
S8	3a./3d.	**pale violet** ..	10	15
S9	6a./6d.	**reddish-mauve** .	25	30
S10	R1/1/–	**bistre-brown** ..	40	45
S7/10		**set** (4)	75	1·00

S7a—For details of this variety see Great Britain, No. S16b. (Row 8/2).

Number issued—2½a., 93,689; 3a., 105,246; 6a., 105,064; 1r., 80,853.

For more detailed information on the issues and Postal History of Bahrein see "The Postal Agencies in Eastern Arabia and the Gulf" by Neil Donaldson (Available from Bridger & Kay Ltd.).

BARBADOS

The island was settled in 1627 and has remained a British possession since that time.

Following the use of handstamps or other manuscript marks, a Crowned Circle PAID Frank was registered at the G.P.O. in London on October 3rd, 1849; and was thereafter struck in red to indicate prepayment of postage on overseas letters (See Introduction).

The use of this Frank ceased after Barbados stamps were issued for foreign postage but it was again used – struck in black – during a shortage of ½d. stamps (Feb.-Mar., 1893), of 1d. stamps (Jan., 1896) and of ¼d. stamps (Jan.-May, 1896).

1849-1855 PAID Frank		*On Cove*
VF1		—

All stamps from V1 to V71 are (*recess*), **Perkins Bacon and Co.**

1852 (Apr. 15th)–55. Local Stamps. No Wmk. Blued paper. Imperf. Sheets 10 x 11.

V1	½d.	**yellow-green**	..		—	£325
V2	½d.	**deep green**	..	..	£55	£140
V3	1d.	**blue**	..	..	£12	£75
V4	1d.	**deep blue**	..	..	5·00	£30
V5	2d.	**greyish-slate** (8/54)		£160		—
		a bisect vert (1d.) on cover ('54)			‡	£1850
V6	4d.	**brownish red** ('55)		£16		£200
		a bisect diag. (2d.) ..			—	—

V1/6—(and all stamps of these denominations issued up to No. V64) bear no indication of value, and were identified only by colour. The original order for Nos. V3 and V5 specified 'Blue' and 'Purple' respectively, but the colour of the second printing of V5 turned out to be very similar to that of the 1d. stamp.

The 2d. stamp was not therefore issued until 1854 when a shortage of 1d. stamps necessitated its use; it was then usually bisected, each half being used as a 1d. stamp (Aug.-Sept., 1854).

The 1d. and 2d. stamps would have been issued earlier than April 15th had the first consignment not been lost in the wreck of S.S. Amazon. These two values, together with the ½d were specifically intended for the 'Inland Post'; but they probably later became valid for foreign mail. The designation of the Barbados Postmaster changed from "Inland Postmaster" to "Colonial Postmaster" between July 27th and November 11th, 1854; and the 4d. stamps were ordered by him in his new capacity. It was not until 1858, however, that Barbados was given control over her overseas mail.

Numbers printed—V1/2 130,000: V3/4 350,000: V5 10,000: V6 50,000.

(lost in the S.S. Amazon: V3/4 50,000: V5 10,000)

Prepared but not issued (Blued paper.)

| V7 | ? | slate-blue | .. | .. | £10 | — |
| V8 | ? | slate | .. | .. | .. | £200 | — |

These stamps both have yellow patchy gum, differing from No. V5 which has smooth even gum. There was only one printing of No. V5; and it seems likely that Nos. V7/8 were intended to be blue (V3/4) stamps, and were witheld from issue because they were unsatisfactory shades.

1855 (Feb. 20th)-57. As before but white paper.

V9	½d.	yellow-green	..	£200	£75
V10	½d.	green ..	..	..	£50	£110
V11	1d.	pale blue	..	..	£25	£30
V12	1d.	deep blue	..	..	£10	£25
	a	bisect vert (½d.) on			
		piece (10/57) ..		‡	—

V12 is known with part of the papermaker's watermark T. H. SAUN(ders)

1858. No Wmk. Imperf. Sheets 11 x 10.

V13	6d.	pale rose-red	..	£250	£50
V14	6d.	deep rose-red	..	£300	£70
V15	1/–	brown-black..	..	£75	£50
V16	1/–	black	..	..	£50	£30

Die Proofs of both values exist in black on India paper. Plate Proofs of the 1/– exist in black on wove paper.

Numbers printed—V13/14 82,500: V15/16 55,000.

In 1909 reprinted proof impressions of the 6d. were made on Small Star watermark paper in the following colours: black, blue, orange, green, deep green, reddish mauve, purple, brown, red-brown and vermilion.

1860-61. As Nos. V9/12. (No Wmk.) but perforated.

(a) Pin Perf. 14.

V17	½d.	yellow-green	..	£500	£100
V18	1d.	pale blue	..	..	£500	£55
V19	1d.	deep blue (10.7.60)	£500	£55

(b) Pin Perf. 12¼.

| V20 | ½d. | yellow-green | .. | £1200 | £200 |
| V21 | 1d. | blue | .. | .. | .. | — | £400 |

(c) Pin Perf. 14 x 12¼.

| V22 | ½d. | yellow-green | .. | .. | — | £750 |

(d) Perf. 14-16 (Clean Cut) 1861.

V23	½d.	deep green ..	..	£22	6·00
	a	double print	..	..	—	—
V24	1d.	pale blue	..	..	£200	£10
V25	1d.	blue	..	..	..	£250	£10
	a	double print	..	..	—	£250
	b	bisect (½d.) on cover	‡	£750

1861-70. As before. (No Wmk.).

(a) Perf. 14-16 (Rough).

V26	½d.	deep green	..	..	6·00	5·00
V27	½d.	green ..	..	..	4·00	4·00
V28	½d.	blue-green	..	..	£25	£30
	a	imperf (pair)	..	£160	—
V29	½d.	yellow-green	..	£15	£15
	a	imperf (pair)	..	—	—
V30	½d.	grass green ..	..	£10	£5
	a	imperf (pair)	..	£160	—
V31	1d.	pale blue	..	..	£15	4·00
	a	imperf (pair)	..	£175	—
	b	bisect diag. (½d.) on			
		piece (11/63) ..		‡	£150
V32	1d.	deep blue	..	..	£10	3·00
V33	4d.	dull rose-red ('61)..	£21	£10
	a	imperf (pair)	..	£250	—
V34	4d.	dull brown-red ('65)	£35	£14
	a	imperf (pair)	..	£300	—
V35	4d.	lake-rose('68)	..	£24	£18
	a	imperf (pair)	..	£300	—
V36	4d.	dull vermilion ('69)	£65	£30
	a	imperf (pair)	..	£300	—
V37	6d.	rose-red ('61)	..	£70	8·00
V38	6d.	orange-red ('64)	..	£30	£10
V39	6d.	orange and ver	..	£25	£15
	a	imperf (pair) thick			
		paper	..	..	£150	—
V40	6d.	bt or-ver ('68)	..	£20	8·00
	a	imperf (pair) thin			
		paper	..	..	£200	—
V41	6d.	dl orange-vermilion		
		('70) ..	..	..	£20	8·00
V42	6d.	orange ('70) ..	..	£32	£10
V43	1/–	brown-black ('63) ..	£20	7·00
V44	1/–	black ('66) ..	..	£10	8·00
	a	imperf between			
		(horiz pair)	..	£1750	—
	b	double print	..	—	—

(b) Perf. 11-13 (1863).

| V45 | ½d. | green .. | .. | .. | £1750 | — |
| V46 | 1d. | blue | .. | .. | .. | £800 | — |

V45/46 are not known used.

Numbers printed—V33, 50,000: V34, 24,200: V35, 11,000: V36, 22,000: V37, 100,000: V38, 50,000: V39, 63,250: V40, 41,000: V41/42, 55,000: V43, 50,000: V44, 30,250.

1863 (June). Prepared for use but not issued.

| V47 | 1/– | blue | .. | .. | .. | £5000 | — |

50,000 stamps were printed in error in the colour of the 1d. stamp. They were never placed on sale, and No. V43 was supplied by the printers in their place.

1870-71. As before but with Watermark. Perf. 14-16 (Rough).

(a) Wmk. Large Star.

V48	½d.	green ..	..	..	£20	7·00
	a	imperf (pair)	..	£160	—
V49	½d.	yellow-green	..	£40	£22
V50	1d.	blue	..	..	£300	£15
	a	on blued paper	..	£375	£22
V51	4d.	dull vermilion	..	£175	£16
V52	6d.	orange vermilion	..	£160	£18
	a	imperf (pair)	..	—	—

V53	1/–	**black**	..	..	..	£70	£14
	a	imperf (pair)		..		—	—
	b	imperf between					
		(pair)	..	..		—	—

(b) Wmk. Small Star (1871).

V54	1d.	**blue**	..	..	..	£25	4·00
V55	4d.	**dl rose-red**		..	..	£200	£15
V56	6d.	**orange-vermilion**		..	£100	£12
V57	1/–	**black**	..	..	..	£40	£12

1872. As before. Wmk. Small Star.

(a) Perf. 14½-15½ (Clean Cut).

V58	1d.	**blue**	..	..	..	£70	3·00
	a	bisect diag (½d.) on					
		cover ('73)		..		‡	£350
V59	6d.	**orange-vermilion**		..	£160	£12
V60	1/–	**black**	..	..	..	£40	5·00

(b) Perf. 11-13 x 14½-15½.

| V61 | ½d. | **green** | .. | .. | .. | £65 | 5·00 |
| V62 | 4d. | **dl vermilion** | | .. | .. | £90 | £18 |

1873. As before. Wmk. Large Star. Perf. 14½-15½ (Clean Cut).

V63	½d.	**green**	..	..	..	£60	7·00
V64	4d.	**dl rose-red**		..	..	£185	£45
V65	6d.	**orange-vermilion**		..	£185	£25
	a	imperf between					
		(horiz pair)		..		£750	—
	b	imperf		..	..	£70	—
V66	1/–	**black**	..	..	..	£32	5·00
	a	imperf between					
		(pair)	..	..		—	—

V65*b* The Royal Collection contains a used copy (30.8.74).

1873. Wmk. Small Star (sideways – two points up). Sheets 3d. 12 x 10.

(a) Perf. 14 (June).

| V67 | 3d. | **brown-purple** | .. | £175 | £60 |

(b) Perf. 15½ x 15. (Feb. 18th).

| V68 | 5/– | **dull rose** | .. | .. | £400 | £250 |
| SPV68 | (H/S) | **ovpt specimen** | £250 | ‡ |

Die Proofs of both values exist in black on card; and of the 5/– also on India paper.

Plate Proofs of both values exist in black on white wove paper; and of the 5/– in deep rose on white and on yellow paper.

Numbers printed—V67, 20,000 : V68, 10,000.

1874 (May). Wmk. Large Star. Sheets 12 x 10.

(a) Perf. 14.

| V69 | ½d. | **deep green** | .. | .. | 7·00 | 5·00 |

V70	1d.	**deep blue**	..	..	£24	2·50
	a	on blued paper		..		—	—
	b	bisect diag or horiz					
		(½d.) on piece					
		(5/75)	..	..		‡	£225

(b) Perf. 14½-15½ (Clean Cut).

| V71 | 1d. | **deep blue** | .. | .. | — | £750 |
| | *a* | imperf (pair) | | .. | | — | — |

Die Proofs of both values exist in black on white card and on India paper.

Plate Proofs of both values exist in black on white wove paper.

Numbers printed—V69, 66,000 : V70/71, 330,000.

The Perkins Bacon Dies, Rollers and Plates were handed to the Crown Agents on November 17th, 1874.

1875-78. As before but printed (*recess*) by De La Rue from the same plates. Wmk. Crown CC (sideways on 6d. and 1/–). Sheets V73 12 x 10.

(a) Perf. 12½.

V72	½d.	**bright green**	..	..	5·00	3·00
V73	4d.	**deep red**	..	..	£70	7·00
V74	6d.	**yellow**	..	..	£300	£40
V75	1/–	**violet** (aniline)		..	£250	£25

V73—Perkins Bacon Die Proofs in black on white card and on India paper, and Plate Proofs in black on white wove paper exist although they never printed from this new plate.

(b) Perf. 14.

V76	½d.	**bright green** ('76)	..	3·50	2·50
V77	1d.	**ultramarine**		..	£10	2·50
V78	1d.	**dull blue**		..	8·00	1·00
V79	1d.	**grey-blue**		..	9·00	1·00
	a	wmk. sideways		..		—	£800
	b	bisect diag (½d.) on					
		piece ('77-'78)		..		‡	£165
V80	3d.	**mauve** ('78)		..	£35	7·00
V81	4d.	**red** ('78)		..	£40	£10
V82	4d.	**carmine**		..	£65	4·00
V83	4d.	**crimson-lake**		..	£165	5·00
V84	6d.	**chrome-yellow** ('76)		£55	4·00
V85	6d.	**yellow**		..	£70	£10
V86	1/–	**violet** (aniline)		..	£575	£25
V87	1/–	**purple**		..	£55	3·75
	a	bisect vert (6d.)					
		on piece (1/80)		..		‡	—
V88	1/–	**mauve**		..	£110	3·00
SPV76/88	**specimen set** (6v)	..	£400	‡

V79*a*—Only two known to exist.

(c) Perf. 14 x 12½.

| V89 | 4d. | **red** | .. | .. | .. | £4500 | — |

Type I   Type II   Type III

1878 (March). No. V68, with lower denomination label removed, locally surcharged (sideways in either direction) in black twice and perforated vertically down the centre.

(a) With Type I (7mm high: curved serif).

V90	1d.	on half 5/- dull rose	£1000	£250
	a	unsevered pair ..	£3000	£950

(b) With Type II (7mm high: straight serif).

V91	1d.	on half 5/- dull rose	£1200	£350
	a	unsevered pair ..	—	£900

(c) With Type III (6mm high).

V92	1d.	on half 5/- dull rose	£1200	£350
	a	unsevered pair ..	£3500	£1000

(d) Unsevered pairs with different Types se-tenant.

V93	Types I and II	..	—	£1600
	a without central			
	perforation	..	—	£5500
V94	Types I and III		—	—

All stamps from V95 to E14 are (*typo*), **De La Rue. Perf. 14.**

1882-86. Wmk. Crown CA. Sheets 240 – four panes each 6 x 10.

V95	½d.	dull green ..	..	2·75	1·00
V96	½d.	green ..	.. ..	2·50	1·00
V97	1d.	rose ..	.. ..	6·50	1·00
		a bisect vert or diag			
		(½d.) on cover			
		('88 '89) ..	..	‡	£185
V98	1d.	carmine	..	2·50	70
V99	2½d.	ultramarine..	..	£13	1·50
V100	2½d.	deep blue ..	..	£16	1·25
V101	3d.	deep purple ('84) ..		£30	£18
V102	3d.	mauve	.. ..	3·50	4·50
V103	4d.	grey ..	..	£65	4·00
V104	4d.	pale brown ('84) ..		2·50	1·75
V105	4d.	deep brown	..	2·50	1·00
V106	6d.	olive-black ('86) ..		£18	£10
V107	1/-	chestnut ('86)	..	£12	£12
V108	5/-	bistre ('86) ..	..	£120	£130
V95/108		**set** (9v)	..	£230	£150
SPV106/108		**specimen set**(3v)		£70	‡

Numbers printed : V108, 2,400.

1892. Nos. V104/105 locally surcharged 'HALF-PENNY' in black serif capitals.

V109	½d. on 4d. pale brown ..		30	70
	a hyphen omitted ..		2·00	2·50
	b surcharge double ..		—	—
	c surcharge double			
	(one red, one			
	black)		£275	£275
	d surcharge double			
	(one red, one			
	black) with hyphen omitted ..		£500	£500

	e surcharge treble			
	(two red, one			
	black)		—	—
V110	½d. on 4d. deep brown ..		50	90
	a hyphen omitted ..		3·00	4·00

1892-1903. Wmk. Crown CA. Sheets 240 – four panes, each 6 x 10.

V111	¼d.	gr-blk and car ('96)		30	40
V112	½d.	dull green ..	..	15	40
V113	1d.	carmine ..	..	30	30
		a bisect diag (½d.) on			
		piece (12/95) ..		‡	—
V114	2d.	slate-blk and or			
		('99)		3·50	2·00
V115	2½d.	ultramarine..	..	3·00	80
V116	5d.	grey-olive ..	..	4·50	3·25
V117	6d.	mauve and carmine		4·50	3·50
V118	8d.	orange and ult	..	2·25	5·50
V119	10d.	dk bl-grn and car..		6·50	8·00
V120	2/6	bl-blk and orange		£18	£19
		a wmk. inverted ..		£50	—
V121	2/6	vio and grn ('03)	..	£30	£32
V111/121		**set** (11v) ..	..	£70	£70
SPV111/121		**specimen set** (11v)	£65		‡

V121 was issued during the reign of King Edward VII, but is listed here as a matter of convenience.

1898. Diamond Jubilee. Wmk. Crown CC. Sheets 120 – two panes, each 12 x 5.

V122	¼d.	grey and carmine..		40	45
		a on blued paper ..		9·00	£10
V123	½d.	dull green ..	..	90	45
		a on blued paper ..		9·50	9·50
V124	1d.	rose ..	..	1·75	70
		a on blued paper ..		£11	£12
V125	2½d.	ultramarine..	..	4·50	1·00
		a on blued paper ..		£12	£12
V126	5d.	olive-brown ..		8·00	9·00
		a on blued paper ..		£65	£65
V127	6d.	mauve and carmine		£10	8·50
		a on blued paper ..		£28	£28
V128	8d.	orange and ult	..	9·00	8·00
		a on blued paper ..		£25	£28
V129	10d.	bl-grn and carmine		£15	£16
		a on blued paper ..		£35	£40
V130	2/6	bl-blk and orange		£15	£16
		a on blued paper ..		£25	£26

V122/130	set (9v)	.. ..	£60	£55
V122a/130a	set (9v. blued paper)		£185	£200
SPV122/130	specimen set (9v)		£85	‡

Numbers printed—V122/125, 500,000 each:
V126, 18,400 : V127, 15,280 :
V128, 20,000 : V129, 12,160 :
V130, 10,000.

1904-10. As Nos. V111/121 but Wmk. Multiple Crown CA. Sheets 120 – two panes, each 6 x 10.

E1	¼d.	**grey and carmine**..	40	40
E2	¼d.	**brown** ('09).. ..	30	35
E3	½d.	**dull green**	90	25
E4	½d.	**blue-green** ('09) ..	90	65
E5	1d.	**carmine**	70	25
E6	1d.	**red** ('09)	60	30
E7	2d.	**greyish-slate** ('10)	5·00	6·00
E8	2½d.	**blue**	3·00	60
E9	2½d.	**bright blue** ('10) ..	7·50	2·75
E10	6d.	**mauve and carmine**	£10	9·50
E11	6d.	**dl and bt pur** ('10)	9·00	9·00
E12	8d.	**orange and ult** ..	£16	£16
E13	1/–	**black/green** ('10) ..	£15	£16
E14	2/6	**violet and green** ..	£26	£28
E1/14		**set** (14v)	£90	£90
SPE2/13		**specimen set** (7v)		
		(1909/10)	£38	‡

1906-07. Nelson's Death Centenary. (*recess*) **De La Rue. Designer, Mrs. G. W. Goodman. Perf. 14. Sheets 12 x 5.**

(a) Wmk. Crown CC (1906). All values exist on thick white paper, and on thin bluish paper. Centres in black.

E15	¼d.	**grey**	55	65
E16	½d.	**pale green**	2·00	70
E17	1d.	**red**	2·00	45
E18	2d.	**yellow**	4·50	6·50
E19	2½d.	**bright blue**	5·50	6·00
E20	6d.	**mauve**	£15	£17
E21	1/–	**rose-red**	£16	£17
E15/21		**set** (7v)	£40	£45
SPE15/21	**specimen set** (7v)		£70	‡

E15 and E17 are known with watermark inverted.

(b) Wmk. Multiple Crown CA (6.7.07). Centres in black.

E22	¼d.	**grey**	90	90
E23	2d.	**yellow**	8·00	9·00
E24	2½d.	**bright blue**	£13	£14
E22/24		**set** (3v)	£20	£22

A colour variety of E24, frequently referred to as 'Indigo', is believed to be the result of climatic effect.

Numbers issued—E22, 50,000 : E23, 12,000 : E24, 27,000.

1906 (Aug. 15th). Tercentenary of Annexation (in 1605). (*recess*). **De La Rue. Designer, Lady Carter. Wmk. Multiple Crown CA (sideways.) Perf. 14. Sheets 5 x 12.**

| E25 | 1d. | **blk, bl and green** .. | 8·00 | 2·50 |
| SPE25 | | **specimen** (1v) .. | £40 | ‡ |

1907. Kingston Relief Fund. No. V114 (Wmk. Crown CA) surcharged by T. E. King and Co. in vermilion in a setting 6 x 2 on panes 6 x 10.

(a) Normal Surcharge (Jan. 25th).

E26	1d. on 2d. **sl-blk and or**	2·00	2·50
	a no stop after "1d."	7·00	7·50
	b surcharge double	£450	—
	c surcharge tete beche (pair) ..	£475	—

(b) Inverted surcharge (Feb. 25th ?).

E27	1d. on 2d. **sl-blk and or**..	2·00	2·50
	a no stop after "1d."	7·00	7·50
	b surcharge double	£450	—

E27—As a result of 2 sheets of the first setting being found inverted, a further 6,000 were then overprinted with surcharge inverted and issued on March19th, 1907, all second setting.

This stamp was sold for 2d. and was valid for 1d. postage; the other 1d. being given to alleviate distress caused by the Jamaica earthquake.

Withdrawn—April 25th, 1907.

*D

1912 (**July 23rd – Aug. 13th**) (*typo*) **De La Rue. Wmk. Multiple Crown CA. Perf. 14. Sheets 120 – two panes, each 6 x 10.**

G1	¼d.	**brown** (23/7)	10	10
G2	¼d.	**dp chocolate** ('16)	15	15
G3	½d.	**green** (23/7)	10	10
G4	1d.	**red**	50	30
G5	1d.	**scarlet** (11/15)	2·00	50
G6	2d.	**slate and grey**	1·50	3·50
G7	2½d.	**bright blue**	1·25	1·00
G8	3d.	**purple/yellow**	1·25	3·00
G9	3d.	**purple brown/buff**	1·75	3·00
G10	4d.	**red and black/yel**	1·25	4·00
		a on pale yellow	3·00	4·00
G11	6d.	**pur and dl pur**	3·00	3·75
G12	1/–	**black/green**	5·00	7·00
G13	1/–	**gr blk/bl grey**	6·00	7·00
G14	2/–	**blue and pur/bl**	£32	£32
G15	3/–	**violet and green**	£32	£32
G1/15		**set** (11v)	£80	£85
SPG1/15		**specimen set** (11v)	£45	‡

1916 (**June 16th**)**-20.** (*recess*) **De La Rue. Wmk. Multiple Crown CA. Perf. 14.**

(**a**) **Thick paper except G29/31/35 (on thin paper). Sheets 12 x 5.**

G16	¼d.	**deep brown**	25	30
G17	¼d.	**chestnut brn** (4/18)	30	30
G18	¼d.	**dull brown** (11/18)	40	50
G19	½d.	**green**	40	35
G20	½d.	**deep green** (4/18)	40	35
G21	½d.	**yel-grn** (10/18)	35	35
G22	1d.	**rose-red**	4·50	2·75
G23	1d.	**carmine**	1·50	50
G24	1d.	**scarlet** (7/17)	1·50	50
G25	1d.	**deep scar** (2/20)	3·00	1·50
G26	2d.	**grey**	2·75	3·75
G27	2d.	**slate**	3·00	4·00
G28	2½d.	**ultramarine**	60	90
G29	3d.	**purple/yellow**	1·50	1·50
G30	3d.	**pur brn/pl yel** ('19)	9·00	9·00
G31	4d.	**carmine-red/yel** (23.6.16)	1·25	4·00
G32	4d.	**scarlet/yellow**	1·50	4·25
G33	6d.	**purple**	1·50	2·00
G34	6d.	**reddish purple**	2·00	2·00
G35	1/–	**black/green**	3·25	3·00
G36	1/–	**gr-blk/bluish grey**	3·50	3·00
G37	2/–	**purple/blue**	£16	£16
G38	3/–	**deep violet**	£30	£32
G16/38		**set** (11v)	£60	£60
SPG16/38		**specimen set** (11v)	£65	‡

G16/23/24 are known with wmk. inverted.

G27 is known with wmk. reversed.

G22/23/24/28 are known with wmk. inverted and reversed.

A Proof of G16 exists in deep green on thick wove paper, Perf. 14.

(**b**) **Medium paper. New plates from re-engraved Die without circular border line. Sheets 6 x 5.** (**February 18th, 1918**).

G39	4d.	**black and red**	60	2·50
G40	3/–	**grn and dp violet**	£14	£15
G41	3/–	**grn and bt violet**	£90	£100
SPG39/40		**specimen set** (2v)	£50	‡

An imperf Colour Trial of G40 is known in deep brown and yellow on unwatermarked paper with overprint 'Specimen'.

WAR TAX

1917-18. War Tax. No. G4 overprinted WAR TAX in black sans serif capitals by De La Rue.

(**a**) **On white paper.**

G42	1d.	**br red** (10.10.17)	25	30
		a imperf (pair)	£600	—
G43	1d.	**dl carmine** (5/18)	50	50
G44	1d.	**car-rose** (7/19)	1·00	1·00
SPG42		**specimen**	£20	‡

(**b**) **On bluish-grey paper** (**18.2.18**).

G45	1d.	**pale red**	50	50

1920 (**Sept. 9th**)**-21. Victory.** (*recess*) **De La Rue. Perf. 14. Sheets ¼d. – 6d. 12 x 5. (Wmk. upright). 1/– – 3/– 6 x 5 (Wmk. sideways).**

(**a**) **Wmk. Multiple Crown CA.**

G46	¼d.	**blk and bistre brn**	25	45
G47	¼d.	**pl gr and bistre**	20	20
G48	½d.	**blk and bt yel-grn**	25	45
G49	½d.	**pl gr and yel-grn**	20	15
G50	1d.	**blk and vermilion**	30	40
G51	2d.	**black and grey**	1·00	3·25
G52	2½d.	**indigo and ult**	2·00	3·25
G53	2½d.	**indigo and azure**	2·50	3·50
G54	3d.	**black and purple**	1·00	2·00
G55	4d.	**blk and bl-green**	1·00	3·00

G56	6d.	**blk and brn-orange**	1·50	3·00
G57	6d.	**black and ochre** ..	1·75	3·00
G58	1/–	**blk and bt green** ..	4·50	7·00
G59	2/–	**black and brown** ..	9·00	£13
G60	3/–	**black and orange**..	£20	£24

(b) Wmk. Multiple Script CA (Aug. 22nd 1921)

G61	1d.	**black and ver** ..	3·75	40
G46/61		**set (12v)**	£40	£50
SPG46/61		**specimen set (12v)**	£80	‡

G46/47 exist with wmk. inverted and reversed.

G48/49/54 exist with wmk. inverted.

G59 exists with wmk. inverted (*sideways to right*).

A Proof of G60 is known in blue and deep green on unwatermarked paper, perf. 14, with overprint 'Specimen'.

1921 (Nov. 14th)-24. (*recess*) **De La Rue. Perf. 14. Sheets 12 x 10.**

(a) Wmk. Multiple Crown CA.

G62	3d.	**purple/pale yellow**	50	1·75
G63	4d.	**red/pale yellow** ..	90	1·75
G64	1/–	**black/emerald** ..	3·75	7·00

(b) Wmk. Multiple Script CA.

G65	¼d.	**brown**	25	10
G66	¼d.	**deep brown** ..	30	10
G67	½d.	**green**	25	30
G68	½d.	**pale green**	30	30
G69	1d.	**red**	30	30
G70	1d.	**bt rose-carmine** ..	1·75	50
G71	2d.	**grey**	1·25	30
G72	2½d.	**ultramarine**.. ..	70	1·25
G73	6d.	**reddish purple** ..	1·25	3·00
G74	1/–	**blk/em (18.9.24)** ..	£16	£17
G75	2/–	**purple/blue** ..	£16	£18
G76	3/–	**deep violet**	£20	£24
G62/76		**set (12v)**	£60	£70
SPG62/76		**specimen set (12v)**	£50	‡

G65/66 exist with wmk. reversed.

G69/70 exist with wmk. inverted.

1925-35. (*recess*) **De La Rue. Wmk. Multiple Script CA. Sheets 10 x 6 (G90). 10 x 8 (G77-79, G85-86). 10 x 12 (G80).**

(a) Perf. 14.

G77	¼d.	**brown**	10	10

G78	¼d.	**grey-brown** ..	15	15
G79	½d.	**green**	10	10
G80	½d.	**grey-green**	15	15
G81	1d.	**rose**	10	10
G82	1d.	**rosine**	10	10
G83	1d.	**scarlet**	15	15
G84	1½d.	**orange**	1·75	45
G85	2d.	**grey**	30	75
G86	2½d.	**blue**	65	35
G87	2½d.	**bt ultramarine** ..	2·00	10
G88	3d.	**brn/yellow ('35)** ..	1·75	1·75
G89	3d.	**or-brn/pl yel** ..	35	30
G90	3d.	**yel-brn/pl yel** ..	40	30
G91	4d.	**red/yellow**	60	60
G92	4d.	**brown-red/yellow**	75	70
G93	4d.	**rosine/pl yellow**..	60	60
G94	6d.	**purple**	90	90
G95	6d.	**mauve**	1·00	90
G96	1/–	**gr-blk/green** ..	2·25	2·00
G97	1/–	**black/green** ..	2·00	3·25
		a on pale green ..	2·50	3·00
		b on blue-green ..	2·25	3·00
G98	1/–	**brn-blk/bt yel-grn**	2·75	5·50
G99	2/–	**purple/blue** ..	3·75	5·75
G100	2/6	**carmine/blue** ..	£15	£20
G101	3/–	**deep violet**	9·00	£12
G77/101		**set (13v)**	£30	£40
SPG77/101		**specimen set (13v)**	£65	‡

(b) Perf. 13½ x 12½ (1932).

G102	½d.	**green**	30	10
G103	½d.	**dull green**	40	10
G104	1d.	**scarlet**	40	10
G105	1d.	**rosine**	50	10
G106	1½d.	**orange**	45	25
G107	1½d.	**red-orange**	50	25
G108	2½d.	**bt ultramarine** ..	2·50	40
G109	1/–	**black/emerald** ..	5·50	6·50
G102/109		**set (5v)**	9·00	7·00

1927 (Feb. 17th). Tercentenary of Settlement. (*recess*) **Bradbury Wilkinson. Wmk. Multiple Script CA. Perf. 12½.**

G110	1d.	**carmine**	60	60
SPG110		**specimen (1v)** ..	£20	‡

1935 (May 6th). Silver Jubilee. (*recess*)

Waterlow and Sons. Wmk. Multiple Script CA. Perf. 11 x 12. Sheets 6 x 10.

G111	1d.	**dp blue and scar** ..	10	15
G112	1½d.	**ult and grey** ..	30	40
G113	2½d.	**brn and dp blue** ..	1·25	1·00
G114	1/–	**slate and purple** ..	4·50	5·00
G111/114		**set** (4v) ..	6·00	6·00
SPG111/114		**specimen set** (4v)	£20	‡

Remainders were withdrawn on December 31st, 1935.

1938 (Jan. 3rd) -48 Design, Seal of Colony. (*recess*) **De La Rue. Sheets 10 x 12.**

(a) Perf. 13¼ x 13 (C).

1	½d.	**green**	10	10
	a	sage green (/41) ..	15	10
	b	booklet pane of ten ..	£15	—
2	½d.	**bistre** (16/10/42) ..	5	5
	a	yellow buff (5/8/48)	5	5
3	1d.	**scarlet-red**	£30	1·00
4	1d.	**blue-green** (16/10/42)	20	5
	a	green	15	5
5	1½d.	**orange**	15	10
	a	red-orange (12/6/47)	15	10
	b	booklet pane of six ..	£10	—
6	2d.	**red-claret** (3/6/41) ..	20	20
7	2d.	**carmine-red**(20/9/43)	10	10
8	2½d.	**ultramarine**	20	25
	a	blue (17/2/44) ..	50	75
9	3d.	**dp brown**	25	25
	a	brown (17/2/44) ..	20	10
	b	line over horse's head	£30	£20
10	3d.	**blue** (1/4/47) ..	15	15
	a	ultramarine (18/12/47	40	75
	b	line over horse's head)	£20	£20
11	4d.	**dp grey**	20	10
	a	joined scroll ..	£20	£20
	b	flying mane ..	£25	£20
	c	black (18/12/47) ..	50	20
	d	grey-black (5/8/48) .	15	10
12	6d.	**violet**	15	5
	a	pale violet	20	5
13	8d.	**dp magenta** (9/12/46)	50	30
	a	magenta (18/12/47)	40	30
14	1/–	**olive-green**	3·00	1·00
	a	olive (9/42) ..	1·10	40
	b	brn-olive (19/11/45)	60	10
	c	dp ol-grn (11/12/46)	75	25
	d	olive-brown (5/8/48)	50	10
15	2/6	**reddish-purple** ..	2·00	70
	a	pale purple ..	3·00	80
16	5/–	**greyish-indigo**		
		(3/6/41)	3·50	1·40
SP 1/16		**specimen set** perf (14)	£50	‡

(b) Perf. 13¾ x 14 (L).

17	1d.	**scarlet-red** (3/1/38) .	2·00	1·00

As before but Perf. 14 (C or L). (Nos. 18, 19, 21, 23 Line; Nos. 20a, 24 Comb.; Nos. 20, 22 (L and C).

18	½d.	**sage green** (8/42) ..	£15	1·00
19	1d.	**bt scarlet-red** (10/40)	1·25	10
	a	booklet pane of ten ..	£20	—
20	1d.	**blue-grn** (16/10/42) ..	20	5
	a	green (5/8/48) ..	10	5
21	1½d.	**orange** (12/41) ..	30	10
22	2d.	**carmine-red**(11/9/44)	10	10
23	3d.	**brown** (/41)	20	20
	a	line over horse's head	£20	£20
24	4d.	**grey-black**(11/9/44)	20	20
	a	joined scroll ..	£25	£25
	b	flying mane ..	£25	£25
1/24		**set** (16 v)	8·00	3·00

11a   11b

Nos. 11a/24a—A curved line joins the top right scroll, Row 7/8.

Nos. 11b/24b—This variety consists of the seahorse having an upright tuft of mane, somewhat resembling a plume, Row 4/1.

9b

Nos. 9b/10b/23a — Occurs on all printings, Row 4/10.

No. 13a—A later release 5/8/48 similar in shade was printed in fluorescent-aniline ink.

ONE PENNY

1947 (April 21st) Nos. 7 and 22 surcharged by the Barbados Advocate Co., Bridgetown.

(a) Perf. 13¼ x 13 (C).

25	1d./2d.	**carmine-red** ..	30	55
	a	broken N's ..	3·00	3·00
	b	short Y ..	3·00	3·00
	c	broken E ..	3·00	3·00

(b) Perf. 14 (C).

26	1d./2d.	**carmine-red** ..	35	55
	a	broken N's ..	4·00	4·00
	b	short Y ..	4·00	4·00
	c	broken E ..	4·00	4·00

The surcharge has several constant varieties, the most noteworthy being illustrated as follows :—

25a/26a
Row 2/8

ONE PEN NY

ONE PENNY

25b/26b
Row 6/2

25c/26c
Rows 7/4 &
11/4

ONE PENNY

A double surcharge is reported to exist, but we have not seen this.

1939 (June 27th) Tercentenary of General Assembly. (*recess*) **De La Rue. Perf. 13½ x 14 (C). Sheets 6 x 10.**

S4	½d. green	..	..	15	15
S5	1d. scarlet	..	..	20	20
S6	1½d. orange	..	..	80	50
S7	2½d. ultramarine		..	1·00	1·25
S8	3d. light brown		..	1·00	1·50
S4/8	set (5)	..	..	3·00	3·50
SP S4/8	specimen set perf(5)		£30	‡

1946 (Sept. 18th) Victory. As Aden.

S9	1½d. orange	..	..	5	5
	a double flag	..	2·00	2·00
S10	3d. chocolate-brown	..	10	10
SP S9/10	specimen set perf(2)	£14	‡

S9a—This variety is in the form of a second flag (*one below the other*) at the stern of the launch, Row 5/2.

1948 (Nov. 24th) Silver Wedding. As Aden.

S11	1½d. orange	..	..	10	10
S12	5/– bluish-slate	..	4·00	4·00

1949 (Oct. 10th) U.P.U. As Aden.

S13	1½d. red-orange	..	..	10	10
S14	3d. indigo	..	..	25	25
S15	4d. grey	..	..	..	40	40
S16	1/– sage-green	..	..	60	60
S13/16	set (4)	..	..	1·20	1·30

1950 (May 1st) Designs, 1c. to 60c. (Views and Scenes in Colony); $1.20 (Map); $2.40 (Seal); 3c. (W. L. Eunica); 8c. (Frances W. Smith): 60c. (W. L. Edricia, Grenada). (*recess*) **Bradbury, Wilkinson. Perf. 13½ x 13½ (C) (Other Values). Designs, 4c., 48c., $1.50, V. Sheets 10 x 10.**

27	1c. slate-indigo	..	5	10
28	2c. emerald	..	..	10	5
29	3c. choc and slate-grn		10	5
30	4c. rose-carmine	..	10	10
31	6c. bright blue	..	..	15	15
32	8c. blue and pur-brown	15	15
33	12c. blue-grn and ol-grey	40	20
	a grey-grn and ol-grn		
	(10/3/54)	60	40
34	24c. dp scar and grey-blk	40	35
35	48c. purple-violet	..	1·50	1·25
36	60c. dp green and lake	..	2·00	1·50
37	$1.20 dp car and olive-grn	3·00	2·00
38	$2.40 grey-black	..	..	5·00	4·00
27/38	set (12)	..	..	£12	£10

1951 (Feb. 16th) West Indies University College. As Antigua.

S17	3c. brown and slate-grn	10	10
S18	12c. blue-grn and sepia-blk	30	30

SPECIAL ISSUES

1937 (May 14th) Coronation. As Aden.

S1	1d. red	..	..	..	20	20
S2	1½d. yellow-brown	..	25	25
S3	2½d. blue	..	..	..	70	70
SP S1/3	specimen set perf (3)	£14	‡

1952 (April 15th) Centenary of First Barbados Postage Stamps. Design, Replica of original Stamps. Printers (*recess*) **Waterlow & Sons. Perf. 13½ x 13¼ (C). Sheets 10 x 10.**

S19	3c. grey-grn and bluish-slate	..	..	10	10

S20	4c.	**blue and rose-carmine**	15	15
S21	12c.	**bluish-slate and**		
		emerald	20	20
S22	24c.	**red-brown and black**	30	35
S19/22		**set** (4)	75	80

Number issued—3c., 574,860; 4c., 271,120; 12c., 339,854; 24c., 219,187.

POSTAGE DUE STAMPS

1934-48. (*typo*) **De La Rue. Wmk. Multiple Script CA. Perf. 13¾ x 14. Sheets 6 x 10.**

PD1	½d.	**deep green** (10.2.35)	20	20
		a on rough paper ('47)	40	30
PD2	1d.	**black** (2.1.34)	60	40
		a bisect (½d.) on cover	—	£140
		b on rough paper ('47)	80	90
PD3	3d.	**carmine** (13.3.47) ..	3·50	1·50
		a on smooth paper ('48)	4·50	2·50
SP PD1/3		**specimen set** (3v) ..	£25	‡

PD2*a*—This bisect was officially authorised from March, 1934 until supplies of the ½d. stamp were available in February, 1935. In some cases the half stamp was surcharged ½d. in red or in black in manuscript.

1950 (Dec. 8th) As No. PD1, etc., but currency changed.

PD4	1c.	**dp green**	25	35
PD5	2c.	**black**	30	40
PD6	6c.	**rose-carmine** ..	85	1·20

As Nos. PD4/6, but printed on chalk-coated paper.

PD7	1c.	**dk green** (29/11/51)	10	15
PD8	2c.	**black** (20/1/53) ..	15	15
PD9	6c.	**car-red** (20/1/53) ..	40	50

Watermark Varieties (Type A)

(See Introduction for details)

PD7*a*	1c. Crown missing ..	£20	—
PD7*b*	1c. St. Edward's Crown ..	£15	—
PD8*b*	2c. St. Edward s Crown ..	£15	—
PD9*a*	6c. Crown missing ..	£25	—
PD9*b*	6c. St. Edward's Crown ..	£20	—

GERMAN PROPAGANDA LABELS.

The 1944 German imitations of the G.B. 1937 Definitives ½d to 3d (see after Great Britain for details) were also overprinted in black "LIQUIDA-TION/OF EMPIRE/BARBADOS" within a vertical rectangular frame. £150.

BARBUDA

This small island originally belonged to the Codrington family, subsequently becoming a dependency and using the stamps of Antigua.

From October 31st 1890 until 1903 the stamps of Leeward Islands were used and from 1903 until 1922 both Leeward Islands and Antigua stamps were in concurrent use.

The stamps here listed were in use for a comparatively short time; and thereafter until 1968 the stamps of Antigua were again used, as well as unoverprinted Leeward Islands issues (until July 1st 1956). From November 1968 Barbuda again used its own stamps, concurrently with those of Antigua.

1922 (July 13th) Stamps of Leeward Islands (King George V), overprinted "BARBUDA" in black, or red (G2 and G11).

(a) Wmk. Multiple Crown CA. Die II.

G1	3d.	**dl pur/pl yel** (C) ..	1·50	3·50
G2	1/–	**black/emerald** (C)	4·00	6·50
G3	5/–	**green and red/ pale yellow** (C)	£85	£110

(b) Wmk. Multiple Script CA. Die II.

G4	½d.	**deep green** ..	1·50	3·25
G5	1d.	**scarlet**	1·50	3·25
G6	2d.	**slate-grey**	1·75	3·75
		a wmk. inverted ..	£30	—
G7	2½d.	**bright blue** ..	1·75	4·50
		a wmk. reversed ..	£30	—
G8	6d.	**dl and brt pur** (C)	4·00	8·50
G9	2/–	**purple and blue/ blue** (C)	£12	£17
G10	3/–	**brt grn and vio** (C)	£26	£35
G11	4/–	**black and red** (C)	£32	£45
G1/11		**set** (11v)	£165	£225
SPG1/11		**specimen set** (11v)	£150	‡

BASUTOLAND

The territory came under British protection in 1843, was annexed in 1868, became a part of Cape Colony in 1871, and was made a Crown Colony in 1884.

From 1880 to 1933 the stamps of Cape of Good Hope and the Union of South Africa were in use and may be recognised by the cancellations.

1933 (Dec. 1st) Printers (recess) Waterlow. Wmk. Mult. Script CA. Perf. 12½. Sheets 12 x 5.

G1	½d. **emerald**	.. ..	35	45
	a bt emerald	..	70	90
G2	1d. **dp red**	.. ..	25	50
	a carmine red	..	75	75
G3	2d.**rose purple**	..	50	70
	a dp bt purple	..	1·25	1·75
G4	3d. **bright blue**	..	60	1·75
G5	4d. **grey** ..	.. ..	1·25	2·50
G6	6d. **brown orange**		1·75	3·25
G7	1/– **red orange**	.. ..	4·00	6·50
G8	2/6 **sepia** ..	.. ..	£11	£18
G9	5/– **violet**	.. ..	£30	£32
G10	10/– **olive green**	..	£80	£85
G1/10	**set** (10)	.. ..	£125	£145
SP G1/10 **specimen set** perf (10)			£85	‡

1935 (May 4th) Silver Jubilee. Printers (recess) De La Rue. Wmk. Mult. Script CA. Perf. 13½ x 14. Sheets 6 x 10.

G11	1d. **dp blue and carmine**		25	30
G12	2d. **ult and grey**	..	50	1·00
G13	3d. **brown and dp blue** ..		1·75	2·00
G14	6d. **slate and purple**	..	2·75	3·75
G11/14	**set** (4)	.. ..	5·00	7·00
SP G11/14 **specimen set** perf (4)		£20	‡

Numbers issued—99,000 sets.

1938 (April 1st)-52 Printers (recess) Waterlow & Sons. Perf. 12¼ (L). Sheets 6 x 10

1	½d. **yellow-green**	..	20	10
	a green (1/44)	..	10	5
	b pale green (14/5/52)		10	5
2	1d. **scarlet**	.. ..	10	5
	a tower variety	..	£15	£16
	b scarlet rose (1/10/46)		15	15
	c tower variety	..	£16	£16
	d carmine lake	..	6·00	—
	e tower variety	..	£20	£20
3	1½d. **dull pale blue**	..	20	10
	a light blue (8/12/47) .		10	10
4	2d. **red-purple**	..	20	20
	a mauve-pur (10/12/45)		10	15
5	3d. **dp blue**	.. ..	10	15
6	4d. **grey**	.. ..	30	30
	a slate-grey (23/1/50)		25	25
7	6d. **yellow-ochre**	..	30	30
	a orange-ochre (1/10/46)3		50	50
8	1/– **dp orange**	..	50	60
	a pale reddish-orange (14/5/52)	..	40	50
9	2/6 **sepia**	.. ..	2·00	2·00
10	5/– **bright violet** ..	..	3·50	3·50
11	10/– **sage-green**	..	7·00	8·00
	a dp ol-grn (1/10/46)		7·00	8·00
1/11	**set** (11)	.. ..	£14	£15
SP 1/11 **specimen set** perf (11)		£40	‡

2c/e A flaw resembling a tower is to be found in hill top Row 2/4 (see illustration).

SPECIAL ISSUES

1937 (May 12th) Coronation. As Aden.

S1	1d. **scarlet** ..	.. ..	10	10
S2	2d. **red-purple**	.. ..	15	15
S3	3d. **dp blue**	..	30	30
SP S1/3 **specimen set** perf (3)		£12	‡

1945 (Dec. 3rd) Victory. Nos. S33–5 of South Africa, overprinted Basutoland.

			Pair M	Pair U
S4	1d. **dp brn and car**	..	10	10
	a aniline centre	..	1·00	—
	b barbed wire Row 9/6		2·00	—
S5	2d. **slate blue and pur-vio**		10	15
S6	3d. **dp blue and blue** ..		15	15
SP S4/6 (**3 pairs**) perf specimen		—	‡

1947(Feb.17th) Royal Visit. Designs, Portraits of Royal Family. Printers (*recess*) **Waterlow & Sons. Perf. 12½ (L). Sheets 10 x 6 or 6 x 10.**

S7	1d.	scarlet	5	5
S8	2d.	green	10	10
S9	3d.	ultramarine	10	10
S10	1/–	dull mauve	15	15
S7/10		set (4)	40	40
SP S7/10	specimen set perf (4)	£40	‡

1948 (Dec. 1st) Silver Wedding. As Aden.

S11	1½d.	ultramarine	10	10
S12	10/–	olive-grey	4·00	4·00

1949 (Oct. 10th) U.P.U. As Aden.

S13	1½d.	dull ultramarine	10	15
S14	3d.	indigo	20	25
S15	6d.	orange	30	35
S16	1/–	beech-brown	40	45
S13/16		set (4)	90	1·10

POSTAGE DUE STAMPS

1937-47 Printers (*typo*) **De La Rue. Perf. 13¾ x 14 (C). Sheets 6 x 10.**

PD1	1d.	carmine-red (/37)	60	60
	a	dp carmine-red (rough paper) (/47)	3·00	3·00
PD2	2d.	pur-vio	1·00	1·00
	a	(-/47) rough paper	2·50	2·50
SP PD1/2	perf specimen	£20	‡

1951. As before but printed on chalk-coated paper.

PD3	1d.	dp car-red (24/10/51)	20	25
PD4	2d.	pur-vio (6/11/52)	20	25
	a	thick "d"	6·00	6·00

PD4*a*—The "d" and dot below are a thicker type on R9/6, R10/6.

Watermark Varieties (Type A)

(See Introduction for details).

PD3a	1d. Crown missing	£22	—
PD3b	1d. St. Edward's Crown	£18	—
PD4b	2d. Crown missing	£22	—
PD4c	2d. St. Edward's Crown	£14	—

OFFICIAL STAMPS

1934 (May 4th) Stamps of 1933 issue overprinted OFFICIAL.

GO1	½d.	emerald	£1750	£650
GO2	1d.	scarlet	£450	£400
GO3	2d.	bright purple	£350	£300
GO4	6d.	brown orange	£1650	£950
GO1/4		set (4)	£4000	£2250

Numbers sold—½d. x 23, 1d. x 34, 2d. x 54 6d. x 26, plus four of each in the Royal Collection.

BECHUANALAND

Following a long unsettled period emigrant Boers established the Republic of Stellaland in January 1883 and stamps were issued in February 1884. Subsequently, this territory was annexed in 1885 by Great Britain as the Colony of British Bechuanaland; and the Stellaland stamps continued in use until the first British administration stamps were issued on December 2nd, 1885. British Bechuanaland was incorporated into Cape Colony in November 1895, and then used the stamps of the Cape until the Union of South Africa was created in 1910.

A British Protectorate was also proclaimed in 1885 over a much larger area of Bechuanaland lying north of the newly established Colony; and British Bechuanaland stamps were also used there.

I BRITISH BECHUANALAND

1885 (Dec. 2nd)-86. Stamps of Cape of Good Hope overprinted in black or red (No. V2) by W. A. Richards and Sons, Capetown. Original stamps Typo De La Rue. Perf. 14. Sheets 240 – four panes, each 6 x 10. Overprint Setting 120 – two panes, each 6 x 10.

(a) Wmk. Crown CC.

V1	4d.	blue ('86)	£23	£27
SPV1	specimen (1)		—	—

(b) Wmk. Crown CA.

V2	½d.	slate	6·00	7·00
	a	overprint double (red and black)	£270	—
V3	3d.	claret	£11	£14
SPV3	specimen (1)		—	‡

(c) Wmk. Anchor.

V4	½d.	grey-black ('86)	3·50	3·50
	a	'B' omitted	—	—
	b	overprint double	£250	£250
V5	1d.	rose-red	3·50	3·50
	a	'B' omitted	—	—
	b	overprint double	—	£725
V6	2d.	bistre	£12	£10
	a	'B' omitted	—	—
	b	overprint double	—	—
V7	6d.	purple ('86)	£15	£19
V8	1/–	green (11/86)	£120	£80
	a	'B' omitted	—	—
SPV4/5	specimen pair		—	‡

V2*a* is believed to be from a Proof sheet.

V4*a*/5*a*/6*a*/8*a* The 'B' of 'British' is omitted.

V4*b* is only known unused.

V5*b* is only known used with '534' (Kuruman) postmark.

V6*b* is only known used with '638' (Mafeking) postmark.

Until as late as March 1886 these stamps were postally cancelled in manuscript or with temporary rubber postmarks.

Forgeries of the overprint on all values have a full stop after 'Bechuanaland'.

BRITISH

BECHUANALAND

1887 (Oct.) No. V176 of G.B. overprinted in black by De La Rue.

V9	½d.	vermilion	70	60
	a	overprint double	£800	—
SPV9	specimen (1)		£50	‡

1888 (Jan. 19th) Typo De La Rue. Perf. 13½ -14. (a) Wmk. Orb (G.B.). Sheets 12 x 10.

V10	1d.	lilac and black	9·00	2·50
V11	2d.	lilac and black	£10	2·50
V12	3d.	lilac and black	2·50	2·50
V13	4d.	lilac and black	£18	4·75
V14	6d.	lilac and black	£17	£13

(b) Wmk. 'VR' in script, reading upwards. Sheets 12 x 7.

V15	1/–	green and black	£17	6·50
V16	2/–	green and black	£20	£10
V17	2/6	green and black	£22	£15
V18	5/–	green and black	£50	£42
V19	10/–	green and black	£95	£95

(c) Wmk. Two Orbs (G.B.) sideways. Sheets 10 x 6.

V20	£1	lilac and black	£450	£500
V21	£5	lilac and black	£1200	£600
SPV10/21	specimen set (12v)		£550	‡

1888 Prepared for use but not issued. As Nos. V10/14.

V22 8d. **lilac and black** .. — —

1888 (Aug. 7th) Nos. V10/15 locally overprinted by P. Townshend and Co. at Vryburg in black or red (Nos. V25 and V26) or green (No. V24).

V23	1d. on 1d.	**lilac and blk** ..	4·00	2·50
V24	2d. on 2d.	**lilac and blk** (Aug.) ..	—	£375
V25	2d. on 2d.	**lilac and blk** (Sept.) ..	5·00	3·00
V26	4d. on 4d.	**lilac and blk** ..	£38	£35
V27	6d. on 6d.	**lilac and blk** ..	£32	£16
V28	1/– on1/–	**grn and blk** ..	£38	£27
SPV23/28		**specimen set** (less V27) 4v	—	‡

V24/25—The first sheets of the 2d. value were overprinted in green; but, as the colour did not show up clearly, the printer was told to change the colour to red.

V27—An overprint in blue is recorded but is believed to be bogus.

There are a number of minor varieties of overprint, including the figure '2' with curved foot. arising from the worn state of the type.

1888 (Dec.) No. V12 locally surcharged in black by P. Townshend and Co. at Vryburg. Setting 12 x 5.

V29 ½d. on 3d. **lilac and blk** .. £35 £35

A number of varieties are recorded, many of them cancelled with the Vryburg datestamp of August 8th and 22nd 1890. These are believed to have come from Printer's spoiled sheets which were not destroyed and which were subsequently discovered by a postal official who had access to the datestamp.

The varieties include inverted surcharge, 'Pneny,' 'Helf Panny', and 'Ponny'.

Number surcharged—1,440.

1889 Stamp of Cape of Good Hope overprinted in green by W. A. Richards & Sons, Capetown. Original stamp Typo De La Rue. Wmk. Anchor. Perf. 14. Sheets 240 – four panes, each 6 x 10. Overprint setting 6 x 10.

V30	½d. **slate**	3·75	6·00
a	overprint double ..	—	—
b	overprint double, one inverted	£200	—
c	overprint double, one vertical	£200	—
d	overprint omitted, in pair with normal ..	£425	—
e	'British' omitted ..	£525	—
SPV30	**specimen** (1)	—	‡

V30e was caused by gross misplacement of the overprint.

There is some doubt as to the status of these varieties, which may have come from Printers spoiled sheets.

1891 (Nov.)-94 Stamps of Cape of Good Hope overprinted in black by W. A. Richards & Sons, Capetown. Original Stamps Typo De La Rue. Wmk. Anchor. Perf. 14. Sheets 240 – four panes, each 6 x 10. Overprint setting 120 – two panes, each 6 x 10.

(a) Reading upwards (Nov. 1891).

V31	1d.	**rose-red**	6·00	7·00
a		dots omitted ..		
b		'British' omitted ..	—	£100
V32	2d.	**bistre**	2·25	2·50
a		stop omitted ..	£85	
SPV31/32		**specimen pair** ..	£175	‡

(b) Reading downwards.

V33	1d.	**rose-red** ('92) ..	80	80
a		dots omitted ..	£20	£20
b		'British' omitted ..	£100	—
V34	2d.	**bistre** (6/94) ..	1·75	80
a		dots omitted ..	£38	£45
b		'British' omitted ..	£130	£130
c		overprint double ..	£385	£325
SPV33/34		**specimen pair** ..	—	‡

V31a/33a/34a—The dots are omitted from the 'i' in 'British'.

V31b/33b/34b were caused by misplacement of the overprint.

V32a—The stop is omitted after 'Bechuanaland' Row 3/3 (Left pane).

It is believed that Nos. V33/34 may also have been overprinted in 1891 but no used copies are known earlier than the dates shown.

BRITISH
BECHUANALAND

1891 (Dec.)-94 Nos. V151, 180, 185, 190, 195 of G.B. overprinted in black by De La Rue.

V35	1d.	**lilac** (Die II) ..	90	50
V36	2d.	**green and carmine**	60	1·00
V37	4d.	**grn and dp brn** ..	2·25	1·25
		a bisect vertically (2d.) on cover..	‡	£550
V38	6d.	**purple/rose-red** ..	2·50	1·75
V39	1/-	**green** (-/7/94) ..	5·50	8·50
		a bisect diagonally (6d.) on cover ..	‡	—
V35/39		**set (5v)**	£13	£12
SPV35/39		**specimen set (5v)**	£75	‡

V37a—Used at Palapye Station on November 22nd 1899 and initialled by the Postmaster. Care should be taken in the purchase of this variety, as members of the Bechuanaland Border Police later persuaded the Postmaster to provide them with cancelled and initialled bisects on covers which were subsequently back-stamped at other Post Offices with back-dated postmarks.

V39a—Used at Kanye on December 6th, 1904 on a registered cover, similarly initialled.

The sale of British Bechuanaland stamps ceased when the Colony was incorporated into Cape Colony on November 16th, 1895; and remaining stocks were handed over for use in the Protectorate.

II BECHUANALAND PROTECTORATE

BRITISH	BRITISH
Protectorate	Protectorate
	Fourpence
BECHUANALAND	BECHUANALAND
Type I	Type IV

1888 (Aug.)-89 No. V9 further overprinted and surcharged in black by P. Townshend & Co. at Vryburg.

(a) Type I (large capital 'P') (16mm).

V40	½d.	**vermilion** ..	2·00	3·25
		a 'Protectorate' double	£90	—

(b) Type II (small capital 'P') (15mm).

V41	½d.	**vermilion**	£18	£18
		a 'Protectorate'	£24	£24
		inverted ..	—	—
		b 'Protectorate' double	—	—
		c 'Protectorate' double	£24	£24
		both inverted ..	£220	£180
		d 'Portectorate' inverted ..	—	—

(c) Type III (larger lower-case letters) (19mm).

V42	½d.	**vermilion**	£21	£23
		a 'Protectorrte' ..	—	—
		b 'Protectorate double'	£125	—

(d) Type IV (as Type I with surcharge) 1889

V43	4d. on ½d.	**vermilion** ..	4·00	4·00

1888 (Aug.) Nos. V10/19 overprinted and surcharged in black by P. Townshend & Co. at Vryburg.

V44	1d. on 1d.	**lilac and black**	2·25	3·25
V45	2d. on 2d.	**lilac and black**	6·50	6·50
V46	3d. on 3d.	**lilac and black**	£32	£35
V47	4d. on 4d.	**lilac and black**	£38	£38
V48	6d. on 6d.	**lilac and black**	£20	£18
		a 'O' omitted ..	£320	£320
V49	1/-	**green and black**	£28	£20
		a 'O' omitted ..	£375	£375
V50	2/-	**green and black**	£100	£100
		a 'O' omitted ..	£1000	—
V51	2/6	**green and black**	£210	£200
		a 'O' omitted ..	£1250	—
V52	5/-	**green and black**	£425	£450
		a 'O' omitted ..	£1750	—
V53	10/-	**green and black**	£1100	£1100
		a 'O' omitted ..	£3500	—
SPV44/51		**specimen set** less V46/47) 6v	—	‡

V48a/53a— The first 'o' in 'Protectorate' is missing.

1888 (Aug.) No. V26 (No. V13 with red surcharge) overprinted as No. V40 (Type I) in black.

V54	4d. on 4d.	**lilac and black** ..	£24	£17

1889 Stamp of Cape of Good Hope overprinted in green by W. A. Richards & Sons, Capetown. Original stamp Typo De La Rue. Wmk. Anchor. Perf. 14. Sheets 240 – four panes, each 6 x 10. Overprint setting 6 x 10.

V55	½d.	**slate**	1·75	3·00
		a overprint double ..	£140	£150
		b 'Bechuanaland' omitted ..	£225	—
		c 'Protectorate' omitted and 'Bechuanaland' double	—	—

V55b/c were caused by gross misplacement of the overprint.

1896 (Dec.)-97 Stamp of Cape of Good Hope overprinted in black. Original stamps Typo De La Rue. Wmk. Anchor. Perf. 14. Sheets 240 – four panes, each 6 x 10. Overprint setting 120 – two panes, each 6 x 10.

Measurements:

1st figure—Distance between lines of overprint.
2nd figure—Length of 'BECHUANALAND'.

(a) By Taylor and Marshall 13mm/16mm.

V56	½d.	**green** (15/12/96)	1·00	2·00

(b) By Townshend & Co. 13½mm/15mm.

V57	½d.	**green** (19/3/97)	8·00	£10

(c) By W. A. Richards & Son. 10½mm/15mm.

V58	½d.	**green** (9/7/97)	4·00	5·00
SPV56		**specimen** (1)	—	‡

The dates are those of delivery by the Printers. No. V56 is not known used before 1897.

British Bechuanaland had been absorbed into Cape Colony in November 1895; and it is believed that this overprint was an error, and should have been BECHUANALAND PROTECTORATE. Nevertheless, as previously issued British Bechuanaland overprinted stamps continued in use in the Protectorate, the error either passed un-noticed or was not considered unacceptable.

Numbers surcharged—V56 24,000; V57 18,240; V58 48,000.

BECHUANALAND PROTECTORATE

1897 (Oct.)-1902 Nos. V176/177/151/180/182/185/190 of G.B. overprinted in black by De La Rue.

V59	½d.	**vermilion**	45	90
V60	½d.	**blu-grn** (25/2/02)	45	90
V61	1d.	**lilac** (Die II)	45	75
V62	2d.	**grn and carmine**	2·25	2·50
V63	3d.	**pur/yel** (–/12/97)	3·75	3·75
V64	4d.	**grn and dp brn**	5·00	5·50
V65	6d.	**purple/rose-red**	£12	£13
V59/65		**set** (7v)	£22	£25
SPV59/65		**specimen set** (7v)	£90	‡

1904-13 Nos. E1/3, E9 (De La Rue printings)

and E73/74 (Somerset House printings) of G.B. overprinted in black by De La Rue.

E1	½d.	**blu-grn** (–/3/06)		2·25	2·00
E2	½d.	**yel-grn** (–/11/08)		2·50	2·50
E3	1d.	**scarlet** (–/4/05)		2·50	1·50
E4	2½d.	**ultra** (29/11/04)		4·75	4·75
		a stop after 'P'		£400	
E5	1/–	**grn and scar** (1912)		£10	£13
E6	1/–	**grn and car** (1913)		£13	£16
E1/6		**set** (6v)		£33	£37

E4a A full stop appears between 'P' and 'R of PROTECTORATE.

1910 Stamp of Transvaal (KE 7) overprinted "Bechuanaland Protectorate" in two lines in blue for fiscal use.

E7	6d.	**black and orange**	£38	£42

Although not intended for such use, a number were postally used. A cover to London dated "OC 22 10" is in the Royal Collection.

1912 (Sept.) No. G13 of G.B. overprinted as E1/6.

G1	1d.	**bright scarlet**	1·75	1·50
		a no cross on crown	—	£35

1914-24 Stamps of G.B. (Nos. G19/49) similarly overprinted by De La Rue. Watermark Single Cypher.

G2	½d.	**green**	70	60
G3	1d.	**scarlet**	70	60
G4	1½d.	**red-brown**	90	1·25
G5	2d.	**orange** (Die I)	1·25	1·50
G6	2d.	**or** (Die II) (1924)	6·50	7·50
G7	2½d.	**ultramarine**	1·50	1·75
		a stop after 'P'	—	—
G8	3d.	**dull reddish violet**	3·50	5·00
G9	4p.	**slate-green**	2·75	4·50
G10	6d.	**reddish purple C**	3·00	3·75
		a plum	4·50	5·00
G11	1/-	**bistre-brown**	5·00	5·50
G2/11		**set** (10V)	£25	£30
SPG2/11		**specimen set** (9v)	£40	‡

G7a See Note after E4a.

1914-20 Stamps of G.B. (Nos. G52/64) overprinted "BECHUANALAND PROTECTORATE".

(a) Waterlow printings 1914.

G12	2/6	**deep sepia-brown**	£100	£100
		a overprint double.		
		one albino	£210	—
G13	5/-	**rose-carmine**	£125	£125
		a overprint double,		
		one albino	£350	—
SPG12/13		**specimen** (2V)	£80	‡

(b) De La Rue printings 1916-20.

G14	2/6	**grey-brn** (1916) ..	£100	£100
G15	2/6	**dp brown** (1920)	£120	£120
		a overprint double,		
		a overprint treble,		
		two albino ..	—	—
G16	5/-	**brt carmine** (1920)	£200	£200
		a overprint double,		
		one albino ..	£250	—
		b dp carmine ..	£200	£200

(c) Bradbury Wilkinson printings 1920-23.

G17	2/6	**chocolate brown**	£100	£100
		a overprint double,		
		one albino ..	—	—
G18	5/-	**rose-red**	£175	£175
G19	5/-	**deep carmine** ..	£175	£175
		a overprint treble,		
		two albino ..	£300	—

Re-entries occur on the 2/6 value of Bechuanaland from all three printers. Prices from £175.

Re-entries are known on the basic Great Britain stamps as follows :—

Waterlow 2/6—Row 1/2—Row 2/1.
De La Rue 2/6—Row 2/1—Row 10/4.
Bradbury 2/6—Row 1. Nos. 1, 2, 3 and 4.
Row 2/4—Row 3. Nos. 2 and 4.
Row 5/1—Row 7/1.

1922 Stamp of South Africa (KG V) overprinted "Bechuanaland Protectorate" as No. E7 in black thicker type for fiscal use.

G20	1d.	**red**	£15	£15

Although not intended for such use a number were postally used.

1925-27 As Nos. G2/11 but Watermark Multiple Block GVR.

G21	½d.	**green**	90	1·00
G22	1d.	**scarlet**	90	1·25
G23	2d.	**orange** (Die II) ..	1·25	1·50
G24	3d.	**violet**	2·50	3·00
		a wmk. inverted ..	£15	—
		b overprint double,		
		one albino ..	—	—
G25	4d.	**grey-green** ..	2·50	3·50
		a printed on gummed		
		side	—	—
G26	6d.	**purple OC**	5·50	6·00
		a small "AND" ..	6·00	6·50
G27	1/-	**bistre-brown** ..	£10	£11
G21/27		**set** (7V)	£22	£26

G26*a* The "AND" in "BECHUANALAND" is in smaller capitals (position not yet established).

1932 (Dec. 12th) Recess Waterlow. Watermark Multiple Script CA. Sheets 6 x 10. Perf. 12½.

G28	½d.	**green**	25	50
G29	1d.	**scarlet**	40	60
G30	2d.	**brown**	1·00	1·00
G31	3d.	**ultramarine** ..	1·25	1·25
G32	4d.	**orange**	1·00	1·25
G33	6d.	**purple**	1·25	1·50
G34	1/-	**blk and ol-grn** ..	3·00	4·25
G35	2/-	**black and orange**	£12	£14
G36	2/6	**black and scarlet**	£15	£18
G37	3/-	**black and purple**	£22	£27
G38	5/-	**black and ultra** ..	£28	£34
G39	10/-	**black and brown**	£120	£120
G28/39		**set** (12V)	£200	£220
SPG28/39		**specimen set** (12V)	£100	‡

1935 (May 4th) Silver Jubilee. Recess Bradbury Wilkinson. Sheets 6 x 10. Wmk. Multiple Script CA. Perf. 11 x 12.

G40	1d.	**indigo and scarlet**	20	30
		a extra flagstaff ..	£22	—
G41	2d.	**ultra and grey** ..	35	60
		a extra flagstaff ..	£18	—
G42	3d.	**brown and blue** ..	50	90
		a extra flagstaff ..	£22	—
G43	6d.	**slate and purple** ..	1·00	1·25
		a extra flagstaff ..	£22	—
G40/43		**set** (4V)	2·00	3·00
SPG40/43		**specimen set** (4V.)	£18	‡

G40*a*/43*a* Extra flagstaff occurs on No. 49 (Row 9/1).

Remainders were withdrawn on December 31st 1935.

1938 (April 1st) -52 (recess) Waterlow & Sons. Perf. 12½ (L) Sheets 6 x 10.

1	½d.	**green**	70	70
	a	yellow-green (4/43)	1·25	1·25
	b	blue-green (11/9/44)	40	45
2	1d.	**scarlet**	45	50
	a	scarlet-rose (1/10/46)	15	20
3	1½d.	**dull pale blue**	60	60
	a	light blue (4/43)	30	20
4	2d.	**chocolate-brown**	45	50
	a	red-brown (10/12/45)	15	25
5	3d.	**dp ultramarine**	15	25
6	4d.	**orange**	25	40
7	6d.	**red-purple**	1·75	1·25
	a	purple (11/9/44)	1·25	1·00
8	1/–	**olive-green and black**	50	80
	a	olive and blk (21/5/52)	2·25	2·50
9	2/6	**dp carmine and black**	2·00	2·25
10	5/–	**dp ult and black**	2·50	3·00
	a	dp ult and grey black (10.46)	7·00	9·00
11	10/–	**dp choc and black**	9·00	9·50
1/11		**set (11)**	£16	£18
SP 1/11		**specimen set** perf (11)	£45	‡

SPECIAL ISSUES

1937 (May 12th) Coronation. As Aden.

S1	1d.	**scarlet**	20	20
S2	2d.	**yellow-brown**	20	25
S3	3d.	**dp blue**	25	40
SP S1/3		**specimen set** perf (3)	£17	‡

1945 (Dec. 3rd) Victory. Nos. S33–5 of South Africa, overprinted Bechuanaland.

			Pair M	Pair U
S4	1d.	**dp brn and car**	15	20
	a	aniline centre	75	—
	b	barbed wire R9/6	2·00	—
S5	2d.	**slate-blue, pur-vio**	20	30
S6	3d.	**dp blue, blue**	30	40
	a	overprint omitted vert pair with normal	£1000	—
SP S4/6		**specimen set** (3 prs)	£40	‡

1947 (Feb. 17th) Royal Visit. Designs, etc., as Basutoland, S7–10. Sheets 10 x 6 and 6 x 10.

S7	1d.	**scarlet**	10	10
S8	2d.	**green**	10	10
S9	3d.	**ultramarine**	10	10
S10	1/–	**dull mauve**	30	30
S7/10		**set (4)**	60	60
SP S7/10		**specimen set** (4) perf	£35	‡

1948 (Dec. 1st) Silver Wedding. As Aden.

S11	1½d.	**ultramarine**	15	15
S12	10/–	**black**	5·00	6·00

1949 (Oct. 10th) U.P.U. As Aden.

S13	1½d.	**dull ultramarine**	20	20
S14	3d.	**indigo**	20	20
S15	6d.	**reddish-mauve**	40	40
S16	1/–	**sage-green**	70	70
S13/16		**set (4)**	1·50	1·50

POSTAGE DUE STAMPS

1926 Postage Due stamps of G.B. (Nos. GD10, 9, 13) overprinted "BECHUANALAND PROTECTORATE" as E1/6 (½d. and 1d.) or in two horizontal lines (2d.).

GD1	½d.	**emerald**	35	40
GD2	1d.	**carmine**	35	40
GD3	2d.	**agate**	55	70
GD1/3		**set (3V)**	1·25	1·50

1932 (Dec. 12th) Typo De La Rue. Watermark Multiple Script CA. Perf. 14.

GD4	½d.	**sage-green**	1·00	1·25
GD5	1d.	**carmine**	50	75
GD6	2d.	**violet**	1·25	1·50
GD4/6		**set (3V.)**	2·75	3·50
SPGD4/6		**specimen set** (3V.)	£20	‡

1944 (July) Typo De La Rue. Perf. 31¾ x 14 (C). Rough thick paper. Sheets 6 x 10.

PD1	½d.	**olive-green**	1·00	1·00
PD2	1d.	**dp carmine**	1·50	1·50
PD3	2d.	**violet and pur-vio**	2·00	2·00

The paper and shades differ from original 1932 issue and frame of PD3 is F.A.

1947 (July) As Nos. PD1–3, but smooth and thinner paper, and changed shades.

PD4	½d.	**dull olive-green**	1·00	1·25
PD5	1d.	**rose-carmine**	1·50	1·70
PD6	2d.	**dull purple-violet**	2·00	2·00
	a	thick "d"	£10	£10

PD6*a*—The "d" after "2" is thicker on Row 9/6 and Row 10/6.

BERMUDA

The islands were settled in 1609 after Sir George Somers was shipwrecked on his way to Virginia, and they have been British possessions since that time.

Following the use of other handstamps or manuscript marks Crowned Circle PAID Franks were registered at the G.P.O. in London on August 1st 1845 (St. George's and Ireland Island) and on November 13th, 1846 (Hamilton) and were thereafter struck in red to indicate prepayment of postage on overseas letters. Uncrowned Franks were similarly used from 1864. (See Introduction).

1845-65 PAID Franks	On Cover
VF1 **St. George's**	£2500
VF2 **Ireland Island**	£6000
VF3 **Hamilton**	£1500
VF4 **Bermuda (1864)**	£1000

None of these PAID franks were directly impressed on *inland* letters, the postage on which was paid in cash and retained by the Postmasters.

A box was provided outside the Post Office for inland letters and cash to cover the postage; and it was the failure of the public to "post" cash with their letters that led to the creation of the Postmasters' stamps.

POSTMASTERS' STAMPS

1848-63 Adhesives prepared and issued by Wm. B. Perot and R. Ward (Hamilton) and J. H. Thies (St. Georges) for the prepayment of local letters mailed in the P.O. letter boxes out of office hours.

(a) First Perot Issue. Made from the current Hamilton datestamp.

VO1	1d.	**black on bluish-grey** (1848-49)	— £30000
VO2	1d.	**red on thick white paper** (1853) ..	— £50000
VO3	1d.	**red on bluish laid paper** (1854) ..	— £70000
VO4	1d.	**red on thick blue paper** (1856) ..	.. £75000

Numbers recorded — VO1 3 (1848); 2 (1849); VO2 2 unused; 1 used. VO3 2. VO4 1.

(b) Second Perot Issue. Made from the Hamilton Crowned Circle (Pen Cancelled).

VO5	1d.	**red on bluish laid paper** (1861)	— £50000

Number recorded — 4.

(c) As above but prepared by R. Ward (Blue Crayon Cancelled).

VO6	1d.	**red on creamy white laid paper** (1862?)	— £45000

Number recorded — 2.

Robert Ward succeeded W. B. Perot as Hamilton Postmaster in June 1862 and the two copies of VO6 (one on horizontally laid and the other on vertically laid paper) are believed to have been prepared some time after October 1862.

(d) Thies Issue. Made from the St. Georges Crowned Circle.

VO7	1d.	**car-red on buff** (1860-63) ..	— £35000

Number recorded — 5.

GOVERNMENT ISSUES

Details of the quantities of stamps printed and/or issued, including those surcharged and overprinted will be found tabulated at the end of the listing.

1865-74 *(typo)* **De La Rue. Perf. 14. Wmk. Crown CC. Various frames.**

V1	1d.	**pale rose (shades)** (25/9/65) ..	£10	3·00
		a rose-red (shades)	£14	3·00
		b rose-red imperf...	£12000	£5500
		c rose-red wmk. inverted	£30	£30
V2	2d.	**dl blue** (14/3/66)	£25	7·00
		a bright blue ..	£27	7·00
		b dl blue wmk. inv.	—	£70
V3	3d.	**yel-buff** (10/3/73)	£175	£40
		a orange (2/7/74)	£180	£45
		b **yel-buff** wmk. inverted	£400	£100
		c yel-buff wmk. reversed ..	£600	£40
V4	6d.	**dull pur (shades)**, (25/9/65) ..	£300	£40
		a wmk. inverted ..	—	£100
V5	6d.	**dull mauve (shds)**, (7/9/75) ..	£12	£12
		a deep dull mauve (2/7/75) ..	£250	£150
		b dull mauve wmk. inverted ..	£240	£30
V6	1/-	**green shades**, (25/9/65) ..	£20	£15
		a dark green	£40	£30
		b pale light green	£100	£70
		c wmk. inverted (shades) ..	£200	£100

1874 Provisional Issue. Surcharged "THREE PENCE" locally by handstamps diagonally upwards in black.

(i) Fancy italic capitals with plain "P" in "PENCE".

V7	3d. on 1d.	**rose-red** (4/3/74) ..	£2500	—
		a partial double surcharge	—	—
V8	3d. on 1/-	**grn** (12/3/74)	£450	£350
		a partial double surcharge	—	—

(ii) Fancy italic capitals with initial or fancy "P" in "PENCE".

V9	3d on 1/-	**grn** (29/3/74?)	£600	£50
		a partial double surcharge	—	—

(iii) Roman capitals

V10	3d. on 1/-	**grn** (19/5/74)	£450	£400
		a dble or partial dble surcharge	—	—

V7 The 3d. on 1d. was an essay of which one pane (60 stamps) was made. Used examples are known the majority post-dated by duplex cancellations, but a few exist cancelled by the horizontal oval bar cancellation current 1865-79. Dangerous forgeries of the provisionals exist and certificates are recommended.

1875 Provisional Issue. Surcharged "One Penny" in two lines (typeset) by the Bermuda Royal Gazette.

V11	1d. on 2d.	**bt bl** (23/4/75)	£575	£150
		a round "O" ..	£700	£250
		b no stop after "Penny" ..	£1500	£500

V12	1d. on 3d.	**yellow-buff** (8/5/75) ..	£400	£200
		a round "O" ..	£500	£250
V13	1d. on 1/-	**grn** (11/3/75)	£300	£150
		a round "O" ..	£500	£250
		b no stop after "Penny" ..	£900	£450
		c sur. inv. ..	—	£2500

The round "O" occurs several times in each setting which is believed to have been of 30 stamps. The no stop variety is believed to have occured in only one printing of the 1d. on 1/- (April 16th) and the printing of the 2d. (April 21st). Forgeries of these provisionals exist and certificates are recommended.

1880 As V1/6 (*typo*) **De La Rue. Perf. 14. Watermark Crown CC.**

V14	½d.	**stone** (25/3/80) ..	1·50	2·00
		a wmk. inverted ..	£15	£20
		b retouch above Queen's head	£30	£30
V15	4d.	**orange**	3·00	2·00

V14*b* The background lines above the head are clearly retouched on No. 10 upper left pane. The cliche was replaced for the ½d. 1892 but the frames of Nos. 4, 10 and 16 were damaged in the process.

1882-1903 As Nos. V3/6 and wmk. Crown CC, but Perf. 14 x 12½ (line). Received 3/3/80 but not issued until the dates below.

V16	3d.	**yel-buff** (c. 5/82)	£75	£25
V17	6d.	**bt mauve** (c. 6/03)	£12	£12
V18	1/-	**green** (c. 1894) ..	£30	£35
		a imperf. hor., vert. strip of 3 ..	—	—
		b imperf. vert. at right with sheet margin attached	—	—
		c wmk. inverted ..	£50	£50

V18*a* 24 vertical strips originally existed, of which 15 are now recorded. A vertical pair and a single with 1/3rd of the stamp above are known used 20 examples of V18*b* originally existed of which 11 are now recorded.

1833-1904 As before. Perf. 14. Wmk. Crown CA.

V19	½d.	**dl-grn** (–/10/92)	1·00	1·00
		a deep grey-green	1·00	1·00
		b damaged frames (3 stamps) ..	—	—
V20	1d.	**dull rose-red** (c. 12/83) ..	£20	3·00
		a dull red ..	£25	5·00
		b dull rose ..	£25	5·00
		c dl rose-red wmk. inverted	£120	£70
V21	1d.	**car-rose** (–/3/86)	£10	125
		a wmk. inverted ..	£75	£20
V22	1d.	**carmine** (1888)	£10	1·25
V23	1d.	**aniline carmine (shades)** (1890)	1·00	50
		a wmk. inverted ..	£25	£10
V24	2d.	**bt blue** (–/12/86)	8·00	2·00
		a dull blue ..	5·00	2·00
V25	2d.	**ani pur** (–/7/93)	5·00	2·00
V26	2d.	**brn pur** (–/6/97)	2·00	2·00

V27	2½d.	**pl ultra** (–/11/84)	3·50	50
		a bright ultramarine	4·00	75
		b deep ultramarine	£12	1·50
		c wmk. inv. (V27 and 27a only)	£35	£30
V28	3d.	**grey** (–/1/86) ..	6·00	4·00
V29	4d.	**or-brn** (–/1/04)	£12	£15
		a wmk. reversed ..	£180	—
V30	1/-	**olive-brn (shades)** (–/7/93) ..	£10	£12
V31	1/-	**yel-brn (shades)** (–/11/97) ..	£15	£20
		SPV19, V25, V26, V30 only **specimen set of 4**	£70	‡

1901 Provisional. The 1/– printed in grey surcharged "ONE FARTHING" in two lines by De La Rue. Perf. 14. Wmk. Crown CA.

V32	½d. on 1/-	**dull grey** (11/1/01) ..	25	25
		a bluish grey (c. 18/3/01)	25	50
		b damaged "G" in "FARTHING"	3·00	5·00
SPV32		**specimen (1)**	£25	‡

1902-3 (*typo*) **De La Rue. Perf. 14. Wmk. Crown CA.**

E1	½d.	**blk and green** ..	5·00	2·50
E2	1d.	**brn and car** ..	4·00	30
E3	3d.	**pur and sage** ..	2·00	2·50
		a magenta and sage ..	4·00	2·50

1906-9 Wmk. Mult. Crown CA. Perf. 14.

E4	¼d.	**brown and violet** ..	1·00	1·50
E5	½d.	**black and green** ..	4·00	2·50
E6	1d.	**brn and rose-car** ..	3·50	40
		a wmk. inverted	£30	—
E7	2d.	**grey-grn and orange**	4·00	5·00
E8	2½d.	**brn and ult**	6·00	£12
E9	4d.	**pl-blu and pur-brn** ..	4·00	5·00

1908-10 Wmk. Mult. Crown CA. Perf. 14.

E10	½d.	**green**	2·50	2·00
E11	1d.	**red**	2·50	50
E12	2½d.	**ultramarine** ..	£10	8·50
E1/E12		**set (12)** ..	£50	£45
SP E1/E12		**specimen set (10)** .	£145	‡

1910-1925 (*recess*) **De La Rue. Wmk. Mult. Crown CA. Perf. 13¾ x 14 (Comb.) except ½d. (part of one printing). Perf. 14 (line). Sheets 12 x 10.**

G1	¼d.	**brown**	1·00	1·00
		a pale-brown ..	50	1·00
G2	½d.	**green**	50	40
		a pl-yellow-green ..	1·00	90
		b dp-blue-green ..	2·50	1·50
		c green (P14 line) ..	£10	£10
		d green wmk. inverted	£50	—
G3	1d.	**red** (plate I) ..	1·00	50
		a rose-red	3·00	50
		c rose-red wmk. inverted	£80	—
G4	1d.	**car** (plate II) ..	5·50	2·50
G5	2d.	**grey**	2·00	3·00
G6	2½d.	**ultramarine** ..	1·50	1·50
		a pale-ult ..	2·00	1·50
		b thick paper ..	4·00	3·00
		c wmk. inverted ..	£20	—
		d wmk. reversed ..	£20	—
		e wmk. inverted and reversed	£20	—
G7	3d.	**purple/yellow** ..	2·25	2·50
G8	4d.	**red/yellow** ..	2·25	2·50
		a pl-rose-red/yellow .	3·00	3·00
G9	6d.	**bright-claret** ..	8·00	£10
		a purple	6·00	8·00
		b claret	5·00	6·00
G10	1/-	**black/green** ..	8·00	8·00
		a black/pl-blue-green	6·00	6·00
		b jt-black/pl-olive ..	5·00	5·00
G1/G10		**set (9)**	£24	£22
SP G1/G10		**specimen set (9)**..	£20	‡

1918-1927 (*typo*) **De La Rue. Wmk. Mult. Crown CA. Perf. 14 (comb). Sheets 12 x 5.**

G11	2/-	**pur and blu/pl-blu**..	6·00	£12
		a wmk. reversed (only one sheet of sixty known)	£350	—
G12	2/6	**blk and red/pl-blue**	£13	£18
G13	4/-	**black and carmine**..	£24	£28
G14	5/-	**green and bt red/ lemon yellow** ..	£25	£30
		a grn and red/yellow	£30	£35
		b wmk. inverted (several sheets known) ..	£175	—
G15	10/-	**grn and bt-red/ pl-bluish-green** ..	£70	£80
		a green and red/pale-bluish-green ..	£70	£80
G16	£1	**pur and blk/sal-red**	£325	£225
		a pur and blk/crimson	£325	£250
		b wmk. inverted (two sheets known 120 stamps) ..	—	—
G11/G16		**set (6)**	£1100	£375
SP G11/G16		**specimen set (6)**	£325	‡

Care should be taken when purchasing used copies as these are known with forged cancellations on cleaned fiscally used stamps.

For details concerning Damaged Scroll (Row 1/12) and Broken Crown (Row 2/12) flaws see notes after G55.

1918 (May 4th) G3, G3a, overprinted in De Vinn capitals by the Bermuda Press.

G17	1d. **red** (plate I)	..	30	30
	a rose-red (plate I)..		20	40

1920 (Feb. 5th) G4 overprinted in Ionic capitals by the Bermuda Press.

G18	1d. **carmine** (plate II)	..	40	50

1920 (Nov. 11th) 1d., 2½d. 1921 (Jan. 10th) other values. 1st Issue of Tercentenary of Representative Institutions. (*typo*) **De La Rue. Perf. 14 (C). All values Wmk. Mult. Crown CA sideways 'A' except 1d., 2½d., 6d., which are Wmk. Mult. Script CA sideways 'B'. Sheets 5 x 12.**

G19	¼d. **deep-brown** (A) ..		50	80
	a pl-brown ..	..	75	1·00
	b wmk. inverted	..	£20	£30
	c wmk. reversed	..	£20	£30
	d wmk. 'C' of CA omtd		—	—
	e wmk. 'A' of CA omtd		—	—
G20	½d. **green** (A)	..	1·00	2·25
	a wmk. inverted	..	£40	—
	b wmk. reversed	..	£40	—
G21	1d. **carmine** (B)	..	80	1·00
G22	2d. **grey** (A)	..	4·50	6·00
	a wmk. inverted	..	£45	—
	b wmk. 'C' of CA omtd		—	—
G23	2½d. **ultramarine** (B)	..	4·00	6·00
G24	3d. **dull-pur/yellow** (A)		5·50	£12
G25	4d. **blk-red/yellow** (A) .		£10	£15
G26	6d. **dull and bt-pur** (B) .		£12	£15
G27	1/- **blk/blu-grn** (A) ..		£15	£17
G19/27	**set** (9)	..	£50	£70
SP G19/27	**specimen set** (9)..		£115	‡

Both wmks. are normal when top of Crown points to right looking at sheet from front of stamp.

The damaged wmk. varieties (G19*d/e* etc.) may exist on all values.

1921 (May 12th) 2nd Issue of Tercentenary of Representative Institution. (*recess*) **De La Rue. Perf. 14 (L). All values Wmk. Mult. Crown CA sideways 'A', except ¼d., ½d., 1d., which are Wmk. Mult. Script CA sideways 'B'. Sheets 5 x 12.**

G28	¼d. **brown** (B) ..	..	1·50	2·00
	a red-brown (B)	..	1·50	2·00
G29	½d. **green** (B)	..	1·50	2·00
	a wmk. inverted (B)..		£10	—
G30	1d. **dp-carmine** (B)	..	1·00	70
	a wmk. 'C' of CA omtd		—	—
G31	2d. **slate-grey** (A)	..	8·00	£10
G32	2½d. **bt-ult** (A)	..	5·00	5·00
	a wmk. 'C' of CA omtd		—	—
	b wmk. 'A' of CA omtd		—	—
G33	3d. **pur/yellow** (A)	..	6·00	7·50
G34	4d. **red/yellow** (A)	..	8·00	£10
	a wmk. reversed	..	£40	—
G35	6d. **purple** (A)	..	7·50	9·00
	a wmk. 'C' of CA omtd		—	—
G36	1/- **black/green** (A)	..	£15	£17
G28/36	**set** (9)	..	£50	£60
SP G28/36	**specimen set** (9) .		£115	‡

Both wmks. are normal when top of Crown points to left looking at sheet from front of stamp.

The damaged wmk. varieties (G32*a/b* etc.) may exist on all values.

Plates of 1d.

Plate I.   Plate II.

Plate III.   Plate IV.

Plate I—On MCA only. Thin to medium paper. Wmk. clearly visible (compare G17–17a).

Plate II—On MCA. In carmine on thick unsurfaced paper. Wmk. almost invisible (compare G18). On Script: Thin "1" with pointed serifs.

Plate III—Heavy "1" with square serifs. Inner frame of value tablet retouched on most stamps.

Plate IV—Entire design redrawn (new die) "1" with long square serifs.

Plates of 2½d.

Plate I.

Plate II.

Plate I—Small thick "2½d."

Plate II—Redrawn die. Tall thinner "2½d."; also inner frame line of value tablet clear cut.

1922-1934 (*recess*) **De La Rue. Wmk. Mult. Script CA. Perf. 13¾ x 14 or 14 (C) until 1928–30, except 1d. No. G40 and G40a, which is Perf. 13¾ or 13¾ x 14 (line) and 2½d. No. G44b (part of one printing only), Perf. 14 line. After 1928-30 Perf. 13¾, 13¾ x 14, or 14 x 13¾ line.**

G37	¼d.	**pl-brown**	45	60
	a	dp-brown	1·00	1·50
	b	brown	60	60
G38	½d.	**green**	30	20
	a	dp-green	60	40
	b	blue-green	75	40
	c	pl-green	40	20
G39	1d.	**red-car** Plate II	1·50	50
	a	scar	1·00	50
	b	rose-car	1·50	50
G40	1d.	**rose-car** Plate III	1·50	50
	a	scar	1·50	50
G41	1d.	**scar** Plate IV	40	35
	a	rose-red	50	40
	b	car	60	40
	c	car-lake (Dry print wide frame 19 mm.)	1·50	60
G42	1½d.	**red-brown**	2·50	80
G43	2d.	**dove-grey**	80	90
	a	dove-grey (wmk. revd)	£25	—
	b	dp-grey	1·50	1·00
	c	slate-grey	1·50	1·00
	d	dp-slate-grey	1·50	1·00
	e	pl-grey (Dry print wide frame 19 mm.)	2·00	2·00
G44	2½d.	**pl-sage-green**	6·00	7·00
	a	yel-sage-grn	3·00	3·00
	b	sage-green (Perf. 14)	4·00	4·00
	c	dp-sage-grn	2·00	2·00
	d	dp-sage-grn (wmk. inverted)	£20	—
G45	2½d.	**ult** Plate I	2·00	1·00
	a	wmk. inverted	£20	—
G46	2½d.	**ult** Plate II	1·50	1·00
G47	3d.	**ult**	£10	£14
	a	wmk. inverted	£45	—

G48	3d.	**reddish-pur/yel**	1·50	1·00
	a	pur/bt-yel	2·50	1·50
	b	dull-pur/yel	2·50	1·50
G49	4d.	**red/yellow**	1·50	1·00
	a	bt-red/yel	3·00	2·50
	b	scar/yel	2·00	2·50
G50	6d.	**red-claret**	2·00	1·75
	a	pl-claret	4·00	3·50
G51	1/–	**jet-blk/em-grn**	7·00	6·00
	a	grey-blk/green	8·00	6·00
	b	sep-blk/yel-grn	£15	£17
G37/51		**set** (12)	£32	£30
SP G37/G51		**specimen set** (12)	£60	‡

(½d.–1/- Late dry printings of some values have a slightly wider frame 19 mm. instead of usual 18½ mm.)

Re-entries and retouches are a specialised study on the Ship types on both watermarks and we strongly recommend the handbook by M. H. LUDINGTON "BERMUDA SHIP TYPE", Published 1955 by Junior Philatical Society.

1924/1932 (*typo*) **De La Rue. Wmk. Mult. Script CA. Perf. 14 (C). Sheets 12 x 5.**

G52	2/–	**pur and blu/pl blu**	£12	5·00
	a	pur and blue/deep greyish-blue	£14	5·00
G53	2/6	**blk and pl red/pl blue**	£20	£10
	a	blk and dp red/dp blue	£20	£10
	b	grey-blk and pl or-vermilion/blue	£450	£450
	c	blk and car-red/dp blue	£20	£10
	d	blk and dp-dl ver/greyish-blue	£20	£18
G54	10/-	**grn and lake/pl em**	£90	£80
	a	pl grn, red/emerald	£90	£80
	b	dp grn, dp red/ dp emerald	£90	£85
G55	12/6	**grey and dp maize**	£200	£200
	a	grey-blk and dp maize	£200	£200
	b	on ordinary paper	£800	£350
G52/55		**set** (4)	£300	£300
SPG52/55		**specimen set**	£120	‡

G53*b* There are three shades within the vermilion range; all are rare but the pale orange vermilion is the most striking and the scarcer stamp. The other two shades are pale dull vermilion and bright vermilion; the later shade G53*d* is a deeper dull slightly blurred printing.

G55 See also F1.

Damaged Scroll
Row 1/12

Broken Crown
and Damaged Scroll
Row 2/12

Twenty one different head plate flaws exist, some of which do not occur on wmk Mult Crown CA issues. The two most notable (illustrated above) are damage to upper right scroll on stamp No. 12 (Row 1/12) and Broken Crown on stamp No. 24 (Row 2/12) which also has damage to the scroll. Both flaws were repaired on a number of occasions and each may be found in various states and are best collected in either vertical pairs or blocks of four. Listed below are those issues where these two flaws are known to exist, and the prices quoted being a guide for mint copies of each value. Fine used copies would attract an additional premium. The other flaws, some of which are quite noticeable, are worth up to 10 times the normal value. In the table below suffix 'A' denotes Damaged Scroll (Row 1/12) and suffix 'B' the Broken Crown (Row 2/12).

G11 A & B	from £60 each
G12 A	from £130 each
G13 A & B	from £240 each
G14 A & B	from £250 each
G15 A & B	from £300 each
G16 A & B	from £550 each
G52 A & B	from £120 each
G53 A & B	from £180 each
G54 A & B	from £260 each
G55 A & B	from £500 each
F1 A & B	from £600 each

1935 (May 6th) Silver Jubilee (*recess*) **Waterlow & Sons. Wmk. Mult. Script CA. Perf 11 x 12 Sheets 6 x 10.**

G56	1d.	**blue and scarlet** ..	20	20
G57	1½d.	**ult and grey** ..	35	35
G58	2½d.	**brn and dk blue** ..	70	80
G59	1/–	**slate and purple** ..	4·50	5·00
G56/59		**set** (4)	5·50	6·00
SPG56/59		**specimen set** (4) ..	£22	‡

1936 (April 14th) Various Pictorial Designs (*recess*) **Bradbury, Wilkinson. Perf 12 (L). Wmk. Mult. Script CA. Sheets 6 x 10.**

G60	½d.	**green**	10	5
		a yellow-green ..	15	5
		b blue-green ..	10	5
G61	1d.	**black and red** ..	15	10
G62	1½d.	**black and choc** ..	25	25
G63	2d.	**blk and pl blue** ..	2·00	2·00
G64	2½d.	**lt blue and dk blue**	50	60
G65	3d.	**black and scarlet** ..	1·50	1·75
G66	6d.	**car-lk and pur-vio***	1·00	20
		a rose and lake-vio..	1·00	30
		b car and dp violet..	1·00	30
		c dp car and violet ..	1·00	30
		d lake and violet ..	1·00	30
		e booklet pane of 6 ..	£10	£12
G67	1/–	**green**	4·00	4·50
G68	1/6	**brown**	25	20
G60/68		**set** (9)	9·00	£10
SP.G60/68		**specimen set** (9) ..	£30	‡

*Later printings of 6d. are listed under 33 and 33a.

1938 (Jan. 20th)-53 Designs, 1d., 1½d. ("J. W. Clise" and "Monarch of Bermuda"); 2d. (Bermuda Yacht "Lucie"); 2½d., 1/– (Horseshoe Beach, Southampton Parish); 3d. (St. David's Lighthouse); 7½d. ("Longtail" bird-with Arms of Bermuda and Flower, (*Sisyrinchium Bermudiana*). **Printers** (*recess*) **Bradbury, Wilkinson. Perf 12 (L). Design, 7½d. H. Sheets 6 x 10.**

1	1d.	**black and rose-red** ..	7·00	3·00
		a blk and rose-scar (/40)	50	10
		b black and rose ..	20	10
		c booklet pane of 6 ..	4·00	5·00
2	1½d.	**dp blue and choc-brn**	30	30
		a dp blue and brown ..	40	30
		b dp blue and pur-brn	50	30
		c booklet pane of 6 ..	8·00	£10
3	2d.	**sky-blue and black** ..	£10	5·00
		a sky-blue and sepia-black (/39)	£10	5·00
4	2d.	**pale ult and scarlet** (12/11/40)	60	60

a pale ult and car-red (7/42) £10 £12
b bt blue-scarlet .. 80 80
c booklet pane of 6 .. £10 £12
5 2½d. **It blue and dk blue** .. 1·50 80
6 2½d. **sky-blue and sepia-grey** (18/12/41) .. 80 40
a pale blue and drab (5/3/43) 25 25
b ult and sepia .. 25 25
c booklet pane of 6 .. £12 £14
7 3d. **black and scarlet** .. 2·00 1·50
8 3d. **blk and dp blue** (16/7/41) 50 30
a blk and dk blu (7/43) 30 25
b black-greenish blue 1·50 50
c booklet pane of 6 .. £3 —
9 7½d. **black, blue and pea-green** (18/12/41) .. 40 50
a blk, blue and grn (5/3/43) 50 50
10 1/- **green** 60 40
a yellow-green (thinner paper) (/42) .. 1·00 1·00
b blue-green (13/6/49) 50 30

Copies of No. 1 with vermilion frames are changelings.

Printers (*typo*) **De La Rue. Perf. 14 x 13¾ (C). £1 Wmk. Multiple Crown CA. Sheets 12 x 5.**

11 2/- **purple and bt blue/grey-blue** (*ch*) .. £12 3·00
a pur and dp-blue/mottled blue (sub) (7/6/42) .. 2·00 1·50
b pur and blue/mottled blue (*sub*) .. .. 2·00 1·50
c pur and dp blu/pl blue (*sub*) (5/3/43) .. 6·00 2·00
d pur and lt blue/pl blue (*sub*) .. .. .. 2·50 1·00
e dl pur and blu/pl blu (*sub*) (13/6/49)(centre FA) .. .. 2·00 2·00
12 2/6 **blk and car/grey-blue** (*ch*) .. .. .. 6·00 4·00
a blk and car/pl blue (*sub*) (/42) .. 5·00 2·00
b blk and dl red/pl blue (*sub*) (5/3/43) .. 3·00 2·00
c blk and or red/pl-blue (*sub*) .. .. .. 2·50 2·00
13 5/- **dp grn and red/yel** (*ch*) .. .. .. £14 5·00
a grn and car/pl yel (*sub*) (5/3/43) .. 6·00 3·00
b green and red/pale yellow (*sub*) .. 5·00 3·00

c pea-green and car/pale yellow (*sub*) (11/12/46) .. .. 4·00 3·00
14 10/- **grn and dp lk/yellow green** (*ch*) £30 £40
a blue-grn and dp red/grn (*ch*) (7/39) .. £40 £40
b grn and dp red/grn (*sub*) (5/3/43) .. £10 £10
c grn and red/grn (em back) (*sub*) (5/2/47) 5·00 6·00
15 12/6 **grey and dp maize**(*ch*) £30 £30
aa grey and maize (*ch*) £12 £12
a grey and maize (*sub*) (5/3/43) £12 £12
b grey and yel (*sub*) (/47) £225 £225
bb grey-grn and yel (*sub*) .. £400 £350
c grey and maize (*ch*) (21/7/48) £15 £15
d grey and brownish maize (*thin paper*) (*ch*) £20 £20
16 £1 **pl purple and black/crimson** (*ch*) .. £45 £35
a pur and blk/salmon-red (*ch*) (/42) .. £15 £14
b bluish pur and black/salmon red (*ch*) .. £18 £14
c pur and jet black/salmon red (*ch*) .. £14 £14
SP1/16 **specimen set**(16v)perf £140 ‡

First printings of 2/- to £1 stamps have shorter and more irregular lines of shading across the King's face, leaving a wider blank space down the front, particularly on the forehead.

No. 11*a*—The paper used for this printing has been treated with a coat of deep blue ink and the stamps produced presented a blotched and/or lined appearance. With no two stamps quite alike and the whole issue being the result of a single experiment. The stamps were withdrawn 16/11/44.

No. 14*b*—is reported to exist watermark sideways.

Nos. 15*b*/15*bb*—There are two printings of the rare 12/6 "lemon" shade. One has a grey-green centre (15*bb*), and the frame of this very rare shade is slightly paler yellow. A number of copies of this shade are known addressed to Prague and dated early in 1947 but most of this printing was used by the Government Office administering the "poll" or landing tax on visitors to the island.

No. 15*b* should not be confused with some copies of No. 15*c* which have a rather yellowish maize frame. A certificate from an expert committee is advisable.

No. 15*aa* has thick brown gum.

No. 15*c* has clear colourless gum.

No. 16—This first printing can be distinguished by the clear crimson shade of the paper itself. The centre portion of the design is lighter and the lines finer than is the case in later printings.

As No. 11, etc., but Perf. 14¼ (L).

17 2/- **pur and bt blu/grey-blue** (*ch*) (6/41) .. £15 5·00
18 2/6 **blk and car/grey-blue** (*ch*) (6/41) £35 £12

19 5/- **grn and car/yellow**
  (*ch*) (6/41) .. .. £18 6·00
20 10/- **grn and car/grn** (*sub*)
  (6/41) £15 £15

As No. 11, etc., but Perf. 13¼ x 13 (C).

21 2/- **dl pur and dp-blu/lt** 3·00 1·00
  blue (*sub*) (15/2/50)
  a pl smoky purple centre
  (*sub*) .. .. 2·00 1·00
  b reddish purple centre
  (*sub*) .. .. 3·00 1·00
22 2/6 **blk and verm/pl blue**
  (*sub*) (10/10/50) .. 3·00 2·00
  a black and car-red/pl
  blue (*sub*) (18/6/52) 2·00 2·00
23 5/- **pea-grn and car/pl yel**
  (*sub*) (15/2/50) .. 3·50 1·50
  a grn and red/yellow
  (*ch*) (10/10/50) .. 2·50 1·50
  b pl grn centre (*ch*) .. 4·00 3·00
24 10/- **grn and verm/grn**
  (*sub*) (19/9/51) .. 7·00 8·00
  a grn and dl red/grn
  (*sub*) (16/4/53) .. 4·00 5·00
25 12/6 **grey and yellow** (*ch*)
  (10/10/50) £10 £10
  a grey/dp yellow (*ch*) 9·00 £10
26 £1 **vio and blk/crimson**
  (*ch*) (7/12/51) .. £10 £10
  a bt violet centre (*ch*) £30 £40
1/26 **set** (20v) £13 £14

Nos. 21/21*b* occur on vertical and horizontal mesh papers, but we have not listed these to avoid a too specialised listing.

The Scroll Varieties

Type A

On stamp 60 (R5/12); all prices are for singles, same price mint or used. This flaw exists in several states and was retouched on the plate several times.

2/-	A11*a*	..	..	..	£60
	A11 *b/c*	..	..	..	£40
	A17	..	..	..	£90
2/6	A12*a*	..	..	..	£60
	A12*b*	..	..	..	£60
	A18	..	..	..	£100
5/-	A13*a*	..	..	..	£90
	A19	..	..	..	£100
10/-	A14*b*	..	..	..	£100
	A20	..	..	..	£90
12/6	A15*a*	..	..	..	£100
£1	A16*a*	..	..	..	£120
	A16*b*	..	..	..	£120

There is also a scroll flaw on Stamp No. 59, so these varieties are well collected in plate pairs. Price about 40 per cent. higher than single of Stamp 60.

Type B

On stamp No. 1 only on the March, 1943 printing of two denominations. The shading is missing from the upper side of the right hand scroll.

2/-	B11*c*	..	..	..	..	£45
£1	B16*a*	..	..	..	..	£65

1940 (Dec. 20th) No. 1a (and shade) surcharged HALF PENNY and original value obliterated by X's by Hamilton Press.

27 ½d./1d. **blk and rose-scar** 25 30
  a black and scarlet 60 60

These stamps were surcharged at Hamilton, Bermuda. There are three spacings between the X's and Penny on the same sheet. The respective measurements being 12½mm. (this setting is scarcer than the other two) and 13½mm. and 14mm. There is also a slight difference in the thickness of the paper used.

1950-1 As No. 1a, etc., but Perf. 12 x 11¾ (C).

28 1d. **black and scarlet-red**
  (10/7/50) 20 40
  a black and dl-red (9/52) 30 40
29 1½d. **dp blue and choc-brn**
  (10/10/50) 20 30
  a blue and pur brn (7/51) 30 30
30 2d. **pale ult and car-red**
  (10/7/50) 30 40
  a bt blue and dp car-red
  (9/52) 40 50
31 2½d. **sky-blue and sepia-**
  grey (23/9/52) .. 30 40
32 3d. **black and dp blue**
  (2/7/51) 30 40
  a blk and lt blue (9/52) 40 50
33 6d. **lake and pur-violet**
  (2/7/51) 80 80
  a car lake and vio (1/52) 80 80
34 1/- **blue-green** (/51) .. 1·00 1·00
  a deep blue-green
  (10/12/52) .. .. 1·25 1·25
25/34a **set** (7) .. .. 3·00 3·50

No. 34 was released in London 2/7/51, but on sale in Colony some months earlier.

SPECIAL ISSUES

1937 (May 14) Coronation. As Aden.

S1	1d. **scarlet**	10	10
S2	1½d. **yellow-brown** ..	20	10
S3	2½d. **blue**	60	60
SP	S1/3 **specimen set** perf (3)	£14	‡

1946 (Nov. 6th) Victory. As Aden.

S4	1½d. **chocolate-brown** ..	10	10
S5	3d. **deep blue**	10	10
SP	S4/5 **specimen set** perf (2)	—	‡

1948 (Dec. 1st) Silver Wedding. As Aden.

S6	1½d. **chestnut-brown** ..	10	10
S7	£1 **rose-carmine**	£22	£25

1949 (April 11th) 100th Anniversary of Bermuda's First Stamp. Design, Incorporating Postmaster Perot's Stamp, King's Portrait and Sisyrinchium Bermudiana. Printers (*recess*) **Bradbury, Wilkinson. Perf 13¼ (C). Sheets 6 x 10.**

S8	2½d. **blue and grey-brn** ..	20	20
S9	3d. **black and dull blue**	25	25
S10	6d. **pur-vio and green** ..	30	30
S8/10	**set** (3)	60	60

1949 (Oct. 10th) U.P.U. As Aden.

S11	2½d. **slate**	15	15
S12	3d. **indigo**	20	25
S13	6d. **purple**	25	35
S14	1/- **quartz-green** ..	45	45
S11/14	**set** (4)	1·00	1·10

POSTAL FISCALS

1937 As No. G 55, but inscribed REVENUE at both sides: authorised for postal use between February and April and in November 1937.

F1	12/6d. **grey and deep maize**	£125	£175

The price for used copies is 'on piece'. This stamp exists with Damaged Scroll (Row 1/12) and Broken Crown (Row 2/12); for details see after G55.

GERMAN PROPAGANDA LABELS

The 1944 German imitations of the G.B. 1937 Definitives ½d. to 3d. (see after Great Britain for details) were also overprinted in black "LIQUIDATION/OF EMPIRE/BERMUDA Is" within a vertical rectangular frame.

Price (6v) unused or cancelled—£175.

Numbers of stamps printed or issued including those surcharged or overprinted for postal use but excluding those overprinted "Cancelled" or overprinted/perforated "Specimen". Figures in brackets thus ( ) are the numbers sold as officially reported. Letters in brackets after the quantities are references to the footnotes following this table of issues.

Queen Victoria

V1	.. ..	2,147,524
V2	.. .. ..	618,840
V3	.. .. ..	103,640
V4/V5	.. .. ..	281,520
V6	.. .. ..	116,820
V8/V9/V10	.. ..	13,500 (a)
V11/V12/V13 ..	.. ..	40,800 (b)
V14	.. .. ..	487,440
V15	.. .. ..	486,480
V16	.. .. ..	50,400
V17	.. .. ..	50,640
V18	.. .. ..	24,000
V19	.. .. ..	721,440
V20/V21/V22/V23	.. ..	4,873,680
V24/V25/V26 ..	.. ..	437,760
V27	.. .. ..	2,677,440
V28	.. .. ..	120,960
V29	.. .. ..	24,480
V30/V31	.. ..	71,520
V32	.. .. ..	1,214,880

King Edward VII

E1	.. ..	361,440
E2	.. ..	2,175,840
E3	.. .. ..	74,160
E4	.. ..	368,640
E5	.. .. ..	365,280
E6	.. .. ..	1,483,920
E7	.. .. ..	70,560
E8	.. .. ..	489,120
E9	.. .. ..	72,000
E10	.. .. ..	366,960
E11	.. .. ..	1,465,920
E12	.. .. ..	488,640

King George V

G1	.. ..		711,360
G2	.. .. ..		3,264,960
G3/G4 ..	.. ..		8,266,920
G5	.. .. ..		126,000
G6	.. .. ..		3,426,880
G7	.. .. ..		126,420
G8	.. .. ..		48,060
G9	.. .. ..		123,480
G10	.. .. ..		122,040
G11	.. .. ..		28,820
G12	.. .. ..		20,580 (c)
G13	.. .. ..		30,120
G14	.. .. ..		112,260 (c)
G15	.. .. ..		81,540 (c)
G16	.. .. ..		18,360
G17	.. .. ..		360,000 (d)
G18	.. ..		240,000 (e)
G19	.. ..	146,260	(146,140) (f)
G20	.. ..	147,800	(147,620)
G21	.. ..	975,120	(972,840)

G22	73,720	(48,800)
G23	247,800	(247,740)
G24	73,120	(29,380)
G25	73,140	(23,460)
G26	74,340	(32,040)
G27	73,395	(24,495)
G28	151,510	(151,330)
G29	150,070	(149,890)
G30	1,009,270	(1,009,150)
G31	72,610	(35,290)
G32	252,790	(252,670)
G33	73,870	(36,850)
G34	73,650	(25,890)
G35	74,190	(38,310)
G36	76,005	(27,225)
G37		341,040
G38		5,161,634
G39/G40/G41		25,754,760
G42		1,991,760
G43		377,455
G44		1,888,880
G45/G46		5,341,900
G47		65,400
G48		371,590
G49		239,580
G50		336,000
G51		182,280
G52		68,520
G53		271,890 (c)
G54		384,240 (c)
G55		292,500 (c)
G56		(885,242)(g)
G57		(1,191,602)(g)
G58		(397,829)(g)
G59		(58,802)(g)
G60		7,441,620
G61		2,150,580
G62		1,898,520
G63		324,700
G64		1,160,280
G65		220,680
G66		3,623,080 (h)
G67		179,460
G68		863,630 (j)

King George VI

1	11,579,344
2	13,002,720
3	315,720
4	2,831,440
5	2,415,180
6	313,200
7	744,600
8	2,695,860
9	1,136,020
10	1,226,460
11	372,420
12	160,260
13	168,780
14	88,200
15	496,980 (c)
16	81,180
17	16,740
18	27,240
19	18,660
20	11,400
21	191,220
22	173,040
23	197,580
24	86,700

25	539,520 (c)
26	183,000
27	348,000 (k)
28	4,841,400
29	4,408,500
30	1,815,720
31	991,800
32	2,524,200
33	2,152,200
34	886,420
S1	(758,417)
S2	(648,049)
S3	(410,989)
S4 to S10	(l)
S11	(196,860)
S12	(269,202)
S13	(304,270)
S14	(148,240)
F1	12,000 (m)

Stamps for Booklets.

A special printing of stamps for booklets was sent to the Colony between 10 Nov. 1947 and 22 January 1948. The values and quantities printed were:—

1d., 1½d., 2d. and 2½d. .. .. 123,000 of each
3d. 246,000
6d. 369,000

The quantity of booklets made up is unknown.

The quantities of these stamps are NOT included in the main listing.

Notes

(a) Surcharged on V6 between March/May 1874. The quantity is included against V6.

(b) Surcharged on V2a, V3 and V6. Individual quantities being on (i) 2d., 4,800; (ii) 3d., 12,000; and (iii) 1/–, 24,000.

(c) The 2/6, 5/–, 10/–, and 12/6d. KGV and 12/6d. KGVI values were mainly required for fiscal use.

(d) Overprinted on G3.

(e) Overprinted on G4—480 copies were spoiled and destroyed.

(f) Where both printed/issued and sold quantities are given the balance were destroyed.

(g) All remainders of G56/G57/G58/G59 were destroyed on 31/12/1935.

(h) Printings from 1951 onwards are listed under Number 33.

(j) Includes 1951 and 1952 printings.

(k) The quantity overprinted is included in the number printed/issued for Number 1.

(l) The quantities printed, issued or sold have never been disclosed.

(m) Issued for fiscal use, a few used copies are known.

BRITISH GUIANA

The Dutch colonies of Berbice, Demerara and Essequibo were captured by the British in 1781, and subsequently passed successively into French and Dutch owernship. They were finally recaptured by the British in 1803 and were formally ceded to Great Britain in 1814-15. The three colonies were united as British Guiana in 1831 (County Union).

Following the use of handstamps or other manuscript marks, a Crowned Circle PAID Frank was registered at the G.P.O. in London on March 1st, 1856; this was intended to indicate prepayment of postage on overseas letters, but no example has been found. An uncrowned Frank was also registered in 1863.

From May, 1858 to April, 1860 contemporary G.B. stamps were in use and were cancelled with "AO 3" (Georgetown) or "AO 4" (New Amsterdam) in transverse ovals of horizontal bars. British Guiana stamps became valid for use on foreign mail from May, 1860.

1858-60 Stamps of Great Britain identified by their Catalogue Nos. after prefix 'GT' or 'NA'.

(I) Used at Georgetown (Demerara): 'A 03'.

GT V39	1d.	rose-red	..	
GT V44	4d.	rose	..	..
GT V45	6d.	lilac	..	..
GT V47	1/-	green	..	..

(II) Used at New Amsterdam (Berbice): 'A 04'.

NA V39	1d.	rose-red	..	..
NA V51	2d.	blue		
NA V44	4d.	rose		
NA V45	6d.	lilac	..	..
NA V47	1/-	green	..	..

1850 (July 1st)-51. Local stamps. Type set at the Office of the Royal Gazette, Georgetown. No Wmk. Imperf and without gum. Sheets 4 x (?).

		Cut square	Cut round
V1	2c. blk/rose (1.3.51) ..	—	£20000
V2	4c. black/orange ..	£8000	£1500
V3	4c. blk/pl yel (pelure)		
	(2/51) ..	£9500	£1850
V4	4c. blk/lem yel (9/51) ..	£9500	£1850
V5	8c. black/green	£4000	£950
V6	12c. black/blue	£1650	£900
V7	12c. black/indigo (12/50)	£3500	£1050
V8	12c. black/pl blue (3/51)	£3000	£900
	a straight-footed '2' ..	£9000	£7500
	b '1' of '12' omitted ..		‡ £13500

None of these stamps are known mint. Each stamp was intended to be initialled by a member of the Post Office staff as a precaution against forgery, but a few copies are known without initials.

Initials, as under, are normally in black ink; but are also found in red or violet ink, or black pencil.

E.T.E.D. (Dalton, the Colonial Postmaster)
E.D.W. (Wight, clerk to Colonial Post Office).
J.B.S. (Smith, clerk to Imperial Post Office).
H.A.K. (Killikelly, letter carrier).
W.H.L. (Lorimer or Lortimer).

Numbers recorded—V1, 6: V2, 15: V3, 9: V4, 8: V5, 33: V6/7/8, 55.

1852 (Jan. 1st). (litho) Waterlow and Sons. Surface coloured paper without watermark. Imperf. Sheets 10 x 10 (?).

V9	1c. black/magenta ..	£3850	£2200
V10	4c. black/deep blue ..	£4250	£2400

Prices for fine unrubbed copies.

There are two types of each within the sheet, showing differences in the waves at the left and in the left outline of the upper sail. The two types of V9 may be more easily recognised, one having a stop after 'GUIANA' and the other not having a stop.

Neither type of V10 has a stop after 'GUIANA'.

For a short time after issue these stamps were also initialled (E.D.W.).

Reprints of both values, with the stamps set closer together in the sheet, were made in 1865 on thicker paper and perf. 12½—Price £8.

The inscription 'PATIMUS' was an error on the part of the engraver, and should have been 'PETIMUS'.

Number printed—V9 and V10, 50,000.

1853-59. (litho) Waterlow and Sons. No Wmk. Imperf. Sheets 10 x 10.

V11	1c. vermilion	.. ..	£1000	£300
V12	4c. deep blue	.. ..	£350	£200
V13	4c. blue ('55)	.. ..	£325	£165
V14	4c. pale blue ('58?)	..	£325	£165

V11 is also known in a distinctive reddish-brown shade, which may have come from a Proof sheet.

V12/14—The 4c. was created from the 1c. Die, the bottom label being cut away and a new one substituted. This accounts for the white line normally found above the bottom label, but

which in certain sheet positions was re-touched and shows as a coloured line.
See V20/27 for later printings.

1856 (Feb.). *(Typeset)* **Baum and Dallas at the Office of the Official Gazette, Georgetown. No Wmk. Imperf. and without gum. Sheets 4 (?) in vertical row.**

(a) On surface-coloured paper.

V15	1c. **blk/magenta** (Apr.)	—	£400000
V16	4c. **black/magenta** ..	—	£2500
V17	4c. **blk/rose car** (Sept.)	—	£2500
V18	4c. **black/blue** (Oct.) ..	—	£12500

(b) On paper coloured right through.

V19	4c. **blk/dp bl** (Aug.) ..	—	£20000

This provisional issue was necessitated by a shortage of Nos. V11/14 caused by Waterlows supplying only 5,000 stamps instead of 50,000 ordered in November, 1854.

None of the provisionals are known mint, and all the used copies are initialled E.T.E.D., E.D.W. or C.A.W. (Watson). Only one example of V15 has been recorded.

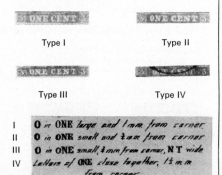

Type I   Type II

Type III   Type IV

I   O *in* ONE *large and 1 mm from corner.*
II   O *in* ONE *small and 1 mm from corner*
III   O *in* ONE *small, 1 mm from corner,* N T *wide*
IV   *Letters of* ONE *close together, 1½ m m from corner*

1857-60. As Nos. V11/14 but fresh *(litho)* **transfers with various value labels, all having the white line above the bottom label.**

V20	1c. **dl red** (Type I) (3/57)	£750	£250
V21	1c. **brnish red** (Type I) (6/59)	£1250	£250
V22	1c. **dull red** (Type II) ..	£850	£250
V23	1c. **brnish red** (Type II)	£1400	£250
V24	1c. **dull red** (Type III) ..	850	£250
V25	1c. **brnish red** (Type III)	£850	£500
V26	1c. **dull red** (Type IV) ..	£700	£175
V27	4c. **blue** (Type V) (5/60)	—	—

Reprints of both values, from fresh transfers, were made in 1865 on thin paper and perf. 12½.

Type V (V27)

1860 (July)-66 *(litho)* **Waterlow and Sons. No Wmk. Sheets 1c., 2c., 4c. – 10 x 10: 8c. – 10 x 5: 12c. – 10 x 4: 24c. – 10 x 2.**

(a) Perf. 12. Thick paper (1860-61).

V28	1c. **pale rose**	..	£175	£40
V29	1c. **reddish brn** (11/61)		£60	£22
V30	2c. **deep orange** ..		£30	£12
V31	2c. **pale orange** ..		£30	£12
V32	4c. **deep blue** ..		£50	£12
V33	4c. **blue** ..	..	£50	£12
V34	8c. **brownish rose**	..	£65	£14
V35	8c. **pink** ..	..	£65	£14
V36	12c. **lilac** ..	..	£95	£12
V37	12c. **grey-lilac** ..	..	£70	£12
V38	24c. **deep green** ..	..	£185	£20
V39	24c. **green** ..	..	£185	£20

V28 on thin paper, perf. 12½, is from an 1865 reprint.

V36/37 are occassionally found with large red '5d, surcharge. This was an accountancy mark denoting the proportion of postage payable to Great Britain.

Numbers printed—V28, 50,000: V30/31, 60,000: V32/33, 40,000: V34/35, 15,000: V36/37, 40,000: V38/39, 7,000.

Stamps of this and subsequent 'unwatermarked issues may be found showing parts of the paper-maker's watermarks.

1860:   A. COWAN & SONS/EXTRA SUPER-FINE/AC&S.
1863/65: T. H. SAUNDERS, 1863.
1863/67: ORIGINAL/TURKEY MILL/KENT.
      (letters of lower two lines large.)
1863/72: T. H. SAUNDERS.
1867/74: J. WHATMAN.
1873/74: W. KING.
1874/75: ORIGINAL/TURKEY MILL/KENT.
      (letters of lower two lines small.)

(b) Perf. 12. Thin paper (1862).

V40	1c. **brown** ..	..	..	£65	£30
V41	1c. **black** ..	..	..	£12	6·00
V42	2c. **orange** ..	..	..	£12	6·00
V43	4c. **blue** ..	..	..	£18	6·00
V44	4c. **pale blue** ..	..	..	£16	6·00
V45	8c. **pink** ..	..	..	£18	£10
V46	12c. **dull purple** ..	..	£18	£10
V47	12c. **purple** ..	..	..	£18	£10
V48	12c. **lilac** ..	..	..	£18	£10
V49	24c. **green** ..	..	..	£95	£12

Numbers printed—V40, 30,000: V42, 20,000: V43/44, 35,000.

Although the practice was expressly forbidden by a Post Office Notice of April, 9th, 1862, covers are known bearing 4c. rate made from bisected 8c. or trisected 12c. stamps, and 2c. rate from bisected 4c. (1861-71).

Several hundred sheets of Nos. V40/42/43/44 were found to have become stuck together in August, 1862. The consequent shortage of these values resulted in the provisional issue of October, 1862. (*See* V66/75).

(c) Perf. 12½-13. Thin paper (1862-63).

V50	1c. **black**	..	7·00	3·00
V51	2c. **orange** ..	..	£12	4·00
V52	4c. **blue** ..	..	£12	4·00
V53	8c. **pink** ..	..	£30	£12
V54	12c. **brown-lilac** ..	..	£90	£14
V55	24c. **green** ..	..	£100	£14

Numbers printed—V41/V50, 54,000: V51, 66,000:
V52, 60,000: V45/V53, 15,000:
V46/47/54, 42,000: V49/55, 7,000.

(d) Perf. 12½-13. Medium paper (1863).

V56	1c. **black** ..	..	6·00	2·00
V57	2c. **deep orange** ..		8·00	3·00
V58	2c. **orange** ..	..	8·00	3·00
V59	4c. **greyish blue** ..	..	£12	4·00
V60	4c. **blue** ..	..	£12	4·00
V61	8c. **pink** ..	..	£25	9·00
V62	12c. **brown-lilac** ..	..	£55	£14
V63	24c. **green** ..	..	£30	£10
V64	24c. **deep green** ..	..	£50	£10

Numbers printed—V56, 60,000: V57/58, 78,000:
V59/60, 60,000: V61, 18,000:
V62, 40,000: V63/64, 54,000.

(e) Perf. 10. Medium paper (1866).

V65	12c. **grey-lilac** ..	..	£50	£10

1862 (Sept.). (*Typeset*), **G. Melville at the Office of the Official Gazette, Georgetown. No Wmk. Roulette 6. Sheets 6 x 4, containing three types of frame.**

Type I	Type II
Nos. 1-12	Nos. 13-20

Type III
Nos. 21-24

V66	1c. **blk/dl rose** (Type I)	£300	£65
	a wrong ornament ..	—	£75
V67	1c. **blk/dl rose** (Type II)	£300	£50
	a wrong ornament ..	—	£60
	b italic 'S' in 'POST-AGE'	—	£60

V68	1c. **blk/dl rose** (Type III)	£500	£85
	a wrong ornament ..	—	—
	b broken ornament ..	—	—
	c 'C' for 'O' in 'POST-AGE'	—	£85
V69	2c. **blk/lem yel** (Type I)	£300	£60
	a wrong ornament ..	—	£65
V70	2c. **blk/lem yel** (Type II)	£325	£65
	a wrong ornament ..	—	—
	b italic 'S' in 'POST-AGE'	—	£75
	c 'TWC' for 'TWO' ..	—	£80
	d italic 'S' in 'CENTS'	—	£80
	e italic 'T' in 'TWO' ..	—	£80
V71	2c. **blk/lem yel** (Type III)	£500	£80
	a wrong ornament ..	—	£95
	b broken ornament ..	—	£95
	c 'C' for 'O' in 'POST-AGE'	—	£95

V66*a*/V69*a* Row 1/1 Fourth from top at left. Row 2/6 Third from top at right. ⎫ As 4c. (Type I) ⎬ ⎭

V67*a*/V70*a*. Row 3/3. Top row above IA of GUIANA   As 4c. (Type III)

V67*b*/V70*b*   Row 3/5.

V68*a*/V71*a*   Row 4/5. Second from left at bottom   As 4c. (Type III)

V68*b*/V71*b*   Row 4/6. Second from left at top.

V68*c*/V71*c*	Row 4/6.
V70*c*	Row 3/1.
V70*d*	Row 3/4.
V70*e*	Row 3/6.

The ONE CENT was printed first and then, using the same frames and substituting the new value, the TWO CENTS. It follows that all varieties on the 1c. sheets (except those affecting the words of value) are repeated on the 2c. sheets. Nos. V70*c/d/e* are peculiar to the 2c.

There are many other examples of broken letters small and narrow letters and additional black bars, etc., all of interest to the Specialist.

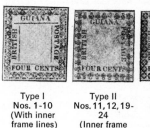 

Type I	Type II	Type III
Nos. 1-10	Nos. 11,12,19-24	Nos. 13-18
(With inner frame lines)	(Inner frame lines on Nos. 11 and 12 only)	(Without inner frame lines)

V72	4c. **blk/dk bl** (Type I) ..	£300	£50
	a wrong ornament ..	—	£60
	b ornament omitted ..	—	£60
	c italic 'S' in 'CENTS'	—	£60
V73	4c. **blk/dk blue** (Type II Framed)	£325	£60
V74	4c. **blk/dk blue** (Type II Unframed)	£325	£80

V75 4c. **blk/dk blue** (Type III)

	a	wrong ornament ..	£700	£200
	b	italic 'S' in 'CENTS'	—	£225
	c	italic 'S' in 'BRIT-ISH'	—	£225
			—	£225

V72a Row 1/6. Fourth from top at left
Row 2/2. Second from right at top } As 4c. (Type III)
V72b Row 2/4. At right above 'G' of 'POSTAGE'.
V72c Row 2/2.
V75a Row 3/1. Bottom row under 'E' of 'CENTS'. } As 1c. (Type III)
V75b Row 3/2.
V75c Row 3/3.

There are many other examples of broken and small letters, inverted and sideways ornaments, etc., all of interest to the Specialist.

These provisionals were initialled "R.M.,Ac.R.G." (R. Mather, Acting Receiver-General) before sale — in black (1c.), in red (2c.) and in white (4c.). They were withdrawn from sale as soon as the definitives (V50-52) were received on October 8th, 1862, but are known used as late as February 19th, 1863.

Unsold sheets, mostly imperforate but some rouletted, without initials, came on the market at a later date. (Price from £375).

Collectors are warned that this issue has been extensively forged.

1863 (Aug.)-75. As Nos. V28/65 but new design for 24c. (and additional 6c. and 48c.) and the space between value and 'CENTS' on the 1c., 2c., 4c., 8c. and 12c. reduced to 1mm. No Wmk. Sheets 6c. – 10 x 9: 24c. and 48c. – 10 x 5.

(a) Perf. 12½-13. (1863-64).

V76	1c. **black**	8·00	5·00
V77	2c. **orange-red**	9·00	1·50
V78	2c. **orange**	8·00	1·50
V79	6c. **blue**	£22	£10
V80	6c. **greenish blue** ..	£22	£10
V81	6c. **deep blue** ..	£22	£10
V82	6c. **milky blue** ..	£26	£10
	a **stop before 'VICISSIM'** ..	—	—
V83	8c. **pink**	£26	5·00
V84	8c. **carmine**	£26	5·00
V85	12c. **grey-lilac** ..	£80	5·00
V86	12c. **brown-lilac** ..	£95	6·00
V87	24c. **yellow-green** ..	£28	4·00
V88	24c. **green**	£28	4·00
V89	24c. **blue-green** ..	£42	8·00
V90	48c. **pale red**	£30	£12
V91	48c. **deep red**	£30	£12
V92	48c. **carmine-rose** ..	£50	£12

(b) Perf. 12.

V93	24c. **green**	£55	6·00
V94	24c. **yellow-green** ..	£26	4·00

(c) Perf. 10. (1866).

V95	1c. **black**	4·00	1·50
	a **imperf between (horiz pair)** ..	—	—
V96	1c. **grey-black**	5·00	2·00
V97	2c. **orange**	3·00	1·50
V98	2c. **red-orange** ..	7·00	1·50
V99	4c. **slate-blue** ..	£15	4·00
	a **imperf between (vert pair)** ..	—	—
V100	4c. **blue**	£16	3·00
V101	4c. **pale blue** ..	£19	4·00
V102	6c. **milky blue** ..	£28	7·00
V103	6c. **ultramarine** ..	£28	9·00
V104	6c. **dark blue** ..	£28	8·00
V105	8c. **pink**	£28	5·00
V106	8c. **brownish pink** ..	£28	5·00
V107	8c. **carmine**	£28	5·00
V108	12c. **pale lilac** ..	£52	6·00
V109	12c. **grey lilac** ..	£28	6·00
V110	12c. **brownish grey** ..	£28	6·00
V111	12c. **lilac**	£28	6·00
V112	24c. **dark green** ..	£52	4·50
V113	24c. **bluish green** ..	£45	4·50
V114	24c. **yellow-green** ..	£40	4·50
V115	48c. **crimson**	£75	£12
V116	48c. **red**	£70	£12
	a **stop after 'P'** ..	—	—

V116a—A stop appears after the 'P' in 'PETIMUS-QUE'.

(d) Perf. 15. (1875).

V117	1c. **black**	7·00	2·00
V118	2c. **orange**	£33	4·00
V119	2c. **orange-red** ..	£33	4·00
V120	4c. **bright blue** ..	£70	£25
V121	6c. **ultramarine** ..	£70	£15
V122	8c. **deep rose** ..	£40	£15
V123	12c. **lilac**	£110	£15
V124	24c. **yellow-green** ..	£145	£15
V125	24c. **deep green** ..	£145	£15

Imperforate stamps from these issues are of doubtful status and may have come from Proof sheets.

1876 (July 1st)-82. (typo) **De La Rue. Sheets 6 x 10 (later printings from 1879, 120 – two panes, each 6 x 10).**

(a) Wmk. Crown CC.

(i) Perf. 14.

V126	1c. **slate**	2·00	50
	a **imperf between (horiz pair)** ..	—	—
V127	2c. **orange**	7·50	90
V128	4c. **blue**	£17	5·50
V129	6c. **brown**	£15	5·50
V130	8c. **rose**	£15	2·50
V131	12c. **pale violet** ..	£17	3·50

V132	24c. **emerald-green**	..	£17	5·00
V133	48c. **red-brown** ..	..	£22	7·50
V134	96c. **olive-bistre**		£110	£90
V126/134 **set** (9v)		..	£215	£115
SPV126/134 **specimen set** (9v)			£100	‡

Numbers printed—V129, 78,520: V130, 376,740:
V131, 325,700: V132, 98,280:
V133/V134, 30,000 each.

(ii) **Perf. 12¼.**

| V135 | 4c. **blue** .. | .. | .. | £350 | £90 |

(iii) **Compound Perf. 14 x 12¼.**

| V136 | 1c. **slate** .. | .. | .. | — | £90 |

(b) **Wmk. Crown CA (Jan. 27th, 1882).**

V137	1c. **slate** ..	..	1·75	40
V138	2c. **orange**	..	4·50	70
	a value doubly printed	..	—	—
V139	4c. **blue** ..	..	£15	6·50
V140	6c. **brown**	..	4·00	4·00
V141	8c. **rose** ..	..	£20	1·00

Numbers printed—V137, 3,185,580: V138.
3,853,620: V139,165,960: V140,
125,040: V141, 753,120.

Under-ordering and delays in the supply of
V126/127 resulted in the many provisionals issued
between 1878 and 1882, listed hereafter.

**1878. Various stamps, as indicated, locally
overprinted with broad black bars, ruled in
ink with broad-nibbed pens.**

(a) **Ordinary stamps, for issue as 1c.**

(i) With two horizontal bars (April 17th).

| V142 | 6c. **brown** (No. V129).. | £14 | £14 |

Numbers overprinted—4,500 (On sale for 18 days).

Authority was also given for 4c. stamps to be
bisected and each half used as a 2c. stamp, but no
such bisects were issued.

(ii) With horizontal and vertical bars (November 6th).

| V143 | 6c. **ult** (No. V103) | .. | £30 | £10 |
| V144 | 6c. **brown** (No. V129).. | £30 | £12 |

(b) **Official stamps, for issue as 1c. (V145/
146/148/149) or as 2c. (V147/150/151).**

(i) With horizontal bar through 'OFFICIAL' (Aug.).

V145	1c. **black** (No. V95/V01)	£24	£12
V146	1c. **slate** (No. V126/V06)	£24	8·00
V147	2c. **or** (No. V127/V07) ..	£24	£12

The use of Official stamps had ceased from June
14th, 1878 and remaining stocks were thus available
for public use.

(ii) With two horizontal bars and one vertical bar
(November 23rd).

V148	4c. **bl** (No. V128/V08) ..	£24	£12
V149	6c. **brn** (No. V129/V09)	£24	£12
V150	8c. **rose** (No. V105/V03)	£24	£12

(iii) With one horizontal bar and one vertical bar
(November 23rd).

| V151 | 8c. **rose** (No. V130/V010) | £30 | £15 |

**1881. Various stamps, as indicated, locally
overprinted with broad (1-4mm.) black bars,
ruled in ink with broad-nibbed pens, and
subsequently surcharged.**

Type I   Type II

Type III   Type IV

(a) **Ordinary stamps surcharged in black.**

(i) No. V134 (December 21st).

V152	1	on 96c **olive-bistre**	2·00	2·00
		(Type I)	—	—
		a bar in red ..	—	—
		b bar omitted ..	—	—
V153	2	on 96c. **olive-bistre**	2·00	4·00
		(Type II) ..	—	—
		a bar in red	—	—
		b bar omitted	—	—
V154	2	on 96c. **olive-bistre**	7·00	6·00
		(Type III) ..	—	—
		a bar in red ..	—	—
		b bar omitted	—	—
		c se-tenant with		
		(Type II) ..	—	—

V153—The Type II surcharge appears on the first
five horizontal rows.

Numbers issued—V152,11,000: V153/154,10,132.

(ii) No. V116 (December 28th).

V155	1	on 48c. **red** (Type IV)	5·00	2·00
		a bar omitted	—	—
		b straight serif ..	—	—

V155*a*—The 1 has a straight serif on Row 2/2.

Number issued—9,900.

Type V   Type VI

(b) **Official stamps surcharged in black
(December 28th).**

(i) With Type IV

V156	1	on 12c. **brnish pur**		
		(No. V86/V04) ..	£14	£10
		a bar in red	—	—

| V157 | 1 | on 48c. **red-brown** (No. V133/V013) | £23 | £15 |

Numbers issued—V156, 2,438 : V157, 1,800.

(ii) With Type V.

V158	2	on 12c. **pale violet** (No. V131/V011)	£30	£22
		a two bars	—	—
		b surcharge double	£160	£120
V159	2	on 24c. **em-green** (No. V132/V012)	£200	—
		a surcharge double	—	—

(iii) With Type VI.

V160	2	on 12c. **pale violet** (No. V131/V011)	£12	7·00
		a two bars	—	—
		b surcharge double	—	—
		c se-tenant with Type V .. surcharge double (one Type V and one Type VI)	—	—
V161	2	on 24c. **em-green** (No. V132/V012)	£14	7·00
		a surcharge double	—	—

V158/161—Type V and VI surcharges both occur in the sheet.

Numbers issued—V158/160, 6,360 : V159/161, 6,000.

It should be noted that Nos. V157-161 were never issued as Official stamps without the surcharges.

(iv) With Type II (As No. V153).

| V162 | 2 | on 24c. **green** (No. V112/V05) .. | £30 | £20 |

Number issued—1,276.

Type I   Type II
(Two Masts)   (Three Masts)

1882 (Jan. 9th). Type set, Baldwin and Co.' Georgetown. No Wmk. Perf. 12. Diagonally perforated SPECIMEN.

Sheets 1st Setting (Three printings) 3 x 4, SPECIMEN upwards (lower left to upper right).

Type I   Nos. 5, 6, 7, 8, 11, 12.

Type II   Nos. 1, 2, 3, 4, 9, 10.

2nd Setting (Four printings) 2 x 6. SPECIMEN downwards (upper left to lower right).

Type I   Nos. 3, 7, 8, 9, 11, 12.

Type II   Nos. 1, 2, 4, 5, 6, 10.

V163	1c. **blk/mag** (Type I) ..	£12	9·00
	a without SPECIMEN	£20	£20
	b imperf. between (pair)	—	—

V164	1c. **blk/mag** (Type II) ..	9·00	9·00
	a without SPECIMEN	£22	£22
V165	2c. **blk/yel** (Type I) ..	£14	9·00
	a without SPECIMEN	£20	£20
V166	2c. **blk/yel** (Type II) ..	£15	£12
	a without SPECIMEN	£22	£22
	b bisect diag (1c.) on cover	‡	—

The stamps were perforated SPECIMEN instead of being initialled as a precaution against forgery. In both settings half the stamps have SPECIMEN inverted.

There are many examples of broken and small figures and letters etc., all of interest to the Specialist. These provisionals were withdrawn from sale on January 27th, 1882 when supplies of Nos. V137/138 were received.

Numbers printed—V163/164, 42,396 : V165/166, 24,132.

Numbers sold—V163/164, 30,396 : V165/166. 12,132.

1888 (Oct. 1st)-90 (*typo*) **De La Rue. As Nos. V137/141 but specially printed in double fugitive colours and without value in lower label. Wmk. Crown CA. Perf. 14. Sheets 6 x 10.**

(a) Overprinted and surcharged in black.

V167	1c. **dl purple** (8/89) ..	50	50
V168	2c. **dl purple** (5/89) ..	50	50
V169	3c. **dl purple** (10/89) ..	50	50
V170	4c. **dull purple**	1·00	70
	a large '4'	9·00	6·50
V171	6c. **dull purple** ..	1·75	1·00
	a straight top	3·75	2·00
V172	8c. **dl pur** (8/89) ..	70	70
V173	10c. **dl pur** (10/89) ..	2·00	1·75
V174	20c. **dl pur** (10/89) ..	4·25	3·50
V175	40c. **dl pur** (10/89) ..	4·25	5·00
V176	72c. **dull purple** ..	6·50	6·00
V177	$1 **green**	£110	£75
V178	$2 **green**	£55	£45
V179	$3 **green**	£32	£27
V180	$4 **green**	£90	£75
	a large '4'	£250	£250
V181	$5 **green**	£55	£45
V167/181	**set** (15v)	£350	£275

V170*a*—The figure '4' is taller and its foot extends below CENTS on all stamps in the third vertical row.

V171*a*—The figure '6' has an open straight top on all stamps in the fourth and sixth vertical rows.

V180*a*—The figure '4' is taller on all stamps in the second vertical row.

Numbers sold (for postal and revenue uses)—
V167, 123,000: V168, 34,500:
V169, 86,708: V170, 83,071:
V171, 122,981: V172, 29,084:
V173, 26,386: V174, 11,978:
V175, 4,120: V176, 4,555:
V177, 146: V178, 544: V179,
9,326: V180, 1,133: V181,
14,160.

(b) No. V168 (further surcharged '2' in red at the Office of the Official Gazette (June 6th, 1889).

V182   '2' on 2c. **dull purple** ..   50   50

This surcharge was applied in order to prevent fraudulent conversion of the 2c. stamp into a 72c. stamp. Inverted and double surcharges were privately produced by an employee in the printing office.

Number issued—273,000.

(c) Nos. V177/V180 further locally surcharged 'One Cent' in red serif letters in two lines with two bars obliterating the previous DOLLAR surcharge. (July 15th, 1890).

V183	1c. on $1 **green**	..	1·00	70
	a surcharge double		—	£25
V184	1c. on $2 **green**	..	50	1·00
	a surcharge double		£45	—
V185	1c. on $3 **green** ..		1·00	70
	a surcharge double		£35	—
V186	1c. on $4 **green** ..	..	2·00	2·75
	a surcharge double			
	b large '4' (No.			
	V180*a*) ..	..	9·00	7·50
	c surcharge double			
	(No. V180*a*)	..	£40	—

Numbers surcharged—V183, 121,800: V184,
111,000: V185, 110,000: V186,
54,000.

1889 (Sept. 6th)-1900 (*typo*) **De La Rue. Wmk. Crown CA. Perf. 14. Sheets 6 x 10.**

V187	1c. **dl pur and sl grey**..	70	50
V188	1c. **sea-green** ('91) ..	25	20
V189	2c. **dl pur and orange**	60	30
V190	2c. **dl pur and car** (6/00)	1·75	30
V191	4c. **dl pur and ult** ..	1·75	1·75
V192	4c. **dl pur and cobalt** ..	5·50	1·50
V193	5c. **ult** ('91)	1·75	50
V194	6c. **dl pur and brown** ..	8·50	3·75
V195	6c. **dl pur and maroon**	4·50	2·25
V196	8c. **dl pur and rose** ..	2·75	1·75
V197	8c. **dl pur and greenish**		
	black (10/90) ..	2·25	2·50
V198	12c. **dl and bt purple** ..	4·50	1·00
V199	12c. **dl pur and mauve**..	3·50	1·25
V200	24c. **dl pur and green** ..	4·50	1·75

V201	48c. **dul pur and orange-**		
	red	8·50	3·75
V202	72c. **dl pur and red-brn**	9·00	5·50
V203	72c. **dl pur and yel-brn**..	£15	£14
V204	96c. **dl pur and carmine**	£24	£22
V205	96c. **dl pur and rosine**..	£32	£26
V187/205	**set** (14v)	£65	£35
SPV187/205	**specimen set** (14v)	£115	‡

See also Nos. E1/6.

1898 (July 18th). Queen Victoria's Jubilee (1897). (*recess*) **De La Rue. Wmk. Crown CC (sideways on V206/209/211). Sheets 12 x 5 (V207/208/210): 6 x 10 (V206/209/211).**

V206	1c.	**blue-black and**		
		carmine ..	..	2·00	60
V207	2c.	**brown and indigo**..	2·25	70
		a imperf between		
		(pair)	£1000	—
V208	2c.	**brown and blue** ..	4·75	60
V209	5c.	**green and sepia** ..	7·50	3·50
		a imperf between		
		(pair)	—	—
V210	10c.	**bl-blk and or-red** ..	9·50	6·50
V211	15c.	**red-brn and blue** ..	9·50	7·00
V206/211		**set** (5v)	£32	£18
SPV206/211		**specimen set** (5v)	£50	‡

V206—May be found with Mount Roraima pale and ill-defined, or darker and well-defined. The former came from the original vignette plate which was damaged in the course of printing, and the latter from the balance of the order printed from a new vignette plate.

Numbers printed—V206, 787,500: V207/208,
884,040: V209, 306,900: V210,
153,600: V211, 154,680.

1899. Nos. V209/210/211 surcharged TWO CENTS. in black sans serif capitals at the Daily Chronicle Office.

V212	2c. on 5c. **grn and sepia**			
	(June 15th)	..	1·00	1·00
	a stop omitted	..	9·00	9·00

V213 2c. on 10c. **bl-blk and or**
-red (Feb. 22nd).. 60 70
  a stop omitted .. 7·50 7·50
  b 'GENTS' for
    'CENTS' .. £16 £16
  c surcharge inverted £85 £100
V214 2c. on 15c. **red-brn and**
blue (Feb. 22nd).. 1·50 1·50
  a stop omitted .. £14 £14
  b surcharge double.. £170 —
  c surcharge double,
    one without stop — —
  d surcharge inverted £120 £130

V212*a* Row 9/5.
V213*a* Row 5/5 (1st Setting). Row 2/9
(2nd Setting).
V213*b* Row 5/7 (1st Setting only).
V214*a* Row 9/2.

Numbers surcharged—V212, 207,900 : V213,
96,600 (1st) : 30,000 (2nd) :
V214, 124,680 (1st) ; 6,000 (2nd)

V214*b*—One sheet of 60, less 23 copies recovered and destroyed.

V214*d*—One sheet of 60.

1901-07. As Nos. V188/201 but new colours and new value. Wmk. Crown CA. Perf. 14.

E1 1c. **grey-green** ('07) .. 90 30
E2 2c. **dl pur and blk/red**
('01) 60 20
E3 6c. **grey-black and ult**
('02) .. .. .. 4·25 4·75
E4 48c. **grey and pur-brown**
('01) £17 £16
E5 48c. **brownish-grey and**
brown ('07) .. £14 £14
E6 60c. **grn and rosine** ('03) £30 £30
E1/6 **set** (5v) £48 £48
SPE2/6 **specimen set** (4v) .. £50 ‡
Number printed : E6, 10,080.

1905-10. As before but Wmk. Multiple Crown CA. Sheets 120 – two panes, each 6 x 10.

E7 1c. **gr-grn OC** (2/05) .. 25 25
E8 1c. **blue-green** ('10) .. 70 35
E9 2c. **purple and black/**
red OC (2/05) .. 40 30
E10 2c. **rose-red** (2/05) .. 2·00 35
E11 4c. **dl purple and ult OC**
(7/05) .. .. 7·50 6·50
E12 4c. **brn and pur** (2/07) .. 2·00 1·25
E13 5c. **dl pur and bl/bl OC**
(5/05) .. .. 2·75 2·00
E14 5c. **ult** (2/07) .. .. 1·00 45
E15 6c. **gr-blk and ult OC**
(9/05) .. .. 8·50 9·00
E16 6c. **gr and blk** (2/07) .. 6·00 3·00
E17 12c. **dl and bt purple OC**
(2/05) £13 £12
E18 12c. **or and mauve** (2/07) 3·00 2·00
E19 24c. **dl pur and grn OC**
(3/06) .. .. 3·75 3·75
E20 48c. **gr and pur-brn OC**
(5/05) £10 £11
E21 60c **grn and rosine OC**
(2/05) £10 £12
E22 72c. **pur and or-brn C**
('07) £19 £19

E23 96c. **blk and ver/yel C**
(11/05) £22 £22
E7/23 **set** (17v) £105 £100
SPE8/23 **specimen set** (7v) .. £60 ‡
Number printed : E21, 10,320.

1905 Revenue Stamp overprinted POSTAGE AND REVENUE in black by De La Rue. Wmk. Multiple Crown CA. Perf. 14. Sheets 6 x 10.

E24 $2·40 **grn and vio C** .. £200 £250
SPE24 **specimen** (1v) .. £55 ‡
Number issued—5,280.

Collectors should beware of cleaned fiscally used copies of this stamp with AMACURA cancellation.

1909. Redrawn. Wmk. Multiple Crown CA. Perf. 14. Sheets 240 – four panes, each 6 x 10.

E25 2c. **rose-red** .. .. 1·00 35

In this redrawn type there are two background lines above '2 CENTS' instead of three (as on No. E10) and the 'S' is spaced farther away from the end of the tablet. The flag is closer to the masthead.

Booklets containing 12 x 1c. and 18 x 2c., in panes of six, were placed on sale on June 14th, 1909

1913-21 (*typo*) **De La Rue. Wmk. Multiple Crown CA. Perf. 14. Sheets 120 – two panes, each 6 x 10.**

G1 1c. **yellow-green** .. 60 40
G2 1c. **bl-grn/bluish** ('17) .. 45 25
G3 2c. **carmine** 40 20
G4 2c. **scarlet** ('16) .. 40 20
  a wmk. sideways .. — —
G5 4c. **brn and br purple C**.. 1·25 60
G5A 4c. **dp brn and pur /bluish**
C .. .. .. 1·50 50
G6 5c. **bright blue** 60 60
G7 5c. **pl ult/bluish grey** .. 90 60
G8 6c. **grey and black** .. 70 70
G9 12c. **orange and violet C** 1·00 80
G10 12c. **dl or and pur/bluish**
C .. .. .. 1·50 80
G11 24c. **dl purple and green** 2·00 2·00
G12 48c. **gr and pur-brn C** .. 3·75 4·50
G13 48c. **sepia and pur-brn C** 4·00 4·50

G14	60c.	**green and rosine C** ..	£10	£10
		a on bluish	£12	£10
G15	72c.	**pur and or-brn C** ..	£13	£13
G16	96c.	**blk and ver/yel C** ..	£15	£15
		a white back ('13) ..	£12	£12
		b on lemon ('16) ..	£12	£13
		c on pale yellow ('21)	£14	£15
G1/16		**set (11v)**	£43	£43
SPG1/16		**specimen set (11v)**	£75	‡

G4—From May, 1917 this stamp was printed in sheets of 240 (four panes, each 6 x 10) : this was achieved by bolting together key Plates 1 and 2, so that Plate No. 1 appears in the top margin and Plate No. 2 in the lower margin.

G5—is known with inverted watermark.

1918 (Jan. 5th). War Tax. No. G4 overprinted War Tax in black serif letters by De La Rue (Sheets – 240).

| G17 | 2c. | **scarlet** .. .. .. | 25 | 25 |

1921 (Dec.)-27. As Nos. G1/16 but Wmk. Multiple Script CA. G18/25 O: G26/30 C.

G18	1c.	**green** (7/22)	25	20
G19	2c.	**rose-carmine** ..	40	25
G20	2c.	**violet** (5/23) ..	40	25
G21	2c.	**reddish-violet** ..	25	15
G22	4c.	**brn and bt pur** (10/22)	75	30
G23	6c.	**bt blue** (11/22) ..	75	45
G24	12c.	**dl or and vio** (5/22)..	1·00	90
G25	12c.	**dp or and dp violet**..	1·25	90
G26	24c.	**dl purple and green**	1·75	1·75
G27	48c.	**blk and pur** (10/26)..	4·00	4·25
G28	60c.	**green and rosine**		
		(10/26)	7·50	7·50
G29	72c.	**dl pur and or-brn**		
		(7/23)	9·00	8·50
G30	96c.	**black and red/yellow**		
		(11/27)	£10	£12
G18/21		**set (11v)**	£33	£35
SPG18/21		**specimen set (11v)**	£80	‡

1931 (July 21st). Centenary of County Union.

(recess) **Waterlow and Sons. Wmk. Multiple Script CA. Perf. 12¼. Sheets 6 x 10. or 10 x 6.**

G31	1c.	**emerald-green** ..	45	45
G32	2c.	**brown**	65	65
G33	4c.	**carmine**	2·00	1·50
G34	6c.	**blue**	3·75	4·00
G35	$1	**violet**	£22	£24
G31/35		**set (5v)**	£27	£28
SPG31/35		**specimen set (5v)**	£35	‡

Numbers printed—G31, 411,600 : G32, 4,811,400 : G33, 600,000 : G34, 242,760 : G35, 24,120.

1934 (Oct. 1st)-50. *(recess)* **Waterlow and Sons Wmk. Multiple Script CA. (sideways on horizontal designs). Sheets 6 x 10 or 10 x 6.**

(a) Perf. 12½.

G36	1c.	**green**	10	10
G37	2c.	**red-brown**	15	10
		a watermark sideways	—	—
G38	3c.	**scarlet**	10	10
		a wmk. Crown missing		
		(Type B) ..	—	—
G39	4c.	**slate-violet**	45	30
		a imperf between (vert		
		pair)	—	£2500
		b imperf horizontally		
		(vert pair) ..	—	£2500
G40	6c.	**dp ultramarine** ..	1·00	1·00
G41	12c.	**red-orange** ..	10	10
G42	24c.	**purple**	3·00	3·00
G43	48c.	**black**	7·00	7·50
G44	50c.	**green**	8·50	9·00
G45	60c.	**red-brown**	£20	£19
G46	72c.	**purple**	1·50	1·50
G47	96c.	**black**	£20	£22
G48	$1	**bright violet**	£22	£24
G36/48		**set (13v)**	£80	£85
SPG36/48		**specimen set (13v)**	£45	‡

(b) Perf. 12½ x 13½. Dec. 30th, 1943.

| G49 | 3c. | **scarlet** .. .. .. | 10 | 10 |

(c) Perf. 13 x 14 (3c.) or 14 x 13 (12c.).

G50	3c.	**scarlet** (28.4.49)	15	15
G51	12c.	**red-orange** (1.7.50)	10	25

G38*a*—Is believed to have been found only in Booklet panes. (See Introduction for details).

G39*a*—One horizontal line of perforations was missed on one sheet, giving ten vertical pairs imperf between. No mint pairs are known and only one postally used pair on cover (19.9.36), the remainder having been fiscally used at the Royal Bank of Canada, Georgetown.

G39*b*—18-26 copies survived from a sheet of 60.

G37—500 Coils each containing 500 stamps in joined strips were supplied in September, 1934.

Booklets containing 4 x 1c., 8 x 2c. and 4 x 4c., were supplied in September, 1934 (400 Booklets only). G38 was also incorporated in Booklets from June, 1945.

Numbers printed—G36, 2,086,420 : G37, 6,201,300 : G38, 224,480 : G39, 1,112,900 : G40, 350,280 : G41, 222,420 : G42, 172,140 : G43, 70,020 : G44, 26,400 : G45, 52,800 : G46, 26,400 : G47, 64,140 : G48, 26,400.

Three values of this issue continued in use during the reign of King George VI when additional supplies were printed as under –

G49/50	18 million (See Nos. 13 and 17).
G51	6½ million (See No. 20).
G46	98,960 (Withdrawn from sale June 1st, 1945).

1935 (May 6th). Silver Jubilee. (*recess*) **De La Rue. Wmk. Multiple Script CA. Perf. 13¼ x 14. Sheets 6 x 10.**

G52	2c.	**ult and grey**	10	10
G53	6c.	**brown and dp blue**	75	70
G54	12c.	**green and indigo** ..	1·00	1·25
G55	24c.	**slate and purple** ..	2·25	2·25
G52/55		**set** (4v)	4·00	4·00
SPG52/55		**specimen set** ..	£18	‡

Imperf Die Proofs of the frames only are known in black on thin paper. A similar Proof of an essay for a proposed 10c. value is also known.

Numbers sold—G52, 1,886,819 : G53, 139,016 : G54, 85,067 : G55, 77,913.

Remainders were withdrawn on December, 31st, 1935.

1938 (Feb. 1st)-52 Designs, 1c., 3c., 6c., 24c., 60c (Colonial Activities); 2c,. 12c., 36c., 48c., $1, $2 (Views in Colony); 4c. (**Map of South America); 96c. (Sir Walter Raleigh & Son); $3 (Victoria Regia Lilies). Printers** (*recess*) **Waterlow & Sons. Perf. 12½ (L). Designs, 2c., 4c., 6c., 96c., V. Sheets 10 x 6 or 6 x 10.**

1	1c.	**yellow-green**	15	5
	a	green (8/4/46)	5	5
	b	booklet pane of 4 ..	2·00	—
2	2c.	**violet-black**	5	5
	a	booklet pane of 4 ..	3·00	—
3	4c.	**red and grey-black** ..	5	5
	a	pr. imperf. horiz.	£1000	£1000
4	6c.	**dp ultramarine** ..	5	5
	a	ultramarine	10	5
5	24c.	**blue-grn** (*wmk. up-right*) (3/4/38) ..	7·00	3·00
	a	blu-grn (*wmk. side-ways*) (/41)	70	15
	b	grn (*wmk. sideways*)	1·00	15
6	36c.	**violet** (7/3/38) ..	25	20
7	48c.	**orange**	45	20
8	60c.	**chocolate-brown** ..	60	40
	a	brown (/43)	60	40
	b	red-brn (8/4/43) ..	50	40
9	96c.	**deep plum**	1·25	80
10	$1	**bright violet**	90	50
11	$2	**reddish-pur** (11/6/45)	2·00	2·50
12	$3	**reddish-chest** (2/7/45)	3·00	4·00
	a	terracotta (13/12/46)	8·00	7·00
1/12		**set** (12)	9·00	8·00
SP1/12		**specimen set** (perf (12)	£45	‡

No. 3*a*—A sheet imperf. horizontally was discovered in the colony in 1947.

As before but Perf. 12½ x 13½ (L).

13	3c.	**scar-red** (30/12/43) ..	10	10
14	96c.	**dp plum** (20/3/44) ..	1·50	1·50

13—See also No. G49.

As before but Perf. 12¾ x 13¾ (C).

15	1c.	**green** (/49)	5	5
	a	booklet pane of 4 ..	2·00	3·00
16	2c.	**violet-black** (28/4/49)	5	5
	a	booklet pane of 4 ..	3·00	—
17	3c.	**carmine-red** (/49) ..	15	15
	a	booklet pane of 4 ..	6·00	—
18	4c.	**red and grey-black** (12/1/52)	5	5
19	6c.	**dp ult** (24/10/49) ..	5	5
20	12c.	**vermilion** (1/7/50) ..	1·00	2·25
	a	bright vermilion ..	10	10
21	36c.	**violet** (13/12/51) ..	60	50
22	48c.	**orange** (14/6/51) ..	60	70

24	96c.	**dark plum** (8/2/51)	..	1·50	1·50
25	$1	**bright violet** (/51)	..	£85	£100
26	$2	**reddish-pur** (9/8/50)		2·00	3·00
27	$3	**reddish-chestnut**			
		(29/10/52)	.. ..	5·00	5·00
15/27		**set** (11) (less 25)	..	9·00	£11

17—See also No. G50.

20—See also No. G51.

Overprints "Marine Detachment" on 1c., 2c., 3c., 12c., 36c. and $1 are bogus and not officially issued.

SPECIAL ISSUES

1937 (May 12th) Coronation. As Aden.

S1	2c.	**light brown**	.. ..	5	5
S2	4c.	**grey-black**	.. ..	10	10
S3	6c.	**blue**	.. ..	25	30
SP	S1/3	**specimen set** perf (3)		£13	‡

1946 (Oct. 21st) Victory. As Aden.

S4	3c.	**carmine-red**	.. ..	5	5
S5	6c.	**deep blue**	.. ..	5	5
SP	S4/5	**specimen set** perf (2)		£14	‡

1948 (Dec. 20th) Silver Wedding. As Aden.

S6	3c.	**scarlet**	.. .. ..	10	10
S7	$3	**ches-brn** (*all recess*) ..		5·00	6·00

1949 (Oct. 10th) U.P.U. As Aden.

S8	4c.	**carmine-rose**	..	10	10
S9	6c.	**indigo** ..	..	15	15
S10	12c.	**orange**	.. ..	30	35
S11	24c.	**quartz-green**	..	60	60
S8/11		**set** (4) ..	..	1·00	1·20

1951 (Feb. 16th) West Indies University College. As Antigua.

S12	3c.	**blk and car-red**	..	15	10
S13	6c.	**black and blue**	..	25	15

POSTAGE DUE STAMPS

1940 (March 1st)-50 (*typo*) **De La Rue. Perf. 13¾ x 14 (C). Rough Paper. Sheets 6 x 10.**

PD1	1c.	**green** ..	.. ..	50	50
PD2	2c.	**black**	.. ..	50	50
PD3	12c.	**deep scarlet** ..	..	75	80
	a	scar (smooth paper)			
		(/50)	.. ..	90	70

1952. Chalk-surfaced paper.

PD4	1c.	**green** ..	.. ..	10	10
PD5	2c.	**black** ..	.. ..	10	10
PD6	4c.	**blue** ..	.. ..	10	10
PD7	12c.	**scarlet**	.. ..	10	10

Watermark Varieties (Type A)

(See Introduction for details)

PD4a	1c.	Crown missing	..	£20	—
PD4b	1c.	St. Edward's Crown	..	£12	—
PD5a	2c.	Crown missing	..	£20	—
PD5b	2c.	St. Edward's Crown	..	£12	—
PD6a	4c.	Crown missing	..	£12	—
PD6b	4c.	St. Edward's Crown	..	£10	—

OFFICIAL STAMPS

1875 (April?). Nos. V95/V97/V105/V86/V112 overprinted OFFICIAL in sans serif letters by Waterlow and Sons. No Wmk. Perf. 10.

(a) In red (16 or 17mm. x 3½mm.).

VO1	1c.	**black** ..	.. ..	5·00	5·00
	a	imperf between			
		(pair)	.. ..	—	£400

(b) In black (13¼ or 14½mm. x 2mm.).

VO2	2c.	**orange** ..	.. ..	£25	4·00
VO3	8c.	**rose** ..	.. ..	£60	£25
VO4	12c.	**brownish purple**			
		(p. 12½-13) ..		£175	£75
VO5	24c.	**green** ..	.. ..	£100	£40

Numbers Printed—VO1, 37,500: VO3, 40,000: VO3, 5,000: VO4, 3,000: VO5, 2,000.

Many of these stamps were converted for use as Ordinary stamps in 1878-81 (See Nos. V145/151 and V156/162); and the actual numbers used as Officials is consequently less than shown above (Used as Official stamps – VO4, 562: VO5, 724).

1876 (January?)-78. Nos. V126/V133 overprinted OFFICIAL in black sans serif letters by De La Rue (16 x 2½mm.). Wmk. Crown CC. Perf. 14.

VO6	1c.	**slate** ..	.. ..	£45	£20
	a	imperf between			
		(pair)	.. ..	—	£12
VO7	2c.	**orange** ..	.. ..	£14	4·00
VO8	4c.	**blue** ..	.. ..	£22	9·00
VO9	6c.	**brown** ..	.. ..	£400	£100
VO10	8c.	**rose** ..	.. ..	£375	£90

Prepared for use but not issued as OFFICIAL stamps.

VO11	12c.	**pale violet** ..	..	£220	—
VO12	24c.	**green** ..	..	£300	—
VO13	48c.	**red-brown** ..	..	£350	—

Numbers printed—VO6, 24,120: VO7, 40,620: VO8, 13,200: VO9, 6,840: VO10, 6,240: VO11, 6,360: VO12, 6,360: VO13, 1,800.

Many of these stamps were also converted for use as Ordinary stamps in 1878-81 (See Nos. V145/151 and V156/162); and the actual number used as Officials is consequently less than shown above. Although VO11/13 were never issued as Official stamps, a few mint copies of VO11 and VO12 are known, but none of VO13. Virtually the entire printing of these three stamps was converted for use as Ordinary stamps in 1881.

The use of Official stamps ceased from June 14th, 1878. Collectors are warned of forged overprints, especially on the De La Rue Crown CA watermarked stamps (Nos. V137/141).

BRITISH HONDURAS

The territory was originally settled in 1638; and, after Spanish attacks in 1779, was re-settled in 1783 under Jamaican administration.

Following the use of other handstamps or manuscript marks, a Crowned Circle PAID Frank was registered at the G.P.O. in London on November 13th, 1841 and was thereafter struck in red to indicate prepayment of postage on overseas letters.

From May, 1858 to March, 1860 contemporary G.B. stamps were in use and were cancelled with "AO6" in a transverse oval of horizontal bars.

The Crowned Circle Frank was again used from April 1st, 1860, and also an Uncrowned Frank, until the first British Honduras stamps were issued (See Introduction).

1841-65 PAID Franks   *On Cover*

VF1		..	..	£350
VF2	**(1860)**	..	..	£350

1858-60 Stamps of Great Britain identified by their Catalogue Nos. after prefix 'BH'. Used at Belize: 'A O6'

BH V39	1d.	**rose-red**	..
BH V44	4d.	**rose**	
BH V45	6d.	**lilac**	.. ..
BH V47	1/-	**green**	.. ..

All stamps from V1 to G37 are (*typo*) **De La Rue.**

1866 (Jan.). No Wmk. Perf. 14. Sheets 240 – four panes, each 6 x 10. (1d. – two panes: 6d. and 1/- – one pane each).

V1	1d.	**pale blue**	..	£28	£26
	a	imperf between (pair)	.. ..	—	
V2	1d.	**blue**	.. ..	£28	£26
V3	6d.	**rose**	..	£90	£55
V4	1/-	**green**	..	£90	£55
	a	in horiz pair with 6d.		£9000	—
	b	in vert pair with 1d.		£9500	—

The sheet layout of the first printing was unusual in that the top two panes were 1d. stamps, the lower left 1/- and the lower right 6d. stamps; the panes being separated by gutter margins. Later printings were of the 1d. stamps only (in sheets of 120 – two panes, each 6 x 10).

Numbers printed—V1/V2, 60,000 : V3/V4, 12,000 each.

1872-79. As before, but Wmk. Crown CC.
(a) Perf. 12½. Sheets V7/8 120 – two panes, each 6 x 10.

V5	1d.	**pale blue**	.. ..	£30	£10
V6	1d.	**deep blue**	.. ..	£30	£10

V7	3d.	**red-brown**	.. ..	£60	£40
V8	3d.	**chocolate**	.. ..	£60	£40
V9	6d.	**rose**	.. ..	£85	£15
V10	6d.	**bright rose-carmine**		£140	£20
V11	1/-	**green** ..	.. ..	£140	£17
V12	1/-	**deep green**	..	£100	£12
	a	imperf between (pair)	.. ..	—	£9000

(b) Perf. 14. Sheets V16 6 x 5.

V13	1d.	**pale blue**	.. ..	£20	£10
V14	1d.	**blue**	.. ..	£18	7·50
	a	imperf between (horiz pair)	..	£900	—
V15	3d.	**chestnut**	.. ..	£50	£10
V16	4d.	**mauve** (8/79)	..	£75	7·50
V17	6d.	**rose**	.. ..	£135	£100
V18	1/-	**green** ..	.. ..	£100	£10
	a	imperf between (pair)	.. ..	—	—

1882-87. As before, but Wmk. Crown CA. Perf. 14.

V19	1d.	**blue** ('84)	.. ..	£12	£10
V20	1d.	**rose** (10/84)	..	£10	9·00
	a	bisect diag (½d.) on cover	..	—	—
V21	1d.	**carmine**	.. ..	£20	£12
V22	4d.	**mauve** ('82)	..	£38	4·00
V23	6d.	**yellow** ('85)	..	£150	£95
V24	1/-	**grey** ('87)	..	£150	£85
SPV24		**specimen** (1v)	..	£50	‡

1d. stamps in rose, yellow or grey (Perf. 12) were Colour Trials.

The 3d. stamp exists imperf with this watermark, but was not issued.

$$ \underset{\text{Type I}}{\overset{\displaystyle 2}{\text{C E N T S}}} \qquad \underset{\text{Type II}}{\overset{\displaystyle \mathbf{2}}{\textbf{CENTS}}} $$

1888 (Jan. 1st). New Currency locally surcharged in black (Type I).

(a) Wmk. Crown CC.

(i) Perf. 12½ (Nos. V8/9).

V25	2c.	on 6d. **rose**	..	£60	£60
V26	2c.	on 6d. **deep rose**	..	£75	£75
V27	3c.	on 3d. **chocolate**	..	£3500	£1800

(ii) Perf. 14. (Nos. V15 and V17).

V28	2c. on 6d. **rose**	..	£45	£45
	a surcharge double	..	£550	—
	b bisect diag (1c.) on cover	..	—	£70
	c surcharge inverted	..	—	—
	d small curved '2'	..	£325	—
V29	3c. on 3d. **red-brown**	..	£36	£36
	a misplaced '3'	..		

There were two trial printings of V28. No. V28*c* comes from the first, on which Row 5/1 was inverted; and No. V28*d* comes from the second trial printing.

V29*a*—The '3' appears over the 'C' of 'CENTS'.

(b) Wmk. Crown CA. (Nos. V20/22/23/24).

V30	2c. on 1d. **rose**	4·50	9·00	
	a surcharge inverted..	£525	£525	
	b surcharge double ..	£525	£525	
	c bisect (1c.) on cover	—	£60	
V31	10c. on 4d. **mauve** ..	£18	9·00	
V32	20c. on 6d. **yellow** ..	£18	£12	
V33	50c. on 1/– **grey**	£170	£200	
	a bisect diag (25c.) on cover	—	—	
	b '5 CENTS'	£3250	—	

1888 (May)-91. New Currency. Nos. V21/V24. surcharged by De La Rue in black (Type II). Wmk. Crown CA. Perf. 14. (Nos. V34/V37 were special printings in new colours).

V34	1c. on 1d. **dl green** ('91)	35	35
V35	2c. on 1d. **carmine**	35	80
	a bisect diag or vert (1c.) on cover ..	—	£45
V36	3c. on 3d. **red-brown** ..	50	1·00
V37	6c. on 3d. **ult** ('91) ..	1·25	3·00
V38	10c. on 4d. **mauve** ..	1·25	1·25
	a surcharge double ..	£500	—
V39	20c. on 6d. **yellow** ('89) ..	4·00	8·50
V40	50c. on 1/– **grey** (7/88) ..	£10	£18
V34/40	**set** (7v)	£17	£32
SPV34/40	**specimen set** (7v)	£175	‡

V36 was not issued on Crown CA paper without this surcharge.

Numbers printed—V34, 284,280: V35, 240,600: V36, 239,640: V37, 75,600: V39, 30,000. (V38, 75,400: V40, 6,300 – 1st printings only).

1888-91. Previously surcharged stamps again surcharged locally.

(a) No. V33 surcharged 'TWO' in red (1888).

V41	2c. on 50c. on 1/– **grey** ..	£25	£30
	a bisect diag (1c.) on cover	—	£70
	b surcharge in black..	£5000	£4750
	c surcharge double (black and red) ..	£4750	£4500

V41*b/c*—Only nine copies of each are believed to exist.

(b) Nos. V36/37/38 surcharged 'FIVE' '6' '15' with bar obliterating the previous surcharge. (In red on V44 and V45). (1891).

V42	5c. on 3c. on 3d. **red-brn**		
	a surcharge double ..	1·25	2·50
	b spaced 'IV' ..	—	—
	c surcharge double ..	£16	£18
	(spaced 'IV') ..	£80	—

V42*b/c*—The I and V of FIVE are wider spaced on Row 2/6.

V43	6c. on 10c. on 4d. **mauve**	70	2·50
	a '6' and bar inverted	£1350	£350
	b '6' only inverted ..	—	£1350
V44	6c. on 10c. on 4d. **mauve**	60	2·50
	a '6' and bar inverted	£190	£17
	b '6' only inverted ..	—	£1350

V43*b*/44*b*—Only six copies of each exist, as the error occurred only once on the pane and was corrected after six panes of each had been printed.

The surcharge 'SIX', with or without bar, in red has long been considered to have been an Essay. Nevertheless, copies are known used on cover, and this variety of the surcharge may have been issued. Price used £50.

V45	15c. on 6c. on 3d. **ult** ..	5·50	7·50
	a surcharge double ..	—	—

1891-99. Wmk. Crown CA. Perf. 14. Sheets 12 x 20. (Nos. V49 and V51 inscribed "POSTAGE, POSTAGE": see also V69/70).

V46	1c. **dull green** ('95) ..	35	50
V47	2c. **carmine-rose** ..	35	45
V48	3c. **brown**	60	1·50
V49	5c. **ultramarine** ('95) ..	7·50	80
V50	6c. **ultramarine**	1·25	70
V51	10c. **mauve and grn** ('95)	4·50	4·25
V52	12c. **pl mauve and green**	£18	3·25
V53	12c. **violet and green** ..	4·50	4·25
V54	24c. **yellow and blue** ..	2·50	4·25
V55	24c. **orange and blue** ..	8·50	£11
V56	25c. **rd-brn and grn** ('98)	£12	£15
V57	50c. **grn and car** ('99) ..	£10	£12
V58	$1 **grn and car** ('99) ..	£17	£18
V59	$2 **green and ult** ('99)..	£38	£45
V60	$5 **green and black** ('99)	£220	£270
V46/60	**set** (13v)	£340	£380
SPV46/60	**specimen set** (13v)	£120	‡

1899. Nos. V49/V51/V56/V40 locally overprinted 'REVENUE' in small black serif capitals.

(a) Overprint 12mm.

V61	5c. **ultramarine**	2·00	2·00
	a 'BEVENUE'	£19	£20
	b narrow 'U'	—	—
V62	10c. **mauve and green** ..	3·00	3·25
	a 'BEVENUE'	£70	—
	b narrow 'U'	—	—
	c 'REVENU'	—	—
V63	25c. **red-brown and grn**	2·50	3·25
	a 'BEVENUE'	£36	£39
	b narrow 'U'	—	—
	c 'N' omitted	—	—
V64	50c. on 1/– **grey**	£60	£60
	a 'BEVENUE'	£1350	—

V61*a*-V64*a*—The 'B' for 'R' variety is on Row 6/4.
V61*b*-V63*b*—The narrow 'U' is on Row 1/5.

(b) Overprint 11mm. (From the same sheets as 12mm. overprint).

V65	5c. **ultramarine**	2·00	2·25
V66	10c. **mauve and green** ..	6·00	6·50
	a 'REVENU'	£160	£80
V67	25c. **red brown and grn**..	3·00	3·25
V68	50c. on 1/– **grey**	£50	£50
	a se-tenant with 12mm. overprint (vert pair) ..	—	

V68a—The Royal Collection contains a block of nine (Rows 6-7-8/3-5) in which only the lower three stamps have the 11mm. overprint.

1900-01. As Nos. V49 and V51, but inscribed 'POSTAGE & REVENUE' and new colours. Sheets 120 – two panes, each 6 x 10.

V69	5c.	grey-black and ult/blue	1·25	1·00
V70	10c.	dl pur and grn ('01)	2·50	4·25
SPV69/70		specimen (2v) ..	£25	‡

V70—An imperf Colour Trial exists in green and black on unwatermarked paper.

1902-10. As before but Head of King Edward VII (all inscribed 'POSTAGE & REVENUE').

(a) Wmk. Crown CA (1902-04).

E1	1c.	gr-grn and grn ('04)	2·75	4·50
E2	2c.	pur and black/red ..	50	50
E3	5c.	pl grey and blue/blue	2·00	2·00
		a large 'C'	—	—
E4	5c.	dk gr and blue/blue	1·50	1·50
		a large 'C'	—	—
E5	20c.	dl and bt purple ('04)	6·50	8·50
E1/5		set (4v)	£11	£14
SPE1/5		specimen set (4v) ..	£35	‡

(b) Wmk. Multiple Crown CA (1905-10). E13/E19 are all C.

E6	1c.	gr-grn and grn O ..	50	50
E7	1c.	grn and dk grn C ..	60	60
E8	1c.	blue-green ('10) O ..	80	70
E9	2c.	pur and blk/red OC	50	25
E10	2c.	carmine ('08) O ..	40	35
E11	5c.	gr-blk and bl/bl C ..	1·00	70
		a large 'C'	—	—
E12	5c.	ult ('10) O	1·50	70
		a large 'C'	—	—
E13	10c.	dl pur and em-grn ('07)	3·25	4·25
E14	25c.	dl pur and or ('07) ..	7·25	7·25
E15	25c.	black/green ('10) ..	6·00	9·00
E16	50c.	gr-grn and car ('07)	£12	£13
E17	$1	gr-grn and car ('07)	£21	£23
E18	$2	gr-grn and blue ('07)	£60	£65
E19	$5	gr-grn and blk ('07)	£220	£240
E6/19		set (13v)	£300	£350
SPE6/19		specimen set (13v) ..	£140	‡

E3a/4a/11a/12a—The C is larger on Row 1/4 in both panes.

E2/3/4—Exist with inverted watermark.

1913-22. Perf. 14. Sheets 120 – two panes, each 6 x 10.

(a) Wmk. Multiple Crown CA. G1/10 O: G11/24 C.

G1	1c.	blue-green	20	20
G2	1c.	yellow-green ('16) ..	35	45

G3	1c.	dp blue-green (3/17)	50	60
		a on bluish paper ..	1·00	60
G4	2c.	red	35	45
		a on bluish paper ..	2·75	2·75
G5	2c.	bt scarlet ('16) ..	35	35
G6	2c.	dl scarlet ('17) ..	90	90
G7	2c.	bt car-red (11/20) ..	1·50	1·50
G8	3c.	orange ('17)	25	30
		a on bluish paper ..	50	50
G9	3c.	yel-or (11/20) ..	1·00	90
G10	5c.	bright blue	1·00	1·00
G11	10c.	dl pur and yel-grn ..	2·50	2·75
G12	10c.	dl pur and bt green ..	3·00	3·00
G13	25c.	grey black/green ..	2·50	3·00
G14	25c.	black/blue-green ..	2·50	3·00
G15	25c.	jet blk/gr-grn (olive back)	3·00 2·50	4·75 4·75
G16	25c.	gr and blk/emerald (11/20)	2·50	4·75
G17	50c.	pur and blue/blue ..	4·75	5·00
G18	$1	black and carmine ..	9·00	£10
G19	$1	blk and bt red (8/17)	£12	£13
G20	$2	pur and blue-green	£38	£40
G21	$2	dl pur and yel-grn (9/19)	£42	£45
G22	$2	dl violet and gr-grn (2/20)	£42	£45
G23	$5	purple and blk/red..	£180	£190
G24	$5	bt pur and blk/bt red (12/21)	£200	£190
G1/24		set (10v)	£225	£240
SPG1/24		specimen set (10v)	£95	‡

G7/G9—Both came from printings specifically made for Booklets and, although G9 was sold in sheet form, the whole printing of the 2c. was used to make up booklets with the exception of the vertical strips from the centres of the sheets (last vertical row of left hand pane and first vertical row of right hand pane with centre gutter).

Booklets were made up with panes 5 x 2.

(b) Wmk. Multiple Script CA. (1.12.21).

G25	1c.	green	1·25	75

1915 (Aug.-Dec.). Nos. G1, G4, and G10 overprinted by De La Rue with moire pattern in violet.

G26	1c.	green (Dec.)	75	2·25
G27	1c.	yellow-green	40	1·25
G28	2c.	scarlet (Nov.)	45	60
G29	5c.	bt blue (Aug.)	50	2·25
G26/29		set (3v)	1·25	4·00

Numbers overprinted—G26/27, 60,240: G28, 180,000: G29, 121,080.

The overprint was applied in order that the stamps might readily be recognised and invalidated in the event of war-time seizure by the enemy.

1916 (Aug. 23rd). War Tax. No. G26 locally overprinted WAR in small black serif capitals in panes 6 x 10.

G30	1c. **green and violet** ..	20	20
	a small 'A'	8·00	—
	b overprint inverted ..	£60	£65

G30*a*—The 'A' in 'WAR' is smaller on Row 2/3.

Number overprinted—117,000.

1917 (March 3rd)-18. Nos. G2, G3 and G8 similarly overprinted (without moire pattern).

G31	1c. **yellow-green** ..	25	40
	a small 'A'	£10	—
G32	1c. **blue-green/bluish** ..	25	50
	a small 'A'	£10	—
G33	3c. **orange/bluish** (3/18)	45	60
	a small 'A'	£18	—
	b overprint double ..	£130	—

G31*a*/32*a*/33*a*—The 'A' in 'WAR' is smaller on Row 2/3.

G32—One sheet was found with inverted watermark and one with reversed watermark.

1918 (May)-19. Nos. G3a (and later special printings) and G8 overprinted WAR by De La Rue in large black sans serif capitals (G34 and G37 in panes 6 x 10).

G34	1c. **bl-grn/bluish grey** ..	30	45
	a thin narrow 'A' ..	£10	—
G35	1c. **deep green** (5/19) ..	45	60
	a thin narrow 'A' ..	£15	—
G36	1c. **dull green** (5/19) ..	70	60
	a thin narrow 'A' ..	£10	—
G37	3c. **dl or/bluish gr** (9/18)	30	80
	a thin narrow 'A' ..	£10	—
SPG34/37	**specimen pair** ..	£45	‡

G34*a*/37*a*—The 'A' in WAR is narrower and has a short left limb on Row 1/4.

G35/36 were overprinted in complete sheets (two panes, each 6 x 10) and the variety only occurred on the right hand panes.

1921 (Mar. 9th). Peace Commemoration. (*recess*) **De La Rue. Wmk. Multiple Crown CA (sideways). Perf. 14. Sheets 5 x 12.**

G38	2c. **rose-red**	2·00	1·50
SPG38	**specimen** (1v) ..	£21	‡

1921. As before, but without 'PEACE'. Wmk. Multiple Script CA.

G39	4c. **slate**	3·50	1·25
SPG39	**specimen** (1v) ..	£21	‡

1922-33. (*typo*) **De La Rue. Perf. 14. Sheets 120 – two panes, each 6 x 10.**

(a) Wmk. Multiple Crown CA (1922).

G40	25c. **gr-blk and blk/grn C**	4·00	7·00
G41	25c. **jet blk and blk/grn C**	5·00	7·00
G42	$5 **pur and blk/red C** ..	£190	£220

(b) Wmk. Multiple Script CA (1922-33). G43/51 O: G52/58 C.

G43	1c. **green** ('29)	25	40
G44	2c. **brown**	20	20
G45	2c. **chocolate**	20	20
G46	2c. **rose-carmine** ('27) ..	20	20
G47	2c. **scarlet** ('31)	20	20
	a booklet pane ..	£10	—
G48	3c. **orange** ('33)	1·00	90
G49	4c. **grey** ('29)	90	50
G50	5c. **ultramarine**	90	50
G51	5c. **milky blue** ('23) ..	90	1·50
G52	10c. **dl pur and sage-grn** ..	70	60
G53	10c. **bright purple and deep sage-green** ..	1·00	80
G54	25c. **black/green**	1·25	1·50
	a on blue green ..	2·00	1·50
G55	50c. **dl pur and bl/bl** ..	4·00	5·00
G56	50c. **mauve and bl/bl** ..	5·00	5·00
G57	$1 **black and scarlet** ..	£10	£15
G58	$2 **yel-grn and bt pur** ..	£24	£30
G43/58	**set** (11v)	£40	£50
SPG43/58	**specimen set** (11v)	£90	‡

G47—Was mainly used to make up Booklets (Panes 5 x 2).

Imperf Colour Trials of G50 exist in black and green, brown and green, black and brown on unwatermarked paper.

BELIZE

RELIEF   FUND

PLUS

3 CENTS

1932. Belize Hurricane Relief Fund. Nos. G43, G46, G48, G50 (in black) and G49 (in red) overprinted and surcharged by De La Rue.

G59	1c. + 1c. **green**	60	2·25
G60	2c. + 2c. **rose-carmine** ..	90	2·25
G61	3c. + 3c. **orange**	1·25	3·50
G62	4c. + 4c. **grey**	1·75	4·00
G63	5c. + 5c. **ultramarine** ..	4·00	8·50
G59/63	**set** (5v)	8·00	£20
SPG59/63	**specimen set** (5v)	£70	‡

G61 was not issued without overprint until 1933.

1935 (May 6th). Silver Jubilee. (*recess*)
Bradbury Wilkinson. Wmk. Multiple Script
CA. Perf. 11 x 12. Sheets 6 x 10.

G64	3c. **ult and grey-black** ..		30	35
	a extra flagstaff	..	£18	—
G65	4c. **green and indigo**	..	40	45
	a extra flagstaff	..	£65	—
G66	5c. **brn and dp blue**	..	1·25	1·50
G67	25c. **slate and purple**	..	2·50	3·00
	a extra flagstaff	..	£90	—
G64/67	**set** (4v)	.. ..	4·00	5·00
SPG64/67	**specimen set** (4v)	£20	‡

G64*a*/67*a*—Extra flagstaff occurs on No. 49 (R9/1).

Numbers printed—G64, 81,690 : G65, 62,900 :
G66, 73,780 : G67, 44,691.

Remainders were withdrawn on December 31st,
1935.

1938 (Jan. 10th)-47 Designs, 1c. (Maya Figur-
ines) ; 2c., 3c., 4c., 5c., 10c., 50c., $2 (Products
of Colony) ; 15c., 25c., $1 (Scenes in Colony) ;
$5 (Arms of Colony). Printers (*recess*)
Bradbury, Wilkinson. Perf. 11¼ x 11½ (C).
Designs, 2c., 3c., $1, $2, $5, V. Sheets 10 x 5
or 5 x 10.

1	1c. **pur-mag and grn** (14/2)		10	5
	a vio-mag and green			
	(12/2/47)	.. ..	10	5

2	2c. **blk and dp scar** (14/2)		10	5
	3c. **pur-violet and choc**			
	(10/1/38)	.. ..	15	10
3	*a* dl pur-vio and brn			
	(2/11/42)	.. ..	10	10
4	4c. **black and dp green**			
	(10/1/38)	.. ..	15	10
	a blk and grn (17/4/46)		10	10
5	5c. **red-pur and sl-blue**			
	(10/1/38)	.. ..	15	10
	a mauve-pur and sl-blu			
	(21/2/45)	.. ..	10	10
6	10c. **green and red-choc**			
	(14/2) ..	.. ..	20	10
7	15c. **choc and grey-blue**			
	(14/2) ..	.. ..	30	20
	a dp choc and dp blue			
	(20/1/47)	.. ..	25	20
8	25c. **dp vio-blue and grn**			
	(14/2) ..	.. ..	60	30
	a dp blue and green			
	(20/11/42)	..	50	30
9	50c. **blk and dp pur** (14/2)		1·00	1·00
	a blk and reddish-pur			
	(12/2/47)	.. ..	70	60
10	$1 **dp scar and olive-grn**			
	(28/2/38)	.. ..	2·00	1·25
11	$2 **indigo and maroon**			
	(28/2/38)	.. ..	4·00	3·50
12	$5 **dp car and dp brn**			
	(28/2/38)	.. ..	£12	£10
1/12	**set** (12)	.. ..	5·00	5·00
SP 1/12	**specimen set** perf (12)	£40	‡

1947 As No. 2 but Perf. 12 (L).

13	2c. **blk and dp scar**	..	80	80

This stamp was sent out to the Colony, January
27th, 1947, and placed on sale some three months
later.

SPECIAL ISSUES

1937 (May 12th) Coronation. As Aden.

S1	3c. **orange**	.. ..	10	10
S2	4c. **deep grey**	.. ..	10	10
S3	5c. **blue**	.. ..	15	15
SP S1/3	**specimen set** perf (3)	£13	‡

1946 (Sept. 9th) Victory. As Aden.

S4	3c. **chocolate-brown** ..		5	5
S5	5c. **deep blue**	..	10	10
SP S4/5	**specimen set** perf (2)	£13	‡

1948 (Oct. 1st) Silver Wedding. As Aden.

S6	4c. **green**	.. ..	10	10
S7	$5 **chocolate**	.. ..	£10	£11

1949 (Jan. 10th) 150th Anniversary of Battle
of St. George's Cay. Designs, 1c. to 4c., St.
George's Cay (*reef*). **Other Values, H.M.S.**

Merlin. Printers (*recess*) **Waterlow & Sons. Perf. 12½ (L).**

S8	1c. **ult and yel-grn**	..	10	10
S9	3c. **blue and lt brown** ..		15	15
S10	4c. **olive and pl violet** ..		20	20
S11	5c. **choc-brn and grey-**			
	blue ..	..	25	25
S12	10c. **grn and choc-brn** ..		30	35
S13	15c. **emerald and sl-blue**		40	50
S8/13	**set (6)** ..	.. ..	1·25	1·50

1949 (Oct. 10th) U.P.U. As Aden but all four values entirely *recess* **printed.**

S14	4c. **green** ..	.. ..	10	10
S15	5c. **indigo** ..	.. ..	30	30
S16	10c. **dull brown**	.. ..	50	60
S17	25c. **azure** ..	.. ..	1·00	1·20
S14/17	**set (4)** ..	.. ..	1·80	2·00

1951 (Feb. 16th) West Indies University College. As Antigua.

S18	3c. **purple and brown** ..		15	15
S19	10c. **green and brown** ..		30	35

POSTAGE DUE STAMPS

1923-46. (*typo*) **De La Rue. Wmk. Multiple Script CA. Perf. 13¾ x 14. Sheets 6 x 10.**

(a) Smooth paper (1923).

GD1	1c. **black** ..	.. ..	30	45
GD2	2c. **black** ..	.. ..	25	40
GD3	4c. **black** ..	.. ..	50	70
GD1/3	**set (3v)**	.. ..	1·00	1·50
SPGD1/3	**specimen set (3v)** ..		£22	‡

(b) Rough paper (1944-46).

PD1	1c. **black** ('46)	.. ..	40	50
PD2	4c. **black** ('44)	.. ..	50	60

LOCAL ISSUES

Issued by Messrs. Cuthbert Bros. of Belize to cover local postal charges on letters carried by their steam launch between Belize and the island of St. George's Caye.

1894. (*typewritten*). **Horizontally laid paper, Imperf.**

L1	3c. **black** ..	.. ..	—	—

These stamps were cancelled with a straight line "CUTHBERT BROS" in blue or mauve.

BRITISH SOLOMON ISLANDS

Following the declaration of a British protectorate in 1893 postage on outgoing mail was either paid in cash or with stamps of New South Wales.

From 6th July, 1906 letters were marked with a PAID handstamp, cash being forwarded to cover the cost of N.S.W. stamps to be affixed in Sydney. The first Post Office was opened at Tulagi in 1907 when the inter-island local stamps (E1/7) were issued. Until 3rd September, 1907 when the Protectorate was admitted to the U.P.U., outgoing letters bearing the local stamps were additionally franked with N.S.W. stamps (or, from May 10th, 1907, with the stamps of *any* Australian State).

1907 (14th Feb.) (*litho*) **W. Smith & Co., Sydney. Designer, C. M. Woodford. No Wmk. Perf 11. Sheets 6 x 10.**

E1	½d. **pale ultramarine** ..	6·50	£13
	a deep ultramarine ..	8·50	£13
E2	1d. **rose-red**	£17	£18
E3	2d. **dark blue**	£17	£18
	a hor.pair imperf. betwn	£3500	—
E4	2½d. **yellow-orange** ..	£18	£21
	a vert. pair. imperf btwn	£1800	—
	b hor. pair, imperf. btwn	£1800	£1650
E5	5d. **emerald**	£30	£42
E6	6d. **chocolate**	£42	£42
	a dp chocolate	£42	£42
	b vert. pair imperf. btwn	£1500	—
	c hor. pair imperf. btwn	—	—
E7	1/– **purple**	£58	£60
E1/E7	**set (7)**	£185	£210

This issue is difficult to find well centred and the perforations are very rough. The existence of E6c is not confirmed with any certainty.

Numbers issued—E1, 45,364; E2, 25,598; E3, 20,641; E4, 12,072; E5, 8,310; E6, 7,853; E7, 7,281.

1908-1911 (1st Nov.) (*recess*) **De La Rue. Wmk.**

Mult. Crown CA sideways. Perf. 14. Sheets 6 x 10.

E8	½d.	**grn** (*brn gum thin paper*)		60	1·00
		a brown gum ..		1·00	1·25
E9	1d.	**carmine**	..	1·25	1·75
		a brn gum thin paper		1·25	2·00
E10	2d.	**grey** ..	..	1·75	2·00
E11	2½d.	**ultramarine**	..	2·25	3·50
E12	4d.	**red/yellow**	..	3·75	5·50
E13	5d.	**olive** ..	..	£10	6·75
E14	6d.	**reddish-purple**	..	£50	6·75
E15	1/–	**black/green** ..	..	£10	£10
E16	2/–	**purple/blue**	..	£27	£30
E17	2/6	**red/blue**	..	£42	£55
E18	5/–	**green/yellow**	..	£75	£80
E8/18		**set** (11)	..	£180	£200
SP.E8/18		**specimen set** (11) ..		£130	‡

Numbers issued—

E8, 102,240; E9, 115,260; E10, 63,886;
E11, 28,503; E12, 19,331; E13,17,084;
E14, 16,126; E15, 13,194; E16, 5,622;
E17, 4,994; E18, 4,431.

1913 (**Feb. 27th-April**) (*typo*) **De La Rue. Wmk. Mult. Crown CA. Perf. 14. Sheets 120 – two panes each 6 x 10.**

G1	½d.	**green** (April 1st)	..	1·50	2·00
G2	1d.	**red** (April 1st) ..		1·75	7·00
G3	3d.	**purple/yellow** ..		2·00	5·50
		a on orange buff back		2·75	£11
G4	11d.	**pl purple and red**	..	7·00	9·00
G1/4		**set** (4) ..	..	£15	£34
SP.G/14		**specimen set** (4)	..	£30	‡

Numbers issued—
G1,124,440; G2, 123,120; G3, 30,480; G4, 30,480

1914/23 (*typo*) **De La Rue. Wmk. Mult. Crown CA. Perf. 14. Sheets 120 – two panes, each 6 x 10.**

G5	½d.	**green** ..	..	80	2·25
		a yellow-green	..	80	2·25

G6	1d.	**carmine**	..	..	80	1·75
		a scarlet	..	..	1·50	3·50
		b rose		..	2·00	3·50
G7	2d.	**grey** ..		..	1·75	5·50
		a silver-grey ..		..	2·00	6·00
G8	2½d.	**ultramarine** ..			2·00	4·50
G9	3d.	**pl purple/yellow** ..			£13	£22
G10	4d.	**black, red/yellow**			6·00	5·50
G11	5d.	**dl purple and olive**			9·00	£11
		a brownish-pur, ol ..			9.00	£13
G12	6d.	**dl pur, red-pur**	..		4·25	£11
G13	1/–	**black/green**	..		7·50	£11
		a black/olive	..		7·50	£11
G14	2/–	**dp pur, blue/blue**			£11	£17
		a pl pur, blue/blue ..			£11	£17
G15	2/6	**blk and red/blue** ..			£15	£18
		a grey and red/blue			£17	£20
G16	5/–	**grn and red/yel**	..		£30	£35
		a on orange-buff ..			£30	£38
G17	10/–	**grn and red/grn**	..		£85	£100
G18	£1	**pur and blk/red**	..		£225	£225
G5/G18		**set** (14) ..			£400	£450
SPG5/18		**specimen set** (14)			£190	‡

Numbers issued—
G9, 6,960; G17, 6,120

1922-31 Wmk. Mult. Script CA. Perf. 14.

G19	½d.	**green** ..	..	..	40	70
		a deep green		..	40	70
G20	1d.	**red** ..	..	..	6·00	6·00
G21	1d.	**pale violet** ..		..	1·00	2·00
G22	1½d.	**rose-scarlet**		..	1·25	50
		a pale rose ..		..	1·50	70
G23	2d.	**slate-grey** ..		..	1·00	1·75
G24	3d.	**pale ultramarine** ..			90	2·25
		a bt ultramarine		..	1·00	2·25
G25	4d.	**blk and red/yel** ..			1·75	4·75
G26	4½d.	**red-brown** ..		..	4·25	5·00
G27	5d.	**dull purple, olive** ..			2·25	4·75
G28	6d.	**dull-pur, red-pur** ..			2·25	4·00
G29	1/–	**black/emerald** ..			3·25	5·75
G30	2/–	**pur and blue/blue**			£11	£17
G31	2/6	**blk and red/blue** ..			£14	£21
G32	5/–	**grn and red/yel** ..			£22	£29
G33	10/–	**grn and red/em** ..			£110	£120
G19/33		**set** (15) ..		..	£180	£225
SP.G33/36		**specimen set** (15)			£135	‡

G22 is inscribed "POSTAGE-POSTAGE" (as G1/4).

1935 (**6th May**) **Silver Jubilee** (*recess*) **De La Rue. Wmk. Script. CA. Perf 13½ x 14. Sheets 6 x 10.**

G34	1½d.	**dp blue and car** ..		60	80
G35	3d.	**brn and indigo** ..		2·25	3·25
G36	6d.	**lt blue and olive** ..		3·50	5·50

G37 1/– **slate and purple** .. 6·00 7·50
G34/37 **set** (4) £12 £17
SP.G33/36 **specimen set** perf. £25 ‡

Numbers issued—
G34, 177,480; G35, 40,140; G36, 39,000;
G37, 39,600.

1939 (Feb. 1st)-51 Designs, ½d. (Spears and Shields); 1d. (Native Policeman and Chief); 1½d. (Auki Is.); 2d. (Native House and Canoe); 2½d. (Roviana Canoe); 3d. (Roviana Canoes); 4½d., 10/– (Native House and Palms); 6d. (Coconut Plantation); 1/– (Breadfruit); 2/– (Tinakula); 2/6 (Megapodes Birds); 5/– (Canoe). /Printers, (recess) De La Rue, 2d., 3d., 2/–, 2/6, Perf. 13½ (C); Waterlow & Sons, Other Values, Perf. 12½ (L). Sheets 6 x 10 or 10 x 6.

1	½d. **dp blue and green** ..	10	15
2	1d. **dp brown and violet**	10	20
3	1½d. **myrtle and lake-car**..	20	25
4	2d. **chest and grey-blk** ..	30	30
	a red-brn and grey-blk (23/10/44)	25	25
5	2½d. **mag and olive-grn** ..	30	35
	a imperf. between pair	£2350	—
6	3d. **black and ult**	25	30
	a sl-blk and bt ult (5/43)	75	1·00
7	4½d. **yel-grn and choc** ..	5·00	6·00
8	6d. **sl-vio and dp claret**..	50	50
	a sl-vio and pur-claret (29/11/51)	60	60
9	1/– **green and black** ..	70	85
10	2/– **black and orange** ..	1·50	2·00
	a sl-blk and or (5/43)..	2·00	2·25
11	2/6 **blk and dl pur-violet**	7·00	7·50
	a sl-blk and pur-vio (5/43)	7·50	8·00
12	5/– **em-grn and red** ..	4·00	4·50
13	10/– **sage-grn and mag** (27/4/42)	8·00	9·00
1/13	**set** (13)	£27	£30
SP1/12	**specimen set** perf (12)	£60	‡

5*a* A part sheet was found by a U.S. serviceman and taken back to U.S.A.

Number issued—No. 7, 70,000.

1951 (Nov. 29th)-54 As Nos. 4*a* **and 6 but Perf. 12 (C).**

14	2d. **red-brn and grey-blk**..	20	25
	a indian-red and black (16/6/54)	30	35
15	3d. **black and ultramarine**	25	60

SPECIAL ISSUES

1937 (May 13th) Coronation. As Aden, but Printers, Bradbury, Wilkinson. Perf. 11 x 11¾ (C).

S1	1d. **violet** ..	..	..	25	25
S2	1½d. **carmine-red**	..		25	25
S3	3d. **deep blue**	..	..	35	40
SP.S1/3	**specimen set** perf (3)			£15	‡

Numbers issued—
S1, 631,480; S2, 301,420; S3, 507,600.

1946 (Oct. 15th) Victory. As Aden.

S4	1½d. **carmine-red** ..	..	10	10
S5	3d. **deep blue**	..	..	15	15
SP S4/5	**specimen set** perf (2)		£14	‡

Number issued—
S4, 778,500; S5, 768,240.

1949 (March 14th) Silver Wedding. As Aden.

S6	2d. **black**	15	15
S7	10/– **lake-magenta** ..	7·00	8·00

Numbers printed—
S6, 373,000; S7, 125,000.

1949 (Oct. 10th) U.P.U. As Aden.

S8	2d. **beech-brown**	..	15	25
S9	3d. **indigo** ..	..	..	25	30
S10	5d. **green** ..	..	..	40	50
S11	1/– **slate-black** ..	..	60	75
S8/11	**set** (4) ..	..	..	1·35	1·60

Number printed—
S8, 455,000; S9, S10, S11, 340,000 each.

POSTAGE DUE STAMPS

1940 (Sept. 1st) Printers (typo) Bradbury, Wilkinson. Perf. 12 (L). Sheets 12 x 10.

PD1	1d. **emerald**	..	..	40	50
PD2	2d. **deep red**	..	..	60	80
PD3	3d. **brown** ..	..	..	80	1·00
PD4	4d. **deep blue**	..	..	1·00	1·50
PD5	5d. **deep green**	..	..	1·50	2·00
PD6	6d. **magenta**	..	..	2·00	3·00
PD7	1/– **violet** ..	..	..	4·00	6·00
PD8	1/6 **turquoise-green**	..	8·00	£10
PD1/8	**set** (8) ..	..	..	£16	£24
SP D1/8	**specimen set** (8)	..	£40	‡

BRUNEI

After a chequered early history, the State became a British Protectorate in 1888. Prior to 1906 the Local Stamps which were valid only within Brunei and Labuan were occasionally used in conjunction with Labuan stamps on foreign mail. A Brunei post office at Brooketon in Sarawak also handled letters for Kuching.

The first Brunei Post Office was opened on October 11th 1906.

1895 Local Stamps. Litho (in Sarawak). No Wmk. Perf. 13¾. Sheets 10 x 5.

V1	½c.	**brown** ..	..	..
V2	1c.	**venetian red** ..	..	
V3	2c.	**black** ..	..	
V4	3c.	**blue** ..	..	..
V5	5c.	**grey-green** ..	..	
V6	8c.	**slate-purple** ..	..	
V7	10c.	**red-orange** ..	..	
V8	25c.	**grey-green** ..	..	
V9	50c.	**sage-green** ..	..	
V10	$1	**olive-green** ..	..	
V1/10		**set (10v)** ..	.. £12	£50

Exist used on covers with Labuan stamps. Price from £25 each.

1906 (Oct. 11th) Stamps of Labuan. (Recess Waterlow & Sons; No Wmk. Sheets 10 x 10). Special printings. Perf. 13½, overprinted or overprinted and surcharged in red at the Government Press in Singapore. Setting – overprint 10 x 5, surcharges 10 x 5.

E1	1c.	**blk and pur** ..	6·50	9·00
		a grey-black overprint	£550	£600
E2	2c. on 3c.	**blk and sepia**	2·00	2·50
		a 'BRUNEI' double ..	£1150	—
E3	2c. on 8c.	**blk and verm**	£11	£11
		a 'TWO CENTS' double ..	£1800	—

b 'TWO CENTS' omitted in vert pair with normal £2000 —

E4	3c.	**blk and sepia**	£11	£11
E5	4c. on 12c.	**blk and yel** ..	1·25	2·50
E6	5c. on 16c.	**grn and brn**..	£11	7·50
E7	8c.	**blk and verm**	3·00	4·00
E8	10c. on 16c.	**grn and brn**..	2·50	3·25
E9	25c. on 16c.	**grn and brn**..	£40	£45
E10	30c. on 16c.	**grn and brn**..	£32	£40
E11	50c. on 16c.	**grn and brn**..	£32	£40
E12	$1 on 8c.	**blk and verm**	£32	£40
E1/12		**set (12v)** ..	£180	£210

E1*a* was, in fact, a Colour Trial which was rejected; but one sheet was sent to the Colony and issued in error.

E2*a*—One sheet sold.

E3*a*/3*b*—On one sheet the surcharge intended for the lower half was printed one row up, Row 5 consequently all being double surcharge and Row 10 without surcharge. The Royal Collection contains the first two vertical columns of the sheet complete with margins.

A re-entry below 'COLONY' occurs on all values of the basic stamps. Row 8/10. Price 4/5 times normal.

Numbers issued—E1, 4,900; E2, 15,000; E3/4/6, 5,000 each; E5, 20,000; E7, 8,000; E8, 9,000; E9/10/11/12, 2,000 each.

All stamps from E13 to G37 are Recess De La Rue. Perf. 14.

1907 (Feb. 26th). Wmk. Multiple Crown CA. Sheets 12 x 5.

E13	1c.	**grey-blk and pl grn**	60	90
E14	1c.	**black and green** ..	60	90
E15	2c.	**grey-blk and scar** ..	80	1·50
E16	2c.	**black and scarlet** ..	80	1·50
E17	3c.	**black and brown** ..	4·00	4·00
E18	4c.	**grey-blk and mauve**	3·75	4·00
E19	4c.	**blk and reddish pur**	£13	£15
E20	5c.	**grey-blk and blue** ..	£13	£15
E21	8c.	**grey-blk and orange**	3·00	6·00
E22	10c.	**grey-blk and grn** ..	6·50	7·50
E23	25c.	**blue and ochre** ..	9·00	£11
E24	30c.	**violet and black** ..	9·00	£11
E25	50c.	**green and brown** ..	9·00	£11
E26	$1	**red and grey** ..	£30	£40
E13/26		**set (11v)** ..	£85	£110
SPE13/26	**specimen set (11v)**	£65	‡

Imperforate copies of No. E17 in slate and overprinted SPECIMEN are Printer's samples.

Double Plate printing—lowest line of shading in vignette is dotted.

Single Plate printing—lowest dotted line removed.

1908-20 As before but new colours and values.

(a) Double Plate printing.

E27	1c.	green ..	..	..	40	80
E28	2c.	grey-blk and brn ('11)	..	..	50	45
E29	2c.	black and brown ..			50	45
E30	3c.	scarlet	..	..	90	90
E31	5c.	black and orange..			2·50	2·50
E32	5c.	blk and dp orange			2·50	2·50
E33	8c.	blue and indigo	..		2·50	2·50
E34	30c.	pur and or-yel ('12)			2·75	2·75
E35	$1	blk and red/blue ('12)	..	..	9·00	£12
E36	$5	car/grn ('12)		..	£40	£50
E37	$25	black/red ('11)	..		£250	£300

(b) Single Plate printing.

E38	1c.	green ('11) ..	..	25	30
E39	3c.	scarlet ('16)	..	5·50	5·50
E40	4c.	claret ('12) ..	..	40	40
E41	4c.	lake-brown ('20) ..		50	50
E42	5c.	orange ('16)	..	90	1·00
		a '5c' inserted	..	£42	£42
E43	8c.	ultramarine ('16)	..	1·50	3·25
E44	10c.	pur/yel ('12)	..	80	80
		a on pale yellow	..	70	90
		b on thick paper	..	80	80
E45	25c.	lilac ('12) ..	..	1·25	1·25
E46	25c.	deep lilac	..	..	1·25	1·25
E47	50c.	black/green ('12)	..	6·00	9·00
		a on blue-green	..	4·25	5·50
E27/47		set (13v)	..	..	£310	£375
SPE27/47		specimen set (13v)	£120	‡

E42a—The top left value tablet was missed on Row 1/8 when the values were pantographed; and was hand-engraved.

Hand engraved

Normal

1922 (May) Singapore Exhibition. Nos. E38/47, E28 and E35 overprinted in black at Singapore. Setting 6 x 1, from which ten stereos were taken to overprint complete sheets.

G1	1c.	green	..	..	..	1·50	5·50
G2	2c.	black and brown	..	..	3·00	5·50
G3	3c.	scarlet ..		..	..	3·75	9·00
G4	4c.	claret ..		..	..	3·00	£12
G5	5c.	orange ..		..	..	4·50	£17
		a '5c' inserted	..		..	£85	£195
G6	10c.	purple/yellow..		..	..	6·00	£22
G7	25c.	deep lilac	..	..	..	£14	£34
G8	50c.	black/blue green	..	..	£35	£75
G9	$1	blk and red/blue	..	..	£45	£75
G1/9		set (9v) ..		..	..	£115	£250

G5a See Note after E42a. (Row 1/8).

Numbers sold—G1, 15,099; G2, 10,721; G3, 10,399; G4, 9,905; G6, 9,618; G7, 7,236; G8, 5,494; G9, 5,272.

1924-37 As before but new colours and values, and new horizontal design (6c. and 12c.). Single Plate printing (except G30 and G32). Wmk. Multiple Script CA. Sheets 12 x 5 or 5 x 12 (6c. and 12c.)

G10	1c.	black ('26) ..	..		20	25
G11	2c.	brown	..	..		40	50
G12	2c.	reddish brown	..		40	50
G13	2c.	green ('33) ..	..		25	25
G14	2c.	yellow-green	..		25	25
G15	3c.	green ..	..	..		70	1·25
G16	4c.	maroon	..	..		1·25	1·00
G17	4c.	orange ('29)	..		80	45
G18	4c.	yellow-orange	..		80	45
G19	5c.	orange-yellow	..		60	60
		a '5c' inserted	..		£50	£50
G20	5c.	grey ('31) ..	..		2·50	2·00
		a '5c' inserted	..		£95	£95
G21	5c.	chocolate ('33)	..		40	50
		a '5c' inserted	..		£25	£25
G22	6c.	black ..	..	..		1·75	2·00
G23	6c.	scarlet ('31)	..		2·00	4·00
G24	8c.	ultramarine ('27)	..		1·50	1·25
G25	8c.	grey-black ('33)	..		1·25	90

G26	10c.	purple/yellow ('37)	4·25	5·00
G27	12c.	blue	2·75	3·00
G28	12c.	greenish blue ..	£35	£40
G29	25c.	slate-purple ('31)..	2·50	3·00
G30	30c.	pur and or-yel ('31)	2·50	3·00
G31	50c.	black/emerald ('31)	4·00	6·00
G32	$1	blk and red/blue		
		('31)	£12	£15
G10/32		set (19v)	£32	£40
SPG10/32		specimen set (19v)	£100	‡

G19a/20a/21a—See Note after No. E42a. (Row 1/8)

G22 is a deeper black and is also 1mm less in width than No. 5.

Later printings of several values from G20 on-wards, other than 6c. and 12c., were in sheets 10 x 5. The reduction in size was achieved by removing two vertical rows from the plates: the sheet-centre markings in top and bottom margins were not altered, and thus became 'off centre' on the smaller sheets.

1941 (Dec.) Prepared for use but not issued. As before but new colours and value. (G35/37 in the horizontal design).

G33	2c.	orange-brown ..	6·00	—
G34	3c.	blue-green	5·00	—
G35	6c.	slate-green ..	£14	—
G36	8c.	red	6·00	—
G37	15c.	ultramarine.. ..	£20	—

On account of the Japanese invasion these stamps were never officially issued without the overprint in Japanese characters. Unoverprinted copies are nevertheless known, both mint and used.

Brunei was occupied by the Japanese from December 16th 1941 to June 10th 1945 and Nos. G10/37 were overprinted with Japanese characters.

During the occupation Brunei, North Borneo and Sarawak were administered as a single territory (North Borneo) and the overprinted stamps of all three States were used throughout the whole area.

Following the re-occupation in 1945 the State was under British Military Administration and the BMA issues of North Borneo and Sarawak were in use until January 2nd 1947.

1947 (Jan. 2nd)-51. As before but new colours. Sheets 10 x 5 or 5 x 10. (3c and 6c in horizontal design).

(a) Perf. 14 (1947-50).

1	1c.	brown	20	20
2	2c.	slate-grey	20	50
3	3c.	grey-green	35	50
4	5c.	orange	40	50
		a '5c' inserted	£12	£12
5	6c.	black	20	45
6	8c.	scarlet	25	20

7	10c.	purple-violet	10	10
8	15c.	ultramarine	40	15
9	25c.	red-purple	15	23
10	30c.	black and orange ..	25	40
11	50c.	black	30	80
12	$1	black and scarlet ..	70	70
13	$1	black and car-red		
		(15/2/50)	1·00	1·00
14	$5	grn and verm (2/2/48)	6·00	7·00
15	$10	grey-blk and plum		
		(2/2/48) ..	£13	£16
1/15		set (14v)	£22	£21
SP1/15		specimen set (14v) ..	£70	‡

4a—See Note after No. E42a (Row 1/8).
5 is a paler black and is also 1mm. wider than No. G22.

(b) Perf. 14¼ x 13½ (1950-51).

16	2c.	sl-grey (25/9/50) ..	50	45
17	2c.	black (27/6/51) ..	15	40
		a sky retouch	1·50	4·00
18	5c.	orange (25/9/50) ..	1·75	2·00
		a '5c' inserted	£20	£20
19	10c.	pur-vio (25/9/50) ..	50	75
20	15c.	red-purple (25/1/51)	25	1·00
21	30c.	blk and or (25/1/51)	25	1·25

17a—A major retouch appears in the sky at top left corner, Row 1/1.

18a—See Note after No. E42a. (Row 1/8).

(c) Perf. 13¼ x 13. (1950-51).

22	8c.	scarlet (25/1/51) ..	15	50
23	50c.	black (25/9/50) ..	75	3·25

SPECIAL ISSUES

1949 (Sept. 22nd) Silver Jubilee of Sultan Ahmed Waddin. Recess De La Rue. Wmk. Multiple Script CA. Perf. 13 x 12¾ (C). Sheets 5 x 10.

S1	8c.	blk and rose-car ..	50	80
S2	25c.	pur-lk and red-or ..	50	35
S3	50c.	black and blue ..	80	90
S1/3		set (3)	1·80	2·00

1949 (Oct. 10th) U.P.U. As Aden.

S4	8c.	carmine-rose	25	40
S5	15c.	indigo	45	45
S6	25c.	reddish-mauve ..	50	60
S7	50c.	slate-black	80	80
S4/7		set (4)	2·00	2·25

BURMA

Contemporary Indian stamps without overprint were used in Burma from 1854 until March 31st, 1937.

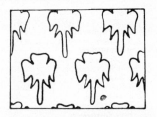

1937 (April 1st) Stamps of India (1926–36 Issues) inscribed "INDIA POSTAGE". Wmk. Multiple Star, overprinted "BURMA" at the Nasik Security Press. The overprint measures 15 mm. (low values), 17½ mm. (Rupee values).

G1	3p.	slate..	15	10
G2	½a.	green	15	10
G3	9p.	deep green	20	10
G4	1a.	chocolate	20	15
G5	2a.	vermilion (small die)	20	15
G6	2½a.	orange	30	20
G7	3a.	carmine	50	40
G8	3½a.	deep blue	50	35
G9	3½a.	grey-blue	2·25	2·75
G10	4a.	sage-green	45	15
G11	6a.	bistre	45	30
G12	8a.	reddish purple	50	35
G13	12a.	claret	70	70
G14	R1	choc and green	80	40
G15	Rs.2	car and orange	2·00	60
G16	Rs.5	ult and purple	4·00	3·25
G17	Rs.10	green and scarlet	8·00	4·50
G18	Rs.15	blue and olive	£32	£20
G19	Rs.25	orange and blue	£55	£40
G1/19		set (18v)	£100	£70

G8, 9, 13 and 18 are known with inverted wmk. The overprint is at the top on all values except G7.

Essays for King George VI definitives were prepared in 1937. Denominations up to 4a. were with frames other than those of the issued stamps; but the Rupee values to Rs10 were all with frames as the issued R1 and Rs2. The King's Head was that used for issued Indian stamps, and was not that used for the issued Burmese stamps.

The following stamps were printed (offset-litho) at the Security Printing Press, Nasik, India, on "Elephant's Head" (mult.) wmk. paper, unless otherwise indicated.

1938 (Nov. 15th)-40 Designs, 1p.–2a., 4a. King's Head (small format) and Perf. 13¾ x 14 (C); 2½a.–8a. (less 4a.) Scenes in Burma and Perf. 13 (C); 1r.–10r. King's Head (large format) and Perf. 13¾ (C). Designs, 2a.,6p., 3a. 3a.6p., 8a., H. Sheets 1–7 and 11, 16 x 20; other Anna values 8 x 16; Rupee values 10 x 12.

1	1p.	vermilion (1/8/40)	10	25
2	3p.	violet..	10	15
3	6p.	bright blue..	5	5
4	9p.	yellow-green	10	20
5	1a.	choc-brn (litho)	5	5
		a (typo)	50	50
6	1½a.	turquoise-green	10	15
7	2a.	dp carmine-rose	15	15
8	2a.6p.	claret..	30	30
		a birds above trees	5·00	—
9	3a.	purple-violet	50	40
10	3a.6p.	ult and blue	1·00	1·50
		a Tick bird	5·00	—
		b extra trees	5·00	—
11	4a.	greenish-blue	20	20
12	8a.	myrtle-green	40	40
13	1R.	dp pur and dp blu	80	45
14	2Rs.	choc-brn and pur..	2·00	80
15	5Rs.	violet and red	6·50	3·50
16	10Rs.	brown and myrtle	£15	£14
1/16		set (16)	£25	£20

5a See Note after India 32 for details of printing differences.

8a A flaw gives the appearance of birds in flight above the trees at left R15/3.

10a A "Tick bird" appears on the flank oft he nearest buffalo.

10b A flaw shows as a large clump of trees in front of the background hills above the farmer's head.

Burma was occupied by the Japanese from early 1942 until the recapture of Rangoon in May 1945.

Prior to the issue of stamps by the Japanese Army Administration in June 1942, stocks of the pre-war issues (G1-G8 and GO8 2-14 and O1-O9) were overprinted in the Irrawaddy Delta area with representations of a Peacock.

1945 (June) As No. 1, etc. but overprinted "MILY ADMN."

17	1p.	vermilion	5	5
		a double overprint	5·00	5·00
18	3p.	violet..	5	10
19	6p.	bright blue..	5	10
20	9p.	yellow-green	5	10
		a basic stamp doubly printed	—	—
21	1a.	choc-brown (typo)	5	10
22	1½a.	turquoise-green	5	10
23	2a.	dp carmine-rose	5	10

24	2a.6p.	**claret**..	5	10
	a	birds above trees	5·00	—
25	3a.	**purple-claret** ..	5	10
	a	double overprint ..	5·00	7·50
26	3a.6p.	**ult and blue** ..	5	10
	a	double overprint ..	5·00	—
	b	vignette double ..	5·00	—
	c	worn vignette ..	5·00	—
	d	Tick bird	5·00	—
	e	extra trees ..	5·00	—
27	4a.	**greenish-blue** ..	—	—
28	8a.	**myrtle-green** ..	5	10
29	1R.	**dp-pur and dp-blu**	15	20
30	2Rs.	**choc-brn and pur**	25	30
31	5Rs.	**violet and red** ..	60	70
32	10Rs	**.brown and myrtle**	1·50	1·50
17/32		**set** (16)	2·50	3·00

24*a* See 8*a*.

26*c* The centre plate became so worn that the inscription "Burma Rice" is virtually omitted.

26*d* See 10*a*.

26*e* See 10*b*.

This set came on the market in quantity after issue and was available under face value.

1946 (Jan. 1st) As No. 2, etc. but colours changed. (*Issued when the Civil Authorities took over from the Military Administration*).

33	3p.	**chocolate-brown**	5	5
34	6p.	**purple-violet** ..	5	5
35	9p.	**grey-green** ..	5	10
36	1a.	**deep blue** (*typo*) ..	10	10
37	1½a.	**vermilion** ..	5	5
38	2a.	**dull claret**	10	10
39	2a.6p.	**greenish-blue** ..	5	5
	a	birds above trees	5·00	—
40	3a.	**dull violet**	10	10
41	3a.6p.	**black and ult** ..	5	10
	a	vignette double ..	5·00	—
	b	Tick bird	5·00	—
	c	extra trees ..	5·00	—
42	4a.	**mauve-purple** ..	10	10
43	8a.	**maroon-lake** ..	10	15
44	1R.	**slate-vio and claret**	15	15
45	2Rs.	**brn and dl ver** ..	30	30
46	5Rs.	**grn and choc-brn**	80	80
47	10Rs	**red-claret and grey-pur** ..	1·75	2·05
33/47		**set** (15)	3·25	3·70

39*a* See 8*a*.

41*b* See 10*a*.

41*c* See 10*b*.

1947 (Oct. 1st) As No. 33, etc., but overprinted "INTERIM GOVERNMENT" (*in Burmese*) **in Rangoon.**

48	3p.	**chocolate-brown**	10	10
	a	overprint error ..	1·50	—
	b	overprint inverted	3·00	—
	c	overprint double ..	1·50	—
	d	overprint error ..	2·00	—
49	6p.	**purple-violet** ..	5	10
	a	overprint error ..	1·50	—
	b	overprint inverted	3·00	—
	c	overprint double ..	1·00	—

50	9p.	**grey-green**	5	10
	a	overprint inverted	3·00	—
	b	overprint double ..	1·50	—
51	1a.	**deep blue**	5	10
	a	overprint inverted	1·50	—
	b	overprint double, both inverted	2·00	—
52	1½a.	**vermilion**	10	10
	a	overprint inverted	1·50	—
	b	overprint double, both inverted	2·00	—
53	2a.	**dull claret**	5	10
	a	overprint error ..	1·50	—
	b	overprint inverted	4·00	—
54	2a.6p.	**greenish-blue** ..	10	10
	a	overprint inverted	4·00	—
	b	birds above trees	5·00	—
55	3a.	**dull violet**	5	10
	a	overprint inverted	1·50	—
	b	overprint double ..	2·00	—
	c	overprint double, both inverted	2·00	—
56	3a.6p.	**black and ult** ..	5	10
	a	overprint inverted	4·00	—
	b	overprint double ..	3·00	—
	c	Tick bird	5·00	—
	d	extra trees ..	5·00	—
57	4a.	**mauve-purple** ..	10	10
	a	overprint inverted	2·00	—
	b	overprint double, both inverted	2·00	—
58	8a.	**maroon-lake** ..	10	15
	a	overprint inverted	2·00	—
	b	overprint double, both inverted	2·00	—
59	1R.	**slate-vio and claret**	25	20
	a	overprint inverted	3·00	—
	b	overprint double, both inverted	3·00	—
60	2Rs.	**brn and dl vermilion**	45	35
61	5Rs.	**grn and choc-brn**..	80	80
62	10Rs.	**red-claret and grey-pur** ..	1·50	1·50
48/62		**set** (15)	3·25	3·50

48*a*/49*a*/53*a* The first character of the overprint was transposed to the end of the same line in error.

48*d* The two end characters of first line of overprint were transposed to front of same line.

54*b* See 8*a*.

56*c* See 10*a*.

56*d* See 10*b*.

SPECIAL ISSUES

1940 (May 6th) Centenary of First Postage

Stamps. No. 8 overprinted and surcharged at Security Printing Press, Nasik.

S1 1a./2a.6p. **claret**	85	90
a double over-print	£15	—
b birds above trees	7·50	—

S1*b* See 8*a*.

1946 (May 2nd) Victory. Designer, A. G. I. McGeoch. Perf. 13 (C). Wmk. sideways Sheets 16 x 8.

S2	9p.	**turquoise-green**	5	5
S3	1½a.	**br purple-violet** ..	5	5
S4	2a.	**carmine-rose** ..	5	5
S5	3a.6p.	**ultramarine** ..	5	5
		a bearded king ..	—	—
S2/5		**set (4)**	20	20

S5*a* A plate flaw gives the King the appearance of having a prominent pointed beard.

Burma became an independent republic 4th January, 1948, and these Victory designs were adapted (with changed portrait) to commemorate change in status, but they are outside the scope of this catalogue.

OFFICIAL STAMPS

Contemporary Indian "Service" stamps were used in Burma until March 31st, 1937.

1937 (April 1st–June) Stamps of India (1926–36 Issues) inscribed "INDIA POSTAGE". Wmk. Multiple Star, overprinted "BURMA

SERVICE" at the Nasik Security Press. The overprint is spaced 11½ mm. between lines. Measurements of BURMA as on ordinary issue: SERVICE 13½ mm. (Anna values)' 19½ mm. (Rupee values). The bulk of the overprinting was done at one operation, but quantities of certain values were overprinted in two operations.

GO1	3p.	**slate**	5	10
GO2	½a.	**green**	25	10
GP3	9p.	**deep green** ..	20	10
GO4	1a.	**chocolate** ..	20	10
GO5	2a.	**vermilion** (small die)	20	10
GO6	2½a.	**orange**	25	20
GO7	4a.	**sage-green** ..	25	15
GO8	6a.	**bistre**	60	50
GO9	8a.	**reddish purple** ..	35	25
GO10	12a.	**claret**	35	45
GO11	R.1	**choc and green** ..	55	45
GO12	Rs.2	**car and orange**	1·50	1·50
GO13	Rs.5	**ult and purple**	4·50	4·00
GO14	Rs.10	**green and scar**	£12	9·00
GO1/O14		**set (14v)** ..	£20	£16

1939 (April 1st) No. 2, etc., overprinted "SERVICE".

O1	3p.	**violet**	5	10
O2	6p.	**bright blue** ..	5	10
O3	9p.	**yellow-green** ..	10	10
O4	1a.	**choc-brn** (*litho*)	10	10
		a ditto (*typo*) ..	70	50
O5	1½a.	**turquoise-green**	30	10
O6	2a.	**dp carmine-rose** ..	15	15
O7	2a.6p.	**claret**	35	35
O8	4a.	**greenish-blue** ..	60	20
O9	8a.	**myrtle-green** ..	65	50
O10	1R.	**dp-pur and dp-blu**	90	70
O11	2Rs.	**choc-brn and pur**	1·50	75
O12	5Rs.	**violet and red** ..	4·25	2·75
O13	10Rs.	**brown and myrtle**	6·50	4·00
O1/13		**set (13)**	£14	8·50

1942 Provisional Issue—Chin Hills District.

When the Japanese occupied the remainder of Burma in March 1942 a substantial area of the Chin Hills remained in British hands until it was finally over-run between November 1943 and March 1944.

Local stocks of Burma Service stamps (O1—O13) were almost exhausted by the middle of 1942, and authority was given for Ordinary Burma stamps to be used on official correspondence provided they were first overprinted "O.H.M.S.". At the same time a Postal Runner Service was established between Falam, the H.Q. of the Chin Hills District, and Aijal, 170 miles away in the Lushai Hills District of Assam.

Ordinary Stamps of Burma, identified by their Catalogue Nos., after prefixes 'CHA', 'CHB' or 'CHC'.

(a) Typed OHMS overprint in black (normally horizontal).

CHA G3	9p.	**deep green** (2)
		a vert. overprint (4)
CHA 3	6p.	**bright blue** (13)
CHA 5	1a.	**choc brown** (6)
		a horiz. & vert.
		overprint (1) ..
CHA 6	1½a.	**turquoise grn** (5)
CHA 7	2a.	**deep car-rose** (2)
CHA 10	3½a.	**ult & blue** (1) ..
CHA 11	4a.	**grnish blue** (1)

(b) Typed OHMS overprint in black and hand-stamped OHMS or OHMs overprint in violet (both normally horizontal, except for typed overprint on CHB 10 which is vertical).

CHB G3	9p.	**deep green** (2)
		a hand-stamped
		only (2) ..
CHB 5	1a.	**choc-brown** (3)
CHB 8	2½a.	**claret** (1) ..
CHB 10	3½a.	**ult & blue** (2) ..
CHN 12	8a.	**myrtle grn** (2)

(c) Typed OHMS overprint in black (horiz.) and hand-stamped 'Service' overprint (diag.)

| CHC 5 | 1a. | **choc-brown** (2) |

The numbers of stamps recorded are indicated in brackets.

Number of Covers recorded:

From HAKA	July 19 - Sept 10	2 (both are
		Falam covers
		re-used)
„	TIDDIM July 24 - Oct 19	5 (one is a
		Falam cover
		re-used)
„	FALAM Aug. 2 - Dec. 4	14

These overprints should only be bought used on official covers with known addresses and hand-writing. Although these stamps were *not* used at Aijal (in Assam) covers may occasionally be found with an AIJAL cancellation, where stamps had been placed on the cover but not cancelled

before despatch from Falam; and registered covers with stamps cancelled at Falam may also be found with an AIJAL registration label, affixed on receipt. Price £175.

In 1943, when stocks of ordinary Burma stamps were also exhausted, ordinary Indian stamps without overprint were used in this area on official correspondence.

1943 Ordinary Stamps of India, identified by their Catalogue Nos., after prefix 'CHI'.

Used at FALAM (March 22 - August 3) : at HAKA (Sept. 15).

CHI 20	3p.	**slate** ('41) ..
CHI 2	½a.	**red-brown** ('37)
CHI 4	1a.	**carmine** ('37) ..
CHI 25	1½a.	**slate-purple** ..
CHI 27	3a.	**bright violet** ..
CHI 29	4a.	**brown** .. ..
CHI 15	2r.	**vio-purple and**
		brown ..

1946 (Jan. 1st) Civil Administration. No. 33, etc., overprinted "SERVICE".

O14	3p.	**chocolate-brown**	10	15
O15	6p.	**purple-violet** ..	10	15
O16	9p.	**grey-green** ..	10	15
O17	1a.	**dp-blue** (*typo*) ..	10	15
O18	1½a.	**vermilion** ..	10	15
O19	2a.	**dull-claret** ..	5	10
O20	2a.6p.	**greenish-blue** ..	5	10
O21	4a.	**mauve-purple** ..	5	10
O22	8a.	**maroon-lake** ..	5	10
O23	1 R.	**sl-vio and claret**	10	15
O24	2Rs.	**brn and dl-verm** ..	40	50
O25	5Rs.	**grn and choc-brn**	80	1·50
O26	10Rs.	**red-claret and**		
		grey-purple ..	1·25	2·25
O14/26		**set** (13)	3·00	5·00

1947 (Oct. 1st) Interim Government. No. O14, etc., overprinted "INTERIM GOVERNMENT" as Nos. 48/62.

O27	3p.	**chocolate-brown**	5	5
O28	6p.	**purple-violet** ..	5	5
O29	9p.	**grey-green** ..	5	5
O30	1a.	**dp-blue** (*typo*) ..	10	5
O31	1½a.	**vermilion**	15	10
O32	2a.	**dull-claret** ..	15	10
O33	2a.6p.	**greenish-blue** ..	15	10
O34	4a.	**mauve-purple** ..	15	10
O35	8a.	**maroon-lake** ..	15	10
O36	1 R.	**sl-vio and claret**	35	30
O37	2Rs.	**brn and dl verm**	60	45
O38	5Rs.	**grn and choc-brn**	1·00	1·50
O39	10Rs.	**red-claret and**		
		grey-purple ..	2·00	2·50
O27/39		**set** (13)	4·50	4·00

GERMAN PROPAGANDA LABELS

The 1944 German imitations of the G.B. 1937 Definitives ½d. to 3d. (see after Great Britain for details) were also overprinted in black "LIQUIDA-TION/OF EMPIRE/RANGOON" within a vertical rectangular frame. Price £120.

CANADA

IMPERFORATE STAMPS

It was formerly the practice to distribute by favour four imperforate sheets of certain stamps, a fifth sheet being placed in the P.O. archives. Being in fairly keen demand with specialists market valuations are quoted.

Until the end of 1929 all stamps were printed by the American Bank Note Co. In 1923 the company changed its name to the Canadian Bank Note Co. The British American Bank Note Co. held the contract between 1930 and 1934, following which the Canadian Bank Note Co. resumed the task of stamp production from the 1935 Silver Jubilee onwards.

Prices for earlier issues are for stamps in average condition. Unmounted and/or well centred mint stamps, and cleanly postmarked used copies are worth a definite premium depending on relative scarcity.

All stamps are Perf. 12, unless otherwise stated.

1903 (July 1st)-1908 Design, portrait of King Edward VII in Robes of State. Designers, the then Prince of Wales, later King George V, and J. A. Tilleard, R.P.S.

E1	1c.	**green**	.. .. ..	5·00	10
	a	pale green	..	5·50	10
	b	deep green	..	6·00	10
E2	2c.	**rose, carmine**	..	5·00	10
	a	pl rose, carmine	..	5·00	10
	b	imperf horizontally			
		(vert. pair)	..	£12	£12
E3	5c.	**dp blue on bluish**	..	£30	1·00
	a	indigo/bluish		£30	1·00
E4	7c.	**yellowish-olive**	..	£24	1·25
	a	greenish-bistre	..	£27	1·25
	b	straw (1912)	..	£90	£10
E5	10c.	**brown, lilac**	.. ..	£65	3·00
	a	dull lilac	..	£65	3·00
	b	pale-dull lilac	..	£65	3·00
E6	20c.	**pl yellowish ol-green**			
		(27/9/04)	..	£180	£12
	a	dp olive-green	..	£180	£14
E7	50c.	**dp violet** (19/11/08)	..	£275	£35
E1/7		**set** (7)	.. .. ..	£550	£65

Imperf. pairs, 1c., £40; 2c., £10; 5c., £200; 7c., £40; 10c., £85. The 2c. imperf was on sale for a number of years in Ottawa, the other values have since emanated from other sources.

Specimen overprint, 20c. overprinted "SPECIMEN" with serifed capitals in horizontal format Price, £70.

Numbers Issued—
1c., 1,470,000,000; 2c., 2,160,000,000; 5c., 66,210,000; 7c., 25,305,000; 10c., 15,080,000; 20c., 3,150,000; 50c., 600,000.

1908 Experimental Coil Perforations. Type Roulette x Imperf. Type II, Imperf. x Roulette and Type II, Imperf. x Perf. 8½.

E8	2c.	**rose carmine**	.. ..	—	—
E9	2c.	**rose carmine**	.. ..	—	—
E10	2c.	**rose carmine**	..	—	—

1908 (July 16th) Quebec Tercentenary. Various designs by Machado. Inscriptions in French. ½c. Princess and Prince of Wales. 1c. Jacques Cartier and Samuel de Champlain, 2c. Queen Alexandra and King Edward, 5c. Champlain's Home in Quebec in 1700, 15c. Champlain's departure for the West, 20c, Cartier's Arrival before Quebec. The colour of the paper varies slightly from white to toned. Sheets 10 x 10.

E11	½c.	**black, brown**	..	3·25	3·25
	a	re-entry	..	£45	£45
E12	1c.	**blue-green**	..	4·50	3·00
E13	2c.	**carmine**	..	8·50	75
E14	5c.	**dark blue**	..	£27	£14
E15	7c.	**olive-green**	..	£45	£16
E16	10c.	**violet**	..	£60	£42
E17	15c.	**red olive**	..	£85	£55
E18	20c.	**dull brown**	..	£110	£70
E11/E18		**set** (8)	..	£300	£185

11a shows as doubling of lower frame lines (Row 5/4).

Prices are for copies of E16, 17, 18 well centred.

All values exist imperf. Price from £60 each (pairs).

Number Issued—

½c., 2,000,000; 1c., 22,530,000; 2c., 35,100,000; 5c., 1,200,000; 7c., 700,000; 10c., 500,000; 15c., 300,000; 20c., 304,200.

1911 King George V. Admiral Type. For the sake of clarity from the philatelic standpoint these issues are listed in the following order:—

Year	Classification	Catalogue Number
Basic Series		
1911–25	Perf. 12	G1–G19
1912	Perf. 8 x Imperr.	G20–G21
1912–24	Imperf. x Perf. 8	G21–G26b
1915–24	Perf. 12 x Imperf.	G27–G30
1915	do. Toronto trial	G31
1931	Perf. 12 x 8	G32
1924	Experimental Papers Perf. 12	G33–G34
War Tax Series		
1915	Overprints	G35–G37
1915	Inscr. "War Tax"	G38–G39
	Inscr. ITC Perf. 12	G40–G41c
	Inscr. ITC Perf. 12 x 8	G42–G42a
	Inscr. ITC Imperf. x Perf. 8 . ..	G43–G44a
Provisionals		
1926	2 cents overprints ..	G46–G47

1911 (Dec. 22nd)-1925 King George V "Admiral" type. On whitish wove paper, medium thickness. The value tablets on the $1.00 value are oval in shape.

G1	1c. **yellowish-green** (22/12/11) (**Die I**)	2·50	5
	a dp yellowish-green (Die I)	2·50	5
	b greyish-grn (Die I)	2·50	5
	c dp bluish-grn (Die I)	2·50	5
G2	1c. **yel** (7/5/22) (**Die I**)..	2·50	10
	a yel (–/10/24) (Die II)	2·00	51
G3	2c. **rose-red** (22/12/11) (**Die Ia**)	2·50	5
	a bt rose-red (Die Ia)	3·00	5
	b dl rose-red (Die Ia)	3·00	5
	c red (Die Ia) ..	2·00	5
	d car-red (Die Ia) ..	2·00	5
	e dp red-lake (Die Ia)	2·00	5
G4	2c.**dp dk green** (6/6/22) (**Die Ia**)	2·25	10
	a dl yel-grn (–/–/24) (Die Ib)	2·50	10
G5	3c. **drab-brown** (6/8/18) (**Die I**)	4·25	10
	a dull brown (Die I)	4·25	10
	b brn-ochre (Die I) ..	3·75	10
	c dp intense brown (Die I)	3·75	10
G6	3c. **car** (14/12/23) (**Die I**)	2·25	10
	a car (–/10/24) (Die II)	5·25	20
G7	4c. **ol-yel** (3/7/22) ..	7·25	85
	a yellow ochre ..	7·25	85
G8	5c. **dp blue** (17/1/12) ..	£32	15
	a indigo ..	£42	15
G9	5c. **dp vio** (2/2/22) ..	4·75	40
	a reddish-violet ..	4·75	40
G10	7c. **pale sage-green** (27/12/11)	£110	£14
G11	7c. **yel ochre** (–/–/12) ..	£16	50
	a intense yel ochre ..	9·00	50
	b pl yellow chrome ..	9·00	50
	c straw	£60	5·00
	d pale sage grn ..	£200	£20
G12	7c. **red-brn** (12/12/24)..	7·50	2·25

G13	8c. **blue** (1/9/25) ..	£10	2·25
G14	10c. **brnish-pur** (12/1/12)	£95	35
	a reddish-purple ..	£55	40
G15	10c. **blue** (20/2/22) ..	£10	30
	a bright blue	£10	30
G16	10c. **bistre-brn** (1/8/25)	£10	30
	a yellow-brown ..	£10	30
G17	20c. **ol-grn** (23/1/12) ..	£18	40
	a dp yel olive	£18	30
G18	50c. **sepia** (26/1/12) ..	£27	1·50
	a grey black	£80	4·00
G19	$1 **dp brn or** (2/7/23) ..	£55	2·50
	a pale brn, orange ..	£55	2·50
G1/19:	(19 values, basic colours)	£350	£25

G4/G9 For these values on thin paper refer to numbers G33 and G34. Imperf. pairs, 4c., 5c. (violet), 7c., (red-brn), 8c., 10c., (brn), 20c., 50c., $1.00 all £35 each. 1c. £3, 2c. £4, 3c. £2.

Numbers Issued—

1c. (grn), 3,218,400,000; 1c. (yel), 1,278,760,000; 2c. (red), 3,043,450,000; 2c. (grn), 1,200,000,000; 3c. (brn), 2,044,000,000; 3c. (car), 1,520,000,000; 4c., 75,900,000; 5c. (blue), 198,000,000; 5c. (vio), 1,000,000,000; 7c. (G11–12b) 103,200,000; 8c., 24,200,000; 10c. (pur) 148,700,000; 10c. (blue), Data not available; 10c. (brn), 85,895,000; 20c., 96,966,000; 50c., 11,070,000; $1.00, 1,865,000.

The numbers given above for the 2c. green and 5c. violet include the quantities produced for the 1924 Experimental issue on thin paper. See numbers G33 and G34.

Die I

Die II

Die I

Die II

Notes on the dies.

1. The 1c. and 3c. Die I, (1911) the inscription "CENT" or "CENTS" rests upon the second line above the foot of the design, whilst the "ONE" or "THREE" is well clear of the medallion. With Die II (1924) the "CENT" or "CENTS" inscription rests upon the first line above the foot of the design, Only a single thin line separates the "ONE" or "THREE" inscription from the lower corner of the medallion.

In general the Die I lettering is smaller and neater than that of Die II. The 1c. green and 3c. brown (all shades) only exist Die I.

Die Ia

Die Ib

2. The 2c. The Die of the 2c. value was reworked, thus producing the two types. (Ia and Ib) Die Ia. Lower right corner slightly bent. The re-worked Die Ib shows a smaller extension to the right from the lower right hand corner frame line. The inscription "TWO CENTS" is slightly larger. The 20c. value was also reworked.

Stamps of this issue exist imperforate on one or two adjacent sides from booklets. See under booklet panes.

1912 (Sept.) "Admiral" type, as G1 etc., but Perf. 8 x Imperf. from coils. Sold from automatic vending machines.

G20 1c. **greyish-grn (Die I)** ..	£37	£15
G21 2c. **rose-red (Die I)** ..	£37	£15

Numbers Issued—
1c., 3,330,000; 2c., 4,005,000.

1912-1924 "Admiral" type as G20/1 but Imperf. x Perf. 8.

G21 1c. **yel-grn** (1912) **(Die I)**	5·50	60
a greyish-grn (Die I) ..	5·50	60
G22 1c. **yel** (1932) **(Die I)** ..	5·50	3·25
a Imperf. between vert. pair on thick soft paper	£125	—
b yel (1924) (Die II)..	7·00	5·00
c imperf. between vert. pair (Die II) ..	£20	£20
G23 2c. **dl rose red** (1912) **(Die Ia)** ..	7·00	15
a car-red (Die Ia) ..	7·00	15
b dp red lake (Die Ia)..	£12	2·50
G24 2c. **dp dark green** (1922) **(Die Ia)** ..	5·00	2·00
a imperf. between vert pair, on thick soft paper (Die Ia)	£150	—

b **dl yel green** (1924) (Die Ib)	5·00	2·00
c imperf. between vert pair (Die Ib) ..	£12	£12
G25 3c. **deep intense brown** (−/11/18) **(Die I)** ..	3·25	15
G26 3c. **car** (1924) **(Die I)** ..	£12	3·00
a imperf. between vert pair, on thick soft paper (Die I) ..	£200	—
b car (1924) (Die II) ..	£16	£11

Numbers G22*a*, G24*a* and G26*a* constitute the very first printings of the 1c, 2c, and 3c, values in the new colours. Two sheets were produced at the request of a gentleman of influence in Ottawa. Twenty other sheets were also produced and found their way into the hands of another private collector who subsequently sold them to a Montreal dealer. The colours of the stamps are darker than the later printings, being damp printed on thick soft whitish paper with pebbly gum. The impression of the printing does not show through on to the back of the stamp.

As many complaints were received by the Postal Authorities regarding the way in which numbers G22*a*, G24*a* and G26*a* were not made available to the public the 1c. and 2c. values were "reissued". These constitute numbers G22*c* and G24*c*. They were dry printed on thinner more creamy paper with smooth gum. Both on the second dies. The impression of the printing does show through on the back of the stamp. 100,000 produced against 2,200 of the very first printing. The 3c. carmine was not "reissued" as this would have made necessary the manufacture of a new plate for the production of only 100,000 stamps

Numbers Printed—
1c. (grn. G21/a), 180,005,000; 1c. (yel, G22/b), 25,700,000; 2c. (red G23/a/b), 171,747,500; 2c. (grn, G24/b), 158,197,000; 3c. (brn, G25), 126,300,000; 3c. (car, G26/b), 47,585,000.

1915 (Sept.)-1924 "Admiral" type, as G1 etc., but Perf. 12 x imperf. Sold from automatic vending machines.

G27 1c. **yel-grn** (−/9/15) **(Die I)**	2·00	2·00
a blue-grn (Die I) ..	9·00	6·00
G28 2c. **dl rose-red** (−/9/15) **(Die Ia)**	9·00	9·00
a bt car-red (Die Ia) ..	9·00	9·00
G29 2c. **dp grn** (−/9/24) **(Die Ia)**	£60	£50
G30 3c. **brn** (1921) **(Die I)** ..	3·00	3·00

Numbers Issued—
1c., 18,050,000; 2c. (red), 14,290,000; 2c. (grn), 250,000; 3c., Data not available.

1915 Trial Coil Perf. Used in the automatic vending machines, Toronto P.O., Ontario. Perf. 12 + two large holes x imperf. The two large holes are 3.5 mm in diameter and 5,75 mm. apart.

G31 1c. **greyish-green (pair) (Die I)**	£35	£25

1921 (June 24th) As G6a but Perf. 12 x 8.

G32	3c. **carmine (Die II)**	..	4·00	4·00

1924 (Oct. 19th) Experimental Issue. Thin paper.

G33	2c. **green**	.. ..	2·25	1·25
G34	5c. **deep violet**	..	6·50	4·50
G34A	7c. **red-brown** ..	..	£110	£70
G33/34A	**set** (3)	.. ..	£112	£75

The experimental printing on thin paper as listed above was produced by the printers on their own initiative and not as a result of the instructions received from the Postal Authorities.

1915 (Feb. 22nd) Overprinted "WAR TAX" diagonally. Overprinted in black (5c. and 20c.) or red (50c.). Originally intended only for taxation purposes but nevertheless used for postal payment owing to a vaguely worded official document.

G35	5c. **blue** ..	.. ..	£110	£110
G36	20c. **olive-green** ..	..	£27	£27
	a dp yellow-olive	..	£27	£27
G37	50c. **sepia** ..	.. ..	£38	£38
G35/37	**set** (3) ..	.. ..	£160	£160

By December 30th, 1915 all three values were no longer available for postage.

1915 Inscribed "WAR TAX".

G38	1c. **yel-grn** (15/4/15) ..	2·25	10
G39	2c. **rose-car** (−/3/15) ..	2·25	15
	a carmine-red	..	2·25	15
G38/G39	**set** (2)	.. ..	4·00	25

1916 War Tax Issue. Inscribed "ITC". Perf. 12.

G40	2c.+1c. **rose-red** (1/1/16)			
	(Die I)	4·25	60
	a bt car-red (Die I)	4·00	50
	b scarlet (Die I) ..	4·50	75
	c dp carmine-red		
	(−/9/16) (Die II)	£47	2·00
G41	2c.+1c. **brown** (16/9/16)		
	(Die I)	£110	6·00

	a dp brn (28/8/16)			
	(Die II)	6·50	10
	b brn (Die II) ..	6·50	10
	c yellowish-bistre		
	brn (Die II) ..	2·00	10
G40a/G41b	**set** (2)	5·00	50

Die I

Die II

Notes on the Dies.

1. Die I. The lines below "ITC" but within the medallion are horizontal and cross hatched.

2. Die II. Horizontal lines below "ITC" as before but the right hand area under the large T consists of diagonal dots and lines only. The rest of the cross hatching below the large T consists of one single horizontal line only.

1916 As War Tax issue G40 etc., above, but Perf. 12 x 8.

G42	2c.+1c. **car-red (Die I)** ..	8·50	9·50
	a bt rose-red (Die II)	8·50	7·50

1916 As War Tax issue G40 etc. above, but Imperf. x Perf. 8 (Coils).

G43	2c.+1c. **lt rose-red (Die I)**	£35	3·00
	a dp rose-red (Die I)	£35	3·00
G44	2c.+1c. **brown (Die I)** ..	£55	2·50
	a dp blk-brn (Die II)	7·50	1·75
	'a pair G43/G44 ..	—	—

1917. 50th Anniversary Confederation.

G45	3c. **brown**	£10	40
	a dp dk brown	£10	40

Number Issued—98,650,000.

Imperf. pair—£25

For a similar design but 2c. green see G49.

2 CENTS   **2 CENTS**

G46   G47

1926 (Oct. 12th) etc. Provisional Overprints. Overprinted "2 CENTS" in a single line (G46) or two lines (G47).

G46	2c. on 3c. **car** (12/10/26)..	£25	£25
	'a' Die II ..	—	—
G47	2c. on 3c. **carmine**		
	(10/11/26) ..	£10	£10
G46/G47	**set** (2) ..	£30	£30

G47 Variations exist in the positioning of the "2" over the "N" of "CENTS".

1927 (June 29th) 60th Anniversary Confederation. Commemorative issue inscribed "1867-1927 CANADA CONFEDERATION". Inscribed in both English and French. 1c., Sir J. A. Macdonald, 2c., The Fathers of Confederation, 3c., Ottawa Parliament Buildings, 5c., Sir W. Laurier, 12c., Map of Canada 1867-1927.

G48	1c. **orange**	1·25	50
G49	2c. **green**	60	10
G50	3c. **carmine**	3·75	2·50
G51	5c. **violet**	1·75	1·25
G52	12c. **dark blue** ..	3·50	2·00
G48/G52	**set** (5)	8·50	6·00

Number Issued—

1c., 148,034,000; 2c., 333,757,000; 3c. 15,431.000; 5c., 26,627,000; 12c., 7,492,000.

1927 (June 29th) 60th Anniversary Confederation Historical issue. Inscribed in English

only. 5c., D. McGee, 12c., Sir W. Laurier and Sir J. A. Macdonald, 20c., R. Baldwin and L. H. Lafontaine.

G53	5c. **violet**	1·75	1·00
G54	12c. **green**	4·00	2·50
G55	20c. **carmine**	6·50	3·00
G53/G55	**set** (3)	£11	6·00

Number Issued—

5c. 20,349,000; 12c., 5,273,000; 20c., 7,632,000

1928 (Sept. 21st) Air Mail Stamps.

G56	5c. **olive, brown** ..	3·25	1·25

Imperf. pair £45. Imperf. between pair (horiz. or vert) £50.

Number Issued—5,050,000.

1928 (Oct. 17th)-1929 The so-called "Scroll Type". 1c.-8c., portrait of King George V., 10c., Mount Hurd, 12c., Quebec Bridge, 20c., Harvesting with Horses, 50c., Schooner "Bluenose", £1, Ottawa Parliament Buildings. First regular bi-lingual definitives.

G57	1c. **orange**	1·00	15
G58	2c. **green**	35	10
G59	3c. **dark carmine** ..	8·50	4·50
G60	4c. **bistre**	6·25	2·25
G61	5c. **dark violet**	2·25	1·00
G62	8c. **dark blue**	5·25	2·75
G63	10c. **green**	4·75	50
G64	12c. **grey**	£12	4·00
G65	20c. **dark carmine** ..	£17	5·00
G66	50c. **dark blue**	£160	£35
G67	$1 **olive-green**	£220	£50
G57/67	**set** (11)	£400	£90

Numbers Issued—

1c., 278,652,000; 2c., 1,131,188,000; 3c., 11,000,000; 4c., 10,020,000; 5c., 21,421,900; 8c., 12,100,000;

10c., 36,077,000; 12c., 4,330,000; 20c., 7,008,600; 50c., 1,044,900; $1, 560,950.

This set is known imperf. and imperf. between pairs, but these were not regularly issued.

1928 (Nov. 5th) Scroll Type as G57 etc., but Imperf. x Perf. 8.

G68	1c. orange (–/–/28)	8·00	8·00
G69	2c. green (5/11/28)	6·00	1·00

G68/69 mainly exist pre-cancelled, 1c. price £2, 2c. price 75p.

Number Issued—
G68,10,000,000 plus 8,515,000 pre-cancelled; G69, 83,259,000.

1930 (July 6th)-1931 Perf. 11. Maple Leaf Issue. All designs include a maple leaf in the top corners. 1c.–8c., King George V., 10c., Parliamentary Library, Ottawa, 12c., The Old Citadel, Quebec, 20c., Harvesting with tractor, 50c., Memorial Church, $1, Mount Edith Cavell. Rotary (R) or Flat bed printed (F).

G70	1c. or (17/7/30) (Die I)		
	(R)	20	15
G71	1c. grn (6/12/30) (Die I)		
	(R)	60	10
G72	1c. grn (Die II) (R)	1·00	5
G73	2c. grn (6/7/30) (Die I)		
	(R)	50	5
G74	2c. scar (17/11/30) (Die I) (R)	50	5
G75	2c. scar (Die II) (R)	1·00	10
G76*	2c. brn (4/7/31) (Die I)		
	(R)	2·00	1·25
G77	2c. dp brn (Die II) (R)..	60	10
G78	3c. scar (13/7/31) (R) ..	1·50	10
G79	4c. ochre (5/11/30) (F)	5·00	4·00
G80	5c. dk vio (18/6/30) (F)	2·50	2·50
G81	5c. vio (7/7/30) (R)	4·00	3·50
G82	5c. blue (13/11/30)/(F)	2·00	10
G83	8c. blue (13/8/30) (F) ..	9·00	5·00
G84	8c. or (5/11/30) (F)	4·00	3·00
G85	10c. ol-grn (5/11/30) (F)	4·00	80
G86	12c. gry-blk (4/12/30) (F)	8·00	2·50
G87	13c. violet (1/12/30) (F)	£14	2·00
G88	20c. red (4/12/30) (F) ..	£14	6·00

G89	50c. blue (4/12/30) (F)	£125	8·00
	a pale blue (F)	£125	8·00
G90	$1 dk ol (2/12/30) (F)	£125	8·00
G70/90	(17 values, No Die variations)	£300	£45

Imperf. 1c. green (Die II) One sheet known. £50 per pair.

Number Issued—
G83, 887,500; G89, 2,811,400; G90, 606,350.

Notes on the dies.

1c. Die I. Three thick coloured lines above one thin coloured line below the ornament above "POSTAGE". Small curved line in the ball ornament below the "A" of "CANADA".

1c. Die II. Four thick coloured lines above "POSTAGE" and a full semi-circular line within the ball ornament below the "A" of "CANADA".

Die I   Die II

2c. Die I. Three thick coloured lines between the "P" of "POSTES" and the ornament below the "C" of "CANADA". Small curved line in the ball ornament below the "C" of "CANADA".

2c. Die II. Four thick coloured lines above "POSTES" and a full semi-circular line within the ball ornament below the "C" of "CANADA".

The various Rotary printings may be identified by the presence of "ridging" clearly visible on the back of the stamp. The ridges are some 5 mm. apart and run horizontally across each stamp.

1930 (June 27th)-1934 Maple Leaf Issue as G70 etc., but Imperf. x Perf. 8½ (Coils).

G91	1c. orange (Die I)	6·00	4·50
G92	1c. green (Die I) ..	3·50	3·50
G93	2c. green (Die I) ..	2·50	1·25
G94	2c. scarlet (Die I)	4·50	1·50
G95	2c. brown (Die I)	3·50	50
G96	3c. scarlet ..	4·50	50
G91/96	set (6V)	£24	£11

1930 (Dec. 4th) Air Mail Stamp. P11.

G97	5c. dp brown	£18	£10

Number Issued—400,000.

1931 (Sept. 30th) Design, Sir G. E. Cartier. P.11.

G98 10c. ol-green (shades) .. 5·00   15

Number Issued—64,300,000.

6

1932 (Feb. 22nd) Airmail provisional overprint. G56 overprinted as above.

G99 6c. on 5c. olive-brown .. 4·50   1·25

In pair, one stamp without overprint, £100 Overprint inverted. Overprint double £45 each. Overprint triple £50. Status of these errors—is possibly irregular.

Number Overprinted—2,000,000.

1932 (June 21st) Provisional overprint, as above. Perf. 11.

G100 3c. on 2c. scar (Die I)   1·50   1·00
G101 3c. on 2c. scar (Die II)   60   20

Number Overprinted—58,265,000.

1932 (July 12th) Imperial Economic Conference, Ottawa. Designs, 3c., King George V., 5c., The Duke of Windsor when Prince of Wales, 13c., Allegory of the British Empire. Perf. 11.

G102 3c. scarlet 50   10
G103 5c. blue .. .. .. 3·50   1·25
G104 13c. green .. .. .. 4·50   2·75
G102/4 set (3) .. .. 8·00   4·00

Numbers Issued—

3c., 100,700,000; 5c., 8,300,000; 13c., 2,000,000.

6   6

OTTAWA CONFERENCE 1932

1932 (July 12th) Imperial Economic Conference, Ottawa. Airmail Stamp. G97 overprinted in blue. Perf. 11.

G105 6c. on 5c. deep brown   9·00   5·00

Number Issued—500,000.

1932 (Dec. 1st) "Medallion" type. Design of the 3c., Ottawa Conference issue adapted for definitive use. Perf. 11. Printed by Rotary (1c., 2c. and 3c.), or Flat Bed processes (4c., 5c. and 8c.).

G106 1c. green 25   10
G107 2c. sepia 40   10
G108 3c. scarlet 60   10
G109 4c. bistre .. .. .. £18   3·00
G110 5c. blue .. .. .. 2·00   10
G111 8c. red-orange .. .. 9·00   2·00
G106/11 set (6) .. .. .. £30   5·00

Copies of the three low values are to be found bearing the characteristics of the flat bed process. (See note following numbers G70–G90). These are not Flat Bed printings but Rotary printings on dry pre-gummed paper.

The so-called two dies on the 3c. value are generally regarded as being differences occasioned by printing and relief variations.

1933 (August 15th) Medallion Type. As G106 etc., but Imperf. x 8½.

G112 1c. green (3/11/33) .. 8·00   1·00
G113 2c. sepia (15/8/33) .. 9·00   50
G114 3c. scarlet (16/8/33) .. 5·00   15
G112/4 set (3) .. .. .. £22   1·50

1933 (May 18th) Preliminary Meeting U.P.U.

F

Congress, Ottawa. Perf. 11. Design, Parliament Buildings, Ottawa.

G115 5c. dark blue ..   ..   6·00   2·00
Number Issued—5,100.000.

1933 (July 24th) World's Grain Exhibition and Conference, Regina, Saskatchewan. G88 overprinted in red as above.

G116 20c. red £25   £10
Number Issued—1,561,000.

1933 (August 17th) Centenary of the First Steamship Crossing of the Atlantic by the Royal William. Design, The S.S. Royal William after S.S. Killet. Perf. 11.

G117 5c. dark blue ..   ..   6·00   2·00
Number Issued—4,854,000.

1934 (July 1st) Fourth Centenary of Jacques Cartier's Discovery of Canada. Design, Jacques Cartier approaching land after a Vignette made by the British American Bank Note Co. in the 1870's Perf. 11. Sheets 200 – two panes, each 10 x 10.

G118 3c. dark blue ..   ..   4·00   1·25
    a wide spacing between stamps. Horiz.
    pair ..   ..   ..   £48   —

5 mm. spacing between stamps instead of the normal 3½ mm. Some 500 pairs exist.

Number Issued—12,370,000.

1934 (July 1st) 150th Anniversary of Arrival of the United Empire Loyalists in Canada. Design, the U.E.L. Monument, Hamilton, Ontario. Perf. 11.

G119 3c. deep olive-green ..   £18   8·00
Number Issued 3,000,000.

1934 (August 16th) 150th Anniversary of Province of New Brunswick. Design, The Seal of New Brunswick. Perf. 11. Sheets 200 – two panes, each 10 x 10.

G120 2c. red brown ..   ..   2·50   1·00
Number Issued—5,050,000.

From 1935 most sheet issued stamps are Perf 12 unless otherwise stated.

1935 (May 4th) Silver Jubilee. Designs, 1c., Queen Elizabeth when Princess, 2c., King George VI., when the Duke of York, 3c., King George V. and Queen Mary, 5c., The Duke of Windsor when Prince of Wales, 10c., Windsor Castle, 13c., The Royal Yacht, "Britannia". Sheets 10 x 10, except 3c. and 10c. which are 5 x 10.

G121 1c. green   20   10
    a weeping princess
    flaw ..   ..   £60   —

			£20	—
	b retouch	.. ..	£20	—
G122	2c. **brown**	.. ..	35	10
G123	3c. **carmine**	.. ..	80	10
G124	5c. **blue** ..	.. ..	2·25	1·25
G125	10c. **green** ..	.. ..	2·50	1·25
G126	13c. **deep blue**	.. ..	3·50	2·50
G121/126	**set (16)**	.. ..	8·50	5·00

The Weeping Princess flaw on the 1c. shows a large coloured blob below the right eye (left on the stamp) of the Princess. Position, Row 4/1 Upper right hand pane of Plate 1. The flaw was subsequently retouched, but traces can still nevertheless be detected.

Numbers Issued—

1c., 30,500,000; 2c., 31,000,000; 3c., 60,425,000; 5c., 3,050,000; 10c., 3,125,000; 13c., 1,100,000.

1935 (June 1st) Definitives. First designs to include the so called "secret dates". Designs, 1c. to 5c. and 8c., King George V., 6c., Daedalus—inscribed "AIR", 10c., Royal Canadian Mounted Policeman, 13c., The Confederation Conference at Charlottetown, 1864, 20c., Niagara Falls, 50c., Parliament Buildings, Victoria, British Colombia, $1, Champlain Monument, Quebec.

G127	1c. **green** ..	.. ..	15	10
G128	2c. **brown**	.. ..	15	10
G129	3c. **carmine**	.. ..	30	10
	a printed on the gummed side	..	£75	—
G130	4c. **yellow**	.. ..	1·50	25
G131	5c. **blue** ..	.. ..	1·50	10
	a imperf. between horiz. pair ..	..	£200	—
G132	6c. **red-brown** ..		2·00	75
G133	8c. **orange**	.. ..	1·50	50
G134	10c. **carmine**	.. ..	4·00	10
G135	13c. **purple**	.. ..	4·00	25
G136	20c. **olive-green** ..	..	£20	50
G137	50c. **violet** ..	.. ..	£22	3·50
	a re-entry	.. ..	£75	—
G138	$1 **blue** ..	.. ..	£75	8·00
G127/138	**set (12)**	.. ..	£105	£12

The re-entry on the 50c. shows a heavy line through the lower part of the inscription "CANADA". Position, Row 5/5 lower right hand pane. Plate 1.

Number Issued—

G137, 2,416,000; G138, 818,000.

1935 (July 20th) As G127 etc., above but Imperf. x Perf. 8 (Coils).

G139	1c. **green** (5/11/35)	..	9·00	1·50
G140	2c. **brown** (14/10/35)	..	9·00	50
G141	3c. **carmine** (20/7/35)	..	5·50	20
G139/141	**set (3)** ..	.. ..	£22	2·00

1937-41 Definitives. Designs, 1c.–8c. (Portrait of King from Photo by Bertram Park); 10c. (Memorial Chamber, Parliament Buildings, Ottawa); 13c. (Entrance, Halifax Harbour); 20c. (Fort Garry Gate, Winnipeg); 50c. (Entrance, Vancouver Harbour); $1 (Chateau de Ramezay, Montreal). Designs, 13c., 20c., 50c., $1, H; others, V.

1	1c. **green** (1/4/37)	..	15	5
2	2c. **brown** (1/4/37)	..	20	5
3	3c. **car-red** (1/4/37)	..	30	5
4	4c. **yellow** (10/5/37)	..	1·50	30
5	5c. **blue** (10/5/37)	..	90	15
6	8c. **orange** (10/5/37)	..	1·50	25
7	10c. **pl rose-car** (15/6/38)		7·00	15
	a rose-car (3/8/38)	..	7·00	15
8	13c. **blue** (15/11/38)	..	8·00	20
9	20c. **lt brown** (15/6/38)	..	£18	30
10	50c. **green** (15/6/38)	..	£32	5·00
11	$1 **pur-vio** (15/6/38)	..	£65	7·50
	a vert. pr. imperf. between		£200	—
	b flu. aniline (/41?)	..	£70	8·00
1/11	**set (11)** ..	.. ..	£120	£30

Imperf. pairs as 1c. to 8c. at £30 pair, 10c. to $1 at £50 pair.

Note—

Various values exist printed on paper with ribbed effect on the underside. The wire mesh on which the pulp is laid in the first instance is the cause of this, and the variety has no connection with laid paper.

11*b* These fluorescent aniline stamps can be readily distinguished from the ordinary variety, as the ink is visible through the back of the stamp, apart from the fluorescent reaction under the quartz lamp.

Die proofs exist in issued colours various values —(£400 each).

Numbers Issued—
1c., 1,393,677,600; 2c., 1,163,103,550; 3c., 2,633,940,000; 1c., 24,074,000; 5c., 133,102,302; 8c., 14,035,353; 10c. (No. 7), 10,186,690; 10c. (No. 7a), 54,019,523; 13c., 13,028,291; 20c., 30,499,240; 50c., 4.924,100; $1, 2,210,219.

As before but Imperf. x Perf. 8 (Coils).

12	1c.	green (15/6/37)	..	70	40
13	2c.	brown (18/6/37)	..	85	15
14	3c.	car-red (15/4/37)	..	1·20	15
12/14	set (3)	..	..	2·75	70

Number Issued—
1c., 23,021,500; 2c., 34,565,000; 3c., 57,827,000.

1942 (July 1st)-43 War Effort Designs, 1c.–5c. (less 4c. slate) (King's Portrait); 4c. (Grain Elevator); 8c. (Farm Scene); 10c. (Parliament Buildings); 13c. (Tank); 20c. (Corvette); 50c. (Munitions); $1 (H.M.C.S. "Iroquois"). Designs, 4c. (19), 8c., 13c., 20c., 50c., $1 H. Others V.

15	1c.	green	..	..	15	5
16	2c.	brown	..	..	25	5
		a imperf between pair		£850	—
17	3c.	carmine-red	..	..	40	5
18	3c.	purple (30/6/43)	..	40	5
19	4c.	slate (grain elevator)	..	1·00	50
20	4c.	carmine-red (King)				
		(9/4/43)	..	..	30	5
21	5c.	blue	..	..	50	5
22	8c.	red-brown	..	..	1·25	20
23	10c.	brown	..	..	2·00	5
24	13c.	grey-green	..	..	3·00	2·50
25	14c.	grey-grn (16/4/43)	..	4·25	40
26	20c.	dp choc-brown	..	3·00	10
27	50c.	bright violet	..	£18	1·50
28	$1	blue	..	..	£70	6·00
15/28	set (14)	..	..	£95	£11

Imperf. pairs as 1c. to 8c. at £30 a pair, 10c. to $1 at £85 pair.

Number Issued—
1c., 2,533,900,000; 2c., 470,710,000; 3c. (No. 17), 605,750,000; 3c. (No. 18), 2,118,190,000; 4c. (No. 19), 7,900,000; 4c. (No. 20), 3,149,175,000; 5c., 174,100,000; 8c., 22,978,621; 10c., 157,680,577; 13c., 4,000,000; 14c., 14,878,673; 20c., 62,028,166; 50c., 16,486,515; $1, 6.195,600.

As before but Imp. x Perf. 8 (Coils).

29	1c.	green (9/2/43)	..	45	60
30	2c.	brown (6/10/42)	..	1·25	70
31	3c.	car-red (6/10/43)	..	70	70
32	3c.	purple (18/8/43)	..	1·25	40
33	4c.	car-red (18/8/43)	..	1·50	25
29/33	set (5)	..	..	..	5·00	2·50

Number Issued—
1c., 26,000,000; 2c., 8,465,000; 3c. (No. 31), 9,975,000.

As before but Imp. x Perf. 12 (Booklets).

34	1c.	green (23/12/46)	..	30	30
35	3c.	purple (23/12/46)	..	40	40
36	4c.	car-red (23/12/46)	..	50	50
34/36	set (3)	..	..	1·00	1·00

These stamps are from booklets in strips of three with outer edges imperf.

As before but Imp. x Perf. 9½ (Coils).

37	1c.	green (13/7/48)	..	2·00	2 00
38	2c.	brown (1/10/48)	..	7 00	7·00
39	3c.	purple (2/7/48)	..	3·00	3·00
40	4c.	car-red (22/7/48)	..	3·00	3·00
37/40	set (4)	..	..	£14	£14

The dates given with Nos. 37–40 refer to when the stamps were delivered to P.O. Dept.: all were issued to public shortly afterwards.

Number Issued—
1c., 8,675,000; 2c., 3,195,000; 3c., 45,990,000; 4c., 47,590,000.

1946 (Sept. 16th) Designs, 8c. (Ontario Farm Scene); 10c. (Great Bear Lake); 14c. (St. Maurice River Power Station); 20c. (Combine-Harvester); 50c. (Lumbering in Br. Columbia); $1 (Train Ferry "Abegweit").

41	8c.	dull red-brown	..	1·00	50
42	10c.	sage-green	..	1·25	5
43	14c.	deep sepia	..	2·00	10
44	20c.	slate-grey	..	2·50	10
45	50c.	deep green	..	£22	1·00
46	$1	reddish-purple	..	£42	2·00
41/46	set (6)	..	..	£65	4·00

Number Issued—
8c., 15,100,000; 10c., 118,250,000. 50c., 13,970,000; $1, 15,375,000.

All values appeared in strips of three as Nos. 34–36. No. 64 was also issued in booklet pane of four, and Nos. 65–66 in panes of six, all with outer edges of panes imperf.

1950 (Jan. 19th) Designs as No. 47, etc., but POSTES POSTAGE omitted.

67	1c. green	..	..	10	5
68	2c. deep sepia	..	..	15	10
69	3c. purple	..	..	15	15
70	4c. carmine-red	..	..	15	5
71	5c. blue	..	..	60	60
67/71	set (5)	..	..	1·00	75

1949 (Nov. 15th)-51 Designs, 1c.–5c. (King's Portrait from photographs by Dorothy Wilding with POSTES POSTAGE incorporated in design); 10c. (Fur Drying and Wigwam); 50c. (Oil Well); $1 (Fish and Fisherman). Designs, 10c., 50c., $1 H; others, V.

Stamps without inscription POSTES and POSTAGE were printed and ready for issue when a decision was made to incorporate the two words in the design. Later, the original stamps were released for sale at the Philatelic Bureau, Ottawa, to avoid speculation in stamps of same set which were said to have leaked out.

47	1c. green	..	..	10	5
48	2c. deep sepia	..	..	10	5
49	2c. sage-grn (25/7/51)	..		10	5
50	3c. purple	..	..	10	5
51	4c. carmine-red	..	..	15	5
52	4c. or-verm (25/7/51)	..		20	5
53	5c. blue	..	..	50	10
54	10c. dk pur-brn (1/10/50)			80	10
55	50c. dp green (1/3/50)	..		£12	1·25
56	$1 ultramarine (1/2/51)			£60	8·00
47/56	set (10)	..	..	£70	9·00

Number Issued—
1c., 802,855,400; 2c. (No. 48), 201,920,000; 2c. (No. 49), 652,946,800; 3c., 1,357,315,100; 4c. (No. 51), 709,940,000; 4c. (No. 52), 790,680,000; 5c., 95,308,100; $1 4,460,000.

Number Issued—
1c., 84,000,000; 2c., 10,200,000: 3c., 101,300,000; 4c., 101,100,000; 5c., 5,000,000.

As No. 67, etc., but Imp. x Perf. 9½ (Coils).

72	1c. green (20/1/50)		..	30	45
73	3c. purple (20/1/50)		..	50	65

Number Issued—
1c., 2,660,000; 3c., 3,085,000.

As No. 47, etc., but Imp. x Perf. 9½ (Coils).

57	1c. green (18/5/50)		..	50	50
58	2c. deep sepia (18/5/50)			1·50	1·50
59	2c. sage-green (9/5/51)		..	75	75
50	3c. purple (18/5/50)		..	1·50	1·50
61	4c. car-red (18/5/50)		..	4·50	4·50
62	4c. or-verm (27/10/51)		..	1·50	1·50
57/62	set (6)	..	..	£10	£10

AIR STAMPS

Number Issued—
1c., 8,675,000; 2c. (No. 58), 3,195,000; 2c. (No. 59), 7,331,500; 3c., 26,625,000; 4c. (No. 61), 10,980,000; 4c. (No. 62), 9,645,000

1938 (June 15th) Design, Seaplane over Riverboat S.S. "Distributor III" on Mackenzie River.

A1	6c. blue	..	..	1·00	15

Imperf. pair, £40.

Number Issued—29,008,650.

As No. 47, etc., but Imp x Perf. 12 (Booklets).

63	1c. green (18/5/50)		..	10	10
64	3c. purple (18/5/50)		..	15	15
65	4c. car-red (18/5/50)		..	2·50	2·50
66	4c. or-verm (9/10/51)		..	50	50
63/66	set (4)	..	..	3·00	3·00

1942-3 Design, Grounded Plane, etc.

A2	6c. blue (1/7/42)	..	..	2·00	40
A3	7c. blue (16/4/43)	..	..	35	10
	a dl grey-blue (/45)	..		50	10

Imperf. pairs as 6c. or 7c. at £50.

Number Issued—
6c., 14,990,000; 7c., 97,793,352.
1946 (Sept. 16th) Design, Geese in Flight.
A4 7c. **blue** 40 10
   a ditto (*thin paper*) (/49) £40 —
   Number Issued—72,350,000.

SPECIAL ISSUES

**1937 (May 10th) Coronation. Sheets 200 —
four panes, each 5 x 10.**
S1 3c. **carmine-red** 15 5
Imperf. pair £45.
   Number Issued—51,400,000.

1939 (May 15th) Royal Visit. Designs, 1c.
(Princesses Elizabeth and Margaret); 2c.
(National War Memorial, Ottawa); 3c.
(King and Queen). Design, 2c. V.
S2 1c. **black and green** .. 15 5
S3 2c. **black and brown** .. 10 5
S4 3c. **black and carmine** .. 10 5
S2/4 **set** (3) 30 15
Imperf. pairs as 1c., 2c., 3c. at £35 pair.
   Number Issued—
1c., 50,043,000; 2c., 50,224,000; 3c., 100,000,000

**1947 (March 3rd) 100th Anniversary of Birth
of Alexander Bell. Sheets 10 x 5.**
S5 4c. **light blue** 10 10
   a blue 40 10
   Number Issued—25,050,000.

1947 (July 1st) Canadian Citizenship. (*Actually
issued on the 80th Anniversary of Founding of
Dominion*). **Sheets 10 x 5.**
S6 4c. **blue** 10 10
   Number Issued—25,100,000.

**1948 (Feb. 16th) Marriage of Princess
Elizabeth. Design from Photograph by
Dorothy Wilding. Sheets 10 x 10.**
S7 4c. **blue** 10 5
   Number Issued—50,010,000.

**1948 (Oct. 1st) Century of Responsible
Government. Sheets 5 x 10.**
S8 4c. **slate** 10 5
   Number Issued—50,300,000.

**1949 (April 1st) Newfoundland's Entry as
Tenth Canadian Province. Design, Cabot's**

ship "Matthew" (from model by Ernest Maunder). Sheets 5 x 10.

S9 4c. green 10 5

Number Issued—50,850,000.

1949 (June 26th) 200th Anniversary of Founding of Halifax, Nova Scotia. Design, Founding of Halifax, 1749 (after painting by C. W. Jeffries). Sheets 5 x 10.

S10 4c. purple-violet 10 5

Number Issued—25,450,000.

1951 (June 25th) Prime Ministers. Designs, 3c. (Sir R. L. Borden). 4c. (Rt. Hon. Mackenzie King). Sheets 10 x 10.

S13 3c. turquoise-green .. 10 5
S14 4c. carmine-rose 15 5

Number Issued—
3c., 50,800,000 ; 4c., 49,953,000.

1951 (Sept. 24th) Centenary of First Postal Service of Provinces. Designs, 4c. (Train of Bytown and Prescott Railway, 1851, and diesel electric loco. drawing regular passenger train), 5c. (Side-paddle wheel steamship "City of Toronto" and Canadian National Steamship "Prince George"), 7c. (Stagecoach of 1851 and "North Star" type of Airliner); 15c. (Reproduction of "Three Penny Beaver"). Sheets S20/225 x 10; S23 10 x 10.

S20	4c. black ..	..	..	30	10
S21	5c. purple	..	..	2·00	1·25
S22	7c. blue ..	..	..	80	40
S23	15c. red ..	..	..	80	20
S20/23	set (4) ..	..	..	3·75	2·00

Number Issued—
4c., 49,750,000; 5c., 5,050,000; 7c., 19,900,000.

1951 (Oct. 26th) Royal Visit. Sheets 5 x 10.

S24 4c. violet 10 5

Number Issued—50,300,000.

SPECIAL EXPRESS DELIVERY STAMPS

1898 (June 28th) Perf. 12.

SD1 10c. **yellow-green** . £20 3·00
   a dp grn (–/12/13) .. £20 3·00
   b dl blue-green ..
     (–/8/20) .. £20 3·00

SD1*a* The shade of deep green is due to a heavy re-entering of all the subjects on the plate.

SD1*b* are from Plate 2.

Number Printed—3,666,850.

1922 (August 21st) Perf. 12.

SD2 20c. **carmine** .. .. £22 3·00

Number SD2 may be found measuring 41 x 25½ mm. Damp Paper printing, or 42½–43 x 26 mm., Dry Paper printing.

Number Printed—2,300,000.

1927 (June 29th) 60th Anniversary Confeder-

ation. Design, Mail-carrying in 1867 and 1927. Perf. 12.

SD3 20c. **orange**   ..   ..   5·00   5·00

Imperf between pair (horiz. or vert.) £50.

Number Printed—671,400.

1930 (Sept. 2nd) Inscribed "TWENTY CENTS" at base. Perf. 11.

SD4 20c. **brown-red**   ..   ..   £20   6·00

Number Issued—950,000.

1932 (Dec. 24th) Inscribed "CENTS" at base. Perf. 11.

SD5 20c. **brown-red**   ..   ..   £12   7·50

Number Issued—600,000.

1935 (June 1st) Design, Allegory of Progress. Perf. 12.

SD6 20c. **scarlet**   ..   ..   2·50   2·25
     a Imperf. pair   ..   £40   —

Number Issued—883,814.

1938-9. Design, Canadian Coat of Arms on Lined Background.

SD7 10c. **green** (1/4/39)   ..   2·00   1·50
SD8 20c. **car-red** (15/6/38)   ..   £12   £12

Imperf. pairs 10c. at £40, 20c. at £40.

Number Issued—
10c., 2,305,450 ; 20c., 200,000.

1939 (March 1st) No. SE2 surcharged.

SD9 10c./20c. **carmine-red** ..   2·50   2·00

Number Issued—300,000.

1942 (July 1st) Design, Coat of Arms flanked by Flags.

SD10 10c. **green** ..   ..   ..   1·50   70

Imperf. pair, £35.

Number Issued—3,276,404.

1946 (Sept. 16th) Design, Coat of Arms flanked by Olive and Laurel Branches (*Emblems of Peace and Victory*).

SD11 10c. **green**   ..   ..   1·25   40

SPECIAL AIR EXPRESS DELIVERY

STAMPS

1942-3. Design, Trans-Canada Plane in Flight (*flying to left*).

AS1 16c. **dp ult** (1/7/42)   ..   1·25   75
AS2 17c. **dp ult** (16/4/43)   ..   1·50   1·00

Imperf. pairs as 16c. and 17c. at £40 pair.

Number Issued—
16c., 814,841 ; 17c., 868,689.

1946 Designs, Trans-Atlantic Plane over Quebec *(flying to right)*.

(a) Circumflex accent over E in EXPRES.
AS3 17c. **dull ult** (16/9/46) ..   2·25   2·25

(b) Grave accent over E in EXPRES.
AS4 17c. **dull ult** (12/46) ..   2·25   2·50

Number Issued—No. AS3, 300,000.

OFFICIAL STAMPS

The perforated initials (O.H.M.S.) are to be found inverted, sideways, etc., with valuations the same.

1939 (July) Nos. 1–11 perforated O.H.M.S.

O1	1c. **green** ..	..	..	4·00	70
O2	2c. **brown** ..		..	4·00	70
O3	3c. **carmine-red** ..		..	70	60
O4	4c. **yellow** ..		..	5·00	2·00
O5	5c. **blue**	..	..	90	30
O6	8c. **orange**	..	..	1·20	1·30
O7	10c. **pl rose-carmine**	..	£30	3·00
	a rose-carmine	..	..	3·00	60
O8	13c. **blue**	..	..	4·50	75
O9	20c. **light brown** ..		..	3·00	75
O10	50c. **green** ..	..	..	6·00	3·50
O11	$1 **purple-violet**	..	..	£21	£15
O1/11	**set** (11)	..	..	£40	£22

Nos. O1–O9 exist with letters perforated in two sizes (4 *or* 5 *punch holes high*). The others are 4 punch holes high only.

1942-3. Nos. 15–28 *(War Activities)*, **perforated O.H.M.S.**

O12	1c. **green** ..	..	..	45	15
O13	2c. **brown** ..	..	..	45	15
O14	3c. **carmine-red** ..		..	45	15
O15	3c. **purple**	..	..	30	15
O16	4c. **slate** ..	..	..	6·70	2·40
O17	4c. **carmine-red** ..		..	60	30
O18	5c. **blue**	..	..	60	30
O19	8c. **red-brown** ..		..	1·50	1·50
O20	10c. **brown** ..	..	..	1·20	1·30
O21	13c. **grey-green** ..		..	6·00	4·50
O22	14c. **grey-green** ..		..	1·50	90
O23	20c. **dp choc-brown** ..		..	1·50	90
O24	50c. **bright violet** ..		..	7·50	3·00
O25	$1 **blue**	..	..	£15	7·50
O12/25	**set** (14)	..	..	£40	£20

1946. Nos. 41–46 *(Peace Time Activities)*, **perforated O.H.M.S.**

O26	8c. **dull red-brown**	..	9·00	3·00
O27	10c **sage-green** ..		..	1·50	90
O28	14c. **deep sepia** ..		..	1·50	90
O29	20c. **slate-grey** ..		..	3·00	1·20
O30	50c. **dp green** (No. 45) ..		7·50	6·00
O31	$1 **reddish-purple** ..		£15	£10
O26/31	**set** (6) ..	..	..	£35	£20

1949 (Nov.) Nos. 48–50, perforated O.H.M.S.

O32	2c. **deep sepia**	..	..	60	45
O33	3c. **purple** ..	..	..	60	45

1949 (Sept.–Oct.) Various Stamps *(Nos. of original stamps given after each value)* **overprinted O.H.M.S.**

O34	1c. **green** (No. 15)			
	(22/9/49) ..	..	1·25	1·25
O35	2c. **brown** (No. 16) ..		£11	£11
	a stop after S omitted		£22	£20
O36	3c. **purple** (No. 18) ..		1·00	60
O37	4c. **car-red** (No. 20) ..		80	25
O38	10c. **sage-grn** (No. 42) ..		1·50	25
	a stop after S omitted		£22	£20
O39	14c. **dp sepia** (No. 43) ..		3·50	60
	a stop after S omitted		£22	£20
O40	20c. **slate-grey** (No. 44) ..		9·00	1·00
	a stop after S omitted		£20	£16
O41	50c. **dp green** (No. 45) ..		£150	£80
	a stop after S omitted		£250	£120
O42	$1 **reddish-pur** (No. 46) ..		£40	£28
	a stop after S omitted		£300	£150
O34/O42	**set** (9) ..	..	..	£200	£115

Number Issued—

1c., 1,500,000; 2c., 500,000;
3c., 1,500,000; 4c., 3,000,000;
10c., 1,000,000; 14c., 600,000;
20c., 400,000; 50c., 30,000;
$1, 65,000.

1949 (April)-50 Nos. 47–51 and 55 overprinted O.H.M.S.

O43	1c. **green** (No. 47)	..	20	15
O44	2c. **dp sepia** (No. 48) ..		35	20
O45	3c. **purple** (No. 50) ..		40	25
O46	4c. **car-red** (No. 51) ..		60	20
O47	5c. **blue** (No. 53)			
	(15/11/49) ..	..	80	40
	a stop after S omitted		£15	£12
O48	50c. **dp grn** (No. 55)			
	(1/3/50) ..	..	£22	£11
O43/O48	**set** (6) ..	..		£23	£12

Number Issued—

1c., 2,000,000; 2c, 1,000,000;
3c., 2,000,000,; 4c., 5,500,000;
5c., 800,000; 50c., 95,000.

1950 (Oct. 24th)-51 Stamps overprinted G.

O49	1c. **green** (No. 47)	..	10	10
O50	2c. **dp sepia** (No. 48) ..		30	15
O51	2c. **sage-grn** (No. 49)			
	(25/7/51) ..	..	15	10
O52	3c. **purple** (No. 50)			
	(30/9/50) ..	..	25	15
O53	4c. **carmine-red** (No. 51)			
	(30/9/50) ..	..	40	10
O54	4c. **or-verm** (No. 52)			
	(1/5/52) ..	..	40	10
O55	5c. **blue** (No. 53)	..	60	40
O56	10c. **sage-grn** (No. 42) ..		1·75	20
O57	10c. **dk pur-brn** (No. 54) ..		1·25	20
	a overprint omitted in pr. with normal		£275	£150
	This error should only be collected in marginal blocks.			
O58	14c. **dp sepia** (No. 43) ..		4·25	£125
O59	20c. **sl-grey** (No. 44) ..		£11	50

O60	50c.	**dp grn (No. 55)**	..	9·00	3·50
O61	$1	**reddish-pur (No. 46)**		£65	£40
O62	$1	**ult (No. 56)** (1/2/51)		£55	£38
O49/O62	**set** (14)			£130	£80

Number Issued—
2c. (No. O50), 1,500,000;
4c. (No. O53) 10,000,000;
10c. (No. O56), 975,000;
14o., 600,000; 20c., 700,000;
$1 (No. O60), 60,000;
$1 (No. O61) 40,000.

OFFICIAL—SPECIAL ISSUE

1939 Royal Visit (*Nos. S2–S4*) **perforated O.H.M.S.**

OS2	1c.	**black and green**	..	£45	£20
OS3	2c.	**black and brown**	..	£45	£20
OS4	3c.	**black and carmine**	..	£45	£20
OS2/4	**set** (3)	..	..	£130	£55

OFFICIAL—AIR STAMPS

1939-46. Nos. A1–4 perforated O.H.M.S.

OA1	6c.	**blue** (1/7/39)	..	6·00	1·50
OA2	6c.	**blue** (/42)	..	6·00	1·50
OA3	7c.	**blue** (/43)	..	4·50	80
OA4	7c.	**blue** (/46)	..	4·50	80

1949 (Sept.) No. A4 overprinted O.H.M.S.

| OA5 | 7c. | **blue** | .. | .. | 4·50 | 1·25 |
| | *a* | stop omitted after S | | £30 | £12 |

Number Issued—400,000.

1950 (Sept. 30th) No. A4 overprinted G for official use.

| OA6 | 7c. | **blue** | .. | .. | 4·50 | 2·00 |

Number Issued—400,000.

OFFICIAL—SPECIAL EXPRESS DELIVERY STAMPS

1938-46. Nos. SE1–3–5 perforated O.H.M.S.

OSE1	10c.	**grn** (/38)	..	6·00	2·50
OSE2	10c./20c.	**car-red** (/40)		—	—
OSE3	10c.	**grn** (/42)	..	4·50	3·00
OSE4	10c.	**grn** (/46)	..	4·50	2·50

1950 (Jan.) No. SE5 overprinted O.H.M.S.

| OSE5 | 10c. | **green** | .. | .. | 7·50 | 8·00 |

Number Issued—175,000.

1950 (Sept. 30th) No. SE5 overprinted G.

| OSE6 | 10c. | **green** | .. | .. | £15 | £15 |

Number Issued—160,000.

OFFICIAL—AIR SPECIAL EXPRESS DELIVERY STAMPS

1942-7. Nos. AS1–4 perforated O.H.M.S.

OAS1	16c.	**dp ult** (/43)	..	9·00	6·00
OAS2	17c.	**dp ult** (/43)	..	9·00	6·00
OAS3	17c.	**dl ult (Circumflex**			
		e) (2/47)..	..	£25	£15
OAS4	17c.	**dl ult (Grave e)**			
		(/47)	..	..	£35	£25

POSTAGE DUE STAMPS

1906 (July 1st) Perf. 12.

ED1	1c.	**violet**	..	..	..	3·00	1·25
ED2	2c.	**violet**	..	..	..	4·50	75
ED3	5c.	**violet**	..	..	..	5·00	75
ED1/3	**set** (3)	..	..		£12	2·50

All values exist imperf. without gum.

Number Printed—
1c., 16,000,000; 2c., 44,178,000; 5c., 13,000,000

1924 (Oct.) Design as ED1 etc., above. Experimental Issue. Thin paper.

GD1	1c.	**reddish-violet**	..	6·00	5·00
GD2	2c.	**reddish-violet**	..	6·00	5·00
GD3	5c.	**reddish-violet**	..	6·00	5·00
GD1/3	**set** (3)	..	..	£18	£15

The note after G34 also applies to the above issue.

Numbers Printed—included with ED1–ED3 above.

1928 (July 3rd) Additional values.

GD4	4c.	**violet** ..	..	..	£18	£10
GD5	10c.	**violet** ..	..	..	£14	5·00
GD4/5	(2)	..	..	..	£32	£15

1930 (August 14th)-1932. Perf. 11.

GD6	1c.	**purple** (14/7/30)..	2·00	2·00
GD7	2c.	**purple** (21/8/30)..	2·00	40
GD8	4c.	**purple** (11/8/30)..	2·00	2·00
GD9	5c.	**purple** (12/12/31)	3·00	2·00
GD10	10c.	**purple** (24/8/32)..	£35	4·00
GD6/GD10	(5)	..	..	..	£40	£10

Imperf. varieties exist.

1933 (Dec. 12th)-1934 Perf. 11. First bi-lingua

Postage Dies.

GD11	1c.	**violet** (5/5/34) ..	2·50	2·00
GD12	2c.	**violet** (2;/12/33)	2·00	50
GD13	4c.	**violet** (12/12/33)	2·50	1·50
GD14	10c.	**violet** (20/12/33)	4·00	2·00
GD11/GD14 (4) ..		.. ..	£11	6·00

Imperf. varieties exist.

1935-48.

PD1	1c.	**pur-vio** (14/10/35)	15	10
PD2	2c.	**pur-vio** (9/9/35) ..	15	10
PD3	4c.	**pur-vio** (2/7/35) ..	15	10
PD4	5c.	**pur-vio** (11/8/48)	20	10
PD5	6c.	**pur-vio** (16/1/59)	80	50
PD6	10c.	**pur-vio** (16/9/35)	30	10
PD1/6	**set** (6)	.. ..	1·50	1·00

A 3c. was issued in 1965.

COMPLETE BOOKLET PANES

(Unused)

1903-8 King Edward VII Issue.

EP1 2c. **pane of 6** £400

1911-25 King George V. Admiral type.

GP1	1c. **green, pane of 6** ..	8·00
GP2	1c. **yel, pane of 4 plus 2**	
	labels	£21
GP3	1c. **yel, pane of 6** ..	£12
GP4	2c. **red, pane of 6** ..	8·00
GP5	2c. **green, pane of 4 plus**	
	2 labels	£18
GP6	2c. **green, pane of 6** ..	£130
GP7	3c. **brown, pane of 4 plus**	
	2 labels	£30
GP8	3c. **car, pane of 4 plus 2**	
	labels	£12

1928-29 King George V. Scroll type.

GP9	1c. **pane of 6**	£12
GP10	2c. **pane of 6**	£12
GP11	5c. **pane of 6**	£40

1930-31 King George V. Maple Leaf Issue.

GP12	1c. **green, pane of 4 plus**	
	2 labels	£45
GP13	1c. **green, pane of 6** ..	£18
GP14	2c. **green, pane of 6** ..	£20

GP15	2c. **scarlet, pane of 6** ..	8·00
GP16	2c. **brn, pane of 4 plus**	
	2 labels	£50
GP17	2c. **brown, pane of 6** ..	£18
GP18	3c. **scarlet**	£18

1932 King George V. Medalion type.

GP19	1c. **pane of 4 plus 2**	
	labels	£40
GP20	1c. **pane of 6**	£10
GP21	2c. **pane of 4 plus 2**	
	labels	£45
GP22	2c. **pane of 6**	£10
GP23	3c. **pane of 4 plus 2**	
	labels	£18
GP23	3c. **pane ditto Die II** ..	£18

1935 King George V.

GP24	1c. **pane of 4 plus 2**	
	labels	£40
GP25	1c. **pane of 6**	8·00
GP26	2c. **pane of 4 plus 2**	
	labels	£40
GP27	2c. **pane of 6**	£10
GP28	3c. **pane of 4 plus 2**	
	labels	£12

1937 Issue K.G. VI.

P1	1c. **pane of 4 plus 2 labels**	..	5·00
P2	1c. **pane of 6**		2·00
P2	2c. **pane of 4 plus 2 labels**	..	6·00
P3	2c. **pane of 6**		4·00
P4	3c. **pane of 4 plus 2 labels**	..	2·00

1942 Issue War Effort.

P5	1c. **pane of 4 plus 2 labels**	..	4·00
P6	1c. **pane of 6**		2·00
P7	1c. **pane of 3**		1·00
P8	2c. **pane of 4 plus 2 labels**		5·00
P9	2c. **pane of 6**		4·00
P10	3c. **red pane of 4 plus 2 labels**		2·00
P11	3c. **pur pane of 4 plus 2 labels**..		2·00
P12	3c. **purple pane of 6**		4·00
P13	3c. **purple pane of 3**		2·00
P14	4c. **pane of 6**		3·00
P15	4c. **pane of 3**		2·00
P16	7c. **air pane of 4**		2·00

1949 Issue K.G. VI Head.

P17	1c. **pane of 3**		1·00
P18	3c. **pane of 3**		1·00
P19	3c. **pane of 4 plus 2 labels**	..	2·00
P20	4c. **pane of 3**		8·00
P21	4c. **pane of 6**		8·00

1951 New Colour.

P22	4c. **pane of 6 (vermilion)**	..	3·00
P23	4c. **pane of 3 (vermilion)**	..	2·00

CAYMAN ISLANDS

The three islands comprising the Colony were ceded, with Jamaica, to Great Britain by the Treaty of Madrid in 1670. There was no permanent settlement of the islands until 1833, and they remained a dependency of Jamaica until August 6th. 1962.

The first Post Office was opened at Georgetown in 1889; and both Ordinary and Official stamps of Jamaica were used, with cancellation GRAND CAYMAN or CAYMAN BRAC. There has yet been no substantiation of the use of Jamaican stamps overprinted "Cayman Islands".

All stamps to G26 are (*typo*) **by De La Rue. Perf. 14. Unless otherwise indicated.**

1901 (Feb. 19). Wmk. Crown CA. Sheets 120 – two panes, each 6 x 10.

V1	½d. **deep green**	2·20	2·70
V2	½d. **pale green**	45	85
V3	1d. **rose-carmine**	2·40	1·10
V4	1d. **pale carmine**	3·50	3·75
SPV1/4	**specimen set** (2v)	£50	‡

1902 (Jan.)-03. Wmk. Crown CA. Sheets as before.

E1	½d. **gr-grn** (15/9/02)	1·75	1·75
E2	1d. **carmine** (6/3/03)	3·50	3·00
E3	2½d. **bright blue**	5·00	6·50
	a broken 'M'	£25	£25
E4	6d. **brown**	£15	£15
E5	1/– **orange**	£30	£35
E1/5	**set** (5v)	£50	£58
SPE1/5	**specimen set** (5v)	£70	‡

Imperf copies of E5 are from Plate proofs.

E3*a*—The first down-stroke of the letter 'M' is broken off short on No. 27 in both panes.

Numbers printed—E3, 13,560: E4, 5,000: E5, 2,000.

1905 (Mar.)-07. As before but Wmk. Multiple Crown CA.

E6	½d. **green**	50	90
	a broken frame	£20	£20
E7	1d. **carmine** (18.10.05)	3·00	4·00
	a broken frame	£30	£30

E8	2½d. **bright blue**	2·00	4·00
	a broken frame	£25	£25
E9	4d. **brn and bl** (13.3.07)	£18	£20
	a broken frame	£40	£40
E10	6d. **brown**	£14	£16
E11	6d. **ol and rose** (13.3.07)	£18	£20
E12	1/– **orange**	£35	£40
E13	1/– **vio and grn** (13.3.07)	£35	£40
E14	5/– **salmon and green**	£160	£180
E6/14	**set** (9v)	£280	£300
E9/11/13/14	**specimen set** (4v)	£95	‡

E6*a*-E9*a*—A semicircular indentation occurs in the top of the frame line below the first 'A' in "Cayman" at Row 1/6 (left pane only).

Imperf copies of E13 are from Plate proofs.

Numbers issued—E6, 24,600: E7, 12,000: E8, 22,740: E10, 2,594: E12, 2,435: E14 6,000.

1907 (Aug. 30th). No. E7 surcharged "One Halfpenny' in black at the Government Printing Office, Jamaica.

E15	½d. on 1d. **carmine**	£38	£45

Number printed—4,800.

1907 (Nov.). No. E14 surcharged in black by the Postmistress, using a handstamp made up from printers type.

E16	½d. on 5/– **sal and grn** (26/11)	£250	£300
	a surcharge inverted	£6000	—
	b surcharge double	£3000	£3000
	c surcharge double, one inverted	—	—
	d surcharge omitted, in pair with normal	£10000	
E17	1d. on 5/– **sal and green** (23/11)	£185	£225
	a surcharge double	£3500	—

E16*d*—One example of this variety occurred on R10/4.

Numbers printed—E16, 1,800: E17, 2,160.

Both surcharges have been forged, and Collectors are advised to purchase copies with Certificates. A number of genuine used copies are known with cancellations after March, 1909: these were mint copies sent back to the Islands by collectors requiring used copies. Price from £150.

1908 (Feb. 12th). No. E9 similarly surcharged by the Inspector of Police.

E18	2½d. on 4d. **brown and bl**	£2000	£2250
	a surcharge double	£10000	£10000
	b surcharge double, one inverted	£10000	—
	c broken frame	£7000	—

E18*c*—See note under E6*a*-E9*a*.

Number printed—480.

Collectors are warned of forgeries of this surcharge which should only be purchased with a Certificate.

No. E26 was similarly surcharged 1D. and 396 copies were placed on sale on May 12th, 1908. This surcharge was intended for Fiscal use only, and the few known postally used copies were cancelled by favour or un-noticed when used on covers with several other stamps. The surcharge is known double and also inverted. Price for normal £120.

During May, 1908, and again in October, during shortages of stamps, covers were franked in manuscript "Postage Paid" or "Pd ¼d." and initialled "G.A.P." by the Postmistress (Miss G. A. Parsons) or "W.G.McC" by the Postmaster who succeeded her in June, 1908 (W. G. McCausland). The datestamp also appears on such covers. Price from £125.

1907 (Dec. 27th)-09. As Nos. E6/14 but Inscribed "POSTAGE & REVENUE". E19/23 O: Remainder C.

(a) Wmk. Multiple Crown CA.

E19	½d.	**dull green**	60	70
E20	½d.	**green**	75	80
E21	1d.	**carmine**	60	70
E22	1d.	**cerise**	1·00	1·00
E23	2½d.	**ult** (30/3/08)	3·00	4·00
E24	3d.	**pur/yel** (30/3/08)	3·00	4·00
E25	3d.	**pl pur/brownish yel**	4·00	5·00
E26	4d.	**black and red/yellow** (30/3/08)	£30	£35
E27	6d.	**dull and bright pur** (2/10/08)	3·00	4·00
E28	6d.	**dl pur and vio pur**	4·00	7·00
E29	1/–	**blk/grn** (5/4/09)	4·00	7·00
E30	5/–	**grn and red/yellow** (30/3/08)	£40	£50

(b) Wmk. Crown CA (30.3.08).

E31	1/–	**black/green**	£17	£22
E32	10/–	**grn and red/green**	£200	£225
E19/32		**set** (10v)	£260	£325
SPE19/32		**specimen set** (9v – excluding E29)	£140	‡

Numbers issued—E26, 2,400: E31, 6,000: E32, 3,000.

1908 (June 30th)-09. Local stamps (*litho*) De La Rue. Wmk. Multiple Crown CA. Perf. 14. Sheets 120 – two panes, each 6 x 10.

E33	¼d.	**brown**	10	20
E34	¼d.	**grey-brown**	40	60
		a imperf between stamp and margin	£40	—
E33/34		**specimen** (1v)	£20	‡

E34—One sheet was imperforate between right vertical row and margin.

Although originally intended for inland mail, the use of this stamp on foreign mail was later permitted.

1912 (April 24th)-20. Wmk. Multiple Crown CA. Sheets 120 – two panes, each 6 x 10. G1/9 O: Remainder C.

G1	¼d.	**brown** (10.2.13)	15	25
G2	¼d.	**deep brown**	20	25
G3	½d.	**green**	25	60
G4	½d.	**deep green**	35	60
G5	1d.	**red** (25.2.13)	60	80
G6	2d.	**slate**	60	1·25
G7	2d.	**pale grey**	80	1·25
G8	2½d.	**bt blue** (26.8.14)	2·25	4·00
G9	2½d.	**dp bt blue** (9.11.17)	3·25	4·00
G10	3d.	**pur/yel** (26.11.14)	4·00	4·25
		a white back (19.11.13)	2·00	3·00
		b on lemon (12.3.18)	2·00	3·00
		c on orange-buff ('20)	2·00	3·50
		d on pl yellow ('20)	3·00	4·00
G11	4d.	**blk and red/pl yel** (25.2.13)	1·00	1·75
		a on lemon	1·50	2·50
G12	6d.	**dl and bt purple** (25.3.13)	2·00	3·25
G13	1/–	**black/blue-green** (15.5.16)	3·50	4·50
		a white back (19.11.13)	3·25	4·59
G14	2/–	**slate vio and bt bl/bl**	8·00	£12
G15	2/–	**slate lilac and bt bl/blue**	8·00	£12
G16	3/–	**green and plum**	£12	£15
G17	3/–	**dl green and plum**	£13	£16
G18	5/–	**green and red/yel**	£35	£42
G19	10/–	**deep green and red/green** (2/15)	£90	£100
		a white back (19.11.13)	£90	£100
		b on blue-green (olive back) (5.10.18)	£80	£90
G1/19		**set** (13v)	£145	£165
SPG1/19		**specimen set** (13v)	£130	‡

WAR
STAMP.
1½d

Type I

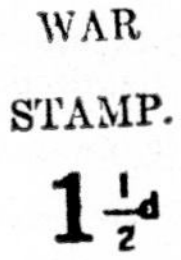
WAR
STAMP.
1½d

Type II

Type III

WAR STAMP
1½d

Type IV

1917-19. War Tax. No. G8 surcharged and overprinted.

(a) In Kingston, Jamaica. (26.2.17).

G20	1½d. on 2½d. **deep blue**			
	(Type I)	75	2·00
	a no fraction bar ..	£20	£24
G21	1½d. on 2½d. **deep blue**			
	(Type II)	40	2·00
	a no fraction bar ..	£10	£12

G20*a*—Occurs on Row 6/4 (left hand pane).

G21*a*—Occurs on several stamps including Row 7/4 (right hand pane) and Row 9/4-5 (left hand pane).

G20—The vertical spacing between STAMP and 1½d. varies considerably.

(b) By De La Rue in London. (4.9.17).

G22	1½d. on 2½d. **deep blue**			
	(Type III)	£550	£600
G23	1½d. on 2½d. **deep blue**			
	(Type IV)	40	50
SPG23	**specimen** (1v) ..	£25	‡

(c) Special printing in changed colour (De La Rue) (4.2.19).

G24	1½d. on 2½d. **orange** (Type			
	IV)	60	1·25
SPG24	**specimen** (1v) ..	£35	‡

Numbers issued—G20, 23,940 : G21, 50,700 : G22, 420 : G23, 48,000 plus : G24, 240,000.

Type V   Type VI

1919-20. War Tax. Nos. G3 and G7 overprinted or overprinted and surcharged.

(a) By De La Rue with Type V. (4.2.19).

G25	½d. **green**	25	35
SPG25	**specimen** (1v) ..	60	1·25

(b) In Kingston, Jamaica with Type VI in black. (10.3.20).

G26	1½d. on 2d. **grey**	£12	£15
	a broken '1' in fraction		

G26*a*—Occurs on Rows 1/2 and 3/2 (left hand pane).

A second printing of G26 was made with Type VI in red on April 7th, 1920; but it was not issued and only a single copy is known.

Numbers issued—G25, 240,000 plus : G26, 71,400.

1921 (April 4th)-26. (*recess*) **De La Rue. Perf. 14 (L or C). Sheets 12 x 10.**

(a) Wmk. Multiple Crown CA.

G27	3d.	**pur/orange buff** ..	1·25	2·50
		a on pale yellow ..	£15	£22
G28	4d.	**red/yel** (1.4.22) ..		
G29	1/-	**black/green** ..	75	2·50
G30	5/-	**yel-grn/pl yel** ..	£20	£25
G31	5/-	**bl-grn/pl yel** ..	£22	£25
G32	5/-	**dp grn/orange buff**	£22	£25
		(19.11.21) ..	£30	£35
G33	10/-	**car/grn** (19.11.21) ..	£60	£70
G27/33		**set** (5v)	£80	£100
SPG27/33		**specimen set** (5v) ..	£95	‡

Imperf copies of G27 and G28 are from Plate proofs.

G27 exists with watermark inverted.

Numbers printed—G27*a*, 840 : G32, 3,000.

(b) Wmk. Multiple Script CA.

G34	½d.	**yel-brown** (1.4.22) ..	20	30
G35	½d.	**chestnut** ..	25	35
G36	½d.	**pl gr-grn** (1.4.22) ..	30	40
G37	1d.	**dp carmine** (1.4.22) ..	25	50
G38	1½d.	**orange brown** ..	60	1·00
G39	2d.	**slate-grey** (1.4.22) ..	60	90
G40	2½d.	**bt blue** (1.4.22) ..	70	90
G41	3d.	**pur/lem** (29.6.23) ..	70	90
		a on pale buff ..	1·50	1·75
G42	4½d.	**sage-green** (29.6.23) ..	1·00	3·25
G43	6d.	**claret**	2·50	4·00
G44	6d.	**dp claret**	6·50	£10
G45	1/-	**blk/grn** (15.5.25) ..	2·00	4·50
G46	2/-	**vio/blue** (1.4.22) ..	6·00	£12
G47	3/-	**violet** (1.4.22) ..	£14	£20
G48	5/-	**grn/yel** (15.5.25) ..	£20	£22
G49	10/-	**car/grn** (15.9.26) ..	£65	£75
G34/49		**set** (14v)	£110	£145
SPG34/49		**specimen set** (14v) ..	£150	‡

Imperf copies of G42 and G44 are from Plate proofs.
G34—exists with watermark inverted.

1932 (Dec. 5th). Centenary of the Assembly of Justices and Vestry. (*recess*) **Waterlow and**

Sons. Wmk. Multiple Script CA. Perf. 12½. Sheets 6 x 10.

G50	¼d.	**brown**	50	75
G51	¼d.	**red-brown**	50	75
G52	½d.	**green**	70	80
G53	1d.	**scarlet**	70	80
G54	1½d.	**red-orange**	1·00	1·25
G55	2d.	**grey**	1·25	1·50
G56	2½d.	**ultramarine**	1·40	2·00
G57	3d.	**olive-green**	2·50	4·00
G58	6d.	**purple**	£10	£14
G59	1/–	**black and brown** ..	£16	£20
G60	2/–	**black and ult** ..	£32	£38
G61	5/–	**black and green** ..	£90	£110
G62	10/–	**black and scarlet** ..	£250	£350
G50/62		**set** (12v)	£375	£450

SPG50/62 **specimen set** (12v) £250 ‡

Remainders were withdrawn on May 5th, 1934.

1935 (May 1st)-36. (*recess*) **Waterlow and Sons. Wmk. Multiple Script CA. Perf. 12½. Sheets H 5 x 12: V 10 x 6.**

G63	¼d.	**black and brown** ..	15	15
G64	½d.	**ult and yel-green** (1.1.36)	20	20
G65	1d.	**ult and scarlet** ..	2·00	70
G66	1½d.	**black and orange** ..	75	75
G67	2d.	**ult and purple** ..	75	80
G68	2½d.	**bl and blk** (1.1.36) ..	3·00	1·00
G69	3d.	**blk and olive-grn** ..	1·25	1·00
G70	6d.	**bt purple and black** (1.1.36)	4·50	5·00
G71	1/–	**ult and or** (1.1.36) ..	3·25	3·00
G72	2/–	**ult and black** ..	£25	£28
G73	5/–	**green and black** ..	£32	£36
G74	10/–	**black and scarlet** ..	£70	£80
G63/74		**set** (12v)	£140	£150
SPG63/74		**specimen set** (12v)	£100	‡

G64/68/70/71—were placed on sale after the following set had been withdrawn.

1935 (May 6th). Silver Jubilee. (*recess*) **De La Rue. Wmk. Multiple Script CA. Perf. 13½ x 14. Sheets 6 x 10.**

G75	½d.	**black and green** ..	30	30
G76	2½d.	**brown and dp blue**	1·00	1·50
G77	6d.	**lt bl and olive-green**	2·00	2·50
G78	1/–	**slate and purple** ..	3·00	4·25
G75/78		**set** (4v)	5·00	8·00
SPG75/78		**specimen set** (4v) ..	£30	‡

Remainders were withdrawn on December 31st, 1935.

1938 (May 5th)-47. Designs, ¼d., 1½d. and 2/– (Beach View); 1d. and 3d. (Map of Islands); ½d. and 1/– (Dolphin Fish); 2½d. and 5/– (Schooner); other values (Hawksbill Turtles). Designs, 2d., 6d., 10/–, V. Sheets Horiz., 5 x 12; others 10 x 6 or 6 x 10.

(a) Perf. 12½ (L). Printers (*recess*) **Waterlow & Sons.**

1	¼d.	**orange**	10	20
		a pl red-or (17/12/45) ..	10	20
2	1d.	**rose-red**	10	15
		a scarlet-red (17/12/45)	15	20
3	1½d.	**black**	15	25
4	2½d.	**light blue**	15	35
5	2½d.	**reddish-or** (25/8/47) ..	1·50	60
6	3d.	**orange**	30	75
		a reddish-or (17/12/45)	30	75
7	3d.	**light blue** (25/8/47) ..	60	60
8	2/–	**yellow-green**	5·00	8·00
		a green (16/7/43) ..	4·00	5·00
		b dp green (26/8/48) ..	4·50	5·50
9	5/–	**lake**	4·00	4·50
		a crim-lake (16/7/43) ..	3·50	4·50

(b) Perf. 11¾ x 13 (C). Printers (*recess*) **De La Rue.**

10	½d.	**green**	10	20
11	2d.	**violet**	35	35

12	6d.	dp olive-green	..	1·25	2·00
	a	brn-olive (8/7/47)		1·00	1·25
13	1/-	chestnut-brown	..	1·50	2·00
	a	red-brn (17/12/45)		1·50	2·00
14	10/-	chocolate	.. ..	8·00	5·50
	a	sepia (12/3/45)	..	9·00	8·00
1/14		set (14)	.. ..	£18	£20
SP1/14		specimen set (14)		£75	‡

As No. 1 but Perf. 13½ x 12¼ (L).

| 15 | ¼d. | orange (16/7/43) | .. | 15 | 30 |

As Nos. 10–14 but Perf. 14 (L).

16	½d.	green (16/7/43)	..	10	20
	a	yellow-green	..	15	25
17	2d.	violet (16/7/43)	..	20	30
18	6d.	dp ol-grn (16/7/43)		75	60
19	1/-	red-brn (16/7/43)	..	1·00	1·20
20	10/-	choc-brn (16/7/43)	..	8·00	£11
	a	sepia-brown			
		(17/12/45) ..	..	9·00	£12

1950 (Oct. 2nd) Designs, ¼d. (Cat Boat); ½d., 1½d., 6d., 9d. (Island Views and Scenes); 1d. (Turtle); 2d. (Cayman Seamen); 2½d. (Map of Islands); 3d. (Parrot Fish); 1/- (Turtles in "Crawl"); 2/- ("Ziroma"); 5/- (Boat-building); 10/- (Government Offices, Grand Cayman). Printers (*recess*), Bradbury, Wilkinson. Perf. 11½ x 11¼ (C). Sheets 5 x 12.

21	¼d.	ultramarine and rose		25	35
22	½d.	purple and green	..	25	35
23	1d.	olive and dp grey-blue		40	50
24	1½d.	grn and greyish-brn .		30	35
25	2d.	purple and lake-car ..		40	50

26	2½d.	turquoise and grey	..	60	30
27	3d.	emerald and light blue		1·00	1·00
28	6d.	red-brown and dp blue		1·00	1·00
29	9d.	car-red and grey-grn		2·00	2·00
30	1/-	brn and orange red ..		2·00	2·50
31	2/-	grey-vio and dull lake		3·50	4·50
32	5/-	olive and grey-violet		5·00	7·00
33	10/-	black and rose	..	8·00	£10
21/33		set (13)	.. ..	£22	£28

SPECIAL ISSUES.

1937 (May 13th) Coronation. As Aden, but Printers Bradbury, Wilkinson. Perf. 11 x 11¾ (C).

S1	½d.	green	.. ..	40	20
S2	1d.	carmine	.. ..	40	40
S3	2½d.	deep blue	.. ..	75	1·00
SP S1/3		specimen set perf (3)		£20	‡

1946 (Aug. 26th) Victory. As Aden.

S4	1½d.	black	.. ..	15	15
	a	row 1/3 re-entry thickening of top frame lines above and below IS of Islands	..	5·00	5·00
S5	3d.	yellow-orange	..	15	15
	a	stop after date	..	5·00	5·00
SP S4/5		specimen set perf (2)		£20	‡

SP5a—A full stop appears after the date Row 2/1.

1948 (Nov. 29th) Silver Wedding. As Aden.

| S6 | ½d. | green | .. .. | 15 | 15 |
| S7 | 10/- | slate-violet | .. | 8·00 | £10 |

1949 (Oct. 10th) U.P.U. As Aden.

S8	2½d.	orange-yellow	..	25	35
S9	3d.	indigo	.. ..	40	50
S10	6d.	dull olive	..	50	1·00
S11	1/-	beech-brown	..	1·00	1·50
S8/11		set (4) ..	..	2·00	3·00

CEYLON

All stamps printed (*recess*) by De La Rue,
unless otherwise stated.

1938-49 Designs, 2r. (Guard Stone, Anuradhapura), Other Values (Views and Scenes
in Ceylon), Wmk. upright except where indicated S (*sideways*). Paper of varying thickness. Designs 2c., 5c., 6c., 20c., 2r., V. Sheets
6 x 10 or 10 x 6.

(a) Perf. 11¾ x 13 (C).

1 2c. **blk and car** (25/4/38)	1·00	20
2 3c. **blk and dp blue-grn**		
(21/3/38)	2·00	20
3 50c. **blk and pur-vio**		
(25/4/38)	£17	4·00

(b) Perf. 11¼ x 11½ (C). Printers (*recess*)
Bradbury, Wilkinson.

4 2c. **blk and dp-car**		
(17/2/44)	10	10
a blk and car (23/7/45)	10	10
b wmk. inverted ..	—	£50
5 3c. **blk and dp-grn**		
(14/5/42)	10	10
a blk and grn (19/2/43)	15	15
6 6c. **blk and grey-blue**		
(1/1/38)	10	10
a black and steel-blue		
(22/9/47) ..	10	15
7 10c. **black and light blue**		
(S) (1/2/38) ..	15	15
a blk and light-blue		
(1/6/44) ..	15	15
b blk and slate-blue		
(7/7/48) ..	15	15
8 15c. **green and red-brown**		
(S) (1/1/38) ..	10	15
a green and maroon (S)		
(4/9/42) ..	20	15
b dp grn and red-brn		
(23/7/45) ..	20	15
9 20c. **black and slate-blue**		
(15/1/38) ..	15	15
10 25c. **dp prussion-blue and**		
choc (S) (15/1/38)	10	15
a blue-black and red-		
brn (S) (19/2/43)	1·00	75
b dp prussian-blue and		
chocolate (/44) ..	20	15
c dp blue and chocolate		
(4/12/47) ..	20	15
d dk blue and dk brown		
(22/6/49) ..	10	15
11 30c. **car and dp green** (S)		
(1/2/38)	1·00	70
a car and dp green		
(16/4/45) ..	90	60
12 50c. **blk and red-purple-**		
violet (14/5/42) ..	40	15

a black and purple ..	40	15
b black and violet ..	40	15
13 1r. **dk violet and choc**		
(S) (1/2/38) ..	1·50	50
a dk vio and choc (/44)	1·50	50
14 2r. **blk and rose-car**		
(1/2/38)	1·00	50
15 2r. **blk and vio** (15/3/47)	90	50
SP1/15 **specimen set** (inc. 29)		
perf (14)	£40	‡

Bradbury, Wilkinson took over printing of 2c.,
3c., 50c. from De La Rue, when works of latter firm
was bombed.

**(c) Perf. 13½ (C). (As Nos. 1-3 plus 5c.
"Palm" Design).**

16 2c. **blk and car** (25/4/38)	10	15
17 3c. **blk and dp blue-grn**		
(21/3/38)	15	15
18 5c. **sage and orange**		
(1/1/43)	35	15
19 50c. **blk and pur-vio**		
(25/4/38)	1·00	40

(d) Perf. 13½ x 13 (C). As Nos. 1-3.

20 2c. **blk and car** (/38) ..	3·00	20
21 3c. **blk and dp blue-grn**		
(/38)	£30	50
22 50c. **blk and pur-vio** (/38)	£18	2·00

As Nos. 2 and 3 but Perf. 14 (L).

23 3c. **blk and dp blue-grn**		
(7/41)	6·00	50
24 50c. **blk and pur-vio** (4/42)	5·00	2·00

As Nos. 1-3 and 18 but Perf. 12 (C).

25 2c. **blk and car** (22/4/49)	10	15
26 3c. **blk and dp blue-grn**		
(14/1/46)	10	15
27 5c. **sage and orange** (/47)	15	15
a pale sage and red-		
orange (8/3/48) ..	15	15
28 50c. **blk and pur-vio**		
(14/1/46)	50	20

No. 5*a* is on thinner paper than No. 5.
10*b* First London release, 16/4/45.
13*a* First London release, 14/1/46.

1938-52 Perf. 13¾ x 14 (C) (*typo*). Sheets 120—
two panes each 6 x 10.

29 5r. **grn and dp pur-brn**		
(10/10/38)	3·00	1·00
a grn and lt pur-brn		
(sub) (19/2/43) ..	2·50	75
b grn and dp brn-plum		
(ch) (11/9/50) ..	2·50	75
30 10r. **grey-grn and orange**		
(ch) (1/2/52) ..	6·00	5·00
1/30 **set** cheapest perfs (14)	£12	8·00

30—First issued for revenue purposes, it was subsequently authorised for postal use from 1 December
52—14 March 54, The word Revenue appears
on side panels.

1940-1. Nos. 6 and 9 surcharged 3 cents.

31	3c./6c. **blk and grey-blue** (16/5/41) ..	20	10
32	3c./20c. **black and slate-blue** (5/11/40) ..	20	30

Number issued—
3c/6c., 1,800,000; 3c./20c., 900,000.

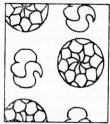

1950 (Feb. 4th) Designs, 4c. (Dancer); 15c. (Vesak Orchid); Other Values (Views and Scenes in Ceylon). Printers (recess) Bradbury, Wilkinson. Wmk. "Lotus Flowers and Sri". Design, 1r., H. Sheets 10 x 5.

(a) Perf. 12 x 12¾ (C).

34	4c. **pur-brn and dp scar**	10	10
35	5c. **green** ..	10	10
38	15c. **dp emer and pur-vio**	15	10
39	30c. **yel and car-red** ..	20	15

(b) Perf. 11¼ x 11½ (C).

40	75c. **ult and vermilion** ..	35	15
41	1r. **indigo and brown** ..	40	20
34/41	**set (6)**	1·25	75

1951-4 Designs, 2c. (Ruhuna National Park);

3c. (Ancient Guard Stone, Anuradhapura); 6c. and 10r. (Harvesting Rice); 10c. (Coconut Palms); 10c. (King Coconuts); 25c. (Sioiviya Fresco); 35c. (Star Orchid, Phaius bicolor); 40c. (Rubber Plantation); 50c. (Outrigger Canoe); 85c. (Tea Plantation); 2r. River Gal Dam); 5r. (Bas-relief, Anuradhapura). Printers (photo) Courvoisier, Switzerland. Perf. 11¾ (C). No wmk. Granite paper. Designs, 40c., 50c., 2r. Hor. Sheets 10 x 10.

42	2c. **brown and blue-green** (15/5/54)	10	10
43	3c. **blk and vio** (15/5/54)	10	10
44	6c. **sepia-black and green** (15/5/54)	10	10
45	10c. **grey and dp green** (1/8/51)	10	10
45a	10c. **orange and brown** (1/12/54)	10	10
46	25c. **orange and ult.** (15/3/56)	10	10
47	35c. **brn-red and dk gren** (Type 1) (1/2/52) (a)	25	10
	a ditto (Type 2) (/54?)	20	10
48	40c. **dk brown** (15/5/54)..	15	10
49	50c. **bluish-slate** (15/3/54)	15	10
50	85c. **black and gry-green** (15/5/54)	30	15
51	2r. **sepia brown and lt blue** (15/5/54) ..	75	30
52	5r. **brown and orange** (15/3/54)	1·50	50
53	10r. **brown** (15/3/54)	5·00	1·50
42/53	**set (12)**	7·50	3·00

47 Type 1—No dot above third character, second line in Tamil.
Type 2—Dot added in corrected inscription

SPECIAL ISSUES

1937 (May 12th) Coronation. As Aden but Printers (recess) Bradbury, Wilkinson. Perf. 11 x 11½ (C).

S1	6c. **carmine-red**	10	10
S2	9c. **green**	15	25
S3	20c. **deep blue**	35	35
SP S1/3	**specimen set** perf (3)	£15	‡

1946 (Dec. 10th) Victory. As Aden.

S4	6c. **deep blue**	10	15
S5	15c. **brown**	10	15
	a reddish-brown ..	20	20
SP S4/5	**specimen set** perf (2)	£15	‡

1947 (Nov. 25th) New Constitution. Designs

COOK ISLANDS

(Views in Ceylon). Designers, R. Tenison and M. S. V. Rodrigo. Printers (recess) Bradbury, Wilkinson. Perf. 11¾ x 11 (C). Designs, 10c., 25c., V. Sheets S6, S8, 5 x 12; S7, S9, 10 x 6.

S6	6c. black and blue ..	10	15
S7	10c. blk,orange and car ..	15	20
S8	15c. myrtle-grey and fuchsia	20	25
S9	25c. ochre and em-green	30	30
SP56/9	specimen set perf (4)	£40	‡

Number issued—
6c., 8,000,000; 10c., 3,000,000; 15c., 1,250,000; 25c., 1,200,000.

1949 First Anniversary of Independence. Designs, 4c. and 15c. (Dominion Flag); 5c. and 25c. (Dr. S. Senanayake, Prime Minister). Printers (recess, but flag typo) Bradbury, Wilkinson. Perf. 12¾ x 12½ (C). 15c.; Perf. 12 x 12¾ (C) (Other Values). Wmk. "Script C.A." (4c. and 5c.) and "Lotus Flowers and Sri" (15c. and 25c.). Designs, 5c., 25c., V. Sheets 10 x 10.

S10	4c. yellow, carmine and lt brown (4/2/49)	10	15
S11	5c. sepia and myrtle (4/2/49) ..	15	20
S12	15c. yellow, carmine and salmon (5/4/49) .	25	20
S13	25c. sepia and blue (5/4/49)	25	25
S10/13	set (4)	75	75

Number issued (locally)—
4c., 9,171,071; 5c., 16,755,839; 15c., 1,393,777; 25c., 1,176,963·

1949 (Oct. 10th) U.P.U. Designs (Globe and Methods of Mail Transport). Printers (recess) De La Rue. Wmk. "Lotus Flowers and Sri". Perf. 12 (C) (5c. and 15c.) and Perf. 13¼ x 13 (C) (25c.). Design, 25c., H. Sheets 5 x 10 or 10 x 5.

S14	5c. choc and myrtle-grn	15	15
S15	15c. blk and car-lake ..	40	20
S16	25c. grey-black and ult..	50	20
S14/16	set (3)	1·00	50

Number issued (locally)—5c., 14,436,792; 15c., 1,097,631; 25c., 1,601,542.

1933-38 Designs. 1/- (Portrait of King from photo by B. Park); Other Values (Island Scenes). Designer, J. Berry. Printers (recess) Govt. Printing Office, Wellington (from plates engraved by Bradbury, Wilkinson). Wmk. "N.Z. Star" (single). Perf. 14 (L). Sheets 8 x 10 or 10 x 8.

X1	½d. black and green ..	30	40
X2	1d. black and scarlet ..	35	45
X3	2d. black and brown ..	40	50
X4	2½d. black and blue ..	50	60
X5	4d. black and bt blue	60	60
X6	6d. black and orange ..	1·00	1·00
1	1/- black and violet ..	75	1·00
2	2/- blk and reddish-choc	1·75	2·50
3	3/- blue and em-grn ..	3·50	4·00
X1/3	set (9)	9·00	£11

Number Printed—

X1, 591,040; X2, 535,600; X3, 552,800; X4, 72,240; X5, 55,200; X6, 70,000; 1/2, 60,000 each; 3, 40,000.

1940 (Sept. 2nd) Printers (recess) Bradbury. Wilkinson. Wmk. "N.Z. Star" (mult). Perf. 13½ x 14 (C). Sheets 8 x 10.

4	3d./1½d. blk and red-pur ..	10	15

A change in postal rates prior to issue created a demand for a 3d. stamp, hence the surcharging. This stamp was not issued without surcharge.

Number Issued—343,520.

1943-50 Designs, as New Zealand No. PF48, etc. (Arms of Dominion type) overprinted COOK ISLANDS in red or black. Wmk. "NZ. Star" (mult). Perf. 14 (C).

5	2/6 brown (3/46) ..	2·00	3·00
	a wmk. inv. ..	2·00	4·00

6	5/–	green (red) (11/43)	3·00	3·50
		a wmk. inv.	3·00	4·00
7	10/–	rose-car (10/48) ..	8·00	9·00
		a wmk. inv.	9·00	£12
8	20/–	dull pink (11/47) ..	£10	£12
		aa wmk. inv.	£12	£16
8a	£3	green (red) (28/5/53)	£30	£35
		b wmk. inv. ..	£30	£40
8c	£5	blue (red) (25/10/50)	£60	£70
		d wmk. inv.	£50	£80
5/8c		set (6)	£105	£130

**1944-6 Designs, ½d. (Capt. Cook landing); 1d.
(Capt. Cook); 2d. (Maori Canoe); 2½d.
(Working Cargo); 4d. (Port Avarua); 6d.
(R.M.S. "Monowai"). Designer, L. Mitchell.
Printers** (*recess*) **Govt. Printing Office.
Wellington** (*from plates engraved by Perkins.
Bacon*). 1/– **to** 3/– (*as Nos.* 1—3). **Wmk. "N.Z.
Star"** (*mult*) (*sideways* ¼d., 1d., 1/– *and* 2/–).
**Perf. 14 (L). Designs, 2d., 2½d., 4d., 6d., 2/-,
3/- H. Sheets 8 x 10 or 10 x 8.**

9		½d. blk and myr-grn		
		(11/44)	30	20
10		1d. blk and dp car (3/45)	15	15
11		2d. blk and lt brn (2/46)	40	35
12		2½d. blk and grey-blue		
		(5/45)	40	30
13		4d. blk and dp blue		
		(4/44)	30	40
14		6d. blk and or (6/44) ..	35	35
15		1/– blk and violet (9/44)	40	40
16		2/– black and chest		
		(8/45)	80	1·00
17		3/– blue and em-grn		
		(6/45)	2·00	2·50
9/17		set (9)	5·00	5·50

Number Issued—½d. 494,760; 1d. 518,720;
2d. 321, 440; 2½d 151, 600; 4d. 122,960; 6d.
119,760; 1/– 110,560; 2/– 99,040; 3/– 79,120.

**1949 (Aug. 1st) Designs, 1d. Capt. Cook and
Map, Hervey Is.); 2d. (Rev. J. Williams and
Map, Rarotonga); 3d. (Map, Aitutaki and
Palms); 1/- (Map and statue of Capt. Cook);
3/- (M.V. "Matua"; Other Values (Views and
Scenes). Designer, J. Berry, Printers** (*recess*)
Waterlow & Sons. Wmk. "N.Z. Star" (*mult*).

**Perf. 13¼ x 13½ (C). Designs, 1/-, 2/-, 3/- V.
Sheets 12 x 10 or 10 x 12.**

21		½d. pur-vio and red-brn	15	25
22		1d. orange-brn and grn	35	35
23		2d. choc and dp crimson	25	30
24		3d. em-grn and ult	20	30
		a wmk. sideways ..	75	1·00
25		5d. emerald and violet	60	90
26		6d. black and carmine	35	40
27		8d. sage and orange	60	80
		a wmk. inverted	—	—
28		1/– pl blue and choc-brn	1·00	1·20
29		2/– yel-brn and car-rose	2·50	2·75
30		3/– pl blue and blue grn	3·00	3·50
21/30		set (10)	9·00	£10

SPECIAL ISSUES

**1937 (June 1st) Coronation. New Zealand,
Nos. S1—3, overprinted COOK ISLANDS.**

S1	1d. carmine	.. ..	10	10
S2	2½d. dp blue	.. ..	15	15
S3	6d. reddish-orange	..	20	30

Number Issued—1d. 737,572; 2½d. 569,108;
6d. 541,657.

**1946 (June 1st) Peace. New Zealand, Nos.
S19, etc. overprinted COOK ISLANDS in
blue or black.**

S4	1d. emerald-green	..	10	10
S5	2d. purple (blue)	..	10	15
S6	6d. choc and vermilion		15	15
S7	8d. black and lake (blue)		20	25
S4/7	set (4)		50	60

Number Printed—1d. 720,000; 2d. 720,000;
6d. 480,000; 8d. 480,000.

CYPRUS

Cyprus came under British Administration following the Treaty of Berlin, and the first British Post Office was opened in Larnaca on July 27th, 1878. Until 1881 contemporary G.B. stamps were used and were cancelled by Town Numerals in upright ovals of horizontal bars.

1878-1881 Stamps of Great Britain identified by their Catalogue Nos. after prefixes 'LC', 'NS', 'KY', 'LM', 'PS', 'FG', 'PY' or 'HQ'.

(I) Used at Larnaca : '942'

LC V108	½d.	**rose-red** (Various Plates) ..
LC V49	1d.	**rose-red** (Various Plates) ..
LC V111	1½d.	**lake-red** (Pl. 3)
LC V51	2d.	**blue** (Pl. 9) ..
LC V52	2d.	**blue** (Various Plates) ..
LC V122	2½d.	**rosy mauve** (Various Plates) ..
LC V123	2½d.	**blue** (Various Plates) ..
LC V139	2½d.	**blue** (Pl. 21) ..
LC V133	4d.	**sage-green** (Pl. 15, 16) ..
LC V115	6d.	**pale buff** (Pl. 11)
LC V126	6d.	**grey** (Various Plates) ..
LC V136	8d.	**orange** ..
LC V127	1/–	**green** (Pl. 12, 13)
LC V143	1/–	**orange-brown** (Pl. 14) ..
LC V101	5/–	**rose** .. ..

(II) Used at Nicosia : '969'

NS V108	½d.	**rose-red** (Various Plates).. ..
NS V49	1d.	**rose-red** (Various Plates).. ..
NS V52	2d.	**blue** (Pl. 14, 15)
NS V122	2½d.	**rosy mauve** (Various Plates) ..
NS V123	2½d.	**blue** (Pl. 20) ..
NS V139	2½d.	**blue** (Pl. 21) ..
NS V131	4d.	**vermilion** (Pl. 15)
NS V133	4d.	**sage-green** (Pl. 16) .. ..
NS V126	6d.	**grey** (Pl. 16) ..

(III) Used at Kyrenia : '974' (to 1880)

KY V108	½d.	**rose-red** (Pl. 1)
KY V49	1d.	**rose-red** (Various Plates) ..
KY V52	2d.	**blue** (Pl. 13, 15)
KY V122	2½d.	**rosy mauve** (Various Plates) ..
KY V133	4d.	**sage-green** (Pl. 16) ..
KY V126	6d.	**grey** (Pl. 16) ..

(IV) Used at Limassol : '975' (to 1880)

LM V108	½d.	**rose-red** (Various Plates) ..
LM V49	1d.	**rose-red** (Various Plates) ..
LM V111	1½d.	**lake-red** (Pl. 3)
LM V52	2d.	**blue** (Pl. 14, 15)
LM V122	2½d.	**rosy mauve** (Various Plates) ..

LM V123	2½d.	**blue** (Various Plates) ..
LM V133	4d.	**sage-green** (Pl. 16) ..

(V) Used at Paphos : '981'

PS V108	½d.	**rose-red** (Pl. 13 15) .. ..
PS V49	1d.	**rose-red** (Various Plates) ..
PS V52	2d.	**blue** (Pl. 15) ..
PS V122	2½d.	**rosy mauve** (Various Plates) ..

(VI) Used at Famagusta : '982'

FG V108	½d.	**rose-red** (Pl. 11, 13) ..
FG V49	1d.	**rose-red** (Various Plates).. ..
FG V52	2d.	**blue** (Various Plates).. ..
FG V122	2½d.	**rosy mauve** (Pl. 13, 16) ..
FG V126	6d.	**grey** (Pl. 15) ..
FG V127	1/–	**green** (Pl. 12) ..
FG V143	1/–	**orange-brown** (Pl. 14) ..

(VII) Used at Polymedia (Limassol) : 'D 47' (with 3 bars) (to 1880).

PY V108	½d.	**rose-red** (Pl. 11)
PY V49	1d.	**rose-red** (Various Plates) ..
PY V52	2d.	**blue** (Pl. 15) ..

(VIII) Used at Head-Quarter Camp (Nicosia) : 'D48' (with 3 bars) (to 1880).

HQ V108	½d.	**rose-red** (Pl. 13, 20) .. ..
HQ V49	1d.	**rose-red** (Various Plates) ..
HQ V52	2d.	**blue** (Pl. 15) ..

'D47' and 'D 48' cancellers with *four* bars above and *four* bars below were used in Great Britain.

1880 (April 1st) Stamps of Great Britain (QV) overprinted "CYPRUS" in black sans-serif capitals by De La Rue.

V1	½d.	**rose (Pl. 12, 15, 19)**		
		from	£40	£45
		a overprint double (Pl 15)	—	£1500
V2	1d.	**red (Pl. 174–220)**		
		from	5·00	£10
		a overprint double (Pl. 208).. ..	£1300	—
		b overprint double (Pl. 218).. ..	£980	—
		c overprint omitted in pair with normal (Pl. 208).. ..	£3000	—
V3	2½d.	**rosy-mauve (Pl. 14, 15)** from	1·00	1·50
		a large thin "C" (Pl. 14, 15) from ..	£10	9·00
		b wmk. inverted (Pl. 15)	£12	£10

V4	4d.	**sage-green (Pl. 16)**		£90	£85
V5	6d.	**grey (Pl. 16)**	..	£175	£135
V6	1/–	**green (Pl. 13)**	..	£425	£225
V1/6		**set** (6v)	..	£650	£475

V2*c* comes from a sheet which lacked the overprint on the top row of twelve.

V1 (Pl. 12), V2 (Pl. 216), V3 (Pl. 14) and V4–V6 exist handstamped "Specimen".

Numbers Issued—V1, 68,640; V2, 338,880; V3, 319,584; V4, 13,449; V5, 3,360; V6, 2,280.

1881 No. V2 surcharged in black at the Government Printing Office. Nicosia.

(a) February: HALF-PENNY measures 18mm.

V7	½d. on 1d.	**red (Pl. 174-220)**			
		from	.. ..	£18	£17
		a "Y" omitted (all			
		plates) from		£300	£260

(b) April. No hyphen. 16–16½mm.

V8	½d. on 1d.	**red (Pl. 201, 216, 218)** from	..	£40	£48
		a surcharge double (Pl. 201)	..	£725	—

(c) June. 13mm.

V9	½d. on 1d.	**red (Pl. 201, 205, 215, 217, 218)** from	.. ..	£14	£18
		a surcharge double (Pl. 201)	..	—	—
		b surcharge double (Pl. 205)	..	£225	—
		c surcharge double (Pl. 215)	..	£200	£200
		d surcharge treble (Pl. 205)	..	—	—
		e surcharge treble (Pl. 215)	..	£250	—
		f surcharge treble (Pl. 217)	..	—	—
		g surcharge treble (Pl. 218)	..	—	—
		surcharge quadruple (Pl. 205)			
		h ruple (Pl. 205)		£700	—
		surcharge quadruple (Pl. 215)		£625	—
		overprint ("CYPRUS") double (Pl. 218)	.. ..	£1100	—

V7*a* is from Row 2/7.

The above provisionals were all withdrawn on July 1st, 1881.

(d) June. "30 PARAS".

V10	30pa. on 1d.	**red (Pl. 201, 216, 217, 220)** from	.. ..	£45	£37
		a surcharge double, one inverted (Pl. 216)	..	£850	—
		b surcharge double, one inverted (Pl. 220)	..	£575	£550

All stamps from V11 to G69 are (*typo*) De La Rue. Perf. 14. Sheets, 240 – four panes, each 6 x 10.

See Introduction for details of Dies I and II.

1881 (July 1st) Wmk. Crown CC. Die I.

V11	½pi.	**emerald-green**	..	£85	£30
		a imperf.	.. ..	£450	—
		b wmk. inverted	..	—	—
V12	1pi.	**carmine**	.. ..	£90	£30
V13	2pi.	**blue** ..	.. ..	£90	£30
V14	4pi.	**pl olive-green**	..	£300	£90
		a imperf.	.. ..	—	—
V15	6pi.	**olive-grey** ..	..	£400	£120
V11/15		**set** (5v)	.. ..	£800	£275

Die Proofs in black on glazed card, and imperf. Imprimaturs are known for all values.

All except V12 exist overprinted "Specimen".

Numbers Issued—V11, 199,800; V12, 101,340; V13, 180,840; V14, 10,800; V15, 5,760.

Various QV stamps may be found overprinted "POSTAL SURCHARGE" and/or initialled "J. A. B." The initials are those of J. A. Bulmer, Postmaster from August, 1879 to May, 1883, who used such stamps for accounting purposes.

$$\frac{1}{2} \qquad \frac{1}{2} \qquad \frac{1}{2} \qquad \frac{1}{2}$$

Local Type   **London Type**

1882 Nos. V11 and V12 surcharged in black.

(a) Local Type at Government Printing Office, Nicosia.

V16	½ on ½pi.	**emerald-green**	£75	£20

(b) By De La Rue. Fractions 8½mm. apart.

V17	½ on ½pi.	**emerald-green**	£1500	£225
		a small "1" at right	£2500	£900
		b large "1" at left	£4000	£600

(c) By De La Rue. Fractions 6–7mm. apart.

V18	½ on ½pi.	**emerald-green**	£1500	—

(d) May 22nd (Government Printing Office). "30 PARAS".

V19	30pa. on 1pi.	**rose**	£380	£100
		a surcharge double, one inverted ..	—	—

1882-84 As V11 etc. but wmk. Crown CA. (Die I).

V20	½pi.	emerald-green ..	£1000	£120
V21	½pi.	dull green ..	2·25	50
V22	30pa.	pl mauve (6/82) ..	£10	8·00
V23	1pi.	carmine	£14	2·00
V24	2pi.	blue ..	£22	2·00
V25	4pi.	pale olive-green..	£60	£12
V26	4pi.	deep olive-green	£65	£12
V27	6pi.	olive-grey ..	£18	8·00
V28	12pi.	orange-brn ('84)	£60	£17
V20/28		set (7v)	£165	£45
SPV28		specimen (I) ..	£40	‡

Die Proofs of V22, bi-coloured and imperf. exist as Essays for the subsequent 1894 issue.

1882-86 No. V20 surcharged, as before, in black.

(a) Local Type at Government Printing Office, Nicosia.

V29	½ on ½pi.	emerald-green	£30	£700
	a	surcharge double ..	—	£425
	b	one fraction omitted ..	—	—

(b) By De La Rue. Fractions 8½mm. apart.

V30	½ on ½pi.	emerald-green	£55	7·00
	a	small "1" at right	£600	£120
	b	large "1" at left	£425	£100

(c) By De La Rue. Fractions 6–7mm. apart.

V31	½ on ½pi.	emerald-green..	£60	£28

Care should be taken when acquiring used copies.

1886 As V20/V28 but Die II.

V32	½pi.	dull green	1·50	50
V33	30pa.	mauve	1·50	1·25
V34	1pi.	carmine	4·25	1·50
V35	2pi.	blue	6·50	1·00
V36	4pi.	pale olive-green..	£11	4·50
V37	4pi.	olive-green ..	£22	5·00
	a	inscriptions omitted ..	—	—
V38	6pi.	olive-grey ..	£40	£60
V39	12pi.	orange-brown ..	£40	£40
V32/39		set (7v)	£120	£105

V37a (blank upper and lower tablets) were used at Troodos.

V39 exists overprinted "Specimen".

Numbers Issued—V20/V28 and V32/V39 (combined figures) ½p., 2,840,040; 30pa., 187,920; 1pi., 323,460;; 2pi., 802,860; 4pi., 79,200; 6pi., 48,240; 12pi., 19,000.

1894 (Aug. 8th)-96 As before (Die II).

V40	½pi.	green and carmine	1·50	40
V41	30pa.	br mauve and grn	1·50	40
V42	1pi.	carmine and blue	2·00	40
V43	2pi.	blue and purple ..	2·00	50
V44	4pi.	green and purple	4·50	2·00
V45	6pi.	sepia and green	4·50	3·00
V46	9pi.	brn and car (8/94)	8·00	4·50

V47	12pi.	or-brn and blk ..	7·50	£14
V48	18pi.	sl and brn (8/94)	£20	£14
V49	45pi.	grey-pur and blue (8/94)	£35	£35
V40/49		set (10v)	£80	£70
SPV40/49		specimen set (10v)	£130	‡

Essays exist with values in Shillings; and Die Proofs of all values are known in black on glazed card.

1903 Wmk. Crown CA.

E1	½pi.	green and carmine	1·75	60
	a	wmk. inverted ..	£15	—
E2	30pa.	mauve and green	1·00	1·00
E3	1pi.	carmine and blue	4·75	1·50
E4	2pi.	blue and purple ..	£11	3·50
E5	4pi.	ol-grn and pur ..	£17	6·00
E6	6pi.	sepia and green ..	£30	£32
E7	9pi.	brn and carmine	£60	£70
E8	12pi.	chest and black ..	8·00	£10
E9	18pi.	black and brown	£50	£60
E10	45pi.	dl purple and blue	£150	£200
E1/10		set (10v)	£325	£350
SPE1/10		specimen set (10v)	£175	‡

Die Proofs without value exist in black on glazed paper; and imperforate Plate Proofs in issued colours.

Numbes Issued—E7, 2,400; E9, 3,600; E10, 2,400.

1904-10 As before, but wmk. Multiple Crown CA.

E11	5pa.	bistre and black (1/08)	25	50
E12	10pa.	orange and green (12/06)	60	75
E13	10pa.	yellow and green	£14	7·50
E14	½pi.	green and car ..	50	20
	a	wmk. inverted ..	£12	—
E15	30pa.	purple and green	2·50	1·00
E16	30pa.	vio and grn ('10)	2·75	1·00
E17	1pi.	carmine and blue	75	40
E18	2pi.	blue and purple	1·75	50
E19	4pi.	ol-grn and pur ..	9·00	3·25
E20	6pi.	sepia and green	8·50	4·00
E21	9pi.	brown and car ..	3·75	4·25
	a	wmk. inverted ..	£25	—
E22	9pi.	choc and car ..	3·75	4·25
E23	12pi.	chest and black ('06)	£18	£12
E24	18pi.	black and brown	£22	8·00
E25	45pi.	purple and blue	£35	£32
E11/10		set (12v)	£95	£60
SPE11/E13		specimen set (2)	£50	‡

Imperforate examples of E15 in various colour are Colour Trials.

1912-23 Wmk. Multiple Crown CA.

G1	10pa.	orange and green	70	90
		a wmk. sideways	£15	—
G2	10pa.	yel-or and br-grn	1·00	90
G3	10pa.	brn-or and grn ..	1·00	90
G4	½pi.	green and car ..	90	80
G5	½pi.	yel-grn and car..	1·25	80
G6	30pa.	violet and green	90	70
G7	1pi.	carmine and blue	1·25	80
G8	1pi.	rose-car and blu	4·75	2·00
G9	1pi.	dp rose-car and blue	4·75	2·00
G10	2pi.	blue and purple	2·50	1·00
G11	4pi.	ol-grn and pur ..	2·50	1·00
G12	6pi.	sepia and green	2·50	1·25
G13	9pi.	brown and car ..	£11	8·00
G14	9pi.	pl brn and car ('14)	£12	£10
G15	12pi.	chestnut and blk	4·00	5·00
G16	18pi.	blk and brn ('14)	£11	£11
G17	45pi.	pu and blu ('14)	£30	£30
G18	10s.	grn and red/yel ('23)	£350	£500
G19	£1	pur and blk/red ('23)	£950	£1200
G1/17		set (13v)	£1350	£1750
SPG1/17		specimen set (13v)	£375	‡

Many of the values G1 to G17 may be found on a bluish paper from war-time printings.

Number issued: G18 3,017.

1921-23 As before, but wmk. Multiple Script CA.

G20	10pa.	orange and green	50	70
G21	10pa.	grey and yellow ('22) ..	2·75	3·00
G22	30pa.	violet and green	80	50
G23	30pa.	green ('23) ..	1·25	75
G24	1pi.	carmine and blue	3·50	5·50
G25	1pi.	vio and red ('22)	2·75	3·00
G26	1½pi.	yel and blk ('22)	1·50	2·25
G27	2pi.	blue and purple	3·75	3·50
G28	2pi.	car and blu ('22)	4·25	5·50
G29	2¾pi.	blu and pur ('22)	5·50	7·00
G30	4pi.	ol-grn and pur ..	3·25	3·75
G31	6pi.	sepia and green	6·00	6·50
G32	9pi.	brown and car ..	£10	£15
		a yel brn and car	£15	£20
G33	18pi.	blk and brn ('23)	£50	£55
G34	45pi.	pur and blu ('23)	£85	£90
G20/34		set (15v)	£165	£175
SPG20/34		specimen set (15v)	£150	‡

Number Issued: G34 2,584.

1924-28 Wmk. Multiple Script CA (except £1 which is Multiple Crown CA).

G35	¼pi.	grey and chest ..	25	30
G36	½pi.	black	50	75
G37	½pi.	grn and dk grn (C)	50	50
G38	½pi.	blue-grn and grn	75	50
G39	½pi.	dp grn and grn ..	1·00	75
G40	¾pi.	yellow-green ..	50	85
G41	¾pi.	deep green ..	75	40
G42	¾pi.	black (C) ..	50	15
G43	¾pi.	grey and blk (C)	50	15
G44	1pi.	pur and chest ..	30	30
G45	1pi.	brown-purple and chestnut	40	40
G46	1½pi.	orange and black	70	1·00
G47	1½pi.	yel-or and blk ..	70	1·00
G48	1½pi.	scarlet	80	60
G49	1½pi.	deep scarlet ..	80	60
G50	2pi.	car and green ..	1·50	1·75
G51	2pi.	yel and blk (C)..	1·75	2·25
G52	2½pi.	bright blue ..	1·50	50
G53	2½pi.	dull blue ..	1·50	50
G54	2¾pi.	blue and purple	75	1·50
G55	4pi.	sage-grn and pur	1·25	1·75
G56	4½pi.	blk and brn-or/ emerald ..	2·25	3·90
G57	4½pi.	grey-blk and yel-or/emerald ..	2·25	3·00
G58	4½pi.	jet black and or/emerald ..	2·50	3·25
G59	6pi.	ol-brn and grn ..	2·25	3·00
G60	6pi.	ol-grey and blu-green	2·50	3·25
G61	6pi.	dp ol-grn and blue-green ..	2·50	3·25
G62	9pi.	brn and dl vio ..	2·50	3·50
G63	9pi.	choc and violet..	2·75	3·50
G64	12pi.	chest and black	3·50	9·50
G65	18pi.	black and orange	9·00	9·00
G66	45pi.	purple and blue	£14	£18
G67	90pi.	grn and red/yel..	£65	£70
G68	£1	pur and blk/red (C)	£175	£200
G69	£5	blk/yel ('28) ..	£3500	£2850
G35/69		set (22v)	£3700	£3200
SPG35/69		specimen set (22v)	£700	‡

1928 (Feb. 1st) 50th Anniversary of British Administration. (*Recess*) **Bradbury, Wilkinson. Wmk. Multiple Script CA. Perf. 12. Sheets 12 x 5 (V.), 10 x 6 (H.).**

G70	¾pi.	deep purple	55	30
G71	1pi.	black and blue ..	75	80
G72	1½pi.	scarlet	1·75	1·50
G73	2½pi.	light blue ..	75	1·25
G74	4pi.	brown	3·50	4·75
G75	6pi.	blue	4·25	5·50
G76	9pi.	maroon	3·75	3·75
G77	18pi.	black and brown	8·00	9·50
G78	45pi.	violet and blue ..	£25	£30
	a	pale lilac and blue	£25	£30
G79	£1	blue and brown..	£185	£185
G70/79		set (10v)	£225	£230
SPG70/79		specimen set		
		(10v)	£190	‡

Unsold remainders were withdrawn on January 31st 1929 and destroyed.

Colour trials were made in the following colours on unwatermarked paper, overprinted "B. W. & Co./ Specimen" (in red on 1p., 4p., 45p. and in black on other values).

¾p. bistre; 1pi. blue and black; 1½pi. deep brown; 2½pi. purple and brown; 4pi. blue; 6pi. violet; 9pi. green; 18pi. blue and orange; 45pi. black and brown; £1 purple and red.

1934 (Dec. 1st) (*Recess*) **Waterlow & Sons. Wmk. Multiple Script CA (sideways on G81, G84-89). Perf. 12½. Sheets 6 x 10.**

G80	¼pi.	ult and chestnut	15	35
	a	imperf between		
		(vert pair) ..	£2750	£2750
G81	½pi.	green	15	35
	a	imperf between		
		(vert pair) ..	£2500	£2500
	b	imperf between		
		stamp and upper		
		margin ..	—	—
G82	¾pi.	black and violet	20	15
	a	imperf between		
		(vert. pair) ..	£2750	—
G83	1pi.	black and brown	50	70
	a	imperf between		
		(hor. pair) ..	£2500	£2500
	b	imperf between		
		ver. pair ..	£2500	—
	c	imperf between		
		stamp and up-		
		per margin ..	—	—
G84	1½pi.	carmine	40	30
G85	2½pi.	ultramarine ..	50	70

G86	4½pi.	blk and crimson	2·50	1·25
G87	6pi.	black and blue ..	2·25	3·50
G88	9pi.	sepia and violet..	2·25	2·50
G89	18pi.	blk and ol-grn ..	£10	7·00
G90	45pi.	green and black	£35	£25
G80/90		set (11v)	£50	£38
SPG80/90		specimen set		
		(11v)	£60	‡

1935 (May 6th) Silver Jubilee. (*Recess*) **Waterlow & Sons. Wmk. Multiple Script CA. Perf. 11 x 12. Sheets 6 x 10.**

G91	¾pi.	ult and grey ..	15	15
G92	1½pi.	indigo and scarlet	1·25	1·25
G93	2½pi.	brown and blue..	3·25	3·75
G94	9pi.	slate and purple	6·50	7·50
G91/94		set (4v)	£10	£12
SPG91/94		specimen set (4v)	£24	‡

Unsold remainders were withdrawn on January 1st 1936 and destroyed.

1938 (May 12th) -55. Designs, 4½p. (Map of Cyprus); 45p. (Cyprian Forest Scene); 90p. and £1 (Portrait King George VI); Other Values (Ruins and Existing Buildings of Historical Importance). Printers (*recess*) **Waterlow & Sons. Perf. 12½ (L). Designs, 4½p., 6p., 9p., 18p., £1, V. Sheets 6 x 10.**

1	¼p.	ult and buff-bown..	15	10
	a	ult and red-brown		
		(16/7/45) ..	15	10
2	½p.	dp green	10	10
	a	green (16/10/44) ..	10	10
3	½p.	bright violet (2/7/51)	25	10
4	¾p.	black and pale violet	70	10
5	1p.	orange	25	10
6	1½p.	carmine-red ..	40	30
7	1½p.	bright violet (15/3/43)	15	10
8	1½p.	green (2/7/51) ..	60	15
9	2p.	blk and red (30/1/42)	15	10
10	2½p.	dp ultramarine ..	1·25	2·00
11	3p.	dp ult (30/1/42)	20	10
	a	dp vio-blue (19/8/47)	20	10
12	4p.	dp ult (2/7/51) ..	75	15
13	4½p.	grey	15	10

a slate-grey (16/10/44)	15	10		
14 6p. **black and pale blue**..	60	40		
a blk and celeste (4/42)	60	40		
15 9p. **black and dp purple**	35	20		
a black and bright red-purple (15/6/55) .	35	20		
16 18p. **blk and olive-green**..	70	50		
a black and dp. olive (16/10/44) ..	70	50		
b black and sage (19/8/47) ..	2·50	1·25		
17 45p. **green and black** ..	1·75	1·00		
18 90p. **mauve and black** ..	7·00	9·00		
19 £1 **scarlet and blue-blk**	£15	£15		
1/19 **set** (19)	£28	£26		
SP 1/19 **specimen set** perf (16)	£75	‡		

1944. As Nos. 5 and 9 but perforations changed.

Perf. 13½ x 12½ (L).

20 1p. **orange**	£60	8·00

Perf. 12½ x 13½ (L).

21 2p. **black and red** ..	25	20

SPECIAL ISSUES

1937 (May 12th) Coronation. As Aden, but Printers Bradbury, Wilkinson. Perf. 11 x 11¾ (C).

S1 ¾p. **grey**	25	10
S2 1½p. **carmine-red** ..	60	35
S3 2½p. **blue**	1·00	90
SP S1/3 **specimen set** perf (3)	£16	‡

1946 (Oct. 21st) Victory. As Aden.

S4 1½p. **slate-violet**	10	10
S5 3p. **grey-blue**	10	10
SP S4/5 **specimen set** perf (2)	£20	‡

1948 (Dec. 20th) Silver Wedding. As Aden.

S6 1½p. **bright violet**	15	15
a extra decoration ..	5·00	5 00
S7 £1 **bluish-slate**	£22	£25

S6*a* A flaw on breast of King appears as an extra medal on Row 3/5.

1949 (Oct. 10th) U.P.U. As Aden, but all recess.

S8 1½p. **dull violet**	30	40
S9 2p. **carmine**	50	65
S10 3p. **dull indigo**	1·00	1·25
S11 9p. **purple**	2·00	1·75
S8/11 **set** (4)	3·75	4·00

DOMINICA

The island was originally ceded to Great Britain by the Treaty of Paris in 1763; it was subsequently captured by the French and finally restored to Great Britain.

Following the use of other handstamps or manuscript marks, a Crowned Circle PAID Frank was registered at the G.P.O. in London on May 17th, 1845 and was thereafter struck in red to indicate prepayment of postage on overseas letters. (See Introduction).

From May, 1858 to March, 1860 contemporary G.B. stamps were in use and were cancelled with "AO7" in a transverse oval of horizontal bars.

The Crowned Circle Frank was again used from April 1st. 1860 until the first Dominican stamps were issued.

See also under Leeward Islands (until December 31st, 1939).

1845-74. PAID Frank   *On Cover*
VF1   £475

1858-60 Stamps of Great Britain identified by their Catalogue Nos. after prefix 'DM'.

Used at Roseau: 'A O7'.

DMV39	1d. **rose red**	—	—
DMV51	2d. **blue**	—	—
DMV45	6d. **lilac**	—	—
DMV47	1/– **green**	—	—

All stamps to G52 are (*typo*) **by De La Rue. Perf. 14, unless otherwise indicated.**

1874 (May 4th)-79. Wmk. Crown CC. Sheets 6 x 10.

(a) Perf. 12½.

V1	1d.	**lilac**	£120	£28
V2	6d.	**green**	£175	£40
V3	1/–	**dl magenta**	£175	£35
SPV1/V3		**specimen set** (3)	£250	‡

(b) Perf. 14.

V4	½d. **olive-yellow** ('79)		8·00	£10
V5	1d. **lilac** ('77)		4·00	3·00
	a bisect vert or diag (½d.)		—	£700
V6	2½d. **red-brown** ('79)		£75	£15
V7	4d. **blue** ('79)		£50	6·00
	a malformed 'CE'		£900	£175
V8	6d. **green** ('77)		£70	£12
	a malformed 'S'		£750	£150
V9	1/– **magenta**		£60	£25
V4/9	**set** (6v)		£260	£65
SPV4, 6, 7, 9	**specimen set** (4)		£250	‡

V7*a*—The 'C' in 'PENCE' is smaller than the other letters; and the second 'E' has weak middle and lower horizontal strokes, and is slightly squat.

Numbers issued—(1st printing) V1, 28,440: V2, 13,980: V3, 14,100: V4, 15,420.

Type I   Type II   Type III

1882-83. No. V5 bisected and surcharged.

(a) With Type I in black (25.11.82).

V10	½d. **on half 1d. lilac**		£50	£20
	a surcharge inverted		£300	£250

(b) With Type II in red (25.11.82).

V11	½d. **on half 1d. lilac**		£15	£15
	a surcharge inverted (13.8.84)		£300	£125
	b surcharge double		£750	—

(c) With Type III in black, reading upwards or downwards (March, 1883).

V12	½d. **on half 1d. lilac**		£20	£25
	a surcharge double		£325	—

1883-88. As Nos. V4/9 but Wmk. Crown CA.

V13	½d. **olive-yellow**		3·00	4·00
V14	½d. **dl green** ('86)		1·00	4·00
V15	1d. **lilac** ('86)		—	£750
	a bisect (½d.) on cover			
V16	1d. **rose** ('87)		4·00	5·00
V17	1d. **dp carmine**		1·50	2·00
	a large 'O' in 'ONE'		£80	—
	b bisect (½d.) on cover		—	£750
V18	2½d. **red-brown** ('84)		£55	£10
V19	2½d. **ultramarine** ('88)		3·00	3·00
V20	4d. **grey** ('86)		3·00	3·00
	a malformed 'CE'		£75	£90
V21	6d. **orange** ('88)		£10	£15
V22	1/– **dl magenta**		£100	£100
V13/22	**set** (9v)		£170	£140
SP.V14, 15, 19, 20, 21	**specimen set** (5)		£150	‡

V20*a*—See Note under V7*a*.

Numbers issued—V13, 15, 18, 19, 30,000 each: V14, 20, 30,420 each: V16/17, 30,000: V21, 6,000.

Half Penny

1886 (March). Nos. V8/9 surcharged in black.

V23	½d. on 6d. **green**		6·00	£10
V24	1d. on 6d. **green**		£10000	
	a horiz. bar thicker		—	£6500
V25	1d. on 1/– **mag** (6/86)		8·00	£10
	a surcharge double		—	£1200

V24 Twenty-one copies are known, of which only two are unused. On five of the used copies the horizontal bar in the surcharge is much thicker.

From November, 1890 until 1903 only the stamps of Leeward Islands were used in Dominica.

The following issues were in concurrent use with Leeward Islands stamps until December 31st, 1939, after which date Dominica came under the Windward Islands administration.

1903 (Sept.)-06. Wmk. Crown CC. (sideways except on E12). Sheets 5 x 12.

(a) Ordinary paper.

E1	½d.	green and grey-green	1·50	1·85
E2	½d.	green and dp green	1·50	1·85
E3	1d.	sepia and red ..	1·50	75
E4	1d.	grey and red ..	1·80	85
E5	2d.	green and brown ..	6·00	6·00
E6	2½d.	grey and bt blue ..	7·50	6·00
E7	3d.	dl pur and gr-blk ..	8·00	8·00
E8	6d.	grey and chestnut..	£10	£10
E9	1/–	mag and gr-grn ..	£18	£17
E10	2/–	gr-blk and purple ..	£18	£20
E11	2/6	gr-grn and maize ..	£18	£20
E12	5/–	black and brown ..	£90	£110
E1/12		set (10v)	£180	£200
SPE1/12		specimen set (10v)	£120	‡

(b) Chalky Paper (1906-07).

E13	½d.	grn and grey-grn ..	2·20	2·25
E14	1d.	grey and red ..	2·00	1·00
E15	2d.	green and brown ..	8·00	8·00
E16	2½d.	gr and bt bl (3.9.07)	9·00	9·50
E17	3d.	pur and grey black	9·00	9·50
E18	1/–	mag and grey-green	£60	£60
E13/18		set (6v)	£90	£90

Numbers printed—E1, 24,000: E2, 60,000: E3, 179,700: E4, 60,480: E5, 16,320: E6, 30,720: E7, 12,360: E8, 12,120: E9/10/11, 6,300 each: E12, 2,520: E13, 14,640: E14, 54,180: E15, 4,680: E16, 7,200: E17, 7,080: E18, 1,920.

1907-08. As before but Wmk. Multiple Crown CA (sideways except on E28). Chalky paper except E19 which exists also on Ordinary paper.

E19	½d.	green	1·00	1·00
	a	ordinary paper ..	1·25	1·50

E20	1d.	grey and red	1·00	60
E21	2d.	green and brown ..	6·00	6·00
E22	2½d.	grey and bt blue ..	9·00	£11
E23	3d.	dl pur and grey-black	9·00	£11
E24	6d.	blk and chnt ('08) ..	£35	£38
E25	1/–	mag and gr-grn ..	£15	£18
E26	2/–	gr-blk and purple ..	£27	£30
E27	2/6	gr-grn and maize ..	£30	£32
E28	5/–	black and brown ..	£50	£60
E19/28		set (10v)	£170	£195

Numbers printed—E19, 54,720: E20 140,280: E21, 15,900: E22, 14,880: E23, 14,340: E24 4,080: E25, 6,840: E26, 4,200: E27, 4,000: E28, 4,140.

1908-21. As before but changed colours and G15 portrays head of King George V. G1/8 on Ordinary paper. Certain stamps, although given a G prefix were in fact issued during the reign of King Edward VII.

G1	½d.	blue-green	80	1·00
G2	½d.	dp green ('18) ..	1·00	1·50
	a	on bluish paper ..	2·00	2·50
G3	1d.	carmine-red	1·00	60
G4	1d.	scarlet ('16)	1·00	75
	a	on bluish paper ..	2·00	2·50
G5	2d.	grey ('09)	3·00	4·00
	a	on bluish paper ..	5·00	6·00
G6	2d.	slate ('18)	3·50	4·50
G7	2½d.	blue	3·00	6·00
G8	2½d.	bt blue	2·50	5·00
G9	3d.	pur/yel ('09) OC ..	2·50	4·00
	a	on pale yellow ..	5·00	6·00
G10	6d.	dl and bt pur ('09) C	8·00	9·50
G11	6d.	dl purple ('15) O ..	4·00	6·00
	a	on bluish paper ..	£10	£10
G12	1/–	black/green OC ..	5·00	5·50
G13	2/–	pur and bl/bl ('19) O	£13	£16
G14	2/6	blk and red/bl('21) O	£20	£24
G15	5/–	red and grn/yel ('14)		
		C	£45	£55
G1/15		set (11v)	£95	£115
SPG1/15		specimen set (11v)	£95	‡

Numbers printed—G1/2, 106,000: G3/4, 390,000: G5/6, 23,880: G7/8 56,940: G9, 27,120: G10/11, 21,240: G12, 18,120.

WAR TAX

Type I	Type II

1916 (Sept.). War Tax. No. G1 overprinted and surcharged in London with Type I in red. Sheets 5 x 12.

G16	½d. on ½d.	blue-green ..	20	1·00
	a	small 'O' in 'ONE'..	5·00	8·00

Number issued—250,000.

1918 (March 18th). No. G1 overprinted locally with Type II in black.

G17	½d.	**blue-green**	40	2·00
	a	overprint inverted ..	—	—
	b	albino surcharge ..	5·00	8·00
SPG17		**ovpt. specimen** ..	£25	‡

G17*a*—It is believed that one sheet was discovered with the overprint inverted and that all copies, except for ⊞ in the Royal Collection, were destroyed.

G17*b*—A number of sheets each contained between one and six stamps showing 'ONE HALFPENNY" (as Type I) in albino 5mm. below "WAR TAX". Due to blanking out of surcharge not being complete.

This overprint may be found in thick type on stamps in deep green (thin paper) and dull green (thick paper); and in thin type on stamps in dull green (thick paper).

Type III

Type IV

1918 (June). Nos. G1 and G9 overprinted in London with Type III in black (G18) or red (G19).

G18	½d.	**blue-green**	15	60
	a	on bluish paper ..	2·00	3·00
G19	3d.	**purple/lemon** ..	20	1·50

1919-20. Special printing of G7 in changed colour overprinted and surcharged or surcharged only in London. Sheets 5 x 12.

(a) With Type IV in red.

G20	1½d. on 2½d.	**orange** ..	15	1·25
	a	short fraction bar ..	£30	£40

(b) Surcharged only (as in Type IV) in black (10.6.20).

G21	1½d. on 2½d.	**brown-or** ..	1·50	3·00
	a	short fraction bar ..	£30	£40
G22	1½d. on 2½d.	**dl yel-or** ..	2·00	4·00
SPG16/22		specimen set less		
		G17 (5v) ..	£100	‡

G20*a*/21*a*—Occur on Row 6/5, the fraction bar measuring 2½mm. instead of the normal 3½mm.

1921. As Nos. G1/14 but Wmk. Multiple Script CA.

G23	½d.	**blue-green**	70	2·25
G24	1d.	**carmine-red** ..	75	1·25
G25	1½d.	**orange**	3·00	4·00
G26	2d.	**grey**	5·00	6·00
G27	2½d.	**bt blue**	1·50	5·00
G28	6d.	**reddish purple C** ..	5·00	8·00
G29	6d.	**plum**	6·00	9·00
G30	2/–	**pur and blue/blue** ..	£25	£30
G31	2/6	**blk and red/blue** ..	£35	£40
G23/31		**set** (8v)	£70	£95
SPG23/31		**specimen set** (8v)	£90	‡

1923 (Feb.)-37. Chalky paper. Centres in black. Sheets 5 x 12.

(a) Wmk. Multiple Script CA.

G32	½d.	**dl green**	20	35
G33	½d.	**myrtle green** ..	30	45
G34	1d.	**bt violet**	50	80
G35	1d.	**reddish violet** ..	80	1·00
G36	1d.	**slate violet** ..	1·00	1·50
G37	1d.	**reddish purple** ..	1·00	1·50
G38	1d.	**rosine** ('33) ..	1·20	1·50
G39	1d.	**scarlet**	1·50	1·75
G40	1½d.	**lt red**	60	90
G41	1½d.	**dp red**	1·00	1·25
G42	1½d.	**red-brown** ('33) ..	1·75	1·60
G43	1½d.	**or-brn** (5/37) ..	2·00	1·75
G44	2d.	**grey**	65	1·00
G45	2½d.	**orange-yellow** ..	1·10	2·00
G46	2½d.	**ult** ('27)	1·25	2·00
G47	3d.	**cobalt**	1·60	2·50
G48	3d.	**blk and red/yel** ('27)	75	1·20
G49	4d.	**brown**	80	2·00
G50	4d.	**dp brown**	95	2·25
G51	6d.	**bt purple**	1·50	3·00
G52	6d.	**pl bt purple** ..	1·75	3·25
G53	1/–	**black/emerald** ..	3·00	2·50
	a	on green ..	3·50	2·50
G54	2/–	**blk and blue/blue** ..	4·00	8·00
G55	2/–	**blk and gr-bl/bl** ..	4·25	9·00
G56	2/6	**blk and red/blue** ..	8·00	£11
G57	3/–	**blk and dl pur/yel** ('27) ..	7·00	£11
G58	3/–	**blk and dp dl pur/yel** ..	7·00	£11
G59	4/–	**blk and red/emerald**	8·00	£14
G60	5/–	**blk and bt grn/yel** ('27)	£16	£19

(b) Wmk. Multiple Crown CA.

G61	3/–	**blk and dp pur/yel** ..	8·00	£14
G62	5/–	**blk and dl grn/yel** ..	£16	£20
G63	£1	**blk and pur/red** ..	£225	£240
G32/63		**set** (21v)	£295	£365
SPG32/63		**specimen set** (19v)	£185	‡

1935 (May 6th). Silver Jubilee. (*recess*) **De La Rue. Wmk. Multiple Script CA. Perf. 13½ x 14. Sheets 6 x 10.**

G64	1d. **dp blue and car** ..	25	35
G65	1½d. **ult and grey**	40	50
G66	2½d. **brown and dp blue**..	2·00	2·20
G67	1/– **slate and purple** ..	3·50	4·50
G64/67	**set** (4v)	6·00	7·00
SPG64/67	**specimen set** (4v)	£25	‡

Remainders were withdrawn on December 31st 1935.

1938 (Aug. 15th) -49 Designs, ½d., 6d., 7d., 2/6 (Fresh Water Lake); 1d., 3d., 2/-, 5/- (Layou River); 1½d., 2½d., 3½d. (Picking Limes); Other Values (Boiling Lake). Printers (*recess*) **Waterlow & Sons. Perf. 12½ (L). Sheets 10 x 6.**

1	½d. **red-brn and yel-grn** ..	5	5
	a choc and green (3/2/44) ..	10	5
2	1d. **grey and scarlet** ..	10	5
	a grey and carmine-red (15/11/49) ..	15	5
3	1½d. **grn and pur-vio** ..	15	5
4	2d. **car-rose and grey** ..	15	5
	a scar and grey (3/2/44)	25	20
5	2½d. **purple and blue** ..	3·00	1·00
	a pur and ult (11/42) ..	20	20
	b imperf bottom margin	—	£300
6	3d. **olive and light brown**	10	10
7	3½d. **ult and pur** (15/10/47)	30	40
8	6d. **emerald and violet** ..	30	30
	a dp emerald and violet (5/11/49) ..	20	25
9	7d. **green and light brown** (15/10/47) ..	30	30
10	1/– **violet and olive-green**	60	30
	a violet and sage-green (15/11/49) ..	50	25
11	2/– **dp slate and pur-vio** (15/10/47) ..	1·00	1·25
12	2/6 **black and vermilion**..	1·00	1·25
13	5/– **lt blue and sepia-brn**	2·00	2·25
14	10/– **black and orange-brn** (15/10/47) ..	7·00	7·00
1/15	**set** (inc. 15) (15) ..	£12	£14
SP1/15	**specimen set** (inc. 15) (15)	£50	‡

No. 5b—Used copies from bottom row with lower margin imperf have been found.

Re-entries.—1½d. (No. 3) vertical frame lines, left bottom corner double (Rows 1/6, 1/9, 3/9). 3d. (No. 6) doubling of vertical frame lines and palms, right bottom corner (Row 4/2). 6d. (No. 8–8a) horizontal frame line, right bottom corner before the value tablet double (Row 2/10). 2/6 (No. 12) lower left corner re-entry Row 3/7. Prices about six times normal.

1940-4 Printers (*photo*) **Harrison & Sons. Perf. 14¾ x 14 (C). Sheets 12 x 10.**

15	¼d. **choc** (*ch*) (15/4/40)..	15	10
	a chocolate (*sub*) (/42)	10	10
	b dull choc-brn (*sub*) (/44)	10	5

1951 (July 1st) Printers (*photo*) **Harrison & Sons. Perf. 14¾ x 14 (C). Sheets as before.**

16	½c. **brown** (*ch*)	10	10

1951 (July 1st) Designs, 6c. (Botanical Gardens); 12c., $1.20 (Fresh Water Lake); 14c. (Layou River); 24c. (Boiling Lake); Other Values (Scenes depicting local occupations and industries). Printers (*recess*) **Bradbury, Wilkinson. Perf. 13 x 13½ (C). Design, $2.40, V. Sheets 5 x 10.**

17	1c. **black and vermilion**	10	10
18	2c. **choc and grey-green**	10	10
19	3c. **emerald and purple**	10	10
20	4c. **brn-orange and sepia**	15	15

21	5c.	black and carmine .	15	15
22	6c.	olive and chestnut .	15	15
23	8c.	green and dp blue ..	20	20
24	12c.	black and emerald..	20	20
25	14c.	ultramarine and pur	20	30
26	24c.	pur and rose-car ..	30	40
27	48c.	emerald and vermilion	80	2·00
28	60c.	scarlet and black ..	1·50	2·00
30	$1.20	emerald grn and blk	3·00	4·00
31	$2.40	dp orange and black	8·00	8·00
16/31		set (15)	£14	£17

SPECIAL ISSUES

1937 (May 12th) Coronation. As Aden but Printers Bradbury, Wilkinson. Perf. 11 x 11¾ (C).

S1	1d.	carmine-red	..	15	20
S2	1½d.	light brown	..	15	10
S3	2½d.	dp blue	..	30	60
SP	S1/3	specimen set perf (3)	£13	‡

1946 (Oct. 14th) Victory. As Aden.

S4	1d.	carmine-red		5	5
S5	3½d.	grey-blue	.. ..	10	10
SP	S4/5	specimen set perf (2)	£13	‡

1948 (Dec. 1st) Silver Wedding. As Aden.

| S6 | 1d. | scarlet | .. .. | 5 | 5 |
| S7 | 10/- | chestnut-brown | .. | 5·00 | 7·00 |

1949 (Oct. 10th) U.P.U. As Aden.

S8	5c.	dull ultramarine	..	10	15
S9	6c.	brown	.. ..	15	20
S10	12c.	purple	.. ..	30	50
S11	24c.	sage-green	.. ..	60	70
S8/11		set (4)	.. ..	1·00	1·50

1951 (Feb. 16th) West Indies University College. As Antigua.

| S12 | 3c. | green and mauve .. | 15 | 15 |
| S13 | 12c. | dp green and carmine | 40 | 40 |

1951 (Oct. 15th) New Constitution. No. 19, etc., overprinted "New Constitution 1951" in black or red.

S14	3c.	emerald and purple	5	10
S15	5c.	black and carmine .	10	15
S16	8c.	grn and dp blue (red)	15	20
S17	14c.	ult and purple (red)	20	25
S14/17		set (4)	50	70

Number issued (London only)—3c., 66,140; 5c., 64,960; 8c., 64,430; 14c., 63,790.

POSTAL FISCALS

1879-86. Nos. V5, V8, V9 and V15 overprinted REVENUE in black sans serif capitals.

(a) Wmk. Crown CC.

F1	1d.	lilac	.. .. ..	£10	2·00
	a	bisect vert (½d.) on cover (1883) ..	‡	—
F2	6d.	green	1·50	2·50
F3	1/-	magenta	4·00	8·00

(b) Wmk. Crown CA.

| F4 | 1d. | lilac ('86) .. .. | 50 | 80 |

1886 (June). No. V17 overprinted in capital and lower case black serif letters.

| F5 | 1d. | carmine .. .. | £10 | £10 |

FALKLAND ISLANDS

A settlement was made by France in 1764 and subsequently passed into Spanish hands. This settlement was destroyed in 1831, and the islands were colonized by Great Britain in 1833.

The first Post Office is believed to have been opened on July 17th, 1861, when prepayment of letters to the United Kingdom was authorised by the G.P.O. Until 1868 the postage paid or due on delivery was marked in red or black respectively in manuscript on the cover; but from March that year pre-payment of postage was additionally indicated by a Frank, which was impressed in conjunction with the dated postmark.

| Type I | Type II |

1868-78 PAID Franks.

				On Cover (with C.D.S.)	On Piece
VF1	**Type I in black**	..	£7000	£800
VF2	**Type II in red**	..	£9000	£900

VF2 was in use from November, 1876 to June, 1878.

Reprints of both Franks were made on paper in 1890. Price from £40 each.

All stamps from V1 to V49 are *(recess)* by Bradbury, Wilkinson. Perf. 14, 14½. Sheets 10 x 6.

1878 (June 19th)-79 No wmk.

V1	1d.	claret	.. .. ..	£125	£120
V2	4d.	grey-blk (9/79)	..	£250	£52
V3	6d.	blue-green	..	£12	£25
V4	1/-	bistre-brown ('78) ..	£12	£22

All values exist imperf. on one or two sides, being marginal copies.

V2 is known with part of the papermaker's watermark showing ("R. TURNER, CHAFFORD MILLS"). £400 £125

V4 exists handstamped "Specimen" in black.

Numbers Issued—V1/V4, 20,000 each.

1883–1902 As before but wmk. Crown CA.
Well centred watermarks are scarce as the size of the stamps did not match the layout of the watermark. Parts of the watermark normally appearing in the margins may be found on stamps ("CROWN AGENTS FOR THE COLONIES").

V5	½d.	blue-green ('91) ..	6·00	7·00
V6	½d.	green ('92) ..	5·00	6·00
V7	½d.	dp yel-grn ('94) ..	5·00	6·00
V8	½d.	yellow-green ('95)	50	1·00
V9	½d.	bluish-grn ('96) ..	6·00	7·00
V10	1d.	claret ('83) ..	£70	£35
		a imperf. between (horiz. pair) ..	—	
V11	1d.	red-brown ('91) ..	£25	£15
V12	1d.	or-red-brn ('91) ..	£16	£16
V13	1d.	russet-brn ('92) ..	£14	£12
V14	1d.	orange-brn ('94)	£10	£10
V15	1d.	br claret ('94) ..	£12	£10
V16	1d.	venetian red ('95)	£12	£10
V17	1d.	pl venetian red ('96)	3·00 4·00	3·00 4·00
V18	1d.	pale red ('99) ..	2·00	2·00
V19	1d.	pl or-red ('02) ..	3·00	3·00
V20	1d.	br orange-red ('02)	4·00	2·00
V21	2d.	purple ('95) ..	2·00	5·00
V22	2d.	pl purple ('98) ..	2·00	5·00
V23	2½d.	pl chalky ult ('91)	£17	£10
V24	2½d.	blue ('92)	£12	6·00
V25	2½d.	pl blue ('92) ..	£12	7·00
V26	2½d.	prussian blue ('94)	£60	£30
V27	2½d.	br ult ('94–98) ..	3·00	5·00
V28	2½d.	dp ult ('02) ..	3·00	5·00
V29	4d.	grey-black ('83) ..	£12	£10
V30	4d.	ol grey-blk ('90) ..	£12	8·00
V31	4d.	grey-blk (wmk rev.) ('94)	—	—
V32	4d.	olive-black ('95) ..	4·00	8·00
V33	6d.	orange-yel ('92) ..	6·00	£10
V34	6d.	yellow ('96) ..	6·00	£10
V35	9d.	vermilion ('96) ..	6·00	£11
V36	9d.	pl vermilion ('96)	7·00	£11
V37	1/–	grey-brown ('96) ..	6·00	£12
V38	1/–	yel-brown ('96) ..	6·00	£12
V5/38		set (8v)	£28	£48
SPV5/38		specimen set (5v except 1d., 4d., 1/–).	£225	‡

V10*a* 2 pairs known.

V11 and V30 exist imperf. on one or two sides, being marginal copies.

For V11 bisected see V44.

The following varieties of watermark are known.

Inverted—V10, V12, V29.

Reversed—V6, V8, V10, V13, V15, V16, V17, V21, V24, V25, V27, V30, V33, V35, V37, (V14 and V31 always found with reversed watermark).

Reversed and Inverted V7, V8, V10, V35.

V31 is unpriced as, despite a reported printing of 3,000 copies, the true shade is very elusive.

SPV5/38 refers to the Bradbury Wilkinson machine overprint. All values are also known with "Specimen" handstamped in black or violet.

Numbers Issued—V5, 60,000; V6 and V23, 40,000 each; V7 and V32, 39,960 each; V8, 214,200; V9, V14, V36, V38, 18,000 each; V10, 10,000; V11, V12, V13, V29, V30, V33, 20,000 each; V15 and V37, 19,980 each; V16/V17,

61,980; V18, 120,000; V19/V20, 60,000; V21, 37,980; V22, 36,000; V24/25, 20,000; V26 and V34, 12,000 each; V27, 55,980; V28, 30,000; V31, 3,000; V35, 19,560.

1885-91 As before, but wmk. Crown CA sideways (Cross on Crown to right looking at back of stamp). Perf. 14, 14½.

V39	1d.	pl claret ('85) ..	£12	£10
V40	1d.	dp claret ('87) ..	£12	£10
V41	4d.	pl grey-black ('85)	£45	£10
V42	4d.	grey-black ('87) ..	£40	£10

V40 and V42 exist imperf. on one or two sides, being marginal copies.

For V39 bisected see V43.

The following varieties of watermark are known.

Inverted—V39–V42.

Reversed (to left or right)—V39–V42.

Numbers Issued—V39/V42, 20,000 each.

1891 Stamps bisected diagonally.

(a) Without surcharge.

			On Cover	On Piece
V43	1d.	pl claret (V39)		
		(Jan. 1st)	£900	£80
V44	1d.	red-brn (V11)		
		(May)	£950	£80

(b) Each half surcharged "½d." On Cover

			On Cover	
V45	1d.	pl claret (V39) (Feb.)	£80	£1200
	a	unsevered pair ..	£400	—
	b	surcharge double ..	£300	—
	c	surcharge inverted	£400	—
	d	surcharge sideways	£250	—
V46	1d.	red-brn (V11) (May)	£60	£120
	a	unsevered pair ..	£700	—
	b	surcharge double ..	£200	—
V47	1d.	or-red-brown (V12) (Dec.)	£30	£50
	a	unsevered pair ..	£80	—
	b	surcharge inverted	£70	—

V45d Prices are for examples showing the fraction at right angles to the vertical side of the stamp. Great care should be exercised in buying abnormals.

The "2" in the original handstamps was broken and replaced towards the end of 1891. All such examples are "Made to Order."

In 1892 a small number of V13 was surcharged on piece and cancelled with the circular Falkland Islands datestamp back-dated to 1891. The 1891 bisects (V43/V47) were all cancelled with a cork obliterator (a circle of small squares) or a metal "F.I." in a vertical oval of horizontal lines. V47 were made to order after Sept. 1891.

The use of bisected stamps was authorised from January 1st, 1891 following a reduction in the Imperial postage rate from 4d. to 2½d. per ½ oz. Their surcharged use was permitted until Sept. 10th, 1891 when supplies of ½d. (V5) and 2½d. (V23) became generally available. Unsurcharged bisects were accepted until July 1892.

1898 (June) Wmk. Crown CC.

V48	2/6	deep blue	..	..	£100	£100
		a re-entry	..	..	£250	£250
V49	5/-	red	..	..	£100	£100
SPV48/49		specimen pair	..	£120	‡

V48a—A strong re-entry in lines below right-hand value tablet.

These stamps may occasionally be found on paper showing a slight blueing.

The issued stamps may be found with "Specimen" handstamped in violet.

Die Proofs exist in black and in issued colours on card. These stamps also exist in green and brown respectively, imperforate and perforated "SPECIMEN".

Numbers Issued—6,000 each.

1904-12 As before, but head of King Edward VII. (Recess) De La Rue. Wmk. Multiple Crown CA. Perf. 14. Sheets 6 x 10 (½d., 1d., 2½d.): 10 x 6 (2d., 6d., 1/-): 6 x 5 (3/-, 5/-).

E1	½d.	br yel-grn ('04) ..	70	1·00
E2	½d.	pl yel-grn (thick paper) ('08)	2·00	3·00
E2A	½d.	deep yellow grn ..	1·25	1·50
E3	1d.	vermilion ('04) ..	1·50	80
E4	1d.	verm (thick paper) ('08)	1·25	1·25
E5	1d.	dull coppery-red ('08)	£50	£10
E6	1d.	orange-verm ('11)	1·00	80
E7	2d.	purple ('04) ..	2·00	8·00
E8	2d.	br reddish-purple ('12)	—	—
E9	2½d.	ultramarine ('04)	7·00	7·00
E10	2½d.	pl ult ('04)	£100	£60
E11	2½d.	dark blue ('12) ..	£95	£70
E12	6d.	orange ('04) ..	£10	£12
E13	1/-	brown ('04) ..	£10	£12
E14	3/-	green ('04) ..	£65	£65
E15	3/-	deep green ('06) ..	£55	£55
E16	5/-	red ('04)	£80	£80
E1/16		set (8v)	£150	£160
SPE1/16		specimen set (8v)	£200	‡

The following varieties of watermark are known :
Inverted—E1, E2, E3, E4, E9, E14.
Reversed—E3, E4, E5, E7, E15—All are scarce.

The ½d., 1d., 2½d., 3/- and 5/- are Line Perf., whereas the 2d., 6d. and 1/- are Comb.

E8 can be identified under ultra violet lamp.

Numbers Issued—E1, 201,120; E2, 104,760; E3, 99,720; E4/E5, 202,620; E6, 101,100; E7, 31,920; E8, 6,360; E9/E10, 51,000; E11, 8,820; E12, 14,580; E13, 15,300; E14, 4,740; E15, 5,010; E16, 6,060.

1906 As before, but wmk. Multiple Crown CA sideways, Sheets 10 x 6.

E17	1d.	vermilion	..	..	45	1·00

Number Issued—96,300.

1912/20 Printers (recess) De La Rue & Co. Wmk. Mult, Crown CA. Perf. 14. Sheets ½d.–1/-, 6 x 10; 3/-£1, 6 x 5.

G1	½d.	green	60	1·00
		a yel-green	80	1·00
		b dp yel-green ..	8·00	£12
		c blue-green/thick grey paper	1·50	4·00
G2	1d.	vermilion	1·25	1·40
		a orange-ver ..	1·75	1·25
		b scarlet	80	1·00
		c scar/thick grey paper	2·25	1·00
G3	2d.	deep purple ..	2·00	3·50
		a reddish purple ..	7·00	8·00
		b purple	1·50	2·50
G4	2½d.	blue	3·00	6·00
		a bright blue ..	3·00	5·00
		b indigo	5·00	7·00
		c milky blue ..	£95	£100
G5	6d.	yellow-orange ..	4·00	7·00
		a brown-orange ..	3·00	5·00
G6	1/-	yellow-bistre ..	£10	£12
		a yel-bis/thick greyish paper	£15	£20
		b bistre	£10	£12
		c bis-brown/thick greyish paper ..	£14	£17
G7	3/-	deep green	£30	£35
G8	5/-	red	£45	£50
G9	5/-	purple	£45	£45
		a maroon	£32	£38
G10	10/-	red/green	£110	£140
G11	£1	black/red	£300	£325
G1/11		set (11)	£470	£550
SP G1/11		specimen set (11)	£325	‡

G2c exists with wmk. reversed on two sheets found at South Georgia in 1923. G2a also exists with wmk. reversed.

G5 exists with wmk. inverted.

G7/11 are Line Perf. as are the 1914 printings of ½d. (26,160), 1d (52,080), 2d (10,200) and 2½d (20,400) : the remainder are Comb.

Numbers issued—G1/1*a*/1*b*, 581,240; G1*c*, 100560; G2/2*a*/2*b*, 762,540; G2*c*, 206,400; G3/3*a*, 91,080; G4/4*a*/4*b*, 128,700; G5, 20,640; G5*a*, 12,120; G6, 10,260; G6*a*, 10,560; G6*b*, 24,000; G6*c*, 23,940; G7, 7,770; G8, 7,440; G9, 9,480; G10, 6,300; G11, 6,240.

1918/20 Overprinted locally in black.

G12	½d.	**pale green**	50	3·00
	a	yellow-green	3·00	4·50
	b	grn/thick greyish paper	4·00	8·00
	c	albino overprint	£400	—
	d	wmk. reversed	—	—
G13	1d.	**vermilion**	35	50
	a	br orange-vermilion	3·00	5·00
	b	scarlet	2·00	3·00
	c	overprint double	£400	—
	d	overprint double one albino	£150	—
	e	scarlet/thick greyish paper	£12	£25
	f	wmk. reversed	—	—
G14	1/-	**yellow-bistre**	£12	£18
	a	dp yel-bistre	3·00	£10
	b	overprint double one albino	£400	£225
	c	bis/thick greyish paper	5·00	£14
	ca	wmk. inverted	—	—
	d	bis-brn/thick greyish paper	6·00	£14
	e	overprint double one albino	£50	—
	f	overprint omitted in pair with normal	£400	£250

G13*c*—58 copies are known from a sheet of 60.
G13*d*—2 sheets (120 copies) are recorded.

Sheets from the 3rd printing are known with Wmk. reversed or inverted.

Numbers issued—

1st and 2nd printings: ½d., 93,000; 1d., 96,000; 1/–, 5,000.

3rd (Reset) printing (May 1920): ½d., 1d., 51,000 each: 1/–, 19,800.

War Stamps were withdrawn in April 1921.

1921/9 Wmk. Mult. Script CA. Sheets as before.

G15	½d.	**green**	40	1·00
	a	yellow-green	70	1·00
	b	bt yel-grn	1·00	1·50
G16	1d.	**scarlet**	1·25	70
	a	scar-ver	40	60
	b	deep dull scarlet	1·25	70
G17	2d.	**reddish-purple**	1·25	1·50
	a	purple	80	1·00
	b	pale purple	1·00	1·00
G18	2½d.	**indigo**	2·50	3·00
	a	dark blue	3·00	4·00
	b	steel blue	2·50	4·00

G19	2½d.	**dp pur/lemon**	1·25	3·00
	a	reddish pur/pl yel	1·25	4·00
G20	6d.	**orange**	2·00	3·00
	a	pale orange	6·00	6·00
G21	1/–	**bistre**	6·50	£10
G22	3/–	**deep green**	£18	£22
G15/22		**set** (8)	£28	£40
SP G15/22		**specimen set** (8)	£125	‡

G16 and G19*a* exist with Wmk. inverted and reversed.

G20 exists with Wmk. inverted and with Wmk. reversed.

Numbers issued—

G15/*a*/*b*, 252,500; G16/*a*/*b*, 498,660; G17, 59,280; G17*a*, 90,120; G18/*a*/*b*, 152,700; G19/*a*, 88,680; G20/*a*, 35,340; G21, 21,060; G22, 14,220.

Remainders destroyed 1/9/29.

1928 (Feb. 7th) G17a surcharged in black in South Georgia for Scandinavian mail.

G23	2½d. on 2d.	**purple**	£450	£550
	a	surcharge double	£10000	—

Only two copies of G23*a* are known.

Number issued—1,179; withdrawn from sale Feb. 22.

1929/36 Printers (*recess*) **Perkins Bacon & Co. Wmk. Mult. Script CA (i) Comb perf. 13.9 on 1929 issue; (ii) Line perf. 13.9, 14.2 or compound on 4d. value and 1936 printings of ½d., 1d., 6d. and 1/-. Sheets 12 x 10.**

G24	½d.	**green**	15	30
	a	bt green ('36)	1·00	1·20
G25	1d.	**scarlet**	20	20
	a	deep red ('36)	2·50	5·00
G26	2d.	**slate grey**	30	50
G27	2½d.	**blue**	30	90
G28	4d.	**orange** (20/11/32)	1·20	2·00
	a	dp orange ('36–'37)	5·00	7·00
G29	6d.	**purple**	2·00	3·00
	a	reddish-pur (1936)	7·00	9·00
G30	1/–	**black/green**	4·00	6·00
	a	blk/emerald ('36)	6·00	7·00
G31	2/6	**carmine/blue**	£14	£18
G32	5/–	**green/yellow**	£20	£26
G33	10/–	**car/emerald**	£50	£60

Wmk. Mult. Crown CA.

G34	£1	**black/red**	£275	£295

G24/34 **set** (11) £350 £400
SPG24/34 **specimen set** perf
(11) .. .. £200 ‡

Numbers Issued—G24, 149,160; G24a, 31,860;
G25, 377,300; G25a, 30,000; G26, 133,200; G27,
330,420; G28, 35,820; G28a, 72,900; G29.
40,260; G29a, 5,520; G30, 25,320; G30a, 5,520;
G31, 17,280; G32, 9,240; G33, 9,120; G34, 8,400.

**1933 (Jan. 2nd) Centenary of British Occupa-
tion, various Pictorial designs. Printers
(recess) Bradbury, Wilkinson. Wmk. Mult.
Script CA. Perf. 12. Sheets 6 x 10.**

G35	½d. **blk and grn**	..	1·25	1·50
G36	1d. **blk and scar**		1·00	1·20
G37	1½d. **blk and blue**	..	1·25	2·00
G38	2d. **blk and brn**		2·25	3·00
G39	3d. **blk and violet**	..	3·25	5·00
G40	4d. **blk and orange**	..	3·50	6·00
G41	6d. **blk and slate**		£22	£25
G42	1/– **blk and ol-grn**	..	£20	£25
G43	2/6 **blk and violet**	..	£60	£75
G44	5/– **blk and yellow**	..	£350	£400
	a blk and yel-orange	.	£600	£650
G45	10/– **blk and chestnut**	..	£450	£500
G46	£1 **blk and car**	..	£1750	£1900
G35/46	**set** (12)	..	£2500	£2900
SPG35/46	**specimen set** perf			
	(12)	..	£950	‡

Care should be taken in purchasing G44a and
allowance should be made for climatic staining.

Forged postmarks (6/1/33) are known on this
issue.

Numbers sold—
G35, 113,606; G36, 94,242; G37, 58,510;
G38, 29,823; G39, 25,690; G40, 27,720; G41,
21,251; G42, 14,587; G43, 9,046; G44, 6,221;
G45, 3,688; G46, 3,128; Remainders destroyed
31/12/33.

**1935 (May 7th) Silver Jubilee. Printers (recess)
Bradbury, Wilkinson. Wmk. Mult. Script CA.
Perf. 11 x 12. Sheets 6 x 10.**

G47	1d. **dp blu and scar**	..	30	20
G48	2½d. **brn and dp blue**	..	50	80
	a re-entry	..	£90	£120
G49	4d. **grn and indigo**	..	75	1·00
G50	1/– **slate and purple**	..	1·50	3·00
	a extra flagstaff	..	£1100	£1100
G47/50	**set** (4)	..	2·25	5·00
SP G47/50	**specimen set** perf			
	(4) ..	..	£30	‡

Extra flagstaff variety. Row 9/1.
Care has to be taken in purchasing this variety
especially when not in positional block.
G48a Re-entry of value tablet and frame is on Row
8, No. 1.

Numbers issued—
G47, 168,840; G48, 99,440; G49, 78,100;
G50, 76,920; G50a, 94.

**1938 (Jan. 3rd) -50 Designs, £1 (Arms of
Colony); Other Values (Scenes and Fauna
of Islands). Designer, G. Roberts. Printers
(recess) Bradbury, Wilkinson. Perf. 12 (L).
Centres black except Nos. 10, 13, 15 and 16.
Sheets 6 x 10.**

1	½d. **green**	..	10	10
	a yellow-green	..	15	15
2	1d. **carmine-rose**	..	4·00	4·00
	a scarlet (/40)	..	40	50
3	1d. **violet** (14/7/41)	..	10	15
	a purple-violet	..	20	25
4	2d. **black and violet**	..	60	80
5	2d. **carmine-red**(14/7/41)	..	25	30
	a red	..	10	15
6	2½d. **blue** (sheep) ..	..	35	50
7	2½d. **blue** (goose) (15/6/49)	..	50	80
8	3d. **blue** (14/7/41)	..	30	20
	a deep blue	..	50	50
9	4d. **purple**	..	40	50
	a bright purple	..	40	50
10	6d. **slate-blk and sepia-**			
	brn		2·00	2·50
	a blk and sepia-brn			
	(28/7/44)	..	2·50	3·00
11	6d. **black** (15/6/49)	..	1·00	1·75
12	9d. **dull grey-blue**	..	60	75
	a sepia and grey-black	..	75	75
13	1/– **blue**		£12	£14
	a dp slate-blue (/41)..		1·00	1·25
	b dp blue (27/5/47)	..	£10	£10
14	1/3 **car-rose** (10/12/46)..		50	60
15	2/6 **slate-black**		£10	8·00
16	5/– **blue and light brown**		£10	£10
	a blue and buff-brown			
	(9/2/50)	..	£10	£10
	b indigo and yel-brown	..	£50	£30
17	10/– **dp orange**		9·00	9·00
18	£1 **violet**		£15	£18
1/18	**set** (17)		£45	£50
SP 1/18	**specimen set** perf (13)		£100	‡

1952 (Jan. 2nd) Designs, 1d. (R.M.S. "Fitz-roy"); 2½d. (Map of Islands); 3d. (Arms of Colony); 4d. ("Auster" Aircraft); 6d. (M.S.S. "John Biscoe"); £1 (Hulk of "Great Britain"); Other Values (Scenes and Fauna of Islands). Printers (recess) **Waterlow & Sons. Perf. 13¼ x 13½ (C). Designs, 3d., 1/-, 2/6, 5/- V. Designer, V. H. Spencer. Sheets 6 x 10 or 10 x 6.**

19	½d.	green	..	..	..	20	20
		a yellow-green(9/4/53)				40	40
20	1d.	scarlet	..	..	..	20	20
21	2d.	violet	..	..	..	40	50
22	2½d.	blk and lt ultramarine				20	25
23	3d.	ultramarine	..	..		20	30
24	4d.	magenta-claret		..		25	35
25	6d.	light brown	..	..		50	50
26	9d.	orange-yellow		..		1·00	1·25
27	1/-	black	..	..	..	1·25	1·25
28	1/3	vermilion	..	..		1·00	1·00
29	2/6	olive-green	..	..		1·50	2·00
30	5/-	purple	..	..	..	2·50	3·00
31	10/-	slate-grey	..	..		4·00	5·00
32	£1	black	..	..	..	£10	£10
19/32		set (14)	..	..		£22	£25

SPECIAL ISSUES

1937 (May 12th) Coronation. As Aden but Printers Bradbury, Wilkinson. Perf. 11 x 11¾ (C).

S1	½d.	green	..	..	..	10	10
S2	1d.	carmine-red		..		15	15
S3	2½d.	dp blue	..	..		25	35
SP S1/3		specimen set perf (3)		£18	‡		

Numbers issued—S1, 318,420; S2, 330,000; S3, 268,140.

1946 (Oct. 7th) Victory. As Aden.

S4	1d.	violet-grey	..	..		10	15
S5	3d.	grey-blue	..	..		15	20
		a major re-entry to crown R8/5 Plate 1		..		£25	£25
SP S4/5		specimen set perf (2)		£20	‡		

Numbers issued—S4, 883,080; S5, 804,300.

1948 (Nov. 1st) Silver Wedding. As Aden.

S6	2½d.	ultramarine	..	..	10	15
S7	£1	dull purple	..	..	£25	£30

Numbers issued—S6, 171,326; S7, 22,956.

1949 (Oct. 10th) U.P.U. As Aden.

S8	1d.	dull violet	..	..	10	15
S9	3d.	indigo	..	..	20	30
S10	1/3	green	..	..	60	80
S11	2/-	azure	..	..	1·10	1·50
S8/11		set (4)	..	..	2·00	2·50

Numbers issued—S8, 618,000; S9, 467,400; S10, 507,000; S11, 497,880.

Stamps of the Falkland Islands may be found cancelled during the period 1911 to 1932 in a variety of markings used on board ships which collected mail from outlying islands and settlements without other postal facilities.

Until 1913 the cancellation was similar to that illustrated, but inscribed "POSTED ON BOARD/ R.M.S. COLUMBUS". Between 1914 and 1920 the same oval cancellation (with "R.M.S. Columbus" erased) was used in conjunction with a straight line "R.M.S. FALKLAND", struck in violet. From 1922 until 1926 the "H.M.C.S. AFTERGLOW" cancellations were struck in black; the first short-lived type was a single line "Posted on H.M.C.S. AFTERGLOW", followed by the illustrated cancellation until 1926.

From 1926 until 1932 "R.M.S. FALKLAND" again used the oval cancellation as in 1914–20 but without date and without the straight line "R.M.S. FALKLAND", struck in blackish violet. After 1932 stamps on mail collected by ships from outlying localities were cancelled on arrival at Port Stanley.

The "AFTERGLOW" cancellation was improperly used in 1927–28 (with date set back to July–August 1926); such usage may be recognised by the space between '2' and '6' in "1926".

FALKLAND ISLANDS DEPENDENCIES

The first Post Office was opened at South Georgia on December 3rd, 1909, and Falkland Island stamps (V5/V42 and E1/E16) were used. Initially, they were cancelled with a circular "Falkland Islands" datestamp; and a small metal handstamp "South Georgia" (21mm. long) was impressed *on the cover* below each stamp.

South Georgia

This "South Georgia" *under*-print was nevertheless occasionally applied as an *over*-print to stamps already on covers, but examples are very scarce indeed. Stamps with the overprint were *not* available to the public.

With the introduction of a "South Georgia" datestamp on July 23rd, 1910 the use of the handstamped underprint was no longer necessary to signify the origin of mail. It continued in use, however, until as late as June, 1912 in conjunction with the new datestamp.

Between mid-October 1911 and mid-February 1912, during a shortage of stamps, covers were franked with a rubber handstamp "Paid . . . At/SOUTH GEORGIA", the amount of postage (1d. or 2½d.) being inserted in manuscript. The frank was initialled "E.B.B." by the acting Magistrate (E. B. Binnie) or "J.I.W." by the Postmaster (J. I. Wilson) and the "South Georgia" datestamp was impressed over it.

In March, 1923 a temporary shortage of 1d. stamps resulted in the locally authorised bisection of the Falkland Islands 2½d. (G4 and G18), each half being used for 1d. postage. The 6d. value (G5) was also bisected, each half being used for 2½d. postage, and a cover to Norway is dated March 30th, 1923.

The 1928 provisional 2½d. on 2d. (G23) was made and used only in South Georgia.

The postal history of South Shetlands dates from November, 1912 when the Government Whaling Officer took a supply of Falkland Islands stamps (up to 2½d. only) to Port Foster on Deception Island. Authority was given from Port Stanley on March 6th, 1913 for *letters* to be obliterated with the words "Port Foster"; but, as the only obliterator available was a "Falkland Islands" datestamp, a handstamped overprint "PORT FOSTER" in serif capitals was applied to stamps which were hen cancelled with the "Falkland Islands" (or NEW ISLAND/FALKLAND Is.") datestamp.

PORT FOSTER

The stamps overprinted were G1 and G2 and also E3; and, although the overprint was normally applied diagonally on a single stamp, horizontal pairs of G1 and G2 are known with the over print horizontally placed across the two stamps. Mint overprinted stamps were *not* available to the public

The use of the overprint ceased the following' year when a large oval rubber datestamp "DECEPTION ISLAND/SOUTH SHETLANDS" was introduced. This datestamp was used in violet or black until 1923 when it was replaced by a circular

"South Shetlands" postmark; the latter continued in use until 1931 when the Post Office was closed.

The postal history of South Orkney and Graham Land dates only from the issue in 1944 of the overprinted stamps.

GRAHAM LAND

1944 (Feb. 13th) -45 As No. 1, etc., Falkland Islands, but overprinted GRAHAM LAND DEPENDENCY OF, in red. Centres black, except Nos. 1a, 6a, 8.

1	½d.	green	.. ..	10	20
		a blue-slate and green (/44)	.. ..	£20	—
2	1d.	violet	.. ..	10	25
3	2d.	carmine-rose	..	10	25
4	3d.	blue	.. .. ..	15	30
5	4d.	purple	.. ..	15	30
6	6d.	sepia-brown	..	60	75
		a bluish-slate and sepia-brown (24/9/45) .		2·50	5·00
7	9d.	dull grey-blue	..	50	60
8	1/–	slate-blue	.. ..	60	75
1/8		set (8)	.. .. ..	2·25	3·25

SOUTH GEORGIA

1944 (Feb. 24th) -45 As before but overprinted SOUTH GEORGIA DEPENDENCY OF, in red. Centres black except Nos. 14a, 16.

9	½d.	green ..	.. ..	10	20
10	1d.	violet	.. ..	10	25
11	2d.	carmine-rose	..	10	25
12	3d.	blue	.. ..	15	30
13	4d.	purple	.. ..	15	30
14	6d.	sepia-brown	..	60	75
		a bluish-slate and sepia-brown (24/9/45)		2·50	6·00
15	9d.	dull grey-blue	..	50	60
16	1/-	slate-blue	.. ..	60	75
9/16		set (8)	.. ..	2·25	3·35

SOUTH ORKNEYS

1944 (Feb. 21st) -45 As before but overprinted SOUTH ORKNEYS DEPENDENCY OF, in red. Centres black except Nos. 22a, 24.

17	½d.	green	.. .. ..	10	20
18	1d.	violet	..	10	25
19	2d.	carmine-rose	..	10	25
20	3d.	blue	.. ..	15	30
21	4d.	purple	.. ..	15	30
22	6d.	sepia-brown	..	60	75
		a bluish-slate and sepia-brown (24/9/45) .		2·50	6·00
23	9d.	dull grey-blue	..	50	60
24	1/–	slate-blue	.. ..	60	75
17/24		set (8)	.. .. ..	2·25	3·25

SOUTH SHETLANDS

1944 (Feb. 5th) -45 As before but overprinted SOUTH SHETLANDS DEPENDENCY OF, In red. Centres black except Nos. 30a, 32.

25	½d. **green**	.. .. ..	10	20
26	1d. **violet**	.. .. ..	10	25
27	2d. **carmine-rose**	..	10	25
28	3d. **blue**	.. .. ..	15	30
29	4d. **purple**	.. ..	15	30
30	6d. **sepia-brown**	..	60	75
	a bluish-slateand sepia-brown (24/9/45)	.	2·50	6·00
31	9d. **dull grey-blue**	..	50	60
32	1/– **slate-blue**	.. ..	60	75
25/32	**set (8)**	.. .. ..	2·25	3·25
1/32	**set (32)**	.. ..	9·00	£13
SP 1/32	**specimen set** perf (32)		£150	‡

ISSUES FOR

THE ENTIRE TERRITORY
(replacing individual sets)

1946 (Feb. 1st) Design, Map of Islands *(litho)* **in Coloured Frame** *(recess)*. **Printers, De La Rue. Perf. 11¾ (C). Wmk. sideways. Centres black. Sheets 10 x 6.**

33	½d. **green**	..	10	15
	a broken arc (*a*)	..	2·00	3·00
	b missing I (*b*)	..	5·00	7·00
	c extra island (*c*)	..	5·00	7·00
34	1d. **violet**	..	10	15
	a broken arc (*a*)	..	2·00	3·00
	b missing I (*b*)	..	5·00	7·00
	c extra island (*c*)	..	5·00	7·00
35	2d. **carmine** ..	..	15	20
	a broken arc (*a*)	..	2·00	3·00
	b missing I (*b*)	..	5·00	7·00
	c extra island (*c*)	·	5·00	7·00
36	3d. **ultramarine** ..	..	20	25
	a broken arc (*a*)	..	3·00	4·00
	b missing I (*b*)	..	7·00	9·00
	c extra island (*c*)	..	9·00	£12
37	4d. **reddish-claret**	..	20	25
	a broken arc (*a*)	..	3·00	4·00
	b black and dp lake	..	3·00	5·00
	c broken arc (*a*)	..	8·00	£10
38	6d. **orange**	..	25	40
	a broken arc (*a*)	..	3·50	4·50
	b missing I (*b*)	..	7·00	9·00
	c extra island (*c*)	..	£10	£12
	d yellow ochre	..	4·00	6·00
	e broken arc (*a*)	..	5·00	6·00
	f missing I (*b*)	..	£15	£18
	g extra island (*c*)	..	£20	£20
39	9d. **dp brown** ..	..	30	60
	a broken arc (*a*)	..	£10	£12

40	1/– **dp purple**	.. ..	50	70
	a broken arc (*a*)	..	£12	£14
33/40	**set (8)**	..	1·75	2·60

No. 38*d*—Also exists in an almost black colour due to poor mixing of ink, which oxidised.

This set can be distinguished from that which follows by certain vignette (*centre*) differences. The lines are thicker and coarser; the line of 50° meridian protrudes slightly beyond frame line at upper left-hand corner; also the meridian passes through the S in COATS.

a) A break occurs in the 80th parallel 6 times on all sheets (Rows 1/4, 1/9, 3/4, 3/9, 5/4 and 5/9) (*see illustration*).

(*b*) On Vignette 1 the I in S SHETLAND Is. is missing (Row 1/2) (*see illustration*).

(*c*) On Vignette 1 an extra island (*a round dot*) appears in the left top corner (Row 3/9).

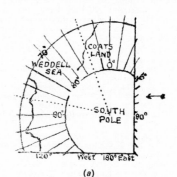

(*a*)

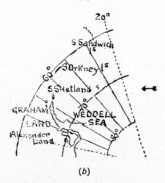

(*b*)

1948 (Feb. 16th) -49 As before but Map *(vignette)* **redrawn. Centres black.**

41	½d. **green**	..	15	1·00
42	1d. **violet**	..	15	1·00
43	2d. **carmine**	..	20	1·20
	a map double	..	£150	—
44	2½d. **dark blue** (6/3/49)	..	30	80
	a dk grey-blue (6/3/49)	..	75	1·20
45	3d. **ultramarine** ..	..	30	90
	a bright ultramarine	..	40	1·00
46	4d. **reddish-claret**	..	50	1·50
	a map double	..	£250	—

47	6d. **orange**	70	2·00
48	9d. **dp brown**	80	2·50
49	1/- **dp purple**	1·50	3·00
41/49	**set** (9)	4·50	£12

In this re-drawn map the lines are finer than before and the Meridian 0° does not cut through S in COATS. A variety occurs on Rows 5/2, 5/4, 5/6, 5/8 and 5/10 in the form of a small dot on the right arm of T in SOUTH POLE (except on 2½d.). Price five times normal.

43*a*—A complete sheet of 2d. map double was found in a London dealer's supply. Variety caused by blanket offset print.

46*a*—We have seen a single mint copy.

SPECIAL ISSUES

1946 (Oct. 4th) Victory. As Aden.

S1	1d. **violet-grey**	5	10
S2	3d. **grey-blue**	10	10
SP S1/2 **specimen set** perf (2)		£30	‡

Numbers issued—S1, 860,520; S2, 831,000.

1948 (Dec. 6th) Silver Wedding. As Aden.

S3	2½d. **ultramarine**	10	15
S4	1/- **slate-violet** (*all recess*)	1·30	1·60

Numbers issued—S3, 299,063; S4, 210,779

1949 (Oct. 10th) U.P.U. As Aden.

S5	1d. **dull violet**	15	20
S6	2d. **carmine**	20	25
S7	3d. **dull indigo**	50	60
S8	6d. **orange**	70	1·00
S5,8	**set** (4)	1·50	2·00

Numbers Issued—S5, 513,600; S6, 405,000
S7, 385,200; S8, 391,380

FIJI

All stamps to G41 are Typo De La Rue perf. 14 unless otherwise indicated.

1903 (Feb. 1st) Wmk. Crown CA. Sheets 240 – four panes each 6 x 10.

E1	½d.	**green and pl green**	40	80
E2	1d.	**dl pur and blk/red** ..	1·75	1·25
E3	2d.	**dl pur and orange** ..	1·00	1·50
E4	2½d.	**dl pur and blue/blue**	6·00	9·00
E5	3d.	**dl pur and mauve** ..	2·25	3·25
E6	4d.	**dl pur and black** ..	2·75	3·50
E7	5d.	**dl pur and green** ..	2·75	3·50
E8	6d.	**dl pur and car** ..	4·00	5·50
E9	1/–	**green and carmine**	9·00	£12
E10	5/–	**green and black** ..	£35	£40
E11	£1	**gry-blk and ultra** ..	£250	£300
E1/11		**set** (11v)	£300	£375
SPE1/11		**specimen set** (11v)	£150	‡

The £1 has been forged (litho) on genuine paper.)

1904-12 As before but Wmk. Multiple Crown CA.

E12	½d.	**grn and pale grn** ..	75	1·00
E13	½d.	**green** (1908) ..	50	80
E14	1d.	**pur and blk/red** ..	90	50
E15	1d.	**red** (1906)	50	80
E16	2½d.	**bright blue** (1910)	1·50	4·00
E17	6d.	**dull pur** (1910) **C**	2·50	4·50
E18	1/–	**green and carmine** (1909) **C** ..	£15	£18
E19	1/–	**blk/grn** (1910) **C** ..	5·00	6·00
E20	5/–	**green and red/ yellow** (1911) **C**	£40	£45
E21	£1	**purple and black/ red** (1912) **C** ..	£200	£225
E12/21		**set** (10v)	£260	£300
SPE13/21		**specimen set** (7v)	£200	‡

1912-23 As before but head of King George V. Wmk. Multiple Crown C.A. Paper ¼d.–4d. O; 5d.–£1 C.

G1	¼d.	**brown** (1916) ..	25	50
G2	¼d.	**dp brown** (1916)	40	60
		a on bluish paper ..	75	80
G3	½d.	**green**	40	50
G4	½d.	**yel-green** (1915) ..	2·00	2·50
		a on bluish paper ..	4·00	5·00
G5	½d.	**blue-green** (1917)	90	90
G6	1d.	**carmine**	90	30
G7	1d.	**bright scar** (1916)	80	70
G8	1d.	**deep rose** (1919)	80	80
G9	2d.	**greyish slate** ..	80	60
		a wmk. sideways ..	£300	—
G10	2½d.	**blue**	2·50	3·50
G11	3d.	**purple/yellow** ..	2·50	3·25
		a on lemon (1915)	3·25	3·75
		b on yel Wmk. side	£200	—
		c on pl yel (Die I) ..	2·25	3·00
G12	3d.	**purple/pl yellow** .. (Die II)	3·00	3·25
G13	4d.	**blk and red/yel** ..	3·00	4·25
		a on lemon ..	3·50	5·00
		b on orange-buff ..	£15	£18
		c on pale yellow (Die I) (1921) ..	6·00	6·00
G14	4d.	**black and red/pl yel** (Die II) (1923) ..	5·00	7·50
G15	5d.	**purple and ol-grn**	3·50	5·00
G16	6d.	**dl and bright pur** ..	2·50	4·00
G17	1/–	**black/green** ..	5·00	7·00
		a white back ..	3·25	3·50
		b blue-green, olive back (1917) ..	4·25	6·00
		c emerald back (Die I) (1921)	3·25	5·50
G18	1/–	**on emerald back** (Die II) (1923) ..	3·25	4·25
G19	2/6	**blk and red/blue** (1916)	£14	£18
G20	5/–	**grn and red/yel** ..	£30	£35
G21	£1	**purple and black/ red** (Die I) ..	£175	£200
G22	£1	**purple and black/ red** (Die II) ..	£175	£200
G1/22		**set** (13v)	£230	£275
SPG1/22		**specimen set** (13v)	£200	‡

1916-19 Nos. G3, G4a, G6, G7, G8 locally overprinted "WAR STAMP" in sans-serif capitals.

G23	½d.	**green**	20	50
G24	½d.	**yellow-green/ bluish** (1916) ..	25	60
		a overprint inverted	£220	—
		b overprint double	—	—
G25	1d.	**carmine**	9·00	£13
G26	1d.	**bright scarlet** ..	60	1·50
		a overprint omitted		
		a overprint omitted in strip with normal	£3000	—
		b overprint inverted	£225	—
G27	1d.	**deep rose** (1919) ..	50	1·00
		specimen pair (½d. and 1d.) ..	£30	‡

G26*a* comes from a sheet on which the overprint was misplaced to the left, appearing on the left margin and on the inter-pane gutter and missing from all the stamps in the last vertical row.

1922-27 As before but Wmk. Multiple Script CA. Paper ¼d. to 6d. O; 1/– to 5/– C.

G28	¼d.	**deep brown** ..	1·00	3·75
G29	½d.	**green**	40	75
G30	1d.	**carmine**	70	1·25
G31	1d.	**violet**	50	30
G32	1½d.	**scarlet**	1·50	2·00
G33	2d.	**grey**	80	30
		a Irish wmk. ..	£300	—
		b value omitted ..	£1250	—
G34	3d.	**blue**	00	00
G35	4d.	**black and red/yel**	2·00	2·50
G36	5d.	**pur and sage-grn**	1·25	2·00
G37	6d.	**dull and bright pur**	1·00	1·50
G38	1/-	**black/emerald** ..	2·50	4·00
G39	2/-	**pur and blue/blue**	£12	£16
G40	2/6	**black and red/blue**	£10	£15
G41	5/–	**green and red/yel**	£25	£30

G28/41 **set** (14v.) .. £55 £75
SPG28/41 **specimen set** (14v) £130 ‡

G33*a* comes from an imperf. part pane printed from Plate 10 on Irish Multiple SE Monogram watermarked paper; a number of the stamps in this pane had pencil lines rules across them.

Although the first Irish definitive stamps on this watermarked paper were printed in Dublin, the plates were made in London. It is believed that a sample of the Irish paper was sent to De La Rue to test its suitability for typographical printing, and that they printed on it from the Fiji plate which was then in similar use.

This variety was never issued either in Fiji or in Ireland and is, in fact, trial printing material.

G33b is known as the centre stamp in a block of nine which shows defective printing of the Duty Plate on three other stamps.

1935 (May 6th) **Silver Jubilee. Recess De La Rue. Wmk. Multiple Script CA. Perf. 13½ x 14. Sheets 6 x 10.**

G42	1½d.	**blue and carmine**	30	60
G43	1½d.	**blue and ani red** ..	2·50	4·50
G44	2d.	**ultra and grey**	50	60
G45	3d.	**brown and blue** ..	1·25	1·75
G46	1/–	**slate and purple** ..	2·50	4·25
G42/46		**set** (4v)	4·50	7·00
SPG42/46		**specimen set** (4v)	£28	‡

Numbers Issued – G42/3 86,000; G44 455,459; G45 54,740; G46 38,519.

G43 comes from a second printing. Remainders withdrawn December 31st 1935.

1938-50 Designs, ½d. (Native Sailing Canoe); 1d. (Native Village); 1½d. (Native Canoe; 2d., 2½d., 6d. (Map of Is.); 2d. (Gov. Offices); 3d. (Canoe and Arms of Fiji); 5d. (Sugar Cane); 8d., 1/5, 1/6 (Arms of Fiji); 1/- (Spearing Fish); 2/- (Suva Harbour); 2/6 (River

Scene); 5/- (Chief's Hut); 10/- (Paw-Paw Tree); £1 (Police Bugler). **Designers,** ½d., 1/-, 2/6 (V. E. Ousey); 3d., 5/- (I. Stinton); 1d., 1½d., 5d. (C. D. Lovejoy); 2d. (Map); 2½d., 6d., 2/- (A. V. Guy). **Printers** (*recess*) **De La Rue,** ½d., 1½d., 2d., 2½d., 6d., 8d., 1/5, 1/6. **Waterlow & Sons, Other Values. Perf.** 13½ (C) ½d., 1½d., 2d., 2½d., 6d. (Die 2). **Perf. 13 x 11¾** (C) 6d. (Die I). **Perf.** 13¾ x 14 (C) 8d., 1/6. **Perf. 14** (L) 1/5. **Perf.** 12½ (L) 1d., 3d., 5d., 1/-, 2/-, 2/6, 5/-, 10/-, £1. **Designs,** ½d., 1d., 5d., 1/-, 10/-, £1 H. **Sheets 10 x 6 or 6 x 10 or 5 x 12.**

1	½d.	**green** (5/4/38) ..	25	25
		a booklet pane of 8 ..	£15	—
		b booklet pane of 10 ..	£20	—
2	1d.	**lt-brn and blue** (5/4/38)	20	20
		a red-brown and blue (7/6/50)	20	20
		b booklet pane of 8 ..	£15	—
		c booklet pane of 10 ..	£20	—
3	1½d.	**car** (Die 1) (5/4/38)	3·00	1·50
4	1½d.	**car** (Die 2) (27/9/40)	80	80
		a dp carmine (Die 2) (10/1/44)	1·50	1·75
5	2d.	**red-brown and green** (Map) (Die 1) (5/4/38) ..	3·50	40
		a booklet pane of 6 ..	£15	—
		b booklet pane of 9 ..	£20	—
6	2d.	**red-brn and grn** (Die 2) (27/9/40) ..	90	2·00
7	2d.	**yel-grn and mag** (Gov. Bldg) (19/5/42) ..	20	25
8	2½d.	**red-brown and green** (6/1/42)	20	20
		a red-brn and blue-grn (10/1/44)	50	50
9	3d.	**blue** (5/4/38)	25	25
		a bright blue ..	25	23
		b re-entry Plate 1 R2/2 top right	£20	£20
10	5d.	**blue and red** (5/4/38)	£11	9·00
11	5d.	**pea-green and red** (1/10/40)	40	50
12	6d.	**black** (Die 1) (5/4/38)	£10	9·00
13	6d.	**black** (Die 2) (1/10/40)	1·50	50
		a slate-black (Die 2) (10/1/44)	£10	8·00
14	8d.	**carmine-red** (5/11/48)	50	60
15	1/–	**yellow and blk** (5/4/38	60	50
16	1/5	**blk and car** (13/6/40)	50	60
17	1/6	**ultramarine** (1/8/50)	70	90
18	2/–	**orange and pur-vio** (5/4/38)	50	80
19	2/6	**emer and brn** (5/4/38)	1·00	1·50
20	5/–	**dp green and purple** (5/4/38)	1·50	1·50
21	10/–	**brn-orange and emer** (13/3/50)	8·50	£10
22	£1	**ult and cherry-red** (13/3/50)	£11	£12
1/22		**set** (21)	£55	£50
SP 1/20		**specimen set** perf (15)	£150	‡

As Nos. 1, 4 and 8 but Perf. 14 (L).

23	½d.	**green** (/41)	1·50	1·00
24	1½d.	**carmine** (Die 2) (/42)	3·50	4·00
25	2½d.	**red-brown and green** (6/1/42)	30	30

As Nos. 1, 4, 7, 8 and 13 but Perf. 12 (C).

26	½d. **green** (26/8/48) ..	25	25
27	1½d. **carmine** (21/7/49) ..	25	30
	a re-entry	£20	£20
28	2d. **yel-grn and magenta** (27/5/46)	25	25
29	2½d. **red-brown and green** (19/1/48)	20	20
30	6d. **black** (Die II) (5/6/47)	35	40

As Nos. 14 and 17 but Perf. 13 x 13¼ (C).

31	8d. **carmine-red** (7/6/50)	50	1·00
32	1/6 **ultramarine** (16/2/55)	1 00	1·50

27a Top frame right corner (Row 4/2) is double.

1½d.

Die I—No figure in boat.

Die 2—Figure in boat.

2d. and 6d.

Die I—Without 180° under ISLANDS.

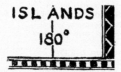

Die 2—With 180° under ISLANDS.

1941 (Feb. 10th) No. 6 surcharged 2½d.

33	2½d./2d. **red-brn and green**	10	10

There are two types of surcharge, one of which has a small spur at the left of the head of "2" and which appears on the 1st, 3rd and 5th vertical rows. The other type appears on the 2nd, 4th and 6th vertical rows.

SPECIAL ISSUES

1937 (May 12th) Coronation. As Aden but Printers Bradbury, Wilkinson. Perf. 11 x 11¾ (C).

S1	1d. **dp purple**	30	30
S2	2d. **dp grey**	40	30
S3	3d. **dp prussian-blue** ..	40	30
SP	S1/3 **specimen set** perf (3)	£20	‡

1946 (Aug. 17th) Victory. As Aden.

S4	2½d. **green**	10	10
	a dble print, one albino	£200	—
S5	3d. **grey-blue**	20	15
SP	S4/5 **specimen set** perf (2)	£18	‡

S4a One sheet was discovered with double impression, one albino.

1948 (Dec. 17th) Silver Wedding. As Aden.

S6	2½d. **green**	15	10
S7	5/– **slate-violet**	4·00	5·00

1949 (Oct. 10th) U.P.U. As Aden.

S8	2d. **magenta**	20	25
S9	3d. **indigo**	30	40
S10	8d. **carmine-red**	50	75
S11	1/6 **azure**	1·00	1·00
	S8/11 **set** (4)	2·00	2·25

HEALTH (CHARITY) ISSUE

1951 (Sept. 17th) Designs, 1d./1d. (Fijian Boys Bathing); 2d./1d. (Fijian Footballer). Printers (recess) Bradbury, Wilkinson. Perf. 13¼ x 13½ (C). Sheets 10 x 6 or 6 x 10.

H1	1d.+1d. **sepia-brown** ..	20	40
H2	2d.+1d. **green**	40	50

Number issued—

1d.+1d., 465,646; 2d.+1d., 465,743.

POSTAGE DUE STAMPS

1917 (Jan. 1st) **Locally type-set on thick yellow-white laid paper without gum. Wmk. figure of Britannia within a crowned oval with the word "DANVERS" above. Perf. 11. Sheets 2d., 7 x 12.** The other values were printed in a composite sheet of 96, consisting of twelve rows of eight stamps – 1d., 1d., 1d., ½d., 4d., 3d., 3d., 3d.

GD1	½d. **black**	.. ..	£150	£140
GD2	1d. **black**	.. ..	£50	£30
GD3	2d. **black**	.. ..	£50	£25
GD4	3d. **black**	.. ..	£65	£35
GD5	4d. **black**	.. ..	£150	£130
GD6	**se tenant strip of 8** (3 x 1d, ½d, 4d., 3 x 3d.)		£2000	—
GD6A	**se tenant strip of 4** (1d., ½d., 4d., 3d.)		£1250	—

1917 (April) **As before but narrow setting: fraction bar in GD7 more nearly vertical. Sheets 7 x 12.**

GD7	½d. **black**	.. ..	£180	£80
GD8	1d. **black**	.. ..	£65	£45
GD9	2d. **black**	.. ..	£220	£220

Numbers printed: GD3 2,604; GD9 4,368 (of which only 420 were sold and 3,948 destroyed).

1918 (June 1) (*Typo*) **De La Rue. Wmk. Multiple Crown CA. Perf. 14. Sheets 6 x 10.**

GD10	½d. **black**	.. ..	75	75
GD11	1d. **black**	.. ..	75	75
GD12	2d. **black**	.. ..	80	1·00
GD13	3d. **black**	.. ..	1·50	2·00
GD14	4d. **black**	.. ..	2·50	2·75
GD10/14	**set (5v)**	.. ..	6·00	7·00
SPGD10/14	**specimen set (5v)**		£60	‡

1940 (July 1st) **Design, Value in White Circle Printers** (*recess*) **Waterlow & Sons. Wmk. Mult. Script CA. Perf. 12½ (L). Sheets 12 x 10.**

PD1	1d. **emerald**	.. ..	30	50
PD2	2d. **emerald**	.. ..	40	70
PD3	3d. **emerald**	.. ..	40	80
PD4	4d. **emerald**	.. ..	70	1·00
PD5	5d. **emerald**	.. ..	1·00	1·25
PD6	6d. **emerald**	.. ..	1·50	1·75
PD7	1/– **dp crimson**	.. ..	2·25	2·50
PD8	1/6 **dp crimson**	.. ..	4·50	5·50
PD1/8	**set (8)** ..	.. ..	£10	£13

GAMBIA

The Gambia was the oldest and smallest British territory in Africa. In 1821 it was placed under Sierra Leone administration, becoming a separate colony in 1843; it was again amalgamated with Sierra Leone from 1866 to 1888.

There was no postal service prior to 1855 when foreign letters were first sent, with cash to defray postage, to the recently opened Post Office in Sierra Leone. The opening of a Post Office at Bathurst probably coincided with the first issue of stamps in 1869; but even as late as 1875, letters were franked with French Colonial Stamps and despatched through Senegal.

1869 (Jan.) *Typo* **and embossed De La Rue. Sheets 5 x 3. No watermark. Imperf.**

V1	4d.	**brown**	£300	£120
V2	4d.	**pale brown**	£250	£130
V3	6d.	**deep blue** ..	£250	£110
V4	6d.	**blue**	£325	£125
V5	6d.	**pale blue** ..	£100	£650
SPV1/5		**specimen set** (2v)	£600	‡

Numbers issued – 4d. 14,265; 6d. 11,640.

1874 (Jan.) **As before, but Wmk. Crown CC.**

V6	4d.	**brown** ..	£210	£120
V7	4d.	**pale brown**	£240	£120
V8	6d.	**deep blue** ..	£200	£140
V9	6d.	**blue** ..	£190	£120
SPV6/9		**specimen set** (2v)	£600	‡

The watermark on this issue is difficult to find and only rarely does it fall centrally on the stamp. It may be found inverted, reversed or inverted and reversed; and stamps may be found with portions of the "CROWN COLONIES" watermark (14 mm or 9 mm letters) normally found in the margins.

Numbers Issued – 4d. 5,190; 6d. 5,160.

1880 (June) **As before, but Perf. 14 (initially Line and later printings Comb.).**

V10	½d.	**deep orange** ..	3·00	5·00
V11	½d.	**pale orange** ..	3·00	5·00
		a embossing double		
		(one inverted)	—	—
		b perf. double (top		
		and sides)	—	—
V12	1d.	**deep lake**	4·00	3·50
		a embossing double	—	—
V13	1d.	**pale lake**	4·00	3·50
V14	2d.	**rose**	£11	7·00
V15	2d.	**pale rose** ..	£11	7·00
		a embossing double	—	—
		b embossing treble	—	—
V16	3d.	**dark ultramarine**	£22	£17
V17	3d.	**pale ultramarine**	£30	£20
		a embossing double	—	—
V18	4d.	**deep brown** ..	£95	£10

V19	4d.	**pale brown** ..	£85	£10
V20	6d.	**deep blue** ..	£45	£30
V21	6d.	**blue**	£45	£30
V22	1/–	**dark green** ..	£120	£75
V23	1/–	**green**	£120	£70
V10/23		**set** (7v)	£275	£140
SPV10/23		**specimen set** (7v)	£35	‡

This issue was originally printed with upright watermark, which may be found inverted or reversed; stamps may also be found with portions of the "CROWN COLONIES marginal watermark. All values were subsequently printed with sideways watermark which may also be found inverted.

Double, and sometimes treble, embossing occurs on all values of 1880-87 issues in some cases one being inverted. Double and treble perforations also occur on the ½d. value (V11 & V25) whilst on the 6d. value (V20, 21, 38 & 39) it can be found off square thus creating the "sloping label" variety and these are worth three to four times normal.

Numbers Issued – ½d. 68,010; 1d. 60,690; 2d. 40,155; 3d. 25,200; 4d. 45, 795; 6d. 11,340; 1/– 7,125.

1886 (Jan.) **-87 As before but Wmk. Crown CA (sideways). Perf. 14 (Comb.).**

V24	½d.	**dark green** ..	60	70
V25	½d.	**grey-green** (1887)	70	90
		a embossing double	—	—
		b embossing double		
		(one inverted)	—	—
		c perf. treble (botm)	—	—
V26	1d.	**dark car** (1887) ..	5·00	6·00
V27	1d.	**crimson** (1887) ..	1·50	1·75
		a aniline	7·00	6·00
		b embossing double	—	—
V28	1d.	**deep lake**	—	£6500
V29	2d.	**dp orange** (1887)	2·25	2·50
V30	2d.	**orange** (1887) ..	2·50	3·00
		a embossing double	—	—
		b embossing treble	—	—
V31	2½d.	**deep ultramarine**	3·50	4·00
V32	2½d.	**slate-blue** ..	3·50	4·00
		a embossing double	—	—
V33	3d.	**dark slate-grey** ..	2·50	4·00
V34	3d.	**grey**	2·50	4·00
		a embossing double	—	—
V35	3d.	**pearl grey** ..	2·50	4·00
V36	4d.	**deep brown** ..	2·50	2·50
		a wmk. upright ..		
V37	4d.	**brown**	2·50	2·50
		a embossing double	..	—
V38	6d.	**dp bronze-green** ..	£12	£14
		a **yellowish-bronze**	£30	£20
V39	6d.	**grey-green** ..	£12	£14
		a embossing double	—	—
V40	1/–	**deep violet** ..	7·00	9·00
V41	1/–	**violet**	6·00	8·00
		a embossing double	—	—
		b embossing double		
		(one inverted) ..	—	—
V24/41		**set** (8v)	£30	£36
SPV24/41		**specimen set** (8v)	£30	‡

V25c: It is believed only five copies existed, one being in the Tapling Collection. For further information about double embossing perforations see note after V23.

V28: This is the colour of V12: a copy is in the Royal Collection. Others are known, all used.

V35: This particular shade comes from sheets having three dots in the left margin and one dot in the right margin – the opposite of the normal marginal markings.

Imperf. copies of the ½d., (V25), 4d. (V37), 6d. and 1/– (V40) are believed to be from Proof Sheets.

Imperf. copies of the ½d. (V25). 4d. (V37), 6d. and 1/– (V40) are believed to be from Proof Sheets.

All values are known with the sideways watermark inverted. Stamps may also be found with portions of the "CROWN COLONIES" marginal watermark.

Numbers Issued – ½d. 226,335; 1d. 118,995; 2d. 82,500; 2½d. 170,370; 3d. 52,470; 4d. 90,600; 6d. 60,150; 1/– 45,000.

All stamps from V42 to G39 are *Typo* (De La Rue). Perf. 14.

1898 (May) -1902 Wmk. Crown CA. Sheets 120 – two panes, each 6 x 10.

V42	½d.	**dull green** ..	1·00	1·20
V43	1d.	**carmine**	1·50	1·00
V44	2d.	**orange and mauve**	1·50	2·50
V45	2½d.	**ultramarine** ..	2·00	3·00
V46	3d.	**rose-purple and blue** (Plate 2) ..	4·00	6·00
V47	3d.	**deep purple and dark blue** (1902)	£30	£50
V48	4d.	**brown and blue**	4·00	7·00
V49	6d.	**ol-grn and car** ..	6·00	£11
V50	1/–	**violet and green**	£10	£15
V42/50		**set** (8v)	£28	£45
SPV42/50		**specimen set** (8v)	£95	‡

V47 only comes from a November 1901 printing from Plate 3. The earliest known use is January 1902 and as it was replaced by the KE7 issue in April 1902, this stamp is rare (2,400 printed).

A constant variety in the form of a malformed "S" in "POSTAGE", resembling a reversed "2", occurs in the right hand panel of Stamp No. 39 of the left hand panes printed from Plate 2; the flaw was corrected on Plate 3.

Numbers Issued – ½d. 87,600; 1d. 127,320; 2d. 30,000 2½d. 45,120; 3d. (V46), 4d., 5d.. 6d. and 1/– 15,000 each; V47 2,400.

1902 (Mar. 13th) -05 As before, but head of King Edward VII.

E1	½d.	**green** (19/4/02)	50	80
E2	1d.	**carmine**	1·00	90
E3	2d.	**orange and mauve** (14/6/02) ..	2·50	3·00
E4	2½d.	**ultra** (14/6/02) ..	5·00	6·00
E5	3d.	**magenta and ultra** (19/4/02) ..	5·00	5·00

E6	4d.	**brown and ultra** (14/6/02) ..	5·00	7·00
E7	6d.	**sage-green and car** (14/6/02) ..	5·00	7·00
E8	1/–	**violet and green** (14/6/02)	£20	£25
E9	1/6	**grn and car/yel** (6/4/05) ..	£12	£18
E10	2/–	**deep slate and or** (14/6/02) ..	£20	£25
E11	2/6	**pur and brn/yel** (6/4/05) ..	£25	£35
E12	3/–	**car and grn/yel** (6/4/05) ..	£30	£40
E1/12		**set** (12v) ..	£130	£165
SPE1/12		**specimen set** (12V)	£130	‡

Numbers Issued – E8 6,000; E9 14,640; E10 7,440; E11 14,640; E12 14,880.

1904 (Aug.) -09 As before, but Wmk. Multiple Crown CA.

E13	½d.	**green** (23/2/06) ..	40	50
E14	½d.	**blue-green** (1909)	40	50
E15	1d.	**carmine**	70	50
E16	1d.	**red** (1909)	40	30
E17	2d.	**orange and mauve** (23/3/06) ..	4·00	5·00
E18	2d.	**grey** (1909) ..	1·20	1·00
E19	2½d.	**blue** (23/2/06) ..	2·00	2·00
E20	2½d.	**blue and ultra** ..	3·50	4·00
E21	3d.	**magenta and ultra** (23/2/06) ..	4·00	4·50
E22	3d.	**pur/yel** (1909) ..	2·50	2·00
		a on lemon yellow	0·00	0·00
E23	4d.	**brown and ultra** (23/2/06) ..	5·00	7·00
E24	4d.	**blk and red/yel** (1909)	1·25	1·50
		a on bright yellow	2·00	2·50
E25	5d.	**grey and black** (6/4/05) ..	5·00	6·00
E26	5d.	**orange and purple** (1909) ..	2·50	2·00
E27	6d.	**sage-grn and car** (23/2/06) ..	3·50	6·00
E28	6d.	**dull and bright pur** (1909)	2·00	2·50
E29	7½d.	**green and carmine** (6/4/05) ..	4·00	6·00
E30	7½d.	**brown and blue** (1909)	2·50	2·75
E31	10d.	**olive-brn and car** (6/4/05) ..	7·50	£10
E32	10d.	**pale sage-grn and carmine** (1909)	2·50	2·75
E33	1/–	**violet and green** (23/2/06) ..	£22	£25
E34	1/–	**blk/grn** (1909) ..	3·00	4·00
E35	1/6	**vio and grn** (1909)	8·00	9·00
E36	2/–	**deep slate and or** (23/2/06) ..	£35	£40
E37	2/–	**pur and blue/blue** (1909)	7·00	9·00
E38	2/6	**blk and red/blue** (1909)	£18	£18
E39	3/–	**yellow and green** (1909)	£25	£30
E13/39		**set** (27v) ..	£165	£195
SPE13/39		**specimen set** (17v, E25, 29, 31 and 1909 issue) ..	£140	‡

Numbers Issued – E14 85,560; E16 146,400; E18 40,320; E22/22a 36,720; E24/24a, E28, E32, E37 16,440 each; E25 14,160; E26, E30, E34, E35, E38, E39 16,680 each; E29, E31 14,400 each; E33 16,800; E36 8,160.

1906 (Apr. 10th) Nos E11 and E12 surcharged in black at Bathurst.

(a) "HALF-PENNY" (Setting 6 x 5) Space between letters and bars 5 mm. (Rows 1, 2 and 5) or 4 mm. (Rows 3 and 4).

E40	½d. on 2/6	**pur and brn/ yel** (5 mm.) ..	£20	£22
	a	"PFNNY" (R2/1) ..	£75	£90
	b	dropped "Y (R5/1) ..	£75	£90
E41	½d. on 2/6	**pur and brn/ yel** (4 mm.) ..	£25	£25

(b) "ONE PENNY" (Setting 6 x 10).

E42	1d. on 3/–	**car and grn/ yel**	£25	£28
	a	sur. double	£1100	—
	b	dropped "Y	£75	£90

E42*a* : The second impression, in grey-black, is slightly below and to the right of the normal black surcharge.

E42*b* is believed to be constant on Nos. 33 and 46.

There are several other minor flaws arising from the use of worn type.

These provisions were in use from April 10th–23rd during a shortage of ½d. and 1d. values, but copies are known used at later dates.

Numbers surcharged – E40/41 3,780 (3,000); E42 4,500 (2,000). The numbers reputed to have been sold are given in brackets: unsold remainders were destroyed on October 16th 1906.

1912 (Sept. 1st) -21 As before, but head of King George V.

G1	½d.	**pale green** ..	40	50
G2	½d.	**deep green** ..	40	50
G3	½d.	**green**	40	50
	a	on thick grey-blue paper	2·50	2·50
G4	1d.	**pale red**	50	40
G5	1d.	**deep red**	50	40

G6	1d.	**red**	40	40
	a	on thick grey-blue paper ..	3·00	3·00
	b	on semi-transparent paper	2·50	2·50
G7	1d.	**scarlet** (1916) ..	50	40
G8	1½d.	**ol-grn and bl-grn**	50	75
	a	dp olive, blu-grn	75	90
G9	2d.	**slate-grey**	50	60
G10	2½d.	**deep blue**	1·75	1·50
G11	2½d.	**blue**	1·50	1·25
G12	3d.	**purple/yellow** ..	50	60
	a	on lemon (1917)	7·00	9·00
	b	on or-buff (1920)	8·00	3·00
	c	on bright yellow	50	90
	d	on pale yel (thin)	60	1·00
G13	4d.	**blk and red/yel** ..	2·00	3·00
	a	on lemon ..	1·50	3·50
	b	on orange-buff	2·50	3·50
	c	on bright yellow	2·50	3·50
	d	wmk. inverted ..	£30	—
G14	5d.	**orange and violet**	75	1·50
G15	6d.	**dull and bright pur**	80	1·20
G16	7½d.	**brown and blue**	1·00	1·50
G17	10d.	**sage-grn and car**	2·50	4·00
	a	dp sage and car	3·00	4·50
G18	1/–	**black/green** ..	1·00	2·00
	a	on blue-green	1·25	3·00
	b	on emerald black	1·50	4·00
G19	1/6	**violet and green**	4·00	5·50
G20	2/–	**pur and blue/blue**	4·00	5·50
G21	2/6	**blk and red/blue**	6·50	6·50
	a	on greenish-blue	7·00	7·00
G22	3/–	**yellow and green**	8·00	9·00
G23	5/–	**grn and red/pale yel C** (1921) ..	£18	£23
	a	on yellow-brown C (1921) ..	£20	£25
G1/23		**set** (17v)	£50	£65
SPG1/23		**specimen set** (17v)	£140	‡

G3*a*/G6*a* were war-time printings.

There is a considerable range of shades of all values.

A constant variety showing a vertical split through the apex of "A" in "POSTAGE" in the right hand panel of Stamp No. 45 in the left hand pane is found on all values except the 5/–. This flaw was repaired in later printings from 1918. The variety is worth 10 times normal.

Numbers Issued – G12 84,840; G13 58,680; G18 36,600; G19 12,240; G20 12,120; G21 12,000; G22 12,120; G23 12,378.

1921-22 As before, but Wmk. Multiple Script CA.

G24	½d.	**dull green** ..	40	75
G25	½d.	**green**	40	75
G26	1d.	**carmine-red** ..	50	60
G27	1d.	**deep red** ..	2·00	3·00
G28	1½d.	**ol-grn and bl-grn**	1·25	2·00
G29	2d.	**grey**	1·25	2·00
G30	2d.	**dark grey** ..	1·00	2·00
G31	2½d.	**blue**	90	2·00
G32	2½d.	**bright blue** ..	2·00	4·00
G33	5d.	**orange and purple**	2·00	4·00
	a	wmk. reversed ..	£15	—
G34	6d.	**dull and bright pur**	2·50	4·00
	a	wmk. reversed ..	—	—
G35	7½d.	**brown and blue**	1·50	4·25
G36	7½d.	**dp brown and blue**	2·00	4·50
	a	wmk. reversed	£20	—

G37	10d.	pl-sage-gr and car	2·00	5·00
		a wmk. reversed ..	£25	—
G38	4/–	black and red (C)	£18	£22
		(1922) ..	£20	£22
G39	4/–	grey-blk and red		
		(C) (1922) ..	£20	£22
		a wmk. inverted	—	—
G24/39		set (10v)	£30	£45
SPG24/39		specimen set (10v)	£90	‡

Number issued – G38/39 12,500.

1922 (Sept. 1st) -38 Recess. De La Rue. Perf. 14 (see Note). Sheets low values 10 x 8: Shilling values 12 x 5.

(a) Watermark Multiple Crown CA.

G40	4d.	pale green ..	60	1·00
G41	4d.	vermilion/yellow	60	1·00
G42	7½d.	purple/pale yel ..	1·50	3·50
G43	7½d.	deep pur/pale yel	1·50	3·50
G44	1/–	deep purple/yel ..	4·00	7·00
G45	1/–	reddish/pur/yel ..	4·00	7·00
		a wmk. inverted	£30	—
G46	5/–	deep grn/deep yel	£22	£25
G47	5/–	blue-grn/pale buff	£22	£25
		a wmk. inverted	£45	—

(b) Watermark Multiple Script CA.

G48	½d.	pale green ..	30	25
G49	½d.	dark blue-green	30	25
G50	1d.	deep brown ..	20	20
G51	1d.	yellow-brown	20	20
G52	1½d.	rose-scarlet ..	35	25
G53	1½d.	rose-carmine ..	40	30
G54	1½d.	crimson-red ..	50	30
G55	2d.	light pearl-grey	50	60
G56	2d.	dark slate-grey ..	60	75
G57	2½d.	yellow ..	50	2·50
G58	2½d.	ochre	50	2·50
G59	3d.	brt ultramarine ..	75	60
G60	3d.	deep steel blue ..	60	50
G61	4d.	red/yellow ..	75	2·00
G62	5d.	sage-green ..	1·50	3·00
G63	6d.	rose-claret ..	1·00	1·00
G64	6d.	claret	1·25	1·25
G65	7½d.	purple/yellow ..	2·00	5·00
G66	10d.	blue ..	2·50	4·00
G67	1/–	purple/yel buff	1·50	2·00
G68	1/–	sepia/orange buff	8·00	8·00
G69	1/–	reddish pur/yel buff	4·00	4·00
		a on orange buff ..	5·00	4·00
		b on yellow ..	6·00	4·00
G70	1/6	deep blue ..	3·50	5·00
G71	1/6	steel blue ..	3·50	5·00
G72	2/–	violet /blue ..	5·00	4·25
G73	2/–	sl-pur/blue ..	6·00	5·00
G74	2/6	deep green ..	5·00	5·50
G75	3/–	violet	7·00	9·00

G76	3/–	slate-purple ..	£95	£150
G77	4/–	brown	6·50	£10
G78	5/–	deep green/yell ..	£10	£15
G79	5/–	blue/grn/lem-yel	£12	£15
G80	10/–	bright olive green	£60	£65
G81	10/–	deep sage-green	£50	£65
G40/81		set (23v) ..	£130	£160
SPG40/81		specimen set (23v)	£250	‡

The above is a simplified listing of a great variety of shades of all values.

Although listed as Perf. 14, there are several different gauges of perf. on this issue.

Pence values Perf. 14 (Line): G40/43 and G48/56, G59/60, G62/66, Perf. 14 x 13¾ (Comb.): G48/61 and G65. Perf. 13¾ (Line): G48/54, G59/60 and G63/64.

Shilling values, Perf. 14 (Line): G44/45 and G67/79. Perf. 13¾ (Comb.): G46/47 and G67/69, G72/73 and G75/81. Perf. 14 x 13¾ (Line): G67/69, G77 and G80/81. Perf. 13¾ x 14 (Line): G67/71 and G78/79.

G76 is 13¾ (Comb.) whereas G75 is 14 (Line).

Numbers Issued – ½d. 498,960; 1d. 380,840; 1½d. 900,960; 2d. 166,000; 2½d. 32,320; 3d. 204,930; 4d. 36,640; 5d. 23,280; 6d. 92,880; 7½d. 29,840; 10d. 25,040; 1/– 74,220; 1/6 15,720; 2/– 30,750; 2/6 28,260; 3/– 10,740; 4/– 21,720; 5/– 19,500; 10/– 10,800.

The 2½d., 4d., 5d., 7½d., 10d., 1/6 and 3/– values were withdrawn and demonetised on August 1st, 1929, and the remaining values were withdrawn in April 1938.

1935 (May 6th) Silver Jubilee. Recess. Bradbury Wilkinson. Wmk. Multiple Script CA. Perf. 11 x 12. Sheets 6 x 10.

G82	1½d.	dp blue and scar	25	25
		a extra flagstaff ..	£35	£42
G83	3d.	brown and dp blue	90	1·00
		a extra flagstaff	£60	£75
G84	6d.	light bl and ol-grn	1·10	1·40
		a extra flagstaff ..	£60	£75
G85	1/–	slate and purple	1·20	1·40
		a extra flagstaff ..	£80	£95
G82/85		set (4v) ..	3·50	4·00
SPG82/85		specimen set (4v)	£25	‡

G82a/85a: Extra flagstaff occurs on No. 49 (Row 9/1).

On a small number of sheets G84*a* and G85*a* the extra flagstaff was erased on the stamp by scratching with a pointed instrument. Price £30 in ⊞ from corner of sheet.

Remainders were withdrawn December 31st, 1935.

1938 (April 1st) -50 Design, Elephant and Palm (*Badge of Colony*). **Printers** (*recess*) **Bradbury, Wilkinson. Perf. (12 L). Sheets 10 x 6.**

1	½d. **blk and emerald-grn**	5	5
2	1d. **mauve-pur and choc**	5	5
3	1½d. **brown-lake and car**	7·00	4·00
	a brn-lake and rose-scar /(40) ..	10	10
4	1½d. **dull blue and black** (2/1/45)	30	40
5	2d. **dull blue and black** ..	20	50
6	2d. **brn-lake and rose-scar** (1/10/43) ..	15	20
7	3d. **light and deep blue** ..	10	15
8	5d. **sage and pur-brown** (13/3/41) .. .	25	35
9	6d. **olive-grn and claret** ..	20	15
	a dp olive and dp claret		

	(30/1/50) ..	15	15
10	1/– **slate and pur-vio** ..	35	30
11	1/3 **chocolate and dull blue** (28/11/46) ..	50	60
12	2/– **carmine and blue** ..	75	90
	a dp car and blue (9/4/45) ..	85	95
13	2/6 **sepia and greyish-olive**	1·50	1·00
14	4/– **vermilion and deep pur**	1·50	1·75
15	5/– **dk blue and vermilion**	1·75	2·00
16	10/– **dp orange and black**	5·00	6·00
1/16	**set** (16)	£12	£13
SP 1/16	**specimen set** perf (12)	£50	‡

SPECIAL ISSUES

1937 (May 12th) Coronation. As Aden but Printers Bradbury. Wilkinson. Perf. 11 x 11¾ (C).

S1	1d. **light brown** ..	10	10
S2	1½d. **carmine-red** ..	15	15
S3	3d. **blue**	25	35
SP S1/3	**specimen set** perf (3)	£15	‡

1946 (Aug. 6th) Victory. As Aden.

S4	1½d. **black**	10	10
S5	3d. **dp blue**	10	15
SP S4/5	**specimen set** perf (2)	£18	‡

1948 (Dec. 24th) Silver Wedding. As Aden.

S6	1½d. **black**	10	10
S7	£1 **dull purple**	8·00	£10

1949 (Oct. 10th) U.P.U. As Aden.

S8	1½d. **slate**	10	10
S9	3d. **indigo**	20	25
S10	6d. **reddish-mauve** ..	40	50
S11	1/– **dull violet**	60	70
S8/11	**set** (4)	1·25	1·50

GIBRALTAR

Gibraltar was captured by British Forces in 1704 and was ceded to Great Britain by the Treaty of Utrecht in 1713. The first Post Office was opened in 1807 as a branch of the G.P.O. London; and from 1857 to 1885 contemporary G.B. stamps were used.

They were cancelled initially by "G" in a transverse oval of horizontal bars, and subsequently by "A26" in small oval of horizontal bars or "A26" in upright oval in duplex with a small Gibraltar datestamp.

The first Gibraltar stamps were issued when the administration of the Post Office was taken over by the Colonial Office. All issues from V1 to V34 were used without overprint in various towns in Morocco Agencies (q.v.) which remained under the control of the Gibraltar Post Office until 1907.

1857-1885 Stamps of Great Britain (Queen Victoria) identified by their Catalogue Nos. after prefix 'G' or 'A'.

(i) Cancelled 'G' in transverse oval of horizontal bars. (3/9/57).

GV22	1d. **red-brown**
GV24	1d. **red-brown**
GV28	1d. **red-brown**
GV33	1d. **red-brown**
GV38	1d. **pale-red**
GV30	2d. **blue**
GV32	2d. **blue**
GV36	2d. **blue**
GV51	2d. **blue**
GV44	4d. **rose-carmine**
GV45	6d. **lilac**
GV47	1/- **green**

(ii) Cancelled 'A26' in transverse oval of horizontal bars or 'A26' in transverse or upright oval of horizontal bars in duplex with named circular date-stamp. (20/2/59).

(a) 1857-83.

AV108	½d. **rose-red**
	(Various Plates)
AV39	1d. **rose-red**
AV49	1d. **rose-red**
	(Various Plates)
AV138	1d. **venetian red**

AV110	1½d.	**rose-red**
AV36	2d.	**blue**
AV51	2d.	**blue**
AV52	2d.	**blue**
AV120	2½d.	**rosy-mauve**
AV121	2½d.	**rosy-mauve**
AV121a	2½d.	**rosy-mauve** (LH-FL)
AV122	2½d.	**rosy-mauve**
AV123	2½d.	**blue**
AV139	2½d.	**blue**
AV53	3d.	**carmine-rose**
AV70	3d.	**rose**
AV78	3d.	**rose**
AV124	3d.	**rose**
AV140	3d.	**rose**
AV144	3d. on 3d. **lilac**
AV44	4d.	**rose-carmine**
AV59	4d.	**bright red**
AV72	4d.	**vermilion**
AV131	4d.	**vermilion**
AV133	4d.	**sage-green**
AV135	4d.	**grey-brown**
AV141	4d.	**grey-brown**
AV45	6d.	**lilac**
AV62	6d.	**lilac**
AV75	6d.	**lilac**
AV75b	*a* wmk. error
AV79	6d.	**lilac**
AV82	6d.	**bright violet** (Hyphen)
AV83	6d.	**dull violet** (No Hyphen)
AV114	6d.	**chestnut**
AV115	6d.	**buff**
AV119	6d.	**grey**

AV126	6d.	**grey**
AV142	6d.	**grey**
AV145	6d. on 6d. **lilac**
AV145a	*a* slanting dots
AV64	9d.	**bistre**
AV65	9d.	**straw**
AV76	9d.	**straw**
AV76a	*a* wmk. error
AV86	9d.	**straw**
AV88	10d.	**red-brown**
AV47	1/-	**green**
AV68	1/-	**green**
AV68a	*a* 'k' circled
AV77	1/-	**green**
AV92	1/-	**green**
AV127	1/-	**green**
AV130	1/-	**orange-brown**
AV143	1/-	**orange-brown**
AV95	2/-	**blue**
AV101	5/-	**rose**

(b) 1880-84.

AV146	½d.	**deep green**
AV147	½d.	**pale green**
AV148	½d.	**slate blue**
AV149	1d.	**lilac (14 pearls)**
AV151	1d.	**lilac (16 pearls)**
AV138	1½d.	**venetian red**
AV156	2d.	**pale rose**
AV157	2d.	**deep rose**
AV158	5d.	**indigo**

(c) 1883-84.

AV160	2d.	**lilac**
AV161	2½d.	**lilac**
AV162	3d.	**lilac**
AV163	4d.	**dull green**
AV165	6d.	**dull green**

1886 (Jan. 1st) Stamps of Bermuda (Q.V.) overprinted "GIBRALTAR" in black sans-serif capitals by De La Rue. The overprinting was done on a special printing of the Bermuda stamps (Wmk. Crown CA. Perf. 14). Sheets 240 — four panes, each 6 x 10.

V1	½d.	**dull green**	..	5·00	5·00
V2	1d.	**rose-red**	..	£12	7·00
V3	2d.	**purple-brown**	..	£40	£20
V4	2½d.	**ultramarine** ..	..	£40	5·00
V5	4d.	**orange-red** ..	..	£50	£55
V6	6d.	**deep lilac**	..	£110	£110
V7	1/-	**yellow-brown**	..	£220	£200
V1/7		**set** (7v)	..	£450	£400
SPV1/7		**specimen set** (7v)		£480	‡

Dangerous forgeries, particularly of V7, exist.

V4 exists with blue/black ovpt—£200   £80.

Numbers Issued—V1, 168,000; V2, 301,680; V3, 24,000; V4, 266,880; V5, 11,040; V6, 8,160; V7, 4,320.

All stamps from V8 to G61 are (*typo*) De La Rue. Perf. 14.

1886 (Dec.) Wmk. Crown CA. Sheets V8/9/11; 240 — four panes, each 6 x 10. V10/12-14: 120 — two panes each 6 x 10.

V8	½d.	**dull green** ..	..	1·50	1·50
V9	1d.	**rose** ..	..	6·00	2·00
V10	2d.	**brown-purple**	..	£16	£16
V11	2½d.	**blue** ..	..	£16	5·00
V12	4d.	**orange-brown**	..	£34	£22
V13	6d.	**lilac** ..	..	£42	£42
V14	1/-	**bistre** ..	..	£100	£95
V8/14		**set** (7v)	..	£210	£175
SPV8/14		**specimen set** (7v)	..	£120	‡

See also Nos. V35 to V41.

V10/11 exist with inverted wmk.

Die Proofs of V9 and V10, without values, are known in black on glazed card. Finished Proofs exist of all values on watermarked paper (imperf.).

Collectors are warned of forgeries of V13 and V14 on genuine paper from which the print of lower values has been removed.

Numbers Issued—V8, 379,680; V9, 970,080; V10, 120,720; V11, 1,309,200; V12, 31,200; V13, 24,360; V14, 20,740.

1889 (July) Nos. V8–V14 surcharged "CENTIMOS" in black sans-serif capitals by De La Rue. Setting 6 x 10.

V15	5c. on ½d.	green	3·00	3·00
V16	10c. on 1d.	rose	3·00	3·00
V17	25c. on 2d.	brn-purple	5·00	6·00
	a short "I" in "CENTIMOS"	£90	£100
	b broken "N" in "CENTIMOS"	£90	£100
V18	25c. on 2½d.	bright blue	6·00	4·00
	a short "I" in "CENTIMOS"	£60	£80
	b broken "N" in "CENTIMOS"	£60	£80
V19	40c. on 4d.	orange-brn	£15	£18
V20	50c. on 6d.	bright lilac	£18	£20
V21	75c. on 1/–	bistre	£20	£22
V15/21		set (7v)	£65	£75
SPV15/21		specimen set (7v)	£130	‡

V17*a*, V18*a* occur on Stamp No. 32 (Row 6/2 in pane of 60).

V17*b*, V18*b* occur on Stamp No. 59 (Row 10/5 in pane of 60).

5   **5**

Type I   Type II

Two varieties of the figure "5" are found on the 5c., 25c., 50c. and 75c. Type II is the scarcer and occurs as indicated below on panes of 60 (6 x 10).

V15 1st, 5th and 6th vertical rows.
V18 2nd and 5th vertical rows.
V17, V20, V21 2nd vertical row.

V20 is stated to be known bisected and used for a 25c. rate, but such use was not authorised.

Numbers Issued—V15, 57,600; V16, 100,800; V17, 55,200; V18, 241,200; V19, 15,000; V20, 15,160; V21, 12,800.

1889 (Nov.) -96 Wmk. Crown CA. Sheets 120 – two panes, each 6 x 10.

V22	5c.	green	30	35
V23	10c.	carmine	30	35
		a bisect diag. (5c) on cover 1891	‡	£750
		b value omitted	£5500	—
V24	20c.	olive-grn (11/95)	2·50	4·00
V25	20c.	olive-grn and brn (6/96)	4·00	4·50
V26	25c.	ultramarine	2·25	50
V27	25c.	dp ult (6/90)	4·00	50
V28	40c.	orange-brown	1·50	2·20
		a bisect diag. (20c.) on cover 1892	‡	£800
V29	50c.	bright lilac	2·00	3·00
		a bisect diag. (25c) on cover 1892.	‡	£650
V30	75c.	olive-green	£15	£16
V31	1p.	bistre	£16	£18
V32	1p.	bistre and ult (6/95)	3·00	4·00
V33	2p.	blk and car (11/95)	6·00	7·00
V34	5p.	slate-grey	£24	£28
V22/34		set (12v)	£80	£85
SPV22/34		specimen set (11v)	£135	‡

V22 exists with inverted wmk.

The bisected stamps V23*a*, V28*a*, V29*a* were only used in Tangier (see under Morocco Agencies). The 20c. (V24 or V25) is reputed to exist bisected and used for a 10c. rate, but no details are available.

V23*b* One pane of 60 missed the second stage (value) of the printing. No used copies are known.

Die Proofs without value, are known in black on glazed card. Plate Proofs exist in issued colours, imperforate. There are various imperforate Colour Trials of the 1p. and 5p. on unwatermarked paper.

Numbers Issued—V22, 2,378,640; V23, 3,900,600; V24, V25, 362,640; V26, V27 3,741,460; V28, 271,200; V29, 240,960; V30, 366,000; V31, 24,720; V32, 121,320; V33, 18,480; V34, 18,480.

1898 (Oct. 1st)-99 Re-issue in Sterling denominations. As V8–V14.

V35	½d.	grey-green	25	60
V36	1d.	carmine	60	40
V37	2d.	brn-pur and ult	4·00	3·50
V38	2½d.	br ultramarine	4·00	1·00
V39	4d.	or-brn and grn	7·50	6·00
V40	6d.	vio and red (1/99)	£10	£10
V41	1/–	bistre and carmine	£11	£13
V35/41		set (7v)	£36	£34
SPV35/41		specimen set (7v)	£90	‡

V39 may be found in various Colour Trials.

Numbers Issued—V35, 1,384,560; V36 3,583,680; V37, 144,600; V38, 589,440; V39 65,640; V40, 36,000; V41 96 000.

1903 (May 1st) **Wmk. Crown CA. Sheets, 120 – two panes, each 6 x 10 (½d.–1/–); 60 (10 x 6) 2/– – £1.**

E1	½d.	**grey-grn and grn**	1·00	1·50
E2	1d.	**dl purple/red**	2·00	1·00
		a "OA" for "CA" in wmk.	—	—
E3	2d.	**grey-grn and car**	3·50	3·75
E4	2½d.	**dl pur and blk/blue**	1·00	1·75
		a large "2" in fraction	£20	£20
E5	6d.	**dl pur and vio**	5·00	6·50
E6	1/–	**grey-brn and car.**	6·50	8·00
E7	2/–	**green and blue**	£32	£32
E8	4/–	**dl pur and grn**	£32	£36
E9	8/–	**dp pur and blk/blu**	£42	£50
E10	£1	**dl pur and blk/red**	£525	£500
E1/10		**set** (10v)	£635	£675
SPE1/10		**specimen set** (10v)	£200	‡

E2a Only one used copy has been recorded.

E4a See note after G20.

Die Proofs exist in black on glazed card. A variety of Colour Trials (2d. and 2/–) exist imperf. on watermarked paper.

1904-08 As before but wmk. Multiple Crown CA. Sheets, 120–two panes, each 6 x 10 (½d.– 1/–); 60 (10 x 6) 2/– – £1.

E11	½d.	**grey-grn and grn (O)** (1/6/04)	50	40
		dl and br green (C) (20/10/05)	50	40
E12	1d.	**lilac/red (O)** (10/10/04)	50	40
		a wmk. inverted	£50	—
		lilac/red (C) (16/9/05)	60	50
		b bisect diag. (½d.) on cover	—	£600
E13	2d.	**grey-grn and car (O)** (9/1/05)	2·25	2·50
		(C) (6/2/07)	2·50	2·70
E14	2½d.	**lilac and blk/blue (C)** (4/5/07)	8·00	9·00
		a large "2" in fraction	£40	£45
E15	6d.	**lilac and vio (O)** (19/4/06)	2·00	3·00
		dl pur and vio (C) (20/4/08)	2·25	3·00
E16	1/–	**blk and car (O)** (13/10/05)	6·00	5·00
		(C) (19/4/06)	6·00	5·50
E17	2/–	**green and blue (O)** (2/2/05)	£30	£32

		(C) (27/10/07)	£30	£32
E18	4/–	**lilac and green (C)** (6/08)	£50	£55
E19	£1	**lilac and black/red (C)** (15/3/08)	£540	£600
E11/19		**set** (9v)	£650	£740
SP E11/19		**specimen set** (7v)	£100	‡

E14a See note after G20.

Numbers Issued—E1/10 and E11/19 (O and C), Combined figures: ½d., 2,098,800; 1d., 3,196,060; 2d., 301,800; 2½d., 420,120; (E14, 24,000 only); 6d., 98,520; 1/–, 133,800; 2/–, 31,140; 4/–, 13,140; 8/–, 7,620; £1, 7,560.

1907-12 As before but new (Universal) colours. Sheets as before.

E20	½d.	**blue-green (O)**	40	30
E21	1d.	**carmine (O)**	40	30
E22	2d.	**greyish-slate (O)** (5/10)	2·00	2·50
E23	2½d.	**ultramarine (O)**	1·60	2·00
		a large "2" in fraction	£18	£20
E24	6d.	**dl and br pur (C)** (16/7/12)	£50	£85
E25	1/–	**grey-blk and blk/ grn (C)** ('10)	6·00	8·00
E26	2/–	**pur and br blue/ blue (C)** (4/10)	£28	£32
E27	4/–	**blk and car (C)**	£40	£45
E28	8/–	**pur and grn (C)** ('11)	£200	£225
E20/28		**set** (9v)	£320	£390
SPE20/28		**specimen set** (9v)	£200	‡

E23a See note after G20.

Numbers Issued—E20, 2,448,960; E21, 7,683,760; E22, 103,200; E23, 605,880; E24, 36,000 (printed); E25, 61,080; E26, 29,940; E27, 17,040; E28, 4,680.

Despite the figures quoted for E24 it is believed that only 1,440 copies were sold as this value only came on sale the day before it was replaced by the K.G. V issue. Used copies with clear dates in July, 1912 are extremely scarce, and the majority of used specimens were cancelled in January, 1914.

1912 (July 17th)-24 As before, but head of King George V. Wmk. Multiple Crown CA. Sheets as before.

G1	½d.	**blue-green (O)**	15	10
G2	½d.	**yel-grn (O)** (4/17)	20	15
G3	1d.	**rose-red (O)**	50	25
G4	1d.	**scarlet (O)** (6/16)	1·00	25
G5	1d.	**car-rose (O)** ('20)	1·25	30
G6	2d.	**pale grey (O)**	1·25	50
G7	2d.	**slate (O)** ('19)	1·75	60
G8	2½d.	**deep blue (O)**	2·00	75
		a large "2" in fraction	£20	£22
G9	2½d.	**pl ult (O)** ('20)	2·00	75
		a large "2" in fraction	£20	£22
G10	6d.	**pur and lilac (C)**	3·00	2·50
G11	6d.	**dk pur and dp mauve (C)** ('19)	3·50	2·75
G12	6d.	**pl pur and vio (C)** ('20)	3·50	2·75
G13	1/–	**black/green (OC)**	2·25	2·00
G14	1/–	**grey-blk and blk/ green (OC)**	2·50	2·50

a on blue-grn (ol black) ('19) ..	3·50	3·50
b on emerald surface ('23) ..	6·00	5·50
c on emerald back ('24) ..	3·00	6·00
G15 2/- **dl pur and blue/ blue (C)**	6·50	6·00
G16 2/- **br pur and dp blue/ grey-blue (C)** (11/16)	7·50	6·00
G17 4/- **blk and car (C)** ..	£17	£21
G18 4/- **black and red (C)**	£18	£22
G19 8/- **dl pur and grn (C)**	£28	£34
G20 £1 **dl pur and blk/red (A)**	£110	£125
G1/20 **set** (10v) ..	£170	£190
SPG1/20 **specimen set** (10v)	£130	‡

Die Proofs, without value, are known in black on glazed card.

G8*a*, G9*a* also E4*a*, E14*a*, E23*a* The "2" in the fraction "½" is larger and the fraction bar is at a steeper angle on Nos. 55 and 115 (sheets of two panes of 60, each 6 x 10).

Type I	Type II

1918 No. G1 overprinted in black sans-serif capitals by Beanland, Malin and Co., Gibraltar.

G21 ½d. (Type I) **green** (April 15th) ..	25	35
G22 ½d. (Type II) **deep green** (June) ..	25	35

1921-32 As before, but wmk. Multiple Script CA. Sheets as before.

G23 ½d. **green (O)** ('27) ..	10	20
G24 1d. **rose (O)** ('21) ..	20	20
G25 1d. **dp scar (O)** ('25)	30	25
G26 1d. **pl dl car (O)** ('25)	20	20
G27 1½d. **chestnut (O)** ('22)	45	30
G28 1½d. **yel-brn (O)** ('24)..	50	30
G29 1½d. **lt brown (O)** ('25)	50	35
G30 2d. **grey (O)** ('21) ..	60	75
G31 2½d. **br blue (O)** ('21)	3·00	3·50
a large '2' in fraction	£24	£27
G32 3d. (3 PENCE) **br blue (O)** ('21) ..	1·00	1·10
G33 3d. (3 PENCE) **dp blue (O)** ..	1·00	1·10
G34 3d. (3 PENCE) **ult (O)** .	1·00	1·10
G35 3d. (3 PENCE) **dl ult (O)**	1·20	1·10
G36 3d. (THREE PENCE) **ult (O)** ('32) ..	1·50	1·00
G37 6d. **pl pur and mauve (C)** ('23) ..	2·00	2·10
G38 6d. **dp pur and mag (C)** ('26) ..	2·20	2·10
G39 6d. **br purple and pl mauve (C)** ('32)	1·75	2·00
G40 1/- **blk/emerald (C)** ('24)	2·00	2·25
G41 1/- **grey-blk and blk/ emerald (C)** ..	2·50	2·50
G42 1/- **jet blk and blk on dl emerald (blue grn back) (C)** ('29) ..	3·00	3·00
G43 1/- **sage-grn and blk (C)** ('29)..	4·50	5·50
G44 1/- **ol-bistre and grey-blk (C)** ('32) ..	4·50	5·50
G45 1/- **ol drab and jet blk (C)** ..	4·50	5·50
G46 1/- **sage and grey-blk (C)** ..	5·00	6·00
G47 1/- **dk ol and blk (C)**	5·00	6·00
G48 2/- **grey-pur and blu/ biue (C)** ('24) ..	7·00	9·50
G49 2/- **reddish pur and blue/blue (C)** ('25) ..	3·00	6·00
G50 2/- **red-brn and blk/ blue (C)** ('29) ..	£12	£14
G51 2/6 **br grn and blk (C)**	7·00	£10
G52 2/6 **yel-grn and blk (C)**	£10	£11
G53 2/6 **blue-grn and jet blk (C)** ..	£12	£12
G54 4/- **blk and car (C)** ('24)	£22	£32
G55 5/- **car and blk (C)** ..	£14	£18
G56 8/- **dl pur and grn (C)** ('24)	£125	£150
G57 10/- **dp ult and blk (C)**	£22	£32
G58 £1 **red-or and blk (C)** ('27)	£175	£180
G59 £1 **yel and blk (C)** ..	£350	—
G60 £1 **pl or and blk (C)**..	£180	—
G61 £5 **vio and blk (C)** ..	£1800	£2000
G23/61 **set** (19v) ..	£2100	£2400
SPG23/61 **specimen set** (19v)	£750	‡

Die Proofs of G36 exist in black on glazed card.

Shades of £1 G59, G60 can be checked against known examples. Used copies which have been in water cannot easily be distinguished from the normal.

1931 (July 1st)-33 (*Recess*) **De La Rue. Wmk. Multiple Script CA. Designer, Capt. H. St. C. Garrood. Perf. A14; B 13½ x 14. Sheets 6 x 10.**

	A		B	
G62 1d. **scar** ..	1·00	1·00	2·50	1·00
G63 1½d. **red-brn**	1·00	1·00	2·00	1·00
G64 2d. **pl grey** ('32)	1·00	1·00	4·00	80
G65 3d. **blue** (1/6/33)	2·00	2·75	6·00	6·00
G62/65 **set** (4v) ..	5·00	5·75	£14	8·75
SPG62/65 **specimen set** (4v)	£55	‡	‡	‡

1935 (May 6th) Silver Jubilee. (*Recess*)
Bradbury Wilkinson. Wmk. Multiple Script
CA. Perf. 11 x 12. Sheets 6 x 10.

G66	2d.	**ult and grey black**	1·00	1·00
		a extra flagstaff ..	£30	£35
G67	3d.	**brown and dp blue**	1·10	1·50
		a extra flagstaff ..	£130	£145
G68	6d.	**green and indigo** ..	3·00	4·25
		a extra flagstaff ..	£80	£90
G69	1/–	**slate and purple** ..	7·00	8·00
		a extra flagstaff ..	£80	£90
G66/69		**set** (4v)	£10	£13
SPG66/69		**specimen set** (4v)	£28	‡

G66*a*/G69*a* Extra flagstaff occurs on No. 49
(Row 9/1).

Numbers Issued—G66, 604,000; G67, 173,000;
G68, 69,000; G69, 55,000.

Remainders were withdrawn on December 31st,
1935.

The following were printed (*recess*) by De La Rue
on "Script CA" wmk. (*upright*) paper, unless
otherwise mentioned.

**1938-51 (Issued, ½d.—3d., 25/2/38; Other
Values, 16/3/38, unless indicated otherwise).**

Designs, ½d. and £1 (King's Head); Other
Values (Views of Colony). (Perf. 14 and 13½
were issued concurrently). Designs, ½d., £1,
V. Others, H. Sheets 120—two panes each
6 x 10.

(a) Perf. 13½ x 14 (C).

1	½d.	**dp green**	5	10
		a olive-green (28/4/49)	10	10
2	£1	**orange**	£18	£20

(b) Perf. 14 (C) (6d. line). Sheets 6 x 10.

3	1d.	**dull chestnut** ..	80	1·00
4	1½d.	**red**	2·50	1·00
5	2d.	**grey**	2·00	75
6	3d.	**blue**	£12	6·00
7	6d.	**car and violet-gray** ..	£22	2·00
8	1/–	**black and green** ..	4·00	8·00
9	2/–	**black and chestnut** ..	£14	£18
10	5/–	**blk and carmine-red**	£18	£22
11	10/–	**black and dp blue** ..	£12	£18

(c) Perf. 13½ (C).

12	1d.	**dull chestnut** ..	75	1·00
		a chestnut-brown(wmk.		
		sideways (/41) ..	25	80
13	1½d.	**red**	£30	£15
14	2d.	**grey**	20	40
		a grey (wmk. sideways)		
		(/41)	£120	£10
15	3d.	**blue**	75	40
16	6d.	**car and violet-grey** ..	3·00	1·50
17	1/–	**black and green** ..	9·00	5·00
18	2/–	**blk and chestnut-brn**	£14	£12
19	5/–	**black and carmine-red**	5·00	6·00

Nos. 12*a* and 14*a* are from coils. Forgeries of
No. 14*a* exist, printed photo litho.

As before but Perf. 13 x 12¾ (C).

20	1d.	**chestnut** (wmk. side-		
		ways) (4/42) ..	10	15
		a choc (wmk. sideways)		
		(27/3/44) ..	50	2·00
		b reddish-chestnut (wmk.		
		sideways) (25/2/46)	15	15
		c red-brown (28/4/49)	15	15
21	1½d.	**purple-slate** (1/1/43)	10	15
		a violet-slate (27/3/44)	10	20
22	2d.	**grey** (wmk. sideways)		
		(/42)	25	30
23	2d.	**carmine-red** (wmk.		
		sideways) (15/7/44)	15	20
		a rose-carmine (wmk.		
		sideways (15/7/47)	15	20
24	3d.	**dull grey-blue** (4/42)	20	25
		a blue (23/4/45) ..	15	20
		b dull greenish-blue		
		(8/2/51) ..	20	25
25	5d.	**orange** (1/10/47) ..	60	70
26	6d.	**car and vio-grey** (/42)	20	30
		aa re-entries from ..	£10	—
		a scarlet and violet-grey		
		(23/4/45) ..	50	50
		b re-entries from ..	£10	—
		c re-entries of vignette	£15	—
27	1/–	**black and green** (4/42)	60	40
		a grey-black and green	60	40
		b re-entry ..	£15	—
28	2/–	**blk and chestnut-brn**		
		(4/42) ..	2·00	2·00

```
        a  blk and red-brown  ..    1·50    1·50
       aa  pale red brn  ..    ..    1·25    1·25
        b  re-entry                  £20      —
29  5/-  black and dp scarlet
             (27/3/44)                3·50    3·50
        a  black and dp carmine
             (22/11/49)    ..         3·00    3·00
       aa  re-entry                   £25      —
30  10/-  slate-blk and dp blue
             (5/43)    ..    ..       £10     £10
        a  black and dark blue
             (27/3/44)    ..          7·00    8·00
        b  re-entry            ..     £30      —
1/30    set (14)    ..    ..          £33     £35
SP 1/30  specimen set perf (11)      £110       ‡
```

22—First placed on sale in Colony about middle of 1942.

26aa/26b/27b/28b/29aa/30b/S14b were re-entered in a number of positions. Frame Plate Rows 1/3 and 4, etc., the castles top right.

26c/S14b Vignette plate shows re-entries in sky and background, at lower right Rows 2/2, 2/6, 5/1, 8/6, 10/3, 10/5, 6d. value only.

27a/28/28a/29a/30a Plate 2 of frame shows broken "R" in GIBRALTAR Row 9/4. Worth six times normal.

SPECIAL ISSUES

1937 (May 12th) Coronation. As Aden but Printers Bradbury, Wilkinson. Perf. 11 x 11¾ (C).

```
S1    ½d. green    ..    ..    ..    15    20
S2    2d. grey    ..    ..    ..     50    60
S3    3d. blue    ..    ..    ..     80    70
SP S1/3 specimen set perf (3)      £20     ‡
```

1946 (Oct. 12th) Victory. As Aden.

```
S4    ½d. pale green    ..    ..    10    15
S5    3d. ultramarine  ..    ..    20    25
SP S4/5 specimen set perf (2)     £22     ‡
```

1948 (Dec. 1st) Silver Wedding. As Aden.

```
S6    ½d. green    ..    ..    ..    10    15
S7    £1  orange-brown    ..       £22    £24
```

1949 (Oct. 10th) U.P.U. As Aden.

```
S8    2d. carmine-rose    ..        30    40
S9    3d. indigo  ..    ..    ..     60    70
S10   6d. purple    ..    ..       1·25   1·35
S11   1/- quartz-green    ..       2·00   2·75
S8/11   set (4) ..    ..    ..     4·00   5·00
```

1950 (Aug. 1st) Legislative Council. Nos. 23, etc., overprinted (letterpress) **NEW CONSTITUTION 1950 by De La Rue, in black or red.**

```
S12   2d. carmine-red    ..         15    20
S13   3d. grey-blue  ..    ..       25    35
S14   6d. carmine and vio-grey      60    75
        a  overprint double  ..    £100   £110
        b  re-entries    ..    ..   £15    £20
S15   1/- black and green (red)    1·00   1·50
S12/15  set (4)  ..    ..    ..     2·00   2·25
```

GILBERT and ELLICE ISLANDS

The various groups of islands were either declared protectorates or were annexed from 1892 onwards, but there was no established postal service until 1911.

Prior to 1911 the small number of outgoing letters was franked with whatever stamps could be obtained from visiting ships, and British, Australian, New Zealand, New South Wales and other stamps were all used. They were pen-cancelled, and such cancellations were often still used on the 1911 issues (E1/11).

1911 (Jan.) Stamps of Fiji overprinted in black or red (R). Wmk. Mult. Crown CA. Perf. 14. Sheets 12 x 10.

```
E1    ½d. green (O)    ..    ..     6·00    £18
E2    1d. red (O)    ..    ..      £40     £50
E3    2d. grey (O)    ..    ..     9·00    £15
E4    2½d. ult (O)    ..    ..     £15     £20
E5    5d. pur and ol-grn (ch)     £28     £27
E6    6d. dull and bt-pur (ch)    £30     £28
E7    1/- blk on grn (R) (ch)..   £28     £35
E1/7    set (7)    ..    ..    ..  £150    £185
SP E1/7  specimen set (7)  ..     £200      ‡
```

Number printed—E1, 12,240; E2, 12,000; E3, 12,360; E4, 9,120; E5, 6,240; E6, 6,000; E7, 6,120.

1911 (Mar. ?) (recess) **Printers De La Rue & Co. Ltd. Wmk. Mult. Crown CA. Perf. 14. Sheets 6 x 10.**

```
E8    ½d. green    ..    ..    ..   1·50    4·00
E9    1d. red    ..    ..    ..     1·50    4·00
E10   2d. slate-grey    ..    ..    1·75    4·50
E11   2½d. ultramarine    ..    ..  1·75    4·50
E8/11   set (4)    ..    ..    ..   6·00    £16
SP E8/11 specimen set (4)  ..      £45       ‡
```

1916 (July 12th) Provisional Issue. Surcharged in black or red on G2 and E11 at FUNAFUTI.

```
GF1   2/- on 1d. (G2)             8 copies
EF2   2/- (R) on 2½d. (E11)      11 copies
EF3   3/- (R) on 2½d. (E.)        3 copies
GF1/EF3 set of 3 values (used)           £2500
```

These provisionals were made by the British District Officer (who was also Postmaster) on the chief island of the Ellice Group. The numeral was applied by rubber stamp on each side of the value tablet in the case of 2/– on 1d. and to the left of the tree in the case of 2/– and 3/– on 2½d.; and " /–" was added in manuscript. One copy of the 2/– on 2½d. is known with the surcharge applied five times and is alleged to have been a "trial" surcharge.

At the time no stamps above 2½d. denomination were available and the surcharging was done at the suggestion of the Resident Medical Officer to defray postage on parcels to be sent by him to England and by his assistant George Kuba (nephew of the then King of Tonga) to Tonga and other Pacific Islands.

The Resident Commissioner of the Gilbert and Ellice Islands, whose headquarters were then on Ocean Island, subsequently stated "The surcharges made by the Postmaster at Funafuti are unauthorised and absolutely valueless".

Nevertheless, most of these stamps were used on parcel mail; and they have maintained a degree of respectability perhaps by virtue of the acceptance from the Resident M.O. of copies by H.M. King George V for his collection.

1912/24 (*typo*) **Printers De La Rue & Co. Ltd. Wmk. Mult. Crown CA. Perf. 14. ½d. to 5/– Die I. £1 Die II. Sheets 120—two panes, each 6 x 10.**

G1	½d. **green** (O)	50	75
	a yellow-green (O)	75	1·50
	b sloping Duty Plate	£80	—
G2	1d. **carmine** (O)	75	1·25
	a rose-carmine (O)	75	1·50
	b scarlet (O)	2·00	3·00
G3	2d. **slate-grey** (O)	5·00	8·00
G4	2½d. **bright blue** (O)	2·00	4·00
G5	3d. **purple/yellow** (*ch*)	80	2·50
G6	4d. **blk and red/yell** (*ch*)	1·00	3·00
G7	5d. **dp-pur and ol-grn** (*ch*)	3·00	9·00
G8	6d. **dull and bt-pur** (*ch*)	1·50	6·00
G9	1/– **black/green** (*ch*)	4·00	8·00
G10	2/– **pur and bl/bl** (*ch*)	£18	£22
G11	2/6 **blk and red/bl** (*ch*)	£20	£25
G12	5/– **bl-grn and red/yell** (*ch*)	£23	£30
G13	£1 **pur and blk/red** (*ch*)	£500	£750
G1/13	**set** (13)	£550	£850
SP G1/13	**specimen set** (13)	£35	‡

G1b Examples are known from a sheet on which the Duty Plate was out of register and sloped left low and right high.

1918 Overprinted in black.

G14	1d. **rose-car** (Die I)	50	2·00

1922/7 Wmk. Mult. Script CA. Perf. 14. Die II.

G15	½d. **green** (O)	40	80
G16	1d. **violet** (O)	90	1·25
G17	1½d. **scarlet** (O)	1·50	2·00
G18	2d. **slate-grey** (O)	2·00	3·50
G19	10/– **grn and red/em** (*ch*)	£140	£175
G15/19	**set** (5)	£140	£180
SP G15/19	**specimen** set (5)	£90	‡

1935 (May 6th) Silver Jubilee (*recess*) **Printers Bradbury, Wilkinson & Co. Wmk. Script CA. Perf. 11 x 12. Sheets 6 x 10.**

G20	1d. **ult and grey-black**	1·00	2·50
G21	1½d. **dp-blue and scarlet**	1·00	2·50
G22	3d. **brn and dp-blue**	3·50	5·50
G23	1/– **slate and purple**	£11	£16
G20/23	**set** (4)	£15	£25
SP G20/23	**specimen set** perf (4)	£28	‡

Number issued—G20, 39,600; G21, 69,940; G22, 39,000; G23, 23,800.

1939 (Jan. 1st)-55 Designs, ½d. (Frigate Bird); 1d. (Pandanus Pine); 1½d. (Canoe crossing reef); 2d. (House and Canoe); 2½d. (Native House); 3d. (Palms and Sea); 5d. (Ellice Is. Canoe); 6d. (Coconut Palms); 1/- (Cantilever

Jetty, Ocean Is.); 2/- (H.M.C.S. "Niṇamoa);
2/6 (Gilbert Is. Canoe); 5/- (Coat of Arms).
Printers Bradbury, Wilkinson, ½d., 2d., 2/6,
Perf. 11½ x 11¼ (C). Sheets 5 x 12. Waterlow
& Sons, 1d., 5d., 6d., 2/-, 5/-, Perf. 12½ (L),
Sheets 10 x 6. De La Rue, Other values, Perf.
13½ (C), Sheets 6 x 10.

1	½d.	**bluish-slate and green**	20	35
2	1d.	**emerald and purple** ..	20	35
	a	P12¾ bt emerald and red-pur (12/5/43)	30	50
3	1½d.	**blk and carmine-red**	35	50
	a	slate-blk and carmine (12/5/43) ..	40	60
4	2d.	**lt chestnut and grey**	25	60
	a	chestnut and slate-grey (12/5/43) ..	75	1·00
	b	chestnut and dp grey (30/10/44) ..	30	70
5	2½d.	**black and olive-green**	25	60
	a	slate-blk and sage-grn (12/5/43) ..	1·25	1·75
6	3d.	**blk and ultramarine** ..	30	50
	a	slate-black and bt ult (12/5/43) ..	1·50	2·00
	b	black and bt blue (30/10/44) ..	30	50
7	5d.	**dp blue and sepia** ..	90	80
	aa	P12¾ dp ult and sepia (12/5/43) ..	1·00	1·00
	a	blue and dp sepia (30/10/44) ..	90	80
8	6d.	**olive and violet** ..	60	75
	a	P12¾ dp olive cold violet (12/5/43) ..	75	90
9	1/-	**blk and turquoise-blue**	50	75
	a	slate-blk and dp turquoise blue (12/5/43)	1·00	1·50
10	2/-	**blue and vermilion** ..	2·75	3·00
	a	P12¾ ult and vermilion (12/5/43) ..	2·75	3·00
11	2/6	**blue and dp emer-grn**	3·50	5·00
12	5/-	**carmine-red and blue**	6·00	7·50
	a	P12¾ car-red and ult (12/5/43) ..	6·50	8·00
	b	car-red and dp blue (30/10/44) ..	6·50	8·00
1/12		**set (12)**	£15	£20
SP 1/12		**specimen set** perf (12)	£35	‡

As Nos. 6 and 9 but Perf. 12 (C).

13	3d.	**black and deep blue** (24/7/55)	75	1·00
13a	1/-	**blk and dp turquoise-blue** (8/5/51) ..	2·00	3·00

SPECIAL ISSUES

1937 (May 12th) Coronation. As Aden.

S1	1d.	violet	.. ..	15	20
	a	lt violet	.. ..	50	50
S2	1½d.	carmine	.. ..	25	40
S3	3d.	blue	.. ..	40	50
SP S1/3	**specimen set** perf (3)			£20	‡

1946 (Dec. 16th) Victory. As Aden.

S4	1d.	reddish-purple	..	15	20
S5	3d.	dp blue	.. ..	20	25
SP S4/5	**specimen set** perf (2)			£15	‡

1949 (Aug. 29th) Silver Wedding. As Aden.

S6	1d.	bright violet	..	15	25
S7	£1	rose-carmine	..	£16	£20

1949 (Oct. 10th) U.P.U. As Aden.

S8	1d.	dull purple	.. ..	30	40
S9	2d.	dark slate	.. ..	40	50
S10	2d.	dull indigo	.. ..	50	75
S11	1/-	azure	.. ..	1·25	2·50
S8/11	**set (4)**	.. ..		2·25	4·00

POSTAGE DUE STAMPS

1940 (Aug.) Printers (*typo*) **Bradbury, Wilkinson. Perf. 12 (L). Sheets 12 x 10.**

PD1	1d.	pale emerald	..	40	1·00
PD2	2d.	red	.. ..	50	1·00
PD3	3d.	brown	.. ..	75	1·25
	a	small "B"	..	£40	
PD4	4d.	blue	.. ..	1·00	2·00
PD5	5d.	myrtle-green	..	1·25	2·50
PD6	6d.	magenta	..	1·50	3·50
PD7	1/-	violet	.. ..	2·50	£10
PD8	1/6	pale blue-green	..	7·50	£20
PD1/8	**set (8)**	.. ..		£15	£40

PD3a Row 10/5. The top loop of "B" in "GILBERT"
is missing, and gives the appearance of a "b".

GOLD COAST

All definitive stamps were printed (*recess*) by Bradbury, Wilkinson.

1938 (April 1st) Design, Christiansborg Castle Accra. Perf. 12 (L). Designs, 1/-, 2/-, 5/- H. Sheets 6 x 10 or 10 x 6.

1	½d. pale green	.. ..	10	10
2	1d. red-brown	.. ..	10	10
3	1½d. scarlet	.. ..	10	10
4	2d. slate	.. ..	15	15
5	3d. blue	..	15	15
6	4d. dp magenta	..	15	15
7	6d. red-purple	.. ..	20	20
8	9d. orange		40	40
9	1/- black and olive	..	40	40
10	2/- dp blue and violet	..	2·50	2·50
11	5/- dp olive-grn and car		5·00	7·00
1/11	**set (11)**	.. ..	9·00	£11

As No. 1, etc., but Perf. 12 x 11¾ (C).

12	½d. green (/40)	.. ..	10	10
	a em-green (22/7/47)		10	10
13	1d. red-brown (/39)	..	10	10
14	1½d. scarlet (/40)	..	10	10
	a car-red (21/1/46)	.	10	10
15	2d. slate (/40)	..	15	15
	a dp grey (10/2/44)	..	15	15
16	3d. blue (/40)	.. ..	15	15
17	4d. dp magenta (/42)	..	15	15
	a bright magenta	..	15	15
18	6d. purple (/39)	..	20	20
19	9d. orange (/44)	..	40	40
	a reddish-orange (16/4/45)	..	40	40
20	1/- blk and dp olive (/40)		40	40
	a blk and olive-green (21/1/46)	..	40	40
21	1/3 chestnut and tur-blue (12/4/41)	..	40	50
	a choc and turquoise-blue (10/2/44)	..	40	50
22	2/- blue and red-vio (/40)		2·00	2·00
	a greenish-blue and pur-vio (10/2/44)		2·50	2·50
23	5/- dp olive-grn and car (/40)	.. ..	4·00	4·00
	a dp olive and dp car (10/2/44)	..	4·50	4·50
24	10/- blk and violet (7/40)		6·00	7·50
12/24	**set (13)**	.. ..	£13	£15
SP 12/24	**specimen set** perf (13)		£55	‡

No stamps were perforated 12 (line) after 1938, but first supplies of the comb perforated stamps (12 x 11¾) were not sent out to the Colony until 1939, 1d. (coils), ½d., 1d. and 6d.; 1940, ½d. (coils), 1½d., 2d., 3d. and 1/–, 2/–, 5/– and 10/–; 1941, 1/3; 1942, 4d.; 1943, 9d.

These stamps were placed on sale as and when required, and no record was kept of dates when released, but stamps postmarked with the year as given after the particular stamp have been noted.

1948 (July 1st) Designs, ½d. (Northern Terr. Mounted Constabulary); 1d. (Christiansborg Castle); 1½d. (Emblem of Joint Provincial Council); 2d. (Talking Drums); 2½d. (Map of West Africa); 3d. (Manganese Mine); 4d. (Lake Bosumtwi); 6d., 1/- (Cocoa Industry); 2/- (Trooping the Colour); 5/- (Surfboats); 10/- (Forest Scene). Perf. 12 x 11¾ (C). Designs, ½d., 2d., 6d., 10/- V. Sheets 6 x 10, Horizontal 5 x 12.

25	½d. emerald	.. ..	15	15
26	1d. dp blue	.. ..	15	15
27	1½d. scarlet	.. ..	15	20
28	2d. chocolate-brown	..	15	15
	a dp brown (24/6/52)		—	—
29	2½d. car-red and bistre-brn		25	30
30	3d. greyish-blue	..	20	20
31	4d. lake-magenta		35	35
32	6d. black and orange	..	35	25
33	1/- blk and red-orange		40	20
34	2/- sage and rose-car	.	80	70
35	5/- purple and grey-blk		3·00	1·50
36	10/- blk and sage-green		4·00	3·00
25/36	**set (12)**	.. ..	9·00	7·00

SPECIAL ISSUES

1937 (May 12th) Coronation. As Aden, but Printers Bradbury, Wilkinson. Perf. 11 x 11¾ (C).

S1	1d. light brown	..	20	20
S2	2d. slate	.. ..	25	25
S3	3d. blue	.. ..	35	35
SP S1/3	**specimen set** perf(3)		£15	‡

1946 (Oct. 14th) Victory. As Aden.
(*a*) **Perf. 13¾ x 14 (C).**

S4	2d. violet	.. ..	25	25
S5	4d. dull lake	.. ..	60	50
SP S4/5	**specimen set** perf (2)		£18	‡

(*b*) **Perf. 13¾ x 13½ (C).**

S6	2d. violet-grey	.. ..	15	15
S7	4d. dull lake	.. ..	15	15

Nos. S4 and S5 were mostly sold in the Colony and Nos. S6 and S7 in London.

1948 (Dec. 20th) Silver Wedding. As Aden.

| S8 | 1½d. **scarlet** | .. | .. | 15 | 10 |
| S9 | 10/– **grey-olive** | .. | .. | 4·00 | 6·00 |

1949 (Oct. 10th) U.P.U. As Aden.

S10	2d. **beech-brown**		20	40
S11	2½d. **orange**	..	30	70
S12	3d. **dull indigo**	..	75	1·25
S13	1/– **quartz-green**	..	1·50	2·25
S10/13	**set** (4)	..	2·50	4·50

POSTAGE DUE STAMPS

1945 Printers (*typo*) **De La Rue. Perf. 13¾ x 14 (C). Rough paper.**

PDX1	½d. **black**	..	..	7·00	6·00
PD1	1d. **black** (/45)	..	..	15	30
PD2	2d. **black** (/45)	..	..	1·25	1·00
PD3	3d. **black** (/45)	..	..	1·25	1·00

Though stamps similar in design were issued in 1923, the 1945 printing can be distinguished by the fact that the impression is deeper and the stamps are printed on rough paper. The ½d. value was obsolete before 1938.

1951-52 Printers (*typo*) **De La Rue. Perf. 13¾ x 14 (C). Chalk-surfaced paper.** (*Stamps printed on uncoated paper were issued previously.*)

PD4	2d. **black** (13/12/51)	..	10	25
PD5	3d. **black** (13/12/51)	..	15	40
PD6	6d. **black** (1/10/52)	..	30	40
PD7	1/– **black** (1/10/52)	..	60	75
	a value variety	..	5·00	6·00

PD7   PD7*a*

PD7*a* The diagonal line in value is more upright than is normal on No. 5 of all rows (10 x 6).

Watermark Varieties (Type A)

(See Introduction for details).

PD4a	2d. Crown missing	..	£22	—
PD4b	St. Edward's Crown	..	£14	—
PD5a	3d. Crown missing	..	£25	—
PD5b	St. Edward's Crown	..	£14	—
PD6a	6d. Crown missing	..	£25	—
PD6b	St. Edward's Crown	..	£18	—
PD7a	1/– St. Edward's Crown	..	£25	—

GRENADA

After an uncertain early history, Grenada was ceded to Great Britain by the Treaty of Paris in 1763. In 1779 it again passed into French hands, but was finally restored to Great Britain four years later. It is now the administrative centre of the Windward Islands, which include Dominica, St. Lucia and St. Vincent and which form the Southern part of the chain of islands stretching from Trinidad to Porto Rico.

Following the use of other handstamps or manuscript marks, Crowned Circle PAID Franks were registered at the G.P.O. in London on November 13th, 1846 (Carriacou) and on October 24th, 1850 (Grenada) and were thereafter struck in red to indicate prepayment of postage on overseas letters (See Introduction).

From May, 1858 to September, 1860 contemporary G.B. stamps were in use and were cancelled with "A15" in a transverse oval of horizontal bars.

The Crowned Circle Franks were again used from October 1st, 1860 until the first Grenada stamps were issued.

1846-61. PAID Franks   *On Cover*

| VF1 | **Carriacou** | .. | .. | — |
| VF2 | **Grenada** | .. | .. | £800 |

No example of VF1 has yet been recorded.

1858-60 Stamps of Great Britain identified by their Catalogue Nos. after prefix 'GA'.

Used at St. George's : 'A15'

GA V39	1d. **rose-red**	..	..
GA V51	2d. **blue**	..	..
GA V44	4d. **rose**	..	..
GA V45	6d. **lilac**	..	..
GA V47	1/– **green**	..	..

All stamps to V40 are (*recess*) **Perkins Bacon and Co. Sheets 12 x 10 unless otherwise indicated.**

1861 (June)-62. No Wmk. Perf. 14-16 (Rough).

V1	1d. **bluish green**	..	..	£1000	£120
V2	1d. **green** (5/62)	..	..	£40	£35
	a imperf between (pair)	..	..	—	—
V3	6d. **rose**	..	..	£380	£45

V1 and V2 exist overprinted SPECIMEN in sans serif capitals.

Die Proofs of both values exist in black on India paper.

Plate Proofs of both values exist imperforate in rose to dark red on white wove paper. A Plate Proof of V3 is also known in brownish red on horizontally laid paper.

Numbers printed—V1/2, 48,000 each: V3, 24,000.

1862 (May). Prepared for use but not issued. No Wmk. Perf. 11½.

V4	6d.	**lake-red**	£400	—

1863 (March)-81. Wmk. Small Star. (S) **indicates that the watermark is sideways.**

(a) Perf. 14-16 (Rough).

V5	1d.	**green** (3/64) ..	£32	£12
V6	1d.	**bluish grn** (S) (5/71)	£60	£15
V7	6d.	**rose** (5/63) ..	£250	£15
V8	6d.	**orange-red** (5/66) ..	£285	£17
V9	6d.	**rose** (S) (4/69) ..	£975	£70
V10	6d.	**vermilion** (5/71) ..	£200	£14
		a double impression..	—	£700

Numbers printed—V5, 96,000: V6, 24,000: V7, 24,000: V8, 48,000: V9, 24,000: V10, 24,000.

(b) Perf. 15. (Clean Cut). January, 1873.

V11	1d.	**dp bluish green** (S)..	£40	£14
		a bisect diag (½d.) on		
		cover	‡	£1850
		b imperf between pair	—	£1000

Number printed—36,000.

(c) Perf. 15. (Intermediate). September, 1878

V12	1d.	**green** (S)	£100	£20
V13	6d.	**dp vermilion** (S) ..	£275	£20
		a double impression..	—	£500

Numbers printed—36,000 each.

(d) Perf. 15. (Rough). December, 1879.

V14	1d.	**pl green** (thin paper)	£150	£10
		a double impression..	—	—

Number printed—72,000.

(e) Perf. 14½. (Rough). April, 1881.

V15	1d.	**green** (S)	£50	£10
		a bisect diag (½d.) on		
		cover	‡	£1750

Number printed—60,000.

1873 (Sept.)-75. Wmk. Large Star. (S) **indicates that the Wmk. is sideways.**

(a) Perf. 15. (Intermediate).

V16	1d.	**bl-grn** (S) (2/74) ..	£40	£14
		a double impression ..	—	—
		b imperf between		
		(pair)	—	—
V17	6d.	**or-ver** (9/73).. ..	£200	£15

Numbers printed—V16, 72,000: V17, 48,000.

(b) Perf. 14. December, 1875.

V18	1d.	**yellow-green** ..	£20	£10
		a bisect diag (½d.) on		
		cover	‡	£1750
V19	1d.	**green**	£28	£12
		a bisect diag (½d.) on		
		cover	‡	—

Numbers printed—V18/19, 120,000.

(c) Perf. 15. (Clean Cut). 1875 (December?).

V20	1d.	**yellow-green** ..	£2500	£750

40 sheets (4,800 copies) were printed on October 13th, 1875 and perforated by Perkins Bacon to replace an equivalent number of sheets of No. V18 badly perforated at Somerset House. Very few copies are known.

V5/20—The sheets of paper used for these stamps were bordered by a watermark of five closely spaced lines broken at the sides by the word POSTAGE. Misplacement of the printing sometimes resulted in one or other of the outer rows of stamps showing the watermark border, either horizontally or vertically.

1875-81. Undenominated Fiscal stamps overprinted for postal use by Perkins Bacon, using mixed letters from two founts varying in height between 1½ and 2mm.

I. In blue (July, 1875). Wmk. Large Star. Perf. 14.

V21	1/–	**dp mauve**	£200	£12
		a "SHLLIING" ..	—	£400
		b "S" inverted ..	—	£200
		c "O" omitted ..	—	—
		d "P" omitted.. ..	—	—

V21*b*—The "S" in POSTAGE is inverted.
V21*c*—The"O" in ONE is omitted.
V21*d*—The "P" in POSTAGE is omitted.

The sheet position of these varieties is not known.

Two sheets (240 stamps) were supplied with Specimen overprint in 5mm. black capitals, each overprint covering two stamps.

Die Proofs of the basic stamp exist in black on India paper. Plate Proofs also exist in black.

Number printed—60,000.

II. In black. (April, 1881). Perf. 14½.

(a) Wmk. Large Star (sideways on V22 and V23).

V22	½d.	**pl mauve**	£15	6·00
V23	½d.	**dp mauve**	6·00	6·00
		a imperf (pair) ..	£100	—
		b overprint double ..	£90	—
		c hyphen omitted ..	£50	—
		d "P" omitted	£60	—
		e "P" omitted (imperf)	—	—
		f wmk. upright ..	—	—
		g "P" omitted (wmk.		
		upright) ..	—	—
V24	2½d.	**rose-lake**	£15	7·00
V25	2½d.	**claret**	£20	7·00
		a imperf (pair) ..	£150	—
		b imperf between		
		(horiz pair) ..	£750	—

	c	no stop	£60	£35
	d	"PENCF"	£90	£40
V26 4d.		**blue**	£40	£10

(b) Wmk. Broad Star.

V27 2½d.		**rose-lake**	£60	£14
	a	no stop	£175	£80
	b	"PENCF"	£175	£90
V28 2½d.		**claret**	£125	£40
	a	no stop	£350	£125
	b	"PENCF"	£400	£175
V29 4d.		**blue**		

V23c—The hyphen between HALF and PENNY is omitted Row 8/4.

V23d/e/g—The "P" in POSTAGE is omitted Row 9/4.

V25c/27a/28a—There is no stop after PENNY Rows 3/4, 6/2, 8/3, 8/12 and 9/7.

V25d/V27b/V28b—Row 8/12.

V27/28/29—The Broad Star Wmk. was otherwise only used by South Australia.

Numbers printed—V22/23, 60,000 : V24/25/27/28, 60,000 : V26/29, 60,000.

1883-1891. Undenominated Fiscal stamps overprinted in green for Revenue use by Perkins Bacon, and subsequently overprinted or surcharged locally in black for postal use.

POSTAGE

Type I　　　　　　Type II

I. January 1883. Wmk. Small Star. (upright or sideways). Perf. 14½.

(a) Horizontally with Type I.

V30 1d.		**orange and green** ..	£80	£25
	a	overprint inverted ..	£700	£350
	b	overprint double ..	£450	£200
	c	"S" inverted ..	£275	£150
	d	no stop	£150	£45
	e	bisect diag (½d.) on piece (Jan. '83)	‡	£950

V30—is also known with POSTAGE overprint in manuscript in red or black.

V30d—There is no stop after POSTAGE.

(b) Diagonally twice (both lower left to upper right) with Type I on each stamp which was then bisected, each half being used as ½d.

V31		Half of 1d. **or and grn**	£250	£100
	a	unsevered pair ..	—	£450
	b	overprint inverted ..	—	£350

(c) Diagonally twice (Type II) the stamps being then bisected, each half being used as ½d.

V32		Half of 1d. **or and grn**	£80	£60
	a	unsevered pair ..	—	£400
	b	lower overprint omitted in unsevered pair	—	—
	c	overprints reversed	—	—

V32c—Both overprints were applied upper left to lower right, the lower overprint being inverted.

POSTAGE.

II. 1886. Overprinted and surcharged. Perf. 14.

(a) Wmk. Large Star.

V33 1d.		on 1½d. **or and grn** (10/86)	£20	£15
	a	"1d. POSTAGE" inverted	£140	£100
	b	"1d. POSTAGE" double	£140	£100
	c	"THRFE" (green overprint) ..	£100	£80
	d	"PFNCE" (green overprint) ..	£100	£80
	e	"HALH" (green overprint ..	£100	£80
	f	bisect diag (½d.) on cover	‡	£450
V34 1d.		on 1/– **or and grn** (12/86)	£20	£15
	a	no stop	—	—
	b	"SHILLNG" (green overprint) ..	£175	£125
	c	wide spaced "ONE SHILLING" (grn overprint) ..	£200	£150
	d	bisect diag (½d.) on cover	‡	£550

(b) Wmk. Small Star.

V35 1d.		on 4d. **or and green** (11/86)	£60	£30

V33c/d/e and V34b/c are errors in the original green overprinting done by Perkins, Bacon.

V34a—There is no stop after "POSTAGE".

V34c—The space between "ONE" and "SHILLING" measures 3½mm.

The basic Fiscal stamps used for V33/35 were in sheets 12 x 10. They were divided horizontally into panes 12 x 5 for the local overprinting.

The setting of 60 was re-arranged for each of the three stamps.

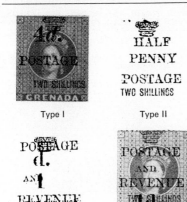

Type I

HALF
PENNY

Type II

POSTAGE
TWO SHILLINGS

PO**S**TAGE
d.

AN**1**

R**EVENU**E
TWO SHILLINGS

POSTAGE
AND
REVENUE
TWO SHILLINGS
1d.
GRENADA

Type III

Type IV

III. 1888-91. Overprinted and surcharged on the 2/– orange and green Revenue stamp. Wmk. Small Star (sideways). Perf. 14½.

The basic Fiscal stamps used for V36/40 were again in sheets 12 x 10; and the *a* and *b* varieties are all in the green overprint applied to the full sheet.

 a wide space (2½mm.)
 between "TWO"
 and "SHILLINGS"
 Rows 1/4 and 10/3
 b first "S" in "SHIL-
 LINGS" inverted

The subsequent overprinting was done on half sheets in a setting 12 x 5.

(a) March 31st, 1888. (Type I).

There were two settings of this type. On V36 the space between "4d." and "POSTAGE" measures 4mm., and on V37 the measurement is 5mm.

V36	4d.	(4mm.)	£20	£15
		a wide space	£60	£45
		b "S" inverted ..	£120	£90
		c upright "d"	£100	£75
		d imperf between		
		(horiz pair) ..	—	—
V37	4d.	(5mm.)	£25	£25
		a wide space	£60	£45
		b "S" inverted ..	£120	£90

V36c—The "d" is upright instead of italic Row 5/6.

(b) December, 1889. (Type II).

V38	½d.	.. ..	£20	£20
		a wide space	£45	£45
		b "S" inverted ..	£140	£65
		c overprint (Type II)		
		double	£110	£120
		d "POSTAGE" omitted	—	—

(c) December, 1890. (Type III).

This overprint consists of the word "POSTAGE AND" superimposed on the 2/– Revenue stamp which had previously been overprinted "1d. REVENUE" as a Fiscal provisional.

V39	1d.	.. ..	£40	£40
		a wide space	£85	£50
		b "S" inverted ..	£200	—
		c overprint inverted ..	£125	—
		d bisect diag (½d.) ..	‡	£500

(d) January, 1891. (Type IV).

V40	1d.	.. ..	£20	£20
		a wide space	£45	£30
		b "S" inverted ..	£140	—
		c stop omitted ..	£75	—

V40c—The stop after 1d. is omitted Row 3/8.

All stamps from V41 to G72 are (*typo*) **De La Rue. Perf. 14 unless otherwise indicated.**

HALFPENNY

ONE PENNY

1883. (Feb.). Wmk. Crown CA. Sheets 240 – four panes, each 6 x 10. (Inscribed "Postage")

V41	½d. **dl green**	1·00	1·00
		a tete beche (vert pair)	4·00	8·00
V42	1d. **carmine**	£14	4·00
		a tete beche (vert pair)	£80	£90
		b imperf (pair) ..	—	—
V43	2½d. **blue** (5/83)	6·00	2·00
		a tete beche (vert pair)	£20	£20
		b imperf (pair) ..	—	
V44	4d. **grey** (5/83)	5·00	6·00
		a tete beche (vert pair)	£14	£14
V45	6d. **mauve** (5/83) ..	7·00	7·00
		a tete beche (vert pair)	£20	£24
V46	8d. **grey-brown**	£14	£14
		a tete beche (vert pair)	£35	£40
		b imperf (pair) ..	—	—
V47	1/– **violet** (4/83)	£60	£50
		a tete beche (vert pair)	£325	£385
		b imperf (pair) ..	—	—
V41/47	**set** (7v)	£95	£85
V41a/47a	**set** (7 tete beche pairs)	£425	£550

1887 (Jan.). Wmk. and Sheets as before (Postage and Revenue).

V48	1d. **carmine**	60	60
		a tete beche (vert pair)	2·00	£10

V41a/48a—These tete beche pairs were the result of an unusual sheet layout in which, for the sake of economical production, each alternate horizontal row was inverted in relation to the adjacent rows. Th᠎ central portion of the stamp consisted of the Turks Islands key-plate (Die I) with the top and bottom label frames removed.

A constant variety, consisting of a white diagonal line above the seventh diamond in the right hand border, occurs on all values on R6/1 in the lower left pane.

Numbers printed—V51, 12,240: V52, 120,000;
V53, 12,000: V54, 60,000:
V55, 36,000: V56, 17,880:
V57/58, 11,760 each.

Withdrawn from sale on July 24th, 1902 and
remainders destroyed.

1891 (Jan.). No. V46 surcharged locally in black.

V49	1d.	on 8d. **grey-brown** ..	£15	£15
		a tete beche (vert pair)	£40	—
		b surcharge inverted..	£150	£150
		c stop omitted ..	£120	£120
		d bisect diag (½d.) ..	—	—

V49c—The stop after 1d. is omitted Row 6/5.

Type I   Type II

1891 (Dec.). No. V46 surcharged locally in black in a setting 6 x 10. The top five rows are Type I and the bottom five rows are Type II.

V50	2½d.	on 8d. **grey brown** ..	£18	£15
		a tete beche (vert pair)	£60	—
		b surcharge inverted..	£275	£350
		c surcharge double ..	—	—
		d surcharge double,		
		one inverted ..	£200	£200
		e surcharge treble ..	—	£400
		f comma for stop ..	—	—

V50f—A comma follows the 'd' instead of a stop
Row 3/5.

1895 (Sept.)-99. Wmk. Crown CA. Sheets 240 – four panes, each 6 x 10.

V51	½d.	**mauve and grn** (9/99)	50	75
V52	1d.	**mauve and car** (5/96)	90	40
V53	2d.	**mauve and brown**		
		(9/99)	£13	£15
V54	2½d.	**mauve and ult** ..	4·00	1·50
V55	3d.	**mauve and orange**..	7·00	7·00
V56	6d.	**mauve and green** ..	4·00	6·00
V57	8d.	**mauve and black** ..	£11	£13
V58	1/–	**green and orange** ..	£13	£15
V51/58		**set** (8v)	£50	£55
SPV51/58		**specimen set** (8v)	£70	‡

1898 (Aug. 15th). 400th Anniversary of Columbus' discovery of Grenada. (*recess*) **De La Rue. Wmk. Crown CC. Perf. 14. Sheets 12 x 5.**

V59	2½d.	**ultramarine**	9·00	9·00
		a on bluish paper ..	£18	£20
SPV59		**specimen** (I)	£45	‡

V59a—This variety has been faked and care should
be taken to ensure that mint copies clearly show
the bluish tint through white gum and that used
copies show the blue of equal density in the
front and on the back.

Proofs on unwatermarked wove paper are known
imperforate in several colours.

Number printed—506,400.

1902. As V51/58 but head of King Edward VII. Wmk. Crown CA. Sheets 120 – two panes, each 6 x 10.

E1	½d.	**dl purple and green**	50	75
E2	1d.	**dl purple and car** ..	60	50
E3	2d.	**dl purple and brn** ..	3·00	4·00
E4	2½d.	**dl purple and ult** ..	3·50	4·25
E5	3d.	**dl purple and or** ..	3·00	3·00
E6	6d.	**dl purple and green**	5·00	7·00
E7	1/–	**green and orange** ..	9·00	£11
E8	2/–	**green and ult** ..	£18	£25
E9	5/–	**green and carmine**	£30	£35
E10	10/–	**green and purple** ..	£95	£120
E1/10		**set** (10v)	£160	£200
SPE1/10		**specimen set** (10v)..	£120	‡

E1/2/3—On apparently toned paper came from a
1904 printing which was climatically affected.

Imperforate Colour Trials are known for most
values on unwatermarked paper.

E1/2/3/8/9/10—Unsold stocks were withdrawn
and destroyed in December, 1905.

1904-06. As before but Wmk. Multiple Crown CA. Ordinary paper, except later printings of E15/16/18 which were C.

E11	½d.	**purple and grn** ('05)	5·00	6·00
E12	1d.	**purple and carmine**	3·00	2·50
E13	2d.	**pur and brn** ('05) ..	£10	£10
E14	2½d.	**pur and ult** ('05) ..	£10	£10
E15	3d.	**pur and or** ('05) ..	4·50	6·00
E16	6d.	**pur and grn** ('06) ..	6·00	6·00

E17	1/–	grn and or ('05)	..	£10	£11
E18	2/–	grn and ult ('06)	..	£20	£28
E19	5/–	grn and car ('06)	..	£40	£45
E20	10/–	grn and pur ('06)	..	£150	£175
E11/20		(set 10v)	.. ..	£250	£280

1906. (*recess*). **De La Rue. Wmk. Multiple Crown CA. Perf. 14. Sheets 6 x 10, except E22 (12 x 10).**

E21	½d.	green..	.. ..	60	60
E22	1d.	carmine	.. ..	40	40
E23	2d.	orange	.. ..	2·50	3·50
E24	2½d.	blue	..	4·00	4·00
E25	2½d.	ultramarine..	..	5·50	4·50
E21/24		set (4v)	..	£12	£12
SPE21/24		specimen set (4v)..		£35	‡

1908-11. (*typo*). **De La Rue. Sheets 6 x 10. C.**

(a) Wmk. Crown CA.

| E26 | 1/– | black/green .. | .. | £13 | £17 |
| E27 | 10/– | green and red/green | | £120 | £140 |

(b) Wmk. Multiple Crown CA.

E28	3d.	dl purple/yellow	..	1·75	3·00
E29	6d.	dl purple and lilac ..		7·50	9·00
E30	1/–	black/green ('11)	..	4·00	6·00
E31	2/–	blue and purple/blue		£12	£15
E32	5/–	green/yellow	..	£35	£45
E26/32		set (7v)	.. ..	£190	£225
SPE26/32		specimen set (7v)..		£120	‡

Die Proofs of the vignette exist 'Before' and 'After' hardening.

1913 (Jan. 3rd)-22. Wmk. Multiple Crown CA. Sheets 120 – two panes, each 6 x 10. G1/13 O; G14/23 C.

G1	½d.	yellow-green	..	35	40
G2	½d.	green ..	.. ..	30	40
G3	½d.	deep green	..	35	50
		a on bluish paper	..	1·00	1·50
G4	1d.	rose ..	.. ..	70	60
G5	1d.	carmine	.. ..	70	60
G6	1d.	scarlet ('16)	..	50	30
G7	1d.	red ..	.. ..	50	50
		a on bluish paper	..	1·25	1·50
G8	2d.	orange	.. ..	60	90
G9	2d.	brown-orange	..	60	90
G10	2d.	dp yellow-orange	..	60	90
G11	2½d.	bt blue..	.. ..	1·50	1·75
G12	2½d.	dp blue	.. ..	1·50	1·75

G13	2½d.	pl dl blue ('20)	..	2·50	3·50
G14	3d.	purple/yellow	..	70	1·20
		a white back (3/14)		1·20	3·00
		b on lemon ('17)	..	1·75	2·75
		c on pl yellow ('21)..		2·00	3·00
G15	6d.	purple and lilac		1·75	3·00
G16	6d.	pur and reddish vio		1·75	3.00
G17	1/–	black/green ..	..	2·75	3·50
		a white back (3/14)..		1·50	3·50
		b on blue-green, olive			
		back ('17)	..	£22	£25
		c on emerald back			
		(6/22)	.. ..	1·50	3·00
		d on emerald ..	..	1·50	3·00
G18	2/–	pur and blue/blue	..	3·50	5·00
G19	2/–	lilac and bl/gr-bl	..	4·00	5·00
G20	2/–	dp purand bl/dl bl ..		4·00	5·00
G21	2/–	blackish purple and			
		blue/greenish blue			
		(mottled) ('21) ..		4·00	5·00
G22	5/–	grn and red/yellow		£11	£17
		a on pl yellow ('21)..		£18	£25
G23	10/–	grn and red/grn	..	£38	£48
		a on emerald back			
		(6/22)	.. ..	£40	£50
G1/23		set (10v)	••	£55	£75
SPG1/23		specimen set (13v)..		£150	‡

1916 (June 1st). War Tax. Nos. G5/6/7 overprinted WAR TAX in black. Setting 6 x 10.

(a) In serif capitals at the Government Press at St. George's.

G24	1d.	carmine	.. ..	2·50	4·50
		a overprint inverted ..		£110	—
		b small "A" IN "WAR"		5·00	£10
		c small A' in 'TAX' ..		7·00	£12
G25	1d.	red ..	.. ..	2·50	4·50
		a small 'A' in 'WAR'..		5·00	£10
		b small 'A' in 'TAX'..		7·00	£12
		c △ for 'A' in 'TAX'..		£10	£15
SPG24		specimen (I) ..		£28	‡

G24b/25a—The 'A' in 'WAR' is 2mm. high instead of 2¼mm. Rows 5/5, 7/2, 8/6, (both panes).

G24c/25b—The 'A' in 'TAX' is 1½mm. high, instead of 2¼mm. Row 2/5 (both panes).

G25c—Row 10/2 (left hand panes only).

(b) In sans serif capitals in London.

G26	1d.	scarlet (9/16)	..	40	40
G27	1d.	car/bluish (5/18)	..	40	40
SPG26		specimen (I)..	..	£22	‡

G27 was a special printing of the basic stamp.

1921-32. As G1/23 but Wmk. Multiple Script CA. G28/47 O; G48/72 C.

G28	½d.	green ..	.. ..	25	35
G29	½d.	blue-green	.. ..	25	35
G30	1d.	carmine	.. ..	25	30
G31	1d.	brown ('23)	..	30	30
G32	1d.	yellow brown		30	30
G33	1d.	chocolate-brown ..		35	35
G34	1½d.	rose-red (6/22)	..	35	40
G35	2d.	orange..	.. ..	40	60
G36	2d.	bt dp orange..	..	40	60
G37	2d.	dp grey ('26)..	..	60	1·00
G38	2d.	slate-grey	.. ..	60	1·00
G39	2d.	silver-grey	..	60	1·00
G40	2½d.	dp dl blue ('21)	..	60	1·00
G41	2½d.	grey (6/22)	.. ..	80	2·75

G42	2½d. **dl slate grey**	80	2·75
G43	2½d. **bt blue** ('26)	1·20	1·50
G44	2½d. **ultramarine** ('31) ..	1·20	1·50
G45	2½d. **ult and gr-bl** ('32) ..	1·20	1·75
G46	3d. **blue** (6/22)	1·40	2·75
G47	3d. **dp blue**	1·50	2·75
G48	3d. **pur/yel** (lem yel back)		
	('26)	70	1·70
G49	3d. **dl reddish pur/yel**..	70	1·70
G50	3d. **dl pur/pl yel**	70	1·70
G51	4d. **blk and red/yel** ('26)		
	a lemon back	70	3·00
G52	5d. **pur and sage-grn**		
	(27.12.22)	1·25	3·50
G53	5d. **brnish pur and dp**		
	sage green.. ..	1·40	3·50
G54	5d. **bt pur and olive-grn**	1·50	3·50
G55	6d. **brownish pur and**		
	redish violet ..	1·50	3·50
G56	6d. **pl purple and lilac** ..	1·50	3·50
G57	6d. **dl pur and mag** ('23)	1·50	3·50
G58	6d. **blk and car** ('26) ..	1·75	3·00
G59	9d. **pur and blk** (27.12.22)	1·50	3·50
G60	9d. **bt pur and blk** ..	1·50	3·50
G61	9d. **brn-pur and blk** ..	1·50	3·50
G62	1/– **black/emerald** ..	3·00	7·00
	a wmk. inverted ..	8·00	£10
G63	1/– **chestnut** ('26) ..	7·50	£10
G64	2/– **blkish pur and blue/**		
	grnish bl (mottled)		
	('22)	7·00	£10
G65	2/– **reddish pur and**		
	blue/greyblue('25)	7·00	£10
G66	2/– **pur and bl/grnish bl**		
	('27)	7·00	£10
G67	2/– **dp pur and bl/grnish**		
	blue ('28)	7·00	£10
G68	2/6 **blk and red/bl** ('29)	£10	£15
G69	3/– **grn and vio** (27.12.22)	£12	£17
G70	3/– **yel-grn and vio** ..	£12	£17
G71	5/– **grn and red/yel** ('23)	£18	£25
	a on yellow buff ..		
G72	10/– **grn and red/em** ('23)	£35	£45
G28/72	**set** (23v)	£120	£150
SPG31/70	**specimen set** (23v)	£240	‡

G29 was made up in vertical coils from sheets, with a coil join every ten stamps.

1934 (Oct. 23rd)-36. (*recess*) **Waterlow and**

Sons. Wmk. Multiple Script CA (sideways on Horizontal design). **Sheets V 10 x 6: H 6 x 10.**

(a) Perf. 12½.

G73	½d. **green**	30	35
G74	1d. **black and sepia** ..	40	40
G75	1½d. **black and scarlet** ..	75	75
G76	2d. **black and orange** ..	80	80
G77	2½d. **blue**	50	75
G78	3d. **blk and olive-green** ..	80	1·00
G79	6d. **black and purple** ..	1·40	1·75
G80	1/– **black and brown** ..	2·75	3·50
G81	2/6 **black and ult** ..	£10	£15
G82	5/– **black and violet** ..	£17	£20
G73/82	**set** (10v)	£30	£40
SPG73/82	**specimen set** (10v)	£55	‡

(b) Perf. 12½ x 13½ or 13½ x 12½ (G84). 1936.

G83	½d. **green**	2·50	6·00
G84	½d. **black and sepia** ..	1·50	3·00
G85	1½d. **black and scarlet** ..	2·50	3·00

G83/84—were made up in coils from sheets.

1935 (May 6th). **Silver Jubilee.** (*recess*) **Waterlow and Sons. Wmk. Multiple Script CA. Perf. 11 x 12. Sheets 6 x 10.**

G86	½d. **black and green** ..	25	25
G87	1d. **ult and grey** ..	30	30
G88	1½d. **dp blue and scarlet**	70	70
G89	1/– **slate and purple** ..	4·00	4·50
G86/89	**set** (4v)	5·00	5·50
SPG86/89	**specimen set** (4v)..	£22	‡

Numbers printed—G86, 175,680: G87, 176,000: G88, 110.000: G89 45,000

Remainders were withdrawn December 31st, 1935.

1937-50 Design, King's Head. Printers (*photo*) **Harrison & Sons. Perf. 14¾ x 14 (C). Sheets 12 x 10.**

1	¼d. **chocolate-brown** (*ch*)		
	(12/7/37)	5	5
	a chocolate-brown (*sub*)		
	(11/42)	10	10
	b chocolate (*sub*)		
	(2/1/45)	5	5
	c chocolate (*ch*)		
	(16/8/50) ..	10	15

1938 (Mar. 16th) -50 Designs, ½d. (Grand Anse Beach); 1½d. (Grand Etang Lake); 2½d. (St. George's); Other Values (King's Head and Badge of the Colony). Printers (recess) Waterlow & Sons. Designs, ½d., 1½d., 2½d., 10/- V. Centres black except Nos. 2, 6, 12, 16. Perf. 12½ (L). Sheets 6 x 10 or 10 x 6.

2	½d.	yellow-green	..	1·00	20
	a	blue-green (10/9/43)		10	10
3	1d.	sepia	..	10	5
	a	dp sepia (10/9/43)	..	15	5
4	1½d.	dp scarlet	..	20	10
	a	scarlet red (10/9/43)		10	5
5	2d.	orange	..	10	5
	a	bright orange	..	20	5
6	2½d.	dp blue	..	15	5
	a	bright blue (20/3/50)		10	5
7	3d.	olive-green	..	1·00	60
	a	olive (/40)	..	1·20	1·00
	b	dp olive (16/8/50)	..	30	30
8	6d.	purple-lake	..	25	15
	a	purple (2/1/45)	..	20	15
9	1/-	light brown	..	35	15
10	2/-	ultramarine	..	80	80
	a	bt ult (2/1/45)	..	1·00	80
11	5/-	violet	..	..	1·50	1·50
1/11		set (11)		3·50	3·10
SP 1/11		specimen set perf (12)			
		(inc. 22)	..	£50	‡

As Nos. 2, etc., but Perf. 12¾ x 13¼ (C).

12	½d.	yellow-green	..	40	60
	a	blue-green (/41)	..	50	75
13	1d.	sepia	..	10	10
	a	dp sepia (/40)	..	15	10
14	1½d.	carmine-red	..	70	50
15	2d.	orange	..	10	10
	a	grey-orange	..	20	10
16	2½d.	blue (/50)	..	£1000	£70
17	3d.	olive-green (/41)	..	80	60
	a	olive (11/42)	..	80	60
	b	dp olive (15/7/47)	..	70	50
18	6d.	dp purple (11/42)	..	30	15
	a	purple (15/7/47)	..	40	15
19	1/-	light brown (11/42)	.	50	40
20	2/-	ultramarine (/41)	..	2·50	1·25
	a	bt ult (15/7/47)	..	2·00	1·25
21	5/-	violet (15/7/47)	..	2·25	2·50

Values in both perforations (where no dates are given) were issued at the same time, along with No. 22.

No. 7 with frames of bright green or orange are fakes.

Nos. 12, 12a were both issued in coils.

Design, Seal of Colony. Printers (recess) De La Rue. Perf. 11¾ x 13 (C). Sheets 6 x 10.

22	10/-	steel-blue and carmine			
		(16/3/38) (n)	..	6·00	6·00

Perf. 13¾ x 14 (L).

23	10/-	slate-blue and carmine			
		(/40) (n)	..	..	£30	£30

Perf. 11¾ (L).

24	10/-	bluish-sl and dl car			
		(10/9/43) (n)	..	£70	£80

Perf. 14 (L).

25	10/-	dull bluish-grey and rose-car (10/9/43) (n)		£25	£30
	aa	dp slate and br car-rose (10/43) (n)		5·00	6·00
	a	bluish-slate and dp car (/44) (w)		£15	£12
	aaa	bluish-slate and dp claret (/44) (w)	..	£25	£25
	b	slate and car-rose (15/7/47) (w)	..	£10	£12
	c	bluish-slate and dull car-rose (/48) (n)		£10	£12

No. 23, though apparently part of the first consignment, was not placed on sale before 1940. Nos. 24 and 25 were released in London simultaneously. No. 25 has a blurred centre which is particularly noticeable in the outline of crow's nest on the mast. No. 25aaa has a very deep claret frame. Forged copies of No. 24 exist made from the common stamp and re-perforated. No. 25c was put on sale in the Colony some time late in 1948.

(n) Stamps printed with damped paper. Design about 23½mm. wide.

(w) Stamps printed with dry paper. Design about 24½mm. wide.

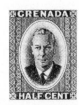

1951 (Jan. 8th) Designs, ½c.–12c. (Portrait of King); Other Values (Badge of Colony). Sheets 10 x 10.

H

(a) Perf. 11½ (C). Printers (*recess*) **Bradbury, Wilkinson. Centres black.**

26	½c.	red-brown	.. ..	10	10
27	1c.	emerald	.. ..	10	10
28	2c.	sepia	.. ..	10	10
29	3c.	carmine	.. ..	15	15
30	4c.	orange	.. ..	15	15
31	5c.	violet	.. ..	15	15
32	6c.	olive-green	.. ..	15	15
33	7c.	blue	.. ..	20	20
34	12c.	purple	.. ..	20	20

(b) Perf. 11½ x 12½ (C). Printers (*recess*) **De La Rue. Sheets 10 x 5.**

35	25c.	sepia	.. ..	60	60
36	50c.	dp blue	.. ..	80	90
37	$1.50	orange	.. ..	5·00	4·00

(c) Perf. 11¾ x 13 (C). Printers (*recess*) **De La Rue** (*large format*).

38	$2.50	slate-blue and car-rose	.. ..	8·00	9·00
	a	re-entry	.. ..	£30	£30
26/38		**set** (13)	.. ..	£15	£15

38*a* occurs on Nos. 1, 4 and 6 of the bottom row.

SPECIAL ISSUES

1937 (May 12th) Coronation. As Aden, but printers Bradbury, Wilkinson. Perf. 11 x 11¾ (C).

S1	1d.	violet	.. ..	10	10
S2	1½d.	carmine-red	..	10	15
S3	2½d.	blue	.. ..	15	20
SP S1/3		specimen set perf (3)	£15	‡

1946 (Sept. 25th) Victory. As Aden.

S4	1½d.	carmine-red	..	10	10
S5	3½d.	grey-blue	.. ..	15	15
SP S4/5		specimen set perf (2)	£20	‡

1948 (Oct. 27th) Silver Wedding. As Aden.

S6	1½d.	scarlet	.. ..	10	10
S7	10/–	greenish-slate	..	5·00	6·00

Number issued (Colony only)—1½d., 98,110; 10/–, 4,160.

1949 (Oct. 10th) U.P.U. As Aden.

S8	5c.	dull violet-blue	..	10	10
S9	6c.	dp olive	.. ..	15	15
S10	12c.	reddish-mauve	..	35	35
S11	24c.	beech-brown	..	60	60
S8/11		**set** (4)	.. ..	1·00	1·00

Number issued (Colony only)—5c., 61,824; 6c., 29,593; 12c., 35,076; 24c., 27,580.

1951 (Feb. 16th) West Indies University College. (See Antigua.)

S12	3c.	black and dp red	..	20	15
S13	6c.	black and olive	..	30	30

Number issued (Colony only)—3c., 85,685; 6c., 63,967.

1951 (Sept. 21st) New Constitution 1951. No. 29, etc., overprinted in black or red by Bradbury, Wilkinson.

S14	3c.	black and carmine	.	10	15
S15	4c.	black and orange	..	15	15
S16	5c.	black and violet (red)	15	15
S17	12c.	black and purple	..	20	30
S14/17		**set** (4)	.. ..	60	75

Number issued—3c., 106,140; 4c., 104,576 5c., 114,659; 12c., 113,221.

POSTAGE DUE STAMPS

1892 (April 18th). (*typo*). **De La Rue. Wmk. Crown CA. Perf. 14. Sheets 6 x 10.**

VD1	1d.	black	.. .. ..	4·00	2·00
VD2	2d.	black	.. .. ..	5·00	2·00
VD3	3d.	black	.. .. ..	7·00	3·00
SPVD1/3		specimen ovpt (3)	£65	‡

1892—Nos. V46 and V45 surcharged locally in black.

(a) August.

VD4	1d.	on 8d. grey-brown	..	£30	4·00
	a	tete beche (vert pair)	£125	—
VD5	2d.	on 8d. grey-brown	..	£70	£10
	a	tete beche (vert pair)	£300	—

Collectors are warned of forged mint copies of VD5.

(b) October.

VD6	1d.	on 6d. mauve	.. ..	4·00	2·00
	a	tete beche (vert pair)	£20	—
	b	surcharge double	..	—	£25
VD7	2d.	on 6d. mauve	.. ..	£10	3·00
	a	tete beche (vert pair)	£30	—

There are innumerable examples of additional commas, colons and stops appearing before or after "SURCHARGE" and "POSTAGE" on all four stamps.

1906 (July)-11. As Nos. VD1/3 but Wmk. Multiple Crown CA.

ED1	1d. **black** ('11)	50	65
ED2	2d. **black**	75	85
ED3	3d. **black** (9/06)	1·00	1·50

1921 (Dec.)-45. As before but inscribed "POSTAGE DUE". Wmk. Multiple Script CA.

(a) Smooth paper. (1921-22).

GD1	1d. **black**	50	50
GD2	1½d. **black** (15.12.22) ..	75	75
GD3	2d. **black**	75	75
GD4	3d. **black**	1·00	1·00
GD1/4	**set** (4v)	3·00	3·00
SPGD1/4	**specimen set** (4v) ..	£40	‡

(b) Rough paper (1945).

PD1	1d. **black**	75	1·00
PD2	3d. **black**	1·00	1·00

1952 (March 1st). As before, but values in Cents.

PD3	2c. **black C**	5	10
PD4	4c. **black C**	10	10
PD5	6c. **black C**	15	20
PD6	8c. **black C**	15	20

Watermark Varieties (Type A)

(See Introduction for details)

PD3a	2c. Crown missing ..	£20	—
PD3b	St. Edwards Crown	£12	—
PD4a	4c. Crown missing ..	£20	—
PD4b	St. Edward's Crown	£14	—
PD5a	6c. Crown missing ..	£25	—

PD5b	St. Edward's Crown	£20	—
PD6a	8c. Crown missing	£30	—
PD6b	St. Edward's Crown	£22	—

SEMI POSTAL ISSUES

1914 (Sept.)-18. Red Cross Fund. Locally typeset. Sheets 2 x 5 (stamps imperf on outer edge) without gum.

(a) September, 1914. Perf. 11.

GSP1	1 fraction **red**	1·75	—

(b) 1916. Dates 1914/1915 included in design. Roul 6.

GSP2	¼d. **red**	2·00	—

(c) December, 1916. Dates 1914/1915/1916/1917 included. Perf. 11.

GSP3	¼d. **red**	1·50	—

(d) 1918. As GSP3 but with '1918' added. Perf. 11. The stamps in the right hand vertical column of the sheet are inverted in relation to those in the left hand vertical column.

GSP4	¼d. **red**	2·00	—

These labels were issued by the Red Cross for the benefit of their funds. Although they had no postal validity they may be found with postal concellations; and it is believed that they were also recognised as 'official franks' on Red Cross correspondence, which was entitled to carriage postage free.

HONG KONG

The island was ceded to Great Britain in 1841 and the colony was subsequently enlarged by the cession of the Kowloon peninsula in 1861 and the lease of the "New Territories" in 1898.

The first Post Office was opened in 1842 and, following the use of other handstamps, Crowned Circle PAID Franks were registered at the G.P.O., London on October 17th, 1843 (double circle) and 1853 (single circle), being struck in red to indicate prepayment of postage on overseas letters, (see Introduction).

The Hong Kong stamps issued in 1862 were cancelled "B62" or "62B" in a transverse oval of horizontal bars: this cancellation is also known on G.B. stamps (1862-1878) although the use of such stamps was not authorised in Hong Kong.

1844-53 PAID Franks.

		On Cover
VF1	**(1843)**	£750
VF2	**(1853)**	£800

All stamps to G46 are Typo De La Rue. Perf. 14. Sheets 240 – four panes, each 6 x 10, unless otherwise indicated. Prices for fine well centred copies.

1862 (Dec. 8th) No Wmk. Perf. 14.

V1	2c. **brown**	..	£100	£30
V2	2c. **deep brown** ('63)	..	£175	£35
V3	8c. **yellow-buff**	..	£140	£25
V4	12c. **pale greenish blue**	..	£100	£22
V5	18c. **lilac**	..	£120	£20
V6	24c. **green**	.. ..	£160	£35
V7	48c. **rose**	.. ..	£425	£85
V8	96c. **brownish grey**	..	£425	£70
SPV1/8	**specimen set** various
	types (7v)	..	from £425	‡

Numbers printed—V1, 216,240; V2, 106,560; V3, 317,280; V4, 322,800; V5, 279,120; V6, 222,240; V7, 48,480; V8, 33,120.

1863-71 As before but Wmk. Crown CC

(a) Perf. 14.

V9	2c. **deep brown** ('64)	..	£30	£10
V10	2c. **brown** ('67)	..	£26	3·00
V11	2c. **pale yellow-brown**		£30	4·00
V12	4c. **grey**	.. ..	£15	4·00
V13	4c. **slate**	..	£15	2·00
V14	4c. **deep slate**	..	£18	3·00
V15	4c. **greenish grey**	..	£32	£15
V16	4c. **bluish slate** ('67)	..	£70	3·00
V17	6c. **lilac**	.. ..	£65	4·00
V18	6c. **mauve** ('67)	..	£65	6·00
V19	8c. **pl dl orange** ('64)	..	£65	5·00
V20	8c. **brownish or** ('67)	..	£45	5·00

V21	8c. **bright orange**	..	£50	3·00
V22	12c. **pl greenish blu** ('64)		£95	£10
V23	12c. **pl blue** ('71)	..	7·00	4·00
V24	12c. **deep blue**	.. ·	£40	4·00
V25	18c. **lilac** ('65)	..	£425	£90
V26	24c. **green** ('64)	..	£50	6·00
V27	24c. **pale green** ('67)	..
V28	24c. **deep green**	..	£70	8·00
V29	30c. **vermilion**	..	£100	£12
V30	30c. **or-verm** ('67)	..	£100	7·00
V31	30c. **mauve** (14/8/71)	..	£40	3·00
V32	48c. **pale rose**	..	£75	£16
V33	48c. **rose-carmine**	..	£75	£14
V34	48c. **deep claret**		—	—
V35	96c. **olive-bistre** ('64)	..	£2200	£225
V36	96c. **brownish grey** ('65)		£70	£14
V37	96c. **brownish blk** ('67)	..	£100	£10

See also Nos. V42/45 and V55/56.

(b) Perf. 12½ (1870).

V38	4c. **grey**	.. ..	£900	£120
V39	4c. **dark grey**	.. ..	£900	£120
SPV9/37	**specimen set** various
	types (11v)	..	from £750	‡

V34—The Royal Collection contains a mint copy, and one used copy is recorded: it is possible that this shade was a colour change.

V9/39—All except V35 exist with inverted watermark; and many values are known with watermark reversed or inverted and reversed.

Lithographed forgeries exist on unwatermarked paper, usually with a neat 'B62' cancellation. No. V25 was also forged on paper with an impressed watermark.

Die Proofs of all values exist in black and in issued colours on white glazed card.

Numbers printed—V9, 572,880; V10/11, 4,008,000; V12/16, 4,224,000; V17, 583,200; V18,3,360,000; V19, 363,600; V20/21, 5,280,000; V22, 129,600; V23/24, 1,008,000; V25, 149,520; V26, 330,000; V27/28, 1,818,000; V29, 463,200; V30, 588,000; V31, 2,400,000; V32, 123,840; V33, 747,600; V35, 12,480; V36, 114,240; V37, 799,200.

(The above figures include quantities later surcharged).

1876-77 Nos. V25 and V31 locally surcharged in black by the Government Printers Noronha & Sons.

V40	16c. on 18c. **lilac** (4/77)	..	£200	£50
	a spaced 'n t'		£475	£95
V41	28c. on 30c. **mauve** (6/76)		£120	£17
SPV40/41	**specimen** (2v)		£225	‡

V40*a*—The 'n' and 't' of 'cents' are spaced 1mm instead of ½mm and the word measures 10mm instead of 9½mm.

Numbers printed—V40/41, approx. 36,000 each.

These surcharges have been forged, both on genuine and on forged stamps.

1877 (Aug.)-80 As Nos. V9/39 but new colours and value.

V42	2c.	**dull rose** (8/79)	£10	4·00
V43	2c.	**rose** (10/80) ..	£14	5·00
V44	16c.	**yellow** ..	£120	£18
V45	48c.	**brown** (8/79)	£90	£27

SPV42/45 **specimen set** (3v)   £175   ‡

Although Nos. V42 and V45 were despatched to the Colony in July 1879, they were apparently not put on sale until the following year.

Imperforate Colour Trials of No. V42 exist on unwatermarked paper in a variety of colours.

Numbers printed—V42, 390,000; V43, 400,800; V44, 238,080; (including quantities later surcharged); V45, 299,280.

1879 (April 1st–Nov.) Nos. V25 and V44 locally surcharged in black by Noronha & Sons for use on postcards.

(a) April 1st.

V46	3c. on 16c.	**yellow** ..	—	—
		a short 'T'	—	—
V47	5c. on 18c.	**lilac**	—	—
		a short 'T'	—	—

(b) No. V47 handstamped 'THREE' in black (November).

V48 3c. on 5c. on 18c. ..   ..   —   —

V46/48 were surcharged for use on postcards only, and they were not intended to be sold other than affixed to cards; mint copies are nevertheless known.

V46 was originally affixed to a yellow card and V47 to a blue card; but the colour of both cards was changed to white in July 1879.

V48 was required on account of a shortage of No. V46.

Hong Kong currency, hitherto 96 cents — 1 dollar was changed from March 1st 1880 to 100 cents — 1 dollar.

5
cents.

10
cents.

1880 (March-May) Nos. V21/23/25/26/44

locally surcharged in black by Noronha & Sons.

V49	5c. on 8c.	**bt or** (May) ..	£50	£20
		a surcharge inverted ..	—	—
		b surcharge double ..	—	—
V50	5c. on 18c.	**lilac** (March)	£40	£18
V51	10c. on 12c.	**pl blue** (Mar.)	£40	£18
V52	10c. on 12c.	**blue** (Mar.) ..	£40	£18
V53	10c. on 16c.	**yellow** (May)	£120	£45
		a surcharge inverted ..	—	—
V54	10c. on 24c.	**green** (May)	£60	£20

V49*a*—14 used copies are known.

V49*b*—2 used copies are known, the second surcharge being almost directly over the first.

V53*a*—2 used copies are known.

These surcharges, including the varieties, have been expertly forged; and collectors should exercise care in purchasing these stamps.

Numbers printed—between 72,000 and 120,000 of each value.

1880 (Nov.) As Nos. V9/39 but new values.

V55	5c.	**blue** ..	£18	5·00
V56	10c.	**mauve** ..	£22	4·00

SPV55/56 **specimen set** (2v)   £50   ‡

Numbers printed—V55, 573,600; V56, 741,600.

1882 (May)-96 As before, but Wmk. Crown CA.

(a) Perf. 14.

V57	2c.	**rose-lake** (7/82) ..	£12	6·00
V58	2c.	**rose-pink** ..	£20	£10
V59	2c.	**carmine** ('83) ..	1·50	30
		a bisect vert (1c.) ..	‡	—
V60	2c.	**aniline carmine** ..	2·00	30
V61	4c.	**grey** (4/96) ..	80	30
V62	5c.	**pale blue** (5/82) ..	2·00	30
V63	5c.	**blue** ..	2·00	30
V64	10c.	**mauve** (5/82) ..	£75	3·00
V65	10c.	**dp blue-green** ('83)	£200	£10
V66	10c.	**green** ('84) ..	£10	1·00
V67	10c.	**purple/red** (1/1/91)	2·00	25
V68	30c.	**yellowish green** (1/1/91) ..	£20	£12
V69	30c.	**grey-green** ..	8·00	4·50

See also Nos. V93/98.

(b) Perf. 12 (1882).

V70 2c. **rose-lake** £3000 £1750

SPV67/68 **specimen pair** ..   £80   ‡

V69 was printed in a highly fugitive ink and copies which have faded or have been affected by moisture closely resemble the much scarcer yellowish green printing (No. V68).

Numbers printed—V64, 586,800; V65, 292,800.

20 CENTS

1885 (June) As Nos. V29/35/45 but special printings in altered colours (Wmk. Crown CA) subsequently surcharged in black by De La Rue. Setting of V73 – one horizontal row of six applied ten times to the pane.

V71	20c. on 30c. **orange-red** ..	£10	3·00
	a surcharge double ..	£800	—
V72	50c. on 48c. **yellowish brn**	£22	5·00
V73	$1 on 96c. **grey-olive** ..	£35	£14
SPV71/73	**specimen set** (3v) ..	£95	‡

Imperforate Colour Trials for No. V73 exist in grey, mauve, and dull green on watermarked buff and yellow paper.

(See also Nos. V77/88).

1891 (Jan.-Feb.) Nos. V31 and V66 locally surcharged in black by Noronha & Sons. Setting 6 x 10.

V74	7c. on 10c. **grn** (Jan. 1st)	£12	£10
	a antique 't' ..	£100	£80
	b surcharge double ..	£500	£300
V75	14c. on 30c. **mauve** (Feb. 1st). ..	£20	£20
	a antique 't' ..	£200	£150

V74a/75a—The 't' in 'cents' is from the wrong font on R1/1. Its lower loop projects below the other letters, and its stem bisects the crossbar.

The lower loop of the 't' is damaged or broken on Rows 4/3, 8/4, 8/5 and 9/6 and stamps from these positions should not be confused with the variety from R1/1.

V74b may be found in differing positions from different panes.

Collectors are warned of excellent forgeries of the normal surcharges.

1841
Hong Kong
JUBILEE
1891

1891 (Jan. 22nd) Golden Jubilee of Cession.

No. V59 locally overprinted in black by Noronha & Sons. First Setting (6 printings); 6 x 2 applied five times to the pane. Second Setting: probably 6 x 10.

V76	2c. **carmine**	£45	£38
	a short 'U'	£90	£90
	b tall 'K'	£90	£90
	c broken 'N' ..	£90	£90
	d spaced 'O N' ..	£175	£175
	e short 'J'	£90	£90
	f broken '1'	£90	£90
	g bent 'E'	£90	£90
	h overprint double ..	£1250	£1250

The varieties a–g were not all constant through the six printings of the First Setting. V67a, b and g may also be found on the Second Setting, together with other varieties (e.g. no crossbar to 'H') which do not occur on printings of the First Setting.

V76a—Short 'U' in 'JUBILEE'. Row 1/1 of the Setting (6 x 2).

V76b—Tall, narrow 'K' in 'KONG'. Row 1/3 of the Setting (6 x 2).

V76c—Broken 'N' in 'KONG'. Row 1/4 of the Setting (6 x 2).

V76d—'O N' spaced in 'HONG'. Row 1/5 of the Setting. (6 x 2).

V76e—Short 'J' in 'JUBILEE'. Row 1/6 of the Setting (6 x 2).

V76f—Broken first '1' in '1891'. Row 2/1 of the Setting (6 x 2).

V76g—Bent top bar in second 'E' in 'JUBILEE'. Row 2/6 of the Setting. (6 x 2).

V76h—May be found in two forms, the more common being that with the second overprint about 1mm. away horizontally. The more important variety, of which there were only 18 copies (3 rows of six), shows the second 11½mm. above or below the normal and lying across two stamps in the vertical column.

The overprint has been forged on stamps on both Crown CA and Crown CC paper.

Number printed—1st Setting, 48,000; 2nd Setting 2,000.

(On sale for three days only).

1891 (Jan. 1st) As Nos. V71/73 but surcharged in black by De La Rue on special printings in altered colours (V79/80) and on Nos. V68/69.

V77	20c. on 30c. **yel'ish grn** ..	£25	£25
V78	20c. on 30c. **grey-green** ..	£20	£20
V79	50c. on 48c. **dull purple** ..	£30	£30
V80	$1 on 96c. **purple/red** ..	£40	£40
SPV77/80	**specimen set** (3v) ..	£110	‡

V78—See Note after No. V69.

20c.   50c. $1

**1891 (Feb. 1st–April 1st). Nos. V77/80
additionally overprinted with black handstamped Chinese characters (denoting the
equivalent of the English surcharge) at top
left by Noronha & Sons.**

V81 20c. on 30c. **yellowish grn** (Feb. 1st) ..	£10	2·00
a '20 CENTS' double ..	—	—
V82 20c. on 30c. **grey-grn** (Feb. 1st) ..	4·00	2·00
V83 50c. on 48c. **dl purple** (Feb. 1st) ..	6·00	2·50
V84 $1 on 96c **pur/red** (April 1st) ..	£26	5·00
a handstamped both sides	£60	—
b pair, one with and one without handstamp	£60	—
SPV81/84 **specimen set** (3v) ..	£110	‡

V81a—This variety is only known on the stamp
with handstamped Chinese characters and is
not recorded on No. V77.

V82—See Note after No. V69.

Despite the fact that such action had been not
found necessary on the similar 1885 surcharges
(V71/73), these Chinese characters were handstamped over the original Chinese denominations
in order that they should agree with the surcharge
made by De La Rue.

Four types of the 20c. overprint and three types
of the 50c. overprint may be distinguished; in
the case of each value one of the types being
much larger than the others. As the overprints
were applied individually to each stamp a wide
variety of errors is known, especially on Nos.
V82 and V83; the better known are listed below:—

a—Handstamp in large type.
b—Handstamp omitted in pair with normal.
c—Handstamp inverted at left.
d—Handstamp double at left.
e—Handstamp double, one inverted, at left.
f—Handstamp both sides.
g—Handstamp both sides and omitted in pair.
h—Handstamp both sides and double in pair.
i—Handstamp normal at left, inverted at right.
j—Handstamp inverted at left, normal at right.
k—Handstamp 20c. both sides and 50c. twice at
left.

Varieties priced from:

V82 (20c.)	V83 (50c.)
£10	£15

**1898 (April) As No. V80 but in altered colour.
(a) Surcharged in black by De La Rue.**

V85 $1 on 96c. **black**	£65	£60
V86 $1 on 96c. **grey-black** ..	£65	£60
SPV85/86 **specimen** (1v)	£50	‡

**(b) Additionally overprinted with black hand-
stamped Chinese characters at left, as No.
V84.**

V87 $1 on 96c. **black**	£12	£10
V88 $1 on 96c. **grey-black** ..	£12	£10
a omitted in pair with normal	£28	—
b inverted at left	£28	—
c double at left	£28	—
d double, one inverted, at left ..	£24	—
e both sides ..	£30	—
f both sides and omitted in pair	£35	—
g both sides and double in pair	£40	—
h normal at left, inverted at right	£28	—
i inverted at left, normal at right	£28	—
j double at left, once at right	£30	—
SPV87/88 **specimen** (1v)	£45	‡

The need for the altered colour arose from the
discovery in September 1897 of bogus copies of
No. V84 created by a Chinese official in a branch
post office. The fraud was achieved by applying
forged surcharges, in English and Chinese, to
copies of the 10c. purple/red (No. V67).

No. V84 was immediately withdrawn from sale
and replaced temporarily by a Fiscal $2 surcharged
$1 (Nos. VF13/14) until Nos. V85/86 were
received in the Colony.

**1898 (April 2nd-16th) Nos. V68/69 locally
surcharged in black by Noronha & Sons.
Setting – one horizontal row of 12 applied
twenty times to the complete sheet of four
panes.**

(a) April 16th.

V89 10c. on 30c. **yellowish grn**	—	—
V90 10c. on 30c. **grey-grn** ..	£50	£100
a spaced '1 0'	—	—

V89 has not yet been recorded without the additional
Chinese overprint.

(b) Additionally overprinted with black hand-stamped Chinese characters at left. (April 2nd).

V91	10c. on 30c. **yellowish grn**	£25	—
V92	10c. on 30c. **grey-grn** ..	6·00	£10
	a spaced '1 0'	£40	£40
	b large hand-stamp ..	£40	£40
	c omitted in pair with normal ..	—	—
SPV91/92	**specimen** (1v)	£70	‡

V90*a*/92*a* occurred only on the last stamp on each row of the two right hand panes in the first (of five) printings made between April and September 1898. The space between '1' and '0' is 1½mm. instead of the normal 1mm.

V92*b* occurred on certain sheets only of the second printing. The character measures 5 x 4mm instead of the normal 4 x 3mm.

V90/92—See Note after No. V69.

V91—This shade was used for only one small printing.

1900-02 As Nos. V57/69 but new colours and value.

V93	2c.	**dull green**	60	20
		a booklet pane ..	—	—
V94	4c.	**carmine** ('01) ..	40	25
		a booklet pane ..	—	—
V95	5c.	**yellow** ('01) ..	1·50	1·00
V96	10c.	**ultramarine** ..	1·50	75
V97	12c.	**blue** ('02) ..	4·00	6·00
V98	30c.	**brown** ('01)..	3·00	4·00
V93/98		**set** (6v)	£10	£12
SPV93/98		**specimen set** (6v)	£60	‡

V93/94 were issued in Booklet form in 1903. See after No. E15.

1903 (Jan.–July). Wmk. Crown CA.

E1	1c.	**dl purple and brown**	10	10
		a booklet pane ..	—	—
E2	2c.	**dull green**	50	20
E3	4c.	**purple/red**	30	15
E4	5c.	**dl grn and brn-or** ..	1·00	1·00
E5	8c.	**slate and violet** ..	75	50
E6	10c.	**pur and blue/blue** ..	90	40
E7	12c.	**grn and pur/yel** ..	1·75	80
E8	20c.	**slate and chestnut** ..	1·50	80
E9	30c.	**dl grn and blk** ..	2·00	1·50
E10	50c.	**dl grn and mag** ..	5·00	6·00
E11	$1	**pur and sage-grn** ..	£10	7·00
E12	$2	**slate and scarlet** ..	£30	£25
E13	$3	**slate and dl blue** ..	£40	£32
E14	$5	**pur and blue-grn** ..	£50	£45
E15	$10	**sl and or/blue** ..	£300	£175
E1/15		**set** (15v)	£425	£280
SPE1/15		**specimen set** (15v)	£125	‡

E1 appeared also in Booklet form with Nos. V93/94 during the first half of 1903. Some 3,000 Booklets were sold.

1904-11 As before but Wmk. Multiple Crown CA.

(a) Ordinary paper; 1904 (Oct.)-10.

E16	1c.	**brown** ('10).. ..	10	10
E17	2c.	**dull green**	1·00	5
E18	2c.	**deep green** (5/07)	1·00	25
E19	2c.	**green** ('10)	60	20
E20	4c.	**purple/red**	15	25
E21	4c.	**carmine-red** (5/07)	50	20
		a booklet pane ..	—	—
E22	5c.	**dl grn and brn-or** ..	60	50
E23	10c.	**pur and blue/blue** (3/05)	1·29	60
E24	10c.	**bt ult** (5/07) ..	75	15
E25	20c.	**slate and chestnut**	1·00	60
E26	30c.	**dl green and black**	1·25	1·00
E27	50c.	**green and magenta**	3·00	1·75
E28	$1	**pur and sage-grn**	7·00	5·00
E29	$2	**slate and scarlet** ..	£25	£22
E30	$10	**slate and or/blue** (5/05)	£275	£175
E16/30		**set** (14v)	£300	£200

E21 was also issued in Booklet form (four panes of six).

E25—Forged copies, lithographed on unwatermarked paper and perf. 11, are known used from Shanghai in February 1905.

(b) Chalky paper; 1905 (Aug.)-11.

E31	2c.	**dull green** (11/06)	1·00	25
E32	4c.	**purple/red** (11/06)	15	25
E33	5c.	**dl grn and brn-or** (12/06)	70	60
E34	6c.	**or-verm and pur** (9/07)	1·25	60
E35	8c.	**sl and vio** (2/07) ..	1·00	60
E36	12c.	**grn and pur/yel** (12/06)	1·50	1·60
E37	20c.	**sl and chest** (1/07)	1·00	60
E38	20c.	**pur and sage-grn** ('11)	5·00	3·00
E39	30c.	**dl green and black** (9/07)	1·50	1·25
E40	30c.	**pur and or-yel** ('11)	5·00	2·50
E41	50c.	**grn and mag** (5/07)	3·00	2·00
E42	50c.	**black/green** ('10)	4·00	2·50
E43	$1	**pur and sage-grn** (5/07)	7·00	5·00
E44	$2	**sl and scar** (10/05)	£25	£22
E45	$2	**car-red and blk** ('11)	£30	£30
E46	$3	**slate and dull blue**	£32	£30
E47	$5	**pur and blue-green**	£50	£45
E48	$10	**sl and or/blu** (9/07)	£275	£175
E31/48		**set** (18v)	£410	£285
SPE16/47		**specimen set** (23v)	£220	‡

E48—Forged copies exist, made by removing the printing from a genuine low value stamp and substituting a new impression. They may be readily recognised, being on white paper.

1912 (Nov.)-20. Wmk. Multiple Crown CA.
G1/12—O: G13/24—C.

G1	1c.	**brown**	50	15
G2	1c.	**blk brn/bluish**	50	15
		a broken Crown ..	£45	£45
G3	2c.	**deep green**	40	20
G4	2c.	**green**	50	20
G5	4c.	**carmine-red** ..	40	15
G6	4c.	**scarlet** ..	2·00	30
G7	6c.	**yellow-orange** ..	1·50	1·00
G8	6c.	**brown-orange** ..	1·50	75
G9	8c.	**grey**	2·50	1·00
G10	8c.	**slate** ('15) ..	3·50	90
G11	10c.	**ultramarine** ..	3·00	35
G12	10c.	**dp bt ultramarine** ..	2·50	25
G13	12c.	**purple/yellow** ..	1·25	1·00
		a white back (3/14)..	1·50	1·50
G14	20c.	**pur and sage-grn** ..	1·00	40
G15	25c.	**pur and mag** (Type I) (1/14)	2·50	2·00
G16	25c.	**pur and mag** (Type II) (9/19)	6·00	5·00
G17	30c.	**pur and or-yel** ..	5·00	2·50
G18	30c.	**purple and orange**	2·00	60
G19	50c.	**black/blue-green** ..	2·00	75
		a white back (3/14)	1·75	75
		b olive back (5/17) ..	£22	3·00
		c on emerald surface (10/20)	5·00	2·50
		d emerald back ..	2·50	3·00
G20	$1	**pur and blue/blue** ..	6·00	1·25
G21	$2	**car-red and grey blk**	£12	7·50
G22	$3	**green and purple** ..	£22	£10
G23	$5	**green and red/green**	£35	£22
		a white back (3/14)	£30	£20
		b on blue-grn, olive back (5/17)	£45	£20
G24	$10	**pur and black/red** ..	£80	£35
G1/24		**set** (17v)	£165	£75
SPG1/24		**specimen set** (17v)	£220	‡

G2a—The right hand side of the Crown is broken (Row 9/2, lower right pane) : later redrawn.

Type I   Type II

G15/16—The original Die showed an incorrect Chinese character at the top of the left panel (Type I) ; this was later corrected on the Die and a fresh plate laid down (Type II).

1921 (Jan.)-37 As before but Wmk. Multiple Script CA. G25/36—O: G37/46—C.

G25	1c.	**brown**	10	5
G26	1c.	**deep brown** ..	10	5
G27	2c.	**blue-green**	15	10
G28	2c.	**yel-green** (6/32) ..	40	15
G29	2c.	**grey** (4/37)	35	30
G30	3c.	**grey** (11/31) ..	45	25
G31	4c.	**carmine-rose** ..	20	15
G32	4c.	**carmine-red** (6/32)	20	20
		a broken 'KONG' ..	6·00	6·00

G33	5c.	**violet** (11/31) ..	30	10
G34	8c.	**grey**	1·75	2·50
G35	8c.	**orange** ('24) ..	50	40
G36	10c.	**bt ultramarine** ..	25	15
G37	12c.	**pur/yel** (4/33) ..	75	45
G38	20c.	**pur and sage-grn** (12/21)	1·20	25
G39	25c.	**pur and mag** (Type II) (12/21) ..	60	40
		a broken flower ..	£10	£10
G40	30c.	**pur and chrome-yel** (9/21)	1·20	50
G41	30c.	**purple and or-yel** (6/32)	3·25	1·50
G42	50c.	**blk/emerald** (2/25)	1·75	40
G43	$1	**pur and blue/blue** (12/21)	5·00	1·50
G44	$2	**car-red and grey-black** (12/21) ..	£14	5·00
G45	$3	**grn and dl pur** (9/26)	£45	£10
G46	$5	**grn and red/em** (6/25)	£55	£14
G25/46		**set** (18v)	£130	£32
SPG25/46		**specimen set** (18v)	£200	‡

G32a—The top of the lower character (KONG) in the right hand panel is broken off. (Row 9/4, lower left pane) ; later repairs remain identifiable.

Normal   Broken Flower

G39a—The corner floral decoration to the right of the Crown is badly damaged. (Row 1/3, top left pane).

G27 and G31 were issued in Booklets (price $1) in 1929.

1935 (May 6th) Silver Jubilee. Recess Bradbury Wilkinson. Wmk. Multiple Script CA. Perf. 11 x 12. Sheets 6 x 10.

G47	3c.	**ult and grey** ..	60	30
G48	5c.	**green and indigo** ..	2·00	60
		a extra flagstaff ..	£40	—
G49	10c.	**brn and dp blue** ..	3·00	2·50
G50	20c.	**slate and purple** ..	9·00	6·00
G47/50		**set** (4v)	£14	9·00
SPG47/50		**specimen set** (4v)	£35	‡

H*

G48a—Extra flagstaff occurs on No. 49 (Row 9/1), Plate 1 only.

Numbers printed—G47, 1,296,000; G48, 3,396,000; G49, 1,318,000; G50, 654,000.

Remainders were withdrawn on December 31st, 1935.

1938-52 (typo) **De La Rue. Perf. 13¾ x 14 (C).**
Sheets 120—two panes each 6 x 10.

1	1c.	**brown** (24/5/38)	10	5
		a dp brown (8/5/46)	10	5
		b light brown (4/2/52)	10	5
2	2c.	**pale grey** (5/4/38)	10	5
		a pale slate (8/5/46)	10	5
3	4c.	**orange** (5/4/38)	10	5
4	5c.	**green** (24/5/38)	15	5
		a yel-grn (4/2/52)	10	5
5	8c.	**red-brown** (1/11/41)	15	10
		a imperf (12/46)	£1000	—
6	10c.	**violet** (13/4/38)	1·00	20
		a reddish-vio (9/4/47)	20	10
		b dull violet	20	10
7	15c.	**scarlet-red** (13/4/38)	15	10
		a carmine-red (8/5/46)	15	10
		b vermilion	10	5
8	20c.	**black** (1/2/46)	15	10
9	25c.	**ultramarine** (5/4/38)	25	10
		a pale blue	20	10
10	30c.	**yel-olive** (13/4/38)	£12	2·50
11	50c.	**red-pur** (thin paper) (13/4/38)	50	20
		a red-pur (ch) (9/4/47)	30	10
		aa pale purple	20	10
12	80c.	**car-rose** (ch) (2/2/48)	50	25
13	$1	**dull lilac and blue** (ch) (27/4/38)	50	50
		a red-lilac and blue (sub) (/41)	1·00	1·00
		b faulty R	£10	£10
14	$2	**red-orange and grn** (ch) (25/5/38)	£12	4·50
15	$5	**dull lilac and red** (ch) (2/6/38)	4·00	3·00
16	$10	**green and violet** (ch) (2/6/38)	£22	£15
1/16		**set** (16)	£50	£25
SP 1/16		**specimen set** perf (13)	£145	‡

1*b*/4*a* First released in Colony, and later in London on 27/2/52.

5*a* One sheet was found imperforate in a branch post office, but most were used up as singles, on letters to China. A mint vertical strip of 5 however, was bought and preserved. Forgeries exist. Price is for a pair.

11 Prior to 1947, the 50c. stamp was printed on thin paper similar to that used for lower values; after that date paper used for higher values (*chalk-coated*) was employed.

13*b* The diagonal stroke on R is shorter than usual.

1941-45. Design as No. 2, etc., but printed on rough paper by Bradbury, Wilkinson (*from De La Rue plates*), **except 4c., which was printed on smooth paper by Harrison & Sons. Perf. 14¾ x 14 (C).**

17	2c.	**slate-grey** (12/41)	20	20
18	4c.	**orange** (28/9/45)	20	15
19	5c.	**green** (12/41)	10	10
20	10c.	**violet** (12/41)	35	15
22	30c.	**sage** (12/41)	90	1·25
23	50c.	**red-purple** (12/41)	60	50
17/23		**set** (6)	2·00	2·00

As far as is known, No. 18 was not released in London at the end of 1941 with the other values. Supplies which were sent to the Colony were diverted to Australia and South Africa, and were not placed on sale in Hong Kong until the re-opening of the Post Office there under British Administration in 1945.

Hong Kong was occupied by the Japanese from December 25th, 1941 to August 14th, 1945, and throughout this period unoverprinted Japanese stamps were in use. Three such stamps were surcharged specifically for use in the Colony.

Immediately following the Japanese surrender, mail was franked 'HONG KONG/1945/POSTAGE PAID' within an octagonal frame until the pre-war stamps were re-issued on September 28th, 1945.

1946-52. As No. 8, etc., but colours changed.

24	20c.	**scarlet** (1/4/48)	15	15
		a pale car-red (24/4/51)	10	10
25	25c.	**pale sage** (9/4/46)	30	35
26	30c.	**blue** (9/4/46)	10	10
		a bright blue (21/2/50)	15	10
27	$1	**orange and green** (sub) (9/4/46)	75	10
		a orange and green (ch) 21/6/48)	60	10
		b red-orange and dp grn (ch) (30/8/50)	60	10
		c faulty R	£10	£10
28	$2	**vio and red** (sub) (9/4/46)	1·50	25
		a purple-violet and red (ch) (9/4/47)	1·00	25
		b vio and red (ch)	1·00	25
29	$5	**green and violet** (sub) (9/4/46)	5·00	1·00
		a yellow-grn and vio (sub) (8/5/46)	8·00	1·00
		b yellow-grn and vio (ch) (9/4/47)	3·50	75
30	$10	**violet and blue** (sub) (9/4/46)	£14	4·50
		a red-violet and blue (ch) (9/4/47)	£10	4·00

b red-purple and blue
(*ch*) (21/2/50) .. £16 3·00
24/30 **set (7)** .. .. £15 4·00
27*c* See Note after 13*b*.

SPECIAL ISSUES

1937 (May 12th) Coronation. As Aden but printers Bradbury, Wilkinson. Perf. 11 x 11¾ (C).

S1	4c. **green**	.. ..	20	20
S2	15c. **carmine-red**	..	25	25
S3	25c. **blue**	.. .. ..	70	70
SP S1/3	**specimen set** perf (3)		£18	‡

1941 (Feb. 26th) Centenary of British Occupation. 2c. (Hong Kong Street Scene); 4c. ("Empress of Scotland" and Junk); 5c. (The University); 15c. (The Harbour); 25c. (Hong Kong Bank); $1 (China Clipper and Seaplane). Designer, W. E. Jones. Recess Bradbury, Wilkinson. Perf. 13½ x 13 (C). Designs, 2c., 25c. V. Sheets 10 x 6 or 6 x 10.

S4	2c. **orange and chocolate**		30	45
S5	4c. **pur-mauve and car**		60	70
S6	5c. **black and green**	..	20	10
S7	15c. **black and scarlet**	..	70	70
S8	25c. **choc. and dp blue**	..	2·00	2·00
S9	$1 **ult and brn-orange**		7.00	7·00
S4/9	**set (6)**	.. ..	£10	£11
SP S4/9	**specimen set** perf (6)		£60	‡

Numbers printed — S4 1,500,000; S5 1,000,000; S6 4,500,000; S7 1,600,000; S8 720,000; S9 480,000.

1946 (Aug. 29th) Victory. Designers, E. I. Wynne-Jones and W. E. Jones. Recess De La Rue. Perf. 13 x 12¾ (C). Sheets 6 x 10.

S10	30c. **scar-red and dp blue**		50	50
	a scarlet red and blue		3·00	3·00
S11	$1 **scarlet-red and sepia**		1·50	1·50
SPS10/11	**specimen pair** ..		£40	‡

Both values exist with extra Chinese character in left-hand shield top left hand. Block of four at £25 Row 1/2 both values.

1948 (Dec. 22nd) Silver Wedding. As Aden.

S12	10c. **purple**	.. ..	20	20
S13	$10 **rose-carmine**	..	£20	£15

1949 (Oct. 10th) U.P.U. As Aden.

S14	10c. **dull violet**	.. ..	25	25
S15	20c. **carmine**	.. ..	90	90
S16	30c. **dull indigo**	.. ..	60	60
S17	80c. **magenta**	.. ..	3·00	2·00
S14/17	**set (4)**	.. ..	4·50	3·50

POSTAGE DUE STAMPS

1923 (Dec.) Typo De La Rue. Wmk. Multiple Script CA (upright until 1929, thereafter sideways). Perf. 14. Sheets 10 x 10.

GD1	1c. **brown**	.. ..	25	30
GD2	2c. **green** ..		60	90
GD3	4c. **scarlet**	.. ..	80	1·25
GD4	6c. **yellow**	.. ..	2·00	3·00
GD5	10c. **bt ultramarine**	..	2·00	2·25
GD1/5	**set (5v)**	.. ..	5·00	7·00
SPGD1/5	**specimen set** (5v)		£65	‡

1938 (Feb.)-50. As before but Wmk. Multiple Script CA sideways. Sheets 10 x 10.

PD1	1c. **light brown** ..	..	20	25
PD2	2c. **grey** (2/38)	..	50	70
	a slate (*rough*)	..	45	60
PD3	4c. **orange** (2/38)	..	60	75
	a dp orange (*rough*) ..		25	25
PD4	6c. **scarlet** (2/38)	..	90	50
	a rose-red (30/8/50)	..	80	50
PD5	8c. **dp chestnut** (*rough*)			
	(26/2/46)	..	90	1·25
	a chestnut (/50)	..	80	1·00
PD6	10c. **violet** (2/38)	..	75	30
	a bright violet (/50)	..	60	30
PD7	20c. **black** (*rough*)			
	(26/2/46)	..	1·00	1·25
	a black (/50) ..	..	90	1·00
PD8	50c. **dp blue** (19/8/47)	..	1·75	2·00
PD1/8	**set (8v)**	.. ..	5·00	5·50

Stamps similar in design but on chalky paper appeared from March 1956 onwards.

POSTAL FISCALS

1874-84 Typo De La Rue. Revenue Stamps

(issued 1867) authorised for postal use. Wmk. Crown CC. Sheets 240 – four panes, each 6 x 10.

(a) Perf. 15¼ x 15 (1874).

F1	$2	**olive-green**	£28	2·50
F2	$3	**dull violet**	£25	2·50
		a on bluish paper	—	—
F3	$10	**rose-carmine**	£220	£110
SPF1/3		**specimen set (3v)**	£75	‡

(b) Perf. 14 (1884).

F4	$10	**grey-green**	£100	—
SPF4		**specimen (1v)**	—	‡

1882 (Feb.) No. F3 surcharged in black.

F5	12c. on $10 **rose-carmine**	£37·50	£25

1890-1902 As. Nos. F1/2 but Wmk. Crown CA. Perf. 14.

F6	$2	**dl bluish green** ('90)	£30	£10
F7	$3	**dull mauve** ('02)	£32	8·00
		a on bluish paper	—	—
SPF6/7		**specimen (2v)**	£40	‡

Although not issued until 1902 No. F7 had been printed as early as 1890.

1890 (Dec. 24th) Typo De La Rue. Revenue Stamp authorised for postal use for only seven days. Wmk. Crown CA.

F8	2c.	**dull purple**	3·00	2·00
SPF8		**specimen (1v)**	5·00	‡

1891 (Jan. 1st) As No. F4 but in altered colour and Wmk. Crown CA., surcharged in black by De La Rue.

F9	$5 on $10 **purple/red**	£20	£18
SPF9		**specimen (1v)**	£20	‡

Type I	Type II
(Stamp Office)	(Stamp Duty)

1891 (Jan. 1st) Nos. V59 and V67 locally overprinted for Revenue use, but still retaining postal validity.

F10	2c.	**carmine** (Type I)	£22	£25
F11	2c.	**carmine** (Type II)	£10	8·00
F12	10c.	**purple/red** (Type I)	£25	£35

1897 (Sept.) Nos. F1 and F6 locally surcharged in black by Noronha & Sons.

F13	$1 on $2	**olive-green**	4·00	6·00
	a	small 'N' in 'ONE'	—	—
	b	Chinese surcharge omitted	£80	£50
F14	$1 on $2	**dl bluish green**	6·00	8·00
	a	Chinese surcharge omitted	£20	£12
	b	diagonal Chinese surcharge omitted	—	—

Numbers surcharged—F13, 9,360; F14, 3,600.

These provisionals remained on issue until April 1898. See Note under No. V88.

1938 (Jan. 11th) Typo De La Rue. Revenue

stamp authorised for postal use for only eleven days. Wmk. Multiple Script CA. Perf. 14. Sheets 120 – two panes, each 6 x 10.

F15	5c.	**dull green** ..	£15	3·00
	a	used on cover ..	—	7·50

Numbers sold (Jan. 11th-21st 1938)—170,709, of which many were used for fiscal purposes.

GERMAN PROPAGANDA LABELS

The 1944 German imitations of the G.B. 1937 Definitives ½d. to 3d. (see after Great Britain for details) were also overprinted in black "LIQUIDA-TION/OF EMPIRE/HONG KONG" within a vertical rectangular frame.

Price (6v) unused or cancelled .. £175

CHINA

BRITISH POST OFFICES

Following the Treaties of Nanking (1842), Yedo (1858) and Tientsin (1858) a total of 21 Consular Postal Agencies were opened in the Treaty Ports in China and Japan. These offices were controlled by the G.P.O. in London until January 1st 1868 when they came under the Hong Kong Post Office; and Hong Kong stamps used in these Treaty Ports may be recognised by the distinctive cancellations. The offices in Japan were closed in 1879.

Amoy	Nanking
Canton	Newchwang, Manchuria
Chefoo	Niigata
Chinkiang	Ningpo
Foochow	Shanghai
Hakodate	Swatow
Hankow	Tainan, Formosa
Kiukiang	Tamsui, Formosa
Kiungchow (Hoihow)	Tientsin
Kobe	Yokohama
Nagasaki	

In May 1898 Great Britain leased some 250 square miles of Chinese territory based on Wei Hai Wei and British Post Offices, using Hong Kong stamps, were opened at Liu-Kung-Tau (1/9/99) and Port Edward (1/4/04).

Fluctuating rates of exchange necessitated the use from 1917 of specially overprinted stamps at the Chinese Treaty Ports until they finally closed on November 30th, 1922; and at Wei Hai Wei until the leased territory was returned to China on October 1st, 1930.

FOR USE IN THE TREATY PORTS

1917-20 Stamps of Hong Kong (Nos. G1/24) overprinted in black by De La Rue. (Wmk. Multiple Crown CA). G1/7—O: G8/18—C.

G1	1c.	**brown**	15	20
G2	1c.	**black-brown** ..	15	20
	a	broken Crown ..	£90	—
G3	2c.	**green**	25	25
G4	4c.	**carmine-red** ..	15	15
G5	6c.	**brown-orange** ..	25	20
G6	8c.	**slate**	60	25
G7	10c.	**ultramarine** ..	50	15
G8	12c.	**purple/yellow** ..	1·00	75
G9	20c.	**pur and sage-green**	1·25	30
G10	25c.	**pur and magenta**		
		(Type I) ..	1·75	2·50
G11	30c.	**pur and or-yel** ..	2·50	90
G12	50c.	**blk/blu-grn** (olive		
		back) ..	4·00	90
	a	white back ..	5·50	2·00
	b	on emerald surface	2·25	1·50
	c	emerald back ..	1·75	1·00
G13	$1	**reddish pur and bt**		
		blue/blue ..	£10	1·50
G14	$1	**grey-pur and blue/**		
		blue ..	8·00	1·25
G15	$2	**car-red and grey-**		
		black ..	£20	£11
G16	$3	**green and purple** ..	£25	£20
G17	$5	**grn and red/blu grn**		
		(olive back) ..	£24	£24
G18	$10	**pur and blk/red** ..	£60	£60
G1/18		**set** (16v)	£140	£116
SPG12/18		**specimen set** (6v)	£300	‡

G2a—See Note after Hong Kong No. G2a.

G10—See Note after Hong Kong Nos. G15/16.

When the Treaty Port Post Offices closed on November 30th, 1922 remaining stocks of this issue were returned to Hong Kong where they were sold for normal postal use. They continued in use at Wei Hai Wei.

FOR USE IN WEI HAI WEI

1922-27 Stamps of Hong Kong (Nos. G25/44) overprinted in black by De La Rue. (Wmk. Multiple Script CA). G19/25—O: G26/30—C.

G19	1c.	**brown**	20	30
G20	2c.	**green**	40	40
G21	4c.	**carmine-rose** ..	30	30
	a	broken 'KONG' ..	£35	£30
G22	6c.	**orange-yellow** ..	40	80
G23	8c.	**grey**	40	75
G24	10c.	**bt ultramarine** ..	40	50
G25	10c.	**pale ultramarine** ..	50	75
G26	20c.	**pur and sage-grn** ..	60	50
G27	25c.	**pur and magenta**		
		(Type II) ..	90	2·00
	a	broken flower ..	£25	£30
G28	50c.	**blk/emerald** ('27) ..	2·25	3·50
G29	$1	**pur and blue/blue** ..	5·00	7·00
G30	$2	**car-red and grey-**		
		black	£12	£18
G19/30		**set** (11v)	£20	£30
SPG21 & 28		**specimen** (2v) ..	—	‡

G21a—See Note after Hong Kong No. G32a.

G27—See Note after Hong Kong Nos. G15/16.

G27a—See Note after Hong Kong No. G39a.

G22 was not issued without this overprint.

Although this issue was generally intended for use only at Wei Hai Wei copies of Nos. G21 and G29 are known used at Treaty Ports shortly before the offices closed.

INDIA

All stamps to G48 (*typo*) by De La Rue and Co.

1902-1911 Various Frames: all inscribed "POSTAGE" except Nos. E5 and 7 ("POSTAGE AND REVENUE"). Sheets E1/19 240 − two panes, each 12 x 10: E20/30 96 − eight panes (2 x 4), each 4 x 3. Wmk. Large Star. Perf. 14.

E1	3p.	**grey**	10	10
E2	3p.	**slate grey** ('04) ..	5	5
E3	½a.	**yellow-green** ..	15	10
E4	½a.	**green**	15	10
E5	½a.	**green** ('06) ..	5	5
E6	1a.	**carmine**	15	5
E7	1a.	**carmine** ('06) ..	5	5
E8	2a.	**violet**	80	15
E9	2a.	**mauve**	70	10
E10	2½a.	**ultramarine** ..	1·00	10
E11	3a.	**orange-brown** ..	1·50	15
E12	4a.	**olive**	1·50	15
E13	4a.	**pale olive**	1·50	15
E14	4a.	**olive-brown** ...	3·00	1·50
E15	6a.	**olive-bistre** ..	3·25	2·00
E16	6a.	**maize**	3·25	2·00
E17	8a.	**mauve**	2·50	80
E18	8a.	**magenta** ('10) ..	2·50	80
E19	12a.	**purple/red**	3·50	1·75
E20	R1	**green and carmine**	2·00	50
E21	R1	**green and scarlet** ('11)	5·00	50
E22	Rs2	**rose-red and yel-brown**	5·00	2·00
E23	Rs2	**carmine and yel-brown**	5·00	2·00
E24	Rs3	**brn and grn** ('04)	7·50	6·00
E25	Rs3	**red-brn and grn** ('11)	7·50	7·00
E26	Rs5	**ult and vio** ('04) ..	£18	£16
E27	Rs5	**ult and dp lilac** ('11)	£18	£16
E28	Rs10	**grn and car** ('09) ..	£20	8·00
E29	Rs15	**blu and ol-brn** ('09)	£50	£15
E30	Rs25	**brownish-or and blue**	£275	£300
E1/30		**set** (19v)	£380	£365

E30 The used price is for copies with postal cancellations. It is usually found telegraphically used (price £180).

Proofs in black on glazed card, are known for all Anna values, and of head only for R1 and Rs2.

All values to Rs5 are known overprinted "Specimen" or "Cancelled". The ½a. (E5) exists with 'Specimen" handstamp in violet script type.

½a. and 1a. values were made up in Booklets.

1905 No. E4. Surcharged.

E31	¼/½a.	**green**	10	5
		a surcharge inverted	£95	£95

The surcharge has been forged, both mint and used copies being known.

1¼a. Type 'A' (illustrated).

Type 'B' inscribed "As", "ANNAS".

1911 (Dec.)-1926 Various Frames; all inscribed "POSTAGE" except Nos. G5–11 ("POSTAGE AND REVENUE"). Sheets G1/36, 256 − four panes, each 16 x 4; G37/43, as before. Wmk. Large Star. Perf. 14.

G1	3p.	**pale grey**	10	5
G2	3p.	**grey**	5	5
G3	3p.	**slate-grey**	5	5
G4	3p.	**blue-slate** ('22) ..	10	5
		a joined Ps ..	2·50	2·50
G5	½a.	**yellow-green** ..	10	5
		a double print ..	£12	—

G6	½a.	**pale blue-green** ..	10	5
G7	1a.	**rose-carmine** ..	20	5
		a printed both sides	—	—
G8	1a.	**carmine**	10	5
		a imperf	—	—
G9	1a.	**aniline-carmine** ..	25	5
G10	1a.	**pale rose-car (C)**		
		('18)	35	5
G11	1a.	**choc** ('22–'26) ..	5	5
G12	1½a.	**choc (Type A)**		
		('19)	40	5
G13	1½a.	**grey-brn (Type A)**	1·00	40
G14	1½a.	**choc (Type B)**		
		('21)	50	40
G15	1½a.	**rose-car (Type B)**		
		('22–'26) ..	20	5
G16	2a.	**dull purple** ..	35	5
G17	2a.	**mauve**	30	5
G18	2a.	**violet**	1·50	5
G19	2a.	**bright purple** ('19)	1·25	5
G20	2½a.	**ultramarine** ..	1·00	80
G21	2½a.	**ultramarine** ('13)	45	5
G22	2½a.	**orange** ('22–'26)	2·00	1·00
G23	3a.	**dull orange** ..	80	5
G24	3a.	**orange-brown** ..	70	5
G25	3a.	**ult** ('22–'26) ..	5·00	50
S26	4a.	**deep olive**	1·00	5
G27	4a.	**olive-green** ..	60	5
G28	6a.	**bistre**	1·25	40
G29	6a.	**yellow-bistre** ..	1·25	40
G30	6a.	**deep bistre-brown**	1·50	50
G31	8a.	**purple**	2·00	25
G32	8a.	**mauve**	4·00	25
G33	8a.	**deep lilac** ..	3·00	30
G34	8a.	**br aniline-mauve**	3·00	30
G35	12a.	**dull claret**	3·00	30
G36	12a.	**claret**	3·50	40
G37	R1	**brown and green**	4·00	60
G38	R1	**red-brn and blu-**		
		grn	4·00	50
G39	Rs2	**car and brn** ..	4·00	50
G40	Rs5	**ult and vio** ..	£10	1·50
G41	Rs10	**green and scarlet**	£15	3·50
G42	Rs15	**blue and olive** ..	£40	5·00
G43	Rs25	**orange and blue** ..	£65	£10
G1/43		**set** (23v)	£145	£22

G4a A white line in the right hand value tablet gives
Ps the appearance of Rs.

G5a This "double print" variety has been extensively forged: it should only be bought with a
Certificate.

All values are known with Star Wmk. inverted.

The marginal wmk. reading "Star Paper" sometimes appears on stamps instead of the star itself.

Where paper was incorrectly positioned the
bottom row is without any watermark, giving vertical
pairs se-tenant with and without watermark.

Proofs in black of all Anna values (except 1½ as)
are known. Proofs of Rupee values exist – frame and
head separately.

All values except 1½as. (Type B) exist overprinted "Cancelled". The 2½a., 3a. and 12a. are
also known imperforate with the same overprint.

3p., ½a., 1a., 1½a. and 2a. values were made up in
Booklets.

1921. G7, 8 and 9 surcharged NINE PIES.

G44	9p./1a.	**rose carmine** ..	10	5
		a NINE NINE ..	7·50	9·00
		b PIES PIES ..	7·50	9·00
		c surcharge double	£15	8·00
		d surcharge inverted	5·00	7·50
G45	9p./1a.	**carmine**	—	—
G46	9p./1a.	**aniline carmine**..	—	—

There were two settings of the surcharge. In the
first, 44a and 44b each occurred four times in the
sheet of 256 stamps (4 panes, each 16 x 4), the
former at the end of the second row in the fourth,
pane and the latter at the end of the last row in the
third pane. In the second setting only 44b occurred
at the end of the second row in the third pane. These
varieties have been forged.

There were four unissued essays of this surcharge.

1922. G5 and 6 surcharged as E31 at Bombay, Calcutta, Karachi and Madras.

G47	¼/½a.	**yellow-green** ..	5	5
		a surcharge inverted	3·00	3·50
		b surcharge double..	7·00	8·00
		c surcharge double		
		(both inverted) ..	—	—
		d surcharge omitted		
		in pair with nor-		
		mal	£50	—
G48	¼/½a.	**pale blue-green** ..	—	—

The varieties have been extensively forged.

All stamps from G49 (*typo*) by Security Printing
Press, Nasik, on "Multiple Star" wmk. paper
unless otherwise stated.

1926-1941 Various frames as G1–G43: all inscribed "POSTAGE" except Nos. G50, 53, 58, 59, 68 ("POSTAGE AND REVENUE"). Perf. 14. Sheets G49/72 as G1/36 (later printings 16 x 20); G73/78, 96 – four panes, each 4 x 3, and two panes, each 4 x 6 (later printings six panes (2 x 3), each 5 x 4).

G49	3p.	**slate**	—	—
		a joined Ps ..	—	—

G50	½a.	**green**	5	
G51	½a.	**green** ('34) ..	5	5
G52	9p.	**dp green** (offset litho) (22.4.32) ..	5	5
		a typo (27.8.34) ..	10	10
G53	1a.	**chocolate**	5	5
		a tete beche (pair)	40	60
G54	1a.	**chocolate** ('34) ..	5	5
G55	1¼a.	**mauve** ('32) (offset litho)	5	5
		a double print (Die I) ..	£10	£12
		b Die II ('41) (offset litho)	30	40
G56	1½a.	**rose-car (Type B)**	40	5
G57	2a.	**bright purple** ..	50	30
		a stop under "s" ..	4·00	4·00
G58	2a.	**purple**	30	10
		a tete beche (pair)	1·00	1·25
G59	2a.	**vermilion** ('32) ..	5·00	3·00
G60	2a.	**vermilion** ('34) ..	3·50	40
G61	2a.	**vermilion** (small die '36)	1·25	25
G62	2½a.	**orange**	25	5
G63	3a.	**ultramarine** ..	1·25	25
G64	3a.	**blue**	1·25	15
G65	3a.	**carmine** ('32) ..	40	5
G66	3½a.	**dp blu** ('32) (offset litho)	80	15
G67	3½a.	**grey-blue** (offset litho)	1·25	90
G68	4a.	**pale sage-green**	40	5
G69	4a.	**sage green** ..	2·00	5
G70	6a.	**bistre** ('35) ..	6·00	2·75
G71	8a.	**reddish-purple** ..	1·25	5
G72	12a.	**claret**	2·00	10
G73	R1	**chocolate and gr**	1·25	5
		a centre omitted ..	£225	—
G74	Rs2	**car and orange** ..	2·00	40
G75	Rs5	**ult and purple** ..	5·00	1·00
G76	Rs10	**grn and scar** ..	£15	2·00
G77	Rs15	**blue and olive** ..	£20	£10
G78	Rs25	**orange and blue** ..	£20	£12
G49/78		**set** (26v) ..	£85	£35

G49*a* The same variety as on G4*a*.

G52/52*a* Background lines on the offset litho printing are clear and sharp, and the sheets do not have 'Jubilee' Lines.

On the typo printing the lines are less sharp (especially the horizontal lines behind the King's Head), and the sheets have marginal 'Jubilee' Lines.

G55 exists in three sizes, with minor variations due to paper shrinkage:

(i) 18.7mm. wide: 1932 Sheet printing (No 'Jubilee' Line) Die I.

(ii) 18.25mm. wide: 1932 Booklet printing (with 'Jubilee' Line) Die. I.

(iii) 18.4mm. wide: 1941 Sheet printing (No 'Jubilee' Line) Die II.

ONE ANNA THREE PIES

ONE ANNA THREE PIES

DIE I (1932)	DIE II (1941)
Thin letters. Large coloured areas enclosed within letters O, A, R, P.	Thick letters. Smal coloured areas enclosed within letters O, A, R, P.

G57*a* A 'stop' appears under 's' in the right hand value tablet on No. 64 in the sheet.

G61 measures 18.4 x 21.8mm., compared with 19 x 22.6mm (G.60). The Small Die has only five shading lines above the Crown, whereas there were seven lines on the old die.

All values are known with Multiple Star wmk. inverted.

Many values from the early Nasik paintings are known with double or misplaced perforations.

The Rupee values show constant varieties in various positions—'Pearls' missing from the value tablet frame. Prices from 15/–.

1a., 1½a. and 2a. values were made up in Booklets.

1929 (Oct. 22nd) Air stamps. Wmk. Multiple Star (sideways to left or right). Designer, R. Grant. (*Offset litho*). **Perf. 14. Sheets 12 x 12.**

G79	2a.	**dp blu-grn** (Dec. 20th)	30	25
G80	3a.	**blue**	50	90
		a double print ..	£30	£25
G81	4a.	**olive-green** ..	1·50	1·20
G82	6a.	**bistre**	2·00	1·00
G83	8a.	**purple**	2·50	3·50
		a missing tree top	7·50	5·00
		b serif on I ..	£30	£25
G84	12a.	**rose-red** ..	5·00	7·50
G79/84		**set** (6v)	£11	£12

G83*a* The top of the foreground tree is missing on Row 11/6.

G83*b* A pronounced serif on the second "I" of India was corrected in subsequent printings.

INDIA PO

The composite enlargement shows both varieties on the 8a.

All values are known in different shades.

1931 (Feb. 9th) Inauguration of New Delhi Wmk. Multiple Star (sideways to left or right). Designer, H. W. Barr. (*Offset litho*). **Perf. 14. Sheets 12 x 12.**

G85	¼a.	**ol-grn and or-brn**	10	20
		a "F" for "P" ..	2·25	2·50
G86	½a.	**violet and green**..	10	10
G87	1a.	**mauve and choc**..	10	5
G88	2a.	**green and blue** ..	30	30
G89	3a.	**choc and carmine**	80	90
G90	R1	**violet and green**..	5·00	6·00
G85/90		**set (6v)**	6·00	7·00

G85a The word "PURANA" is spelled "FURANA".

All values are known with vignette doubly printed.

Specimen sets exist in issued colours on art paper.

1935 (May 6th) Silver Jubilee. Wmk. Multiple Star (sideways to left or right). (*Offset litho*). **Perf. 14. Sheets 12 x 12.**

G91	½a.	**blk and yel-grn** ..	10	5
		a double print		
		(vignette) ..	7·50	7·50
G92	9p.	**blk and grey-grn**	10	5
G93	1a.	**black and brown**	10	5
		a double print		
		(vignette) ..	7·50	7·50
		b double print		
		(frame) ..	7·50	7·50
G94	1¼a.	**blk and br vio** ..	10	10
G95	2½a.	**blk and or** ..	25	10
G96	3½a.	**blk and dl ult** ..	30	40
		a bird on parapet	4·00	4·50
G97	8a.	**blk and pur** ..	1·25	90
G91/97		**set (7v)**	2·00	1·40

G96a A constant flaw resembling a bird, appears on the parapet of the Golden Temple. Row 9/3.

Reported printing 125,820 sets.

EDWARD VIII ESSAYS

In 1936 two different sets of Essays were prepared, all on unwatermarked paper, for a complete range of stamps bearing the Head of King Edward VIII.

The small format (3p.–1a.) were similar to the issued King George VI stamps, but some had different frames. The Rupee values were all in frames the same as the issued KG VI stamps.

The horizontal format (2a.–12a.) were in frames the same as the issued KG VI stamps, but the two

sets of Essays showed different selections of vignettes, very few of which represented the 'Transport' theme adopted for the issued KG VI stamps.

1937 (Dec. 15th) -40 Designs, 3p.–1a. and 1r.–25r. (Portrait of King-Emperor); 2a.–14a., (Methods of Mail Transport); 3p.–14a., Perf. 13¾ x 14 (C); Other Values, Perf. 13¾ (C). Designs, 2a. to 14a. H. Sheets—1–4, 16 x 20; 5–13; 8 x 20; 14–19, 120—six panes, each 5 x 4.

1	3p.	**slate**	10	5
2	½a.	**red-brown**	10	5
3	9p.	**dp green** (23/8/37) ..	20	15
4	1a.	**carmine** (23/8/37) ..	15	5
		a tete-beche vert. pair		
		(a)	25	15
		b booklet pane of 4 ..	3·00	—
5	2a.	**vermilion**	20	5
6	2½a.	**violet**	30	5
7	3a.	**yellow-green** ..	20	5
8	3½a.	**blue**	35	30
9	4a.	**dp brown**	40	5
10	6a.	**greenish-blue** ..	40	10
11	8a.	**violet-slate**	40	5
12	12a.	**dp crimson**	70	35
13	14a.	**purple** (15/10/40) ..	45	15
14	1r.	**vio-grey and lt brown**	45	5
15	2r.	**vio purple and brown**	1·00	5
		a dp pur and brn ..	1·00	5
16	5r.	**dp green and dp blue**	2·50	10
17	10r.	**vio-pur and red-claret**	4·25	40
18	15r.	**chocolate and dp grn**	7·50	7·00
19	25r.	**slate-vio and pur-vio**	£10	4·50
1/19		**set (19)**	£28	£13

4a This variety is from sheets of stamps which were prepared for booklets. The booklets contained 16 x 1a. stamps.

Most values are known with inverted watermark.

A Postal forgery of the 1r. (No. 14) was made in Nepal and used only from the Indian Embassy in Kathmandu. It was lithographed and perf. 11½ on unwatermarked paper, and is 1mm. taller than the genuine stamp.

1941-3. Perf. 13¾ x 14 (C). Sheets 16 x 20.

20	3p.	**slate** (1/12/41) ..	5	5
21	½a.	**purple** (1/10/41) ..	5	5
22	9p.	**green** (16/8/41) ..	5	5
23	1a.	**rose-carmine** (1/4/43)	5	5

24 1a.3p. **bistre** (1/2/41) .. 30 15
25 1½a. **slate-purple** (*litho*)
      (20/5/42) .. 50 10
    a ditto (*typo*) (/43) .. 10 10
26 2a. **vermilion** (15/5/41) .. 5 5
27 3a. **bt vio** (*litho*) (5/1/41) 70 15
    a ditto (*typo*) (/43) .. 5 5
28 3½a. **blue** (15/5/41) .. 10 5
29 4a. **brown** (15/5/41) .. 15 5
30 6a. **greenish-blue** (15/5/41) 15 5
31 8a. **violet-slate** (15/5/41) 20 5
32 12a. **dp crimson** (15/5/41) 40 5
20/32 **set** (13) .. .. 1·50 70

Original printings of the 1½a. and 3a. were Offset-Litho without Jubilee Lines. Later printings were Typo with Jubilee Lines. The general appearance of Litho printings is clean with distinct fine lines, whereas Typo has a fuzzy appearance with thicker lines which tend to run together.

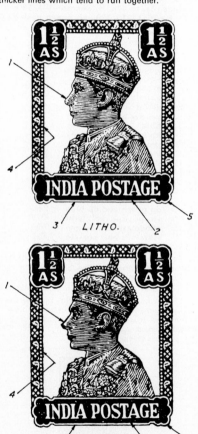

LITHO.

TYPO.

Five points provide positive identification on both values :—

1. *Litho:* The outline of the King's nose is thin and clean.

Typo: The line is thicker and ragged and in some cases the tip of the nose becomes pointed.

2. *Litho:* The background colour of the value tablets and "INDIA POSTAGE" panel is evenly inked with very few blemishes or spots.

Typo: The background colour has numerous small white specks in it. (These can vary considerably.)

3. *Litho:* The base line is thin and has sharp edges.
Typo: The base line is thick and has ragged edges.

4. *Litho:* The inside frame lines of the rows of pearls are thick and clean.
Typo: The lines are thick and ragged.

5. *Litho:* The curves on frame lines remain an even width.
Typo: They bulge and get thicker at the top of the curve.

1946 (Aug. 8th) No. 24 surcharged.
33 3p./1a.3p. **bistre** 5 5

BANTAM ESSAYS

Despite the reduction in paper consumption achieved by the issue of the above set, war-time conditions made further saving desirable. Accordingly, following the example of South Africa, the Nasik Security Press prepared essays for Indian "Bantam" stamps bearing the Head of the King-Emperor: the issue was abandoned when the war ended. These 3 pies essays are exceedingly rare (Price £225).

1949 (Aug. 15th) -51 Designs, Architectural and Archeological Subjects. Designers, T. I. Archer and I. M. Das. Anna values typo as usual, but rupee stamps offset litho. Perf. 13¾ x 14 (3p.–2a., 1r.–10r.), Perf. 13¾ (2½a.–12a. Perf. 13 (C) (15r.). All Comb. Designs, 6p., 6a., 8a., 12a., 2r., 5r., 15r. H. Wmk. Multiple Star. Sheets 34–47, 16 x 20; 48–51, 8 x 20 or 20 x 8; 52, 8 x 16.

34 3p. **dp slate-violet** .. 5 5
    a slate-violet (/51) .. 5 5
35 6p. **purple-brown** .. 5 5
    a red-brown (/51) .. 5 5
36 9p. **pale green** 10 5

37	1a.	**turquoise** (Die I)	10	5
	a	greyish-turquoise		
		(Die I)	10	5
38	1a.	**turquoise** (Die 2)		
		(15/7/50)	10	5
39	2a.	**carmine-red**	10	5
40	2½a.	**maroon-lake** (30/4/51)	20	5
41	3a.	**dp vermilion**	15	5
42	3½a.	**bright blue**	80	50
43	4a.	**maroon-lake**	50	5
44	4a.	**bright blue** (30/4/51)	40	10
45	6a.	**violet**	50	5
46	8a.	**turquoise-green**	1·00	5
47	12a.	**dull blue**	65	5
48	1r.	**purple-violet and grn**	2·00	10
	a	double print (frame)	—	—
49	2r.	**claret and pur-violet**	2·50	15
50	5r.	**grey-grn and maroon**	3·25	30
51	10r.	**maroon and dk blue**	6·00	1·25
	a	double print (centre)	—	—
	b	maroon and lt blue		
		(/52?)	7·00	1·25
52	15r.	**choc and maroon-lake**	8·00	2·00
34/52		**set** (19)	£26	4·50

37—This design wrongly depicted Bodhisattva with left arm outstretched. This was rectified in Die 2 and the right arm is outstretched instead.

Lithographed postal forgeries of Nos. 46 and 48 exist, perf. 11 x 12½ on unwatermarked paper.

SPECIAL ISSUES

Printed as before but by offset-litho unless otherwise stated. Wmk. Multiple Star.

1946 Victory. Designers, Dorothy Cronan and Edward Johangs. Perf. 13 (C). Sheets 8 x 16.

S1	9p.	**green** (8/2/46)	5	5
S2	1½a.	**purple-violet** (2/1/46)	10	5
S3	3½a.	**blue** (2/1/46)	15	5
S4	12a.	**dull crimson** (8/2/46)	25	5
S1/4		**set** (4)	55	20

1947 Dominion Status. Designs, 1½a. (Asokan Capital); 3½a. (National Flag); 12a. (Plane). First Indian stamps printed in English and Hindi. Perf. 14 x 13¾ (C). Design, 1½a. V Sheets—S5, 12 x 12; S6, 8 x 12; S7, 8 x 20.

S5	1½a.	**grey-grn** (15/12/47)	5	5
S6	3½a.	**or, grn, blue** (21/11)	15	5
	a	flaw	3·00	3·00

S7	12a.	**ultramarine** (15/12/47)	40	5
S5/7		**set** (3)	60	15

S6a—A marked flaw appears above the 7 on Rows 5/6.

1948 (May 20th) Inauguration India–U.K. Air Service. Design, "Constellation" Plane in Flight. Perf. 13¾ x 14 (C). Sheets 8 x 20.

S8	12a.	**blk and ultramarine**	40	40

1948 (Aug. 15th) First Anniversary Indian Independence. Printers (photo) Courvoisier, Switzerland. Perf. 11¾ (C). No. wmk. Sheets 10 x 5.

S9	1½a.	**chocolate-brown**	20	5
S10	3½a.	**dull violet**	30	5
S11	12a.	**greyish-green**	1·00	25
S12	10r.	**brown and lake**	£50	£50
S9/12		**set** (4)	£50	£50

The paper is granite and chalk-surfaced.

Number issued—

1½a., 24,680,924; 3½a., 2,226,324; 12a., 3,096,824; 10r., 229,974

1949 (Oct. 10th) U.P.U. Design, Asokan Capital and Globe. Perf. 13 (C). Sheets 8 x 16.

S13	9p.	**myrtle-green**	20	15
S14	2a.	**dp rose**	35	30
S15	3½a.	**blue**	40	30
S16	12a.	**maroon-lake**	80	90
S13/16		**set** (4)	1·50	1·65

1950 (Jan. 26th) Inauguration of Republic. Designs, Allegorical Scenes. Designers, Messrs. J. J. Keymer & Co. Perf. 13 (C). Design 3½a., V. Sheets 8 x 16.

S17	2a.	**rose-carmine**	25	15
S18	3½a.	**ultramarine** ..	35	15
S19	4a.	**violet**	50	25
S20	12a.	**dull lake** ..	1·00	45
S17/20		**set** (4)	2·00	1·00

Number issued—
2a., 19,667,712;   3½a., 1,171,200;
4a., 6,674,048;   12a., 2,483,968.

1951 (Jan. 13th) Centenary of Geological Survey of India. Design, Stegodon Ganesa (predecessor of elephant). Perf. 13 (C). Sheets 8 x 16.

S21	2a.	**black and claret** ..	30	30

1951 (Mar. 4th) First Asian Games. Perf. 14 x 13¾ (C). Sheets 20 x 8.

S22	2a.	**claret and red-orange**	20	25
S23	12a.	**chocolate and blue** .	1·00	75
S22/23		**set** (2)	1·20	1·00

1952 (Oct. 1st) Indian Saints and Poets. Designs, 9p. Kabir (15th Century Saint); **1a. Tulsidas** (16th–17th Century Saint-Poet); **2a. Meera** (15th Century Rajput Princess); **4a. Surdas** (15th–16th Century Saint-Poet); **4½a. Ghalib** (19th Century Urdu Poet); **12a. Tagore** (19th-20th Century Poet and Philosopher). (*Photo*). **Perf. 14 x 13¾ (C). Sheets 160—two panes each 8 x 10.**

S24	9p.	**emerald-green** ..	15	10
S25	1a.	**carmine-red** ..	25	10
S26	2a.	**orange-red** ..	35	10
S27	4a.	**blue**	50	15
S28	4½a.	**magenta** ..	1·00	25
S29	12a.	**deep brown** ..	1·00	50
S24/29		**set** (6) ..	3·25	1·00

STAMP BOOKLETS

Unless otherwise indicated all Booklets have interleaving sheets and are stapled. Outer cover inscriptions and Postal Rates are printed in black. Booklets made up in Match-Book type covers are noted "MB".

Booklets B1, B2 and B6–B14 were made up by De La Rue. (Wmk. Single Star).

Booklets B3–B5 were made up by Stamps and Stationery Department, Calcutta. (Wmk. Single Star).

Booklets B15–B20 were made up by Security Printing Press, Nasik. (Wmk. Multiple Star).

1902 Green Cover. 4 x vertical panes of six Price 12¼a.

B1	½a.	**yellow-green** (E3) ..	£75

Pink Cover. 2 x vertical panes of six. Price 12¼a.

B2	1a.	**carmine** (E6)	£75

1906 Green "MB" Cover. 8 x panes of four Price R1.

B3	½a.	**green** (E5)	£60

Pink "MB" Cover. 4 x panes of four. Price R1.

B4	1a.	**carmine** (E7)	£40

Green "MB" Cover or Pink Regular Cover. Postal Rates included. Price R1.

B5	½a.	**grn** (E5) (4 x panes of four)	
	1a.	**car** (E7) (2 x panes of four)	£60

1911 Green "MB" Cover. 16 x panes of four Price R1.

B6   3p.   **grey** (G2) £60

As before. Postal Rates included. 8 x panes of four. Price R1.

B7   ½a.   **yel-grn** (G5) £40

Pink "MB" Cover. Postal Rates included. 4 x panes of four. Price R1.

B8   1a.   **rose-carmine** (G7) ..   £40

Front Cover: Yellow-Green or Blue-Green Back Cover: Pink. Price R1.

B9   ½a.   **yel-grn** (G5) (4 x
             panes of four) ..   ..
      1a.   **rose-car** (G7) (2 x
             panes of four) £45

Purple Cover. 4 x panes of four. Price Rs2.

B10   2a.   **dull purple** (G16) ..   £40

Purple "MB" Cover. Postal Rates included. 4 x panes of four. Price Rs2.

B11   2a.   **br purple** (G19) £40

1919 As before. 4 x panes of four. Price R1-8-0.

B12   1½a.   **chocolate** (G12) £40

1921 Buff "MB" Cover. Postal Rates included. 6 x panes of four. Price R1-2-0.

B13   NINE PIES on 1a. (Shades)
             (G44-G46)   £45

1922 Lilac "MB" Cover or Brown Regular Cover. Postal Rates included. 4 x panes of four. Price R1.

B14   1a.   **chocolate** (G11) £40

1926 Brown Cover ("MB" stapled: Regular stitched). 4 x panes of four. Price R1.

B15   1a.   **chocolate** (G53) £25

Purple "MB" Cover. 4 x panes of four. Price Rs2.

B16   2a.   **br purple** (G57) £40

As before.

B17   2a.   **purple** (G58) £40

1932 Cinnamon Cover. Stitched (black thread). 4 x panes of four, interleaved. Price R1-4-0.

B18   1¼a.   **mauve** (G55. Die I) ..   £45

Buff Cover. Stiched (black thread). 4 x panes of four, interleaved. Price R1-4-0.

B18A   1¼a.   **mauve** (G55. Die I) ..   £45

Although these two Booklets were normally made up from the special Booklet printing (See Note after G78), Booklet B18A has been seen made up from marginal blocks of four without Jubilee Line.

1934 Buff Cover. Stitched (black thread). 4 x panes of four, interleaved. Price RI.

B19   1a.   **chocolate** (G54) .. ..   —

1937 Brick-red Cover. Stitched (black thread). Postal Rates included. 4 x panes of four. Price R1.

B20   1a.   **carmine** (No. 4) £15

OFFICIAL STAMPS

1902-1909. Stamps of King Edward VII (E1–30) overprinted "On H.M.S.". Nos. EO4 and EO6 inscribed "POSTAGE AND REVENUE", remainder "POSTAGE".

EO1	3p.	grey	.. ..	20	5
		a stop omitted ..	4·00	4·00
EO2	3p.	slate-grey ('05)	5	5
EO3	½a.	green	20	5
EO4	½a.	green ('06)	5	5
		a stop omitted ..	4·00	4·00
EO5	1a.	carmine	5	5
EO6	1a.	carmine ('06)	5	5
		a stop omitted ..	4·00	4·00
EO7	2a.	violet	30	5
EO8	2a.	mauve	5	5
EO9	4a.	olive	15	5
EO10	4a.	pale olive.. ..	15	5
EO11	6a.	olive-bistre ..	15	5
EO12	8a.	mauve	25	5
EO13	8a.	magenta	30	5
EO14	R1	grn and car ('05)	30	5
EO15	Rs2	rose-red and yel-brn	75	20
EO16	Rs2	car and yel-brn	80	20
EO17	Rs5	ult and violet	1·75	60
EO18	Rs10	green and car ..	3·00	1·00
EO19	Rs10	green and scarlet	5·00	2·00
EO20	Rs15	blu and ol-brn ..	5·00	5·00
EO21	Rs25	brownish-or and blu	8·00	9·00
EO1/21		set (15v)	£18	£15

EO1a, 4a and 6a the stop is missing after "M": Row 6/10 and 10/1 of the first pane.

All values to R1 exist overprinted "CANCELLED".

All values to R1 are found with misplaced overprint.

Two sets may be made with the overprint in thick or thin letters.

1925. Official stamps of King Edward VII

(Nos. EO19–21) surcharged diagonally (in words).

EO22	R1 on Rs15	blu and ol-brn	..	75	40
		a surcharge double	£10		—
		b ONF. RUPF.F.	5·00		5·00
EO23	R1 on Rs25	brn-or and blu	..	4·00	4·00
		a surcharge double	£10		—
		b ONF. RUPF.F.	5·00		5·00
		c surcharge also on reverse	£10		—
EO24	Rs2 on Rs10	grn and car	£20		£20
EO25	Rs2 on Rs10	grn and scar	..	80	75
		a surcharge double	£10		—

EO22*b*, 23*b* This variety occurs on Stamp No. 12 in the top left pane.

32 Essays were prepared for these surcharged stamps.

Numbers Issued—EO22, 531,456; EO23, 22,752; EO24, EO25, 429,888.

1926. No. EO11 surcharged diagonally.

EO26	1a. on 6a.	olive-bistre	10	10

1912–1922. Stamps of King George V. (Nos. G1–43) overprinted SERVICE (14mm. on Anna values: 21½mm. on Rupee values). Wmk. large Star

GO1	3p.	grey	.. ..	5	5
GO2	3p.	slate-grey	..	5	5
GO3	3p.	blue-slate	..	5	5
		joined "Ps"		2·50	2·50
GO4	½a.	yellow-green	..	5	5
		a overprint double	£10		—
GO5	½a.	pale blue-green		5	5
GO6	1a.	rose-carmine	..	5	5
GO7	1a.	carmine	.. ..	5	5
GO8	1a.	aniline-carmine		5	5
		a overprint double		—	£22
GO9	1a.	chocolate ('22)		5	5
		a imperf	.. ..	£10	—
GO10	2a.	mauve	.. ..	5	5
GO11	2a.	purple	.. ..	5	5
GO12	4a.	deep olive	..	15	5
GO13	4a.	olive-green	..	10	5
GO14	6a.	yellow-bistre	..	40	20
GO15	6a.	dp bistre-brown		80	30
GO16	8a.	purple	.. ..	50	15
GO17	8a.	mauve	.. ..	30	5

GO18	8a.	br aniline-mauve	1·50	60
GO19	R1	red-brn and blu-grn	.. ..	40	5
GO20	Rs2	rose-car and brn	75	30
GO21	Rs5	ult and violet	..	2·00	75
GO22	Rs10	grn and scar	..	5·00	4·00
GO23	Rs15	blue and olive	..	7·50	7·50
GO24	Rs25	orange and blue	£12	£12
GO/24		set (16v)	£27	£24

O3*a* The same variety as on G4*a*.

O21–O24 also exist on ungummed paper with a shiny overprint. This was from an experimental printing.

All values to 8a. exist overprinted CANCELLED. The Rupee values also exist with large CAN-CELLED handstamp in violet over three stamps.

1921. No. GO6 surcharged NINE PIES as G44.

GO25	9p. on 1a.	rose-carmine	5	5

1925. Offical stamps of King George V (Nos. GO22-24).

I. Surcharged (in words) horizontally.

GO26	R1 on Rs15	blu and ol	3·00	3·00
		a surcharge double ..	£10	—
GO27	R1 on Rs25	or and blu	1·00	50
		a surcharge double..	£10	—
		b surcharge inverted	£65	—

32 essays were prepared for these surcharged stamps.

Number Issued—GO26, 35,712; GO27, 436,224

II. Surcharged diagonally as on No. EO 25.

GO28	Rs2 on Rs10	grn and scar	..	£110	—

1926 Stamps of King George V overprinted SERVICE and surcharged with new value.

GO29	1a. on 1½a.			
		(Type A No. G12)	5	5
		a surcharge and overprint double	4·00	4·00
		b surcharge and overprint inverted	4·00	4·00
GO30	1a. on 1½a.			
		(Type B No. G14)	10	5
		a surcharge and overprint double	4·00	4·00
		b surcharge and overprint inverted	4·00	4·00

c surcharge also on
reverse .. 4·00 —
GO31 Error 1a. on 1a.
(No. G11) .. .. £35 —
GO32 1a. on 2½a.
(No. G21) 20 25

1926-1941 Stamps of King George V (Nos. G49–76) overprinted SERVICE (13½mm. on Anna values: 19½mm. on Rupee values). Wmk. Multiple Stars.

GO33	3p.	slate	5	5
GO34	½a.	green	5	5
GO35	½a.	green ('35)	5	5
GO36	9p.	deep green ..		
		offset litho ('32)	5	5
		a typo ('34) ..	15	15
GO37	1a.	chocolate ..	5	5
		a 14mm. over-		
		print	3·50	1·00
GO38	1a.	chocolate ('36)	5	5
GO39	1¼a.	mauve ('32)('41)	5	5
		a overprint on		
		gummed side		
		(Die I) ..	—	—
GO40	2a.	purple	5	5
GO41	2a.	vermilion ..	30	5
GO42	2a.	vermilion ('35)	5	20
GO43	2a.	ver (small die)		
		('36) ..	15	5
GO44	2½a.	orange	5	5
GO45	4a.	sage-green ..	5	5
GO46	4a.	sage-grn ('35)	20	5
GO47	6a.	bistre ('36) ..	45	50
GO48	8a.	reddish purple	20	5
GO49	12a.	claret	15	5
GO50	R1	choc and grn ..	50	5
GO51	Rs2	car and orange	1·00	40
GO53	Rs10	grn and scar ..	8·00	3·00
GO33/53		set (20v)	£10·50	4·00

GO39 exists in both Dies (see note after G55).

Two sets may be made with overprint Offset Litho or Typo.

For GO39 with 1A. surcharge see O8.

GO39*a* There is some doubt as to the status of this variety.

1937-47 Issue of 1937 overprinted SERVICE.

O1	½a. red-brown (12/3/38)	10	10
O2	9p. dp green (5/10/37)	50	10
O3	1a. carmine (1/11/37)	10	10
O4	1r. violet-grey and lt brn		
	(25/4/38) ..	40	10
O5	2r. violet-pur and brn		
	(25/4/38) ..	90	50
	a dp pur and brn (/47)	80	40
O6	5r. dp green and dp blue		
	(10/10/38) ..	1·75	90

O7 10r. vio-pur and red-claret
(29/9/39) .. 3·00 1·50
O1/7 set (7) .. .. 7·50 3·50

1939 K.G. V Official Stamp (GO 39: Die I), surcharged, with bars obliterating original value.

O8 1a./1½a. red-pur (20/4/39) 10 10

The relative positions of the overprint (SERVICE) and the surcharge vary considerably, both horizontally and vertically.

1939 (June 1st) -42 Perf. 13¾ x 14 (C). Sheets 16 x 20.

O9	3p. slate	10	10
O10	½a. red-brown	10	10
O11	½a. dp pur (1/10/42) ..	10	10
O12	9p. green	10	10
O13	1a. rose-carmine ..	10	10
O14	1a./3p. bistre (2/6/41) ..	10	10
O15	1½a. slate-pur (1/9/42)	10	10
O16	2a. vermilion	10	10
O17	2½a. purple-violet ..	10	10
O18	4a. dp brown	10	10
O19	8a. violet-slate ..	10	10
O9/19	set (11)	1·00	1·00

1948 (Aug. 15th) Nos. S9–12 overprinted SERVICE (*overprint 13½mm. in length, height of letters 2mm.*), **for use of Governor-General's Secretariat.**

O19a	1½a. chocolate-brown ..	£24	£24
O19b	3½a. dull violet ..	£200	£200
O19c	12a. greyish-green ..	£500	£500
O19d	10r. brown and lake ..	£2500	—
O19a/d	set (4)	£3000	—

No. O19a–19d—Forged overprints of all values exist and a certificate should be obtained for these very rare stamps.

O19a exists with genuine overprint, but cancellation struck after issue withdrawn and back dated.

Number overprinted—1½a., 15,950; 3½a., 1,350; 12a., 250; 10r., 20.

Three sheets of each overprinted value were officially reprinted for the 1954 Centenary Exhibition

1950 (Jan. 2nd) -51 3p.–8a. (*small format*), **Perf. 13¾ x 14 (C), Typo, Sheets 16 x 20; 1r.–10r.** (*large format*) **Perf. 13¾ (C), Offset-litho, Sheets O29–31, 11 x 14; O32, 10 x 12.**

O20	3p. **blk-vio** (1/7/50)	..	5	5
O21	6p. **dp choc** (1/7/50)		5	5
O22	9p. **dp em-grn** (1/7/50)		5	5
O23	1a. **dp turquoise** (1/7/50)		5	5
O24	2a. **crimson** (1/7/50)	..	5	5
O25	3a. **vermilion** (1/7/50)	..	10	5
O26	4a. **dp lake** (1/7/50)	..	15	5
O26a	4a. **dp blue** (1/10/51)	..	15	5
O27	6a. **pur-vio** (1/7/50)	..	15	5
O28	8a. **cinnamon-brown** (1/7/50)	..	15	5
O29	1r. **purple-violet**	..	20	5
O30	2r. **lake-red**	..	30	10
O31	5r. **grey-green**	..	1·25	50
O32	10r. **maroon-brown**	..	2·00	1·00
O20/32	**set** (14)	..	4·50	2·00

SEMI-POSTAL ISSUES

1907 (Jan.) Lady Minto's Fete. No wmk. Rough Pin Perf. Sheets ESP1/2 24 (6 blocks of 4): ESP3 5 x 5.

ESP1	4a.	**blue** (Lord Minto)	5·00	£10
ESP2	4a.	**red** (Lady Minto)	5·00	£10
ESP3	R1	**red, green, black**	5·00	£10

Printed by Survey of India in connection with Lady Minto's Fete held in Calcutta, January 28th–February 8th, 1907. A few copies passed through the post, bearing a special "Red Cross" cancellation before the issue was withdrawn. The same "Red Cross" cancellation was used on **ordinary** Indian stamps at the special Post Office at the Fete.

1924. Mount Everest Expedition. No wmk. (*Litho*). **Perf. 11.**

GSP1	No value	**dk blue**	..	3·00	8·00
GSP2	No value	**lt blue**	..	3·00	8·00

Used on covers or cards despatched by members of the expedition in addition to Indian postage stamps. This label had no postal validity, but was used to raise funds for the expedition.

INDIAN NATIONAL ARMY

I. In anticipation of the 'liberation' of India by the Japanese, Subhas Chandra Bhose (leader of the Independence Movement) arranged for the printing at the Government Printing Bureau in Berlin of stamps inscribed "Azad Hind" (Free India). Some 80,000 sets (to As.12) and only 4,000 of the R1 + Rs2 of these unissued stamps came on to the market after the war. Very few of the R1 + Rs2 survived.

1943. Prepared for issue. Designer, Von Axster Heudtlass. (*Photo*) **in sheets of 100 (10 x 10). No wmk. Imperf. or Perf. 10½ (Anna values). R1 + Rs2 Imperf only.**

INA1	½a.	**green**	
INA2	1a.	**carmine**	
INA3	2½a.	**orange**	
INA4	1a.+1a.	**brown**	
INA5	2a.+2a.	**carmine**	Set (9) £5
INA6	2½a.+2½a.	**blue** ..	
INA7	3a.+3a.	**red** ..	
INA8	8a.+12a.	**deep violet**	
INA9	12a+R1	**magenta**	

INA10 R1+Rs2 **black** .. £10
INA11 R1+Rs2 **blk and or** .. £10
INA12 R1+Rs2 **blk, or and grn** £10

INA 1-3 (500,000 each) are believed to have been intended for use in the Andaman and Nicobar Islands.

INA 4-9 (1,000,000 each) and INA10-12 (13,500 total) were intended for use in India.

Although these stamps were never valid for postal use, INA 1-9 are nevertheless known used on covers postmarked 'NETAJI BHAVAN/CAL-CUTTA 23.1.64'.

II. Indian Army soldiers, held prisoners of war in Singapore, were coerced into joining the Indian National Army for service during their attempted invasion of India from Burma. Stamps inscribed "CHALO DELHI" (On to Delhi!) were said to have been issued for use by the I.N.A. in the occupied areas of India during the march on Imphal where the Japanese invasion was halted: they are extremely rare.

1944. (*Typo*) **in Rangoon. No gum. Perf. 11½ or Imperf.**

INA13 1p. (½a.) **plum** .. .. — —
INA14 1a. **green** .. .. — —

Forgeries in slightly larger size were made in Calcutta. The 1a. value also exists in red, believed to be a proof.

CHINA EXPEDITIONARY FORCE

1900 (Aug.)-1904 Stamps of Queen Victoria (1882–1900 Issues) overprinted "C.E.F." at the Government Printing Office, Calcutta.

VC1	3p.	**carmine**	5	5
VC2	½a.	**green**	5	5
VC3	1a.	**brown-purple** ..	15	15
VC4	1a.	**car** (27/2/04) ..	2·25	1·25
VC5	2a.	**ultramarine** ..	30	40
VC6	2½a.	**green**	40	50
VC7	3a.	**orange**	1·00	1·50
VC8	4a.	**olive-green** ..	50	70

VC9	8a.	**magenta**	50	70
VC10	12a.	**purple/red** ..	75	90
VC11	R1.	**green and car** ..	1·25	1·25
VC1/11		**set** (11v)	6·00	6·50

Prepared but not issued.

VC12	1½a.	**sepia**	£15	..

A constant variety 'O' for 'C' is found on all values Row 1/5. Price from £5.

A constant variety, no Stop after "F" is found on all values except 2½a. and 4a. Row 11/3. Price £5 each.

All values are found with misplaced overprint.

The Government of India collection includes an Essay 2½a. surcharged on 4½a. with "C.E.F." overprint.

1904-1909 Stamps of King Edward VII (Nos. E1–20) similarly overprinted.

EC1	3p.	**pale grey**	20	30
EC2	3p.	**slate-grey**	40	50
		a overprint double	£55	£65
EC3	½a.	**green** ('09) ..	40	40
		a overprint double	£35	£40
EC4	1a.	**carmine**	45	50
EC5	1a.	**carmine** ('09) ..	25	25
EC6	2a.	**pale violet** ..	60	40
EC7	2½a.	**ultramarine** ..	50	90
EC8	3a.	**orange-brown** ..	60	90
EC9	4a.	**olive-green** ..	1·25	1·25
EC10	8a.	**magenta**	1·25	1·25
EC11	12a.	**purple/red** ..	1·50	2·50
EC12	R1.	**grn and car** ..	1·50	2·00
EC1/12		**set** (11v)	7·50	£10

All values are found with misplaced overprint.

1913-1921 Stamps of King George V (Nos. G1–38) similarly overprinted. Wmk. Large Star.

GC1	3p.	**slate-grey** ..	20	40
GC2	½a.	**green**	20	45
GC3	1a.	**aniline carmine**	30	90
GC4	1½a.	**choc (Type A)** ..	75	2·00
GC5	2a.	**mauve**	80	2·25
GC6	2½a.	**bright blue** ..	1·00	2·25
GC7	3a.	**orange-brown** ..	1·50	2·75
GC8	4a.	**olive-green** ..	2·25	4·50
GC9	8a.	**mauve**	2·25	4·50
GC10	12a.	**claret**	2·50	5·50
GC11	R1.	**red-brn and blu-green**	7·50	£12
GC1/11		**set** (11v)	£17	£35

Although the KG V issue continued in use until the last Indian Garrison was withdrawn and F.P.O. 5 at Tientsin was closed in September, 1939 these stamps are rarely found used.

INDIAN EXPEDITIONARY FORCES
1914–1922

The I.E.F. stamps were used in all theatres in which units of the Indian Army were on active service.

1914 Stamps of King George V (Nos. G1–38) overprinted "I.E.F." Wmk. Large Star.

GE1	3p.	**slate-grey** ..	5	5
		a overprint double	5·00	5·00
GE2	½a.	**yellow-green** ..	5	5
GE3	1a.	**aniline-carmine**	5	5
GE4	1a.	**carmine**	15	15
GE5	2a.	**mauve**	5	5
GE6	2½a.	**ultramarine** ..	10	15
GE7	3a.	**orange-brown** ..	10	10
GE8	4a.	**olive-green** ..	10	20
GE9	8a.	**purple**	20	20
GE10	8a.	**mauve**	1·25	2·50
GE11	12a.	**dull claret** ..	1·25	2·00
GE12	12a.	**claret**	75	2·50
GE13	R1.	**red-brn and blu-**		
		grn	1·50	3·00
GE1/13		**set (10v)**	2·75	5·00

A constant variety, no Stop after "F" is found on all the Anna values Row 4/12 in top pane.

A constant variety, no Stop after "E" is found on the 3p. and 2a. values.

Several values are known with double overprint, one albino.

All values are found with misplaced overprint.

All values are known with easily recognised forged overprints done on used Indian Stamps.

A bogus overprint also exists on G51.

CONVENTION STATES
OF INDIA

† Denotes dates when stamps were despatched from Central Stamp Store to Post Offices. No records of actual dates of issue were kept.

CHAMBA

1938 Stamps of India (1937 Issue), overprinted CHAMBA STATE.

1	3p.	**slate** (1/9/38) † ..	15	15
2	½a.	**red-brown** (1/9/38) †	20	40
3	9p.	**dp green** (1/9/38) † ..	40	40
4	1a.	**carmine** (1/9/38) † ..	15	20
5	2a.	**vermilion** (27/8/38) †	35	45
6	2½a.	**violet** (27/8/38) † ..	40	45
7	3a.	**yellow-grn** (27/8/38) †	1·50	1·50
8	3½a.	**blue** (27/8/38) † ..	40	70
9	4a.	**dp brown** (27/8/38) †	40	70
10	6a.	**greenish-blue**		
		(27/8/38) † ..	3·00	5·00

11	8a.	**vio-slate** (27/8/38) † ..	70	1·75
12	12a.	**dp crimson** (27/8/38) †	1·50	2·50
13	1r.	**vio-grey and lt brown**		
		(1/9/38) †	3·00	4·00
14	2r.	**vio-purple and brown**		
		(1/9/38) †	4·50	6·50
15	5r.	**dp green and dp blue**		
		(1/9/38) †	9·00	£10
16	10r.	**vio-pur and red-claret**		
		(1/9/38)	£20	£24
17	15r.	**chocolate and dp grn**		
		(1/9/38) †	£35	£42
18	25r.	**slate-vio and pur-vio**		
		(1/9/38) †	£50	£60
1/18		**set (18)**	£120	£150

1942 (May 7th †) -47 As No. 2, etc., overprinted CHAMBA.

19	½a.	**red-brown**	60	60
20	1a.	**carmine**	70	60
21	14a.	**purple** (15/10/47) † ..	2·75	5·00
22	1r.	**vio-grey and lt brown**	5·00	6·00
23	2r.	**vio-purple and brown**	£25	£27
24	5r.	**dp green and dp blue**	£20	£21
25	10r.	**vio-pur and red-claret**	£30	£31
26	15r.	**chocolate and dp grn**	£31	£34
27	25r.	**slate-vio and pur-vio**	£50	£55
19/27		**set (9)**	£135	£150

1942-3 Stamps of India (1941-3 Issue), overprinted CHAMBA.

28	3p.	**slate** (7/5/42) † ..	10	10
29	½a.	**purple** (25/6/43) † ..	10	10
30	9p.	**green** (7/5/42) † ..	10	10
31	1a.	**rose-car** (25/6/43) † .	10	10
32	1½a.	**slate-pur** (23/6/43) †	10	10
33	2a.	**vermilion** (23/6/43) †	10	30
34	3a.	**bt vio** (*typo*) (7/5/42) †	45	90
		a ditto (*litho*) (23/6/43) †	15	30
35	3½a.	**blue** (7/5/42) † ..	15	40
36	4a.	**brown** (7/5/42) † ..	15	40
37	6a.	**greenish-blue** (7/5/42) †	40	80
38	8a.	**violet-slate** (7/5/42) †	70	1·75
39	12a.	**dp crimson** (7/5/42) †	80	1·75
28/39		**set (12)**	2·75	6·00

OFFICIAL STAMPS

1938-40 Postage Stamps of India (1937 Issue), overprinted CHAMBA STATE SERVICE.

O1	9p.	**dp green** (1/9/38) † ..	35	40
O2	1a.	**carmine** (1/9/38) † ..	20	25
O3	1r.	**vio-grey and lt brown**		
		(12/12/40) † ..	£120	£110
O4	2r.	**vio-purple and brown**		
		(9/11/39) † ..	3·50	4·00
O5	5r.	**dp green and dp blue**		
		(9/11/39) † ..	6·00	6·50
O6	10r.	**vio-pur and red-claret**		
		(9/11/39) † ..	£13	£14
O1/6		**set (6)**	£160	£665

1940-3 Official Stamps of India (1939 Issue), overprinted CHAMBA.

O7	3p.	**slate** (12/12/40) † ..	10	10
O8	½a.	**red-brn** (12/12/40) †	40	20
O9	½a.	**dp pur** (25/6/43) † ..	35	10

O10	9p. **green** (12/12/40) † .	10	10
O11	1a. **rose-car** (23/1/41) †	10	10
O12	1a.3p. **bistre** (15/7/41) † ..	3·50	2·00
O13	1½a. **slate-pur** (25/6/43) †	15	35
O14	2a. **vermilion** (12/12/40) †	15	35
O15	2½a. **pur-vio** (23/1/41) †	45	45
O16	4a. **dp brn** (12/12/40) †	50	80
O17	8a. **vio-slate** (12/12/40) †	1·00	1·25
O7/17	**set (11)** 2	6·50	5·50

1942 (May 7th †) As Nos. O3–O6, but overprinted CHAMBA SERVICE.

O18	1r. **vio-grey and lt brn**..	3·00	4·00
O19	2r. **vio-purple and brn**	3·00	4·00
O20	5r. **dp green and dp blue**	6·00	9·00
O21	10r. **vio-purple and red-**claret	£10	£11
O18/21	**set (4)**	£20	£25

GWALIOR

1938-48 Stamps of India (1937) Issue, overprinted GWALIOR in English and Hindi.

1	3p. **slate** (26/8/38) † ..	40	10
2	½p. **red-brown** (20/6/38) †	40	10
3	9p. **dp green** (30/6/39) † ..	£10	8·00
4	1a. **carmine** (28/7/38) † ..	40	10
5	3a. **yel-grn** (30/6/39) † ..	40	35
6	4a. **dp brown** (18/6/38) †	4·00	4·00
7	6a. **greenish-blue** (30/6/39) †	50	50
8	1r. **vio-grey and lt brown** (10/9/42) †	80	1·00
9	2r. **vio-purple and brown** (17/8/48) †	4·00	4·00
10	5r. **dp green and dp blue** (17/8/48) †	£10	£10
11	10r. **vio-pur and red-claret** (17/8/48) †	£15	£16
12	15r. **chocolate and dp grn** (17/8/48) †	£28	£30
13	25r. **slate-vio and pur-vio** (17/8/48) †	£35	£35
1/13	**set (13)**	£100	£100

1942-5 Stamps of India (1941-3 Issue), overprinted as before.

14	3p. **slate** (26/9/42) † ..	10	10
15	½a. **purple** (20/5/43) † ..	10	10
16	9p. **green** (11/2/42) † ..	10	10
17	1a. **rose-car** (20/5/43) † ..	10	10
18	1½a. **slate-purple** (*litho*) (10/9/42) †	50	60
	a ditto (*typo*) 20/5/43) †	15	15
19	2a. **vermilion** (26/9/42) † ..	15	15
20	3a. **bt violet** (26/9/42) † ..	25	25
	a ditto (*typo*) (20/5/43)	3·00	1·50
21	4a. **brown** (26/9/42) † ..	20	30
22	6a. **greenish-blue** (1/8/45) †	2·00	2·00
23	8a. **violet-slate** (3/6/44) †	2·00	2·00
24	12a. **dp crimson** (20/5/43) †	2·00	2·00
14/24	**set (11)**	7·00	7·00

1949 As before but overprinted locally (*a*).

25	3p. **slate**	50	50
26	½a. **purple**	50	50
27	1a. **rose-carmine**	50	50

27a	1a./3p. **bistre**	—	—
28	2a. **vermilion**	1·00	1·00
29	3a. **bright violet** ..	2·50	2·50
30	4a. **brown**	2·50	3·00
31	6a. **greenish-blue** ..	£10	£10
32	8a. **violet-slate** ..	£15	£12
33	12a. **dp crimson** ..	£65	£30
25/33	**set (10)** ..	£95	£55

Due to pressure of other work, Nasik was unable to overprint further supplies of stamps, and the work was undertaken at the Gwalior Government Printing Works. The type used differs from that used in Nasik and the overprint measures 17mm. instead of 13mm. as previously.

OFFICIAL STAMPS

The official stamps of Gwalior are overprinted in Hindi only.

1938-47 Postage Stamps of India (1937 Issue) overprinted (in Hindi) GWALIOR SERVICE.

O1	½a. **red-brown** (5/7/38) †	50	10
O2	1a. **carmine** (5/7/38) † ..	50	10
O3	1r. **vio-grey and lt brown** (7/8/42) †	40	50
O4	2r. **vio-purple and brown** (7/8/42) †	2·50	1·50
O5	5r. **dp green and dp blue** (20/5/43) †	8·00	8·00
O6	10r. **vio-pur and red-claret** (12/7/47) †	£12	£12
O1/6	**set (6)**	£20	£20

1940-2 Official Stamps of India (1939 Issue) overprinted (in Hindi) GWALIOR.

O7	3p. **slate** (8/7/40) † ..	25	20
O8	½a. **red-brn** (8/7/40) † ..	80	50
O9	½a. **dp pur** (15/10/42) †	25	25
O10	9p. **green** (15/10/42) †	25	25
O11	1a. **rose-car** (8/7/40) †	25	25
O12	1a.3p. **bistre** (11/2/42) † ..	40	40
O13	1½a. **slate-pur** (10/9/42) †	30	30
O14	2a. **vermilion** (8/7/40) †	30	30
O15	4a. **dp brown** (7/8/42) †	25	40
O16	8a. **vio-slate** (7/8/42) †	50	60
O7/16	**set (10)**	3·00	3·00

1942 K.G. V Stamp of India (No. G55) overprinted in 1933 (in Hindi) "GWALIOR SERVICE," now surcharged 1A.—1A.

| O17 | 1a./1¼a. **red-purple** (Die I) | 1·50 | 50 |

JIND

1937 (May 10th †) Stamps of India (1937 Issue) overprinted JIND STATE.

1	3p. **slate**	10	10
2	½a. **red-brown**	10	15
3	9p. **dp green** (5/11/37) † ..	15	15
4	1a. **carmine** (5/11/37) † ..	10	10
5	2a. **vermilion**	10	25
6	2½a. **violet**	10	20
7	3a. **yellow-green**	15	20
8	3½a. **blue**	15	20
9	4a. **dp brown**	25	30
10	6a. **greenish-blue**	25	30
11	8a. **violet-slate**	25	30
12	12a. **dp crimson**	50	90

13	1r.	vio-grey and lt brown	1·00	1·50
14	2r.	vio-purple and brown	1·50	2·00
15	5r.	dp green and dp blue	7·00	7·00
16	10r.	vio-pur and red-claret	£12	£13
17	15r.	choc and dp green ..	£38	£40
18	25r.	slate-vio and pur-vio	£45	£50
1/18		set (18)	£100	£110

1941 (Aug. 7th†) As before, but overprinted **JIND.**

19	3p.	slate	1·00	1·00
20	½a.	red-brown	1·00	1·00
21	9p.	dp green	1·00	1·00
22	1a.	carmine	1·00	1·00
23	1r.	vio-grey and lt brown	1·75	2·00
24	2r.	vio-purple and brown	2·75	4·00
25	5r.	dp green and dp blue	6·50	8·00
26	10r.	vio-pur and red-claret	£14	£15
27	15r.	choc and dp green ..	£20	£22
28	25r.	slate-vio and pur-vio	£28	£30
19/28		set (10)	£70	£80

1941-3 Stamps of India (1941-3 Issue), overprinted **JIND.**

29	3p.	slate (11/4/42)† ..	10	10
30	½a.	purple (17/6/43)† ..	10	10
31	9p.	green (11/4/42)† ..	10	10
32	1a.	rose-car (11/4/42)† ..	10	10
33	1a.3p.	bistre (7/8/41)† ..	10	20
34	1½a.	slate-purple (litho)		
		(29/8/42)†	30	30
		a ditto (typo)	1·50	1·00
35	2a.	vermilion (7/8/41)†..	10	10
36	3a.	bt vio (litho) (11/4/42)†	25	25
		a ditto (typo)	1·50	1·00
37	3½a.	blue (7/8/41)† ..	25	30
38	4a.	brown (7/8/41)† ..	10	30
40	6a.	greenish-blue (7/8/41)†	15	40
42	8a.	violet-slate (7/8/41)†	50	60
43	12a.	dp crimson (7/8/41)†	70	80
29/43		set (13)	2·75	3·00

OFFICIAL STAMPS

1937-40 Postage Stamps of India (1937 Issue). overprinted **JIND STATE SERVICE.**

O1	½a.	red-brn (13/12/38)†	60	10
O2	9p.	dp green (5/11/37)†	25	10
O3	1a.	carmine (5/11/37)†	20	10
O4	1r.	vio-grey and lt brn		
		(7/5/40)†	2·00	1·75
O5	2r.	vio-purple and brn		
		(7/5/40)†	4·00	4·00
O6	5r.	dp green and dp blue		
		(7/5/40)†	9·00	9·00
O7	10r.	vio-pur and red-claret		
		(7/5/40)†	£12	£12
O1/7		set (7)	£25	£25

1939 (Dec. 12th†) -43 Official Stamps of India (1939 Issue), overprinted **JIND.**

O8	3p.	slate	10	10
O9	½a.	red-brown	1·25	75
O10	½a.	dp purple (17/6/43)†	10	10
O11	9p.	green	10	10
O12	1a.	rose-carmine ..	10	10
O13	1½a.	slate-pur (12/9/42)†	30	25
O14	2a.	vermilion	15	15
O15	2½a.	purple-violet ..	15	15

O16	4a.	dp brown	40	40
O17	8a.	violet-slate	50	50
O8/17		set (10)	3·00	2·57

1942 (Sept. 18th†) As Nos. O4-7, but overprinted **JIND SERVICE.**

O18	1r.	vio-grey and lt brn ..	2·00	2·00
O19	2r.	vio-purple and brn..	3·00	3·00
O20	5r.	dp grn and dp blue	5·00	8·00
O21	10r.	vio-pur and red-		
		claret	£12	£12
O18/21		set (4)	£20	£23

NABHA

1938 (June 20th†) unless otherwise indicated Stamps of India (1937 Issue), overprinted **NABHA STATE.**

1	3p.	slate	1·00	40
2	½a.	red-brown	25	30
3	9p.	dp green	4·00	4·00
4	1a.	carmine	15	10
5	2a.	.vermilion	15	15
6	2½a.	violet	20	30
7	3a.	yellow-green ..	25	35
8	3½a.	blue	30	40
9	4a.	dp brown	15	35
10	6a.	greenish blue ..	40	80
11	8a.	violet-slate ..	35	80
12	12a.	dp crimson ..	80	1·25
13	1r.	vio-grey and lt brown	1·00	1·25
14	2r.	vio-purple and brown	2·50	3·00
15	5r.	dp green and dp blue	8·00	9·00
16	10r.	vio-pur and red-claret		
		(16/6/38)†	£15	£20
17	15r.	choc. and dp green		
		(16/6/38)†	£33	£40
18	25r.	slate-vio and pur-vio		
		(16/6/38)†	£40	£45
1/18		set (18)	£95	£120

1942 (May 30th†) As before, but overprinted **NABHA.**

19	3p.	slate	4·00	80
20	½a.	red-brown	9·00	5·00
21	9p.	deep green	4·00	1·00
22	1a.	carmine	3·00	1·00
19/22		set (4)	£18	7·00

1941-5 Stamps of India (1941-3 Issue), overprinted **NABHA.**

23	3p.	slate (2/5/42)† ..	10	10
24	½a.	purple (9/1/43) ..	10	10
25	9p.	green (2/5/42)† ..	10	10
26	1a.	rose-car (4/7/45)† ..	10	10
27	1a.3p.	bistre (30/5/41)† ..	10	10
28	1½a.	slate-purple (litho)		
		(22/9/42)†	10	10
		a ditto (typo) 4/7/72†	1·50	1·00
29	2a.	vermilion (16/6/43)†	15	15
30	3a.	bt violet (16/6/43)†	20	20
31	3½a.	blue (31/1/44)† ..	25	25
32	4a.	brown (30/5/41)† ..	25	25
33	6a.	greenish-blur		
		(16/6/43)†	35	30
34	8a.	vio-slate (16/6/43)†	40	45
35	12a.	dp crimson (16/6/43)†	70	1·00
23/35		set (13)	2·75	3·00

OFFICIAL STAMPS

1938 (June 20th) Postage Stamps of India (1937 Issue), overprinted NABHA STATE SERVICE.

O1	9p. **dp green**	40	70
O2	1a. **carmine**	25	30

1940-3 Official Stamps of India (1939 Issue), overprinted NABHA.

O3	3p. **slate** (2/5/42) † ..	10	10
O4	½a. **red-brown** (22/9/42) ‡	20	20
O5	½a. **dp purple** (16/6/43) †	10	10
O6	9p. **green** (10/4/40) † ..	10	10
O7	1a. **carmine** (2/5/42) ..	10	15
O8	1½a. **slate-pur** (22/9/42) †	15	25
O9	2a. **vermilion** (22/9/42) †	15	25
O10	4a. **dp brown** (22/9/42) †	35	40
O11	8a. **vio-slate** (22/9/42) †	50	75
O1/11	**set** (11)	2·25	3·00

1942 (May 2nd) Postage Stamps of India (1937 Issue), overprinted NABHA SERVICE.

O12	1r. **vio-grey and lt brn**	1·00	1·25
O13	2r. **vio purple and brn**	3·50	3·75
O14	5r. **dp green and dp blue**	9·00	9·00
O12/14	**set** (3)	£13	£13

PATIALA

1937-8 (June 1st†) Stamps of India (1937 Issue), overprinted PATIALA STATE.

1	3p. **slate**	6·00	5·00
2	½a. **red-brown**	40	25
3	9p. **dp green** (16/10/37) †	35	30
4	1a. **carmine** (16/10/37) †	15	15
5	2a. **vermilion**	15	20
6	2½a. **violet**	15	40
7	3a. **yellow-green** ..	15	40
8	3½a. **blue**	40	60
9	4a. **dp brown**	40	60
10	6a. **greenish-blue** ..	40	90
11	8a. **violet-slate**	50	90
12	12a. **dp crimson**	1·25	2·00
13	1r. **vio-grey and lt brown**	5·00	5·00
14	2r. **vio-purple and brown**	5·00	5·00
15	5r. **dp green and dp blue**	7·00	7·00
16	10r. **vio-pur and red-claret**	£14	£16
17	15r. **choc and dp green** ..	£26	£26
18	25r. **slate-vio and pur-vio**	£32	£38
1/18	**set** (18)	£95	£100

1941 (May 29th) †-41 As before, but overprinted PATIALA.

19	3p. **slate**	1·00	40
20	½a. **red-brown**	1·00	40
21	9p. **dp green**	4·00	75
22	1a. **carmine**	1·50	75
23	1r. **vio-grey and lt-brown** (22/6/46) †	1·00	80
19/23	**set** (5)	7·00	3·00

1942-5 Stamps of India (1941-3 Issue), overprinted PATIALA.

24	3p. **slate** (2/5/42) † ..	10	10
25	½a. **purple** (29/4/43) † ..	10	10
26	9p. **green** (2/5/42) † ..	10	10
	a overprint omitted, in pr. with normal ..	£550	—
27	1a. **rose-car** (12/4/44) † ..	10	10
28	1a.3p. **bistre** (29/5/41) † ..	25	30
29	1½a. **slate-purple** (*litho*) (10/9/42) †	50	30
	a ditto (*typo*)	10	10
30	2a. **vermilion** (12/4/44) ‡	15	15
31	3a. **bt violet** (12/4/44) ‡	20	20
32	3½a. **blue** (12/4/44) ‡ ..	25	20
33	4a. **brown** (12/4/44) † ..	10	15
34	6a. **greenish-blue** (12/4/44) †	15	15
35	8a. **vio-slate** (12/4/44) †	30	30
36	12a. **dp crimson** (17/5/45)	50	60
24/36	**set** (13)	2·25	2·50

OFFICIAL STAMPS

1937-9 Postage Stamps of India (1937 issue), overprinted PATIALA STATE SERVICE.

O1	½a. **red-brown** (1/6/38) †	50	25
O2	9p. **dp green** (1/6/38) † ..	£25	£25
O3	1a. **carmine** (5/11/37) † ..	60	20
O4	1r. **vio-grey and lt brown** (16/2/39) †	1·00	1·00
O5	2r. **vio-purple and brown** (16/2/39) †	4·00	4·00
O6	5r. **dp green and dp blue** (16/2/39) †	7·00	7·00
O1/6	**set** (6)	£18	£18

Number issued—O2, 4,800 (15 sheets).

1939-40 K.G. V Stamp of India (No. G55).

(**a**) Previously overprinted "PATIALA STATE/ SERVICE"; now surcharged 1A—1A.

O7	1a on 1¼a. **red-purple** (Die I) (/39)	40	35

(**b**) Previously overprinted "PATIALA STATE" now further overprinted "SERVICE" and surcharged 1A—1A (in one operation).

O8	1a. on 1¼a. **red-purple** (Die I) (/40)	30	25

In O7 the "S" and final "E" of "SERVICE" (which measures 9½mm.) always lie under the "T" of "PATIALA" and the "A" of "STATE" respectively; and the position of the surcharge varies in relation to the previous overprint.

In O8, "SERVICE" measures 8¾mm. and always appears in constant position relative to the surcharge, but varying in relation to the position of the previous overprint.

1939-44 Official Stamps of India (1939 issue), overprinted PATIALA.

O9	3p. **slate** (10/6/40) † ..	10	10
O10	½a. **red/brn** (12/12/39) †	10	10
O11	½a. **dp pur** (29/4/42) † ..	10	10
O12	9p. **green** (30/10/39) † .	10	10
O13	1a. **rose-car** (30/10/39) †	10	10
O14	1a.3p. **bistre** (18/6/41) † ..	15	10
O15	1½a. **slate-pur** (7/7/44) †	10	10
O16	2a. **vermilion** (10/6/40) †	10	10
O17	2½a. **pur-vio** (5/10/40) †	20	20
O18	4a. **dp brn** (29/4/43) †...	25	30
O19	8a. **vio-slate** (7/7/44) †	40	40
O9/19	**set** (11)	1·50	1·50

1943-4 As Nos. O4—6, but overprinted PATIALA SERVICE.

O20	1r. **vio-grey and lt brn** (29/4/43) † ..	80	90
O21	2r. **vio-purple and brn** (7/7/44) †	2·00	3·00
O22	5r. **dp green and dp blue** (7/7/44) †	4·50	6·00
O20/22	**set** (3)	7·00	9·00

IRELAND

Prior to 1922 the whole of Ireland formed an integral part of the United Kingdom; and, from 1840 until that year, used the stamps that were in general circulation throughout the kingdom.

Following a long period of unrest, Home Rule was granted on January 16th 1922 to the Provinces of Leinster, Munster and Connaught which — with three Counties in the Province of Ulster — subsequently formed the Irish Free State. The other six Counties in Ulster remained within the United Kingdom and continue to use G.B. stamps.

The Post Office Act of 1922 authorised the overprinting of G.B. stamps and, by an anomalous provision, also permitted the use of the overprinted stamps in certain British Colonies which still used G.B. stamps. This provision was quickly rescinded and examples of the overprinted stamps "used abroad" are exceedingly rare.

PROVISIONAL ISSUES

All the provisional overprints except Nos. G79/81 were made on G.B. stamps Nos. G19 to G49 and G62 to G65 (Bradbury Wilkinson printings).

1922 Overprinted "PROVISIONAL GOVERN-MENT OF IRELAND 1922".

Rialtar Sealaṁaḋ na h Éiŋeann 1922	Rialtar Sealaṁaḋ na h Éiŋeann 1922
No stop after thin "1922"	**"Sealadac" measures 15 mm. "h" and "e" of "heireann" wide spaced base of "e" below level of "h"**

(i) **By Dollard Printing House Ltd.**

(a) **February 17th. In black. Setting 3 x 5 (repeated x 16).**

G1	¼d.	**green**	15	15
		a overprint inverted	£225	£250
		b overprint omitted in vertical pair with normal ..	—	—
		c o'print misplaced	£10	£10
G2	1d.	**scarlet**	25	15
		a overprint inverted	£125	£150
		b overprint double	—	—
		c o'print misplaced	£10	£10
		d wmk. inverted ..	75	25
G3	1d.	**carmine** ..	75	25
G4	2½d.	**bright blue** ..	50	75
G5	3d.	**violet** ..	1·25	75
G6	4d.	**grey-green** ..	2·00	2·00
		a break above "FOUR" ..	£45	—
G7	5d.	**yellow-brown** ..	2·50	2·50
		a o'print misplaced	—	—
G8	9d.	**agate**	6·00	5·00
		a o'print misplaced	—	—
G9	10d.	**turquoise**	5·00	6·00
		a broken frame ..	—	—
G1/9		**set** (8v)	£18	£17

G1a Two sheets (480 copies) exist, with overprint misplaced.

G1b The overprint was so misplaced downwards on one sheet that the first horizontal row in each pane was without overprint.

G2a Three sheets (720 copies) were issued.

G6a A diagonal break occurs in the frame line above the "O" of FOUR" (Row 19/2).

G9a A diagonal break occurs in the left frame line above the "E" of "POSTAGE" (Row 9/1).

G1c/2c/7a/9a Due to movement of the sixteen (4 x 4) stereos (each 3 x 5) the overprint is found so misplaced vertically that "RIALTAS" may be found at the bottom of the stamp, or omitted; and "1922" may be found at the top of the stamp, or omitted.

The ¼d. value with overprint in red is from a Proof Sheet (Price £12). A single copy is known used on cover with G24 from Belvelly, Co. Cork, on April 19th 1922.

Collectors are warned of bogus inverted overprints on other values including G6, G8 and 2d. and 1/– stamps.

G6 is known bisected and used as a 2d. stamp on cover.

Numbers Issued: G1 103,000,000; G2/3 27,000,000; G4 360,000; G5 1,500,000; G6 408,000; G7 504,000; G8 575,000; G9 216,000.

(b) **April 1 (in red) and July (in carmine). Setting as before.**

G10	2½d.	**bright blue** ..	60	85
G11	4d.	**grey-green (R)** ..	4·00	4·00
		a break above "FOUR" ..	£60	—
G12	4d.	**grey-green (C)** ..	£15	£17
		a break above "FOUR" ..	£125	—
G13	9d.	**agate (R)**	7·00	7·00
G14	9d.	**agate (C)**	£60	—
G10/13		**set** (4v)	£25	£27
G11a/G12a See Note under G6a.				

Numbers Issued: G10 312,000; G11/12 432,000; G13/14 624,000.

(c) **February 17. In black. Setting 4 x 5 (repeated x 2).**

G15	2/6	**chocolate-brown**	£18	£20
		a short third line ..	£27	£30
		b re-entry	£100	—
G16	2/6	**sepia-brown** ..	£18	£20
		a short third line ..	£27	£30
		b re-entry	£100	—
G17	5/–	**carmine** ..	£45	£50
		a short third line ..	£90	£90
G18	10/–	**grey-blue** ..	£110	£125
		a short third line ..	£200	£200
		b re-entry ..	—	—
G15/18		**set** (3v)	£170	£195
SPG15/18		**specimen set** (3v)	—	‡

G15a/16a/17a/18a The third line of the overprint (normally 21½mm) measures 21 mm on Rows 1/4, 2/4, 6/4, 7/1, 7/4 and 9/1.

G15b/16b These re-entries occur on Rows 1/3 and 7/1 (Plate 2A).

G18b This re-entry occured on Row 1/1 (Plate 5A).

Numbers Issued: G15/16 40,000; G17 26,000; G18 20,000.

ꞃıⱥlⱥⱥꞃ
Seⱥlⱥⱱⱥċ
nⱥ
héıꞃeⱥnn
1922.

"Sealadac" measures 15 mm. "R" of "Rialtas" centrally placed above "Se" of "Sealadac". The "i" in "Rialtas" extends down below the other letters. Stop after thick 1922.

(ii) June 19th-Aug. By Harrison and Sons Ltd. In glossy black, for vertical and horizontal coils. Sheets of overprinted stamps were cut into vertical or horizontal strips which were joined by use of the sheet margins to provide coils of 500 or 1,000 (vertical) or 480 (horizontal).

G19	½d.	green	60	1·75
G20	1d.	scarlet	60	75
G21	1½d.	red-brown (21/6)	4·00	6·00
		a "PENCF" corr	—	—
G22	2d.	orange (Die I)	5·00	7·00
G23	2d.	or (Die II) (Aug.)	6·00	7·00
		a wmk. inv and rev.	—	—
G19/23		set (5v)	£16	£22

G21a The original error "PENCF" on Row 15/12 was subsequently corrected by the addition of a new lower bar, easily recognised as it is longer than the normal.

G22/23 May be found se-tenant in the same coil; but this variety can of course be readily faked. See above G.B. G19 for details of the two Dies.

Numbers Issued (complete Coils): G19 492; G20 1,454; G21 118; G22 672; G23 820.

ꞃıⱥlⱥⱥꞃ	ꞃıⱥlⱥⱥꞃ
Seⱥlⱥⱱⱥċ	Seⱥlⱥⱱⱥċ
nⱥ	nⱥ héıꞃeⱥnn
héıꞃeⱥnn	1922
1922.	

"Rialtas" measures 11½ mm.	"Sealadac" measures 14½ mm.
"Sealadac" measures 14½ mm.	"h" and "e" of "heireann" close together
"R" of "Rialtas" normally over "e" of "Sealadac"	base of "h" and "e" on same level
Stop after thick 1922	

(iii) By Alex Thom and Co. Ltd.

(a) February 17. In black.

G24	1½d.	red-brown	50	50
		a wmk. inverted	—	—
		b o'print misplaced	—	—
		c "PENCF"	£275	—
		d "PENCF" corr	—	—
G25	2d.	orange (Die I)	1·25	25
		a wmk. inverted	—	—
		b o'print misplaced	—	—
		c overprint inverted	£100	—
G26	2d.	orange (Die II)	1·75	25
		a wmk. inverted	—	—
		b o'print misplaced	—	—
		c overprint inverted	£125	—

G27	6d.	purple (C)	3·50	1·75
G28	1/-	bistre-brown	7·00	5·0
G24/28		set (5v)	£14	5·00

G24b/25b/26b See Note under G1c etc.

G24c/24d: Row 15/12 See Note under G21a.

G25c Four sheets (960 stamps) were purchased in Cork. one having the overprint badly misplaced.

G26c Only one sheet (240 copies) was sold in Wexford.

G25/26 See above G.B. G19 for details of the two Dies.

Although the "R" of "Rialtas" is normally directly over the "e" of "Sealadac", it may be found directly over the "S" (Rows 17/4, 5, 6) or over "Se" in various positions. Where it is centrally placed over "Se", stamps of this issue may be identified by the measurement of "Sealadac" (14½ mm* and the length of "i" in "Rialtas" (cf. 15 mm and long "i" of the Harrison overprint G19/23).

Numbers Issued: G24 960,000; G25/26 9,500,000; G27/28 480,000 each.

(b) June 19th-Nov. 6th. Ad before but bolder, in dull to shiny blue-black, or red (2½d., 4d., 9d values).

G29	½d.	green (23/8)	35	35
G30	1d.	scarlet (10/7)	25	15
		a "Q" for "O"	£650	—
		b rev. "Q" for "O"	£250	—
G31	1½d.	red-brown (21/8)	4·00	1·50
		a "PENCF" corr.	—	—
G32	2d.	or (Die I) (19/6)	£10	75
		a overprint inverted	—	£
G33	2d.	orange (Die II)	1·00	25
		a overprint inverted	—	—
G34	2½s.	blue (R) (23/10)	2·50	3·50
G35	3d.	violet (11/7)	60	75
		a wmk. inv. and rev.	—	—
G36	4d.	gry-grn (R) (8/9)	2·50	2·50
		a break above "FOUR"	£45	—
G37	5d.	yel-brn (11/8)	2·00	3·00
G38	6d.	purple (21/8) C	2·00	1·50
		a wmk. inverted	—	—
G39	9d.	agate (R) (11/8)	3·50	3·50
G40	9d.	ol-grn (R) (6/11)	4·00	5·00
		a "POSTAGE"	—	—
G41	10d.	tur-blue (24/8)	£12	£13
		a broken frame	—	—
G42	1/-	bistre-brn (21/8)	7·00	6·00
		a "ONF"	—	—
G29/42		set (14v)	£50	£40

G30a A white flaw converts the "O" of "ONE" to "Q".

G30b This variety occurs on Row 15/9 of sheets with Control T22, and consists of a marked white flaw running from lower left of the "O" of "ONE" into the left figure tablet.

G31a Row 15/12 See Note under G21a.

G32a/33a One sheet of each were said to have been found in the Dublin area. Although used copies of G33a are known, there is some doubt as to whether these sheets were actually purchased in a Post Office.

G36a Row 19/2 See Note under G6a.

G40a. Row 9/1 (Plate 3B) A white flaw changes the "O" in "POSTAGE" to "Q".

G41a Row 9/1 See Note under G9a.

G42a, Row 8/10 (Plate 3) The lower bar of the "E" in "ONE" is broken.

The "R" of "Rialtas" is normally over the "e" of "Sealadac". but is also found, in various positions in the sheet, over the "S" or over the "Se". In such cases identification of the issue depends upon the intensity and colour of the overprint, best seen *through* the stamp with a strong light behind it.

(c) October 17th (2/6d.) -25th (5/- and 10/-). In shiny blue-black (bold impression).

G43	2/6	**chocolate-brown**	£125	£140
		a "R" over "Se" ..	£175	£200
G44	5/-	**carmine**	£200	£225
		a "R" over "Se" ..	£300	—
G45	10/-	**grey-blue**	£850	£950
		a "R" over "Se" ..	£1200	—
		b re-entry	—	—

G43a/44a/45a The "R" of "Rialtas", normally over the "e" of "Sealadac" is above the "Se" in twelve positions in the sheet (Rows 1/3, 2/3, 3/2, 3/3, 4/3, 7/3, 8/1, 9/1, 9/2, 9/3, 10/2 and 10/4).

G45b, Row 1/1 (Plate 5A).

G43/45 were replaced after less than two months by G63/65 and are consequently very scarce.

RιαLταρ
SεαLαoαċ
nα
ħéιρεαnn
1922.

Wide setting.
"Rialtas" measures
12½ mm.
"Sealadac" measures
15½ mm.

(d) November 21 (½d., 1d., 2d.) -December 4 (1½d., 1/-). In shiny blue-black.

G46	½d.	**green**	35	35
		a o'print jet black	—	—
G47	1d.	**scarlet**	50	50
G48	1½d.	**red-brown** ..	60	70
		a "PENCF" corr'd	—	—
G49	2d.	**orange** (Die II) ..	5·00	5·00
G50	1/-	**bistre-brown** ..	£12	£12
		a "ONF"	—	—
G46/50		**set** (5v)	£18	£18

G46a Comes from a few Proof sheets subsequently placed on sale.

G48a, Row 15/12 See Note under G21a.

G50a, Row 8/10 See Note under G42a.

This was an emergency printing from the master plate pending issue of the stamps with the new overprint. (See G51 etc.)

Numbers Issued: G46 720,000; G47 1,680,000; G48 600,000; G49 1,144,000; G50 240,000.

1922-35 Overprinted "IRISH FREE STATE 1922".

Sαoρsτάτ
Éιρεαnn
1922

Wide spaced date.
Foot of "1" in
"1922" is squared

(i) 1922 (Dec. 11th) -23 (Jan. 16th). By Alex Thom and Co. Ltd. In dull to shiny blue-black, or red (2½d., 4d., 9d.).

G51	½d.	**green** (18/12) ..	15	15
		a no "accent" ..	£550	—
		b inserted "accent"	£60	—
		c "S" over "e" ..	£15	—
		d line over "Saorstat"	£20	—
		e "Sacrstat" ..	5·00	—

G52	1d.	**scarlet** (18/12) ..	15	15
		a no accent ..	£2750	—
		b inserted accent ..	£80	—
		c "S" over "e" ..	£15	—
		d line over "Saorstat"	£20	—
		e "Sacrstat"	5·00	—
		f accent and "t" omitted ..	£1250	—
		g accent and "t" inserted ..	£125	—
		h accent and "at" omitted ..	—	—
		i accent and "at" inserted ..	—	—
		j rev. "Q" for "O" ..	£275	—
G53	1½d.	**red-brn** (21/12) ..	40	50
		a "S" over "e" ..	£20	—
		b "Sacrstat" ..	£10	—
		c "PENCF" corr'd	—	£
G54	2d.	**or** (Die II) (11/12)..	50	50
		a "S" over "e" ..	£15	—
		b "Sacrstat" ..	8·00	—
G55	2½d.	**blue** (6/1/23) ..	1·00	1·00
		a no accent ..	£90	—
		b line over Saorstat"	£15	—
		s "Sacrstat ..	8·00	—
G56	3d.	**violet** (6/1/23) ..	1·25	1·50
		a no accent ..	£140	—
		b "S" over "e" ..	£20	—
		c "Sacrstat" ..	7·00	—
G57	4d.	**gry-grn** (16/1/23)	1·50	1·75
		a no accent ..	£100	—
		b "Sacrstat" ..	7·00	—
		c break above "FOUR" ..	£45	—
G58	5d.	**yel-brn** (29/12) ..	2·00	2·00
		a "S" over "e" ..	£18	—
		b "Sacrstat" ..	7·00	—
G59	6d.	**pur** (C) (28/12) ..	1·00	1·00
		a inserted accent ..	£500	—
		b "S" over "e" ..	£25	—
		c "Sacrstat" ..	7·00	—
		d wmk. inv. and rev.	—	—
G60	9d.	**olive-grn** (28/12) ..	1·50	2·00
		a no accent ..	£175	—
		b line over "Saorstat" ..	£25	—
		c "S" over "e" ..	£25	—
		d "Sacrstat" ..	£12	—
		e "PQSTAGE" ..	—	—
G61	10d.	**tur-blue** (13/1/23)	8·00	9·00
		a "S" over "e" ..	£30	—
		b "Sacrstat" ..	£12	—
		c broken frame ..	—	—
G62	1/-	**bis-brn** (21/12) ..	6·00	6·00
		a no accent ..	£2500	—
		b inserted accent ..	£500	—
		c "S" over "e" ..	£30	—
		d "Sacrstat" ..	£12	—
		e "ONF"	—	—
G63	2/6	**choc-brn** (21/12) ..	£15	£18
		a no accent ..	£250	—
		b reversed accent ..	£350	—
		c "S" over "e" ..	£60	—
		d "Sacrstat" ..	£25	—
		e re-entry ..	£550	—
G64	5/-	**carmine** (28/12) ..	£50	£55
		a no accent ..	£325	—
		b reversed accent	£375	—
		c "S" over "e" ..	£75	—
		d "Sacrstat" ..	£60	—

G65	10/–	**grey-blue** (28/12)	£110	£125
		a no accent ..	£1300	—
		b reversed accent	£1500	—
		c "S" over "e" ..	£200	—
		d "Sacrstat" ..	£150	—
		e re-entry ..	—	—
G51/62		**set** (12v) ..	£23	£25

G52*j* Row 15/9 (Control T22).

The "no accent" varieties (over second "a" of "Saorstat") on the ½d., 1d., 2½d., 3d., 4d., 9d. and 1/- values occurred on Row 15/12 ; and the "inserted accent" varieties on the ½d., 1d., 6d. and 1/– values were official corrections – made by hand (handstamped in dull black, or even in pen or dark crayon) – to rectify the omission.

The numbers of "inserted accent" varieties sold are believed to be: G51*b* 3,867; G52*b* 3,041; G59*a* 623; G62*b* 489; G52*f*; g, h, i also come from Row 15/12.

The "no accent" varieties on the 2/6, 5/– and 10/-values are found on Row 3/2 and Row 8/2 ; and the "reversed accent" on Row 7/4.

The "S" over ' e" varieties are from Row 7/10 and Row 10/10 (values to 1/–) and Row 9/2 (high values) where the S" of 'Saorstat", instead of being to the left of the "e' of "eireann", is above it (all values except 2½d. and 4d.).

The "line over Saorstat" occurs on the ½d. (Row 7/10. 17/3). 1d. (Rows 16/12, 19/8), 2½d. (Row 6/10) and 9d. (Rows 2/5, 7/2) values and consists of a thin straight line lying above the last five letters of the word.

The "Sacrstat" (or broken "O") variety occurs in various positions, notably Row 2/10 (values to 1/–) and Row 5/4 (high values).

G52*j*, Row 15/9 : See Note under G30*b*.
G53*c*, Row 15/12 : See Note under G21*a*.
G57*c*, Row 19/2 : See Note under G6*a*.
G60*e*, Row 9/1 : See Note under G40*a*.
G61*c*, Row 9/1 : See Note under G9*a*.
G62*e*, Row 8/10 : See Note under G42*a*.
G63*e*, Rows 1/3, 7/1 (Plate 2A), Row 1/2 (Plate 3A).
65*e*, Row 6/1 (Plate 2A). Row 1/1 (Plate 5A).

Saorscác
Éireann
1922

Foot of "1" in "1922" is rounded. Second "e" in "eireann" is raised

(ii) **1923 (Mar. 7th) By Harrison and Sons Ltd. In dull or shiny blue black, for vertical and horizontal coils which were made up in the same manner as G19/23.**

G66	½d.	**green** ..	40	75
		a long "1" ..	7·00	—
		b wmk. inv. and rev.	—	—
G67	1d.	**scarlet** ..	1·25	1·50
		a long "1" ..	£30	£35
G68	1½d.	**red-brown** ..	4·00	5·00
		a long "1" ..	£50	£55
		b "PENCF" corr'd	—	—
G69	2d.	**orange** (Die II) ..	75	85
		a long "1" ..	9·00	£10
G66/69		**set** (4v)	6·00	8·00

G66*a*/69*a* The figure "1" in "1922" has a prominent downward extension with serif at foot (normally Nos. 5 and 11 in each horizontal strip of twelve; and Nos. 5 and 10 in each vertical strip of ten).

G68*b*, Row 15/12 : See Note under G21*a*.

Numbers Issued (complete coils) : G66 552; G67 300; G68 48; G69 300.

Most of the 1½d. coils were vertical ; of the other values the majority were horizontal.

(iii) **By Government Printing Works, Dublin Castle (the "Castle" overprints) which took over the overprinting contract on June 25th 1925.**

Saorscác
Éireann Narrow spaced date
1922

(a) **1925 (Aug.) In black or grey-black. The setting for this overprint was five horizontal rows of four, so spaced that the first operation overprinted Rows 1, 3, 5, 7 and 9 whilst Rows 2, 4, 6, 8 and 10 were overprinted in a second operation. It is thus possible to find vertical pairs, se tenant, which show different positioning of the overprint and different intensities of pressure and gloss in the ink.**

G70	2/6	**chocolate-brown**	£18	£18
		a re-entry ..	£125	—
G71	5/–	**carmine**	£40	£40
		a overprint omitted	—	—
G72	10/–	**grey-blue** ..	£95	£95
		a re-entry ..	—	—
G70/72		**set** (3v)	£150	£150

G70*a*. Row 1/3.

G71*a*, Row 10/1 From at least one sheet on which the second printing operation was so misplaced to the right (and sloping upwards) that the overprint intended for Row 10/4 fell on the marginal paper and Row 10/1 was without overprint.

G72*a*. Row 6/1 (Plate 2A).

In 1940 a sheet of G72 with Rows 2, 4, 6, 8 and 10 (overprinted at the second operation) showing a double overprint, one being inverted, was broken up; and subsequently sold. The sheet had originally been defaced by the printers by means of an irregular crayon line running from bottom left to top right of the sheet and should have been subsequently destroyed as "printers' waste".

(b) **1927 (May 10/–: June 2/6 and 5/–). In black or grey-black. The setting for this overprint was the same as that for G70/72 but a mixture of Wide and Narrow Spaced Date cliches was employed (the "Composite" setting), the printing again being done in** two operations. **The position of wide (W) and narrow (N) dates was normally as under at left; but an abnormal make-up is also recorded on the 2/6 and 5/-, as under at right.**

NORMAL 2/6					ABNORMAL 2/6			
W	W	N	N		N	N	N	N
W	W	N	N		W	W	N	N
W	W	W	W		W	W	W	N
W	W	W	W		W	W	W	W
N	W	N	W		N	W	N	N
N	N	N	W		N	W	N	W
W	W	N	N		W	W	N	N
W	W	N	N		W	W	N	N
W	W	N	N		N	N	N	W
W	W	N	W		W	W	N	W

In the abnormal make-up, Rows 2, 4, 6, 8 and 10 are as normal.

Rows 1, 3, 5, 7, and 9 are as normal 5/– and 10/– but with a wide cliché substituted for narrow on Row 9/4.

5/- and 10/-					5/- only			
N	N	N	N		N	N	N	N
N	N	N	N		N	N	N	N
W	W	W	N		W	W	W	N
W	W	W	N		N	N	N	N
N	W	N	N		N	W	N	N
N	W	N	N		N	N	N	N
W	W	N	N		W	W	N	N
W	W	N	N		W	W	N	N
N	N	N	N		N	N	N	N
N	N	N	N		N	N	N	N

In the abnormal make-up, Rows 1, 2, 4, 6, 8, 9, and 10 are as normal.

Rows 3, 5 and 7 are as normal 5/- and 10/-, but with narrow clichés substituted for wide.

G73	2/6	**chocolate-brown**	£150	—
G74	5/-	**carmine**	£300	—
G75	10/-	**grey-blue** ..	£800	—
G73/75		**set** (3 pairs) ..	£1200	—

Prices are for horizontal or vertical pairs showing the two setting se-tenant.

Single copies of the Wide Spaced Date from this printing can be distinguished from Nos. G63/65 (Thom printing) by the colour of the ink, and from the following (G76/78) which bears a much heavier, clearer impression.

A horizontal pair of G73 is known with no accent on the second "a" of "Saorstat" on the wide-setting stamp. It is not known if this variety was constant.

SAORSTÁT ÉIREANN 1922

(c) **1927 (Dec. 9th, 2/6) -28 (Feb., 5/– and 10/–). In deep black. The plates used for this overprinting are believed to have been the same ones as used by Thom for G63/65, but this overprint can be recognized by the deep black colour and by the heavy clear impression which often shows in relief on the back of the stamp. There is also a small ink dot frequently found between the "S" and "a" of "Saorstat" on this issue.**

G76	2/6	**chocolate-brown**	£15	£15
		a circumflex accent	£100	—
		b flat tailed "9" ..	£25	—
		c no accent	£150	—
G77	5/-	**carmine**	£50	£50
		a circumflex accent	£150	—
		b flat tailed "9" ..	£80	—
G78	10/-	**grey-blue** (15/2)	£110	£120
		a circumflex accent	£300	—
		b flat tailed "9" ..	£150	—
G76/78		**set** (3v) ..	£175	£185

G76a/78a, Row 9/2 The accent over the second "a" in "Saorstat' resembles a circumflex accent tilted to the right.

G76c, Row 9/2 The accent gradually failed to print but the impression is clear on the reverse of the stamp.

G76b/78b Row 3/4 The tail of "9" in "1922" is flattened.

(d) **1935 (March-July) Overprinted as before on G.B. stamps Nos. G66/69 (Waterlow re-engraved dies) in black.**

G79	2/6	**chocolate-brown**	£25	£25
		a flat accent	£125	—
G80	5/-	**carmine**	£75	£75
		a flat accent	£125	—
G81	10/-	**indigo**	£300	£300
		a flat accent	£375	—
		b overprint double	—	—
G79/81		**set** (3v)	£400	£400

G79a/81a, Row 9/2 The same plates were used for this printing as for G76/78 and the "flat accent" variety represents further deterioration of the accent over the second "a" in "Saorstat". It is associated with damage to the top of the "a" and with a nick in the top of the last "t".

G81b A total of 8 copies are believed to come from the right hand side of a sheet, the second overprint being fainter and lower. The used copies were all telegraphically used.

DEFINITIVE ISSUES

The following issues were all typographed at the Government Printing Works, Dublin on Gaelic Script SE watermarked paper and perforated 15 x 14 unless otherwise indicated.

1922 (Dec. 6th) -35 Various designs, printed from plates made in London. Sheets 240 – two panes, each 12 x 10.

G82	½d.	**brt grn** (20/4/23)	30	10
		a imperf. x perf. 14. wmk. sideways (11/34) ..	£15	£10
		b booklet pane of six	£20	—
G83	1d.	**carmine** (23/2/23)	15	10
		aa booklet pane of six	£20	—
		a wmk. inverted ..	—	—
		b perf. 15 x imperf. (4/33) ..	£35	£37
		c perf. 15 x imperf. but wmk. inv.	£50	—
		d perf. 15 x imperf. (7/34) ..	£10	6·00
G84	1½d.	**claret** (2/2/23) ..	1·50	15
G85	2d.	**grey-green** ..	15	10
		aa booklet pane of six	£20	—
		ab booklet pane of six (inc. 3 labels)	£30	—
		a wmk. inv. and rev.	—	—
		b retouch in sea (Row 17/12) ..	—	—
		c imperf. x perf. 14 wmk. sideways (11/34) ..	£30	£15
		d perf. 15 x imperf. (1935)	£4000	£600
G86	2½d.	**red-brn** (7/9/23)..	3·00	1·00
		a wmk. inverted ..	—	—
G87	3d.	**blue** (16/3/23) ..	1·50	25
		a wmk. inverted ..	—	—
G88	4d.	**sl-blue** (28/9/23)	2·00	50
G89	5d.	**brt vio** (11/5/23)..	9·00	3·00
G90	6d.	**claret** (21/12/23)	2·00	1·00
G91	9d.	**brt vio** (26/10/23)	£12	4·00
G92	10d.	**brown** (11/5/23)..	£12	6·00
G93	1/–	**light bl** (15/6/25)	£35	3·00
G82/93		**set** (12v)	£75	£18

G82a/G85c Are from special printings for Coils.

G83b Comes from an experimental vertical Coil, and has a single vertical perforation hole at the top of each side. Only 30 Coils were issued (each of 960 stamps).

G83d Comes from a similar experimental vertical Coil (of 960 stamps) but does not have the single vertical perforation hole.

G85d Comes from an experimental verical Coil. Very few mint copies are known, and used copies are very scarce.

Trial printings of the Fiji K.G.V. 2d. (Mult. Scrip CA) are known printed on Gaelic Script SE watermarked paper supplied to De La Rue for testing.

See Fiji G33a.

1929 (June 22nd) Centenary of Catholic Emancipation. Designer Leo Whelan. Sheets 240 – two panes, each 12 x 10.

G94	2d.	**grey-green** ..	50	20
		a retouch	—	—
G95	3d.	**blue**	2·00	1·00
G95	9d.	**violet**	4·00	2·00
G94/96		**set** (3v)	6·00	3·00

G94a A vertical white bar appears in the horizontal shading above the right hand value tablet on early printings only (Row 15/12).

Numbers Issued: G94 23,888,400; G95 1,044,960; G96 850,320.

1930 (Oct. 15th) Completion of Shannon Hydro-Electric Scheme. Designer E. L. Lawrenson. Sheets 120 – two panes, each 6 x 10.

G97	2d.	**agate**	50	30

Number Issued: 19,330,805. Withdrawn 31/2/31.

1931 (June 12th) Bicentenary of the Royal Dublin Society. Designer G. Atkinson. Sheets 240 – two panes, each 12 x 10.

G98	2d.	**blue**	70	30

Number Issued: 20,680,800. Withdrawn 31/8/31.

1932 (May 12th) International Eucharistic Congress, Dublin. Designer G. Atkinson. Sheets as before.

G99	2d.	**grey-green**	50	20
G100	3d.	**blue**	2·50	2·50
G99/100		**set** (2v)	3·00	2·50

Numbers Issued: G99 15,807,475; G100 867,475. Withdrawn 2/7/32.

1932 (Aug. 18th) No. G93 privately overprinted "ATLANTIC AIR MAIL AUGUST 1932" in four lines.

G101	1/–	**light blue**	£300	£500
	a	"1932" omitted	—	—

Price for used is "on cover".

This overprint was intended for use on mail carried by J. A. Mollison on his flight from Dublin to New York. Copies are known cancelled by favour "PORT MEARNOG 16 AU 32". Mint copies are initialled "J.A.M." on the reverse.

1933 (Sept. 18th) Holy Year (1933-34). Designer R. J. King. Sheets as before.

G102	2d.	**grey-green**	50	15
G103	3d.	**blue**	2·00	1·50
G102/3		**set** (2v)	2·50	1·50

Withdrawn 31/3/34.

1934 (July 27th) Golden Jubilee of the Gaelic Athletic Association. Designer R. J. King. Sheets as before.

G104	2d.	**green**	80	25

Withdrawn 31/12/34.

1937 (Sept. 8th) Design, St. Patrick invoking Blessing on Paschal Fire, framed by an outline of the 11th Century Shrine of St. Patrick's Bell. Designer, R. J. King. Chalk surfaced paper. Sheets 8 x 5.

14	2/6	**green**	£40	£40
15	5/–	**ruby**	£55	£55
16	10/–	**dp blue**	£30	£30
14/16		**set** (3)	£125	£125

1940-52 As G82/93 and 14/16 but wmk. Gaelic E.

17	½d.	**emerald-green** (11/40)	5·00	50
	a	wmk. inv	7·00	—
	b	booklet pane of 6	£40	—
18	1d.	**carmine** (10/40)	25	20
	a	wmk. inv	1·00	1·00
	b	booklet pane of 6	4·00	—
	c	booklet pane 3 stamps plus 3 labels	£65	—
19	1½d.	**ruby** (12/40)	4·00	20
	a	wmk. inv	5·00	—
	b	booklet pane of 6	£30	—
20	2d.	**pearl-green** (12/40)	25	15
	a	wmk. inv	75	—
	b	booklet pane of 6	4·00	—
21	2½d.	**lt brown** (3/41)	3·00	25
	a	wmk. inv	4·00	4·00
	aa	booklet pane of 6	£25	—
	b	dp brown (/52)	3·00	25
22	3d.	**blue** (12/40)	75	15
		wmk. inv	2·00	1·00
	aa	booklet pane of 6	6·00	—
	b	ultramarine (/62)	75	15
	c	wmk. inv	2·00	1·00
23	4d.	**steel-blue** (12/40)	75	15
	a	wmk. inv.	1·00	1·00
	b	booklet pane of 6	6·00	—
	c	slate-blue ('47)	75	15
24	5d.	**violet** (7/40)	75	15
	a	wmk. inv	3·00	2·00

25	6d. **purple** (double fugitive ink) (*ch*) (6/42)	..	2·50	50
	a claret (*ch*) (/47)	..	75	15
26	8d. **bright red** (12/9/49) .		50	50
27	9d. **violet** (7/40)	..	75	50
28	10d. **Rembrandt-brown** (7/40)	..	75	50
29	11d. **cerise** (12/9/49)	..	75	75
30	1/– **azure** (6/40)	..	£45	7·00
	set 17/30(14)		£63	£11
31	2/6 **emerald-green** (*sub*) (10/2/43)	..	7·00	1·50
	a pale em (*sub*) (/45)	..	7·00	1·50
	b green (*ch*) (/51)	..	2·50	75
32	5/– **ruby** (*sub*) (15/12/42)		£10	1·50
	a dp ruby (*ch*) (/48?)		4·00	1·00
33	10/– **dp blue** (*sub*) (5/45)	..	£20	5·00
	a ditto (*ch*) (/48?)	..	6·00	3·00
	b pale blue	..	8·00	4·00

The colour descriptions given here are official designations. It is not possible to be more specific about dates of issue, as the stamps with the Gaelic E wmk. were put into circulation without any official record being kept.

All values in this set are believed to exist with watermark inverted.

As No. 5, but Perf. 13¾ x Imp. (Coils) (*thin paper*).

34	1d. **carmine** (/41)	..	£12	£12

As No. 5, but Perf. 14¾ x Imp. (Coils) (*thin paper*).

35	1d. **carmine** (/46)	..	8·00	2·00

AIR STAMPS

1948-9 Designs, 1d. (Angel Victor in flight over Rock of Cashel, Munster); **3d.** (Angel Victor in flight over Lough Derg, Ulster); **6d.** (Angel Victor in flight over Croagh Patrick, Connaught); **1/-** (Angel Victor in flight over Glendalough, Leinster). Designer, R. J. King. Printers (*recess*) Waterlow & Son. Perf. 14¾ x 14 (C). Wmk. Gaelic E. Sheets 120 —two panes, each 6 x 10.

A1	1d. **sepia** (4/4/49)	..	2·50	1·00
A2	3d. **blue** (7/4/48)	..	6·00	1·50
	a major re-entry	..	£30	—
A3	6d. **wine** (7/4/48)	..	40	20
	a re-entry	..	5·00	—
A5	1/– **dark green** (4/4/49)	..	60	35
A1/5	**set** (4)	..	9·50	3·00

A2*a* The H of Hiberniae the lower outer frame line, and the 3 are partially double. Row 6/3 (*sheets with bottom margin perforated*).

A3*a* Row 4/3.

SPECIAL ISSUES

1937 (Dec. 29th) Constitution Day. Design, Allegory of Eire and New Constitution. Designer, R. J. King. Wmk. Gaelic S E. Sheets 120—two panes, each 6 x 10.

S11	2d. **ruby**	..	..	50	40
S12	3d. **blue**	..	..	1·50	1·70

Number issued—

2d., 35,175,095; 3d., 1,291,299.

1938 (July 1st) Temperance Crusade Centenary. Design, Head of Father Mathew. Designer, S. Keating. Wmk. Gaelic S E. Sheets as before.

S13	2d. **agate**	..	..	75	50
S14	3d. **dp blue**	..	..	4.00	4·00

Number issued—

2d., 46,973,640; 3d., 1,387,320.

1939 (Mar. 1st) 150th Anniversary U.S. Constitution and Installation of First President. Designer, G. Atkinson. Wmk. Gaelic S E. Sheets as before.

S15	2d. **scarlet**	..	..	50	60
S16	3d. **dp blue**	..	..	4·00	4·00

Number issued—

2d., 27,950,880; 3d., 1,100,493.

1941 (April 12th) 25th Anniversary of 1916 Easter Rising (*provisional issue*). **Design, as No. 20** (*colour changed*) **and No. 22 but overprinted in green (2d.) and violet (3d.).**

S17	2d. orange-yellow	..	35	35
S18	3d. blue	.. ..	£15	5·00

Number issued—
2d., 28,162,320; 3d., 1,187,280.

All stamps from S19 onwards are on Gaelic E watermarked paper.

1941 (Oct. 27th) Object of issue as April 12th release. Design, Volunteer and G.P.O., Dublin. Designer, V. Brown. Sheets 120— two panes, each 6 x 10.

S19	2½d. blue-black	.. ..	60	15
	a broken pillar (a)	..	2·50	1·50
	b cracked statue (b)	..	2·50	1·50
	c damaged capital (c)		8·00	4·00
	d broken windows (d)		8·00	4·00

The break in the right pillar (a) and also crack in the statue (b) on the top centre of the building occur several times in both panes. The damaged capital (c) of the right pillar is on No. 2/4 (lower pane). The nine damaged windows (d) to the left of the building are on No. 10/1 (upper pane).

Number issued—32,394,840.

1943 (July 31st) 50th Anniversary of Found in Gaelic League. Design, Portrait of Dr. D Hyde. Designer, S. O'Sullivan. Sheets 240— two panes, each 12 x 10.

S20	½d. green	.. .. ..	20	15
S21	2½d. ruby	.. .. ..	40	30

Number issued—
½d., 26,202,965; 2½d., 32,394,840.

1943 (Nov. 13th) Centenary of Announcement of Discovery of Quaternions. Design, Portrgit of Sir W. R. Hamilton. Designer, S. O'Sullivan. Sheets as before.

S22	½d. dp green	.. ..	1·00	30
S23	2½d. chocolate-brown	..	1·25	50

Number issued—
½d., 28,079,520; 2½d., 37,267,200.

1944 (June 30th) -52 Tercentenary of Death of Michael O'Clery. Design, Portrait of Brother O'Clery. Designer, R. J. King. Wmk. sideways. Perf. 14 x 15. Sheets 240—two panes, each 10 x 12.

S24	½d. emerald-green	..	20	10
	a wmk. reversed	..	1·00	—
	b booklet pane of 6	..	6·00	—
S25	1/– brown	..	35	15
	a dark brown (/52)	..	45	15

Adopted as definitive stamps to replace Nos. 17 and 30.

1944 (Aug. 29th) Centenary of Irish Christian Brothers. Design, Portrait of Edmund Ignatius Rice. Designer, S. O'Sullivan. Sheets 240—two panes, each 12 x 10.

S26	2½d. slate	.. .. ..	50	20
	a wmk. inverted	..	—	—

Number issued—37,671,840.

1945 (Sept. 15th) Centenary of Death of

Founder of Young Ireland Movement, Thomas Davis. Design, Sower of Seeds of Freedom. Designer, R. J. King. Sheets as before.

S27	2½d. **blue**	.. .. ..	45	25
	a wmk. inverted	..	—	—
S28	6d. **red-purple**	.. ..	1·60	2·20

Number issued—
2½d., 70,528,080; 6d., 5,564,136.

1946 (Sept. 16th) **Centenary of Births of Michael Davitt and Charles Stewart Parnell.** Design, Country and Homestead. Designer, R. J. King. Sheets 120—two panes, each 6 x 10.

S29	2½d. **scarlet**	.. ..	50	25
S30	3d. **blue**	.. .. ..	1·60	2·20

Number issued—
2½d., 36,938,550; 3d., 2,095,590.

1948 (Nov. 19th) **150th Anniversary of Insurrection of 1798.** Design, Portrait of Theo Wolfe Tone, framed with Laurel Leaves and flanked by Pikeman and Ships, depicting French Expedition. Designer, K. Uhleman. Sheets as before.

S31	2½d. **ruby**	.. ..	60	40
S32	3d. **violet**	.. .. ..	2·50	2·80

Number issued—
2½d., 38,066,160; 3d., 2,158,560.

REPUBLIC OF IRELAND

(Included for convenience of collectors).

1949 (Nov. 21st) **International Recognition.** Design, Leinster House and Arms of the Four

Provinces. Designer, Mrs. M. Brandt. Sheets as before.

S33	2½d. **chocolate-brown**	..	30	25
S34	3d. **dp blue**	.. ..	1·60	1·40

Number issued—
2½d., 53,913,020; 3d., 3,449,900.

1949 (Dec. 5th) **Centenary of Death of Poet, J. C. Mangan.** Design, Portrait of Poet. Designer, R. J. King. Sheets 240—two panes, each 12 x 10.

S35	1d. **green**	.. ..	1·60	50
	a wmk. inv. ..	..	—	—

Number issued—29,992,680.

1950 (Sept. 11th) **Holy Year** (*Annus Sanctus*). Design, Statue of St. Peter (*from St. Peter's Basilica, Rome*). Printers (*recess*) **Waterlow & Son.** Perf. 12½ (C). Sheets 120—two panes, each 10 x 6.

S36	2½d. **bright violet**	..	40	50
S37	3d. **light blue**	.. ..	4·00	4·25
S38	9d. **sepia-brown**	..	4·00	4·75

Number issued—
2½d., 12,887,140; 3d., 890,620; 9d. 1,588,240.

1952 (Nov. 10th) **Centenary of Death of**

Thomas Moore. Design from Portrait by Sir M. Archer Shee. Engraver, W. Vacek. Printers (*recess*) **De La Rue** (Clonskeagh, Dublin). **Perf. 12¾ x 13 (C). Sheets as before.**

S39	2½d. **claret**		**40**	**50**
	a re-entry ..		—	—
S40	3½d. **dp olive**		2·00	1·70

S39*a* 'Thomas Moore' doubled Row 3/6 (Plate 1B).

Number issued—
2½d., 21,574,336; 3½d., 1,308,256.

POSTAGE DUE STAMPS

From 1922 to 1925 contemporary G.B. Postage Due stamps (without overprint) were in use.

1925 (*Typo*) **Government Printing Works.**

Wmk. Gaelic Script SE. Perf. 14 x 15. Sheets 180 – three panes, each 6 x 10.

PD1	½d.	**emerald-green** ..	5·00	6·00
PD2	1d.	**carmine** (20/2) ..	3·75	3·00
		a wmk. inverted ..		—
		b wmk. sideways	£38	£15
PD3	2d.	**dp green** (20/2) ..	6·50	5·00
		a wmk. inverted ..	—	—
		b wmk. sideways	£20	£10
PD4	6d.	**plum** (20/2) ..	2·00	2·00
PD1/4		**set** (4V.) ..	£15	£15

1940-65 As before but wmk. Gaelic E.

PD5	½d.	**emerald-grn** (/42)	6·00	8·00
		a lt emerald (/45)..	8·00	8·00
PD6	1d.	**dp scarlet** (/41)..	60	60
		a dp golden-scar (/52) ..	75	60
PD7	1½d.	**vermilion** (10/11/52)	70	1·25
PD8	2d.	**dp ol-green** (/40)	60	70
PD9	3d.	**blue** (10/11/52) ..	75	80
PD10	5d.	**vio-black** (3/3/43)	70	80
PD11	6d.	**plum** (21/3/60) ..	1·75	80
PD12	8d.	**orange** (wmk. inv) (31/10/62) ..	3·25	3·25
		a ditto (wmk. up) ..	1·75	80
PD13	10d.	**magenta** (27/1/65)	2·75	4·25
PD5/13		**set** (9)	£14	£16

JAMAICA

Jamaica was in Spanish occupation from 1509 until 1655 when it was captured by British Forces. It was ceded to Great Britain by the Treaty of Madrid in 1670.

Although the establishment of a Post Office was authorised soon after, it was not until May, 1858 that contemporary stamps of Great Britain were introduced for use on overseas letters.

The cancellation used was "AO1" in a transverse oval of horizontal bars; and when the use of stamps was extended the following year to internal mail, similar cancellors numbered from A27 to A78 were supplied to Post Offices throughout the island. A79 was supplied in November, 1863 and was never used on G.B. stamps.

G.B. stamps continued in use until August 24th, 1860. The Crowned Circle PAID Franks were never used in Jamaica. An uncrowned Frank was registered for Kingston on April 11th, 1858; on receipt in Jamaica it was struck in black as a datestamp, the word PAID having been cut out (but showing slight traces).

1858-60 Stamps of Great Britain identified by their Catalogue Nos. after prefix 'JA', 'JB' or 'JC'.

Used at Kingston.

(I) 'A O2'

JA V39	1d.	**rose-red**	..
JA V40	1d.	**rose-red**	..
JA V44	4d.	**rose**	.. ..
JA V45	6d.	**lilac**	.. ..
JA V47	1/-	**green**	.. ..

(II) 'A O2' in duplex with date-stamp (May 1859)

JB V39	1d.	**rose-red**	..
JB V44	4d.	**rose**	.. ..
JB V45	6d.	**lilac**	.. ..
JB V47	1/-	**green**	.. ..

(III) Double 'A O2' (May 1859)

JC V39	1d.	**rose-red**	..
JC V44	4d.	**rose**	..
JC V44	*a* on thick glazed paper		
JC V45	6d.	**lilac**	.. ..
JC V47	1/-	**green**	.. ..

1859 (Mar. 1st)-60 Stamps of Great Britain identified by their Catalogue Nos. after prefix 'A27' – 'A78'.

Used at County Post Offices on internal mail.

(Between May 1858 and March 1859 G.B. stamps were cancelled with named date-stamps at certain of these Post Offices).

'A27' ALEXANDRIA

A27 V39	1d.	**rose-red**	..
A27 V36A	2d.	**blue** (Pl. 6)	..
A27 V44	4d.	**rose**	.. ..
A27 V45	6d.	**lilac**	.. ..

'A28' ANNOTTO BAY

A28 V39	1d.	**rose-red**	.. ..
A28 V44	4d.	**rose**	.. ..
A28 V45	6d.	**lilac**	.. ..

'A29' BATH

A29 V39	1d.	**rose-red**	.. ..
A29 V44	4d.	**rose**	.. ..
A29 V45	6d.	**lilac**	.. ..

'A30' BLACK RIVER

A30 V39	1d.	**rose-red**	..
A30 V44	4d.	**rose**	.. ..
A30 V45	6d.	**lilac**	.. ..

'A31' BROWN'S TOWN

A31 V39	1d.	**rose-red**	..
A31 V44	4d.	**rose**	.. ..
A31 V45	6d.	**lilac**	.. ..

'A32' BUFF BAY

A32 V39	1d.	**rose-red**	..
A32 V44	4d.	**rose**	.. ..
A32 V45	6d.	**lilac**	.. ..

'A33' CHAPLETON

A33 V39	1d.	**rose-red**	..
A33 V44	4d.	**rose**	.. ..
A33 V45	6d.	**lilac**	.. ..

'A34' CLAREMONT

A34 V39	1d.	**rose-red**	..
A34 V44	4d.	**rose**	.. ..
A34 V45	6d.	**lilac**	.. ..

'A35' CLARENDON

A35 V39	1d.	**rose-red**	..
A35 V44	4d.	**rose**	.. ..
A35 V45	6d.	**lilac**	.. ..

'A36' DRY HARBOUR

A36 V39	1d.	**rose-red**	..
A36 V44	4d.	**rose**	.. ..
A36 V45	6d.	**lilac**	.. ..

'A37' DUNCANS

A37 V39	1d.	**rose-red**	..
A37 V44	4d.	**rose**	.. ..
A37 V45	6d.	**lilac**	.. ..

'A38' EWARTON

(No example recorded)

'A39' FALMOUTH

A39 V39	1d.	**rose-red**	..
A39 V44	4d.	**rose**	.. ..
A39 V45	6d.	**lilac**	.. ..
A39 V47	1/-	**green**	.. ..

'A40' FLINT RIVER

A40 V39	1d.	**rose-red**	..
A40 V44	4d.	**rose**	.. ..
A40 V45	6d.	**lilac**	.. ..
A40 V47	1/-	**green**	.. ..

'A41' GAYLE

A41 V39	1d.	**rose-red**	..
A41 V44	4d.	**rose**	.. ..
A41 V45	6d.	**lilac**	.. ..
A41 V47	1/-	**green**	.. ..

'A42' GOLDEN SPRING

A42 V39	1d.	**rose-red**	..
A42 V44	4d.	**rose**	.. ..
A42 V45	6d.	**lilac**	.. ..
A42 V47	1/-	**green**	.. ..

'A43' GORDON TOWN

A43 V39	1d.	**rose-red**	..
A43 V44	4d.	**rose**	.. ..
A43 V45	6d.	**lilac**	.. ..

'A44' GOSHEN

A44 V39	1d.	**rose-red**	..
A44 V44	4d.	**rose**	.. ..
A44 V45	6d.	**lilac**	.. ..

'A45' GRANGE HILL

A45 V39	1d.	**rose-red**	..
A45 V44	4d.	**rose**	.. ..
A45 V45	6d.	**lilac**	.. ..
A45 V47	1/-	**green**	.. ..

'A46' GREEN ISLAND
A46 V39 1d. **rose-red**
A46 V44 4d. **rose**   ..   ..
A46 V45 6d. **lilac**   ..   ..
A46 V47 1/- **green**   ..   ..

'A47' HIGHGATE
A47 V39 1d. **rose-red**
A47 V44 4d. **rose**
A47 V45 6d. **lilac**   ..

'A48' HOPE BAY
A48 V39 1d. **rose-red**   ..
A48 V44 4d. **rose**   ..   ..
A48 V45 6d. **lilac**   ..   ..

'A49' LILLIPUT
A49 V39 1d. **rose-red**
A49 V44 4d. **rose**   ..
A49 V45 6d. **lilac**   ..   ..

'A50' LITTLE RIVER
(No example recorded).

'A51' LUCEA
A51 V39 1d. **rose-red**   ..
A51 V44 4d. **rose**   ..   ..
A51 V45 6d. **lilac**   ..   ..

'A52' MANCHIONEAL
A52 V39 1d. **rose-red**   ..
A52 V44 4d. **rose**   ..   ..
A52 V45 6d. **lilac**   ..   ..

'A53' MANDEVILLE
A53 V39 1d. **rose-red**   ..
A53 V44 4d. **rose**   ..   ..
A53 V45 6d. **lilac**   ..   ..

'A54' MAY HILL
A54 V39 1d. **rose-red**
A54 V44 4d. **rose**   ..   ..
A54 V45 6d. **lilac**   ..   ..

'A55' MILE GULLY
A55 V39 1d. **rose-red**   ..
A55 V44 4d. **rose**   ..   ..
A55 V45 6d. **lilac**   ..   ..

'A56' MONEAGUE
A56 V39 1d. **rose-red**
A56 V44 4d. **rose**   ..
A56 V45 6d. **lilac**   ..   ..

'A57' MONTEGO BAY
A57 V39 1d. **rose-red**   ..
A57 V44 4d. **rose**   ..   ..
A57 V45 6d. **lilac**   ..   ..
A57 V47 1/- **green**   ..

'A58' MONTEPELIER
A58 V39 1d. **rose-red**   ..
A58 V44 4d. **rose**   ..   ..
A58 V45 6d. **lilac**   ..   ..

'A59' MORANT BAY
A59 V39 1d. **rose-red**   ..
A59 V44 4d. **rose**   ..   ..
A59 V45 6d. **lilac**   ..   ..

'A60' OCHO RIOS
A60 V39 1d. **rose-red**   ..
A60 V44 4d. **rose**   ..   ..
A60 V45 6d. **lilac**   ..   ..

'A61' OLD HARBOUR
A61 V39 1d. **rose-red**   ..
A61 V44 4d. **rose**
A61 V45 6d. **lilac**

'A62' PLANTAIN GARDEN RIVER
A62 V39 1d. **rose-red**
A62 V44 4d. **rose**   ..   ..
A62 V45 6d. **lilac**   ..   ..

'A63' PEAR TREE GROVE
(No example recorded).

'A64' PORT ANTONIO
A64 V39 1d. **rose-red**   ..
A64 V44 4d. **rose**   ..
A64 V45 6d. **lilac**   ..   ..

'A65' PORT MORANT
A65 V39 1d. **rose-red**   ..
A65 V44 4d. **rose**   ..
A65 V45 6d. **lilac**   ..   ..

'A66' PORT MARIA
A66 V39 1d. **rose-red**   ..
A66 V44 4d. **rose**   ..   ..
A66 V45 6d. **lilac**   ..   ..

'A67' PORT ROYAL
A67 V39 1d. **rose-red**   ..
A67 V44 4d. **rose**   ..   ..
A67 V45 6d. **lilac**   ..   ..

'A68' PORUS
A68 V39 1d. **rose-red**   ..
A68 V44 4d. **rose**   ..   ..
A68 V45 6d. **lilac**   ..   ..

'A69' RAMBLE
A69 V39 1d. **rose-red**   ..
A69 V44 4d. **rose**   ..   ..
A69 V44   *a* on thick glazed paper
A69 V45 6d. **lilac**   ..   ..

'A70' RIO BUENO
A70 V39 1d. **rose-red**   ..
A70 V44 4d. **rose**   ..   ..
A70 V45 6d. **lilac**   ..   ..

'A71' RODNEY HALL
A71 V39 1d. **rose-red**   ..
A71 V44 4d. **rose**   ..   ..
A71 V45 6d. **lilac**   ..   ..

'A72' ST. DAVID
A72 V39 1d. **rose-red**   ..
A72 V44 4d. **rose**   ..   ..
A72 V45 6d. **lilac**

'A73' ST. ANN'S BAY
A73 V39 1d. **rose-red**   ..
A73 V44 4d. **rose**   ..   ..
A73 V45 6d. **lilac**   ..   ..

'A74' SALT GUT
A74 V39 1d. **rose-red**   ..
A74 V44 4d. **rose**   ..   ..
A74 V45 6d. **lilac**   ..   ..

'A75' SAVANNA-LA-MAR
A75 V39 1d. **rose-red**   ..
A75 V44 4d. **rose**   ..   ..
A75 V45 6d. **lilac**   ..   ..
A75 V47 1/- **green**   ..   ..

'A76' SPANISH TOWN
A76 V39 1d. **rose-red**   ..
A76 V44 4d. **rose**   ..   ..
A76 V45 6d. **lilac**   ..   ..
A76 V47 1/- **green**   ..

'A77' STEWART TOWN
A77 V39 1d. **rose-red**   ..
A77 V44 4d. **rose**   ..   ..
A77 V45 6d. **lilac**   ..   ..

'A78' VERE
A78 V39 1d. **rose-red**   ..
A78 V44 4d. **rose**   ..   ..
A78 V45 6d. **lilac**   ..   ..
A78 V47 1/- **green**   ..   ..

All stamps to G30 are *(typo)*. **De La Rue. Perf. 14. unless otherwise indicated.**

1860-63. Various frames. Wmk. Pineapple. Sheets 240 – four panes, each 6 x 10.

V1	1d.	**pl blue**	£24	5·00
V2	1d.	**pl greenish blue** ..	£25	6·00
V3	1d.	**blue**	£22	4·00
V4	1d.	**dp blue**	£27	9·00
	a	bisect diag (½d.) on cover or wrapper	‡	£250
V5	2d.	**rose**	£65	£12
V6	2d.	**dp rose**	£50	£12
V7	3d.	**green** (10.9.63) ..	£50	£10
V8	4d.	**brown-orange** ..	£80	9·00
V9	4d.	**red-orange**	£80	6·00
	a	bisect diag (2d.) on cover (1863)	‡	—
V10	6d.	**dl lilac**	£70	6·00
V11	6d.	**grey-purple**	£110	£10
V12	6d.	**dp purple**	£330	£15
V13	1/–	**yellow-brown** ..	£125	£10
V14	1/–	**purple-brown** ..	£220	£10
V15	1/–	**dl brown**	£80	£10
	a	$ for 'S'	£500	£275

V4*a*—The diagonal bisection of the 1d. stamp was authorised from November 20th, 1861 to November 30th, 1872 when a ½d. stamp had become available for book and newspaper post.

V9*a*—A cover is in the Royal Collection (6.10.63). A Post Office notice of August 28th, 1862 had, however, specifically stated that the only stamp authorised for bisection was the 1d.

V15*a*—The 'S' of 'SHILLING' appears as $ Row 2/2 (top left pane) on all printings.

All values are known with the watermark inverted. In the 3d. and 1/– values there are two types of watermark, one squat and the other elongated.

Imperforate copies of all values are from Proof sheets.

All values exist overprinted 'Specimen'.

1870 (Mar.)-83. As before, but Wmk. Crown CC.

(a) Perf. 14.

V16	½d.	**claret** (20.10.72) ..	4·00	1·00
V17	½d.	**rosy mauve** ('83) ..	4·00	1·00
V18	1d.	**blue** ('73)	£10	50
V19	1d.	**dp blue**	£12	50

V20	2d.	**rose** (4/70)	£13	10
V21	2d.	**dp rose**	£25	20
V22	3d.	**green** (3/70) ..	£40	1·50
V23	3d.	**dp green**	£45	2·00
V24	4d.	**brown-orange** ('72)	£50	2·00
V25	4d.	**red-orange**	£125	2·00
V26	6d.	**mauve** ('71) ..	£15	2·00
V27	6d.	**dp lilac**	£18	2·00
V28	1/–	**pl brown** ('73) ..	£14	4·00
V29	1/–	**dl brown**	£10	4·00
V30	1/–	**dp brown**	£12	4·00
	a	$ for 'S'	£400	£275

V30*a*—As V15*a* (Row 2/2).

(b) Perf. 12½. Sheets 60. (August 27th, 1875).

V31	2/–	**venetian red**	£15	6·00
V32	5/–	**lilac**	£40	£30
V16/32		**set** (9v)	£185	£45

All values are known with the watermark inverted; and all exist overprinted 'Specimen' or 'Cancelled'.

Die Proofs of V16/31/32 exist in black on glazed paper.

Numbers printed—V31, 28,320; V32, 7,680.

1883 (March)-97. As before, but Wmk. Crown CA.

V33	½d.	**yellow-green** ('85)	70	10
V34	½d.	**blue-green**	25	10
V35	1d.	**blue** ('83)	£50	2·00
V36	1d.	**rose** (3.3.85)... ..	£10	60
V37	1d.	**dp carmine**	5·00	40
V38	2d.	**rose** (17.3.84) ..	£55	2·00
V39	2d.	**dp rose**	£55	2·00
V40	2d.	**grey** ('85)	£20	20
V41	2d.	**slate-grey**	£15	20
V42	2d.	**slate**	£10	10
V43	3d.	**sage-green** ('86) ..	3·00	40
V44	3d.	**olive-green**	1·50	40
V45	4d.	**red-orange** (9.3.83)	£200	5·00
V46	4d.	**orange-brown** ..	1·50	10
V47	6d.	**dp yellow** (10/90) ..	5·00	3·50
V48	6d.	**orange-yellow** ..	5·00	2·50
V49	1/–	**pl brown** (3/97) ..	5·00	2·50
V50	1/–	**dp brown**	8·00	5·00
	a	$ for 'S'	£350	£175
V51	2/–	**reddish brown** ('97)	£18	8·00
V52	5/–	**lilac** ('97)	£35	£20
V33/52		**set** (11v)	£180	£35
SPV33/47		**specimen set** (6v)..	£70	‡
		(V33/36/40/43/45/47)		

All values to 6d. exist Perf. 12; but were not issued in this state.

V50*a*—As V15*a* (Row 2/2).

Numbers printed—V51, 28,020: V52, 9,120.

See also Nos. V62/77 (Multiple Crown CA).

1890 (June). No. V46 surcharged "TWO PENCE/HALF-PENNY" in two lines in black sans serif capitals by Camille Vendryes in Kingston.

V53	2½d. on 4d. **or-brown** ..	£10	5·00
	a	wide spaced surcharge	£12	£10
	b	surcharge double ..	£100	£90
	c	surcharge treble ..	—	—
	d	surcharge omitted in pair with normal..	—	—
	e	"PFNNY"	£35	£25
	f	"PFNNK"	£65	£45

V53*a*—The space between the two lines of the surcharge is 1½mm. instead of the normal 1mm (Setting No. 2).

V53*a*—This error occurs on Row 1/3 of the second setting (1mm. space between lines).

G53*f*—This error occurs on Row 2/10 of the second setting (1½mm. space between lines). A broken 'K' was used for 'Y'.

V53*b*—Occurs on all three settings, of which details are given below.

There were three settings of the surcharge—
1. Single setting of 10 in a vertical column, repeated six times on the pane (all spaced 1mm.).
2. Single setting of 12 in two horizontal rows, repeated five times on the pane. The first row (Nos. 1-6) are spaced 1mm., and the second row (Nos. 7-12) 1½mm. (V53*a*).
3. Single setting of 3 in a horizontal strip, repeated twenty times on the pane (all spaced 1½mm.).

No used copies of this setting are known, and it may either have been a reprint or 'prepared for use but not issued'. Most copies of V53*a* can also be from this setting.

Collectors are warned of a forgery of V53*f* in which an unbroken K'' was used and the word is spelt 'PFNNK'.

Number printed—48,000.

1889 (March 8th)-91. Wmk. **Crown CA. Sheets 240 – four panes, each 6 x 10.**

V54	1d.	**dl purple and mauve**	60	10
V55	1d.	**brnish pur and plum**	1·25	15
V56	1d.	**purple and crimson**	1·50	15
V57	2d.	**green**	5·00	1·00
V58	2d.	**dp green** (brn gum)..	2·00	1·00
V59	2½d.	**dl purple and blue** (25.2.91)	2·50	50
V54/59		**set** (3v)	5·00	1·50
SPV54/59		**specimen set** (3v)..	£50	‡

All values exist with watermark inverted.

Jamaican stamps were authorised for use in the Cayman Islands from April 12th, 1889 to February 19th, 1901.

Certain Jamaican stamps, including V54 were overprinted "CAYMAN ISLANDS" but were not issued.

1900 (May 1st)-01. (*recess*) **De La Rue. Design from photograph by Dr. J. Johnston.**

Wmk. Crown CC (sideways). Perf. 14. Sheets 60.

V60	1d.	**carmine**	50	15
	a	wmk. inverted	—	—
	b	wmk. reversed	—	—
	c	wmk. inverted and reversed ..	—	—
V61	1d.	**blk and red** (25.9.01)	1·25	15
	a	wmk. inverted	—	—
	b	wmk. reversed	—	—
	c	wmk. inverted and reversed ..	—	—
	d	imperf between (horiz pair)	£1500	—
	e	imperf between stamp and lower margin	—	—
	f	on blued paper	£60	£60
SPV60/61		**specimen** (2v)	£60	‡

Colour Trials are known of V60 in vermilion, deep lake and bright orange red, imperforate on unwatermarked paper.

V60—Was originally intended for issue on May 24th, 1889 to commemorate Queen Victoria's birthday and Jamaica's adoption of Imperial Penny Postage.

The following stamps (V62/77) were issued during the reign of King Edward VII but are included in the Queen Victoria lists as they bear her portrait.

1905 (May 15th)-11. As Nos. V33/52 but Wmk. Multiple Crown CA.

V62	3d.	**olive-green**	1·00	20
V63	3d.	**sage-green** ('07)	2·00	20
V64	3d.	**pur/yel** (10.3.10)	2·00	1·50
V65	3d.	**pl pur/yel C** (11.7.10)	1·00	50
V66	4d.	**or-brn** (6.6.08)	£16	£14
V67	4d.	**blk/yel C** (21.9.10)	6·00	£10
V68	4d.	**red/yel** (3.10.11)	1·50	2·00
V69	6d.	**or-yel** (27.6.06)	8·00	6·00
V70	6d.	**gldn yellow** (9/09)..	8·00	6·00
V71	6d.	**lilac** (19.11.09)	8·00	6·00
V72	6d.	**purple C** (7/10)	5·00	6·00
V73	1/-	**brown** (11/06)	6·50	5·00
V74	1/-	**dp brown**	£12	5·00
	a	$ for 'S'	£425	£400
V75	1/-	**blk/grn C** (21.9.10)..	3·50	5·00
	a	$ for 'S'	£425	£400
V76	2/-	**venetian red** (11/08)	£38	£25
V/77	2/-	**pur/bl C** (21.9.10)..	6·50	5·00
V62/77		**set** (11v)	£85	£75
SPV64/77		**specimen set** (6v).. (764/67/68/71/75/77)	£60	‡

V74*a*/75*a*—As V15*a* (Row 2/2).

Numbers printed—V62/63, 446,080: V64/65, 57,360: V68, 95,280: V66, 12,960: V67, 12,000: V68, 95,280: V69/70, 50,400: V71/72, 17,500: V73/74, 39,360: V75, 40,800: V76, 6,000: V77 49,500.

Original   Redrawn

1903-11. Sheets 240 – four panes, each 6 x 10.
(a) 1903 (Nov. 16th)-04. Wmk. Crown CA.

E1	½d.	**grey and green** ..	80	10
E2	½d.	**gr-blk and grn**	1·00	10
		a "SER. ET"	£16	£13
		b wmk. inverted ..	—	—
E3	1d.	**gr and car** (24.2.04)..	1·25	10
E4	1d.	**gr-blk and carmine**	1·50	10
		a "SER. ET"	£14	£10
E5	2½d.	**grey and ult** ..	1·75	50
E6	2½d.	**gr-blk and ult** ..	2·00	50
E7	2½d.	**black and blue** ..	2·50	50
		a "SER. ET"	£25	£20
E8	5d.	**blk and yel** (1.3.04)..	£11	£10
		a "SER. ET"	£425	—
E/18		**set** (4v)	£14	£10
SPE1/8		**specimen set** (4v) ..	£45	‡

E2a/4a/7a/8a—On account of damage to the printing plate the word "SERVIET" in the motto below the shield appears as SER.ET on Row 4/2 (top left pane).

Imperforate Colour Trials of the ½d. on watermarked paper include dull purple and blue, red, green; green and red, green; black and blue. Watermark sideways – black and red/red; grey and blue/bluish.

Numbers printed—E1/2, 2,434,080; E3/4, 4,914,480; E/57 1,377,360; E8, 23,520 (98 sheets).

(b) 1905 (Nov. 20th)-11. Wmk. Multiple Crown CA. C (except E12/13).

E9	½d.	**grey and dull green** (24.11.05)	50	10
		a "SER.ET"	£14	£12
E10	1d.	**grey and carmine** ..	4·50	10
E11	2½d.	**gr and ult** (12.11.07)	1·50	60
E12	2½d.	**pl ult O** (21.9.10) ..	2·00	70
E13	2½d.	**dp ult O**	2·00	70
		a "REVENOE" ..	—	—
E14	5d.	**grey and orange-yel** (24.4.07)	£10	£10
		a "SER.ET"	£400	£350
E15	6d.	**dl and bt pur** (18.8.11)	5·50	5·00
E16	5/–	**blk and pl vio** (11/05)	£22	£16
E17	5/–	**gr-blk and violet** ..	£25	£16
E9/17		**set** (7v) ..	£40	£30
SPE12/17		**specimen set** (3v) .. (E12/15/16).	£35	‡

E9a/14a—See under E2a/4a/7a/8a Row 4/2 (top left pane).

The absence of the variety on Nos. E10/11/15/16/17, which were all printed from the same centre plate indicates that the printers corrected it about July, 1905 after printing the ½d. and 5d. (the latter, although not issued until 1907, was printed at the same time as the ½d.).

E13a—This variety was constant on Row 1/5 (top left pane), and also occurs intermittently elsewhere on the sheet.

Numbers printed—E9, 2,472,720: E10, 1,221,120: E11,982,800: E12/13,1,068,400: E14, 12,000 (50 sheets) : E16/17, 17,040: E15 181,680.

(c) 1906. Redrawn designs. Wmk. Multiple Crown CA. Sheets 120 – two panes, each 6 x 10. Ordinary paper.

E18	½d.	**green** (Nov. 8) ..	45	10
E19	½d.	**dp green**	50	10

E20	½d.	**blue-green**	80	10
E21	½d.	**yellow-green** ..	1·25	20
E22	1d.	**rose-red** (Oct. 1) ..	45	10
E23	1d.	**carmine**	50	10
		a wmk. inverted ..	—	—
SPE21/22		**specimen** (2) ..	£20	‡

The 1d. was also issued in Booklets (9.3.12).

1911 (Feb. 3rd). Wmk. Multiple Crown CA. Sheets 120 – two panes, each 6 x 10.

E24	2d.	**grey**	1·50	3·00
E25	2d.	**blue-grey**	2·00	3·00
SPE24		**specimen** (1) ..	£10	‡

The issue of this stamp, nine months after the death of King Edward VII, was as a direct result of a petition submitted in June, 1910 by Jamaican Philatelic Societies.

Numbers printed—E24/25, 121,440.

1912-27. Sheets as before, except G1/4 and some printings of G9 – 240 – four panes, each 6 x 10; and G15 6 x 10; G1/8 O: G9/16 C.

(a) Wmk. Multiple Crown CA. (1912-20).

G1	1d.	**carmine** (5.12.12) ..	15	5
G2	1d.	**scarlet** ('16) ..	20	10
G3	1½d.	**brn-or** (13.7.16) ..	60	10
G4	1½d.	**yellow-orange** ..	2·50	50
		a wmk. sideways ..	—	—
G5	2d.	**grey** (2.8.12)	50	1·00
G6	2d.	**slate**	50	1·00
G7	2½d.	**blue** (13.2.13) ..	50	20
G8	2½d.	**dp bt blue**	60	20
G9	3d.	**pur/yel** (6.3.12) ..	50	40
		a white back (2.4.13)	50	40
		b on lemon ('16) ..	2·25	
G10	4d.	**gr-blk and red/yel** (4.4.13)	1·50	60
		a white back (7.5.14)	1·00	1·00
		b on lemon (28.9.16)	8·00	5·50
		c on pale yellow ('19)	£12	5·50
G11	6d.	**dl purple and purple** (14.11.12)	3·50	2·00
G12	6d.	**dl pur and bt mauve** ('15)	1·25	70
G13	6d.	**dl pur and bt mag.** ..	1·25	70
G14	1/–	**blk/grn** (2.8.12) ..	2·00	2·00
		a white back (4.1.15)	1·50	2·00
		b on blue-green, olive back ('18) ..	3·50	2·00
G15	2/–	**pur and bt blue/blue** (10.1.19)	5·50	6·00
G16	5/–	**green and red/yel** (5.9.19)	£18	£18
		a on pale yellow ('20)	£24	£20
		b on orange-buff ..	£28	£25
G1/16		**set** (10v)	£28	£25
SPG1/16		**specimen set** (10v)..	£75	‡

G1 was originally issued in Booklet form only, and was not available in sheets until February, 1913.

G14/14a are known with the head in purple, and this was at one time assumed to be a rare error of colour. It has, however, been established that it is a changeling due to the effect of moisture on doubly fugitive ink.

(b) Wmk. Multiple Script CA. (1921-27).

G17	½d. **green O** (3.11.27)	..	10	10
G18 6d.	**dl pur and bt lilac C** (21.10.21) ..		7·50	3·50
SPG17/18 **specimen** (2)		..	£30	‡

Type I   Type II

Type III

1916-19. War Tax. Nos. E18/21, G3/4 and G9/a/b overprinted.

(a) In black by the Government Printing Office, Kingston.

(i) With Type I. 1916 (April 1st–Aug.).

G19	½d. **yellow green**	..	10	20
	a no stop	.. ..	4·00	5·00
	b overprint double	..	£28	£28
	c overprint inverted	..	£22	£22
G20	½d. **blue-green**	..	20	20
	a no stop	..	2·50	2·00
G21 3d.	**purple/yellow**	..	1·50	1·25
	a on lemon (6/16)	..	1·25	1·25
	b no stop	..	6·50	6·00
	c on pl yellow (8/16)		1·25	1·00

G19a—The stop after 'STAMP' is omitted Row 8/2 lower left pane.

G19b—75 copies from a sheet which showed varying degrees of doubling only in the lower seven rows of the lower panes was discovered in 1918.

G19c—Although not discovered until 1918 this variety occurred in the first printing.

G20a—The stop after 'STAMP' is omitted Row 3/5 upper right pane and Row 1/1 lower left pane.

G21b—The stop after 'STAMP' is omitted on Row 8/6 or Row 9/6 upper left pane.

(ii) With Type II 1916 (Sept. 1st–Dec.).

G22	½d. **blue-green** (Oct. 2nd)		15	10
	a no stop	.. ..	4·50	3·00
	b 'R' inserted	..	£110	£90
	c overprint omitted in pair with normal		£110	£90

G23	1½d. **orange** (Sept. 1st)	..	15	10
	a no stop	.. ..	2·75	2·00
	b "R" omitted	..	£110	£90
	c 'R' inserted	..	£110	£90
	d "S" omitted..	..	£18	£15
	e "S" inserted	..	£80	—
	f wmk. sideways	..	—	£200
G24 3d.	**pur/lem** (Oct. 2nd)..		35	70
	a no stop	..	7·50	6·00
	b "S" omitted..	..	£75	£60
	c "S" inserted	..	£60	£60
	d overprint inverted	..	£160	—
G25 3d.	**pur/yel** (Dec.)	..	3·50	4·00
	a "S" omitted..	..	£100	£75
	b "S" inserted	..	£100	£75

G22a/G24a—The stop after 'STAMP' is omitted Row 5/1 upper right pane.

G22b—The "R" in 'WAR' was omitted and subsequently inserted by hand Row 1/4 lower right pane.

G22c—This variety was caused by the folding over of the marginal paper in the lower right corner of the lower right pane of one sheet.

G23a—The stop after 'STAMP' is omited.
   Upper left pane Row 8/6.
   Upper right pane Row 4/6, Row 10/4.
   Lower left pane Row 1/1.
   Lower right pane Row 8/6, Row 9/6.

G23b/c—The "R" in 'WAR' was omitted and subsequently inserted by hand Row 1/4 upper right pane.

G23d/e/G24b/c/G25a/b—The "S" in 'STAMP' was omitted and subsequently inserted by hand Row 6/6 upper right pane.

(iii) With Type III. 1917 (March).

G26	½d. **blue-green** (25/3)	..	15	10
	a no stop	.. ..	3·50	3·00
	b stop inserted	..	£70	—
	c "WAR" omitted	..	—	—
	d overprint inverted	..	5·00	3·00
	e overprint (inverted) on gummed side		£22	—
G27 1½d.	**orange** (3/3)	..	10	10
	a no stop	.. ..	4·50	4·00
	b stop inserted	..	£90	—
	c "WAR" omitted	..	—	—
	d overprint inverted	..	£32	£30
	e overprint double	..	£30	£30
	f wmk. inverted	..	—	—
	g wmk. sideways	..	—	—
G28 3d.	**pur/yel** (3/3)	..	20	20
	a no stop	..	5·00	5·00
	b stop inserted	..	£80	—
	c overprint inverted	..	£65	—
	d overprint vertical (reading up)	..	£90	—

G26/27/28a/b—The stop after "STAMP" was omitted Row 7/6 upper left pane and subsequently inserted together with a second impression of the letter "P".

The stop was also omitted Row 2/5 upper left pane and was later corrected by the insertion of an irregular circle or a three-rayed star.

In the 1919 printings the stop was omitted in several positions on the upper right pane—Row 6/6, 7/6, 8/5 and 8/6.

G26c/27c—This variety was caused by an upward shift of the overprint whereby "WAR" appeared in the upper margins and the bottom rows of the panes were overprinted "STAMP" only. The remaining stamps in the sheet showed a reversed overprint (STAMP WAR).

G28d Copies may be found with the overprint appearing partly or wholly twice on one stamp, This is *not* a double overprint; but was caused because the overprint was spaced for horizontal printing, and this spacing did not match the larger vertical measurement of the stamp.

G19/28—Display numerous minor varieties, regular and irregular in the overprints. These include spaced and broken letters, of differing size, colon for stop, raised quads (WARISTAMP).

(b) In red in sans serif 13 x 2½mm. capitals in one line by De La Rue. 1919 (Oct. 4th).

G29	½d.	**green**	..	10	10
G30	3d.	**purple/yellow**	..	75	80
	a	on buff (3.1.20)	..	25	30
	b	small overprint	..	£25	—
SPG29/30		**specimen** (2)	..	£35	‡

G30b—On Row 10/1 of the upper right pane the overprint measures 12½ x 2mm.

1919 (July 4th)-21. (*typo*). **(G31/33)** (*recess*) **(G34/47) De La Rue. Various designs selected by F. C. Cundall (G45/47 designed by the Governor) and frames drawn by Miss Cundall and Miss Wood. Wmk. Multiple Crown CA (sideways on G32/35, G47). Perf. 14 (Line or Comb). Sheets—G31/33 160 – two panes, each 8 x 10 or 10 x 8: G34/35 5 x 8: G36/39/40**

41 10 x 8 or 8 x 10: G37/38/42/43 12 x 5: G44/47 6 x 5 or 5 x 6.

G31	½d.	**grn and olive-grn C**			
		(12.11.20) ..	..	15	10
G32	1d.	**car and or C** (3.10.21)		1·25	20
G33	1d.	**carmine and red C**		1·50	20
C34	1½d.	**dp green** (4.7.19)	..	25	10
G35	1½d.	**yellow green**	..	50	10
	a	part double impression	..	£30	—
G36	2d.	**indigo and green**			
		(18.2.21) ..	..	65	70
G37	2½d.	**deep blue and blue**			
		(18.2.21)	..	6·00	2·00
G38	2½d.	**indigo and deep blue**		1·25	1·00
G39	3d.	**grn and bl** (8.4.21)..		60	20
G40	4d.	**sep and grn** (21.1.21)		1·50	2·00
G41	4d.	**chocolate and pl grn**		2·00	2·00
	a	on thick paper	..		
G42	1/-	**or-yel and red-or**		3·00	2·00
		(10.12.20) ..	..	3·50	3·00
	a	frame inverted	..	£6000	£3000
G43	2/-	**lt blue and brown**			
		(10.12.20) ..	..	£16	6·00
G44	3/-	**violet blue and or**			
		(10.12.20) ..	..	£15	£19
G45	5/-	**dp blue and yel-or**			
		(15.4.21) ..	..	£30	£28
G46	5/-	**bl and ochre-brown**		£25	£23
G47	10/-	**dp myrtle-green**			
		(6.5.20) ..	..	£38	£55
G31/47		**set** (12v)	..	£100	£95
SPG31/47		**specimen set** (12v)		£120	‡

G35a—Amongst sheets from an early printing a number display an apparent indistinct and blurred impression of the centre of the design particularly on Row 8/4 and to a lesser extent on Row 6/4 and 7/4. These varieties arose from re-entries made on the plate in these positions.

G42a—About 10 copies were discovered in March, 1922, the remains of a half sheet (of 30) sent to Manchioneal Post Office. It is believed that the other half of the sheet was sold at Kingston G.P.O., and one copy is known cancelled there.

The following watermark varieties are known—
Inverted ½d., 1d., 1½d., 2d., 2½d., 3d., 1/–, 2/–.
Reversed ½d., 1½d., 2½d., 1/–.
Inverted and reversed 1½d., 2d., 2½d., 2/–.
Upright (normal being sideways) 1½d.

Inverted   Normal

G37/38—The Union Jack at left is inverted. This was corrected on the subsequent issue. (See G58/59).

Numbers issued—G43, 21,540: G44, 6,390: G45/46, 9,341: G47, 7,485.

1921 June) Prepared for use but not issued (*recess*). De La Rue. Perf. 14. Sheets 5 x 8.

(a) Wmk. Multiple Crown CA (upright).

G48	6d.	red and blue-green..	£3000	—
SPG48		specimen (reading upwards) ..	£350	‡

(b) Wmk. Multiple Script CA (sideways).

G49	6d.	red and blue-green..	£3000	—
SPG49		specimen (reading downwards) ..	£350	‡

G48 is known with wmk. reversed.

The issue of this stamp was withheld on account of political unrest in Jamaica at the time. The same design was used in 1955 for the 6d. value of the Tercentenary issue.

Approximately 740 'Specimen' copies had been distributed to U.P.U. member countries before the issue was abandoned.

1921 (Feb. 2nd)-29. As before but Wmk. Multiple Script CA (sideways on G52/55).

G50	½d.	grn and olive-grn C (5.2.22) ..	20	15
G51	½d.	grn and bt yel-grn C	15	10
G52	1d.	carmine and orange C (5.12.22).. ..	50	10

G53	1d.	carmine and red C..	80	10
G54	1½d.	blue-green (2.2.21)..	35	10
G55	1½d.	yellow-green ..	60	25
G56	2d.	indigo and green (4.11.21)	1·50	20
G57	2d.	indigo and pl ol-grn	2·00	20
G58	2½d.	dp blue and blue (4.11.21)	2·00	20
G59	2½d.	indigo and dp blue..	2·50	20
G60	3d.	grn and bl (6.3.22)..	1·00	20
G61	4d.	sep and grn (5.12.21)	50	15
G62	4d.	choc and dl green..	30	15
G63	6d.	blk and bl (5.12.22)..	£10	1·75
G64	6d.	grey and pl blue ..	£10	1·75
G65	1/–	or and rd-or (4.11.21)	2·00	40
G66	1/–	yel-or and brn or ..	1·50	25
G67	2/–	pl bl and brn (5.2.22)	2·00	1·00
	a	lower portion of frame doubly printed ..	—	—
G68	3/–	violet blue and or (23.8.21)	9·00	9·00
G69	5/–	indigo and yel-brn (8.11.23)	£14	£15
G70	5/–	indigo and yel-or ..	£15	£14
G71	5/–	bl and ochre-brn ..	£28	£25
G72	5/–	bl and pl bistre-brn ('29)	£15	£14
G73	10/–	dp myrtle-green (3-4/22)	£28	£50
G50/73		set (13v)	£70	£75
SPG50/73		specimen set (13v)	£120	‡

The following watermark varieties are known—
Inverted ½d., 1d., 1½d., 2½d, 4d., 5/–.
Reversed 1½d., 2½d, 3d., 4d., 1/–, 5/–.
Inverted and reversed 1½d, 2½d.

G58/59—The Union Jack at left is upright. See also G37/38.

G50/55—Were also issued in a Booklet containing three panes (of four) each of the ½d., 1d., and 1½d.

Imperf Plate Proofs on thick wove unwatermarked paper exist in the following colours, with or without SPECIMEN overprint: Price from £35 each.

1½d.	grey-blue .. ..
2d.	mauve and indigo ..
2½d.	green and orange-brown (Union Jack normal)
3d.	brown and green ..
4d.	orange-red and brown
6d.	green and purple (design of G48/49) ..
6d.	brown and carmine (design of G63/64) ..
1/–	carmine and green ..
2/–	green and browm ..
3/–	carmine and green ..
5/–	green and blue ..
10/–	rose-carmine .. ..

1923 (Nov. 1st). Child Welfare. (*recess*).

Bradbury Wilkinson. Designer, F. C. Cundall from photographs by Miss V. F. Taylor. Wmk. Multiple Script CA. Perf. 12. Sheets 12 x 10.

G74	½d. + ½d.	**blk and grn** ..	1·25	1·25
		a on thin paper	2·50	2·50
G75 1d.	+ ½d.	**blk and scar**	6·50	7·00
G76 2½d.	+ ½d.	**blk and blue** ..	£14	£15
G74/76		**set** (3v) ..	£21	£22
SPG74/76		**specimen set** (3v)	£85	‡

These stamps were placed on sale annually from November 1st to January 31st until January 31st, 1927. Unsold remainders were destroyed on 21.2.27.

Despite their sale over four seasons, only £246-3-2 was raised by the ½d. premium for Child Welfare.

Numbers sold—G74, 43,159 : G75, 44,401 : G76, 30,595 :

1929-32. (*recess*). **De La Rue. Wmk. Multiple Script CA. Perf. 14. Sheets 120 – two panes, each 6 x 10.**

G77 1d.	**scarlet** (Die I) ..		30	10
G78 1d.	**car** (Die II) ('32) ..		10	10
G79 1½d.	**chocolate** ..	..	20	20
G80 9d.	**maroon** ..	..	3·75	2·75
G77/80	**set** (4v) ..	..	4·00	3·00
SPG77/80	**specimen set** (3v)..		£30	‡

In Die I the shading below JAMAICA consists only of horizontal lines, whereas in Die II it is formed of diagonal cross hatching. There are other minor differences between the two dies.

1932. (*recess*). **Waterlow and Sons. Wmk. Multiple Script CA** (sideways on G81/82). **Perf. 12¾. Sheets 10 x 6 or 6 x 10.**

G81 2d.	**black and green** ..		2·50	50
	a imperf between		£750	—
	(vert pair) ..		1·50	1·50
G82 2½d.	**grnish-blue and ult**			
	a imperf between			
	(vert pair) ..		£750	—
G83 6d.	**gr-blk and purple**..		3·50	2·25
G81/83	**set** (3v)		7·00	4·00
SPG81/83	**specimen set** (3v)..		£30	‡

1935 (May 6th). Silver Jubilee. (*recess*). **Bradbury Wilkinson. Wmk. Multiple Script CA. Perf. 11 x 12. Sheets 6 x 10.**

G84 1d.	**blue and scarlet** ..		15	15
	a extra flagstaff ..		£25	£25
G85 1½d.	**ult and grey** ..		20	20
	a extra flagstaff ..		£25	£25
G86 6d.	**green and indigo** ..		2·00	2·50
	a extra flagstaff ..		£40	£45
G87 1/-	**slate and purple** ..		2·25	2·75
	a extra flagstaff ..		£80	£85
G84/87	**set** (4v)		4·50	5·00
SPG84/87	**specimen set** (4v)..		£25	‡

G84*a*/87*a*—Extra flagstaff occurs on No. 49 (Row 9/1).

G84—Was also issued in Booklets containing 24 stamps.

Numbers printed—G84, 5,857,000 : G85, 544,160 : G86, 180,696 : G87, 121,951.

Remainders were withdrawn on December, 31st, 1935.

1938 (Oct. 10th) -52 Designs, ½d., 1d., 1½d. **(King's Head); 2d. (Coco Palms, Columbus Cove); 2½d. (Wag Water River, St. Andrew); 3d. (Bananas); 4d. (Citrus Grove); 6d. (Priestman River, Portland); 9d. (Kingston Harbour); 1/- (Sugar Industry); 2/- (Bamboo Walk); 5/- (Isle of Wood and Water); 10/- (KG VI); £1 (Cigar making). Printers (***recess***

De La Rue. ½d.–1½d., Perf. 13½ x 14 (C); 5/-. 10/-, Perf. 14 x 13¾ (C). Waterlow & Sons, Perf. 12½ (L). Designs, 3d., 4d., 6d., 9d., 1/-, 10/-, £1 H. Sheets—Small format 120—two panes, each 6 x 10; Horizontal, 5 x 12; Vertical, 10 x 6 or 6 x10; 5/- and 10/-, 6 x 5 or 5 x 6.

1	½d.	**dp green** (10/10/38) ..	5	5
		a green (5/42) ..	10	5
		aa booklet pane of 6 ..	3·00	—
		b wmk. sideways ..	—	£850
2	½d.	**orange** (25/10/51) ..	10	5
		a dp orange (30/6/52)	10	5
		b booklet pane of 6 ..	2·00	—
3	1d.	**scarlet** (10/10/38) ..	10	5
		a car-red (30/1/50) ..	15	5
		b booklet pane of 6 ..	5·00	—
4	1d.	**green** (25/10/51) ..	15	5
		a booklet pane of 6 ..	5·00	—
5	1½d.	**lt brown** (10/10/38) ..	10	5
		a chocolate-brown (/41)	10	5
		b lt red-brown (/44)	£75	—
6	2d.	**grey and green** ..	10	5
		a grey and dp emer-grn (26/2/47) ..	15	5
7	2½d.	**grey-green and ult** ..	80	80
8	3d.	**pale ult and green** ..	15	5
		a pale ult and dp green (12/1/48)	15	5
9	3d.	**pale green and ult** (15/8/49)	50	5
10	3d.	**grn and red** (1/7/52)	25	10
11	4d.	**lt brown and green** ..	15	10
		a lt brown and blue-grn (4/9/44) ..	15	10
12	6d.	**grey and red-purple** .	25	5
		a grey and red-claret (15/4/46) ..	15	5
13	9d.	**lake**	25	15
		a claret (5/42) ..	20	15
14	1/–	**grn and dp pur-brn** ..	30	15
		a broken chimney ..	£35	£30
		b blue-grn and pur-brn (5/42)	25	10
		c broken chimney ..	£35	£30
15	2/–	**blue and choc-brown**	60	20
		a pale blue-brown ..	60	20
16	5/–	**grey-blue and yellow ochre**	2·50	1·25
		a dp blue and dp orange (5/42)	2·00	1·00
17	10/–	**myrtle-green** ..	5·00	3·50
18	£1	**dp brown and violet** (15/8/49)	£17	£17
1/18		**set** (18)	£28	£22
SP 1/17		**specimen set** perf (13)	£60	‡

As Nos. 6 and 12, but Perf. 12¾ x 13¾ (C).

19	2d.	**grey and green** (/39)	15	10
20	6d.	**grey and red-purple** (10/10/50) ..	15	10

As Nos. 16 and 17, but Perf. 13¼ x 13 (C).

21	5/–	**blue-black and ochre** (blued paper) (24/10/49) ..	4·00	4·00
		a dp blue & brownish-orange (10/10/50)	2·50	2·00
22	10/–	**myrtle-grn** (10/10/50)	6·00	5·00
		a lt myrtle-grn (8/1/52)	7·00	5·00

As No. 6 but Perf. 12¾ x 13 (C).

23	2d.	**grey and green** (/51)	15	15

No. 5*b* This particular printing was on sale in the Colony (*only*) for a short period about the middle of 1944.

Nos. 14*a*/14*c* Two short lines cut through smoke from smaller chimney on all printings up to 1947. Row 11/1 (*see illus.*).

No. 21*a* has a slight blue tinge on the surface, but not so pronounced as No. 21.

The 5/–, in greyish blue and reddish orange, is reported to exist perf 14 (Line).

SPECIAL ISSUES

1937 (May 12th) Coronation. As Aden.

S1	1d.	**red**	10	5
S2	1½d.	**dp grey**	10	5
S3	2½d.	**blue**	40	40
SP S1/3		**specimen set** perf (3)	£13	‡

1945 (Aug. 20th) New Constitution. Designs, 1½d. (Courthouse, Falmouth); 2d. (Charles II and KG VI); 3d. (Institute of Jamaica); 4½d. (House of Assembly); 2/- (Symbols of Art and Learning); 5/- (Jamaican Flag). Printers (*recess*) Waterlow & Sons. Perf. 12½ (L). Designs, 3d., 2/-, 10/- V. Sheets 10 x 6 or 6 x 10.

S4	1½d.	**sepia-brown** ..	10	10
S5	2d.	**green**	60	30
S6	3d.	**ultramarine**	10	15
S7	4½d.	**slate-black**	10	15
S8	2/–	**chocolate-brown** ..	60	80
S9	5/–	**dark blue**	1·00	1·50
S10	10/–	**green**	2·00	3·00
S4/10		**set** (7)	4·00	6·00
SP S4/10		**perf specimen** (7v)	£90	‡

As Nos. S4 and S5 but Perf. 12¾ x 13¼ (C).

S11	1½d.	**sepia-brown** (/46) ..	40	15
		a booklet pane of 4 ..	£12	—
S12	2d.	**green** (/45)	10	20

S11*a* comes from booklets containing 4 x panes of four.

As Nos. S6 and S7 but Perf. 13¼ x 13 (C).

S13	3d.	**ultramarine**	40	45
S14	4½d.	**slate-black** (/46) ..	40	45

1946 (Oct. 14th) Victory. As Aden.
(a) Perf. 13¾ x 14 (C).

S15	1½d.	**purple-brown** ..	10	10
S16	3d.	**grey-blue**	10	10
SP S15/16		**specimen pair** perf	£18	‡

(b) Perf. 13¾ x 13¼ (C).

S17	1½d. **purple-brown**	10	10
S18	3d. **grey-blue**	40	45

1948 (Dec. 1st) Silver Wedding. As Aden.

S19	1½d. **chestnut-brown**	10	10
S20	£1 **rose-carmine**	£16	£18

1949 (Oct. 10th) U.P.U. As Aden.

S21	1½d. **beech-brown**	10	10
S22	2d. **dp green**	15	15
S23	3d. **dull indigo**	30	30
S24	6d. **purple**	45	45
S21/24	**set** (4)	1·00	1·00

1951 (Feb. 16th) West Indies University College. (See Antigua.)

S25	2d. **black and chocolate**	10	10
S26	6d. **grey-blk and pur-lake**	30	20

1925 (Mar. 5th) First Caribbean Scout Jamboree. Designs, 2d. (Scout Badge and Map of Caribbean); 6d. (Scout Badge and Maps of Jamaica and American Continent, adapted from designs by Claude de Souza). Printers (litho) Bradbury, Wilkinson. Perf. 13½ x 13 (C). Sheets—S27, 6 x 10; S28, 5 x 12.

S27	2d. **blue, black and green**	15	15
S28	6d. **grn, blk and crimson**	40	50

Number issued—2d., 2,864,153; 6d., 899,723.

OFFICIAL STAMPS

Type I   Type II

1890 (April 1st). Nos. V33/34 overprinted with Type I in black by Camille Vendryes in Kingston.

(a) 17-17½mm. (Setting 1, 3 and 4).

VO1	½d. **green**	75	60
	a "O" omitted	£170	—
	b one "I" omitted	—	—
	c both "I's" omitted	£225	£225
	d "L" omitted	—	£225
	e overprint inverted	£20	£22

	f overprint double	£20	£22
	g overprint double, one inverted	£125	£125
	h overprint double,one vertical	£250	—
	overprints tete beche (in pair)	—	—

(b) 15-16mm. (Setting 2).

VO2	½d. **green**	5·00	5·00
	a overprint double	£200	—

There were four settings of the overprint—

1. Single setting of 18 in three horizontal rows repeated 3½ times on the pane. The majority of the errors a to i came from this setting.

2. Single setting of 12 in two horizontal rows, repeated five times on the pane. VO1f is also known on this setting.

3. Single setting of 20 in two vertical columns, repeated three times on the pane.

4. Single setting of 6 in a horizontal row, repeated ten times on the pane.

There are numerous minor varieties in all four settings. These include broken and battered letters and irregular spacing.

1890 (April 1st)-91. Nos. V33/34, and V54/58 in changed colours overprinted with Type II by De La Rue.

VO3	½d.	**green** ('91)	35	15
VO4	1d.	**pl rose**	45	15
VO5	1d.	**dp carmine**	60	50
VO6	2d.	**grey**	75	30
VO3/6		**set** (3v)	1·40	50
SPVO3/6		**specimen set** (3v)	£40	‡

The use of Official stamps ceased from January 1st, 1898.

POSTAL FISCALS

Previously issued Fiscal stamps were authorised for postal use from October 1st, 1887. Telegraph stamps are also found postally used, but this was never authorised.

All Fiscal stamps were (typo) De La Rue. Perf. 14 unless otherwise indicated.

Type I   Type II

(a) Wmk. Pineapple.

F1	1d.	**rose**	£30	£35
		a imperf	£150	—

(b) Wmk. Crown CC.

F2	1d.	**rose**	£15	£18
F3	3d.	**purple/lilac** (Type II)	1·25	1·50

(c) Wmk. Crown over CA. (sideways, covering two stamps).

F4	1d.	**rose**	3·50	3·50
		a imperf	—	—

(d) No Wmk. (Type II).

F5	1½d. **blue/blue**	.. ..	£14	£16
	a imperf	.. ..	—	—
F6	1½d. **blue/white**	.. ..	£16	£23
F7	3d. **purple/blue**	.. ..	£14	£16
	a imperf	.. ..	—	—
F8	3d. **purple/lilac**	.. ..	£15	£18
	a imperf	.. ..	—	—
F9	3d. **purple/white**	..	£13	£16

F2 is known with wmk. inverted.

F1/4/8 exist overprinted or perforated 'SPECIMEN'.

The imperforate varieties are very rarely found postally used.

No Wmk. Perf. 15¼ x 15. Sheets 12 x 20.

F10	1/– **rose/bluish**	.. ..	£17	£18
F11	5/– **lilac/bluish**	.. ..	£70	£90
F12	10/– **green/bluish**	..	£70	£90
SPF10/12 **specimen set** (3v)		..	£95	‡

All the above stamps are known with fiscal marks removed and forged or bogus postal cancellations applied

No. F10 is also known cleaned and cancelled with *genuine* postmarks from various Post Offices, including the 'SPANISH TOWN' squared circle of 1900 (but dated 1881).

SEMI POSTAL ISSUES

1915 (Dec. 1st)-16. Red Cross and War Funds.

Printed by Dennison Manufacturing Co. (Framingham, Mass., U.S.A.) on white unwatermarked wove paper. Perf. 12. Sheets 10 x 10.

(a) December 1st, 1915.

GSP1 (½d.) **red** .. .. .. 75 —

(b) December 22nd. As before but overprinted "JAMAICA" in red by Gleaner Co. Ltd. at Kingston.

GSP2 (½d.) **red** .. .. .. 75 —

(c) January 15th, 1916. As before but overprinted in black.

GSP3 (½d.) **red** .. .. .. 60 —
    a overprint inverted .. — —

(d) March 11th, 1916. No. GSP1 overprinted "JAMAICA Half-Penny" in black by Gleaner Co. Ltd.

GSP4 ½d. **red** .. .. .. 75 —

GSP4 was also issued in Booklets containing 12 labels (Price £10).

These labels were issued by the Jamaica War Stamp League for the benefit of their funds, and were officially sold at ½d. in all Post Offices. Although they had no general postal validity they may be found with postal cancellations.

They were also officially authorised for use on correspondence in connection with League or Red Cross business from the Chairman of the League which was entitled to carriage postage free. Such letters bore the signature of Mr. Lewis Ashenheim across a label which was then cancelled with the Post Office datestamp.

GERMAN PROPAGANDA LABELS

The 1944 German imitations of the G.B. 1937 Definitives ½d to 3d (see after Great Britain for details) were also overprinted in black "LIQUIDA-TION/OF EMPIRE/JAMAICA" within a vertical rectangular frame—Price £150.

KENYA, UGANDA and TANGANYIKA

British East Africa (later Kenya) and Uganda were originally administered by the Imperial British East Africa Company which was granted a Charter in 1888. Uganda became a Protectorate in 1894 and British East Africa, renamed the East African Protectorate, followed in 1895: the joint territories being raised to Colonial status in 1920 as Kenya and Uganda.

German East Africa was occupied by British Forces during the first World War and stamps of East Africa and Uganda were overprinted 'G.E.A.' for use there. In 1919 Britain was given a mandate and the territory was renamed Tanganyika.

The joint issue in 1935 for the three territories had its origin in the earlier stamps of British East Africa (1890-1903) and Uganda (1895-1903), subsequently amalgamated postally as the East Africa and Uganda Protectorates and later as Kenya and Uganda, and in the Tanganyika Mandatory issues (1922–1935).

All stamps to G77 are Typo De La Rue. Perf. 14, unless otherwise indicated.

1904-07 As before but Wmk. Multiple Crown CA. E17/25 O and C (except E20—O only): E26/33—C.

E17	½a.	grey-green	30	30
E18	1a.	grey and red ..	60	40
E19	2a.	dl and bt purple ..	2·25	2·25
E20	2½a.	blue	5·00	5·00
E21	2½a.	ult and blue ..	4·00	4·50
E22	3a.	brown and green	3·00	3·75
E23	4a.	grey-grn and blk ..	4·00	4·50
E24	5a.	grey and or-brn ..	5·00	5·50
E25	8a.	grey and pl blue ..	6·00	6·00
E26	R1	green ('07)	9·00	9·00
E27	Rs2	dl and bt pur ('06)..	£16	£14
E28	Rs3	grey-grn and blk ('07)	£20	£20
E29	Rs4	grey and em ('07)..	£20	£27
E30	Rs5	grey and red ('07)..	£26	£27
E31	Rs10	grey and ult ('07)..	£90	£85
E32	Rs20	grey and stone ('07)	£225	£275
E33	Rs50	grey and red-brn ('07)	£900	£825
E17/31		set (14v)	£200	£210
SPE17/32		specimen (10) ..	£120	‡

Specimen set consists of E17/E20, E22, E24, E28/E30 and E32.

1903-04.

(a) Wmk. Crown CA. Sheets 160 – two panes, each 8 x 10.

E1	½a.	green	90	90
E2	1a.	grey and red ..	90	50
E3	2a.	dl and bt purple ..	3·00	3·50
E4	2½a.	blue	9·00	7·50
E5	3a.	brown and green	6·50	7·50
E6	4a.	grey-grn and blk ..	8·00	7·50
E7	5a.	grey and or-brn ..	£16	£17
E8	8a.	grey and pl blue ..	£16	£16

(b) Wmk. Crown CC. Sheets 12 x 5.

E9	R1	green (OC)	8·00	£10
E10	R2	dl and bt purple ..	£16	£17
E11	Rs3	grey-grn and blk ..	£18	£19
E12	Rs4	grey and emerald..	£24	£25
E13	Rs5	grey and red ..	£24	£27
E14	Rs10	grey and ult (OC)	£80	£65
E15	Rs20	grey and stone ..	£350	£250
E16	Rs50	grey and red-brn ..	£700	£700
E1/14		set (14v)	£210	£200
SPE1/14		specimen set (14v)	£100	‡
SPE15		specimen (1) ..	£70	‡
SPE16		specimen (1) ..	£140	‡

Type I (Double Plates)—EAST AFRICA AND UGANDA in tall thin letters.
PROTECTORATES in short letters.

Type II (Single Plate)—EAST AFRICA AND UGANDA in shorter thicker letters.
PROTECTORATES in taller letters.
White lines added around value tablets and above name tablet.

1907-10 As before but new currency (100 Cents —1 Rupee). Sheets 120 – two panes, each 6 x 10 except E38 (240 – four panes, each 6 x 10). E34/38 and 41—O: remainder—C.

E34	1c.	**brown**	20	35
E35	3c.	**grey-green**	20	35
E36	3c.	**blue-green**	15	65
E37	6c.	**red** (Type I)	90	30
E38	6c.	**red** (Type II) ('10)	2·25	30
E39	10c.	**lilac and sage-grn**	3·50	3·50
E40	12c.	**dl and bt purple**	3·50	2·75
E41	15c.	**bright blue**	3·50	4·00
E42	25c.	**grey-grn and blk**	4·00	5·00
E43	50c.	**grey-grn and or-brown**	4·50	6·00
E44	75c.	**grey and pl blue** ('08)	6·50	£10
E34/44		**set** (9v)	£25	£30
SPE34/44		**specimen set** (9v)	£70	‡

1912-22 Wmk. Multiple Crown CA. Sheets G1/14 240 – four panes, each 6 x 10. G15/26 12 x 5.

G1	1c.	**black**	30	20
G2	3c.	**green**	60	20
G3	3c.	**dp blue-grn** ('17)	80	20
G4	6c.	**red**	30	25
G5	6c.	**scarlet** ('17)	1·50	25
G6	10c.	**bright orange**	2·50	25
G7	10c.	**orange** ('21)	2·25	25
G8	12c.	**grey**	1·25	1·00
G9	12c.	**deep slate**	1·75	1·00
G10	15c.	**blue**	1·25	75
G11	15c.	**deep blue**	2·00	1·00
G12	25c.	**blk and red/yel (C)**	1·00	60
		a on lemon ('16)	5·00	4·50
		b on orange-buff ('21)	£10	2·00
		c on pl yellow ('21)	5·00	1·75
		d white back	1·00	1·00
G13	50c.	**blk and lilac (C)**	2·00	1·50
G14	75c.	**black/green (C)**	2·75	3·00
		a white back	2.25	3·75
		b on blue-green (olive back)	5·50	3·75
		c on emerald (olive back)	£30	£30
		d on emerald	5·00	4·50
G15	R1	**black/green (C)**	4·00	3·50
		a on emerald	5·50	5·50
G16	Rs2	**red and blk/blue (C)**	£10	£10
G17	Rs3	**vio and grn (C)**	£10	£11

G18	Rs4	**red and grn/yel (C)**	£18	£17
		a on pale yellow	£20	£19
G19	Rs5	**blu and dl pur C)**	£20	£19
G20	Rs10	**red and grn/grn (C)**	£25	£30
G21	Rs20	**blk and pur/red (C)**	£140	£120
G22	Rs20	**pur and blu/blu (C)** ('18)	£140	£120
G23	Rs50	**car and grn (CO)**	£450	£450
G24	Rs50	**dl rose-red and dl greyish-green**	£450	£450
G25	Rs100	**pur and blk/red (C)**	£1500	£850
G26	Rs500	**grn and red/grn (C)**	£6500	—
G1/20		**set** (15v)	£95	£95
SPG1/22		**specimen set** (17v)	£180	‡
SPG23		**specimen** (1)	£100	‡
SPG25		**specimen** (1)	£325	‡
SPG26		**specimen** (1)	£750	‡

G2 and G4 were also made up in Booklets in 1912. G1/24 overprinted 'G.E.A.' were used during the occupation of German East Africa (later Tanganyika).

1919 No. G5 locally surcharged in black.

G27	4c. on 6c. **scarlet**			15	20
	a surcharge inverted	£35	£40
	b surcharge double	£40	£45
	c surcharge omitted in pair with normal	£85	£130
	d bars omitted	£12	£18
SPG27		**specimen** (1)	£22	‡

G27c/d were caused by an upward shift of the surcharge. In the case of No. G27d the bars intended for the top of the stamps in the bottom row fell *below* the surcharge on the row above.

1921-22 As Nos. G1/23 but Wmk. Multiple Script CA. G28/33—O: G35/39—C.

G28	1c.	**black**	45	25
G29	3c.	**green**	65	65
G30	3c.	**blue-green**	1·75	90
G31	6c.	**carmine**	1·25	60
G32	10c.	**orange**	1·00	25
G33	12c.	**slate-grey**	3·65	7·50
G34	15c.	**bright blue**	2·75	2·75
G35	50c.	**black and lilac**	7·50	7·50
G36	Rs2	**red and black/blue**	£17	£17
G37	Rs3	**violet and green**	£20	£20
G38	Rs5	**blue and dl purple**	£30	£32
G39	Rs50	**carmine and green**	£850	£900

G28/39	set (10v)	.. ..	£80	£85
SPG28/38	specimen set (10v)		£80	‡
SPG39	specimen (1)	..	£160	‡

G28/38 overprinted 'G.E.A.' were used during the occupation of German East Africa (later Tanganyika).

SPG	68	£95	69	£110	70	£175
	71	£185	72	£220	73	£295
	74	£325	75	£435	76	£450
	77	£475				

Cleaned Fiscally used copies of Nos. G68/77 are known with forged postal cancellations.

1922-27. New Currency (100 Cents–1 Shilling).

(a) Wmk. Multiple Script CA (upright). Sheets 240 – four panes, each 6 x 10.

G40	1c. pale brown	30	30
G41	1c. deep brown ('23) ..	60	50
G42	5c. dull violet	60	25
G43	5c. bright violet ..	60	50
G44	5c. green ('27) ..	60	15
G45	10c. green	60	25
G46	10c. black ('27) ..	30	15
G47	12c. black	3·75	5·00
G48	12c. grey-black	1·25	2·50
G49	15c. carmine	50	25
G50	20c. orange-yellow ..	1·25	25
G51	20c. bright orange ..	1·00	15
G52	30c. ultramarine.. ..	60	25
G53	50c. grey	1·00	25
G54	75c. olive	2·50	4·00
G55	75c. greenish olive ..	4·00	4·00

G41 exists with wmk. reversed.

(b) Wmk. Multiple Script CA (sideways). Sheets 5 x 12. Chalky paper.

G56	1/–	bright green ..	2·75	1·25
G57	1/–	yellow-green ..	3·50	2·00
G58	1/–	deep green ..	3·25	2·00
G59	2/–	dull purple ..	3·50	2·75
G60	2/50	brown ('25) ..	£14	£28
G61	3/–	brownish grey ..	7·00	6·00
G62	3/–	black	£11	£11
G63	4/–	grey ('25) ..	£16	£26
G64	5/–	carmine	£13	£13
G65	7/50	or-yel ('25) ..	£25	£48
G66	10/–	bright blue ..	£27	£27
G67	£1	black and orange	£95	£95
G68	£2	grn and pur ('25)	£450	—
G69	£3	pur and yel ('25)	£775	—
G70	£4	blk and mag ('25)	£1300	—
G71	£5	black and blue ..	£1500	—
G72	£10	black and green	£5500	—
G73	£20	red and grn ('25)	£6750	—
G74	£25	black and red ..	£7000	—
G75	£50	black and brown	£12000	—
G76	£75	pur and grey ('25)	£16000	—
G77	£100	red and blk ('25)	£20000	—
G40/67		set (20v)	£200	£230
SPG40/67		specimen set (20v)	£200	‡

1935 (May 1st)-36 Various frames and views. Recess. De La Rue (except G81 and G91 – Typo and Perf. 12 x 13). Wmk. Multiple Script CA. Sheets 10 x 10.

(a) Perf. 14 (G79/80/85/86/88): Perf. 13 (remainder).

G78	1c.	blk and red-brn ..	10	10
G79	5c.	blk and grn (Type I)	10	10
G80	5c.	blk and grn (Type II)	80	40
G81	10c.	blk and yellow (C)	70	10
G82	15c.	black and scarlet	50	10
G83	20c.	black and orange	15	10
G84	30c.	black and blue ..	30	60
G85	50c.	pur and blk (Type I)	60	60
G86	65c.	black and brown ..	70	90
G87	1/–	black and green ..	80	70
G88	2/–	lake and purple ..	3·75	4·75
G89	3/–	blue and black ..	4·75	6·00
G90	5/–	black and carmine	£10	£10
G91	10/–	purple and blue ..	£25	£20
G92	£1	black and red (C)	£48	£43
G78/92		set (14v)	£80	£82
SPG78/92		specimen set (14v)	£60	‡

(b) Perf. 13 x 12 (1936).

G93	5c.	blk and grn (Type I)..	£75	£25
G94	5c.	blk and grn (Type II)	£95	£20
G95	1/–	black and green ..	£300	£20
G96	3/–	blue and black ..	£600	—

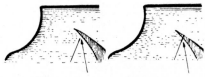

Type I   Type II

G79/80 and G93/94—In Type I the stay rope was not attached to the upper point of the sail. The correction (Type II) was made only on the last printing (late 1937) of the 5c.; it was not corrected on No. G85. (See K.G. VI No. 12/12a).

1935 (May 6th) Silver Jubilee Recess De La Rue. Wmk. Multiple Script CA. Perf. 13½ x 14. Sheets 6 x 10.

G97	20c.	**blue and olive** ..	10	10
G98	30c.	**brown and blue** ..	60	40
G99	65c.	**green and indigo** ..	1·75	1·75
G100	1/–	**slate and purple** ..	2·00	2·00
		a line through 'O' ..	£20	£20
G97/100		**set** (4v)	4·00	4·00
SPG97/100		**specimen set** (4v)	£20	‡

G100*a*—A diagonal line runs through '0' in '1910' on Row 4/2.

Numbers printed—G97, 2,203,750; G98, 264,375; G99, 74,000; G100, 233,750.

1938 (April 11th) 54 Designs, 1c., 20c., 40c., 10/– (Kavirondo Cranes): 5c., 25c., 50c. (Dhow on Lake Victoria): 10c., 1/–, 3/– (Lake Naivasha); 15c., 2/– (Mount Kilimanjaro); 30c., 5/– (Jinga Bridge by the Ripon Falls); £1 Typo (Lion and Palms). Printers, De La Rue. Designs, 1c., 15c., 20c., 30c., 5/– ,10/–, £1 V. Sheets 10 x 10.

(a) Perf. 13¼ (C).

1	1c.	**blk and reddish-brn**	10	20
2	15c.	**black and red** ..	15	10
		a booklet pane of 4 ..	2·00	—
3	20c.	**black and orange** ..	60	20
		a booklet pane of 4 ..	3·00	—
4	30c.	**black and dp blue** ..	1·75	30
5	2/—	**mar and pur-mauve**	4·00	1·00
6	5/–	**black and carmine**	9·00	2·75
7	10/–	**purple and blue** ..	£12	5·00

(b) Perf 13 x 11¾ (C).

8	5c.	**blk and grn** (11/4/38)	10	10
9	5c.	**chocolate and or** (1/6/49)	25	25
10	10c.	**chocolate and or**	10	10
11	10c.	**blk and grn** (1/6/49)	10	15
		a peak retouch ..	8·00	8·00
12	50c.	**dp purple and black**	20	10
		a short stay (Type I)	£50	£30
		b red-purple and black (29/7/47) ..	10	10

13	1/–	**black and brown** ..	25	10
		a peak retouch (/49)	£20	8·00
		b blk and dark brn (9/42)	50	25
14	3/–	**dp blue and black**	1·25	70
		a dk blue and black (29/7/47) ..	1·75	80
15	£1	**blk and crimson** (*ch*) (12/10/38) ..	£42	£20
SP	1/15	**specimen set perf** (13)	£42	‡

No. 3 is known imperf. but is of unknown status. Price (pair) £100.

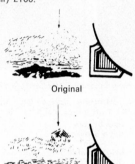

Original

Retouch

11*a*/13*a* Major retouches to the mountain top are to be found on Rows 5/10 and 6/7 (Plate 7B).

12*a*—See Note after No. G96. The same Centre Plate as had been used for No. G85 was used for the first printing of the K.G. VI 50c., after the short stay rope had been extended on 99 subjects *on the Plate*. The exception was on Row 2/5 where the correction was overlooked: 5,127 sheets were printed and placed on sale in May 1938. The Die was then corrected and a new Plate laid down; stamps printed from this Plate were placed on sale in September 1938 and the remainder of the first printing was withdrawn.

Stamps with the extended stay rope may be recognised as being from the first (corrected) plate if the extension is slightly thicker than the lower part of the stay rope. The full length of the stay rope is of constant thickness on all stamps printed from the new Plate.

As No. 10, etc., but Perf. 14 (L).

16	10c.	**choc and or** (/41) ..	£10	75
17	20c.	**blk and or** (/41) ..	3·00	1·00
18	30c.	**blk and dp blue** (/41)	£20	3·75
19	2/–	**maroon and purple-mauve** (/41) ..	7·50	3·00
20	5/–	**blk and car** (/41) ..	3·75	1·50
21	10/–	**red-purple and blue** (/41)..	£10	8·00
22	£1	**black and crim** (*ch*) (/41)..	6·50	5·00
		a blk and crimson (*sub*) (24/2/44) ..	5·50	4·50

As No. 1, etc., but Perf. 13¼ x 13¾ (C).

23	1c.	**blk and choc brn** (/42)..	10	10
		a retouched tablet	8·00	6·00

b	blk and dp red-brown (9/42) ..	10	10
bb	retouched tablet	6·00	3·00
c	blk and dk brn (/46)	20	10
d	retouched tablet	8·00	5·00
e	blk and red-choc (26/9/51) ..	10	10
24 15c.	**blk and red** (2/43) ..	30	30
a	booklet pane of 4 ..	3·00	—
25 15c.	**blk and grn** (1/4/52)	10	25
26 20c.	**blk and orange** (/42)	10	10
a	black and dp orange (26/9/51)	10	10
27 30c.	**blk and dp bl** (9/42)	10	10
a	slate-black and deep blue(24/2/44) ..	20	10
b	black and violet-blue (29/7/47)	20	10
28 30c.	**purple and sepia-brn** (1/4/52) ..	10	10
29 40c.	**black and dp blue** (1/4/52)	20	15
30 2/–	**maroon and pur-mauve** (24/2/44) ..	50	30
31 5/–	**blk and car** (24/2/44)	1·00	50
32 10/–	**purple and blue** (24/2/44)	3·00	1·75

23*a*/*bb*/*d* A flaw on the value tablet at the left bottom corner was crudely retouched Row 9/6 Frame Plate 2.

As No. 9, etc., but Perf. 13 x 12½ (C).

33 5c.	**chocolate and orange** (14/6/50)	10	30
34 10c.	**blk and grn** (14/6/50)	10	10
35 10c.	**brn and grey** (1/4/52)	10	10
36 25c.	**blk and red** (1/4/52)	40	90
37 50c.	**red-purple and black** (10/49)	10	10
a	dot removed (14/6/50) ..	2·00	1·25
b	pair with and without dot	£80	£40
38 1/–	**blk and brn** (10/49)..	£40	£15
a	black and dp-brown (14/6/50) ..	£40	£15
39 3/–	**dark blue and black** (14/6/50)	1·25	1·00

37*a*/*b* The dot which was to be found previously on the scroll at the left bottom corner has been removed by retouching, except on Rows 5/2, 6/1, 7/2, 7/4 and 9/1. Traces are still visible on some stamps however where the retouching was not completely effective.

38*a* The new centre plate used for this printing shows much detail, particularly in the foreground and sky.

As No. 15, but Perf. 12½ (L).

39*a* £1	**blk and crim** (21/1/54)	6·00	6·00
1/39	**set** (20) all colours ..	£13	£10

1941 (July 1st) -42 Contemporary Stamps of South Africa, surcharged and overprinted.

The difficulty in obtaining supplies of stamps from Great Britain during the war was the reason why South African stamps were utilised.

			Pr. M.	*Pr. U.*
40	5c./1d.	**grey and car-red**	35	45
	a	grey and car-red	1·00	1·00
41	10c./3d.	**ultramarine** ..	35	45
42	20c./6d.	**grn and dp orange**	30	45
	a	grn and brnish-orange (/42) ..	75	75
43	70c./1/-	**sepia and chalky-blue** (20/4/42)..	30	45
40/43		**set 4 pairs**	1·25	1·75
SP40/43		**specimen set** (4 prs)	£60	‡

40 This stamp (as South Africa No. 5) measures 18¼ x 22½mm. whilst 40*a* (as South Africa No. 5*a*) measures 18¼ x 22¼mm.

These stamps exist overprinted SPECIMEN in sans serif capitals 26 x 3mm reading diagonally downwards. This overprint was locally hand-stamped, and should not be confused with a much larger hand-stamp with serifed letters later applied to stamps used at the Postal Training School outside Nairobi.

SPECIAL ISSUES

1937 (May 12th) Coronation. As Aden.

S1	5c.	**green**	10	10
S2	20c.	**orange**	10	10
S3	30c.	**blue**	20	25
SP S1/3		**specimen set** perf (3)	£15	‡

1946 (Nov. 11th) Victory. As Aden.

S4	20c.	**reddish-orange** ..	15	10
S5	30c.	**dp blue**	10	10
SP S4/5		**specimen set** perf (2)	£16	‡

Placed on sale prematurely on Oct. 20th at Lindo (Tanganyika).

1948 (Dec. 1st) Silver Wedding. As Aden.

S6	20c.	**orange**	15	15
S7	£1	**rose-carmine** ..	£12	£15

1949 (Oct. 10th) U.P.U. As Aden.

S8	20c.	**red-orange**	15	15
S9	30c.	**indigo**	15	15
S10	50c.	**grey**	25	20
S11	1/-	**beech-brown** ..	50	50
S8/11		**set** (4)	1·00	1·00

1952 (Feb. 1st) Royal Visit. Design as Nos. 11 and 13, with inscription ROYAL VISIT 1952 added to frame plate. Perf. 13 x 12½ (C). Sheets 10 x 10.

S12	10c.	black and green	10	10
S13	1/–	black and brown	70	1·00

Number issued—10c., 1,020,044; 1/–, 320,409.

POSTAGE DUE STAMPS

1928-33 Typo De La Rue. Wmk. Multiple Script CA. Perf. 15 x 14. Sheets 12 x 10.

GD1	5c.	violet	20	30
GD2	10c.	carmine	25	40
GD3	20c.	yellow-green	30	50
GD4	30c.	brown ('31)	1·00	1·25

GD5	40c.	blue	1·50	2·50
GD6	1/–	grey-green ('33)	6·00	7·00
GD1/6		set (6v)	£10	£11
SPGD1/6		specimen set (6v)	£50	‡

1935 (May 1st) Typo De La Rue. Wmk. Multiple Script CA. Perf. 14. Sheets 10 x 10.

GD7	5c.	violet	5	10
GD8	10c.	carmine	10	15
GD9	20c.	green	15	25
GD10	30c.	brown	40	50
GD11	40c.	ultramarine	60	75
GD12	1/–	grey	1·00	1·25
GD7/12		set (6v)	2·25	3·00
SPGD7/12		specimen set (6v)	£35	‡

1942-43 Printers (typo) De La Rue. Perf. 13¾ x 14 (C). Sheets 12 x 20.

PD1	5c.	purple-violet (/43)	15	20
PD2	10c.	carmine-red (/42)	25	30
PD3	20c.	myrtle-green (/43)	35	45
PD4	40c.	dp ultramarine (/43)	1·00	1·25
PD1/4		set (4)	1·75	2·20

Apart from shade differences these printings are on rough paper and can thus be distinguished from the original printing of 1935.

KUWAIT

An Indian Postal Agency was opened on 21st January, 1915, and contemporary Indian stamps were used without overprint until 1923. Their use during this period may only be recognised by the named cancellation (spelt "KOWEIT" or "KUWAIT")

1923 (April 1st) -1924. Stamps of India (1911-22 Issue). Wmk. Star. overprinted KUWAIT at Government Printing Works, Calcutta. The overprint measures 13mm. (thick letters) on the Anna values; 15½mm. (Rupee values). All inscribed "INDIA POST- AGE" except Nos. G1, 2, which are "POST- AGE AND REVENUE".

G1	½a. **green**	.. ..	25	40
	b overprint double	..	£40	—
	c overprint omitted (in vertical pair with normal) ..		£90	—
G2	1a. **chocolate**	.. ..	25	40
	b overprint double	..	£40	—
	c overprint omitted (in vertical pair with normal) ..		£110	—
G3	1½a. **chocolate** (1¼A)		25	40
G4	1½a. **chocolate** (1¼As)	..	5·00	7·50
G5	2a. **mauve**	.. ..	25	30
G6	2½a. **ultramarine**	..	60	2·00
G7	3a. **orange-brown**	..	1·25	4·00
G8	3a. **ultramarine** ('24)	..	2·25	40
G9	4a. **olive-green**	..	2·25	3·50
G10	6a. **yellow-bistre**	..	2·75	3·50
G11	8a. **purple**	.. ..	3·25	4·00
G12	12a. **claret**	.. ..	4·25	5·00
G13	1r. **brown and green**	..	5·00	2·50
G14	2r. **car and yel-brown**	..	£12·50	£15
G15	5r. **ult and violet**	..	£30	£40
G16	10r. **green and scarlet**	..	£60	£75
G1/16	**set** (15v excluding G4)		£120	£150

Used prices are for copies with postal cal- cellations. The Rupee values. especially, are usually found used telegraphically, and are worth about two-thirds of the above prices.

G1*b* The second overprint is ½—¾mm. above the normal and between ¾mm. and 1½mm. to the left.

G2*b* The second overprint is ½mm. to the right of and slightly lower than the normal.

G1*c*/2*c* These stamps were overprinted in sheets of 256 — four panes, each 16 x 4. The varieties arise from an upward shift of the overprint, whereby the lower row was without overprint and an overprint fell on the gutter margin above the pane: on the upper three rows in the pane the overprint falls higher than on the normal stamps.

G1—G5 and G7—G8 exist with inverted over- print: they are genuine, but were probably not sold in the Post Office, although they are known used on cover.

G4 with inverted overprint exists with inverted watermark.

Dangerous forged overprints are known on all values. The inverted overprints have also been forged.

1923 Prepared for use, but not issued. As above, but overprinted "KOWEIT".

G1*a*/16*a* Set (14v excluding G4 and G8) For price, see after GO14*a*.

Only 24 sets were printed, of which the Royal Collection contains ⊞

1929-37. Stamps of India (1926-33 and 1932-36 Issues). Wmk. Mult. Star, over- printed KUWAIT at the Nasik Security Press. The overprint measures 13mm. (thin letters) on the Anna values; 19mm. (Rupee values). All inscribed "INDIA POSTAGE" except G17, 19, 21, 22, 27 "POSTAGE AND REVEN- UE".

G17	½a. **green**	.. ..	10	25
G18	½a. **green** ('34)	.. ..	1·00	25
G19	1a. **chocolate**	.. ..	2·50	25
G20	1a. **chocolate** ('34)	..	75	25
G21	2a. **purple**	.. ..	40	25
G22	2a. **vermilion**	.. ..	£10	£12
G23	2a. **vermilion** ('34)	..	3·00	3·00
G24	2a. **vermilion** ('37) Small die	.. ..	50	50
G25	3a. **blue**	.. ..	2·50	75
G26	3a. **carmine** ('34)	..	2·50	3·00
G27	4a. **sage-green**	..	£10	£15
G28	4a. **sage-green** ('34)	..	2·00	2·00
G29	6a. **bistre** ('37)	..	2·00	3·00
G30	8a. **purple**	.. ..	3·00	4·00
G31	12a. **claret** ('33)	..	4·00	5·00
G32	1r. **chocolate and green**		5·00	£10
G33	2r. **carmine and orange**		£15	£20
G34	5r. **ult and pur** ('37)	..	£35	£75
	a extended 'T'	..	£125	—
G35	10r. **grn and scarlet** ('34)		£50	£70
G36	15r. **blue and olive** ('37) .		£70	£140
	a extended 'T'	..	£200	—
G17/36	**set** (20v.)	.. ..	£200	£350

G24. For details of small die see note after INDIA G61.

*G*34*a*/36*a* The stem of T in KUWAIT extends down-wards ¾mm. on the lower left pane, Row 3, No. 2.

The following values are known with inverted watermark:—G17, 19, 22, 27, 30, 31, 32, 33 and 36.

Forged overprints on the Rupee values may be readily recognised, being only 16mm. in length.

1933 -34. Air Stamps of India (1929 Issue). Wmk. Mult. Star (sideways to left or right), overprinted KUWAIT at the Nasik Security Press. The overprint measures 16mm.

G37	2a.	**deep blue-green**	7·50	9·00
G38	3a.	**blue**	2·00	2·00
		a basic stamp doubly printed	£80	£150
G39	4a.	**drab**	£65	£95
G40	6a.	**bistre** (7/34)	3·00	4·00
G37/40		**set** (4v.)	£75	£105

Numbers issued—

2a., 10,512; 3a., 48,096; 4a., 3,312.

Dangerous forged overprints are known on all values, especially the 4a. A bogus overprint is also recorded on the 12a. India Air Stamp.

1939-45 Stamps of India (1937-46 Issue), overprinted KUWAIT. The overprint measures 12mm. (low values). 19mm. (Rupee values).

1	½a.	**red-brown**	30	30
2	1a.	**carmine**	20	25
3	2a.	**vermilion**	40	40
4	3a.	**yellow-green**	60	70
5	4a.	**dp brown**	80	2·00
6	6a.	**greenish-blue**	1·00	2·50
7	8a.	**violet-slate**	2·00	3·00
8	12a.	**dp crimson**	2·50	4·00
9	14a.	**purple** (/45)	2·00	3·25
10	1r.	**vio-grey and lt brown**		
		a extended 'T'	2·50	2·00
		b overprint, treble one inverted	—	—

1	2r.	**vio-pur and brown**	2·00	1·50
		a extended 'T'	—	—
		b 1st repair	—	—
		c dp pur and brown	50	70
12	5r.	**dp green and dp blue**	4·00	4·00
		a extended 'T'	—	—
		b 2nd repair	—	—
13	10r.	**vio-pur and red-claret**	£12	£14
		a extended 'T'	—	—
		b 2nd repair	—	—
		c overprint double	£75	—
14	15r.	**chocolate and dp grn**	£22	£24
		a extended 'T'	—	—
		b 2nd repair	—	—
1/14		**set** (14)	£45	£55

10*b* Only one copy has been recorded.

10*a*/14*a* The stem of T in Kuwait extends down-wards ¾mm. on the lower left pane, Row 3/2 (See illustration after G36).

1st Repair   2nd Repair

The extended T was subsequently repaired in two stages, as illustrated, leaving minor traces.

11*b* Only the 2r. (earlier shade) has been recorded with 1st repair.

12*b*/14*b* Only the 5r, 10r, and 15r. have been re-corded with 2nd. repair.

13*c* Only one sheet of 120 is known on which the double overprint is less prominent on the right-hand side. Row 3/2 of the lower left pane shows the 2nd repair (as 13*b*).

14 is usually found with wmk. inverted; it is scarce with upright wmk.

Forged overprints on the Rupee values may be readily recognised, being only 16½mm. in length.

Between May 1941 and 1945 Indian stamps without overprint were in use and may be recog-nised by the cancellation ("SUPDT. OF POST OFFICES./PERSIAN GULF." from 24.5.41 to 6.6.41; "EXPERIMENTAL P.O. K-79" from 10.6.41 to 30.9.41, and named KUWAIT can-cellations from October 1941).

Between May 1941 and January 1942 the very small amount of mail for U.K. was despatched in the Diplomatic Bag to London where it was franked with G.B. stamps and posted.

Collectors are warned of forged "KUWAIT PERSIAN GULF" cancellation dated 19th Novem-ber, 1942, or with date omitted, on Indian stamps without overprint (1941/43 issue and 1937 Rupee values).

The Indian Victory stamps (S1—4) were issued (without overprint) in Kuwait in 1946, but are very scarce with Kuwait postmarks.

1945 Stamps of India (1941-3 Issue), overprinted KUWAIT.

15	3p.	slate	.. .. ..	10	10
16	½a.	purple	.. .. ..	10	10
17	9p.	green	.. ..	10	15
18	1a.	rose-carmine	..	15	15
19	1½a.	slate-pur	.. ..	15	15
20	2a.	vermilion	.. ..	15	20
21	3a.	bright violet	..	20	20
22	3½a.	blue	.. .. ..	20	20
23	4a.	brown	.. ..	35	50
24	6a.	greenish-blue	..	3·00	3·00
25	8a.	violet-slate	..	25	30
26	12a.	dp crimson	.. ..	30	40
15/26		set (12)	.. ..	5·00	5·50

A similar overprint on the 1¼a. of this issue of India is bogus.

1948 (April 1st) -49 Stamps of Great Britain overprinted KUWAIT, and surcharged by Harrison & Sons. The change from Indian to G.B. stamps coincided with change of administration.

27	½a./½d.	green	.. ..	10	10
28	1a./1d.	scarlet	.. ..	10	15
29	1½a./1½d.	red-brown	..	10	15
30	2a./2d.	dull orange	..	10	15
31	2½a./2½d.	ultramarine	..	10	15
32	3a./3d.	purple-violet	..	10	15
		overprint albino in pair with normal	..	£800	£900
34	6a./6d.	pale purple	..	15	20
35	1r./1/-	bistre-brown	..	30	25
36	2r./2/6	green	.. ..	1·00	1·00
37	5r./5/-	red	.. ..	3·00	3·00
	a	T Guide Line	..	—	—
38	10r./10/-	ult (4/7/49)	..	£12	6·00
27/38		set (11)	..	£17	£11

32a—Five sheets of the 3 Anna value were sold in Kuwait in early 1949 on which a small number of stamps in the lower left corner were wholly or partly without overprint and/or surcharge on account of inadequate inking of the plate.

One sheet was preserved and shows Row 19/1 "3 ANNAS" albino, Row 20/1 overprint and surcharge albino, Row 20/2 "KUW" of "KUWAIT" very faint and "3 ANNAS" albino, Row 20/3 "ANNAS" very faint, and Row 20/4 and 5 the first "A" and the "S" of "ANNAS" faint.

From the second sheet a strip (Row 20/1-4) was preserved mint. The other sheets were broken up, the variety unnoticed; but two pairs survived, one used on piece (13th March, 1949) of which the left hand stamp shows 3 ANNAS albino whilst the first "A" and the "S" of ANNAS are faint on the right hand stamp; and the other a vertical pair, the top stamp being normal except for faint first "A" in ANNAS and the lower stamp lacking both overprint (except for "T") and surcharge.

A few single used copies from these sheets are also known.

37a See G.B. 18*b* (Row 2/7).

Number issued—½a., 443,355; 1a., 460,535; 1½a., 424,579; 2a., 479,423; 2½a., 394,239; 3a., 1,243,707; 6a., 1,853,344; 1r., 445,074; 2r., 48,807; 5r., 43,154; 10r., 19,351.

Crude and easily recognised forged and bogus overprints exist on many values in all the foregoing issues. They were handstamped on used Indian (or G.B.) stamps.

1951 (May 3rd) -55 As No. 27, etc., but colours changed (Nos. 45—7 as Nos. 34—6 of G.B.), similarly overprinted and surcharged.

39	½a./½d.	dull orange	..	10	10
40	1a./1d.	ultramarine	..	10	10
41	1½a./1½d.	green	..	10	10
42	2a./2d.	red-brown	..	10	15
43	2½a./2½d.	scarlet	..	15	20
44	4a./4d.	lt blue (2/10/50)	..	15	15
45	2r./2/6	green (Type I)	..	2·00	1·00
	a	extra bar in ovpt		£90	£80
	b	Type II ('53)	..	£45	£20
	c	Type III (/55)	..	£100	£35
46	5r./5/-	red	.. ..	3·00	3·50
	a	extra bar in ovpt		£80	£70
47	10r./10/-	ultramarine	..	5·00	3·50
	a	Type II ('53)	..	£25	£20
	b	Type III	..	—	£100
39/47		set (9)	.. ..	£10	8·50

Type I

45 Type I. "KUWAIT" in sharp letters.
"2" and "RUPEES" in line, overall measurement 16mm.

Type II

45 Type II. "KUWAIT" in slightly heavier, worn type.

"2" raised in relation to RUPEES", overall measurement 15½mm.

45 Type III. As Type II but space between bars and 'K' of KUWAIT is only 2¾mm instead of 3mm. The surcharge is set slightly further to the left of KUWAIT.

KUWAIT

1O RUPEES

Type I

47 Type I. Letters clean-edged and with D-shaped loops to 'R' and 'P'.

'1' and 'O' spaced 1 mm.

KUWAIT

1O RUPEES

Type II

47 Type II. Letters worn and with small circular loops to 'R' and 'P'.

'1' and 'O' spaced ¾mm. (the 'O' being further away from 'R')

47 Type III. Appearance as Type II, but the two lines of overprint are 10mm apart instead of 9mm. Only a few used copies have been recorded.

45/46 A third (thinner) bar appears on part of the printing only.

45a between the normal two bars Row 7/2

A single copy has been recorded on which a third thinner bar appears *below* the normal two bars (Sheet position not known).

46a above the normal two bars Row 2/2

Number issued—½a., 446,569; 1a., 486,629; 1½a., 253 725; 2a., 467,487; 2½a., 245,675; 4a., 433,391; 2r., 59,975; 5r., 48,117; 10r., 36,050.

SPECIAL ISSUES

1948 (May 1st) Silver Wedding Issue of Great Britain, overprinted KUWAIT and surcharged.

S1	2½a./2½d.	**ultramarine**	10	10
S2	15r./£1	**dp blue**	£25	£28
	a	short bars	—	—

S2a The bars cancelling the Sterling value on Row 3/4 are 3mm. long, compared with 3½mm. on the rest of the sheet.

Number issued—2½a., 179,060; 15r., 21,703.

1948 (July 29th) Olympic Games Issue of Great Britain, overprinted KUWAIT and surcharged.

S3	2½a./2d.	**ultramarine**	10	15
S4	3a./3d.	**violet**	15	20
S5	6a./6d.	**reddish-purple**	30	45
	a	'H.L.P.' retouch	£40	—
S6	1r./1/–	**bistre-brown**	60	75
S3/6		**set** (4)	1·00	1·50

S5a—Initials H.L.P. erased from the Jubilee lines below Nos. 118/119/120, Cyl. 9 stop (See Great Britain S14b).

Number issued—2½a., 89,264; 3a., 91,203; 6a., 83,677; 1r., 83,395.

1949 (Oct. 10th) U.P.U. Issue of Great Britain, overprinted KUWAIT and surcharged.

S7	2½a./2½d.	**ultramarine**	10	20
	a	Indian lake	£35	£35
S8	3a./3d.	**pale violet**	20	35
S9	6a./6d.	**reddish-mauve**	40	60
S10	1r./1/–	**bistre-brown**	80	85
S7/10		**set** (4)	1·50	2·00

S7a—For details of this variety see Great Britain No. S16b. (Row 8/2).

Number issued—2½a., 90,781; 3a., 89,968; 6a., 92,897; 1r., 77,904.

OFFICIAL STAMPS

Between 1915 and 1923 contemporary Indian Service stamps were very occasionally used in Kuwait, and may only be recognised by the named cancellation (spelt KOWEIT or KUWAIT).

1923-4. Stamps of India (1911-22 Issue). Wmk. Star, overprinted KUWAIT SERVICE in two lines at Government Printing Works, Calcutta. The overprint is spaced 9½mm. between lines (Anna values) and 12mm. (Rupee values). Measurements of KUWAIT as on Ordinary issue: SERVICE 14mm. (Anna values); 16½mm. (Rupee values). All inscribed "INDIA POSTAGE" except G01, 02 "POSTAGE AND REVENUE".

GO1	½a.	**green**	15	75
	b	overprint double		
		one albino ..	£35	—
GO2	1a.	**chocolate** ..	15	75
	b	overprint double		
		one albino ..	£20	—
GO3	1½a.	**chocolate** (1½A) ..	40	3·00
GO4	2a.	**mauve**	40	3·00
GO5	2½a.	**ultramarine**	1·25	4·00
GO6	3a.	**orange-brown** ..	1·75	4·00
GO7	3a.	**ultramarine** ('24) .	50	3·00
GO8	4a.	**olive-green** ..	1·00	5·00
GO9	8a.	**purple**	1·25	5·00
GO10	1r.	**brown and green**	3·00	£15
	b	overprint double		
		one albino ..	£30	—
	c	broken 'T' ..	£30	—
GO11	2r.	**car and orange** ..	5·00	£25
	b	broken 'T' ..	£45	—
GO12	5r.	**ult and violet** ..	£10	£45
	b	overprint double		
		one albino ..	£60	—
GO13	10r.	**green and scarlet** ..	£25	£75
GO14	15r.	**blue and olive** ..	£30	£100
GO1/O14		**set** (14v) ..	£75	£275

Used prices are for copies with postal cancellations. The Rupee values, especially, are usually found used telegraphically, and are worth about two-thirds of the above prices.

KUWAIT

GO10*c*/GO11*b* The right arm of the 'T' of KUWAIT is broken off, giving the impression of an inverted 'L' (position not known).

1923 Prepared for use, but not issued. As above, but overprinted "KOWEIT SERVICE".

GO1a/14a Set (13v excluding GO7)—Price for Set, Ordinary and Service (27v) Mint .. £8,000

Only 24 sets were printed, of which the Royal Collection contains ⊞

1929-33 Stamps of India (1926-33 Issue). Wmk. Mult. Star, overprinted KUWAIT SERVICE in two lines at the Nasik Security Press. The overprint is spaced 10mm. between lines (Anna values) and 15mm. (Rupee values). Measurements of KUWAIT as on ordinary issue: SERVICE 13½mm. (Anna values); 19½mm. (Rupee values). All inscribed "INDIA POSTAGE" except GO15, O16, O18, "POSTAGE AND REVENUE".

GO15	1a.	**chocolate** ..	15	5·00
GO16	2a.	**purple**	5·00	£10
GO17	3a.	**blue**	45	5·00
GO18	4a.	**sage-green** ..	1·50	£10
GO19	8a.	**purple**	1·50	£10
GO20	12a.	**claret**	3·00	£15
GO21	1r.	**chocolate and grn**	3·00	£25
GO22	2r.	**car and orange** ..	5·00	£40
GO23	5r.	**ult and pur** ..	£15	£75
GO24	10r.	**green and scarlet**	£30	£90
GO25	15r.	**blue and olive** ..	£40	£175
GO15/O25		**set** (11v) ..	£90	£450

The following values are known with inverted watermark:—GO15, 18, 19, 20, 22, 23 and 25.

Easily recognised forged overprints (on used Indian Service stamps) exist on this and the preceeding issue.

SEMI POSTAL ISSUES

1948   1949

Labels, having the appearance of postage stamps but without denomination, were supplied by the State Secretariat to the Post Office in celebration of the anniversary of accession of Shaikh Ahmad al Jabir (1921-50).

The Post Office affixed them to both incoming and outgoing letters and, although they had no postal validity, they are occasionally found with postal cancellations.

(a) Booklet of 10 panes of 10 (5 x 2 with narrow margin all round), stapled. Line Perf.

SP1	1947	**reddish violet** (p.11)	25	—
SP2	1948	**bluish violet** (p.11½)	75	—

(b) Sheets with Serial Number (vertically upwards) in left margin opposite bottom row.

| SP3 | 1949 | **emerald** (p.11½) .. | 1·50 | — |

For more detailed information on this issue and Postal History of Kuwait see "The Postal Agencies in Eastern Arabia and the Gulf" by Neil Donaldson.

LEEWARD ISLANDS

This group forms the Northern part of the chain of islands stretching from Porto Rico to Trinidad, and included the following Colonies and Dependencies. From May 1858 to March 1860, G.B. stamps were in use, and were cancelled with numbered transverse ovals of horizontal bars, as indicated:—

Antigua (with Barbuda)—AO2, A18

Dominica (transferred to Windward Group 1940)—AO7.

Nevis	— Later St. Kitts—	— AO9
St. Christopher	Nevis–Anguilla	— A12
Montserrat—AO8.		
Virgin Islands (Tortola)—A13.		

Between 1861 and 1876 all these territories first issued their own stamps; but in 1890 the general issue for the Leeward Islands replaced individual issues. From 1899 (Virgin Islands) and 1903 (the remainder) individual issues again appeared and were in concurrent use with the Leeward Islands general issues until June 1956, when the latter were withdrawn and invalidated.

All stamps Typo. De La Rue & Co., unless otherwise stated.

1890 (Oct. 31st) Wmk. Crown CA. Perf. 14. Sheets 120—two panes, each 6 x 10.

V1	½d. **dull mauve and green**	25	20
V2	1d. **dull mauve and rose**	40	20
	a Leeward Is. and duty plate shifted to right	£90	—
V3	2½d. **dull mauve and blue**	1·25	40
V4	4d. **dull mauve and brn-or**	2·50	2·50
V5	6d. **dull mauve and brown**	2·50	2·50
V6	7d. **dull mauve and grey**	2·00	2·50
V7	1/- **green and carmine** ..	£10	£10
V8	5/- **green and blue** ..	£60	£70
V1/8	**set** (8)	£75	£85
SP V1/8 **specimen set**	..	£90	‡

V2*a*—Very few copies are known, from a single pane of 60.

1897 (July 22nd) Queen Victoria's Diamond Jubilee. Overprinted in black on previous issue.

V9	½d. **dull mauve and grn**	3·00	4·00
	a overprint inverted ..	—	—
	b overprint double ..	£150	—
V10	1d. **dull mauve and rose**	3·00	4·00
	a overprint double ..	£150	—
	b overprint triple ..	—	—
V11	2½d. **dull mauve and blue**	4·00	5·00
	a overprint double ..	£150	—
V12	4d. **dull mauve and brn-orange**	£10	£12
	a overprint double ..	£175	—
V13	6d. **dull mauve and brn**	£18	£20
	a overprint double ..	£300	—
V14	7d. **dull mauve and grey**	£20	£22
	a overprint double ..	£350	—
V15	1/- **green and carmine** ..	£70	£90
V16	5/- **green and blue** ..	£550	£600
	a overprint double ..	£2000	—
V9/16	**set** (8)	£650	£700

Numbers sold—V9, 12,963; V10, 12,811; V11, 9,833; V12, 4,747; V13, 2,690; V14, 2,687; V15, 1,743; V16, 784.

The stamps were officially on sale for only one week.

1902 (Aug. 11th) Surcharged in black.

V17	1d. on 4d. **mauve and or** ..	80	2·0(
	a tall narrow O in ONE in pair with normal	9·00	£10
	b surcharge double ..	—	—
V18	1d. on 6d. **mauve and brn**	50	2·00
	a tall narrow O in ONE in pair with normal	£10	£12

Numbers issued—V17/18, 37,200 each.

V19	1d. on 7d. **mauve and grey**	70	2·00

Number issued—37,200.

1902 (Sept. 1) Wmk. Crown CA. Perf. 14.
Sheets as before.

E1	½d. **dull pur and grn** ..	30	40
E2	1d. **dull pur and car** ..	50	20
E3	2d. **dull pur and ochre**..	1·25	1·25
E4	2½d. **dull pur and blue** ..	1·50	2·50
	a malformed 'WA' ..	£20	£20
E5	3d. **dull pur and black** ..	1·25	2·00
E6	6d. **dul! pur and brown** .	1·50	4·00
E7	1/– **green and carmine** .	4·00	4·00
	a dropped 'R' ..	£20	£20
E8	2/6 **green and black** ..	£12	£14
E9	5/– **green and blue** ..	£20	£24
E1/9	**set** (9)	£40	£50
SP E1/9	**specimen set** (9) ..	£80	F

LEEWARD	LEEWARD
Normal	Malformed 'WA'

E4*a*—Row 6/1 (left pane – Plate 2).

E7*a*—The 'R' in 'LEEWARD' is noticeably dropped in Row 1/1 (Plate 2).

1905/8 Wmk. Mult. Crown CA. Perf. 14.
Chalky paper (E10 and E14 also on Ordinary paper).

E10	½d. **dull pur and grn** ..	20	25
E11	1d. **dull pur and car** ..	50	25
E12	2d. **dull pur and ochre**..	1·50	4·00
E13	2½d. **dull pur and blue** ..	6·00	8·00
	a malformed 'WA' ..	£45	£50
E14	3d. **dull pur and blk** ..	3·00	4·00
E15	6d. **dull pur and brn** ..	7·00	9·00
E16	1/– **grn and carmine** ..	£12	£14
E10/16	**set** (7)	£30	£40

E13*a*—See Note under E4*a*.

1907/11 Wmk. Mult. Crown CA. Perf. 14.
E17/21 O; E22/26C.

E17	½d. **brown** (4/7/09) ..	10	30
E18	½d. **green**	20	10
E19	1d. **deep red**	45	20
	a rose carmine ..	6·00	25
E20	2d. **grey**	80	3·00
E21	2½d. **bright blue**	90	2·50
	a malformed 'WA' ..	£30	£30
E22	3d. **purple/yellow** ..	1·50	3·00
E23	6d. **dull and bt-purple** ..	1·50	3·00

E24	1/– **black/green**	5·00	7·50
E25	2/6 **blk and red/blue** ..	£11	£15
E26	5/– **green and red/yel** ..	£30	£32
E17/26	**set** (10)	£50	£65
SP E17/6	**specimen set** (10)	£80	‡

E21*a*—See Note under E4*a*.

See Introduction for details of Dies I and II.

1912 (Oct. 23rd)-22 Wmk. Mult. CA. Perf. 14.
All Die I unless otherwise stated. Sheets as before. G1/5 O; G6/12 C.

G1	½d. **deep chocolate** ..	15	10
	a brown	20	15
G2	½d. **yellow green** ..	25	20
	a green	35	20
	b blue green	35	20
G3	1d. **carmine red** ..	30	10
	a bright scarlet ..	50	15
	b rose scarlet	50	15
	c rose pink	90	90
G4	2d. **grey**	35	80
	a drab grey	50	1·00
G5	2½d. **ultramarine** ..	2·00	3·00
	a bright blue	2·00	3·00
G6	3d. **purple/yellow** ..	30	1·25
	a dp-pur/yellow ..	35	1·50
	b dp-pur/gold-yel ..	1·00	2·00
	c white back	£10	£15
	d dp dull-pur/lemon..	1·00	200
	e dull and dp-purple/ orange buff ..	80	1·50
	f dull and dp-purple/ yellow buff	£10	£12
G7	4d. **grey-blk and red/buff** Die II	50	1·50
	a grey and red/pale yell Die II	80	2·00
G8	6d. **lilac and bt mauve**..	60	1·50
	a dp and br purple ..	80	1·80
G9	1/– **black/green** ..	2·50	2·00
	a white back	£12	£12
	b grey-blk/blue-green (olive back) ..	1·00	1·25
G10	2/– **pur and blue/blue** Die II	3·00	4·00
G11	2/6 **blk and red/blue** ..	£10	8·00
G12	5/– **dull grn and red/yel**	£10	£12
	a white back	£12	£15
	b dp-grn and red-/ lemon	6·00	9·00

	c grn and red/orange buff	.. ..	£20	£25
G1/12	**set** (12)	.. ..	£22	£24

SP G1/12 **specimen set** (12) .. £90   ‡

**1921/32 Wmk. Mult. Script CA. Perf. 14.
G13/22 O; G23/32 C.**

DIE II (1921-29)

G13	¼d. **pale brown**	.. ..	10	10
	a chocolate	.. ..	10	10
	b deep brown		10	10
	c blk brown	.. ..	15	15
G14	½d. **dull green**	..	10	10
	a green		10	10
	b bright green..	..	15	15
G15	1d. **carmine red** ..		10	15
	a rose carmine		15	15
G16	1d. **dull vio and mauve**		25	25
	a violet	..	15	15
	b bright violet	..	20	20
G17	1½d. **carmine red** ..		10	30
	a rose carmine	..	20	30
	b rose red	..	20	30
G18	1½d. **dp red brown**	..	10	15
	a red brown	..	20	25
G19	2d. **grey** ..	..	15	15
	a slate grey	..	20	25
	b deep slate	..	20	25
G20	2½d. **orange yellow**	..	3·00	8·00
G21	2½d. **dull blue**	..	1·00	2·00
	a bright blue ..		30	40
G22	3d. **ultramarine** ..		3·00	4·00
	a deep bright blue	..	7·00	9·00
G23	3d. **purple/lemon**		40	1·20
G24	4d. **blk and red/lemon**	..	40	1·20
	a grey blk and red/yel		50	2·00
G25	5d. **brn-pur and olive** ..		35	1·00
	a dull pur and ol-grn		70	1·20
	b lilac and ol-grn	..	80	1·20
G26	6d. **dull and bt-purple** ..		3·00	5·00
	a dp pur and bt mauve		3·50	6·00
G27	1/– **black/emerald**	..	1·00	2·50
G28	2/– **sl pur and blue/blue**		£10	£12
	a reddish purple and blue/blue	..	4·00	5·00
	b wmk inverted	..	£80	—
G29	2/6 **blk and red/blue**	..	4·00	7·00
	a grey blk and red/blue		6·00	8·00
G30	3/– **yell-grn and bt-blue**		7·00	9·00
	a blue grn and dp vio		8·00	9·50
G31	4/– **black and red**	..	8·00	£10
	a grey-blk and red	..	8·00	£10
G32	5/– **grn and red/yel**	..	£15	£18

G28*b*— only one sheet recorded.

DIE I (1931-32)

G33/37 O; G38/39 C.

G33	¼d. **black brown**	..	10	15
G34	½d. **green** ..	.. ..	10	1·00
G35	1d. **rose red**	.. ..	10	15
G36	1½d. **red brown**	..	40	50
G37	2½d. **ultramarine** ..		70	1·25
G38	6d. **dp-pur and mauve**..		3·00	4·00
G39	1/– **black/emerald**	..	£10	£12

1928 Wmk. Mult. Script CA. Perf. 14. Sheets 12 x 5.

G40	10/– **grn and red/grn** ..	£50	£60

Wmk. Mult. Crown CA. Perf. 14.

G41	£1 **pur and blk/red** ..	£150	£185
G13/41	**set** (22)	£240	£310
SP G13/41	**specimen set** (22)	£160	‡

Numbers issued—G40, 30,300; G41, 12,600.

G40/41—The Damaged Scroll ((Row 1/12) and Broken Crown (Row 2/12) varieties are known (See notes after BERMUDA No. G55).

G40A	Damaged Scroll	..	£200	—
G40B	Broken Crown	.. ..	£300	—
G41A	Damaged Scroll	..	£350	—
G41B	Broken Crown	.. ..	£450	—

1935 (*May 6th*) (*recess*) **Printers, Waterlow & Sons. Wmk. Script CA. Perf. 11 x 12. Sheets 6 x 10.**

G42	1d. **dp-blue and car** ..		10	15
G43	1½d. **ult and grey**	..	25	40
G44	2½d. **brown and dp-blue**		80	1·00
G45	1/– **slate and purple**	..	3·00	4·00
G42/45	**set** (4)	.. ..	4·00	5·50
SP G42/45	**specimen set** perf (4)	£18	‡

1938 (**Nov. 25th**) **-51 Printers** (*typo*) **De La Rue. Perf. 13¾ x 14 (C). Sheets 120—two panes, each 6 x 10.**

(a) (**Small format**).

1	¼d. **brown**	.. ..	10	5
	a light brown (29/9/47)		10	5
	b dp brn (ch) (13/6/49)		10	10
2	½d. **green** ..	.. ..	10	10
	a blue-green (3/42) ..		15	10
	b yellow-green	..	15	10
3	1d. **scarlet** (Die I)	..	70	70
	a scarlet (Die II) (/40)		20	15

b carmine (Die II) (8/42)	35	1·00
c rose-scarlet (Die II) (10/5/44) ..	20	10
d DI flaw	£30	£30
e dull car-rose (Die II) (13/9/48) ..	40	40
f DI flaw (13/9/48)	£30	£30
4 1½d. **dull red-brown** ..	15	10
a dp red-brn (3/12/43)	15	10
b pale brn	10	10
5 2d. **grey**	15	15
a slate (8/42)	20	15
b pale grey (11/42) ..	20	15
c pale slate (29/9/47) .	20	15
d silver grey	20	20
6 2½d. **blue**	20	20
a pale blue (10/5/44).	15	15
7 3d. **dp orange** (ch) ..	2·50	80
a orange (sub) (3/42)	40	30
b orange (thin paper) (11/42)	30	20
c pale orange (thin paper) (10/5/44) ..	25	15
8 6d. **dull and red-pur** (ch)	70	70
b pale and bright purple (blurred imp.) (sub) (8/42)	60	60
d dull and red-purple (sub) (11/42) ..	50	50
e broken E ..	£30	£30
f deep and red-purple (ch) (29/9/47) ..	25	25
g broken E ..	£30	£30
h purple and bt purple (ch) 24/10/51) ..	25	25
9 1/- **blk/ emerald grn** (ch)	1·00	70
a ditto (olive back) (ch)	1·00	70
aa D I flaw exist as 1d. but position on sheet not the same	£60	£60
b blk/grn (sub) (3/42)	40	40
c grey and blk/grn (sub) (8/42)	6·00	4·00
d blk and grey/grn (sub) (11/42)	£15	8·00
10 2/- **pur and dp blue/dull blue** (ch)	2·00	1·50
a red-pur and dp blue/ blue (sub) (3/42)	2·00	1·50
b dp pur and dp blue/ pale blue (sub) (29/9/47) ..	1·50	1·50
11 5/- **grn and red/yel** (ch)	4·00	3·00
a broken E	£50	—
b grn and scar/pale yell (sub) (3/12/43)..	2·50	3·00
c broken E ..	£40	—
d grn and dp red/pale yellow (sub) (1951)	2·50	3·00

(b) (Large format) £1 (wmk. Multiple Crown CA). Perf. 14 x 13¾ (C). Sheets 12 x 5.

12 10/- **grn and red/grn** (ch)	8·00	4·00
a grn and red/grn (sub) (3/12/43) ..	4·00	4·50
aa scroll flaw	£60	—
b grn and red/grn (emer back) (sub) (10/5/44) ..	5·00	5·00
13 £1 **dp purple and black/ crimson-red** (ch) ..	£40	£38
ba purpleand black/deep brick red (/39) ..	£40	£38
a pur and blk/car-red (ch) (3/42) ..	£10	£12
aa scroll flaw ..	£80	—
aaa dp purple and black/ dp car red (11/42)	£10	£12
b pur and blk/salmon-red (ch) (3/12/43)	£10	£10
1/13b (inc. 14/19) **set** (19)	£20	£20
SP 1/13 **specimen set** perf (13)	£60	‡

No. 3—The top of the 1 in Die I is more pointed than in Die II (see illustration).

No. 3a—Whilst Die II was not released in London until 1942, used copies exist postmarked as early as 1940.

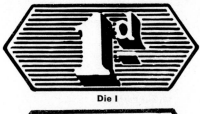

Die I

Die II

Fluorescent aniline ink was used in printing from duty plate of the 1d. stamps released in London 17/11/48 but as the shade was similar to No. 3e a separate listing is not called for.

Nos. 3d/3f—The base of the letter D and I are cut away. Row 7/3 left pane.

No. 7c—The paper used until 1942 for the 3d. stamps was similar to that used for the 6d. value; later, thin paper, as used for lower values, was employed.

Nos. 8e/8g and 11a/11c—The top bar of second E of LEEWARD is missing, Row 4/1 right pane. This flaw was corrected in the 1949 release.

No. 9a—It is possible that this stamp formed part of the first consignment. It was on sale for a considerable period in more than one island.

Nos. 12aa/13aa—See Bermuda for details of Scroll variety Type A which occurred on Row 5/12 of the March and August, 1942 printings of these stamps.

1949 (July 1st) -51 As No. 2, etc., but colours changed and stamps printed on chalk-coated paper.

14	½d.	**grey**	.. .. ..	10	10
	a	slate (/50)	..	20	20
15	1d.	**green**	.. ..	10	15
	a	Dl flaw		£12	£12
16	1½d.	**orange and black**	..	15	15
17	2d.	**scarlet**		15	15
18	2½d.	**black and red-purple**		20	20
19	3d.	**dp blue**	. ..	25	15
14/19		**set** (6)	.. ..	1·00	1·00

No. 14a—Supplies of this value which went to some of the islands were distinctly slate in shade.

No 15a—See Note under No. 3d.

As No. 13, but Perf. 13¼ x 13 (C).

21	£1	**vio and blk/crimson**	-		
		(13/12/51)	.. ..	8·00	8·00

a	wmk. sideways	..	£600	—
aa	frame double print one			
	albino	.. ..	£200	—
b	wmk. inverted	..	£150	—

Only one sheet each of 21a, 21b are known to exist.

No. 21aa—One sheet showed lower rows with clear Albino double print of the frame clearly visible when stamp held at 45 degrees to a light source.

SPECIAL ISSUES

1937 (May 12th) Coronation. As Aden.

S1	1d. **scarlet**	.. ..	20	20
S2	1½d. **light brown**	..	20	20
S3	2½d. **blue**	.. .. ..	30	30
SP S1/3	**specimen set** perf (3)		£15	‡

1946 (Nov. 1st) Victory. As Aden.

S4	1½d. **light brown**	..	10	10
S5	3d. **reddish-orange**	..	10	10
SP S4/5	**specimen set** perf (2)		£18	‡

1949 (Jan. 2nd) Silver Wedding. As Aden.

S6	2½d. **ultramarine**	..	10	10
S7	5/- **grey-green**	.. ..	3·50	4·50

1949 (Oct. 10th) U.P.U. As Aden.

S8	2½d. **slate**	.. .. ..	15	15
S9	3d. **indigo**	.. ..	25	30
S10	6d. **reddish-mauve**	..	50	50
S11	1/- **quartz-green**	..	70	70
S8/11	**set** (4)	.. ..	1·50	1·50

1951 (Feb. 16th) West Indies University College. See Antigua.

S12	3c. **orange and black**	..	10	10
S13	12c. **carmine and dp lake**		30	30

MALAYA

STRAITS SETTLEMENTS

1937-41. Printers (*typo*) **De La Rue. Perf. 13¾ x 14 (C). Chalk-surfaced paper unless otherwise indicated. Sheets 10 x 10.**

(a) Die 1.

1	1c.	**black** (1/1/38) ..	10	10
2	2c.	**yel-grn** (6/12/37) ..	10	10
3	4c.	**orange** (1/1/38) ..	40	10
4	5c.	**chocolate** (19/11/37)	30	10
5	6c.	**scarlet-rose** (10/1/38)	40	10
		a scarlet (/41) ..	20	10
6	8c.	**grey** (26/1/38) ..	60	10
		a booklet pane of 10..	8·00	—
7	10c.	**dp purple** (8/11/37)..	45	10
8	12c.	**ultramarine** (10/1/38)	55	10
9	25c.	**pur and car** (11/12/37)	3·00	30
10	30c.	**purple and orange** (1/12/37)	1·75	50
11	40c.	**scarlet and purple** (20/12/37) .	1·75	50
12	50c.	**blk/emerald** (26/1/38)	60	25
		a brownish-grey and black/green (/39)	4·00	1·00
		b black/green (/41) ..	60	25
13	$1	**blk, car/blue** (26/1/38)	1·00	30
		a blk, scarlet/blue (/40)	2·00	70
14	$2	**grn and car** (21/1/38)	4·00	1·50
15	$5	**grn, car/grn** (21/1/38)	7·00	2·50
		a grn, scar/grn (/41)..	£10	4·00
1/15		**set** (15)	£20	£10
SP 1/15		**specimen set** perf (18)	£80	‡

(b) Die 2. (No. 21 is Perf. 14¾ x 14 (C).

16	2c.	**green** (28/12/38) ..	60	10
		a yellow-green (/41) .	1·00	30
17	2c.	**orange** (6/10/41) ..	25	30
18	3c.	**green** (sub) (5/9/41)	30	35
		a yel-grn (sub) (/41)..	1·00	50
19	4c.	**orange** (29/10/38) ..	2·25	20
20	5c.	**chocolate** (18/2/39)..	70	15
		a booklet pane of 10 ..	8·00	—
21	15c.	**ult** (sub) (6/10/41) ..	1·00	1·00
		a dp ultramarine (sub)	2·00	1·50

Die 1—These stamps were printed in two operations and can be distinguished from Die 2 by the lower tip of the frond at the right side of the stamp which terminates with two points.

Die 2—These stamps were printed in one operation and the palm fronds are cut clear of the oval frame; moreover, the lower frond terminates in a single point.

Die 1   Die 2

PREPARED FOR USE BUT NOT ISSUED.
8c. **rose** (sub) at £6

After issue of No. 36, unoverprinted copies leaked out. Some exist with Singapore cancellations, but these probably did no postal service.

1945-8. As before but overprinted (in Great Britain, Australia or Kuala Lumpur) **BMA in Black or Red for use throughout MALAYA. Chalk-surfaced paper, unless otherwise indicated. Setting 5 x 5.**

(a) Die 1.

22	1c.	**black** (sub) (red) (10/10/45) ..	10	10
		a jet-black (brown gum) (10/10/45) ..	1·00	50
		b magenta overprint ..	—	£25
		c black (10/45) ..	10	10
		d blk (thin paper) (8/46)	1·00	75
23	2c.	**orange** (sub) (9/46)..	40	60
24	10c.	**dp purple** (sub) (10/10/45) ..	10	10
		a dp brown purple (brn gum) (10/45) ..	10	10
		b dull pur (thin paper) (7/46)	30	20
		c purple and dull purple (fugitive ink centre) (sub) (27/1/47) ..	30	25
		d purple (fugitive) (sub) (8/7/47)	10	10
		e magenta-purple (F.A.) (22/3/48) ..	30	20
		f reddish-purple (F.A.) (13/5/48) ..	10	10
25	12c.	**ult** (26/10/45)	35	70
26	25c.	**pur and car-red** (sub) (26/10/45)	20	10
		a purple and carmine (thin paper) (6/46)	75	20
		b purple and scarlet (sub) (15/10/46) .	20	10
		c purple and dp scarlet (22/3/48) ..	20	10
		d double overprint ..	£200	—

27	50c.	**blk/green** (sub) (red)		
		(26/10/45) ..	15	10
	a	black/green (12/45)	20	10
	b	blk/grn (F.A. over-print (sub) (/46)	40	15
28	$1	**black and carmine**		
		(sub) (26/10/45) ..	50	10
	a	black and dp scarlet (sub) (15/10/46)	50	10
29	$2	**grn and carmine-red**		
		(sub) (26/10/45) ..	80	30
	a	grn and scarlet (sub) (15/10/46) ..	1·00	40
30	$5	**green, scarlet/green** (1/11/45) ..	£18	£20
31	$5	**pur and brn-orange** (sub) (12/45) ..	2·50	70
	a	red-purple and yellow orange (sub) (8/7/47) ..	6·00	1·50
22/39		(1 each colour) (16v)	£22	£22
SP22/31		**specimen set perf** (14) ($5 pur/orange only)	£120	‡

(b) Die 2 (No. 38 is Perf. 14¾ x 14 (C).

32	2c.	**orange** (sub) (10/10/45)	10	10
	a	orange (white fore-head) (sub) (/46)	1·00	50
	b	orange (thin paper) (7/46)	50	50
	c	orange-yellow (sub) (27/1/47) ..	10	10
	d	orange (8/7/47) ..	20	10
	e	orange-yel (12/10/48)	20	10
33	3c.	**green** (sub) (10/10/45)	25	10
	a	blue-green (sub) (27/1/47) ..	30	10
	b	green (7/47) ..	50	10
	c	blue-green (/48) ..	25	10
34	5c.	**chocolate** (26/10/45)	15	10
35	6c.	**slate-grey** (sub) (10/10/45) ..	15	10
	a	slate (thin paper) (6/46)	50	25
	b	slate-grey (white fore-head) (sub) (/46)	50	15
	c	slate (sub) (/47) ..	20	10
	d	slate-grey (22/3/48)	20	10
36	8c.	**rose** (sub) (10/10/45)	15	10
	a	red-scar (sub) (2/46)	50	10
	b	dp red (thin paper) (6/46)	50	10
37	10c.	**red-purple** (28/7/48)	15	10
38	15c.	**ult** (black overprint) (sub) (26/10/45) ..	75	2·50
	a	pair overprinted BMA on margin of sheet	£10	£10
39	15c.	**ult** (red overprint) (sub) (12/45)	15	10
	a	dull ultramarine (sub) (15/10/46) ..	20	10
	b	steel-blue (sub) (8/7/47) ..	£10	3·00
	c	blue (27/11/47) ..	80	30
	d	ultramarine (22/3/48)	25	10

Whilst stamps overprinted "B.M.A." were not placed on sale until 10/10/45, the B.M.A. was in control prior to this date, but mail was carried free or charge, thus stamps were not necessary. The "B.M.A." stamps were withdrawn July 10th, 1951.

Postal Forgeries.

These exist of the 50c. B.M.A. made from the 1c. with paper dyed green and 1c. altered to 50c. Also 50c., $1 and $2 Singapore exist as total fakes perforated about perf. 12 on no watermark paper. Printing is good, colours as issued stamps. Worth from £20 each.

OVERPRINTED BUT NOT ISSUED.

8c. **grey** (overprinted as No. 22, etc.) £18.

On return of British Authorities in 1945, a quantity of these stamps was found in Kuala Lumpur and overprinted there, but the arrival of a supply of the 8c. rose made their emission unnecessary and thus a possible clashing with the 6c. grey was avoided. Used copies were proably cancelled a *complaisance.*

Victory stamps for use in the Malayan Union exist, but these were obtained during a destruction operation and were never officially issued. Value about £60 each.

SPECIAL ISSUES

1937 (May 12th) Coronation. As Aden. Perf. 13¾ x 14 (C). Sheets 5 x 10.

S1	4c. **orange**	.. ..	10	10
S2	8c. **dp grey**		10	10
S3	12c. **blue**	.. .. ..	20	20
SP S1/3	**specimen set** perf (3)		£15	‡

POSTAGE DUE STAMPS

1938-51. Printers (*typo*) **Waterlow & Sons. Perf. 14¾ x 14 (C). Sheets 10 x 10.**

PD1	1c. **violet-maroon** (4/38)		25	40
	a purple (/45) ..		50	60
	b purple-violet (/49) .		60	50
PD2	3c. **yellow-green** (/45) .		1·50	1·75
	a emerald-green (/49)		3·00	2·50
PD3	5c. **scarlet** (/45) ..		2·00	2·75
	a pink (/49) ..		2·00	2·75
PD4	8c. **ochre** (/49) ..		5·00	5·00
PD5	9c. **orange-yellow** (/45)		£10	£10
PD6	15c. **slate-violet** (/46) ..		£14	£12
PD7	20c. **deep blue** (/48) ..		3·00	4·00
	a dp vio-blue (6/3/51)		2·50	4·00
PD8	50c. **black** (1/38) ..		1·50	2·00
PD1/8	**set** (8)		£35	£35

Nos. PD1*a*, 2, 3, 5 and 6 were printed on the rough paper used during the war. Stamps of same design in other colours, or values, were issued before 1937.

1951 (Aug. 8th) -52. As No. PD1, etc., but Perf. 14 (L).

PD9	1c. **pur-violet** (21/8/52)		10	10

PD10	3c. **green**	.. ..	60	70
PD11	5c. **pink**	.. ..	80	1·00
PD12	8c. **ochre**	.. ..	20	20
PD13	20c. **dp blue**	.. ..	50	70

JOHORE

All stamps were printed (*typo*) by De La Rue on chalk-surfaced paper unless otherwise mentioned.

1922-40. Design, Portrait of Sultan Sir Ibrahim. Perf. 13¾ x 14 (C). Sheets 12 x 10 (also 10 x 10, and 120—two panes, each 6 x 10).

X1	1c. **dull pur and black** ..		20	15
X2	2c. **green** (/28)		25	25
	a **booklet pane of 10**..		—	—
X3	3c. **pur and sepia** (/28)		60	55
X4	4c. **pur and car** (/24) ..		60	15
	a **booklet pane of 10**..		—	—
X5	5c. **dull pur and sage grn**		25	15
X6	6c. **dull pur and claret**..		25	15
X7	10c. **dull pur and yel** (/22)		25	20
X8	12c. **dull purple and blue**	1·50	60
X9	12c. **ultramarine** (/40) ..	6·50	5·50
X10	21c. **dull pur and orange** (/28)		2·50	1·75
X11	25c. **dull pur and myrtle**		75	60
X12	30c. **dull pur and orange** (/36)		75	70
X13	40c. **dull pur and brn** (/36)	1·25	1·50
X14	50c. **dull purple and red**..	1·00	70
X15	$1 **green and mauve** ..	2·00	80
X16	$2 **green and car** (/23) .	4·00	2·00
X17	$3 **green and blue** (/25)	£12	£13
X18	$4 **green and brn** (/26) .	£13	£14
X19	$5 **green and orange** ..	£17	£13
X20	$10 **green and blk** (/24) .	£50	£40
X21	$50 **green and ult** ..	£375	—
X1/21	**set** (21)	£465	‡
SP X1/21	**specimen set** over-print and perf (21)..	£260	

1940 (Feb.) Design, Sultan Sir Ibrahim. Perf. 13½ (C). Recess printed. Uncoated paper. Sheets 10 x 5.

1	8c. **black and light blue**	40	30
	a blk and pale ult ..	50	40

1949 (May 2nd)-52 Design, Sultan Sir Ibrahim. Perf. 17½ x 18 (C). Sheets 10 x 10.

3	1c. **black**	10	10
4	2c. **orange**	10	10
	a yel-orange (22/1/52)	15	10
	b pale yel (9/12/58) ..	20	10
5	3c. **green**	25	15
	a lt green (2/9/49) ..	20	10
6	4c. **brown**	15	10
	a lt brown (13/3/57) .	15	10
7	6c. **grey**	20	15
	a light grey (22/1/52) .	25	15
	b greenish-grey (17/12/52) ..	50	20
8	8c. **scarlet**	35	45
9	10c. **red-purple**	20	15
	a dp red-pur (24/5/56)	20	10
	b lt red-pur (9/12/58)	20	10
	c imperf pr	£300	—
10	15c. **bright ultramarine** ..	60	30
	a blue (22/1/52) ..	80	40
11	20c. **black and green** ..	50	25
12	25c. **red-pur and orange**..	30	25
	a dp red-pur and orange (22/2/51)	30	25
13	40c. **scarlet and red-pur**	1·00	1·00
14	50c. **black and violet-blue**	60	20
	a blk and blue (21/1/52)	60	20
15	$1 **ult and dp red-purple**	1·00	70
	a blue and red-purple (17/12/52) ..	1·00	70
16	$2 **green and car-red** ..	3·50	1·75
17	$5 **green and dp brown**	6·00	3·50

Watermark Variety (Type A)

(See Introduction for details.)

7c.	6c. St. Edward's Crown ..	£150	—

1952 (Sept. 1st) -56 As before, but new values or colours.

18	5c. **magenta**	15	15
	a bt magenta (18/8/53)	20	15
19	8c. **green**	25	30
20	12c. **scarlet**	30	50
21	20c. **dp blue**	30	20
	a bright blue (23/2/55)	30	20
22	30c. **scarlet and red-pur** (4/9/55) ..	70	50
	a scar and dull lake-pur (24/5/56) ..	70	50
23	35c. **scarlet and red-pur**..	80	60
3/23	**set** (21)	£16	£10

SPECIAL ISSUES

1948 (Dec. 1st) Silver Wedding. As Aden.

S1	10c. **purple**	10	10
S2	$5 **grey-green**	8·00	8·50

Number issued—10c., 812,390; $5, 20,281.

1949 (Oct. 10th) U.P.U. As Aden.

S3	10c.	dull purple	.. ..	15	15
S4	15c.	indigo	.. ..	15	40
S5	25c.	orange	.. ..	50	50
S6	50c.	slate-black	.. ..	70	75
S3/6		set (4)	.. ..	1·40	1·60

Number issued—

10c., 684,457; 15c.. 156,318;
25c., 117,176; 25c., 90,460.

POSTAGE DUE STAMPS

1938 (Jan. 1st) Printers (typo) Waterlow & Sons. Perf. 12½ (L). Uncoated paper. Sheets 10 x 10.

PD1	1c.	crimson	.. ..	1·00	1·25
PD2	4c.	green	..	1·50	2·00
PD3	8c.	ochre	.. ..	2·25	2·75
PD4	10c.	dp brown	.. ..	2·75	3·00
PD5	12c.	dp purple	.. ..	4·50	6·50
PD1/5		set (5)	.. ..	£11	£14
SP PD1/5		perf specimen	..	£30	‡

KEDAH

1937 (June 30th). Design, Sultan Abdul Hamid Halimshah. Printers (recess) Waterlow & Sons. Perf. 12½ (L). Sheets 6 x 10.

1	10c.	ult and sepia	..	50	15
2	12c.	black and deep violet		3·75	3·75
3	25c.	ult and red-pur	..	1·50	1·50
4	30c.	green and red	..	1.50	1·50
5	40c.	black and red-purple		50	2·00
6	50c.	dp brown and blue	..	50	1·50
7	$1	black and green	..	1·25	1·50
8	$2	green and dp brown		£18	£14
9	$5	black and red	..	6·00	8·00
1/9		set (9)	.. ..	£30	£30
SP 1/9		specimen set perf (9)		£55	‡

1938-40. Printers (recess) De La Rue. Sheets 120—2 panes, each 6 x 10. Perf. 14 (L).

10	1c.	black (/38)	.. ..	8·00	5·00
11	2c.	green (/40)	.. ..	25·00	1·50

Perf. 13¾ (L).

11A	1c.	black (/38)	.. ..	8·00	6·00

10,11A—This printing (from new plate) can be distinguished from that issued in 1921 by the shape of the 1's. No. 11a exists in two sizes 18½ x 22½mm. and 19¼ x 22¾mm., through printings having been done on damp and dry paper. The lower stamp is No. 10.

11—In this die the 2's have round drops instead of oval and the c's are slightly larger than the 1921 issue. The upper stamp of illustration is No. 11.

1950 (June 1st) -55. Designs, Sheaf of Rice (1c.-20c.), Sultan Tengku Badlishah (other values). Printers (typo) De La Rue. Perf. 17½ x 18 (C). Sheets 10 x 10.

12	1c.	black	.. .. ..	5	5
13	2c.	orange	.. ..	5	5

14	3c.	**green**	15	10
15	4c.	**brown**	5	5
		a dp brown (24/3/54)	10	5
16	6c.	**grey**	10	10
		a greenish-grey		
		(27/11/52) ..	20	10
17	8c.	**scarlet**	25	40
18	10c.	**red-purple**	15	5
		a dp red-pur (8/2/56)	10	5
19	15c.	**bright ultramarine** ..	40	40
20	20c.	**black and green** ..	40	40
21	25c.	**dp pur and orange** ..	40	10
		a red-purple and orange		
		(27/6/51) ..	30	10
22	40c.	**scarlet and red-pur**	50	1·00
23	50c.	**black and violet-blue**	60	25
		a black and blue		
		(27/11/52) ..	50	25
24	$1	**ult and red-purple** ..	85	50
		a blue and dp red-pur		
		(18/2/53) ..	75	50
25	$2	**green and car-red** ..	2·75	3·75
26	$5	**green and dp brown** .	5·00	7·00

1952 (Sept. 1st) -56 As before, but new values or colours.

27	5c.	**magenta**	15	5
		a bt magenta (24/9/53)	10	5
28	8c.	**green**	25	30
		a dp green (24/9/53) .	30	30
29	12c.	**scarlet**	20	25
30	20c.	**blue**	40	30
		a dp blue (8/2/56) ..	60	30
31	30c.	**scarlet and red-pur**		
		(4/9/55) ..	50	40
32	35c.	**scarlet and red-purple**	50	55
12/32		**set (21)**	£10	£15

SPECIAL ISSUES

1948 (Dec. 1st) Silver Wedding. As Aden.

S1	10c.	**purple**	10	10
S2	$5	**rose-carmine** ..	9·00	£12

Number issued—10c., 346,182; $5, 20,723.

1949 (Oct. 10th) U.P.U. As Aden.

S3	10c.	**dull purple**	15	15
S4	15c.	**indigo**	15	40
S5	25c.	**orange**	50	60
S6	50c.	**slate-black**	80	1·00
S3/6		**set (4)**	1·50	2·00

Number issued—

10c., 283,010; 15c., 89,652;
25c., 84,456; 50c., 74,500.

KELANTAN

1937-40. Design, Sultan Ismail. Printers

(recess) **Bradbury, Wilkinson. Perf. 12 (L). Sheets 10 x 10.**

1	1c.	**olive and ochre** (7/37)	25	25
2	2c.	**emerald-grn** (7/37) ..	25	15
3	4c.	**scarlet-red** (7/37) ..	60	30
4	5c.	**dp chestnut** (7/37) ..	60	25
5	6c.	**crimson-lake** (10/37)	1·50	50
6	8c.	**olive** (7/37)	70	35
7	10c.	**dp purple** (10/37) ..	1·50	80
8	12c.	**blue** (7/37)	75	1·00
9	25c.	**ver and pur** (7/37) ..	1·50	1·50
10	30c.	**pur and scar** (10/37)	4·50	5·00
11	40c.	**red-orange and green**		
		(7/37)	2·75	3·00
12	50c.	**olive and red-orange**		
		(10/37)	5·00	5·50
13	$1	**pur and grn** (10/37)..	3·00	3·75
14	$2	**maroon and crimson**		
		(3/40)	£45	£65
15	$5	**vermilion and crimson-**		
		lake (3/40) ..	£65	£100
1/15		**set (15)**	£125	£170
SP 1/15		**specimen set** perf (15)	£100	‡

1951 (July 11th) -55 Design, Portrait of Sultan Tengku Ibrahim. Printers *(typo)* **De La Rue, on chalk-surfaced paper. Perf. 17½ x 18 (C). Sheets as before.**

16	1c.	**black**	5	5
17	2c.	**orange**	5	5
		a stop omitted ..	5·00	5·00
		b orange-yel (11/5/55)	10	5
18	3c.	**green**	15	25
19	4c.	**brown**	10	5
20	6c.	**light grey**	10	10
		a greenish-grey (16/7/5	30	10
21	8c.	**scarlet**	30	40
22	10c.	**red-purple**	25	20
		a dp red-pur (8/12/53)	10	5
23	15c.	**bright ultramarine** ..	30	30
24	20c.	**black and green** ..	50	50
25	25c.	**red-pur and orange** ..	50	40
		a dp red-pur and orange		
		(8/12/53) ..	40	40
26	40c.	**scarlet and red-pur** ..	70	1·40
27	50c.	**black and blue** ..	50	50
28	$1	**ult and dp red-purple**	90	1·00
		a ult and red-purple		
		(12/2/53) ..	1·25	1·00
29	$2	**grn and carmine-red**	2·00	4·50
30	$5	**green and dp brown**	6·00	£10

17*a*—The stop under 2 in right hand panel is missing on Row 1/2.

K*

1952 (Sept. 1st) -56 As before, but new values or colours.

31	5c. **magenta**	10	10
	a bt magenta (8/12/53)	10	10
32	8c. **green**	20	30
33	12c. **scarlet**	20	30
34	20c. **blue**	40	40
35	30c. **scarlet and red-pur** (4/9/55)	80	65
	a scarlet and lake-pur (27/3/56)	60	65
36	35c. **scarlet and red-pur**	60	1·00
16/36	**set** (21)	£13	£20

SPECIAL ISSUES

1948 (Dec. 1st) Silver Wedding. As Aden.

S1	10c. **purple**	10	10
S2	$5 **rose-carmine** ..	7·00	£11

Number issued— 10c., 225,572; $5, 18,633.

1949 (Oct. 10th) U.P.U. As Aden.

S3	10c. **dull purple**	25	30
S4	15c. **indigo**	30	50
S5	25c. **orange**	60	90
S6	50c. **slate-black**	90	1·40
S3/6	**set** (4)	2·00	3·00

Number issued—10c., 193,979; 15c., 69,160; 15c., 69,618; 25c., 72,435.

MALACCA

All stamps were printed (typo) by De La Rue, on chalk-surfaced paper.

1949 Mar. 1st) -52 Perf. 17½ x 18 (C). Sheets 10 x 10.

1	1c. **black**	15	20
2	2c. **orange**	15	20
3	3c. **green**	20	50
4	4c. **brown**	15	20
5	6c. **greenish-grey** ..	15	40
6	8c. **scarlet**	35	50
7	10c. **red-purple**	20	30
8	15c. **bright ultramarine** ..	45	45
9	20c. **black and green** ..	35	60
10	25c. **dp red-pur and orange**	30	50
	a bt red-pur and orange (13/11/52) ..	40	50
11	40c. **scarlet and red-pur**	70	1·50
12	50c. **blk and violet-blue** ..	55	60
	a blk and blue (13/11/52)	65	60
13	$1 **blue and dp red-pur**	1·25	1·50
	a lt blue and red-purple (22/11/51) ..	1·50	1·50
14	$2 **green and car-red** ..	2·50	3·00
15	$5 **green and dp brown**	3·50	5·00

1952 (Sept. 1st) As No. 1, etc., but new values and changed colours.

16	5c. **magenta** ..	15	35
17	8c. **green**	25	50
18	12c. **scarlet**	30	70
19	20c. **blue**	60	70
21	35c. **scarlet and purple** ..	30	90
1/21	**set** (21)	£11	£17

SPECIAL ISSUES

1948 (Dec. 1st) Silver Wedding. As Aden.

S1	10c. **purple**	10	10
S2	$5 **chocolate**	11	£13

Number issued—10c., 375,006; $5, 18,889.

1949 (Oct. 10th) U.P.U. As Aden.

S3	10c. **dull purple**	15	25
S4	15c. **indigo**	15	25
S5	25c. **orange**	45	55
S6	50c. **slate-black**	60	75
S3/6	**set** (4)	1·25	1·75

Number issued—10c., 328,057; 15c., 79,242; 25c., 81,297; 50c., 69,213.

NEGRI SEMBILAN

All stamps were printed (typo) by De La Rue on chalk-surfaced paper except where otherwise mentioned.

1935-41 Design, Arms of Territory. Perf. 13¾ x 14 (C). Sheets 10 x 10.

X1	1c. **black**	35	20
X2	2c. **green**	45	20
1	2c. **orange** (11/12/41) ..	40	75
2	3c. **green** (21/8/41) ..	35	50
	a green (sub) ..	1·00	75
X3	4c. **orange**	25	20
X4	5c. **brown**	30	15
	a booklet pane of 10 ..	—	—
3	6c. **scarlet** (1/1/37) ..	1·50	1·25
	a stop omitted ..	£10	8·00
4	6c. **grey** (18/12/41) (sub)	75	3·75
	a stop omitted ..	8·00	8·00
X5	8c. **grey**	£75	15
X6	10c. **purple**	30	20
X7	12c. **blue**	65	35
5	15c. **ult** (sub) (1/10/41) ..	1·50	3·00
	a dark ult (sub) ..	4·00	4·00
X8	25c. **purple and scarlet** ..	55	60
X9	30c. **purple and orange** ..	1·50	1·50
X10	40c. **scarlet and purple** ..	70	1·75
X11	50c. **black/emerald** ..	2·00	1·00
X12	$1 **black and red/blue** ..	1·00	1·25
X13	$2 **green/scarlet** ..	£10	7·50
X14	$5 **grn and red/emerald**	7·00	8·00
X1/14	**set** (19)	£27	£30
SP X1/14	**specimen set** perf (15)	£80	‡

3a, 4a—The stop under C in right value tablet is missing on Row 10/9.

PREPARED FOR USE BUT NOT ISSUED.

8c. (**rose**) at £20.

Prepared for issue in 1941, the Japanese occupation prevented this. It was, however, overprinted by Japanese and later unoverprinted copies leaked out.

1949 (April 1st) -52 Design, Arms of Territory. Perf. 17½ x 18 (C). Sheets as before.

6	1c.	**black**	10	10
7	2c.	**orange**	15	10
		a yellow-orange (8/1/52)	10	10
8	3c.	**green**	10	10
9	4c.	**dp brown**	15	10
		a brown (16/6/54) ..	10	10
10	6c.	**greenish-grey** ..	30	10
		a dp greenish-grey (13/12/50) ..	30	10
		b grey (13/12/50) ..	10	10
11	8c.	**scarlet**	25	40
12	10c.	**dp red-purple** ..	20	15
		a red-purple (8/1/52) .	10	10
13	15c.	**dp blue** ..	40	20
14	20c.	**black and green** ..	30	50
15	25c.	**dp red-pur and orange**	25	20
		a red-purple and orange (30/12/52) ..	50	30
16	40c.	**scar and red-purple**..	40	90
17	50c.	**black and violet-blue**	60	40
		a blk and blue (8/1/52)	40	30
18	$1	**blue and dp red-pur**	70	50
		a blue and red-purple (30/12/52) ..	1·00	70
19	$2	**green and car-red** ..	2·00	70
20	$5	**green and dp brown**	5·00	3·00

1952 (Sept. 1st) -56 As before, but new values or colours.

21	5c.	**magenta**	20	10
		a bt magenta (25/8/53)	10	10
22	8c.	**green**	10	30
23	12c.	**scarlet**	15	25
24	20c.	**blue**	50	15
		a dp blue (22/2/56) ..	30	10
25	30c.	**scar and dp red-pur** (4/9/55) ..	40	40
		a scarlet and red-purple (22/2/56) ..	60	40
26	35c.	**scar and red-purple**..	40	40
6/26		**set** (21)	9·00	8·00

SPECIAL ISSUES

1948 (Dec. 1st) Silver Wedding. As Aden.

S1	10c.	**purple**	10	10
S2	$5	**grey-green**	7·00	8·50

Number issued—10c., 496,250; $5, 19,151.

1949 (Oct. 10th) U.P.U. As Aden.

S3	10c.	**dull purple**	15	15
S4	15c.	**indigo**	25	30
S5	25c.	**orange**	40	40
S6	50c.	**slate-black**	60	70
S3/6		**set** (4)	1·30	1·50

Number issued—10c., 452,690; 15c., 103,653; 25c., 94,452: 50c., 74,218.

PAHANG

All stamps were printed (*typo*) by De La Rue on chalk-surfaced paper unless otherwise mentioned.

1935-37. Perf. 14. Sheets 10 x 10.

X1	1c.	**black**	15	25
X2	2c.	**green**	35	25
X3	4c.	**orange**	15	25
X4	5c.	**brown**	40	15
		a booklet pane of 10..	6·00	—
X5	8c.	**grey**	55	15
X6	10c.	**dull purple**	25	15
X7	12c.	**bright ultramarine**..	90	1·00
X8	25c.	**dull purple and scar**	90	75
X9	30c.	**dull pur and orange**	60	1·00
X10	40c.	**scarlet and dull pur**	65	1·50
X11	50c.	**black/emerald** ..	2·50	1·25
X12	$1	**black and red/blue**	1·75	3·00
X13	$2	**green and scarlet** ..	£12	£12
X14	$5	**grn and red/em** ..	6·00	£12
SP X1/14		**specimen set** perf (18)	£50	‡

1937-41 Design, Sultan Abu Bakar. Perf. 13¾ x 14 (C).

1	3c.	**green** (21/8/41) ..	30	40
		ditto (/41) ..	1·25	1·00
2	6c.	**rose** (1/1/37) ..	1·50	1·50
3	8c.	**rose** (11/12/41) ..	50	2·75
4	15c.	**ult** (1/10/41) (sub) ..	80	2·75
1/4		**set** (18)	£28	£38

PREPARED FOR USE BUT NOT ISSUED.

2c. (**orange**) and 6c. (**slate-grey**) at £4 per pair.

These stamps were to have been issued in 1941, but the Japanese occupation prevented this. Later, mint copies appeared on the market, but those with Singapore postmarks are of doubtful status.

1950 (June 1st) -54 Design, Sultan Sir Abu Bakar. Perf. 17½ x 18 (C). Sheets as before

5	1c. **black**	5	5
6	2c. **orange**	5	5
7	3c. **green**	25	20
8	4c. **brown**	5	5
	a dp brown (24/3/54)	20	10
9	6c. **greenish-grey** ..	30	10
	a light grey (10/9/53)	10	10
10	8c. **scarlet**	20	25
11	10c. **red-purple**	20	5
	a dp red-pur (12/6/57)	10	5
12	15c. **bright ultramarine** ..	25	25
13	20c. **black and green**	30	50
14	25c. **red-pur and orange**..	35	20
	a dp red-pur and orange (10/9/53)	30	20
15	40c. **scar and red-purple**..	50	90
16	50c. **black and violet-blue**	60	30
	a black and deep blue (17/12/52) ..	40	30
17	$1 **ult and dp red-purple**	1·00	90
	a ultramarine and red-pur (17/12/52) ..	80	90
18	$2 **grn and carmine-red**	2·00	5·00
19	$5 **grn and dp brown** ..	5·50	£10

1952 (Sept. 1st) -56 As before, but new values or colours.

20	5c. **magenta**	10	5
	a bt magenta (10/9/53)	15	5
21	8c. **green**	30	25
	a dp green (10/9/53)..	20	25
22	12c. **scarlet**	25	30
23	20c. **blue**	30	30
	a dp blue (8/3/56) ..	50	40
24	30c. **scarlet and red-pur** (4/9/55)	50	50
25	35c. **scar and red-purple**..	50	70
5/25	**set** (21)	£10	£20

SPECIAL ISSUES

1948 (Dec. 1st) Silver Wedding. As Aden.

S1	10c. **purple**	10	10
S2	$5 **grey-green**	9·00	£12

Number issued—10c., 389,540; $5, 18,380.

1949 (Oct. 10th) U.P.U. As Aden.

S3	10c. **dull purple**	10	15
S4	15c. **indigo**	15	25
S5	25c. **orange**	35	45
S6	50c. **slate-black**	50	70
S3/6	**set** (4)	1·00	1·50

Number issued—10c., 349,564; 15c., 98,795; 25c., 81,776; 50c., 64,661.

PENANG

All stamps were printed (typo) by De La Rue, on chalk-surfaced paper unless otherwise mentioned.

1949 (Feb. 21st) -54 Perf. 17½ x 18 (C). Sheets 10 x 10.

1	1c. **black**	10	5
2	2c. **orange**	10	5
3	3c. **green**	10	10
4	4c. **brown**	10	10
	a dp brown (12/5/54)	20	10
5	6c. **greenish-grey**	10	10
	a light greenish-grey (27/11/52) ..	20	10
6	8c. **scarlet**	25	35
7	10c. **red-purple**	10	10
8	15c. **bright ultramarine** ..	20	20
9	20c. **black and green** ..	30	25
10	25c. **red-pur and orange**..	20	15
	a dp red-pur and orange (10/9/53) ..	30	15
11	40c. **scar and red-purple**..	35	1·00
12	50c. **black and vio-blue** ..	35	20
13	$1 **blue and dp red-pur**	85	30
	a blue and red-purple (13/12/50) ..	75	25
14	$2 **grn and carmine-red**	1·25	50
15	$5 **grn and dp brown** ..	4·00	1·50

1952 (Sept. 1st) -54 As No. 1, etc., but new values and changed colours.

16	5c. **magenta**	15	15
	a bt magenta (12/5/54)	20	15
17	8c. **green**	15	35
18	12c. **scarlet**	15	30
19	20c. **blue**	25	20
20	35c. **scarlet and purple** ..	35	45
1/20	**set** (20)	8·50	6·00

SPECIAL ISSUES

1948 (Dec. 1st) Silver Wedding. As Aden.

S1	10c. **purple**	10	10
S2	$5 **chocolate**	9·00	£11

Number issued—10c., 773,372; $5, 25,124.

1949 (Oct. 10th) U.P.U. As Aden.

S3	10c. **dull purple**	10	10
S4	15c. **indigo**	10	30
S5	25c. **orange**	35	45
S6	50c. **slate-black**	55	75
S3/6	**set** (4)	1·00	1·50

Number issued—10c., 761,745; 15c., 185,687; 25c., 193,662; 50c., 130,193.

PERAK

All stamps were printed (typo) by De La Rue on chalk-surfaced paper unless otherwise mentioned.

1935-37 Design, Portrait (side face) of Sultan Iskandar. Perf 13¾ x 14 (C). Sheets 10 x 10.

X1	1c. **black**	15	10
X2	2c. **green**	10	10
X3	4c. **orange**	20	10
X4	5c. **brown**	10	10
X5	6c. **scarlet** (1/1/37) ..	1·00	1·00

X6	8c. **grey**	45	15
X7	10c. **dull purple**	15	10
X8	12c. **bright ultramarine**	60	80
X9	25c. **dull pur and scarlet**	50	50
X10	30c. **dull pur and orange**	65	1·00
X11	40c. **scarlet and dull pur**	1·75	2·25
X12	50c. **black/emerald**	1·75	1·25
X13	$1 **black and red/blue**	1·50	1·25
X14	$2 **green and scarlet**	5·00	4·50
X15	$5 **grn and red/emerald**	£14	£10
X1/15	**set** (15)	£25	£22
SP X1/15	**specimen set** perf (15)	£70	‡

1938-41 Design, Portrait (*full face*) **of Sultan Iskandar. Perf. 13¾ x 14 (C). Sheets as before.**

2	1c. **black** (17/4/39)	20	10
3	2c. **green** (13/1/39)	50	15
4	2c. **orange** (30/10/41)	50	60
	a ditto (thin paper) (sub)	25	50
5	3c. **green** (21/8/41)	1·50	80
	a ditto (thin paper)	25	45
6	4c. **orange** (8/5/39)	50	15
	a orange-yellow (thin paper)	2·00	35
7	5c. **chocolate** (1/2/39)	10	10
	a booklet pane of 10	—	—
8	6c. **rose** (1/12/39)	2·75	15
9	8c. **slate-grey** (1/12/38)	50	10
	a booklet pane of 10	—	—
10	8c. **rose-car** (18/12/41)	90	2·00
	a ditto (thin paper)	75	2·00
11	10c. **grey-pur** (17/10/38)	70	15
12	12c. **blue** (17/10/38)	1·25	1·25
13	15c. **ult** (sub) (8/41)	90	4·25
	a blue (sub)	1·50	4·50
14	25c. **pur and red** (1/12/39)	3·50	1·50
15	30c. **purple and orange** (17/10/38)	50	1·00
	a red-purple and orange (thin paper)	1·50	3·00
16	40c. **scar and pur** (2/5/38)	1·75	1·25
17	50c. **black/emer** (17/10/38)	75	80
	a black/green (/41)	1·50	1·00
18	$1 **blk, car/blue** (7/40)	7·00	6·00
19	$2 **grn and red** (1/10/40)	£15	£14
20	$5 **grn, car/grn** (1/41)	£40	£40
2/20	**set** (19)	£70	£70
SP 2/20	**specimen set** perf (19)	£90	‡

1950 (Aug. 17th) -53 Design, Sultan Yussof Izzuddin. Perf. 17½ x 18 (C). Sheets as before.

21	1c. **black**	5	5

22	2c. **orange**	5	5
23	3c. **green**	30	15
	a yellow-grn (15/11/51)	30	10
24	4c. **dark brown**	20	10
	a brown (22/10/53)	10	5
25	6c. **greenish-grey**	30	10
	a grey (22/10/53)	10	5
26	8c. **scarlet**	15	20
27	10c. **red-purple**	30	10
	a dp red-pur (20/6/56)	15	5
28	15c. **bright ultramarine**	25	15
29	20c. **black and green**	25	30
30	25c. **red-pur and orange**	20	10
31	40c. **scar and red-purple**	45	50
32	50c. **blk and violet-blue**	45	15
	a blk and blue (20/11/52)	30	10
33	$1 **blue and dp red-pur**	75	40
	a blue and dp red-pur (20/6/56)	1·00	60
34	$2 **green and car-red**	1·75	80
35	$5 **green and dp brown**	5·00	3·00

1952 (Sept. 1st) -55 As before, but new values or colours.

36	5c. **magenta**	20	10
	a bt magenta (10/11/54)	10	5
37	8c. **green**	15	20
38	12c. **scarlet**	20	20
39	20c. **blue**	25	15
40	30c. **scarlet and red-pur** (4/9/55)	40	35
41	35c. **scar and red-purple**	40	45
21/41	**set** (21)	£11	7·00

SPECIAL ISSUES

1948 (Dec. 1st) Silver Wedding. As Aden.

S1	10c. **purple**	10	10
S2	$5 **grey-green**	7·00	£10

Number issued—10c., 1,199,684 ; $5, 21,522.

1949 (Oct. 10th) U.P.U. As Aden.

S3	10c. **dull purple**	10	10
S4	15c. **indigo**	15	25
S5	25c. **orange**	35	45
S6	50c. **slate-black**	70	80
S3/6	**set** (4)	1·25	1·50

Number issued— 10c., 1,188,203 ; 15c., 238,608 ; 25c., 188,882 ; 50c., 118,896.

PERLIS

All stamps were printed (*typo*) by De La Rue on chalk-surfaced paper unless otherwise mentioned.

1951 (Mar. 26th) Design, Raja Syed Putra, Perf. 17½ x 18 (C). Sheets 10 x 10.

1	1c. **black**	5	10
2	2c. **orange**	5	10
3	3c. **yellow-green**	40	50
4	4c. **brown**	5	10
5	6c. **light grey**	5	10

6	8c.	scarlet	30	40
7	10c.	red-purple	10	10
		a dp red-pur (11/5/55)	15	10
8	15c.	bright ultramarine	50	70
9	20c.	black and yel-green	70	80
10	25c.	red-pur and orange	35	40
11	40c.	scar and red-purple	70	1·00
12	50c.	black and violet-blue	50	50
13	$1	ult and dp red-purple	1·50	2·50
14	$2	green and car-red	2·75	4·50
15	$5	green and dp brown	6·00	£10

1952 (Sept. 1st) -55 As before, but new values or colours.

16	5c.	magenta	5	10
17	8c.	green	35	45
18	12c.	scarlet	20	35
19	20c.	blue	35	40
20	30c.	scar and dp red-pur (4/9/55)	50	55
21	35c.	scar and red-purple	50	80
1/21		set (21)	£15	£22

SPECIAL ISSUES

1948 (Dec. 1st) Silver Wedding. As Aden.

S1	10c.	purple	10	10
S2	$5	chocolate	7·00	£10

Number issued—10c., 145,833; $5, 18,270.

1949 (Oct. 10th) U.P.U. As Aden.

S3	10c.	dull purple	10	25
S4	15c.	indigo	15	40
S5	25c.	orange	35	60
S6	50c.	slate-black	60	80
S3/6		set (4)	1·00	2·00

Number issued—10c., 95,230; 15c., 60,844; 25c., 58,119; 50c., 56,981.

SELANGOR

All stamps were printed (typo) by De La Rue on chalk-surfaced paper unless otherwise mentioned.

1937-41 Design, 2c.–15c., Mosque at Klang; $1, $2, Sultan Hisamud-din Alam Shah. Sheets 10 x 10.

X1	1c.	black	15	10
X2	2c.	green	10	10
X3	4c.	orange	10	40
X4	5c.	brown	10	10
		a booklet pane of 10	—	—
X5	8c.	grey	30	15
X6	10c.	purple	30	10
X7	12c.	blue	1·50	25
X8	25c.	purple and scarlet	90	80
X9	30c.	purple and orange	1·25	1·25
X10	40c.	scarlet and purple	1·50	1·25
X11	50c.	black/green	1·25	70
X12	$1	black and red/blue	3·00	80
X13	$2	green/scarlet	9·00	5·00
X14	$5	grn and red/grn	£20	£12
X1/14		set (14)	£36	£20
SP X1/14		specimen set perf (14)	£65	‡

(a) Perf. 14 x 14¾ (C).

1	2c.	orange (sub) (21/8/41)	20	30

(b) Perf. 13¾ x 14 (C).

2	2c.	orange (21/8/41)	5·00	3·00
		a orange (sub)	3·75	1·50
3	3c.	yellow-grn (21/8/41)	1·00	75
		a ditto (sub)	1·00	75
		b green	50	60
		c blue-green (sub)	15	40
4	6c.	rose (1/1/37)	50	25
5	15c.	ult (sub) (1/10/41)	1·25	2·75
		a dk ultramarine (sub)	3·00	3·00
6	$1	blk, scar/blue (15/4/41)	2·50	3·50
7	$2	grn and crim (7/7/41)	6·50	9·00
2/7		set (6)	£12	£15

PREPARED FOR USE BUT NOT ISSUED.

	8c.	red	£40	—
	$5	green and car/grn	£10	—

Sent out in 1941, the Japanese occupation prevented issue. Thus the bulk of the printing was overprinted, but a few copies without overprint leaked out later.

1949 (Sept. 12th) -55 Design, Sultan Hisamud-din Alam Shah. Perf. 17½ x 18 (C). Sheets 6 x 10.

8	1c.	black	5	10
9	2c.	orange	5	10
10	3c.	green	10	15
11	4c.	brown	5	5
		a dp brown (13/11/52)	20	15
12	6c.	grey	40	15
		a light grey (26/9/51)	15	10
		b greenish-grey (13/11/52)	40	15
13	8c.	scarlet	20	25
14	10c.	red-purple	20	10
		a dp red-pur (17/8/55)	10	5
15	15c.	bright ultramarine	25	10
16	20c.	black and green	40	30
17	25c.	red-pur and orange	30	5
18	40c.	scarlet and red-pur	50	60
19	50c.	black and violet-blue	65	25
		a blk & blue (13/11/52)	45	15
20	$1	ult and red-purple	55	20
		a ult and dp red-purple (17/8/55)	65	30
21	$2	green and car-red	2·00	50
22	$5	green and dp brown	4·00	1·00

1952 (Sept. 1st) -55 As before, but new values or colour.

23	5c.	**magenta**	10	10
	a	bt magenta (17/9/53)	15	10
24	8c.	**green**	25	25
	a	dp green (17/9/53)..	15	30
25	12c.	**scarlet**	25	30
	a	wmk. inverted ..	£40	—
26	20c.	**blue**	40	25
27	30c.	**scar and dp red-pur**		
		(4/9/55)	50	30
28	35c.	**scar and red-purple**..	50	50
8/28		**set** (21)	£10	5·00

SPECIAL ISSUES

1948 (Dec. 1st) Silver Wedding. As Aden.

S1	10c.	**purple**	10	10
S2	$5	**grey-green**	7·00	£12

Number issued—10c., 1,252,340; $5, 25,151.

1949 (Oct. 10th) U.P.U. As Aden.

S3	10c.	**dull purple**	10	10
S4	15c.	**indigo**	15	20
S5	25c.	**orange**	25	35
S6	50c.	**slate-black**	50	55
S3/6		**set** (4)	1·00	1·10

Number issued—10c., 1,346,978; 15c., 268,920; 25c., 233,672; 50c., 155,891.

SINGAPORE

All stamps were printed (*typo*) by De La Rue on chalk-surfaced paper unless otherwise mentioned.

1948 (Sept. 1st) Design as Straits Settlements with SINGAPORE added. Perf. 13¾ x 14 (C). Sheets 10 x 10.

1	1c.	**black**	5	5
2	2c.	**orange**	5	5
3	3c.	**green**	10	5
4	4c.	**brown**	10	5
5	6c.	**grey**	10	5
6	8c.	**scarlet** (1/10/48) ..	10	5
7	10c.	**red-purple**	10	5
8	15c.	**bt ult** (1/10/48) ..	10	5
9	20c.	**blk and grn** (1/10/48)	15	10
10	25c.	**red-pur and orange**		
		(1/10/48)	15	10
11	40c.	**scarlet and dp purple**		
		(1/10/48)	60	75
12	50c.	**blk and blue** (1/10/48)	60	10
13	$1	**blue and dp purple**		
		(1/10/48)	90	10
14	$2	**green and carmine-red**		
		(25/10/48) ..	2·50	1·00
15	$5	**green and dp brown**		
		(1/10/48)	7·00	1·50
1/15		**set** (15)	£11	4·00

Postal Forgeries

See note after Straits Settlements No. 39 regarding forged 50c. $1 and $2 stamps.

1949-55 As Nos. 1—15, but Perf. 17½ x 18 (C).

16	1c.	**black** (21/5/52) ..	10	5
17	2c.	**orange** (31/10/49) ..	10	5
	a	orange-yel (10/12/52)	10	5
18	4c.	**brown** (1/7/49) ..	10	5
	a	dp brown (24/5/51) ..	20	5
19	6c.	**greenish-grey**		
		(10/12/52)	10	5
	a	grey (19/11/53) ..	15	5
20	10c.	**red-purple** (9/2/50)..	25	5
	a	pale red-pur (10/12/52)	20	5
	b	dp red-pur (21/4/55)	15	5
21	15c.	**vio-blue** (9/2/50) ..	15	10
22	20c.	**blk and grn** (31/10/49)	40	25
23	25c.	**red-purple and orange**		
		(9/2/50)	25	10
	a	dp red-pur and orange		
		(21/4/55) ..	40	10
24	40c.	**scarlet and red-pur**		
		(/51)	1·25	1·25
25	50c.	**black and violet-blue**		
		(9/2/50)	70	10
	a	blk and blue (21/5/52)	80	10
26	$1	**blue and red-purple**		
		(31/10/49) ..	1·00	25
	a	blue and dp red-pur		
		(19/11/53) ..	1·50	25
27	$2	**green and carmine-red**		
		(24/5/51)	4·00	1·00
28	$5	**green and dp brown**		
		(19/12/51)	£11	1·50
16/28		**set** (13)	£18	4·00

24—Released in London 24/5/51 but on sale in Colony some months eariler.

Watermark Variety (Type B)

(See Introduction for deta'ls)

26b	$1	St. Edward's Crown ..	£250	—
27a	$2	St. Edward's Crown ..	£250	—

1952 (Sept. 1st) -53 As No. 16, etc., but new values and changed colours.

29	5c.	**magenta**	15	5
	a	bt magenta (19/11/53)	20	5
30	8c.	**yellow-green** ..	30	15
	a	green (25/8/53) ..	40	15
31	12c.	**scarlet**	15	30
32	20c.	**blue**	25	10
	a	vio-blue (25/8/53) ..	30	10
34	35c.	**scarlet and purple** ..	65	60
29/34		**set** (5)	1·50	1·00

SPECIAL ISSUES

1948 (Oct. 25th) Silver Wedding. As Aden.

S1	10c.	**purple**	10	10
S2	$5	**chocolate**	£11	9·00

Number issued—10c. 2,973,270; $5, 54,501.

1949 (Oct. 10th) U.P.U. As Aden.

S3	10c.	**dull purple**	10	10
S4	15c.	**indigo**	25	30
S5	25c.	**orange**	35	45
S6	50c.	**slate-black**	70	80
S3/6		**set** (4)	1·25	1·50

Number issued—10c., 2,580,544; 15c., 577,261; 25c., 681,908; 50c., 409,401.

GERMAN PROPAGANDA LABELS

The 1944 German imitations of the G.B. 1937 Definities ½d to 3d (see after Great Britain for details) were also overprinted in black "LIQUIDA-TION/OF EMPIRE/SINGAPORE" within a vertical rectangular frame.

Prive (6v) unused or cancelled — £125.

TRENGGANU

All stamps were printed (typo) by De La Rue on chalk-surfaced paper unless otherwise mentioned.

1938 Design, Sultan Suleiman. Perf. 13¾ x 14 (C). Sheets X1—X6 120—two panes each 6 x 10; remainder 6 x 5.

X1	1c.	black	.. .. ..	25	15
X2	3c.	green	.. .. ..	35	40
1	3c.	brown	.. .. ..	1·25	1·50
X3	5c.	purple/yellow	..	70	55
X4	6c.	orange	.. .. ..	2·25	40
2	8c.	slate grey	.. ..	1·50	60
X5	12c.	blue	.. .. ..	1·75	2·25
X6	35c.	car/yellow	.. ..	2·25	4·00
X7	$1	purple and blue/blue	8·00	3·50
X8	$3	grn and red/grn	..	£17	£20
3	$5	grn and car/yel	..	£60	£90
X1/3		set (11)	.. ..	£90	£110
SP 1/3,	1c./$5	specimen set perf (11)	.. ..	£80	‡

Other values of a similar design were issued before 1937.

1941 (May 1st) Design as No. 1, etc., but surcharged in black.

4	2c./5c.	red-purple/yel	1·50	1·75
5	8c./10c.	blue	.. ..	2·00	2·75

PREPARED FOR USE BUT NOT ISSUED.

2c. orange, 6c. slate-grey, 8c. rose and 15c. ult, at £60 set.

The Japanese occupation prevented the issue of these stamps in 1941. Subsequently a few copies leaked out.

1949 (Dec. 27th) -54 Design, Sultan Ismail. Perf. 17½ x 18 (C). Sheets 10 x 10.

6	1c.	black	.. .. ..	5	5

7	2c.	orange	.. .. ..	5	5
8	3c.	green	.. .. ..	15	25
9	4c.	brown	.. .. ..	5	5
10	6c.	greenish-grey	..	30	15
		a grey (23/4/54)	..	15	15
11	8c.	scarlet	.. .. ..	15	25
12	10c.	dp red-purple	..	25	10
		a red-purple (24/4/51)	15	10
13	15c.	bright ultramarine	..	25	25
14	20c.	black and green	..	35	45
15	25c.	red-pur and orange..	25	30
16	40c.	scar and red-purple..	80	1·25
17	50c.	blk and violet-blue	..	50	45
		a blk and blue (25/5/53)	35	45
18	$1	ult and dp red-purple	75	80
		a blue and red-purple (25/2/53)	1·00	1·00
19	$2	green and car-red	..	2·50	3·50
20	$5	green and dp brown ..	7·00	£13

1952 (Sept. 1st) -57 As before, but new values or colours.

21	5c.	magenta	.. ..	10	10
		a bt magenta (27/3/57)	20	10
22	8c.	yellow-green	..	40	40
		a green (11/8/53)	..	25	35
23	12c.	scarlet	.. .. ..	20	30
24	20c.	blue	.. .. ..	25	30
25	30c.	scar and dp red-pur (4/9/55)	60	50
		a scarlet and red-purple (27/6/56)	45	50
26	35c.	scar and red-purple..	45	60
6/26		set (21)	.. ..	£13	£20

SPECIAL ISSUES

1948 (Dec. 1st) Silver Wedding. As Aden.

S1	10c.	purple	.. .. ..	10	10
S2	$5	rose-carmine	.. ..	9·00	£11

Number issued—10c₂, 197,807; $5, 18.446

1949 (Oct. 10th) U.P.U. As Aden.

S3	10c.	dull purple	.. ..	20	25
S4	15c.	indigo	.. .. ..	30	50
S5	25c.	orange	.. .. ..	45	65
S6	50c.	slate-black	.. ..	60	70
S3/6		set (4)	.. ..	1·50	2·00

Number issued—10c., 44,913; 15c., 71,742; 25c., 59,987; 50c., 58,755.

POSTAGE DUE STAMPS

1937 (Aug. 10th) Perf. 14 x 13¾ (C) (wmk. sideways). Uncoated paper. Sheets 120—two panes, each 10 x 6.

PD1	1c.	carmine-rose	..	70	1·50
PD2	4c.	green	.. ..	70	1·50
PD3	8c.	yellow	.. ..	5·00	7·50
PD4	10c.	chocolate	.. ..	7·00	£14
PD1/4		set (4)	.. ..	£12	£22
SP PD1/4		perf specimen	..	£40	‡

MALDIVE ISLANDS

The islands were originally occupied by the Portuguese, and passed into Dutch hands in 1645. They were acquired as a British possession in 1796, being dependencies of Ceylon.

1906 (Sept. 9th) Stamps of Ceylon (KE 7. Wmk. Multiple Crown CA. Perf. 14) overprinted "MALDIVES" in black sans serif capitals.

E1	2c.	orange-brown	..	9·00	£11
E2	3c.	green	.. ..	£11	£14
E3	4c.	orange and ultra		£28	£45
E4	5c.	purple (C) ..	..	5·00	5·50
E5	15c.	blue ..	..	£40	£50
E6	25c.	bistre	.. ..	£45	£50
E1/6		set (6v.)	.. ..	£125	£160

Numbers Overprinted — E1 4,400; E2 3,600; E3 2,200; E4 18 800; E5/6 1,200 each.

1909 (May) Recess De La Rue (Minaret of Juma Mosque, Malé). Wmk. Multiple Rosettes. Perf. 14. Sheets 240 — four panes each 6 x 10. Stamp size 18½ x 22½ mm.

E7	2c.	orange-brown	..	1·00	35
E8	3c.	green	.. ..	35	35
E9	5c.	purple	.. ..	35	35
E10	10c.	carmine	.. ..	60	50
E7/10		set (4v.)	.. ..	2·00	1·50

(Reduced size illustration)

1933 As before but (Photo) Harrison and Sons Ltd. Wmk. Script "Harrison and Sons London". Perf. 15 x 14. Sheets 10 x 5. Stamp size 18 x 21½ mm.

G1	2c.	grey ..	.. ..	55	50
G2	3c.	red-brown	..	50	70
G3	5c.	claret (wmk. vert.)		5·00	5·00
G4	5c.	mauve (wmk. hor.)		2·00	2·75
G5	6c.	scarlet	.. ..	90	90
G6	10c.	green	.. ..	40	40
G7	15c.	black	.. ..	75	80
G8	25c.	brown	.. ..	1·00	1·00
G9	50c.	purple		1·25	1·00
G10	R1	blue ..	.. ..	2·00	1·75
G1/10		set (10v.)	.. ..	£13	£13

All values may be found with the watermark horizontal or vertical.

New Currency 100 Larees — 1 Rupee.

1950 (Dec. 24) -52 Design, Fishing Boat and Palm (except Nos. 3 and 5). Printers (recess) Bradbury, Wilkinson. Perf. 13¼ x 13 (C). No wmk. Sheets 5 x 10.

1	2l.	olive-green	.. ..	45	55
		a yellowish-olive (/52)		60	55
2	3l.	blue	.. ..	90	80
3	3l.	blue (fish) ('52)		30	35
4	5l.	green	.. ..	1·25	1·00
5	5l.	emerald (Products) ('52)		15	20
6	6l.	chestnut-brown	..	35	40
7	10l.	scarlet	.. ..	35	40
8	15l.	orange	.. ..	40	45
9	25l.	purple	.. ..	60	50
		a reddish-purple (/52)		45	50
10	50l.	violet	.. ..	75	75
		a greyish-violet (/52)		65	75
11	1r.	dp sepia-brown	..	3·50	4·00
1/11		set (11)	.. ..	8·00	9·00

MALTA

Following a short French occupation, Malta requested British protection in 1802 and this was confirmed by the Treaty of Paris in 1814. The first Post Office was opened in 1857 as a branch of the G.P.O. London; and from then until 1885 contemporary G.B. stamps were used for foreign mails.

They were cancelled initially by "M" in a transverse oval of horizontal bars, and subseqeuntly by "A25" in transverse or upright ovals of horizontal bars alone or in duplex with a small Malta datestamp.

Concurrently from 1860 to 1885 Malta adhesive ½d. stamps were used for internal and inter-island mail only; they were cancelled in similar fashion to the G.B. stamps.

1855 Stamps of Great Britain identified by their Catalogue Nos. after prefix 'C' mainly used from the Crimea and cancelled at Malta with a framed horizontal rectangle of wavy lines.
(See also under British Levant).

CV22	1d. red-brown
CV28	1d. red-brown
CV31	1d. red-brown
CV36	2d. blue
CV12	6d. mauve
CV16	1/- green

1857-85 Stamps of Great Britain (Queen Victoria) identified by their Catalogue Nos. after prefix 'M' or 'A'.

(i) Cancelled 'M' in transverse oval of horizontal bars

MV5	1d. red-brown
MV22	1d. red-brown
MV24	1d. red-brown
MV28	1d. red-brown
MV33	1d. red-brown
MV38	1d pale red
MV39	1d. rose-red
MV10	2d. blue
MV26	2d. pale blue
MV36	2d. blue
MV36A	2d. blue
MV41	2d. blue
MV51	2d. blue
MV43	4d. carmine
MV44	4d. rose-carmine
MV14	6d. violet
MV45	6d. lilac
MV47	1/- green

(ii) Cancelled 'A25' in transverse oval of horizontal bars or 'A25' in transverse or upright, oval of horizontal bars in duplex with named circular date-stamp.

(a) 1857-83.

AV108	½d. rose-red
	Plates (Various)

AV5	1d. red-brown
AV22	1d. red-brown
AV33	1d. red-brown
AV38	1d. pale-red
AV39	1d. rose-red
	Plates 50.51
	(Alph IV)
AV39	1d. rose-red
	Res.Pl. 16
AV49	1d. rose-red
	(Various Plates)
AV138	1d. venetian red
AV110	1½d. rose-red
AV10	2d. blue
AV36	2d. blue
AV51	2d. blue
AV52	2d. blue
AV120	2½d. rosy mauve
AV121	2½d. rosy mauve
AV121a	2½d. rosy mauve
	(LH-FL)
AV122	2½d. rosy mauve
AV123	2½d. blue
AV139	2½d. blue
AV53	3d. carmine-rose
AV70	3d. rose
AV78	3d. rose
AV124	3d. rose
AV140	3d. rose
AV144	3d. on 3d. lilac
AV44	4d. rose-carmine
AV59	4d. bright red
AV72	4d. vermilion
AV131	4d. vermilion
AV133	4d. sage-green
AV135	4d. grey-brown
AV141	4d. grey-brown
AV14	6d. violet
AV45	6d. lilac
AV62	6d. lilac
AV75	6d. lilac
AV75b	b wmk. error
AV79	6d. lilac
AV82	6d. bright violet
	(Hyphen)
AV83	6d. dull violet
	(No Hyphen)
AV114	6d. chestnut
AV115	6d. buff
AV119	6d. grey

AV126	6d. grey
AV142	6d. grey
AV145	6d. on 6d. lilac
AV145a	a slanting dots
AV136	8d. orange
AV64	9d. bistre
AV65	9d. straw
AV76	9d. straw
AV86	9d. straw
AV88	10d. red-brown
AV16	1/- green
AV47	1/- green
AV68	1/- green
AV68a	a 'K' circled
AV77	1/- green
AV92	1/- green
AV127	1/- green
AV130	1/- orange-brown
AV143	1/- orange-brown
AV95	2/- blue
AV100	2/- brown
AV101	5/- rose
AV104	5/- rose
AV104a	a white paper
AV102	10/- grey-green

(b) 1880-84.

AV146	½d. deep green
AV147	½d. pale green
AV148	½d. slate-blue
AV149	1d. lilac (14 pearls)
AV151	1d. lilac (16 pearls)
AV138	1½d. venetian red
AV156	2d. pale rose
AV157	2d. deep rose
AV158	5d. indigo

(c) 1883-84

AV159	1½d. lilac
AV160	2d. lilac
AV161	2½d. lilac
AV162	3d. lilac
AV163	4d. dull green
AV164	5d. dull green
AV165	6d. dull green
AV166	9d. dull green
AV167	1/- dull green
AV169	5/- rose
VA169a	a white paper

All stamps from VL1 to G93 are (*typo*) De La Rue. Perf. 14. unless otherwise indicated.

1860 (Dec. 1st)-63 Local Stamps. No wmk. Sheets 240 — four panes each 6 x 10.

(a) Blued Paper.

VL1	½d.	buff	..	..	..	£600 £300
		a imperf.	..	..		— £4000

(b) White Paper.

VL2	½d.	brn-orange (11/61)			£375 £140
VL3	½d.	buff ('63)	..	..	£370 £140

Die Proofs in black and Plate Proofs in black or yellow exist.

VL1 exists overprinted "Specimen". £300 ‡

Numbers Issued—VL1, 24,000; VL2, 25,440; VL3, 26,160.

1863 (June)-81 (April) As before but wmk. Crown CC (white paper).

VL4	½d.	buff (shades) from	£45	£25
		a wmk. inverted	—	—
VL5	½d.	brn/or (shades) from	£75	£35
VL6	½d.	or (shades) from ..	£55	£28
VL7	½d.	yel (shades) from ..	£30	£22

There were seventeen different printings of VL4/7, ranging from 24,480 of VL4 in 1865 to 51,360 of VL6 in 1873: there is consequently an immense range of shades.

Numbers Issued—VL4, 102,000; VL5, 99,360; VL6, 269,040; VL7, 189,280.

1868-71 As before but Perf. 12½. (VL8 rough: VL9 clean cut).

VL8	½d.	brownish buff ..	£35	£28
		a imperf. between		
		(vertical pair) ..	—	—
VL9	½d.	yel-orange (5/71) ..	£85	£80

Numbers Issued—VL8, 48,000; VL9, 47,280.

1878 (July)-79 As before but Perf. 14 x 12½.

VL10 ½d. yel (shades) from £55 £35

Copies are reported 12½ x 14.

Number Issued—102,480.

1882 (May)-84 As before but wmk. Crown CA. Perf. 14.

VL11	½d.	orange-yellow (shades) from ..	£12	£18
VL12	½d.	reddish-or ('84) ..	£12	£18

There were four different printings of VL11 between May 1882 and 1884, each of approximately 48,000 stamps.

Numbers Issued—VL11, 192,720; VL12, 48,000.

1885 (Jan. 1st) Various Frames. Wmk. Crown CA. Sheets ½d. and 1d.—240 (four panes, each 6 x 10) 2d. to 1/–, 12 x 10.

V1	½d.	green	1·00	50
V2	1d.	rose	£16	£13
V3	1d.	carmine	1·50	1·25
		a printed on gummed side	—	—
V4	2d.	grey	80	1·00
V5	2½d.	dull blue	9·00	1·00
V6	2½d.	bright blue	9·00	1·00
V7	2½d.	ultramarine ..	7·00	1·00
V8	4d.	brown	3·75	3·75
		a imperf. (pair) ('93)	£2750	£1750

V9	1/–	violet	£16	£13
		a imperf. (pair) ..	—	—
V10	1/–	pale violet	£25	£13
V1/10		set (6v)	£28	£19
SPV1/10		specimen set (6v)	£350	‡

V1, V9 and V10 may be found with wmk. inverted.

V8a A sheet of 120 was found in Valetta Post Office on December 16th, 1893.

Die Proofs of all values, with or without value expressed, exist in black.

1886 (Jan. 1st) Wmk. Crown CC. Sheets 12 x 10.

V11	5/–	rose	£55	£50
SPV11		specimen	£100	‡

V11 may be found with wmk. inverted. Die Proofs exist in black on glazed paper.

1899 (Feb. 4th)-1901. (Recess).

(a) Wmk. Crown CA. Sheets 120—2 panes, each 6 x 10.

V12	¼d.	brown (1/1/01) ..	90	60
V13	¼d.	red-brown ..	1·00	60
V14	4½d.	sepia..	7·50	5·50
V15	5d.	vermilion	£13	£13

(b) Wmk. Crown CC. Sheets 12 x 5.

V16	2/6	olive-grey	£17	£14
V17	10/–	blue-black.. ..	£50	£40
V12/17		set (5v)	£85	£70
SPV12/17		specimen set (5v)	£95	‡

V12/V13 may be found with wmk. inverted or sideways to right or left. V17 exists with wmk. inverted, reversed and inverted and reversed

Various Colour Trials, perf. and imperf. are known for all values.

Die Proofs of V16/17 exist on surfaced paper.

The Royal Collection contains a proof of V16 in brown on thick wove paper, imperf. and overprinted "Specimen".

Numbers printed : V14/15 120,000 each.
V16/17 60,000 each.

1902 (July 4th) Nos. V5 and V6 surcharged "One Penny" at Malta Government Printing Office, Valleta.

V18	1d. on 2½d.	**dull blue** ..	50	50
	a	surcharge double ..	£1100	£900
	b	"One Pnney"	£10	£12
V19	1d. on 2½d.	**bright blue** ..	50	50
	a	"One Pnney"	£10	£12

A total of 720,000 stamps was surcharged in panes of 60 (6 x 10). The error V19*b* and V19*a* was made deliberately on Row 9/2 on the orders of the Postmaster who then removed the positional blocks containing the error and sold them at an enhanced price. A subsequent rumour to the effect that the "error" was being forged resulted in an instruction to P.O. clerks to mark all *unsurcharged* 2½d. stamps, before sale, with a small red tick in the top left corner.

The surcharged stamps also exist with overprint 'Specimen". Price £35.

These provisionals were issued during the reign of King Edward VII but are included in the Queen Victoria lists as a matter of convenience.

1903-04 Wmk. Crown CA. Sheets 240 – four panes, each 6 x 10.

E1	½d.	**green**	1·25	25
E2	½d.	**pale green**	1·50	25
E3	1d.	**black and red** ..	2·00	35
E4	1d.	**sepia and scar-lake**	2·50	35
E5	2d.	**purple and slate** ..	5·50	4·50
E6	2½d.	**maroon and blue** ..	7·50	1·50
E7	3d.	**slate and purple** ..	1·50	1·00
E8	4d.	**blk and brn** ('04) ..	£13	£10
	a	imperf. (pair) ..	—	—
E9	1/–	**grey and violet** ..	9·00	6·50
E1/7		**set** (7v)	£38	£22
SPE1/7		**specimen set** (7v) ..	£85	‡

Die Proofs of E1/2 exist in black with or without values.

1904 (Oct. 8th)-11 Wmk. Multple Crown CA. Sheets as before.

(a) (*Typo*).

E10	½d.	**green** (11/04) ..	1·25	25
E11	½d.	**deep green** ('10) ..	1·00	25
E12	1d.	**blk and red** (4/05) ..	2·00	35

E13	1d.	**sepia and scar-lake**	1·75	35
E14	1d.	**red** ('07)	90	30
E15	2d.	**pur and sl** (2/05)..	3·25	1·00
E16	2d.	**grey** ('11)	1·25	1·00
E17	2½d.	**maroon and blue** (8/10/04)..	2·00	1·00
E18	2½d.	**bright blue** ('11) ..	2·00	1·00
E19	2½d.	**pale blue**	2·50	1·00
E20	4d.	**sepia and brown**..	5·50	5·00
E21	4d.	**black and red/yel** ('11)	2·50	2·00
	a	on pale yellow ..	5·00	3·00
	b	on lemon ..	4·00	2·50
E22	1/–	**grey and violet** (12/04) ..	£11	3·00
E23	1/–	**black/green** ('11)	3·75	4·50
E24	5/–	**grn and red/yel (C)** ('11)	£55	£55

(b) (*Recess*) **As Nos. V12/15.**

E25	¼d.	**red-brown** (10/05) (CA to right) ..	65	15
E26	¼d.	**choc** ('10) (CA to left)	60	15
E27	4½d.	**brown** (2/05) ..	7·50	5·00
E28	4½d.	**orange** ('11) ..	3·50	2·50
E29	4½d.	**yellow-orange** ..	4·00	2·50
E30	5d.	**vermilion** (2/05) ..	6·00	3·00
E31	5d.	**sage-green** ..	6·50	6·00
E32	5d.	**pl sage-green** ('10)	3·00	3·00
E10/32		**set** (17v)	£110	£85
SPE10/32		**specimen set** (17v)	£135	‡

E25, E26 may be found with wmk. inverted or upright.

1914 (Jan. 2nd)- 21 Wmk. Multiple Crown CA. Sheets ¼d.–1/– as before: 2/– to 5/–, 12 x 5.

(a) (*Typo*).

G1	¼d.	**brown**	30	20
G2	¼d.	**deep brown** ('19)	40	20
G3	½d.	**green** (1/14) ..	80	20
G4	½d.	**deep green** ('19)..	30	20
G5	1d.	**car-red** (4/14) ..	60	30
G6	1d.	**scarlet** ('15) ..	90	30
G7	2d.	**grey** (8/14) ..	4·50	2·75
G8	2d.	**deep slate** ('19) ..	6·50	6·00
G9	2½d.	**bright blue** (4/14)	45	30
G10	3d.	**purple/or-buff (C)** (3/17)	6·50	7·00
	a	on yel (C) ('20) ..	5·00	5·00
	b	on lemon ..	£10	8·00
G11	6d.	**dl and br purple (C)** (4/14) ..	5·50	5·00
G12	6d.	**dl pur and mag (C)** (12/18)	6·00	6·00
G13	1/–	**black/green (C)** (7/15)	7·00	6·00
	a	white back ('14) ..	6·50	6·00

<table>
<tbody></tbody>
</table>

	b on blue-grn, ol-			
	back		7·00	6·00
	(*c*) on emerald sur-			
	face		6·50	6·00
	d emerald back ('15)		7·50	6·00
G14	1/-	**grey and blk/pale**		
		green	£10	7·00
G15	2/-	**pur and br blue/**		
		blue (C) (4/14)	£27	£22
		a printed both sides	—	—
G16	2/-	**dl pur and blue/**		
		blue (C) ('21) ..	£28	£22
G17	5/-	**green and red/**		
		yellow (1/18) ..	£48	£52

G3, G4 may be found with wmk. inverted or sideways and G13 with wmk. sideways.

The 3d. value on yellow paper with white back was prepared for use but not issued. A corner ⊞ from Plate 1 is in the Royal Collection.

G15/17 are known with Damaged Scroll (Row 1/12) and Broken Crown (Row 2/12)—for details see notes after BERMUDA No. G55.

G15A	Damaged Scroll	£175	—
G15B	Broken Crown	£200	—
G16A	Damaged Scroll	£175	—
G16B	Broken Crown	£200	—
G17A	Damaged Scroll	£225	—
G17B	Broken Crown	£300	—

(b) (*Recess*) **As Nos. E25, E30, V16 and V17 but re-drawn. Sheets as before.**

G18	4d.	**black** ('14) ..	7·50	6·00
G19	4d.	**grey-black** ('15) ..	£13	7·50
G20	5d.	**dp sage-grn** ('14)	6·50	6·50
G21	2/6	**grey-green** ('19)	£27	£30
G22	2/6	**olive-grey** ('20) ..	£27	£30
G23	10/-	**black** ('19) ..	£2750	£2750
G1/22		**set** (14v)	£130	£130
SPG1/22		**specimen set** (12v		
		without 5d. and		
		2/6 values) ..	£160	‡
SPG23		**specimen** (1v) ..	£550	‡

Colour Trials of the 2/6 in sepia and the 10/- in red-brown are known with or without"Specimen" overprint.

The Royal Collection contains a proof of G23 in red-brown on thick wove paper, perf. 14.

1917-18 Nos. G4 and E7 overprinted "WAR TAX" in sans-serif capitals.

G24	½d.	**dp grn on bluish**		
		paper (12/17) ..	35	30
G25	½d.	**dp green on white**		
		paper	40	30
		a imperf pair ..	—	—
G26	3d.	**grey and purple**		
		(3/18) ..	2·75	3·75
SPG24/26		**specimen** (2v) ..	£80	‡

G25 exists with inverted watermark.

1921-22 As before but wmk. Script CA. (*typo*) **except G35 which is** (*recess*). **Sheets as before.**

G27	¼d.	**brown**	40	35
G28	½d.	**green**	85	80
G29	1d.	**scarlet**	40	40
G30	2d.	**grey** ('21)	3·25	80
G31	2½d.	**bright blue** ..	2·00	2·25
G32	6d.	**dull and bright**		
		purple (C) ..	£11	£13
G33	2/-	**purple and bright**		
		blue/blue (C) ..	£75	£78

G34	2/-	**purple and pale**		
		blue/blue (C) ..	£80	£80
G35	10/-	**black**	£425	£425
G27/23		**set** (8v)	£500	£525
SPG27/35		**specimen set** (8v)	£190	‡

Imperf. Plate Proofs of G30 in blue and perf. 14 in carmine, both on unwmk'd. paper, are known.

G3, G4 may be found with wmk. inverted or (Row 1/12) and Broken Crown (Row 2/12) flaws —for details see notes after BERMUDA No. G55.

G33A	Damaged Scroll	£350	—
G33B	Broken Crown	£450	—
G34A	Damaged Scroll	£350	—
G34B	Broken Crown	£450	—

1922 (Jan 12th-April) Various stamps overprinted "SELF-GOVERNMENT" diagonally in sans-serif capitals in black or, where indicated, in red.

(a) Wmk. Crown CC (No. V17).

G36	10/-	**blue-black (R)** ..	£140	£140

(b) Wmk. Multiple Crown CA (Nos. G3–17 and G22).

G37	½d.	**green**	30	25
G38	2½d.	**bright blue** ..	1·25	1·50
G39	3d.	**pur/or-buff (C)** ..	1·00	2·50
G40	6d.	**dl and br pur (C)**	1·25	2·50
G41	1/-	**black/emerald (C)**	2·00	2·25
		a grey and black/		
		pale green ..	5·00	5·00
G42	2/-	**dl purple and blue/**		
		blue (C) (R) ..	£145	£160
G43	2/6	**olive-grey**	£16	£17
G44	5/-	**green and red/**		
		yellow (C) ..	£27	£30

(c) Wmk. Multiple Script CA (Nos. G27-35).

G45	¼d.	**brown**	20	20
G46	½d.	**green**	45	40
G47	1d.	**scarlet**	35	30
		a misplaced tablets	—	—
G48	2d.	**grey**	80	80
G49	2½d.	**bright blue** ..	55	75
G50	6d.	**dl and br pur (C)**	2·00	2·25
G51	2/-	**dl purple and blue/**		
		blue (C) (R) ..	£22	£26
G52	10/-	**black (R)**	£75	£85
G37/52		**set** (16v)	£290	£330

G47*a* comes from a sheet on which the value tablets and "MALTA" tablet have all shifted downwards.

There are a number of varieties showing broken type in the overprint – such as dot for hyphen, broken "O", short "F" etc.

G42, G44 & G51 are known with Damaged Scroll (Row 1/12) and Broken Crown (Row 2/12) flaws —for details see notes after BERMUDA No. G55.

G42A	Damaged Scroll	£600	—
G42B	Broken Crown	£700	—
G44A	Damaged Scroll	£100	—
G44B	Broken Crown	£150	—
G51A	Damaged Scroll	£200	—
G51B	Broken Crown	£250	‡

Numbers overprinted: G36 7,860; G37 378,000; G38 21,480; G39 33,000; G40 50,380; G41 78,240; G42 32,240; G43 21,360; G44 17,640; G45 300,000; G46 290,400; G47 1,080,000; G48 492,000; G49 204 360; G50 40,680; G51 15,120; G52 12,690.

1922 (April 15th) No. G30 surcharged "One/ Farthing" in black serif type at the Government Printing Office, Valletta.

G53 ¼d. on 2d. **grey** 20 20
    a no dot over
       "i" .. .. 5·00 5·00

G53*a* occurs on Stamp No. 40 in the sheet.

1922 (Aug. 1st)-26 Wmk. Multiple Script CA (sideways on G54–69 and G75). Designers, Melita, Caruana Dingli; Melita and Britannia, G. Vella. Sheets ¼d.–6d. 120 (2 panes, each 6 x 10)' 1/– to £1, 8 x 10.

(a) (*Typo*). **Chalk surfaced paper.**

G54	¼d.	**brown** (22/8/22) ..	30	25
G55	¼d.	**chocolate-brown**	30	25
G56	½d.	**green**	25	15
G57	½d.	**yellow-green**	40	15
G58	1d.	**orange and purple**	60	40
G59	1d.	**dp orange and pur**	40	40
G60	1d.	**br violet** (4/24) ..	40	30
G61	1d.	**violet** ..	50	30
G62	1½d.	**brown-red** (10/23)	45	25
G63	2d.	**bistre-brown and**		
		tur (28/8/22) ..	30	20
G64	2½d.	**ultramarine** (2/26)	75	1·50
G65	3d.	**bright ultramarine**		
		(28/8/22) ..	1·25	1·25
G66	3d.	**cobalt**	1·50	1·25
G67	3d.	**blk/yellow** (2/26)	1·25	1·25
G68	4d.	**yellow and br blue**		
		(28/8/22) ..	1·00	1·25
G69	6d.	**ol-grn and violet**	1·25	1·25
G70	1/–	**indigo and sepia**	2·25	2·25
G71	2/–	**brown and blue** ..	5·50	6·00
G72	2/6	**br magenta and**		
		black (28/8/22)	7·50	7·50
G73	5/–	**orange-yel and br**		
		ult (28/8/22) ..	£10	£10
G74	10/–	**sl-grey and brown**		
		(28/8/22) ..	£25	£27

(b) (*Recess*).

G75	£1	**blk and carmine-red**		
		(28/8/22) ..	£90	£95
G76	£1	**blk and carmine-red**		
		('25)	£90	£95
G54/76		**set** (17v)	£140	£145
SPG54/76 **specimen set** (17v)			£240	‡

The wmk. is sideways on G75 and upright on G76.

G54-G59 and G68 exist with inverted watermark.

Die Proofs of the Melita design exist without value in black or sepia. There are Colour Trials of G56 in several shades.

The Royal Collection contains Colour Trials of G75 imperf. on thick paper in blue and brown and in blue and green.

1925 (Nos. G65/66 surcharged "Two pence/ halfpenny" in black serif type at the Government Printing Office, Valletta.

G77	2½d. on 3d.	**cobalt** (3/12)	65	70
G78	2½d. on 3d.	**br ult** (24/12)	65	75

The surcharge normally falls on the upper portion of the stamp, but may be found on the lower half of stamps from a different printing.

1926 (April 1st) Nos. G54/74 overprinted "POSTAGE" in black serif type at the Government Printing Office, Valletta.

G79	¼d.	**brown**	20	25
G80	¼d.	**chocolate-brown**	30	25
G81	½d.	**green**	30	20
G82	1d.	**bright violet** ..	30	40
G83	1½d.	**brown-red**	40	40
G84	2d.	**bistre-brn and tur**	35	45
G85	2½d.	**ultramarine** ..	45	40
G86	3d.	**black/yellow**	50	75
		a overprint inverted	£350	£350
G87	4d.	**yel and br blue** ..	1·25	2·50
		a misplaced over-		
		print	—	—
G88	6d.	**olive-grn and vio**	1·00	65
G89	1/–	**indigo and sepia**	3·00	4·50
G90	2/–	**brown and blue** ..	£25	£27
G91	2/6	**br mag and blk** ..	9·50	£10
G92	5/–	**or-yel and br ult**..	6·00	9·00
G93	10/–	**slate-grey and brn**	£12	£14
G79/93		**set** (14v)	£55	£65

G86*a* has been forged and copies should only be purchased with a certificate.

G87*a* comes from a single sheet on which the overprint was so misplaced laterally that each stamp received an overprint "AGE POST".

1926-27 Wmk. Multiple Script CA. Waterlow. Inscribed "Postage".

(a) (*typo*) **Perf. 15 x 14. Sheets 120 – two panes, each 6 x 10.**

G94	¼d.	**brown**	25	15
G95	½d.	**green**	30	15
		a printed on gum-		
		med side ..	—	—
G96	1d.	**red**	25	25
G97	1½d.	**chestnut** ..	45	20
G98	2d.	**greenish-grey** ..	1·50	1·75
G99	2½d.	**blue**	1·25	40
G100	3d.	**violet**	1·25	1·50
G101	4d.	**black and red** ..	2·75	3·00
G102	4½d.	**lav and ochre** ..	2·75	2·75
G103	6d.	**violet and scarlet**	2·75	2·75

(b) (*Recess*). **Various Vignettes. Perf. 12½. Sheets 10 x 8 (vert. designs) 8 x 10; (horiz.).**

G104	1/–	**black**	2·75	3·00
G105	1/6	**black and green**	6·50	6·50
G106	2/–	**black and purple**	8·00	8·50

G107	2/6	black and verm	9·00	9·00
G108	3/–	black and blue	9·00	9·50
G109	5/–	black and green	£15	£17
G110	10/–	black and car ..	£45	£48
G94/110		set (17v)	£100	£110
SPG94/110		specimen set		
		(17v)	£215	‡

Die Proofs of G104 in black on thin card, and Plate Proofs of G94 in black (imperf. on unwmk'd paper) exist.

1928 (April 1st) No. G103 overprinted "AIR/ MAIL" in black sans-serif capitals.

G111	6d.	violet and scarlet	8·00	£10

1928 (Oct 1st-Dec.) Nos. G94/110 overprinted "POSTAGE AND REVENUE" (in 3 lines) in black serif type (G112/123) and red sans-serif type (G124/130).

G112	¼d.	brown	20	10
G113	½d.	green	15	10
G114	1d.	red	15	50
G115	1d.	chestnut (Dec.)	50	10
G116	1½d.	chestnut	25	30
G117	1½d.	red (Dec.) ..	50	15
G118	2d.	greenish-grey ..	2·00	2·25
G119	2½d.	blue	50	20
G120	3d.	violet	90	60
G121	4d.	black and red ..	90	1·50
G122	4½d.	lav and ochre ..	1·75	1·50
G123	6d.	violet and scarlet	2·00	2·25
G124	1/–	black	1·75	2·00
		a imperf at margin	—	—
G125	1/6	black and green	6·50	7·50
		a imperf. at margin	—	—
G126	2/–	black and purple	8·00	7·00
G127	2/6	black and verm	£11	£12
G128	3/–	black and blue ..	£11	£12
G129	5/–	black and green ..	£22	£28
G130	10/–	black and car ..	£40	£48
G112/130		set (19v)	£100	£115
SPG112/130		specimen set		
		(19v)	£240	‡

1930 (Oct. 20th) As before but inscribed "Postage and Revenue".

G131	¼d.	brown	10	10
G132	½d.	green	20	10
G133	1d.	chestnut	20	10
G134	½d.	red	30	10
G135	12d.	greenish-grey ..	55	70
G136	½d.	blue	55	25
G137	23d.	violet	65	50
G138	4d.	black and red ..	1·00	2·00
G139	½d.	lav and ochre ..	1·25	2·00
G140	6d.	violet and scarlet	1·50	2·00
G141	1/–	black	3·25	4·25
G142	1/6	black and green	6·50	7·00
G143	2/–	black and purple	7·00	8·50
G144	2/6	black and verm	£11	£12
G145	3/–	black and blue ..	£ 3	£17
G146	5/–	black and green	£18	£22
G147	10/–	black and car ..	£50	£60
G131/147		set (17v)	£100	£115
SPG131/147		specimen set		
		(17v)	£140	‡

1935 (May 6th) Silver Jubilee. *(Recess)* **Bradbury Wilkinson. Wmk. Multiple Script CA. Perf. 11 x 12. Sheets 6 x 10.**

G148	½d.	black and green	15	15
		a extra flagstaff ..	£18	—
G149	2½d.	brown and blue	1·75	1·75
		a extra flagstaff ..	£50	—
G150	6d.	lt blue and ol-grn	6·00	6·00
		a extra flagstaff ..	£50	—
G151	6d.	light blue and		
		brownish-grn	£10	£10
G152	1/–	slate and purple	£11	£11
		a extra flagstaff ..	£120	—
G148/152		set (4v excluding		
		G151)	£17	£17
SPG148/152		specimen set (4v		
		excluding G151)	£30	‡

G143*a*/G152*a* Extra flagstaff occurs on No. 49 (Row 9/1).

On a small number of sheets G148*a*, G151 and G152*a* the extra flagstaff was erased on the stamp by scratching with a pointed instrument. G151 sheets are not known *without* the extra flagstaff erased in this manner.

Numbers issued—G148, 95,690; G149, 52,890; G150/151, 43,360; G152, 32,780.

Remainders were withdrawn on December 31st, 1935.

The following stamps were printed *(recess)* by Waterlow & Sons. Perf. 12½ (L).

1938 (Feb. 17th) - 44 Designs, ¼d. (Grand Har-

bour, Valetta); ½d. (Naval Dockyard, H.M.S. "St. Angelo"); 2d. (Victoria and Citadel, Gozo); 2½d. (De l'Isle Adam entering Mdina); 6d. (State of Manoel de Vilhena); 1/- (Girl wearing Faldetta); 1/6 (St. Publius); 2/6 (Statue of Neptune); 5/- (Palace Square, Valetta); 10/- (St. Paul); Other Values (Ruins or Buildings of Historical importance). Designs, ½d., 1½d., 3d., 6d., 1/-, 5/-, 10/- H. Sheets ¼d. 8 x 51; others 10 x 6 or 6 x 10.

1	¼d.	**chocolate**	10	10
		a brown (13/3/44) ..	10	10
2	½d.	**green**	15	10
3	½d.	**red-brown** (8/3/43) ..	10	10
4	1d.	**chestnut-brown** ..	30	10
		a dp chestnut-br. (/41)	40	10
5	1d.	**green** (8/3/43) ..	15	10
6	1½d.	**scarlet**	15	10
		a carmine-red (/41) ..	20	10
7	1½d.	**slate-black** (8/3/43)	10	10
8	2d.	**grey-black**	30	35
		a slate-black (/14) ..	40	35
9	2d.	**scarlet** (8/3/43) ..	15	10
		a car-red (13/3/44)	10	10
10	2½d.	**blue**	25	35
11	2½d.	**violet** (8/3/43) ..	20	15
12	3d.	**violet**	24	45
13	3d.	**blue** (8/3/43)	15	15
14	4½d.	**olive and yel-brown**	45	25
		a olive and orange-brown (13/3/44) ..	35	25
15	6d.	**olive and scarlet** ..	35	30
16	1/-	**black**	70	70
17	1/6	**black and olive** ..	1·75	2·25
18	2/-	**palr green and indigo**	1·75	2·25
19	2/6	**black and scarlet** ..	3·00	2·50
20	5/-	**black and green** ..	5·50	6·00
		a semaphore variety ..	£20	£20
		b black and yellow-gr. (13/3/44) ..	5·00	2·50
21	10/-	**black and dp carmine**	£11	£10
1/21		**set** (21)	£24	£22
SP 1/21		**specimen set** perf (21)	£150	‡

20*a* A printer's guide mark and known to collectors as the "semaphore variety" is to be found on first printing only Row 2/7.

SPECIAL ISSUES

1937 (May 12th) Coronation. As Aden.

S1	½d.	**green**	10	10
S2	1½d.	**scarlet**	10	10
		a carmine-red ..	£150	£150
S3	2½d.	**blue**	40	40
SP S1/3		**specimen set** perf (3)	£20	‡

1946 (Dec. 3rd) Victory. As Aden .(*George and Maltese Crosses incorporated in design*).

S4	1d.	**green**	10	10
S5	3d.	**dp blue**	25	25
SP S4/5		**specimen set** perf (2)	£22	‡

1948 (Nov. 25th). 55 Nos. 1, etc., overprinted SELF-GOVERNMENT 1947 (*diagonally*) **in black or red to commemorate inauguration of New Constitution.**

S6	¼d.	**brown**	10	10
S7	½d.	**red-brown**	20	10
		a lt red-brn (16/5/50)	10	10
S8	1d.	**green**	10	10
S9	1½d.	**slate-black** (red) ..	15	10
		a indigo-blk (16/5/50)	10	10
S10	2d.	**scarlet**	15	10
		a "Flag" variety ..	£10	£10
S11	2½d.	**violet** (red)	10	10
S12	3d.	**blue** (red)	15	15
S13	4½d.	**olive and yel-brn** ..	50	60
S14	6d.	**olive and scarlet** ..	25	25
		a dp olive-grn & scar (26/7/55) ..	40	25
		b F damaged ..	£10	£10
		c F repaired	£10	£10
S15	1/-	**black**	70	70
S16	1/6	**black and olive** ..	1·50	1·50
S17	2/-	**pl grn and ind** (red)	1·75	1·75
S18	2/6	**black and scarlet** ..	3·50	3·50
S19	5/-	**black and grn** (red)	6·00	6·00
S20	10/-	**black and carmine**	£13	£13
S6/20		**set** (15)	£25	£25

S10*a* Flaw at end (roof) of building resembling a flag appears on Row 5/8.

S14*b/c* Top bar of F of overprint is damaged, later repaired but left thicker, on Row 3/1.

1953 (Jan. 8th) As Nos. S8, etc., but colours changed.

S21	1d.	**light grey** (red) ..	10	10
		a grey (5/11/53) ..	15	10
S22	1½d.	**green**	10	10
		a overprint omitted	—	£2750
S23	2d.	**yellowish-ochre** ..	15	10
		a ochre (5/11/53) ..	10	10
		b cracked plate ..	£10	£10
S24	2½d.	**scarlet**	35	35
S25	3d.	**violet** (red)	15	15
S26	4½d.	**olive and ult** (red) ..	35	35
S21/26		**set** (6)	1·00	1·00

S22*a* About six copies of the overprint omitted were found in commercial mail. Mint copies have been reported, but we have not seen a copy.

S23*b* The break runs across second A of MALTA to portrait on Row 5/1.

1949 (Jan. 4th) Silver Wedding. As Aden. (*George and Maltese Crosses incorporated in design*).

S27	1d.	**green**	10	10
S28	£1	**bluish-slate** .. .. (*all recess*) ..	£22	£25

1949 (Oct. 10th) U.P.U. As Aden (*George and Maltese Crosses incorporated in design*).

S29	2½d.	**dull violet**	20	25

S30	3d. **indigo**		40	40
S31	6d. **carmine-red**		1·00	75
S32	1/- **dp grey**		1·50	1·75
S29/32	**set** (4)		3·00	3·00

1950 (**Dec. 1st**) **Princess Elizabeth. Printers** (*recess*) **Bradbury, Wilkinson. Perf. 12 x 11¾(C) Sheets 6 x 10.**

S33	1d. **green**	10	10
S34	3d. **dp ultramarine**	30	30
S35	1/- **black**	75	80
S33/35	**set** (3)	1·00	1·00

1951 (**July 12th**) **7th Centenary of the Scapular. Design, the Virgin Mary handing Carmelite Scapular to St. Simon Stock in 1251. Printers Bradbury, Wilkinson. Perf. 12 x 11¾ (C). Sheets as before.**

S36	1d. **green**	10	10
S37	3d. **violet**	15	15
S38	1/- **slate-black**	1·00	1·00
S36/38	**set** (4)	1·25	1·25

Number Issued—1d, 1,209,560; 3d, 1,184,970; 1/-, 663,570.

POSTAGE DUE STAMPS

1925 Type-set locally. No wmk. Imperf. Sheets 168 – four panes, each 6 x 7.

GD1	½d.	**black/lt cream**	30	40
GD2	1d.	**black/lt cream**	40	60
GD3	1½d.	**black/lt cream**	60	80
	a	straight serif to "1" in fraction	£25	£25
GD4	2d.	**black/lt cream**	70	80

GD5	2½d.	**black/lt cream**	80	90
	a	"2" of fraction omitted	£200	£200
GD6	3d.	**black/grey**	1·00	1·25
GD7	4d.	**black/buff**	1·25	1·40
GD8	6d.	**black/buff**	1·50	1·75
GD9	1/-	**black/buff**	5·00	5·00
GD10	1/6	**black/buff**	8·00	9·00
	a	MALTA in heavy type	—	—
GD1/10		**set** (10v)	£19	£22
GD1/10		**tete-beche set** (10 pairs)	£75	£95

The type was set up in two panes, each 6 x 7, one above the other. After printing down one side the paper was turned round and a similar printing applied to the other side: the left two panes are thus inverted in relation to the right two panes, and down the centre of the sheet there are 14 horizontal tete-beche pairs. Tete-beche pairs of single values can be supplied at five times the price of the normal stamp.

Collectors are warned of dangerous forgeries of GD5*a* which should only be bought with a certificate. This variety was caused on Row 4/10 when the "2" of the fraction fell out during the printing of one side of the sheet.

1925 (*Typo*) **Bradbury Wilkinson. Wmk. Multiple Script CA (sideways). Perf. 12.**

GD11	½d.	**green**	30	30
GD12	1d.	**violet**	40	30
GD13	1½d.	**brown**	40	40
GD14	2d.	**grey**	6·00	6·00
GD15	2½d.	**orange**	70	70
GD16	3d.	**blue**	1·00	1·00
GD17	4d.	**olive-green**	6·00	6·00
GD18	6d.	**purple**	1·00	1·00
GD19	1/-	**black**	1·50	1·50
GD20	1/6	**carmine**	3·00	3·00
GD11/20		**set** (10v)	£20	£20
SPGD11/20		**specimen set** (10v)	£75	‡

1937-46 Printers (*typo*) **Bradbury, Wilkinson. Perf. 12 (L)** (*wmk. sideways*). **Sheets 240, four panes, each 6 x 10.**

PD1	½d.	**emer-gr** (16/10/41)	40	40
PD2	1d.	**purple** (9/4/43)	50	50
PD3	1½d.	**pale brn** (26/6/46)	50	50
PD4	2d.	**sepia** (11/4/37)	6·50	6·50
PD5	2½d.	**dp orange** (26/6/46)	80	80
PD6	3d.	**greyish-blue** (26/6/46)	1·20	1·20
PD7	4d.	**sage gr** (26/6/46)	6·50	6·50
PD8	6d.	**pur-lake** (26/6/46)	1·20	1·20
PD9	1/-	**grey** (9/4/43)	1·75	1·75
PD10	1/6	**dp sclet** (26/6/46)	3·00	3·00
PD1/10		**set** (10)	£22	£22

These later printings not only differ considerably in shade but they are also printed on rough paper. Subsequently printings appeared on chalk-surfaced paper.

MAURITIUS

1938 (Mar. 2nd) **-48 Printers** (*typo*) **De La Rue. Perf. 13¾ x 14 (C). Sheets 120—two panes, each 6 x 10.**

1	2c.	**grey** (9/3/38)	10	5
	a	dp grey (8/4/43)	5	5
2	3c.	**pur and sc** (27/9/38)	10	5
	a	purple-violet and scarlet (8/4/43)	5	5
3	4c.	**dull green (26/1/38)**	10	5
	a	dull bl-gr (8/4/43)	10	5
4	5c.	**violet** (23/2/38)	10	5
	a	dull lavender and lavender (/42)	2·00	1·50
	b	pale vit (8/4/43)	15	10
5	10c.	**carmine-rose** (9/3/38)	15	10
	a	dp car-rd (8/4/43)	10	10
6	12c.	**dull sal** (26/2/38)	15	10
	a	sal-pk (27/8/45)	10	5
7	20c.	**dull blue** (26/2/38)	20	10
	a	dl gr-bl (8/4/43)	20	10
	b	blue (4/12/44)	10	5
8	25c.	**brown-maroon** (*ch*)	40	25
	a	maroon (sub) (8/4/43)	50	20
	b	lake-mar (*ch*) (22/5/47)	50	20
	c	dull mar (*ch*) (19/4/48)	10	10
9	1r.	**blackish-brown** (*ch*)	60	40
	a	grey-brown (sub) (8/4/43)	60	30
	b	ditto (*ch*) (22/5/47)	40	20
10	2.50c.	**dull pale violet** (*ch*)	2·00	1·00
	a	pale lavender (sub) (8/4/43)	1·50	1·50
	b	dull lavender (*ch*) (22/5/47)	7·00	7·50
	c	pale violet (F.A.) (*ch*) (19/4/48)	6·00	7·50
11	5r.	**dull olive** (*ch*)	4·00	3·50
	a	dp olive-green (sub) (8/4/43)	3·25	3·00
	b	deep olive (*ch*) (19/4/48)	5·00	3·50
12	10r.	**purple** (*ch*)	8·00	7·00
	a	ditto (sub) (8/4/43)	5·00	6·00
1/12		**set** (12)	£11	£11
SP 1/12		**specimen set** perf (12)	£35	‡

8/4/43 is the approximate date (*furnished officially*) when the printing was released.

1943 As No. 1, etc., but printed on rough paper by Bradbury, Wilkinson (*from De La Rue plates*) **and Perf. 14¾ x 14 (C).**

13	2c.	**grey**	15	15
14	5c.	**violet**	2·25	60
15	10c.	**carmine-red**	2·00	1·75
16	12c.	**salmon**	5·00	3·00
13/16		**set** (4)	£10	5·00

1950 (July 1st) **Designs, 1c.** (Sugar Factory); **3c.** (Aloe Plant); **12c.** (Map and Dodo); **20c.** (Legend of Paul and Virginia); **24c.** (La Bourdonnais Statue); **35c.** (Govt. House); **1.** (Mauritius Deer); **2r.50** (Port Louis); **10r.** (Arms of Mauritius); Other Values (Views and Scenes in Colony). Printers (*photo*) **Harrison & Sons. Perf. 14¾ x 13¾ (C). Chalk-surfaced paper. Designs, 3c., 4c., 20c., 25c., 50c. V. Sheets 10 x 6 or 6 x 10.**

17	1c.	**purple-magenta**	5	10
18	2c.	**carmine-lake**	5	5
19	3c.	**pea-green**	20	20
20	4c.	**dp grey/green**	10	5
21	5c.	**blue**	10	5
	a	Q for O	2·00	2·00
	b	booklet pane of 4	5·00	—
22	10c	**scarlet-red**	15	20
24	20c.	**bright-ultramarine**	10	10
25	25c.	**brown-lake**	20	20
26	35c.	**purple-violet**	15	15
27	50c.	**emerald**	25	25
	a	booklet pane of 4	£10	—
28	1r.	**grey-sepia**	1·25	60
29	2r.50	**orange**	2·00	1·50
30	5r.	**red-brown**	3·00	3·00
31	10r.	**mineral-blue**	7·00	4·00
17/31		**set** (15)	£14	£10

21*a* A flaw on O (Row 19/9) changes letter to Q.

SPECIAL ISSUES

1937 (May 12th) **Coronation. As Aden.**

S1	5c.	**violet**	5	5
S2	12c.	**scarlet**	10	5
S3	20c.	**blue**	15	15
SP S1/3		**specimen set** perf (3)	£12	‡

1946 (Nov. 20th) **Victory. As Aden.**

S4	5c.	**lilac**	5	5

S5	20c.	**dp blue**	..	..	25	25
	a	blue	..	..	25	25
	b	flag on Tower of				
		Parliament	..	3·00	3·00
SP S4/5		**specimen set** perf (3)		£13	‡

1948 (Mar. 22nd) Centenary of First Mauritius Postage Stamps. Design, incorporating fac-simile of "Post Office" Stamps, issued 21/9/1847. Printers (recess) Bradbury, Wilkinson. Perf. 11½ x 11¼ (C). Sheets 5 x 12.

S6	5c.	**orange and magenta**	5	5
S7	12c.	**orange and green** ..	10	10
S8	20c.	**dp bl and grey-blue**	10	10
S9	1r.	**dp bl and beech-brn**	40	40
S6/9		**set** (4)	60	60

1948 (Oct. 25th) Silver Wedding. As Aden.

| S10 | 5c. | **bright violet** .. | .. | 5 | 5 |
| S11 | 10r. | **lake-magenta** | .. | 6·00 | 7·00 |

1949 (Oct. 10th) U.P.U. As Aden.

S12	12c.	**carmine-rose**	..	10	15
S13	20c.	**indigo** ..	..	..	20	30
S14	35c.	**purple** ..	..	..	30	30
S15	1r.	**sepia** ..	..	..	50	50
S12/15		**set** (4)	..	..	1·00	1·25

POSTAGE DUE STAMPS

1933-8 Printers (*typo*) Waterlow & Sons. Perf. 14¾ x 14 (C). Sheets 6 x 10.

PD1	2c.	**black** (/33) ..	..	5	10
PD1a	4c.	**dp purple-violet**	..	5	10
PD2	6c.	**vermilion**	..	..	5	10
PD3	10c.	**olive-green**	..	..	10	10
PD4	20c.	**pale blue**	..	..	20	15
PD5	50c.	**magenta** (1/3/54) ..	35	25
PD6	1r.	**orange** (1/3/54) ..	50	40
PD1/6		**set** (7)	..	..	1·30	1·20

| SPPD1/6 | **set** perf. **specimen** (5) | £20 | ‡ |

Though similar in design to the 1933 issue, the shades are quite distinct.

MONTSERRAT

The island was originally settled by Irishmen; and was subsequently occupied by France, before being assigned to Great Britain in 1783.

Following the use of handstamps or manuscript marks, a Crowned Circle PAID Frank was registered at the G.P.O. in London on July 15th, 1852 and was thereafter struck in red to indicate prepayment of postage on overseas letters.

From May, 1858 to March, 1860 contemporary G.B. stamps were in use and were cancelled with "AO8" in a transverse oval of horizontal bars.

The Crowned Circle Frank was again used from April 1st, 1860, and an Uncrowned Frank from 1861, until the first Montserrat stamps were issued (See Introduction).

See also under Leeward Islands.

1852-76. PAID Franks			On Cover.
VF1	..	..	£225
VF2 **(1861)**	..	..	£175

1858-60 Stamps of Great Britain identified by their Catalogue Nos. after prefix 'MT'.
Used at Plymouth: 'A08'.

MT V39	1d.	**rose-red**	..	
MT V44	4d.	**rose**	..	..
MT V45	6d.	**lilac**	..	..
MT V47	1/-	**green**	..	..

MONTSERRAT

1876 (Sept.). Nos. V14/17 of Antigua (*recess*). **De La Rue overprinted MONTSERRAT (beneath a bar) in black by De La Rue. Wmk. Crown CC. Perf. 14. Sheets 12 x 10.**

V1	1d.	**red**	..	..	£12	£14
		a inverted 'S' ..		..	£550	£550
		b bisect vert (½d.) on				
		cover (Sept. 1883)			‡	£675
V2	6d.	**green** ..		..	£25	£20
		a inverted 'S' ..		..	£1100	£1000
		b bisect (2½d.) on				
		cover			‡	—
		c blue grn		..	£400	—

V1 may be found with the overprint so misplaced that the bar does not obliterate ANTIGUA.

V2 is also known, unused only, is a blue-green shade. This is believed to be from a Proof Sheet.

V1*b*—This bisect is also found surcharged '½' in black.

V2*b*—This stamp is also known trisected and used with a bisected copy of V1 to make up the 2½d. rate (1884).

V2*c* is not known used.

Numbers issued—V2, 19,300.

See Introduction for details of Dies I and II.

1880 (Jan.). (*typo*). **De La Rue. (Die I) Wmk. Crown CC. Perf. 14. Sheets 6 x 10.**

V3	2½d.	**red-brown**	..	..	£125	£90
V4	4d.	**blue**	..	..	£65	£45
		a bisect diag (2d.)	..		—	—

V4*a*—A bisect, used with a complete stamp on piece (April 26th, 1881), is in the Royal Collection.

1884-85. As V1/2 but Wmk. Crown CA.

(a) Perf. 14.

V5	1d.	**red**	..	..	4·00	8·00
		a inverted 'S' ..		..	£550	£550
		b bisect diag or vert				
		(½d.) on cover				
		Sept., 1887		..	‡	£675
V6	1d.	**rose-red** ('85)		..	8·00	£10

(b) Perf. 12. (May, 1884).

V7	1d.	**red**	..	..	£20	£20
		a inverted 'S' ..		..	£1000	£825
		b bisect vert (½d.) on				
		cover, May, 1884,			‡	£625

V6—The inverted 'S' varieties were corrected before this printing.

1884-85. As V3/4 but Wmk. Crown CA.

V8	½d.	**dl green**	..	..	1·00	2·00
V9	2½d.	**red-brown**	..	..	£65	£50
V10	2½d.	**ultramarine**	..	..	7·00	7·50
V11	4d.	**blue**	..	..	£1000	£150
V12	4d.	**mauve** ..		..	6·00	6·00

Numbers issued—V9, 8,040: V11, 3,900.

From November, 1890 until 1903 only the stamps of Leeward Islands were used in Montserrat.

The following issues were in concurrent use with Leeward Islands stamps until June, 1956.

All stamps from E1 to G55 are (*typo*) **De La Rue. Perf. 14.**

1903. Sheets 120 — two panes, each 6 x 10.

(a) Wmk. Crown CA.

E1	½d.	**gr-grn and grn**	..	80	2·00
E2	1d.	**gr-blk and red**	..	60	60
E3	2d.	**grey and brown**	..	4·50	7·00
E4	2½d.	**grey and blue**	..	3·50	5·50
E5	3d.	**orange and purple** ..		6·00	8·00
E6	6d.	**dl purple and olive**	..	8·00	£10
E7	1/-	**grn and bt pur**	..	£11	£13
E8	2/-	**grn and brn-or**	..	£14	£18
E9	2/6	**green and black**	..	£20	£25

(b) Wmk. Crown CC.

E10	5/-	**black and scarlet**	..	£95	£110
(E1/10		**set** (10v)		£150	£180
SPE1/10		**specimen set** (10v)		£100	‡

1903-08. As before but Wmk. Multiple Crown CA. Chalky paper; and E11/13/15/16 also on Ordinary paper.

E11	½d.	gr-grn and grn	50	60
E12	1d.	gr-blk and red (11/07)	6·50	7·50
E13	2d.	grey and brown	1·00	1·75
E14	2½d.	grey and blue ('05)	1·50	3·25
E15	3d.	orange and purple	2·25	2·50
E16	6d.	dl purple and olive	2·50	2·50
E17	1/−	grn and bt pur ('08)	6·50	7·50
E18	2/−	grn and or ('08)	£18	£25
E19	2/6	grn and black ('08)	£28	£30
E20	5/−	black and red (9/07)	£80	£95
E11/20		set (10v)	£140	£160
SPE11/20		specimen set (10v)	£100	‡

1908-16. As before but changed colours. E21/27 on Ordinary paper: E28/36 on Chalky paper.

E21	½d.	dp green	60	80
E22	½d.	yellow-green ('16)	3·00	1·25
E23	½d.	dk green C (4/10)	80	60
E24	1d.	rose-red	1·25	35
E25	2d.	greyish slate	1·75	3·50
E26	2d.	grey (11/11)	2·00	3·00
E27	2½d.	blue	2·50	3·50
E28	3d.	purple/yellow	1·50	3·50
	a	white back ('13)	2·75	4·00
E29	3d.	brown/yellow	3·50	£30
E30	6d.	dl and dp purple	6·00	8·00
E31	6d.	dl and bt purple	6·00	8·00
E32	6d.	red-purple	7·00	8·00
E33	1/−	black/green	6·00	8·00
E34	2 −	pur and bt bl/bl	£18	£21
E35	2/6	blk and red/blue	£20	£25
E36	5/−	red and green/yel	£50	£55
E21/36		set (10v)	£100	£120
SPE21/36		specimen set (10v)	£100	‡

1914. As E36 but head of King George V.

G1	5/−	red and grn/yel C	£70	£90
SPG1		specimen (1v)	£50	‡

1916 (Oct. 10th)-23. Wmk. Multiple Crown CA. G2/6 on Ordinary paper: G7/14 on Chalky paper. Sheets 120 − two panes, each 6 x 10.

G2	½d.	green		20	35
G3	1d.	scarlet		40	50
G4	1d.	carmine		2·00	1·50
G5	2d.	grey		1·25	2·25
G6	2½d.	bt blue		2·25	3·00
G7	3d.	purple/yellow		1·50	3·00
	a	on pale yellow		2·00	3·00
G8	4d.	gr blk and red/pl yel ('23)		4·50	6·50
	a	on deep yellow		6·00	7·00
¦9	6d.	dl and dp purple		3·00	6·00
G10	6d.	dk purple and mag (12/17)		3·50	5·00

G11	1/−	blk/bl-green (ol-back)		3·75	6·00
G12	2/−	purple and blue/blue		9·00	£13
G13	2/6	black and red/blue		£20	£20
G14	5/−	green and red/yel		£28	£35
G2/14		set (11v)		£70	£95
SPG2/14		specimen set (11v)		£80	‡

1917-19 War Tax. No. G2 and previously unissued 1½d. value overprinted WAR STAMP in sans serif capitals in London.

(a) In bright red. (Oct. 1917).

G15	½d.	dp green (thin bluish paper)	15	35

(b) In dull red. (Jan. 1918).

G16	½d.	dl green (thicker bluish paper)	2·00	—

(c) In scarlet. (May, 1918).

G17	½d.	blue-green	2·00	—

(d) In black. (June, 1918).

G18	½d.	blue-green (medium bluish paper)	30	40
	a	wmk. inverted	—	—

(e) In black (Thinner Letters). (Oct., 1918).

G19	½d.	dl green (medium greyish-blue paper)	—	—

(f) In black. (Mar., 1919). (2mm. space between WAR and STAMP).

G20	1½d.	black and orange	15	30
G21	1½d.	blk and dp or-brn	20	40
G15/21		set (3v)	60	1·00
SPG15/21		specimen set (3v)	£45	‡

The length of the fraction bar varies between 1 mm. and 1½mm., the shorter variety being found on Nos. 3 and 6 of Rows 2, 4, 6, 8 and 10. The longer variety is found on Row 1/1, 7/1, 9/1 and 9/4.

The '1' and '½' are closer together on Row 9/2.

1922-29. As Nos. G2/14 but Wmk. Multiple Script CA. G22/44 on Ordinary paper: G45/55 on Chalky paper.

G22	¼d.	chocolate		30	50
G23	¼d.	brown		30	50
G24	¼d.	dp brown		40	75
G25	¼d.	dl brown		60	1·00
G26	½d.	green		20	20
G27	½d.	dl green		30	30
G28	1d.	violet		30	30
G29	1d.	reddish violet		40	40
G30	1d.	carmine ('29)		90	1·00
G31	1½d.	orange		2·25	2·50
G32	1½d.	pl orange-yellow		2·50	3·50
G33	1½d.	carmine		30	70
G34	1½d.	rosine		40	90
G35	1½d.	scarlet		50	1·00
G36	1½d.	red-brown ('29)		40	80
G37	1½d.	chestnut		50	1·00
G38	2d.	grey		80	1·00
G39	2d.	greenish-grey		1·00	2·00
G40	2½d.	dp bt blue		2·00	3·00
G41	2½d.	pl bt blue ('26)		1·00	2·00
G42	2½d.	orange-yellow ('23)		2·00	3·00
G43	3d.	dl blue ('23)		80	1·75
G44	3d.	pl dl blue		1·00	2·00
G45	3d.	purple/yellow ('27)		1·00	2·00
G46	4d.	blk and rd/pl yellow		80	1·50
G47	4d.	gr-blk and rd/pl yel		1·00	2·00

G48	5d.	**dl purple and olive**..	3·50	6·00
G49	6d.	**pl and br purple** ..	1·00	2·50
G50	1/–	**black/emerald** ..	4·75	6·00
G51	2/–	**pur and blue/blue**..	4·00	6·00
G52	2/6	**black and red/blue**..	£14	£16
G53	3/–	**green and violet** ..	£12	£14
G54	4/–	**black and scarlet** ..	£14	£16
G55	5/–	**grn and red/pl yellow**	£20	£25
G22/55		**set** (21v)	£80	£105

SPG22/55	**specimen set** (21v)	£200	‡

1932 (Apr. 18th). Tercentenary of Foundation. (*recess*). De La Rue. Wmk. Multiple Script CA. Perf. 14. Sheets 6 x 5.

G56	½d.	**green** ..	..	80	80
G57	1d.	**scarlet**..	..	80	1·00
G58	1½d.	**red-brown**	..	1·50	2·50
G59	2d.	**grey** ..	..	1·75	2·75
G60	2½d.	**ultramarine**	..	1·75	4·00
G61	3d.	**orange**..	..	3·00	4·50
G62	6d.	**violet** ..	..	6·50	8·50
G63	1/–	**olive-brown**	..	£15	£18
G64	2/6	**purple** ..	..	£60	£65
G65	5/–	**chocolate**	..	£120	£125
G56/65		**set** (10v)	..	£200	£225

SPG56/65	**specimen set** (10v)	£120	‡

The undenominated Die Proof exists in black on cream paper.

A Die Proof of G62 is known in blue on cream paper.

1935 (May 6th). Silver Jubilee. (*recess*). Waterlow and Sons. Wmk. Multiple Script CA. Perf. 11 x 12. Sheets 6 x 10.

G66	1d.	**dp blue and scarlet**	55	35
G67	1½d.	**ult and grey**	35	80
G68	2½d.	**brown and blue** ..	2·00	3·00
G69	1/–	**slate and purple** ..	7·25	8·00
G66/69		**set** (4v)	£10	£12

SPG 66/69	**specimen set** (4v)	£30	‡

Number issued—G69, 39,800.

Remainders withdrawn on December 31st, 1935.

1938 (Aug. 2nd) Designs, ½d., 3d., 1/-, 5/-, £1 (Carr's Bay); 1d., 1½d., 2½d. (Sea Island Cotton Plantation); Other Values (Botanic Station, Grove). Printers (*recess*) **De La Rue. Perf. 13 x 13¼ (C). Sheets 6 x 10.**

1	½d.	**dp green**	..	10	15
2	1d.	**rose-carmine**	..	10	10
3	1½d.	**purple**	..	2·00	1·50
4	2d.	**orange**	..	2·00	1·00
5	2½d.	**blue**	..	10	20
6	3d.	**chocolate-brown**	..	30	30
7	6d.	**purple-violet**	..	60	50
8	1/–	**dp lake**	..	1·50	1·00
9	2/6	**bluish-slate**	..	1·00	1·25
10	5/–	**dp rose**	..	6·00	6·00
1/10		**set** (10)	..	£13	£12

SP 1/10	**specimen set** perf (10)	£8	£25	‡

As No. 1, etc., but Perf. 14 (L).

11	½d.	**dp green** (/42)	..	10	10
12	1d.	**rose-red** (/42)	..	15	10
		a car-rose (/48)	..	10	10
13	1½d.	**purple** (/41) ..		10	10
		a dp purple (/48)	..	10	10
14	2d.	**orange** (/41) ..	..	15	10
		a dp orange	..	10	10
15	2½d.	**blue** (/43)	..	10	10
16	3d.	**chocolate** (/42)	..	30	30
		a chestnut-brown (/44)	..	2·00	2·00
		b red-br (14/8/45) ..		20	20
17	6d.	**purple-violet** (/42)	..	20	20
		a slate-violet ..		40	30
18	1/–	**dp lake** (/42)	..	40	30
		a lake	..	50	50
19	2/6	**slate-black** (/43)	..	2·00	2·00
		a pale slate ..		1·50	2·00
20	5/–	**dp rose** (/42)	..	2·50	2·50
		a rose-carmine	..	2·00	2·00

Nos. 12*a*/13*a*/16*a*—These printings were received from the Colony but actual date of issue had not been recorded.

No. 16*b* is printed on somewhat thinner paper.

1948 (April 1st) Designs as Nos. 4 and 1, but new values. Perf. 12 (C).

21	10/–	**jay blue**	..	7·00	8·00
22	£1	**black** ..	..	£14	£17
11/22		**set** (12)	..	£25	£30

SP21/22	**perf. specimen** ..	£70	‡

1951 (Sept. 17th) Designs, 1c., $2.40 (Govt. House); 2c., $1.20 (Sea Island Cotton Cultivation); 3c. (Map of Presidency), 4c., 24c. (Picking Tomatoes); 5c., 12c. (St. Anthony's Church); 6c., $4.80 (Badge of Presidency); 8c., 60c. (Cotton Ginning). Printers *(recess)* **Bradbury, Wilkinson. Perf. 11¼ x 11¼ (C). Sheets 5 x 10.**

23	1c.	grey-black		10	10
24	2c.	green		10	10
25	3c.	lt chestnut-brown		10	10
26	4c.	red		15	15
27	5c.	bright purple		15	15
28	6c.	sepia		20	30
29	8c.	dp blue		25	25
30	12c.	blue and brown		40	40
31	24c.	carmine and green		80	90
32	60c.	black and red		2·00	2·00
33	$1.20	green and blue		4·00	4·50
34	$2.40	black and green		5·00	5·00
35	$4.80	black and dp purple		9·00	£10
23/35		set (13)		£20	£22

SPECIAL ISSUES

1937 (May 12th) Coronation. As Aden.

S1	1d.	scarlet	..	..	10	15
S2	1½d.	light brown	..	..	10	15
S3	2½d.	blue	..	..	..	20	25
SP	S1/3	specimen set perf (3)		£13	‡

1946 (Nov. 1st) Victory. As Aden.

S4	1½d.	reddish-purple	..	10	10
S5	3d.	chocolate	..	..	15	15
SP	S4/5	specimen set perf (2)		£13	‡

1949 (Jan. 3rd) Silver Wedding. As Aden.

S6	2½d.	ultramarine	..	10	10
S7	5/–	rose-carmine	..	4·00	5·00

1949 (Oct. 10th) U.P.U. As Aden.

S8	2½d.	violet-blue	..	..	15	20
S9	3d.	brown	..	..	..	15	25
S10	6d.	purple	..	..	50	60
S11	1/–	purple	..	..	70	80
S8/11		set (4)	..	..	1·50	1·75

1951 (Feb. 16) West Indies University College. (See Antigua).

S12	3c.	black and claret	..	15	15
S13	12c.	black and violet	..	30	30

MUSCAT AND EASTERN ARABIAN AGENCIES

An Indian Postal Agency was opened at Muscat on May 1st, 1864, and contemporary Indian stamps were used without overprint (except S1-15 and 01-10) until December 29th, 1947, when Indian stamps to 2r. overprinted "PAKISTAN" (see Pakistan 1-15) were introduced. The use of Indian and Pakistani stamps throughout this period may only be recognised by the cancellation— "309", "23", K-4" "MASKAT" and finally, "MUSCAT".

At Guadur, a dependency of Muscat until September 8th, 1958, an Indian Postal Agency was opened on April 12, 1868. The use of Indian and, from November 1947, Pakistani stamps (see Pakistan 1-17, 21-37, S1-S7, etc.) may be recognised by the cancellation— "24 ","K41"", "GWADUR" and "GUADUR". Surcharged G.B. stamps were *not* used at Guadur.

Preceding the Nasik 'PAKISTAN' overprints, a very small number of Indian stamps from 3p.—2r. was handstamped "PAKISTAN" and put on sale in Muscat Post Office on December 20, 1947. These are exceedingly rare and less than six covers have survived. Although the handstamped overprints were not sold in Guadur Post Office, they were valid for use there and the ½a. and 2a. values are known on cover which are of great rarity.

An Indian Postal Agency was opened at Dubai on August 19, 1909; Indian stamps were used without overprint until October 1947 when Indian stamps to 2r. overprinted "PAKISTAN" (see Pakistan 1-15) were introduced. Their use during this period may be recognised by the named DUBAI cancellation. EXPERIMENTAL P.O. K-46 and K-77 cancellations may be found on mail emanating from Dubai and Sharjah during the period 1941-43, but these cancellations were applied in Karachi on Paquebot latters.

The issue of G.B. stamps surcharged in Annas and Rupees coincided with change of administration, and they were intended for general use in all British Postal Agencies in the area. They had validity and were used in Bahrain and Kuwait as well as in Muscat, Dubai and (from August 1950) Doha (Qatar). Cw 7 and 8 were sold in Kuwait Post Offices in 1951 and 1953 due to a shortage of these values overprinted KUWAIT.

FOR USE IN MUSCAT AND GUADUR

1947 (Dec. 20) Stamps of India (Nos. 21, 3, 23, 25 and 26) handstamped "PAKISTAN" diagonally upwards or downwards by the Postmaster at Muscat. The overprint is in black Serif capitals and normally measures 20 mm x 3 mm, but heavy application of the rubber stamp occasionally gives an overprint measuring up to 22 mm.

M2	½a.	**purple**	..	£50	—
M3	9p.	**deep green**	..	£75	—
M4	1a.	**rose-carmine**		—	—
M6	1½a.	**slate-purple**	..	—	—
M7	2a.	**vermilion**	..	£75	—

Although all values up to Rs2 are believed to have been overprinted we only list those which are known to have survived. Price for used copies on cover with MUSCAT or GUADUR cancellation from £175.

Although a large variety of "PAKISTAN" hand stamped overprints were made on the stamps of India in 1948, this overprinted issue was peculiar to Muscat. It was on sale for only nine days until Pakistan stamps (Nos. 1-15) were introduced on December 29, 1947; the unsold stock was then destroyed, but the stamps were valid for use until March 31st, 1948 in Muscat, and thereafter in Guadur.

FOR GENERAL USE

1948 (April 1st) Stamps of Great Britain surcharged by Harrison & Sons, London.

1	½a./½d.	**green**	.. ..	5	5
2	1a./1d.	**scarlet**	.. ..	5	5
3	1½a./1½d.	**red-br** Type I	..	10	10
4	1½a./1½d.	**red-br** Type II	..	10	10
5	2a./2d.	**dull orange**	..	10	15
6	2½a./2½d.	**ultramarine**	..	10	15
7	3a./3d.	**purple-violet**	..	10	5
8	6a./6d.	**pale purple**	...	10	15
		a surcharge omitted in pair with normal	..	£1250	—
9	R1/1/-	**bistre-brown**	..	40	60
10	R2/2/6	**green**	.. ..	4·00	7·50
1/10		**set (9)**	.. ..	4·75	8·00

8a A single example of this variety is known; Row 20/2 bearing only a very faint impression of 'AS of "ANNAS". (Cylinder 36: Sheet No. 27204).

Number issued — ½a. 138,285; 1a. 117,548; 1½a. 97,146; 2a. 77,116; 2½a. 78,759; 3a. 356,061; 6a. 385,885; 1r. 56,179; 2r. 20,518.

From 1950 British Forces in Sharjah and elsewhere in Eastern Arabia used stamps of the foregoing and following issues, which were cancelled with British F.P.O. date-stamps (Nos. 171 and 756 and, later No. 518 and others).

1951 (May 3rd)-55. As No. 1, etc., but colours changed (No. 17 as No. 34 of Great Britain), similarly surcharged.

11	½a./½d.	**dull orange** ..	10	15
12	1a./1d.	**ultramarine** ..	15	15
13	1½a./1½d.	**green** Type I ..	20	25
13A	1½a./1½d.	**green** Type II ..	20	25
14	2a./2d.	**red-brown** ..	15	15
15	2½a./2½d.	**scarlet** ..	20	20
16	4a./4d.	**lt blue** (2/10/59)	25	25
17	R2/2/6	**green** Type I ..	4·00	3·00
		a Type II ('55) ..	£25	£15
		aa raised 's' ..	—	—
11/17		**set** (7)	3·00	3·00

$$1 \frac{1}{2}$$

ANNAS

3/4/13/13A Type I The figure 1 measures 3¼ mm. (top half of sheet).

$$1 \frac{1}{2}$$

ANNAS

Type II The figure 1 measures 3½mm. (bottom half of sheet).

17 (Type I) "2" and "RUPEES" level, and in line with the lower of the two bars cancelling "2/6"; overall measurement 15¾mm.

17*a* (Type II) "2' raised in relation to "RUPEES" and the whole surcharge is below the lower bar; overall measurement 15½mm.

Number Issued—½a, 181,280; 1a, 143,706 1½a, 77,953; 2a, 110,785; 2½a, 67,748; 4a, 103,516; 2r. 34,859.

SPECIAL ISSUES

FOR USE IN MUSCAT ONLY

1944 (Nov. 20th) Bicentenary of Al-Busaid Dynasty. Stamps of India (*No. 20, etc.*), overprinted "AL BUSAID 1363" (*in Arabic*).

S1	3p.	**slate**	5	10
S2	½a.	**purple**	5	10
S3	9p.	**green**	5	15
S4	1a.	**rose-carmine** ..	5	15
S5	1½a.	**slate-purple** ..	5	15
		a o'print double ..	—	—
S6	2a.	**vermilion** ..	5	15
S7	3a.	**bright violet** ..	5	5
S8	3½a.	**blue**	10	20
S9	4a.	**brown** ..	10	20
S10	6a.	**greenish-blue** ..	10	30
S11	8a.	**violet-slate** ..	15	40
S12	12a.	**dp crimson** ..	20	50
S13	14a.	**purple** ..	30	60
S14	RI	**vio-grey and lt br** ..	40	1·00
S15	RS2	**vio-pur and brown**	60	2·50
S1/15		**set** (15)	2·25	6·25

S5*a*—We are no longer entirely satisfied that the 1½a. exists with genuine double overprint; it and other values may be found with 'ghost' second overprints resulting from a touch of the over-printing type.

Genuinely used copies of this issue are very scarce and many are found with forged or bogus cancellations.

The overprints have also been forged, usually on used Indian stamps.

FOR GENERAL USE

1948 (May 1st) Silver Wedding Issue of Great Britain surcharged.

S16	2½a./2½d.	**ultramarine** ..	10	10
S17	R15/£1	**dp blue**	£22	£24

Number Issued—2½a. 137,789; 15r. 20,656.

1948 (July 29th) Olympic Games Issue of Great Britain surcharged.

S18	2½a./2½d.	**ultramarine** ..	10	20
S19	3a./3d.	**violet** ..	15	20
		a crown flaw ..	£20	£20
S20	6a./6d.	**reddish-purple**	20	20
S21	R1 1/-	**bistre-brown** ..	50	70
		a surcharge dble.	£175	—
18/21		**set** (5)	95	1·25

S19*a* For details of this variety, see G.B. No. SI3*a* (Row 20/2).

S21a A sheet of 120 stamps sold in London was found with double surcharge. No used copies are known (Cylinder 3 : Sheet No. 21164).

Number Issued—2½a. 73,998; 3a. 72,226; 6a. 68,904; 1r. 66,867.

1949 (Oct. 10th) U.P.U. Issue of Great Britain surcharged.

S22	2½a./2½d. **ultramarine**	..	10	15
	a Indian lake		£20	£30
S23	3a./3d. **pale violet**	..	20	25
S24	6a./6d. **reddish-mauve**		35	40
S25	R1/1/- **bistre-brown**		60	70
S22/25	**set** (4)	.. ..	1.20	1·50

S22a For details of this variety, see G.B. No. S16*b*. (Row 8/2).

Number Issued—2½a. 70,462; 3a. 64,843; 6a. 62,797; 1r. 60,093.

OFFICIAL STAMPS

Prior to 1948 Indian Service stamps were occasionally used in Muscat, Guadar and Dubai, only to be recognised by the named cancellations.

Indian stamps overprinted I.E.F. (see after India: GE1 etc.) are recorded used in Guadur in 1916.

FOR USE IN MUSCAT ONLY

1944 (Nov. 20th) Bicentenary of Al-Busaid Dynasty. Stamps of India (*No.* 09, *etc.*) **overprinted "AL BUSAID 1363"** (*in Arabic*).

O1	3p.	**slate**	.. .. ..	5	10
O2	½a.	**dp purple**	.. ..	5	10
O3	9p.	**green**	.. ..	5	15
O4	1a.	**rose-carmine**	..	5	15
O5	1½a.	**slate-purple**	..	5	15
O6	2a.	**vermilion**	..	5	15
O7	2½a.	**purple-violet**	..	5	20
O8	4a.	**brown**	.. ..	10	25
O9	8a.	**violet-slate**	..	15	50
O10	R1	**vio-grey and lt brn**		40	1·50
O1/10		**set** (10)	.. ..	90	3·00

For more detailed information on the issues and Postal History of Muscat and the Arabian Gulf Agencies, including Bahrain and Kuwait, see "The Postal Agencies in Eastern Arabia and the Gulf" by Neil Donaldson.

NAURU

The island was annexed by Germany in 1888, occupied by Australian Forces in 1914 and administered by the Commonwealth Government under Mandate from 1919.

From July 14, 1905 to September 8, 1914, a German Post Office operated, using the stamps of the Marshall Islands. Until the appearance of the G.B. overprinted stamps Australian stamps overprinted "N.W. PACIFIC ISLANDS" were in use.

1916/23 overprinted in black on 1912/21 issues of Great Britain. Overprint 12¼ mm. long.

G1	½d. **deep green**	..	15	30
	a green	..	20	40
	b yellow-green	..	1·00	1·50
	c NAUP.U	..	£125	—
	d short stroke to N	..	£20	—
	e dble ovpt.. one albino		£40	—
G2	1d. **bright scarlet**	..	20	40
	a rose red	..	40	80
	b NAUP.U	..	£125	—
	c short stroke to N	..	£20	—
	d dble ovpt. one albino		£50	—
G3	1½d. **red brown**	..	£22	£32
	a short stroke to N	..	£100	—
G4	2d. **orange Die I**		50	70
	a NAUP.U	..	£125	—
	b short stroke to N	..	£30	—
	c dble ovpt. one albino		£90	—
G5	2d. **orange Die II**	..	£25	£32
G6	2½d. **blue**	..	90	1·25
	a bt ultramarine	..	1·00	1·40
	b NAUP.U	..	£135	—
	c short stroke to N	..	£30	—
	d dble ovpt. one albino		£90	—
G7	3d. **blue violet**	..	1·25	1·50
	a NAUP.U	..	£145	—
	b short stroke to N	..	£30	—
	c dble ovpt one albino		£90	—
G8	4d. **pale grey, green**	..	1·50	2·00
	a NAUP.U	..	£150	—
	b short stroke to N	..	£40	—
	c dble ovpt. one albino		£90	—
G9	5d. **yellow-brown**	..	2·50	3·25
	a NAUP.U	..	£175	—
	b short stroke to N	..	£45	—
	c dble ovpt. one albino		£80	—
G10	6d. **reddish purple**	..	3·00	4·00
	a NAUP.U	..	£185	—
	b short stroke to N	..	£45	—
	c dble ovpt. one albino		£90	—
G11	9d. **agate**	.. ..	4·00	5·00
	a short sroke to N	..	£50	—
	b dble ovpt. one albino		£90	—

G12	1/- **bistre**	.. .. ..	5·00	7·00
	a short stroke to N	..	£60	—
	b dble ovpt. one albino		£95	—
G1/12	**set** (11)	.. ..	£42	£55
SP G1/12	**specimen set** (11)		£120	‡

G1*c*/2*b*/4*a*/6*b*/7*a*/8*a*/9*a*/10*a*—NAUP.U Row 6/2.

G1*d*/2*c*/3*a*/4*b*/6*c*/7*b*/8*b*/9*b*/10*b*/11*a*/12*a*—Short first stroke to N. Row 1/8 of upper and lower panes.

G4—Die I. Inner frame line at top and sides of stamp close to solid of background. Four complete lines of shading between top of head and oval frame line. White line around TWOPENCE thin.

G5—Die II. Wider space between inner frame line and solid background. Three lines between top of head and oval frame line. White line around TWOPENCE thicker.

The second 'U' of the overprint has the appearance of a horseshoe on Row 6/5 (both panes).

Numbers recorded (and Controls where known) : G1*e*, 360 (H16, I16, V23) ; G2*d*, 120 (N19) ; G4*c*, 240 (H16, J17?) ; G6*d*, (G15) ; G7*c*, G8*c*, G9*c*, G11*b*, G12*b*, 120 of each (all H16).

Overprint 13¼ mm. long (1924).

G13	½d. **bright green**	.. ..	5·00	8·00
G14	1d. **scarlet**	.. ..	5·00	8·00
G15	1½d. **red brown**	.. ..	5·00	9·00
	a dble ovpt. one albino		—	—
G16	2d. **orange Die II**	..	£14	£21
G13/16	**set** (4)	.. ..	£28	£45

Numbers overprinted : G13, 10,560 ; G14, 11,520 ; G15, 9,840 ; G16, 11,040.

Overprinted in black or red (R). Waterlow printing.

G17	5/- **rose carmine**	..	£1100	£1000
G18	10/- **indigo** (R)	.. ..	£4000	£3000
	a dble ovpt. one albino		£4500	£4500
SP.G17/18	**specimen set** (2)		£400	‡

It is reported that two sheets (80 copies) of the 10/- value exist.

De La Rue printing.

G19	2/6 **deep brown**	..	£600	£650
	a dble ovpt. one albino		—	—
G20	2/6 **chestnut brown**	..	£100	£110
G21	2/6 **brown**	.. ..	£100	£110

G22	5/-	**bright carmine**	..	£150	£160
G23	10/-	**grey blue** (R)	..	£375	£400
G24	10/-	**Cambridge blue** (R)		£750	£800
SPG19/24		**specimen** H/S (3)		£350	‡

Bradbury Wilkinson printing.

G25	2/6	**chocolate brown**	..	£90	£100
		a dble ovpt. one albino		—	—

G26	2/6	**grey-brown**	..	..	£90	£100

Re-entries occur on the De La Rue and Bradbury printings of the 2/6 value of Nauru. Prices from £325.

Re-entries are known on the basic Great Britain stamps as follows:—

De La Rue 2/6—Row 2/1—Row 10/4.
Bradbury 2/6 —Row 1. Nos. 1, 2, 3 and 4.
—Row 2/4/Row 3, Nos. 2 and 4.
—Row 5/1—Row 7/1.

1924-34 Printers (*recess*) **Commonwealth Treasury, Melbourne. Rough surfaced greyish paper. No wmk. Perf. 11. Sheets 12 x 10.**

G27	½d.	**chestnut**	..	..	1·00	1·25
G28	1d.	**green** ..	..	..	1·00	1·25
G29	1½d.	**scarlet**	..	..	1·50	2·00
G30	2d.	**orange**	..	..	1·50	2·00
G31	2½d.	**indigo blue**	..		3·00	6·00
		a greenish blue	..		3·50	6·00
G32	3d.	**pale grey blue**	..		2·00	3·50
G33	4d.	**sage green**	..		2·50	4·00
G34	5d.	**brown**	..		2·50	4·00
G35	6d.	**dull violet**	..		4·00	5·00
G36	9d.	**olive brown**	..		4·50	6·00
G37	1/-	**lake red**	..		5·00	7·00
G38	2/6	**grey green**	..		£12	£16
G39	5/-	**claret** ..	..		£35	£45
G40	10/-	**yellow**	..	..	£55	£65
G27/40		**set** (14)	..	..	£130	£140

1935 (12th July) Silver Jubilee, on shiny surfaced paper.

G41	1½d.	**scarlet**	..	..	15	35
G42	2d.	**orange**	..	..	35	50
G43	2½d.	**dull blue**	..	..	1·00	1·00
G44	1/-	**lake red**	..	..	2·00	2·20
G41/44		**set**	..	..	..	3·50	4·00

Number issued—100,000 each.

1937-49 Design, ''S S Century'' Printers (*recess*) **and Engravers, Com. Treasury, Melbourne. Perf. 11¼ (L). Sheets 12 x 19.**

1	½d.	**light brown**	..	..	2·00	3·00
2	1d.	**yellow-green**		..	1·50	1·60
3	1½d.	**scarlet-red**	..	..	50	1·00
4	2d.	**orange**	..	..	60	1·00
5	2½d.	**grey-blue**	..	..	80	1·00
		a slate-blue (/49)	..	65	1·00
		b imperf between vertical pair	..	..	£1750	—
		c imperf between horizontal pair	..	£1750	£1750
6	3d.	**pale greenish-blue**		1·00	1·20
		a grey-blue (/47)		1·00	1·20
7	4d.	**sage-green**	..	..	1·20	1·30
8	5d.	**grey-brown**	..		1·00	1·10
9	6d.	**pale violet**	..		1·10	1·25
10	9d.	**dull olive**	..	..	2·50	3·00
11	1/-	**dull red-lake**	..		2·75	3·00
12	2/6	**myrtle-green**	..		£10	£10
13	5/-	**claret** ..	..		£35	£37
14	10/-	**orange-yellow**	..		£50	£58
1/14		**set** (14)	..	..	£100	£110

Whilst the stamps have a gloss when printed, this has a tendency to disappear if the stamps remain in the Colony for any length of time. Nevertheless, stamps printed from 1937 onwards can be readily distinguished by their shades and general smooth appearance. Earlier printings are on matt surfaced paper and shades generally duller. Listed G27/G40.

As No. 1, but Perf. 14 (L).

15	½d.	**light brown** (/42)		50	90

SPECIAL ISSUES

1937 (May 10th) Coronation. Printers (*recess*) **Australian Note & Stamp Printing Works** (*John Ash*). **Perf. 11¼ (L.) No wmk. Sheets 5 x 8.**

S1	1½d.	**red**	..	..	10	10
S2	2d.	**orange**	..	..	10	10
S3	2½d.	**blue**	..	..	10	10
		a re-entry	..	..	£20	£20
S4	1/–	**lake-purple**	..		25	25
S1/4		**set** (4)	..	..	50	50

S3*a* Upper frame line doubled on No. 19.

Number Issued — S1 532,500; S2 490,500; S3 500,000; S4 480,000.

NEVIS

The island was colonized from England in 1628 and, except for a short period of French occupation in 1782-83, has remained British.

Following the use of other handstamps or manuscript marks, a Crowned Circle PAID Frank was registered at the G.P.O. in London in September, 1852, and was thereafter struck in red to indicate repayment of postage on overseas letters. (See Introduction).

From May, 1858 to March, 1860 contemporary G.B. stamps were in use and were cancelled with "AO9" in a transverse oval of horizontal bars.

The Crowned Circle Frank was again used from April 1st, 1860 until the first Nevis stamps were issued. See also No. V48.

See also under Leeward Islands.

1852-61. PAID Frank.   *On Cover*

VFI £900

1858-60 Stamps of Great Britain identified by their Catalogue Nos. after prefix 'NS'

Used at Charlestown : 'A09'

NS V39	1d.	**rose-red**	. . . .
NS V51	2d.	**blue** . .	. . . .
NS V44	4d.	**rose** . .	. . . .
NS V45	6d.	**lilac** . .	. . . .
NS V47	1/–	**green**	. . . .

1861-76. (recess). **Nissen and Parker, London. Design: The Great Seal of the Colony within various frames, all based on the frames of equivalent G.B. stamps. No Wmk. Sheets 3 x 4.**

(a) Blued paper. Perf. 13.

V1	1d.	**lake**	. .	. .	£65	£45
V2	4d.	**dl rose**	. .	. .	£230	£65
V3	6d.	**pearl grey**	. .	. .	£200	£95
V4	1/–	**pale green**	. .	. .	£330	£80

(b) Greyish paper. Perf. 13.

V5	1d.	**dull lake**	. .	. .	£14	£14
V6	4d.	**dull rose**	. .	. .	£30	£25
V7	6d.	**grey**	. .	. .	£25	£18
V8	1/–	**green**	. .	. .	£65	£25

(c) White wove paper. Perf. 15. (1866-76).

V9	1d.	**dl vermilion** . .		. .	£12	£13
V10	1d.	**vermilion**		. .	£12	£13
V11	1d.	**lake-red** ('71)		. .	£12	£13
V12	4d.	**orange-yellow**		. .	£45	£12
V13	4d.	**dp orange-yellow**		. .	£45	£12
V14	1/–	**pale blue-green**		. .	£65	£16

V15	1/–	**blue-green**	. .	. .	£65	£16
V16	1/–	**deep blue-green**		. .	£65	£16
V17	1/–	**yellow-green** ('76)		. .	£350	£50
		a cross on hill		. .	£800	£175
V18	1/–	**dp yellow-green**		. .	£350	£50
		a on vertically laid paper		. .	£4500	£1250
		b cross on hill (laid paper)		. .	—	—

V17*a*/18*b*—A cross-shaped flaw appears near the summit of the background hills. Row 3/3.

Imperforate sheets on thin white wove paper, as follows, are Colour Trials :

1d. lake	1d. red	
4d. grey-lilac	4d. deep blue	4d. yellow
6d. grey	6d. violet	
1/– deep green		

Imperforate sheets on thick white card, as follows, are Proofs :

1d. green	1d. blue-green
4d. violet (2 shades)	
6d. orange (2 shades)	
1/– deep rose (2 shades)	1/– lake

Impressions were taken in black from each of the four plates in 1931. Price from £10 each.

Numbers printed—V9/11, 74,180 : V12/13, 26,624 : V14/18, 11,008.

1876-78. As before, but lithographed from transfers from the recess plates.

(a) Perf. 15.

V19	1d.	**pl vermilion-red**	. .	6·00	7·00
		a imperf (pair)	. .	£100	—
V20	1d.	**vermilion-red**	. .	6·00	7·00
		a imperf (pair). .	. .	—	—
		b bisect vert (½d.) on cover	. .	‡	£200
V21	1d.	**dp vermilion-red**	. .	6·00	7·00
V22	1d.	**dull lake-red** . .	. .	6·00	7·00
V23	1d.	**lake-red**	. .	6·00	7·00
V24	4d.	**orange-yellow**	. .	£65	£15
V25	4d.	**orange** . .	. .	£65	£15
		a imperf (pair)	. .	—	—
		b imperf between (vert pair)	. .	£1200	—
V26	6d.	**brnsh grey** (2/78)	. .	£65	£60
V27	6d.	**grey** (2/78) . .	. .	£65	£60
V28	1/–	**pale green**	. .	£18	£35
		a cross on hill	. .	£90	£110
		b imperf (pair)	. .	—	—
		c imperf between (horiz pair)	. .	£1000	—
		d cross on hill (imperf at left)	. .	—	—
V29	1/–	**deep green**		£18	£35
		a faint cross . .	. .	£60	£85

V20*b*—This bisect, used with two copies of No. V31 on piece dated 25.3.83, is in the Royal Collection

V28*a*/28*d*—See V17*a*/18*b*.

V29*a* is the same variety, but the lines forming the cross have become very faint.

(b) Perf. 11¼. (Nov. 1878).

V30 1d.	**vermilion-red** ..	9·00	£17
	a bisect (½d.) on cover	‡	£300
	b imperf (pair) ..	£85	—
	c imperf between (horiz pair) ..	—	—
	d imperf between stamp and right margin	—	—
	e imperf between stamp and lower margin	—	—

Numbers printed—V19/23, 36,000 : V24/25, 15,000 : V26/27, 1,200 : V28/29, 4,204 : V30, 1,200.

See Introduction for details of Dies I and II.

1879-80. *(typo).* **De La Rue. (Die I) Wmk. Crown CC. Perf. 14. Sheets 6 x 10.**

V31 1d.	**lilac** ('80)	£14	£13
	a bisect diag (½d.) on cover	‡	£175
V32 2½d. **red-brown**		£45	£40

Numbers issued—V31, 15,780 : V32, 2,400.

1882-90. As before, but Wmk. Crown CA.

V33 ½d.	**green** (11/83) ..	2·25	2·50
	a imperf (pair) ..	—	—
V34 1d.	**lilac**	£30	£13
	a bisect vert (½d.) on cover ..	‡	£175
V35 1d.	**carmine** (11/83) ..	1·75	2·25
	a imperf (pair) ..	—	—
V36 1d.	**dull rose**	6·50	5·00
V37 2½d.	**red-brown**	£45	£35
V38 2½d.	**ultramarine** (11/83)	3·00	3·00
	a imperf (pair) ..	—	—
V39 4d.	**blue**	£135	£30
V40 4d.	**grey** (11/83) ..	3·00	3·00
	a imperf (pair) ..	—	—
V41 6d.	**green** ('83) ..	£160	£160
V42 6d.	**chestnut** (10/88) ..	£13	£18
	a imperf (pair) ..	—	—
V43 1/–	**pale violet** (3/90) ..	£45	£48
	a imperf (pair) ..	—	—

V34*a*—This bisect, used with two unsevered stamps on piece dated 27.3.83, is in the Royal Collection.

Numbers issued—(Figures in brackets indicate additional numbers sold as remainders in 1892): V33, 48,753 (7,227): V34, 19,980 : V35/36, 45,188 (5,872): V37, 1,080 : V38, 8,215 (5,045): V39, 7,140 : V40, 21,948 (4,332): V41, 1,020 : V42, 2,156 (2,944): V43, 583 (1,457).

1883 (Sept. 4th). No. V34 overprinted "NEVIS" and surcharged "½d." twice (vertically) prior to bisection.

(a) In black, reading upwards.

V44 ½d.	**on half 1d. lilac** ..	£125	£20
	a surcharge double ..	—	£125
	b unsevered stamp ..	—	—
	c unsevered stamp one surcharge omitted	—	—

(b) In black, reading downwards.

V45 ½d.	**on half 1d. lilac** ..	—	—

(c) In violet, reading upwards

V46 ½d.	**on half 1d. lilac** ..	—	—
	a surcharge double ..	—	—

(d) In violet, reading downwards

V47 ½d.	**on half 1d. lilac** ..	—	—
	a unsevered stamp ..	—	—

1885-86. No. V36 overprinted with the Crowned Circle PAID Frank to indicate surcharge.

V48 6d.	on 1d. **dull rose** ..	—	—

POSTAL FISCALS

1866(?) No. V18a handstamped "Revenue".

F1 1/–	**dp yellow green** ..	—	£500

1882. Nos. V19/21, V25, V27 and V28/29 overprinted "Revenue" in black serif letters.

F2 1d.	**bright red**	9·00	—
	a overprint inverted ..	—	—
F3 1d.	**rose**	9·00	4·00
F4 4d.	**orange**	£13	—
F5 6d.	**grey**	£22	—
F6 1/–	**green**	£35	—

1883 (Oct. ?). Nos. V34, V39 and V41 overprinted REVENUE in black sans serif capitals by De La Rue.

F7 1d.	**lilac**	6·00	7·00
	a bisect vert (½d.) on cover	‡	—
F8 4d.	**blue**	4·50	7·00
F9 6d.	**green**	4·50	7·00
F10 1/–	**mauve**	£10	£10

F7*a*—This bisect, used with two unoverprinted copies of No. V34 on piece, is in the Royal Collection.

From November, 1890 until 1903 only the stamps of Leeward Islands were used in Nevis.

From 1903 the stamps of St. Kitts-Nevis were in concurrent use with those of Leeward Islands until June, 1956.

NEWFOUNDLAND

The island was originally discovered in 1497, settled in 1583, and proclaimed a British Colony in 1713. Labrador was ceded in 1809, and in 1949 the joint territory joined the Dominion of Canada.

The first Post Office was opened at St. Johns in 1809, and various PAID Franks were used in overseas mail until 1857.

1846-57 PAID Franks   On Cover

VF1   —

VF2 **(1849)**   —

1857 (Jan. 1st) First Issue, various square (1d. and 5d.), triangular (3d.) and vertical (2d., 4d., 6d., 6½d., 8d. and 1/–) designs depicting the Royal Crown and heraldic flowers of the United Kingdom. Recess Perkins, Bacon and Co. Sheets: 1d. 120 (12 x 10): 3d. 80 (8 pairs x 5 pairs); 5d. 40 (8 x 5) Remainder 20 (5 x 4).

(i) Imperf. Thick porous wove paper, with mesh. No watermark.

V1	1d. **brown violet**	..	£25	£70
	a re-entry	..	£40	—
	b bisected (½d.) on			
	cover	..	‡	—
V2	2d. **scar ver** (15/2/57)	..	£7000	£3000
	a scratched plate line			
	thro "2"	..	—	—
	b bisected (1d.) on cover		‡	—
V3	3d. **green** (Type I)	..	£120	£200
V4	3d. **green** (Type II)	..	£120	£200
V5	4d. **scarlet vermilion**	..	£3500	£2000
	a bisected (2d.) on			
	cover	..	‡	—
V6	5d. **brown violet**	..	£80	£150
V7	6d. **scarlet vermilion**	..	£5000	£1500
	a bisected (3d.) on			
	cover	..	‡	—
V8	6½d. **scarlet vermilion**	..	£1200	£1450
V9	8d. **scarlet vermilion**	..	£140	£200
	a bisected (4d.) on			
	cover	..	‡	£1500
V10	1/– **scarlet vermilion**	..	£8500	£2250
	a bisected (6d.) on			
	cover	..	‡	£6000

V3/4 Types I and II alternate through the sheet, se tenant (base to base).

This arose from the method of transferring impressions from the Master Die to the Plate. Two impressions were taken base to base from the Master Die on to a small steel plate which was then worked over by hand, thereby creating two different types. The Plate was built up from a transfer roller created from this secondary die with the pair of 3d. stamps.

Numbers Issued – V1 70,000; V2 3,000; V3/4 16,000, V5 5,000; V6 11,000, V7 5.000; V8 2,000; V9 8,000; V10 2,000.

1960 (ii) Imperf. Thinnish to thick wove paper, no mesh. No watermark.

V11	2d. **orange**	..	£140	£185
	a scratched plate	..	—	—
	b watermarked		£225	£250
	c scratched plate with			
	wmk	..	—	—
V12	3d. **green to dp green**			
	(Type I)	..	£15	£60
	a watermarked	..	£30	£80
V13	3d. **green to dp green**			
	(Type II)	..	£15	£60
	a watermarked	..	£30	£80
V14	4d. **orange**	..	£1000	£500
	a watermarked	..	£1400	£700
	b bisected (2d.) on			
	cover		‡	£4000
V15	5d. **chocolate-brown**	..	£15	£60
	a watermarked	..	£30	£80
V16	6d. **orange**	..	£1400	£550
	a watermarked	..	£1750	£650
V17	1/– **orange**	..	£14500	£6000
	a watermarked		—	—
	b bisected (6d.) on			
	cover	..	‡	—

Numbers Issued – V11 5,000; V12/13 6,000; V14 5,000; V15 20,000; V16 10,000; V17 1,000.

1861 (iii) New colours. Imperf. First printing on thick paper. (–/7/61).

V18	1d. **chocolate brown**	..	£25	£80
	a re-entry	..	—	—
	b watermarked	..	£50	£110
	c red-brown	..	£1500	—
V19	2d. **deep rose lake**	..	£80	£200
	a scratched plate	..	—	—
	b watermarked	..	£100	£325
	c scratched plate with			
	wmk.	..	—	—
V20	4d. **deep rose lake**	..	£20	£90
	a watermarked	..	£30	£110
	b bisected (2d.) on			
	cover	..	‡	—
V21	5d. **reddish brown**			
	(shades)	..	£20	£90
	a watermarked	..	£40	£175
V22	6d. **deep rose lake**	..	£20	£110
	a watermarked	..	£15	£110
	b bisected (3d.) on cover		‡	—
V23	6½d. **deep rose lake**	..	£120	£345
	a watermarked	..	£140	£400
V24	1/– **deep rose lake**	..	£150	£300
	a watermarked	..	£225	£400
	b bisected (6d.) on cover		‡	£7500

Numbers Issued – V18 10,080; V19 5,000; V20 15,000; V21 10,000; V22 20,000; V23 5,000; V24 10,000.

(iv) As (iii) above but the second printing on thin paper (–/11/61)

V25	2d. **pale rose lake**	..	£30	£75
	a watermarked	..	£60	£120
V26	4d. **pale rose lake**	..	5·00	£40
	a watermarked	..	£10	£70
V27	6d. **pale rose lake**	..	5·00	£40
	a watermarked	..	£10	£70
V28	6½d. **pale rose lake**	..	£20	£150
	a watermarked	..	£40	£225

V29	8d.	**pale rose lake**	..	£10	£225
		a watermarked	..	£20	£275
V30	1/–	**pale rose lake**	..	8·00	£90
		a watermarked	..	£15	£125

Number Issued – V25 5 000; V26 20,000; V27 50,000; V28 10,000: V29 10,000; V30 15,000.

1865-95 First Pictorial Issue. Designs, 2c., Codfish; 5c., Seal; 10c., The Prince Consort, Prince Albert of Saxe-Coburg Gotha; 12c., Queen Victoria; 13c., Schooner; 24c., Queen Victoria. (Recess) **printed by the American Bank Note Co., New York. Perf. 12. No wmk.**

(i) On thin yellowish paper.

V31	2c.	**yellowish green** ..	£70	£18
		a bisected (1c.) on		
		cover	‡	£1750
V32	5c.	**brown**	£400	£120
		a re-entry from ..	—	—
		b bisected (2½c.) on		
		cover ..	‡	—
V33	10c.	**black**	£150	£30
		a bisected (5c.) on		
		cover ..	‡	£1500
V34	12c.	**pale brown** ..	£200	£90
		a re-entry ..	—	—
		b bisected (6c.) on		
		cover ..	‡	—
V35	13c.	**orange yellow** ..	£45	£32
		a re-entry ..	—	—
V36	24c.	**blue**	£22	£18
		a re-entry ..	—	—

The hitherto regular practice of bisecting stamps ceased during the currency of the above series.

(ii) On white paper of medium thickness.

V37	2c.	**green**	£40	£16
		a on very thin white		
		paper	—	—
V38	10c.	**black**	£70	£20
V39	12c.	**pale brown** ..	£18	£15
		a re-entry ..	—	—
		b chestnut ..	£20	£15
		c re-entry, chestnut	—	—
V40	24c.	**blue**	£300	£150
		a re-entry ..	—	—

V32a Re-entries may be found on many positions on the 5c. plate. Prices depend on the nature and extent of the re-entry and, of course, the condition of the stamp.

V39a, c The re-entry shows a strong doubling around the "U" of NEWFOUNDLAND. Number 25 on the sheet.

V35a The re-entry shows extensive doubling to the lower left of many parts of the design. Number 18 on the sheet.

V40a The re-entry shows a marked doubling of both the inner and outer vertical frame lines. Number 9 on the sheet.

Collectors are warned against so-called proofs of the above series that are in fact from composite sheets of various stamps produced by the American Bank Note Company for examination by prospective clients. Forgeries, mainly lithographic, exist of all values.

1868 (November). New value (1c.) depicting King Edward VII when Prince of Wales in the costume of a Highland Clansman. Recess printed by the National Bank Note Company, New York. Perf. 12 Line. No watermark.

| V41 | 1c. | **dl pur** (Die I) | .. | £20 | £22 |

The first 1c. die (illustrated above) is characterised by the break in the inner oval frame line around the portait occasioned by the positioning of the ribbon bearing the "ONE CENT' inscription. This die was manufactured and used by the National Bank Note Company, whilst the second die was the work of the American Bank Note Company and is characterised by the unbroken inner oval frame line around the portrait, the "ONE CENT" ribbon being placed above the apex of the inner oval frame line. There are many other smaller differences.

Number Printed: 100,000.

1868 (November) -79. Designs as before, except for the new Queen Victoria of the 3c. and 6c. Printed (recess) **by the American Bank Note Company, New York. No wmk.**

(i) Perf. 12 Line.

V42	1c.	**brown purple** (Die			
		II) (–/5/71) ..	£25	£18
V43	3c.	**verm** (–7/70) ..	£145	£60
V44	3c.	**blue** (1/4/73) ..	£90	£10
V45	5c.	**black** (–/11/68) ..	£100	£45
		a re-entry ..	—	—
V46	6c.	**dull rose** (–/7/70)	7·00	6·00

For details concerning the two dies of the 1c. refer to the note after V41.

The 3c. and 6c. values were necessitated by a reduction in the inland letter rate that came into force May 9th 1870. Lithographed forgeries exist of both values.

For note on the 5c. re-entries see note for V32a.

For the 6c. crimson lake shade, printed by the British-American Bank-Note Company in Montreal, see under number V65.

(ii) Rouletted 8

| V47 | 1c. | **dk pur** (1877) .. | £40 | £20 |
| V48 | 2c. | **blue-grn** (1879) .. | £90 | £70 |

V49	3c.	**blue** (1877)	..	£90	7·00
V50	5c.	**blue** (1876)	..	£140	8·00
		a re-entry ..	..	—	—
		b imperf ..	..	—	—
		c imperf. re-entry ..		—	—

The roulettes were either the products of experimentation by the American Bank Note Company or simply by the necessity to use the rouletting machines in order to fulfill.

For note on the 5c. re-entries see note for V32*a*.

1880-94 Old 6c. and 12c., new ¼c. and re-drawn 1c., 2c., 3c., 5c. and 10c. designs (as illustrated above) recess printed by the British–American Bank Note Company, Montreal, (*a*) on white to yellowish wove paper. Perf. 12 Line.

V51	½c.	**rose-red**	..	..	3·00	2·50
V52	½c.	**black**		..	2·00	1·75
V53	1c.	**violet brown**		..	7·00	5·00
V54	1c.	**grey brown**			6·00	4·50
V55	1c.	**red brown**		..	9·00	6·00
V56	1c.	**blue green**		..	2·00	1·00
V57	1c.	**green**	..	..	1·75	1·00
V58	1c.	**yellowish green**			2·00	1·50
V59	2c.	**yellow green**		..	£14	5·00
V60	2c.	**orange vermilion**			3·00	2·00
V61	3c.	**pale dullish blue**			£15	4·50
V62	3c.	**bright blue**		..	£35	2·00
V62A	3c.	**deep brown**		..	5·00	2·00
V63	5c.	**pale dull blue**		..	£15	5·00
V64	5c.	**deep blue** ..		..	£30	2·25
V64A	5c.	**bright blue**		..	5·00	2·50
V65	6c.	**crimson lake**		..	5·00	5·00
V66	10c.	**black**	..	..	£18	£12
		a line thro "CE" of				
		"CENTS"		..	£50	£30
V67	12c.	**deep brown**		..	£12	£14

1890. New design. Recess printed by the British–American Bank Note Company, Ottawa on unwatermarked medium white wove paper. Sheets 10 x 10. Perf. 12 Line.

V68	3c.	**slate to dp slate**		5·00	20
		a imperf (pair)		—	—
		b imperf. between			
		(pair) ..	..	£380	—
V69	3c.	**grey lilac**	..	£380	—
V70	3c.	**brown lilac**	..	5·00	20
V71	3c.	**slate violet**	..	6·00	1·00

A vast range of shades may be found on the 1890 3c., the above list being the groups of shades rather than specific variations. It is generally considered than many of the existing shade variations can be attributed to the effect of outside climatic and other influences rather than to variations of the ink supplies used during the printing process. Examples on pink paper are from a consignment shipwrecked on route and subsequently recovered, the pink colour being caused by the chemical effect produced by the salt water.

1896 As Nos. V51/62 but re-issued in brighter colours.

V72	½c.	**orange vermilion**		£20	£22
V73	1c.	**deep green**	..	2·00	1·25
V74	1c.	**deep brown**	..	9·00	6·00
V75	2c.	**green**	..	8·00	6·50
V76	3c.	**deep blue** ..	..	8·00	5·00
V77	3c.	**chocolate-brown**		£13	£12
V72/77		**set of 6 values** ..		£60	£45

Numbers Printed – 20,000 of each value.

1897 (June 24th) First Commemorative Series. 60th year of Queen Victoria's reign and 400th Anniversary of the Discovery of Newfoundland by John Cabot. Various designs all recess printed by the American Bank Note Company, New York.

Designs as follows: 1c., Queen Victoria; 2c., inscribed "Cabot – him that found the new Isle", but in fact showing Holbein's portrait of Cabot's son; 3c., Cape Bonavista; 4c., Caribou-hunting; 5c., mining; 6c., logging; 8c., fishing; 10c., inscribed "Cabot's ship the 'Matthew' leaving the Avon," although the same ship was used by the printers in the 3c. design of 1892 United States landfall of Columbus series. 12c., Snow Partridge; 15c., seals; 24c., salmon fishing; 30c., Seal of the Colony; 35c., iceberg; 60c., King Henry VII.

All values dated 1497–1897. Sheets 10 x 10. Perf. 12 Line. No watermark.

V78	1c.	**deep green**	..	1·25	1·25
V79	2c.	**carmine rose**	..	1·25	1·25
V80	3c.	**bright blue**	..	1·50	1·00
V81	4c.	**olive green**	..	5·00	2·25
V82	5c.	**violet**	..	2·50	2·25
V83	6c.	**red-brown**	..	2·25	2·25
V84	8c.	**red-orange**	..	6·00	4·00
V85	10c.	**black brown**	..	9·00	4·00
V86	12c.	**dark blue**	..	£14	4·00
V87	15c.	**scarlet**	..	9·00	4·50
V88	24c.	**dl grey violet**	..	7·00	6·00
V89	30c.	**slate**	..	£14	9·00
V90	35c.	**red**	..	£18	£20
V91	60c.	**black**	..	8·00	8·00
V78/91		**set of 14 values** ..		£90	£65

L*

V81 In fact the 4c. value is based upon a photograph made available by Mr. H. Clay Pierce, showing himself on his extensive Newfoundland estates standing by a large caribou that he had just shot. It is understood that Mr. Pierce made a contribution to the Jubilee Fund.

The 2c., 3c., and 6c values exist bisected on cover, but these are unofficial.

The four highest values are to be found with a small red circular cancellation over one corner of the stamp. Copies thus postmarked are from cancelled to order stocks sold in 1920.

A 2c. surcharge in red on the 60c. is an essay made in 1918.

Numbers Printed: V78/79/81/82/83 400,000 each; V80 1,000,000; V84/85/86/87 200,000 each; V88-V91 100,000 each.

One sheet of each value was overprinted SPECIMEN vertically in red.

ONE CENT   ONE CENT

Type I   Type II

ONE CENT

Type III

1897 (Oct.) As Nos. V68/71 surcharged in black. Setting 10 x 5 (repeated twice to each sheet).

V92	1c. on			
	3c.	**grey-purple (I)**	5·00	5·00
	a	surcharge omitted in vert. pair	£1250	—
	b	surcharge double, one diagonal	£650	—
	c	surcharge in red	£200	—
	d	surcharge in red and black	£200	—
V93	1c. on			
	3c.	**grey-purple (II)**	£25	£25
	a	surcharge in red	£600	—
	b	surcharge in red and black	£600	—
V94	1c. on			
	3c.	**grey-purple (IIa)**	£130	£130
	a	surcharge in red	£2750	—
	b	surcharge in red and black	£2750	—
V95	1c. on			
	3c.	**grey-purple (III)**	£75	£75
	a	surcharge in red	£1300	—
	b	surcharge in red and black	£1500	—

The surcharge appears on stamps of different shades. A total of 400 sheets (=40,000 stamps) was surcharged – one sheet in red (V92c. 93a, 94a, 95a), one sheet in black over red (V92d, 93b, 94b, 95b), and 798 sheets in black. The two sheets (red, and black over red) were essays, but were subsequently issued and sold at the Post Office.

In each half sheet (10 x 5) Nos. 1–40 (the first four horizontal rows) have the Type I surcharge, No. 41 has Type IIa, Nos. 42–48 have Type II and Nos. 49–50 have Type III. Type IIa is the same as Type II but with wider spacing (2 mm) between "ONE" and "CENT".

The smallest block showing all three major Types is of four stamps (Nos. 38, 39, 48, 49).

Numbers Issued: V92 31,760; V93 5,558; V94 794; V95 1,588.

V92c/d 80 each
V93a/b 14 each
V94a/b 2 each
V95a/b 4 each

> **Numerous stamps between V96 and G161 exist imperforate. The majority were not so issued but are Proofs which are nevertheless collectable items. The "Imperf. between" varieties are errors arising from the use of Line Perforators.**

1897-1918 Various Royal Portraits. Recess. American Bank Note Co. Sheets 10 x 10. Perf. 12. No watermark.

V96	½c.	**olive** (–/8/98)	1·25	1·25
	a	imperf. (pair)	£70	—
V97	1c.	**carmine** (–/12/97)	1·75	1·75
V98	1c.	**blue-grn** (–6/98)	1·50	15
	a	imperf. between (vert .pair)	£75	—
	b	bt yel-grn	1·50	15
V99	2c.	**orange** (–/12/97)	1·25	1·25
V100	2c.	**scarlet** (–/6/98)	2·00	25
	a	imperf. (pair)	£90	—
	b	imperf. between (pair)	£120	—
V101	3c.	**orange** (–/6/98)	1·75	30
	a	imperf. (pair)	£110	—
	b	imperf. between (vert. pair)	£110	—
V102	3c.	**red-orange/bluish**	5·00	1·50
	a	imperf. between (horizontal pair)	£85	—
V103	4c.	**violet** (–/10/01)	5·00	1·50
	a	imperf. (pair)	£95	—
V104	5c.	**blue** (–/6/99)	6·00	1·25
V69/104		**set** (9v)	£21	9·00

V102 was a war-time emergency printing issued in June 1918.

1908 (Sept.) Recess American Bank Note Co. Perf. 12.

E1	2c. **lake**	.. ..	8·00	50
	a imperf.	.. ..	£45	—

1910 (Aug. 15) Tercentenary of Colonisation (GUY). Various designs. Litho. Whitehead, Morris and Co. Ltd. Sheets 1c., 2c., 5c., 200 – two panes each 10 x 10, remainder 10 x 10. No watermark.

(a) Perf. 12.

E2	1c. **green**	.. ..	80	50
	a "NFWFOUND-			
	LAND"	..	£30	£40
	b "JANES"	..	£25	£30
	c imperf. between			
	(horizontal pair)		£140	£150
E3	2c. **carmine**	.. ..	1·50	50
	a imperf. (pair)	..	£20	—
E4	3c. **olive**	.. ..	4·50	4·75
	a imperf. (pair)	..	£20	—
E5	4c. **violet** ..	..	4·75	4·75
	a imperf. (pair)	..	£20	—
E6	5c. **bright blue**	..	3·50	3·75
	a imperf. (pair)	..	—	—
E7	6c. **claret (I)**	..	£22	£22
	a imperf. (pair)	..	£30	—
E8	6c. **claret (II)**	..	7·00	7·00
E9	8c. **bistre-brown**	..	£13	£16
E10	9c. **olive-green** ..	..	£13	£16
E11	10c. **purple-slate** ..	..	£18	£18
E12	12c. **pale red-brown**	..	£18	£18
	a imperf (pair) ..	..	£175	—
E13	15c. **black** ..	..	£17	£15
	a imperf. (pair)	..	£175	—
E2/13	**set (11v)**	.. ..	£95	£95

(b) Perf. 12 x 14.

E14	1c. **green** ..	.. ..	75	50
	a "NFWFOUND-			
	LAND" ..	..	£40	—
	b "JANES" ..	..	£25	—
	c imperf. between			
	(horizontal pair)..		£240	£250
	d imperf between (pair)			
	with variety *a* ..		—	—
E15	2c. **carmine** ..	..	1·25	50
	a imperf. between (hori-			
	zontal pair)	..	£175	—

(c) Perf. 14 x 12.

E16	5c. **bright blue**	..	..	3·00	7·00

(d) Perf. 12 x 11.

E17	1c. **green** ..	..	..	60	50
	a "NFWFOUND-				
	LAND" ..	..		£28	£28
	b "JANES" ..	..		£25	—
	c imperf. between				
	(horizontal pair)..			£130	—
	d imperf. between				
	(vertical pair)	..		£140	—
	e imperf. vertical pair				
	with variety *a*	..		—	—

(e) Perf. 12 x 11½.

E18	2c. **rose-carmine**	..	£45	£50

E13 was the first stamp depicting George V as King; it was issued only three months after his accession.

1911 (Feb.) As Nos. E8/13 but Recess printed by A. Alexander and Sons Ltd. from dies engraved by Macdonald and Sons. Sheets as before. Perf. 14.

E19	6c. **claret (II)** ..	..	7·00	7·00
	a imperf. between			
	(horizonral pair)..		£85	—
E20	8c. **yellow-brown**	..	£17	£17
	a imperf. between			
	(horizontal pair)..		£200	—
	b imperf. (pair)	..	£90	—
E21	9c. **sage-green** ..	..	£15	£16
	a imperf. between			
	(horizontal pair)..		£110	—
	b imperf. (pair)	..	£90	—
E22	10c. **purple-black**	..	£28	£28
	a imperf. between			
	(horizontal pair)		£150	—
	b imperf. (pair)	..	£90	—
E23	12c. **red-brown**	..	£22	£22
	a imperf. (pair)	..	£90	—
E24	15c. **slate-green** ..	..	£22	£22
	a imperf. between			
	(horizontal pair)..		£150	—
E19/24	**set (6v)** ..	..	£110	£110

E21 may be found with traces of paper-maker's watermark.

E2a/E14a/E17a No. 41 in right hand pane (corrected in later printings).

E2b/E14b/E17b No. 42 in right hand pane.

E7/8/19 in Die I the "Z" in "COLONIZATION" was reversed: in Die II it is correct. The inscription "Lord Bacon" is incorrect as Sir Francis Bacon took the title of Lord Verulam.

1911 (June 19th) Coronation of King George V. Various Royal portraits and (15c.) Seal of Newfoundland. Recess De La Rue and Alexander and Sons. Sheets 10 x 10. No. watermark. Perf. 13¼ x 14 (comb.) or 14 (line).

G1	1c. **yellow-green**	..	1·00	25

G2	1c.	blue-green	..	..	90	25
G3	2c.	carmine	..	..	1·00	25
G4	2c.	rose-red (blurred)		2·25	50
G5	3c.	red-brown	..	..	7·00	7·00
G6	4c.	purple ..	..	..	7·00	7·00
G7	5c.	ultramarine	..	..	4·00	2·50
G8	6c.	slate-grey	..	..	£10	£10
G9	8c.	greenish-blue	..	£24	£24
G10	8c.	aniline blue	..	£25	£25
		a imperf. (pair)		—	—
G11	9c.	violet-blue	..	..	8·00	8·00
G12	10c.	deep green	..	..	£11	£11
G13	12c.	plum	..	..	£11	£11
		a imperf. (pair)	..	£30	—
G14	15c.	lake	..	..	£10	£10
		a imperf. (pair)	..	£30	—
		b imperf. between			
		(pair)		—	—
G1/14		**set (11v)**	..	..	£90	£90

G4 is from a poor quality war-time printing.

Numbers Printed—G1/2 19,938,400; G3/4 26,065,500; G7 1,035,800; G5 and G6 50,000 each; G8 30,000; G9/10 20,000; G12 22,000; G11, G13 and G14 20,000 each.

1919 (Jan. 2nd) Newfoundland War Effort 1914-1918. Each value is inscribed with the name of a different engagement. Recess De La Rue. Designer J. H. Noonan. No watermark. Perf. 14 (comb.) except G17/19/21 which were line. G15/16/18/22 exist with both perfs. Sheets 1c., 2c., 3c. – 200 – two panes, each 10 x 10. Remainder 10 x 10.

G15	1c.	green ..	..	..	75	50
G16	2c.	scarlet	..	..	80	50
G17	2c.	carmine-red	..	95	35
G18	3c.	brown	..	..	80	40
G19	3c.	red-brown	..	..	80	20
G20	4c.	mauve	..	..	90	75
G21	4c.	purple ..	..	..	90	60
G22	5c.	ultramarine	..	..	1·50	90
G23	6c.	slate-grey	..	..	6·50	7·50
		a double print	..	£50	—
G24	8c.	bright magenta	..	6·00	6·50
G25	10c.	deep grey-green	..	5·00	5·00
G26	12c.	orange	..	..	£16	£16
G27	15c.	indigo ..	..	..	9·00	£11
		a pale indigo		9·00	9·00
G28	15c.	**Prussian blue**	..	—	—
G29	24c.	bistre-brown	..	£12	£15
G30	26c.	sage-green	..	..	9·00	9·00
G15/30		**set (12v)**	..	..	£65	£70

Letterpress forgeries are known of the 4c. and 8c.

Numbers Printed — G15 7,810,000; G16/17 7,749,000; G18/19 11,836,000; G20/21 657,100; G22 1,350,000; G23 48,400; G25 283,400; G27/28 50,000; G24/26/29/30 50,000 each.

1919 (Apr. 12th) Hawker and Grieve Atlantic Flight. No. G18 overprinted in black in five

lines "FIRST/TRANS-/ATLANTIC/AIR POST /April, 1919" by Robinson and Co. Ltd. at the "Daily News" Office. The Postmaster initialled (J.A.R.) all the stamps on the back.

| G31 | 3c. | brown | .. | .. | £6500 | £6000 |

Number overprinted 200; mint 87; used 95; damaged 18.

The flight, on May 18th, ended in failure and the crew was rescued from the Atlantic after covering 1,100 miles. Most of the covers show signs of immersion in the sea.

1919 (April 19) Morgan and Raynham Atlantic Flight. No. G18 overprinted in manuscript by the Postmaster (J. A. Robinson) "Aerial Atlantic Mail. J. A. R."

| G32 | 3c. | **brown** | .. | .. | — | £13500 |

This flight was abortive and the mail was eventually despatched by sea, the covers being backstamped in London on 7/1/20. 182 stamps were overprinted but only ten copies are now recorded. Most of the 60 (possibly 85) covers sent bore unoverprinted stamps.

A few covers are known, however, bearing privately overprinted stamps which were not authorised. The stamps were G15 and G17 (5 each), G18 (1 copy), G22 (3 copies), G29 (2 copies) and G30 overprinted in five lines "1st Atlantic/Air Post/ Martinsyde/Raynham/Morgan". They were cancelled with a bogus double lined date-stamp in purple—"REGISTERED/ 17/May/1919 / St. John's N.F.".

1919 (June 9th) Alcock and Brown (and other) Atlantic Flights. No. V87 overprinted and surcharged in black in four lines "Trans-Atlantic/AIR POST,/1919./ONE DOLLAR" by J. W. Withers at the "Royal Gazette" Office. Setting 5 x 5.

G33	$1 on				
	15c.	**bright scarlet**	..	£60	£60
		a comma omitted		
		after "POST" ..	£85	£90
		b G33*a* and no stop		
		after "1919" ..	£110	£120
		c G33*a* and "AIR		
		POST" shifted		
		right ..	..	£110	£120

G33*a* occurs on Nos. 4, 8, 10, 14, 18, 19, 22 and 24.

G33*b* is on No. 14.

G33*c* is on No. 22 ("A" of "AIR' under "a" of "Trans").

Number Issued – 10,000.

196 covers carried on the first successful trans-Atlantic flight were postmarked at St. John's between June 10th and 13th and most were backstamped in London June 18th or 19th.

1920 Various stamps surcharged "TWO CENTS" or "THREE CENTS" in black serif capitals in two lines. Setting in panes 5 x 5 (a) Sept. 11th. With two bars spaced 10½ mm on V87.*

G34	3c. on 15c.	**scarlet**	..	£40	£40
		a surcharge		
		inverted	£250	—

(b) Sept. 13th. With two bars spaced 13½ mm on V87.

| G35 | 3c. on 15c. | **scarlet** | .. | 4·50 | 5·00 |

(c) Sept. 15th. With two bars spaced 13½ mm on V90.

G36	3c. on 35c.	**red**	3·00	3·50
		a lower bar omitted	£75	£60
		b "THREE" omitted..	£450	—

(d) Sept. 23rd. One bar only on V89.

G37	2c on 30c.	**slate** ..	2·50	2·75
		a surcharge inverted	£150	—

G36*a* occurred on Stamp No. 15 on about half the sheets. Nos. 14 and 21 (and other positions) show the bar partly missing.

G36*b* occurred on Stamps 13 and 14 of a few panes only. Stamps may also be found showing only the upper or lower portion of "THREE" or of "CENTS".

*From the first setting (a) two panes of the 6c. (V83) were surcharged, one in red and one in black. Although these were essays the two panes were sold by the Post Office in October 1921, and one copy of each stamp was postally used.

G37 with red surcharge is an essay.

Numbers Issued – G34 2,975; G34*a* 25; G35 47,000; G36 49,000; G36*a* 1,000; G37 49,950; G37*a* 50.

1921 (Nov.) No. V90 overprinted "AIR MAIL/to Halifax, N.S./1921." in black in three lines. Setting in panes 5 x 5.

Space between "AIR" and "MAIL"
(a) 2¾ mm. Nos. 1–4, 7, 9–14, 16, 18, 20–24.

G38	35c. **red**	.. .. ..	£60	£50
	a no stop after "1921"		£75	£60
	b "1921 ' shifted right		£90	£75
	c G38 inverted	..	£1200	—
	d G38*a* inverted		£900	—
	e G38*b* inverted	..	£2750	—

(b) 1½ mm. Nos. 5, 6, 8, 15, 17, 19, 25.

G39	35c. **red**	.. ..	£65	£55
	a no stop after "1921"		£80	£65
	b "1921" shifted right		£105	£120
	c G39 inverted	..	£1200	—
	d G39*a* inverted		£1650	—
	e G39*b* inverted	..	£3000	—

G38*a* occurs on Nos. 1, 3, 4, 9 11, 13, 14, 16, 21, 23, 24.

G38*b* occurs only on No. 4.

G39*a* occurs on Nos. 5, 15, 25.

G39*b* occurs only on No. 5.

G38*b*/39*b*: the first "1" of "1921" falls below 'f' of "Halifax".

Numbers Issued – 14,000 (including two panes inverted).

The flight for which these stamps were prepared was abondoned, and they were subsequently used in late 1922 and early 1923 for flights from St. John's to Halifax, Nova Scotia.

1923 (July 9th) -24 Various scenic views. Recess De La Due. No watermark. Perf 14 (comb. or line). Sheets 10 x 10.

G40	1c.	**green**	80	15
G41	2c.	**carmine**	80	15
		a imperf. (pair) ..	£80	—
G42	3c.	**brown** ..	80	10
G43	4c.	**brown-violet** ..	1·00	75
G44	5c.	**ultramarine** ..	2·50	75
G45	6c.	**slate** ..	2·50	1·50
G46	8c.	**dull violet** ..	2·50	1·50
G47	9c.	**slate-green** ..	£10	9·00
G48	10c.	**dark violet** ..	2·50	1·00
G49	11c.	**olive-green** ..	3·50	3·00
G50	12c.	**lake** ..	4·00	3·25
G51	15c.	**deep blue** ..	6·00	4·50
G52	20c.	**red-br** (28/4/24)	5·50	4·00
G53	24c.	**sepia** (22/4/24) ..	£24	£22
G40/53		**set** (14v)	£65	£50

1927 (May 18th) De Pinedo Italian Flight. No. V91 overprinted in red in three lines "Air Mail/DE PINEDO/1927" by Robinson and Co. Ltd.

G54	60c.	**black**	£13500	£4250

Number overprinted 300; mint 66; used 230; damaged 4.

The 'plane took off on May 23rd and was forced to make a sea landing only 200 miles short of its objective in the Azores. It was salvaged and completed the flight, reaching Ostia on June 16th. An additional 75 letters were carried, franked with V91 without overprint. (Price £1400).

1928 (Jan. 3rd) -29 "Publicity" issue. Various designs. Recess De La Rue. No watermark. Perf. 13-14 (comb. or line).

G55	1c.	**deep green** ..	1·00	25
G56	2c.	**carmine**	1·00	25
		a bisect (1c.) on cover (24/12/36)	‡	—
G57	3c.	**brown** ..	1·00	25
		a imperf between stamp and margin	£40	—
G58	4c.	**mauve** ..	2·00	1·50
G59	4c.	**rose-pur** (1929)	£10	8·00
G60	5c.	**slate-grey**	2·50	2·00
G61	6c.	**ultramarine** ..	2·00	2·00
G62	8c.	**red-brown** ..	3·00	3·00
G63	9c.	**deep-green** ..	3·00	3·00

G64	10c.	**deep violet**	3·00	2·25
G65	12c.	**maroon**	2·50	2·50
G66	14c.	**brown-purple** ..	3·50	3·50
G67	15c.	**blue**	4·00	3·00
G68	20c.	**grey** ..	2·50	2·00
G69	28c.	**gry-grn** (–/12/28)	8·50	7·00
G70	30c.	**sepia**	4·00	4·00
G55/70		**set** (15v) ..	£40	£35

1929-31 As before but re-engraved by Perkins Bacon. Perf. 13½ – 14 (comb. or line),

(a) No watermark.

G71	1c.	**green** (26/9/29) ..	1·00	40
		a imperf. (pair) ..	£40	—
		b imperf. between		
		(vertical pair)	£60	—
G72	2c.	**scarlet** (10/8/29)	1·00	20
		a imperf. (pair) ..	£60	—
G73	3c.	**red-brown**		
		(10/8/29)	1·00	20
		a imperf. (pair) ..	£40	—
G74	4c.	**reddish purple**		
		(26/8/29) ..	1·75	60
		a imperf. (pair) ..	£40	—
G75	5c.	**grey-grn** (14/2/99)	1·75	60
G76	6c.	**ultra** (8/11/29) ..	5·00	5·00
G77	10c.	**violet** (5/10/29)	3·00	1·50
G78	15c.	**blue** (–/1/30) ..	£14	£14
G79	20c.	**black** (1/1/31) ..	£18	9·00
G71/79		**set** (9v)	£45	£30

(b) Wmk. Arms of Newfoundland (1931).

G80	1c.	**green**	50	50
		a imperf. between		
		(horizontal pair)	£325	—
G81	2c.	**scarlet**	1·00	1·00
G82	3c.	**red-brown** ..	1·50	50
G83	4c.	**reddish-purple** ..	3·50	1·50
G84	5c.	**grey-green** ..	4·00	3·00
G85	6c.	**ultramarine** ..	£10	9·00
G86	8c.	**red-brown** ..	9·00	9·00
G87	10c.	**violet**	5·00	4·00
G88	15c.	**blue**	£12	£12
G89	20c.	**black**	£14	8·00
G90	30c.	**sepia**	£13	£13
G80/90		**set** (11v) ..	£70	£60

There are many recognisable differences in the engravings for the De La Rue printing (G55/70) and the Perkins Bacon printings (G71/90).

1929 (Aug. 23rd) No. G45 surcharged "THREE/CENTS" (above a bar) in red in two lines by Messrs. D. R. Thistle, St. John's. Setting 5 x 5.

G91	3c. on 6c.	**slate**	1·25	1·50
		a surcharge in-		
		verted	£175	—
		b surcharge in-		
		black ..	£300	—

Numbers Issued 100,000 (G91*a* 50).

1930 (Sept. 25th) Boyd and Connor Flight. No. G30 overprinted and surcharged "Trans-Atlantic /AIR MAIL/by B. M./'Columbia'/ September/1930/Fifty Cents" in black in seven lines by Messrs. D. R. Thistle. Setting 2 x 2.

G92	50c. on 36c.	**sage green**	£2750	£3000

Number Issued – 300.

The flight was successfully accomplished October 10-11 1930. 158 covers bearing overprinted stamps were carried, as well as a small number with unoverprinted 50c stamps.

1931 Air Stamps. Printed (*recess*) **Perkins Bacon. Perf. 14. Sheets 10 x 10.**

(a) No watermark. Jan 2nd.

G93	15c.	**chocolate**	2·00	2·50
		a imperf. between		
		(horizontal or		
		vertical pair) ..	£200	—
		b imperf. (pair) ..	£200	—
G94	50c.	**green**	7·00	8·00
		a imperf. between		
		(horizontal or		
		vertical pair) ..	£200	—
		b imperf. (pair	£200	—
G95	$1	**blue**	£20	£22
		a imperf. between		
		(horizontal or		
		vertical pair) ..	£200	—
		b imperf. (pair) ..	£200	—

(b) Wmk. Arms (sideways). Mar. 13th.

G96	15c.	**chocolate**	2·00	2·50
		a imperf. between		
		(horizontal or		
		vertical pair) ..	£200	—
		b imperf. (pair) ..	£125	—
		c pair with/without		
		watermark ..	£12	—
G97	50c.	**green**	£10	£12
		a imperf. between		
		(horizontal or		
		vertical pair) ..	£225	—
		b imperf (pair) ..	£225	—
		c pair with/without		
		watermark ..	—	—
G98	$1	**blue**	£25	£30
		a imperf. between		
		(horizontal of		
		vertical pair) ..	£300	—
		b imperf (pair) ..	£150	—
		c pair with/without		
		watermark ..	—	—

G96c/97c/98c. One stamp showing no trace of the watermark.

Numbers issued: G96 125,000; G97 (May 15th) 20,000; G98 20,000 (less 8,000 for G139).

1932 (Jan 1st) -38 Various Royal Portraits and other designs. Recess Perkins, Bacon and Co. Wmk Arms (sideways on vertical designs). Sheets 10 x 10.

(a) Perf 13½. (Comb.).

G99	1c.	**green**	50	20
		a imperf. (pair) ..	£25	—
G100	1c.	**grey**	20	10
		a imperf. (pair) ..	£25	—
		b booklet pane (4)	£30	—
G101	2c.	**carmine**	50	20
		a imperf. (pair) ..	£30	—
G102	2c.	**green**	30	10
		a imperf. (pair) ..	£25	—
		b booklet pane (4)	£45	—
		c bisect (1c.) on		
		cov (24/12/36)	£90	—
G103	3c.	**orange-brown** ..	30	15
		a imperf. (pair) ..	£30	—
G104	4c.	**violet**	2·00	50
G105	4c.	**carmine**	25	10
		a imperf (pair) ..	£30	—
G106	5c.	**maroon** (Die I) ..	3·00	50
		a imperf. (pair) ..	£50	—
G107	5c.	**violet** (Die I) ..	3·00	50
		a imperf. (pair) ..	£30	—
G108	5c.	**violet** (Die II) ..	40	15
		a imperf. (pair) ..	£30	—
G109	6c.	**light blue**	7·00	6·00
G110	7c.	**brown**	80	75
G111	8c.	**red-brown**	80	60
		a imperf. (pair) ..	£30	—

G112	10c.	**black-brown** ..	50	20
		a imperf. (pair) ..	£30	—
		b grnish-black ..	5·00	—
		c inverted wmk ..	£12	—
G113	14c.	**black**	1·00	70
		a imperf. (pair) ..	£40	—
G114	15c.	**claret**	1·00	70
		a imperf. (pair) ..	£40	—
G115	20c.	**green**	1·00	40
		a imperf. (pair) ..	£45	—
G116	24c.	**bright blue** ..	1·00	1·20
		a imperf. (pair) ..	£50	—
		b doubly printed ..	£425	—
G117	25c.	**slate**	1·00	80
		a imperf. (pair) ..	£50	—
		b imperf between		
		horiz pair	£120	—
G118	30c.	**ultramarine** ..	£12	£12
		a imperf. (pair) ..	£150	—
		b imperf. between		
		(vertical pair) ..	£225	—
G119	48c.	**brn-lake** (1/1/38)	2·50	2·25
		a imperf. (pair) ..	£30	—
G99/119		**set** (20v)	£32	£25

(b) Perf. 13 (Line).

G120	1c.	**green**	£12	£12
		a imperf. between		
		(vertical pair) ..	£60	—
G121	2c.	**carmine**	£12	£12
G122	3c.	**orange-brown** ..	£16	—

(c) Perf. 13¾ (Line).

G123	4c.	**carmine**	£25	

(d) Perf. 14 (Line).

G124	1c.	**grey**	7·00	—
		a booklet-pane (4)	£50	—
G125	2c.	**carmine**	£30	—
G126	2c.	**green**	8·00	—
		a imperf. between		
		(horizontal pair)	£75	—
		b booklet-pane (4)	£45	—
G127	4c.	**carmine**	4·00	—
		a imperf between		
		vert pair	£60	—
G128	5c.	**violet** (Die II) ..	£15	—
		a imperf. between		
		(horizontal pair)	£75	—
G129	7c.	**brown**	£35	—
		a imperf. between		
		(horizontal pair)	£175	—
		b imperf. (pair) ..	£35	—
G130	15c.	**claret**	5·00	8·00
G131	20c.	**green**	£18	—
G132	25c.	**slate**	8·00	8·00
		a imperf. between		
		(vertical pair) ..	£125	—
G133	30c.	**ultramarine** ..	£95	—

(e) Perf. 14 (Line. Small Holes).

G134	1c.	**grey**	£15	—
		a pair with/without		
		watermark	£65	—
G135	2c.	**carmine**	£30	—
G136	2c.	**green**	£12	—
		a pair with/without		
		watermark ..	£30	—
G137	3c.	**orange-brown** ..	£15	—
		a imperf. between		
		(vertical pair) ..	£35	—
G137A	4c.	**carmine**	£20	—
G138	5c.	**violet** (Die I) ..	£20	—

Dies of the 5c. Die I: both antlers same height, Die II: antler at right, pointing to "T" in "POSTAGE", is taller than that pointing to the "S".

For stamps in these designs, but perf. 12½, see Nos. 7–21.

1932 (May 19th) Dornier Atlantic Flight No. G98 overprinted and surcharged "TRANS-ATLANTIC/WEST TO EAST/Per Dornier DO-X/May, 1932./One Dollar and Fifty Cents" over a single bar in red in five lines by Messrs. D. R. Thistle. Setting 2 x 2.

G139	$1·50 on $1	**blue**	£175	£175
		a surcharge inverted	£3500	—

Each overprint within the setting shows slight variations.

The flight was successfully accomplished May 21st–23rd 1932. 8,000 stamps were overprinted (including 20 inverted), and 1,804 covers were carried. They were postmarked:—

St. Johns (May 19th) 1362
St. Johns (May 20) 427
Holyrood (May 20th) 5
? 10

Price from £285 each.

1933 (Feb. 9th) No. G96 overprinted "L. & S. Post" vertically downwards between double vertical bars in black by Messrs. D. R. Thistle. Setting 5 x 5.

G140	15c.	**chocolate**	2·50	3·50
		a pair with/without watermark	£10	—
		b overprint reading upwards	£400	—
		c with and without overprint vert pair	£750	—

One sheet of fifty exists of G140b.

Number Issued – 70,000.

1933 (May 31st) Air Stamps. Various designs. Recess Perkins Bacon. Watermark Arms. Perf. 14 (5c., 30c., 75c.), 11½ (10c., 60c.). Sheets 5 x 10.

G141	5c.	**red-brown**	5·00	6·00
		a imperf. (pair)	£100	—
		b imperf. between (horizontal or vertical pair)	£800	—
G142	10c.	**tangerine orange**	8·00	9·00
		a imperf. (pair)	£100	—
G143	10c.	**Indian yellow**	£600	—
G144	30c.	**light blue**	£15	£18
		a imperf. (pair)	£125	—
G145	60c.	**green**	£30	£32
		a imperf. (pair)	£125	—

G146	75c.	**yellow-brown**	£32	£32
		a imperf. (pair)	£125	—
		b imperf. between (horizontal or vertical pair)	£800	—
G141/146	set (5v)		£80	£85

The colour of G412 is B.C.C.55, and that of G143 is B.C.C.6. A single block of four of G143 is known and was granted a R.P.S. Certificate in August 1962. This block was supplied by the Newfoundland Post Office, along with a part sheet of 46 in the normal colour, against an order for 50 copies. It is not known whether G143 was an error of colour in the printing or a colour trial perforated and issued.

Numbers Issued – G141/142 100,000 each; G144 50,000; G145/146 30,000 each.

1933 (July 24th) Balbo Trans-Atlantic Flight. No. G146 overprinted and surcharged "1933/GEN. BALBO/FLIGHT/$4'50" in black in four lines by Robinson and Co. Setting 2 x 2.

G147	$4·50 on 75c.	**yel-brn**	£300	£300
		a sur invd	£16000	—
		b sur on 10c.) (G142)	£12000	—
		c block of four (normal)	£1100	—
		d flown cover	‡	£400

Each overprint within the setting shows slight variations.

Four copies G147a and eight copies G147b are reported.

Number printed – 8,000. 1,153 covers were carried.

1933 (Aug. 3rd) 350th Anniversary of Annexation by Sir Humphrey Gilbert. Various designs dated "1583, 1933". Recess Perkins Bacon. Watermark. Arms. Sheets 10 x 10.

(a) Perf. 13½ (Comb.).

G148	1c.	**slate**	50	40
		a imperf. (pair)	£25	—
G149	2c.	**green**	50	40
		a imperf. (pair)	£30	—
		b doubly printed	£200	—
G150	3c.	**brown**	75	50
		a imperf. (pair)	£30	—
G151	4c.	**carmine**	75	40
		a imperf. (pair)	£25	—
		b imperf. between (vertical pair)	£50	—
G152	5c.	**violet**	1·00	50
		a imperf. (pair)	£20	—
G153	7c.	**greenish blue**	4·50	5·00

G154	8c.	**vermilion**	4·50	5·00
G155	8c.	**brownish red** ..	£200	—
		a bisect (4c) on cover	‡	£130
G156	9c.	**ultramarine** ..	4·00	4·50
		a imperf. (pair) ..	£75	—
G157	10c.	**brown-lake** ..	3·00	2·00
		a imperf. (pair) ..	£85	—
G158	14c.	**grey-black**.. ..	6·50	8·50
		a imperf. (pair) ..	£35	—
G159	15c.	**claret**	8·00	£11
		a imperf. (pair) ..	£45	—
G160	20c.	**grey-green** ..	4·00	6·00
G161	24c.	**maroon**	8·00	£12
		a imperf. (pair) ..	£65	—
		b imperf. between (horizontal pair)	£150	—
G162	32c.	**olive-black** ..	£10	£15
G148/162		**set** (14v)	£55	£70

(b) Perf. 13¾ (Line). From second printing.

G163	7c.	**greenish blue** ..	9·00	£11
G164	9c.	**ultramarine** ..	5·00	6·00
G165	10c.	**brown-lake** ..	£10	£10
G166	14c.	**grey-black** ...	£12	£12
G167	20c.	**grey-green** ..	8·00	£10
G168	24c.	**maroon**	£15	£18
G169	32c.	**olive-black** ..	£18	£20
G163/169		**set of 7**	£60	£70

1935 (May 6th) Silver Jubilee. Recess. Bradbury Wilkinson. Watermark. Multiple Script CA. Perf. 11 x 12. Sheets 6 x 10.

G170	4c.	**rose**	50	30
G171	5c.	**violet**	50	40
G172	7c.	**blue**	1·00	75
G173	24c.	**olive**	2·00	2·00
G170/173		**set** (4v)	3·50	3·00
SPG170/173		**specimen set** (4v)	£45	‡

This was the only Colonial Silver Jubilee issue printed in monocolour, recognising Newfoundland's unique status.

Numbers printed — G170 1,767,826; G171 1,018,871; G172 196,173; G173 166,174.

Remainders withdrawn Dec. 31st 1935.

1938 (May 12th) Designs, Portraits of Royal

Family. Perf. 13½ (C). Wmk. sideways. Sheets 10 x 10.

2	2c.	**green**	1·00	15
		a pair one no wmk. ..	£65	—
		b imperf. (pair) ..	£30	—
3	3c.	**carmine-red**	1·00	15
		a pair one no wmk. ..	£85	—
		b right hand marginal pair stamp at right being imperf. on three sides ..	£80	—
		c imperf. (pair) ..	£30	—
4	4c.	**light blue**	1·20	15
		a pair one no wmk. ..	£45	—
		b imperf. (pair) ..	£30	—
		c inverted wmk. ..	—	—
5	7c.	**dp slate-blue** ..	—	—
		a imperf. (pair) ..	£30	—

As No. 3, but Perf. 14 (L).

6	3c.	**carmine-red**	£110	£40

1941-8 Designs, 1c (Codfish); 2c., 3c., 4c., 7c. (As Nos. 2–5, but 2c. and 3c. re-drawn); 5c. (Caribou); 8c. (Corner Brook Paper Mills); 10c. (Salmon leaping); 14c. (N'land Dog); 15c. (Seal); 20c. (Transatlantic Beacon); 24c. (Ore Loading, Bell Is.); 25c. (Sealing Fleet); 48c. (Fishing Fleet). Perf 12½ (L). Nos. 7–13 wmk. sideways. Designs, 8c. to 48c. H. Sheets 10 x 10.

7	1c.	**grey**	10	10
8	2c.	**green**	10	5
9	3c.	**carmine-red**	10	5
		a pair one no wmk. ..	£40	—
		b 'A' flaw ..	£10	—
10	4c.	**dull blue**	30	5
		a pair one no wmk. ..	£50	—
12	5c.	**purple** (Die I)	30	10
		a pair one no wmk. ..	£60	—
13	7c.	**dp slate-blue** ..	45	50
		a pair one no wmk. ..	£60	—
14	8c.	**dull scarlet**	45	40
		a pair one no wmk. ..	£60	—
15	10c.	**dp sepia**	55	40
16	14c.	**black**	75	80
17	15c.	**claret**	75	80
18	20c.	**green**	80	75
19	24c.	**dp blue** (S.S. "Willemplein")	1·40	1·10
		a blue (thin paper) (/48)	3·00	4·00
20	25c.	**slate**	1·80	1·20
21	48c.	**brn-lake** (fishing fleet) (/44)	2·50	1·40
7/21		**set** (14)	£10	7·00

9b.—Row 5/9.

12 See note after G138.

Stamps of similar design but Perf. 13½ were issued in 1932. Listed G99, etc.

1943 (Jan. 2nd) Design, Memorial University College, St. John's. Printers (recess) **Canadian Bank Note Co., Ottawa. Perf. 12 (L). No wmk. Sheets 10 x 10.**

22	30c. **rose-carmine**	..	1·00	75

As No. 22, but surcharged TWO CENTS.

23	2c./30c. **rose-car** (23/3/46)	20	30

1947 (April 21st) Design, Queen Elizabeth II as Princess. Perf 12¼ (L). Wmk. sideways. Sheets 10 x 10.

24	4c. **dull blue**	.. ..	20	15

Though released on the Queen's Birthday, the stamp had no specific connection with that event.

AIR STAMPS

1943 (June 1st) Design, Plane over St. John's. Printers (recess) **Canadian Bank Note Co., Ottawa. Perf. 12 (L). No wmk. Sheets 10 x 10.**

A1	7c. **ultramarine**	..	30	30

SPECIAL ISSUES

1937 (May 12th) Coronation. Printers, Bradbury, Wilkinson. Perf 11 x 11¾ (C).

S1	2c. **green**	..	..	..	15	10
S2	4c. **carmine**	..	..	20	20
S3	5c. **dp purple**	..	..	30	30

1937 (May 12th) Supplementary Coronation issue. Designs, 1c. (Codfish); 3c. (Map of Newfoundland, etc.); 7c. (Caribou); 8c. (Corner Brook Paper Mills); 10c. (Salmon leaping); 14c. (N'land Dog); 15c. (Seal); 20c. (Transatlantic Beacon); 24c. (Ore Loading, Bell Is.); 25c. (Sealing Fleet); 48c. (Fishing Fleet). Sheets 10 x 10.

(a) Perf. 14¼ (L).

S4	1c. **grey**	.. ..	20	15
	a	fish-hook variety	..	8·00	£10
	b	pair one no wmk.	..	£10	£12
	c	imperf. (pair)	..	£20	—
S5	3c. **brn-orange** (Die 1)	..	30	25
	a	pair one no wmk.	..	£23	—
	b	imperf. (pair)	..	£15	—
	c	imperf. between (horiz or vert pair)		£120	—
	d	Die 2..	.. ..	30	30
	e	imperf. between (horiz or vert pair)		£175	—
S6	7c. **ultramarine**	..	30	30
	a	pair one no wmk.	..	£40	—
S7	8c. **dull scarlet**	..	60	60
	a	pair one no wmk.	..	£15	—
	b	imperf. (pair)	..	£30	—
	c	imperf. between	..	£275	—
S8	10c. **dp sepia**	..	80	80
	a	imperf. (pair)	..	£40	—
S9	14c. **black**	.. ..	1·50	1·50
	a	pair one no wmk.	..	£17	—
	b	imperf.	.. ..	£40	—
S10	15c. **claret**	.. ..	1·35	1·35
	a	wmk. inverted	..	£25	—
	b	pair one no wmk.	..	£17	—
	c	imperf between (vert pair)	..	£120	—
S11	20c. **green**	.. ..	1·25	1·25
	a	wmk. inverted	..	£30	—
	b	imperf. (pair)	..	£40	—
	c	imperf between (vert peir)	.. ..	£275	—
S12	24c. **blue**	.. ..	1·30	1·30
	a	pair one no emk.	..	£45	—
S13	25c. **slate**	.. ..	1·35	1·35
	a	pair one no wmk.		£45	—

S14 28c. **dp purple** .. .. 2·00 2·00
    a pair one no wmk. .. £45 —
    b imperf. (pair) .. £40 —
    c imperf between (vert
    pair) .. .. .. £275 —

(b) Perf. 13¼ (C).

S15 1c. **grey** .. .. .. 6·00 8·00
    a fish hook variety .. £10 £10
S16 3c. **brn-orange** (Die 1) .. 50 30
    a pair one no wmk. .. £10 —
    b brn-orange (Die 2) 30 30
    c pair one no wmk. .. £45 —
S17 7c. **ultramarine** .. £40 —
S18 8c. **dull scarlet** .. .. 1·75 1·75
S19 10c. **dp sepia** .. 2·00 2·00
    a wmk inverted .. £30 —
S20 14c. **black** £275 £400
S21 15c. **claret** .. .. 2·00 2·00
    a pair one no wmk. .. £20 —
S22 20c. **green** .. .. .. 1·25 1·25
S23 24c. **blue** .. .. .. 2·00 2·00
S24 25c. **slate** .. .. 5·00 5·00
S25 48c. **dp purple** .. .. 8·00 8·00

(c) Perf. 13¾ (L).

S26 1c. **grey** 30 15
    a fish hook variety .. 8·00 —
    b pair one no wmk. .. £10 —
S27 3c. **brn-orange** (Die 1) .. 40 25
    a brn-orange (Die 2) 40 25
S28 7c. **ultramarine** 60 60
S20 8c. **dull scarlet** 80 80
    a pair one no wmk. .. £15 —
S30 10c. **dp sepia** .. .. 1·00 1·00
    a pair one no wmk. .. £25 —
S31 14c. **black** .. .. 1·00 1·00
    a pair one no wmk. .. £17 —
S32 15c. **claret** .. .. 1·75 1·75
    a pair one no wmk. .. £17 —
S33 20c. **green** .. .. 1·75 1·75
    a pair one no wmk. .. £45 —
S34 24c. **blue** .. .. 1·75 1·75
    a pair one no wmk. .. £45 —
S35 25c. **slate** .. .. 1·75 1·75
    a pair one no wmk. .. £25 —
    b bluish-slate .. 2·00 3·00
S36 48c. **dp purple** .. 2·00 2·00
S4/36 **set** (11) cheaper perf. £10 £10

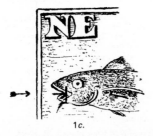

1c.

S4*a*/15*a*/26*a* Lines of a guide mark protrude from mouth of the fish resemble a hook. No. 3/3 and No. 1/7 (diff. plates).

3c Die 1

3c Die 2

S5/16/27 Chief differences between Dies 1 and 2 are to be noted on the King's face. In the case of Die 1 there is less shading on nose and upper lip.

Re-entries are to be found on 1c. (No. 2/1), 7c. (Nos. 3/3 and 4/8), 14c. (Nos. 2/10, 3/10, 4/10 and 5/10) and 25c. (Nos. 10/6 and 10/7). A minor variety (*smoking chimney*) is to be found on 20c. (No. 6/5).

No. S20 14c. perf. 13¼ comb. is a very rare stamp. Only a few mint copies have been found. It is advisable to obtain a certificate from an Expert Committee.

1939 (June 17th) Royal Visit. Printers (*recess*) **Bradbury, Wilkinson. Perf. 13½ x 13¼ (C). No wmk. Sheets 10 x 10.**

S37 5c. **dp ultramarine** .. 55 55

As before, but surcharged. (Nov. 20th).

S38 2c./5c. **dp ult** (brown) .. 60 70
S39 4c./5c. **dp ult** (red) .. 60 70

1941 (Dec. 1st) Honour to Sir Wilfred Grenfell (*for work in Labrador*). **Design, Sir Wilfred Grenfell and his Vessel "Strathcona II". Printers** (*recess*) **Canadian Bank Note Co. Perf. 12(L). No wmk. Sheets 200-two panes, each 10 x 10.**

S40	5c.	**light blue**	30	30
	a	imperf. at left	£85	—

1947 (June 23rd) 450th Anniversary of John Cabot's Discovery of Newfoundland. Design, Cabot aboard the "Matthew" off Cape Bonavista. Printers (*recess*) **Perkins, Bacon. Perf. 12¼ (L). Wmk. sideways. Sheets 10 x 10.**

S41	5c.	**purple-lilac**	20	20
	a	horiz. pair imperf.		
		between	£300	£350

POSTAGE DUR STAMPS

1939 (May 1st) Printers (*litho*) **John Dickinson. Perf. 10—10¼ (L). No wmk. Sheets 10 x 10.**

PD1	1c.	**green**	75	75
PD2	2c.	**vermilion**	1·75	1·75
PD3	3c.	**ultramarine**	1·75	1·75
PD4	4c.	**orange**	3·00	3·00
PD5	5c.	**brown**	1·50	1·50
PD6	10c.	**purple-violet**	1·50	1·50
PD1/6		**set** (6)	£10	£10

As before, but Perf. 11 x 9 (L).

PD7	2c.	**red** (/46)	2·25	2·25
PD8	3c.	**ultramarine** (/49)	3·50	3·50
PD9	4c.	**pale orange** (/46)	3·50	3·50

As before, but Perf. 11 (L).

PD10	1c.	**green** (/49)	1·50	2·50

As before, but Perf. 11 (L) and wmk. "Arms".

PD11	10c.	**purple-violet** (/49)	3·50	9·00
	a	"LUE" variety	£20	£40
	b	imperf. between vertical pair	£200	—
	c	imperf. between vertical pair including "LUE" variety on normal stamp	£325	—

PD11*a* The inscription reads "POSTAGE LUE" Nos. 3/3 and 3/8.

PD11*b* Three sheets are reported to exist, each with one horizontal row imperforate between, i.e. 30 pairs in total.

As before, but Perf. 9 (L).

PD12	3c.	**ultramarine**	£80	—

SEMI-POSTAL ISSUES

1932 (Aug. 11th) WAYZATA. Prepared for proposed Trans-Atlantic Flights, but not issued. (*Recess*) **Bureau of Engraving, Minneapolis. No wmk. Perf. 12. Sheets 4 x 5.**

GSP1	$1	**dark blue**	3·50	‡

These stamps were privately produced in the United States for a projected Air Mail Service. The Scheme was abandoned; and, when the Newfoundland Government repudiated the stamps, the promoters sold them to a dealer in order to re-coup printing costs.

400,000 copies were printed, of which 375,000 were subsequently destroyed.

Newfoundland joined with Canada, 1st April, 1949, and thereby ceased to issue its own stamps.

NEW GUINEA

Originally annexed, in part by Germany in 1884 the whole of the territory was occupied by Australian Imperial Forces in 1914. Initially, German New Guinea and Marshall Islands stamps were used with "G.R.I." overprint; then Australian stamps and finally, Australian stamps with "N.W. PACIFIC ISLANDS" overprint.

Australia was given a Mandate over the whole territory after the 1914-18 War, resulting in the following issues of stamps.

Much of the territory was over-run by the Japanese in the Second World War and Civil Administration was suspended in 1942. Following the Japanese defeat in 1945, Australian stamps without overprint were again used until the combined issue for Papua and New Guinea appeared in October 1952.

See also PAPUA.

1925-28 Recess. Note Printing Branch Commonwealth Bank of Australia (from 1926, Reserve Bank). No watermark. Perf. 11. Sheets 6 x 5.

G1	½d.	orange	50	1·50
G2	1d.	green	60	1·50
G3	1½d.	or-verm (1926)	1·50	1·50
G4	2d.	claret	1·75	2·25
G5	3d.	blue	2·75	2·50
G6	4d.	olive-green	5·00	5·50
G7	6d.	dull yellow-brn	5·50	9·00
G8	6d.	olive-bistre (1927)	5·50	9·00
G9	6d.	pl yel-bis (1928)	6·00	£10
G10	9d.	violet	8·00	£10
G11	1/–	dull blue-green	8·00	£10
G12	2/–	brown-lake	£12	£15
G13	5/–	olive-bistre	£20	£24
G14	10/–	dull rose	£40	£45
G15	£1	dull olive-green	£90	£100
G1/15		set (15v)	£190	£210

An engraved forgery of G15 exists.

Numbers sold: G1 176,640; G2 537,000; G3 823,200; G4 350,100; G5 140,400; G6 36,180; G7 24,000; G8 18,000; G9 23,430; G10 16,620; G11 31,500; G12 17,580; G13 9,000; G14 4,980; G15 2,520.

1931 (June 8th) As before, but overprinted "AIR MAIL" diagonally with silhouette of bi-plane in black.

G16	½d.	orange	40	75
G17	1d.	green	50	80
G18	1½d.	orange-vermilion	1·00	2·25
G19	2d.	claret	1·25	4·00
G20	3d.	blue	1·75	2·25
G21	4d.	olive-green	2·25	3·00
G22	6d.	pale yellow-bistre	2·50	4·00
G23	9d.	violet	2·75	6·00
G24	1/—	dull blue-green	5·50	8·00
G25	2/–	brown-lake	£10	£11

G26	5/–	olive-bistre	£18	£20
G27	10/-	bright pink	£45	£50
G28	£1	olive-grey	£90	£100
G16/28		set (13v)	£175	£200

Numbers sold: G16 60,000; G17 33,750; G18 22,500; G19 22,410; G20 18,330; G21 16,380; G22 16,530; G23 14,370; G24 15,120; G25 12,120; G26 7,170; G27 6,270; G28 4,020.

1931 (Aug. 2nd) Tenth Anniversary of Australian Administration. (*Recess*) **John Ash. No watermark. Perf. 11. Sheets 10 x 3.**

G29	1d.	green	30	35
G30	1½d.	vermilion	2·75	2·75
G31	2d.	claret	1·25	1·50
G32	3d.	blue	1·50	1·50
G33	4d.	olive green	3·00	3·75
G34	5d.	deep blue-green	3·50	4·00
G35	6d.	bistre-brown	3·50	4·25
G36	9d.	violet	3·75	5·50
G37	1/-	pale blue-green	4·50	6·00
G38	2/-	brown-lake	7·50	8·50
G39	5/-	olive-brown	£16	£17
G40	10/-	bright pink	£65	£65
G41	£1	olive-grey	£120	£135
G29/41		set (13v)	£215	£235

Numbers sold: G29 69,000; G30 26,250; G31 172,500; G32 45,000; G33/34/35 18,000 each; G36 12,750; G37 14,250; G38 8,400; G39 5,250; G40 3,000; G41 2,550.

1931 (Aug. 2nd) As before, but overprinted "AIR MAIL" horizontally in two lines with silhouette of bi-plane in black.

G42	½d.	orange	30	45
	a	imperf between stamps and right margin	—	—
G43	1d.	green	65	75
G44	1½d.	vermilion	1·25	1·25
G45	2d.	claret	1·25	1·25
G46	3d.	blue	1·50	1·50
G47	4d.	olive-green	1·75	2·25
G48	5d.	deep blue-green	2·25	3·00
G49	6d.	bistre-brown	4·50	5·50
G50	9d.	violet	4·50	6·00
G51	1/-	pale blue-green	4·50	6·00
G52	2/-	dull lake	7·50	£11
G53	5/-	olive-brown	£14	£20

G54	10/-	bright pink	£65	£65
G55	£1	olive-grey	£100	£100
G42/55		set (14v)	£190	£200

Numbers sold: G42 120,000; G43 51,720; G44 23,700; G45 49,320; G46 52,500; G47 22,250; G48 18,750; G49 18,000; G50 15,750; G51 16,050; G52 9,750; G53 7,500; G54 4,290; G55 3,240.

1932 (June 30th) 34 As Nos. G29/41 but redrawn without commemorative dates. No watermark. Perf. Sheets 10 x 3.

G56	1d.	green	35	35
G57	1½d.	claret	50	90
G58	2d.	vermilion	45	50
G59	2½d.	green (14/9/34)	2·25	4·50
G60	3d.	blue	70	90
G61	3½d.	ani car (14/9/34)	4·50	4·50
G62	4d.	olive-green	90	1·00
G63	5d.	deep blue-green	1·00	1·00
G64	6d.	bistre-brown	1·00	1·50
G65	9d.	violet	4·50	6·50
G66	1/-	blue-green	2·75	5·00
G67	2/-	dull lake	5·00	6·50
G68	5/-	olive-brown	£14	£16
G69	10/-	pink	£55	£55
G70	£1	olive-grey	£75	£75
G56/70		set (16v)	£150	£155

1932 (June 30th) -34 As before, but overprinted "AIR MAIL" horizontally in two lines with silhouette of bi-plane in black.

G71	½d.	orange	30	30
		a overprint omitted	—	—
G72	1d.	green	30	35
G73	1½d.	claret	50	70
G74	2d.	vermilion	90	75
G75	2½d.	green (14/9/34)	1·50	1·25
G76	3d.	blue	1·00	70
G77	3½d.	ani car (14/9/34)	2·25	1·75
G78	4d.	olive-green	1·50	1·50
G79	5d.	deep blue-green	2·25	3·25
G80	6d.	bistre brown	1·75	3·50
G81	9d.	violet	3·00	3·75
G82	1/-	pale blue-green	3·00	3·00
G83	2/-	dull lake	5·00	5·50
G84	5/-	olive-brown	£14	£16
G85	10/-	pink	£50	£45
G86	£1	olive-grey	£75	£45
G71/86		set (16v)	£150	£120

G71a : Two sheets are believed to exist. This value was not normally issued without the "Air Mail" overprint.

1935 (May 1st) (Recess) John Ash. No watermark. Perf. 11. Sheets 10 x 3. Inscribed "POSTAGE".

G87	£2	bright violet	£170	£125
G88	£5	emerald-green	£450	£325

Engraved forgeries of both values exist.

1935 (June 27th) Silver Jubilee. Special printings of Nos. G56 and G58 on shiny paper, overprinted in three lines in black "HIS MAJESTY'S/JUBILEE./1910-1935" by John Ash.

G89	1d.	green	60	60
G90	2d.	vermilion	1·00	1·25
G89/90		set (2v)	1·50	1·75

Numbers Printed – 120,000 each.

During a shortage of stamps in July 1936 the Postmaster on Manus Island (Admiralty Group) franked letters with a circular date-stamp 'MANUS POSTAGE PAID NEW GUINEA' which he then initialled.

AIR STAMPS

1939 (March 1st) As G87/88 but inscribed "AIR MAIL POSTAGE". Printers (recess) Government Stamp Printing Works, Melbourne (John Ash). Perf. 11¼ (L). No wmk. Sheets 6 x 5.

A1	½d.	orange	1·00	50
A2	1d.	green	30	50
A3	1½d.	dull claret	70	1·50
A4	2d.	vermilion	1·50	1·50
A5	3d.	dp blue	2·25	2·50
A6	4d.	sage-green	2·00	2·50
A7	5d.	slate-green	1·25	1·50
A8	6d.	bistre-brown	2·50	3·25
A9	9d.	purple-violet	3·25	4·50
A10	1/-	grey-green	3·75	4·50
A11	2/-	carmine-lake	£14	£16
A12	5/-	brown-olive	£25	£28
A13	10/-	rose-pink	£85	£85
A14	£1	grey-olive	£55	£60
A1/14		set (14)	£180	£195

SPECIAL ISSUES

1937 (May 18th) Coronation. As Nos. S1—4 of Nauru, with changed inscription. Sheets 5 x 6.

S1	2d.	red	15	20
S2	3d.	blue	15	20
		a imperf. between stamp and margin	—	—
S3	5d.	green	20	25
		a re-entry	£20	£20
S4	1/-	lake-purple	35	45
S1/S4		set (4)	75	1·00

S2a One sheet lacked the vertical perfs. at left of first vertical row.

S3a This re-entry is easily visible to the naked eye, as most of design was duplicated, giving the stamp a deeper shade. Row 5/2 (Plate 2A).

Number Issued—2d. 532,500; 3d. 490,500; 5d. 504,000; 1/- 480,000.

OFFICIAL STAMPS

1925-31 Nos. G2-12 overprinted with bold "OS" ("S" has serifs) in black.

GO1	1d.	**green**	60	1·50
GO2	1½d.	**or-verm** (1931) ..	2·50	3·25
GO3	2d.	**claret**	1·00	1·50
GO4	3d.	**blue**	1·25	1·75
GO5	4d.	**olive-green** ..	1·75	2·25
GO6	6d.	**olive-bistre** ..	3·75	7·50
GO7	6d.	**pl yel-bis** (1931)	5·00	7·50
GO8	9d.	**violet**	4·00	8·00
GO9	1/-	**dull blue-green** ..	4·00	8·00
GO10	2/-	**brown-lake** ..	£20	£20
GO1/10		**set** (9v) ..	£40	£55

The original overprinting of all except GO2 and GO7 was on coarse toned paper with vertical mesh and dull brownish gum. Later overprintings in 1931 of all values was on fine white paper with vertical (GO2, GO4, GO5, GO7) or horizontal (remainder) mesh paper with thick shiny white gum.

Numbers sold: GO1 37,950; GO2 15,750; GO3 40,500; GO4 17,400; GO5 16,500; GO6/7 19,500; GO8 16,500; GO9 13,950; GO10 10,800.

1931 (Aug. 2nd) **Nos. G29/39 overprinted**

with smaller "OS" ("S" is sans serif) in black.

GO11	1d.	**green**	70	1·75
GO12	1½d.	**vermilion** ..	1·25	1·75
GO13	2d.	**claret**	1·25	1·75
GO14	3d.	**blue**	1·25	2·00
GO15	4d.	**olive-green** ..	1·25	2·75
GO16	5d.	**deep blue-green**	1·75	3·75
GO17	6d.	**bistre-brown** ..	3·25	6·00
GO18	9d.	**violet**	3·25	6·00
GO19	1/-	**pale blue-green** ..	5·50	8·00
GO20	2/-	**brown-lake** ..	£15	£20
GO21	5/-	**olive-brown** ..	£40	£50
GO11/21		**set** (11v) ..	£65	£95

Numbers sold: GO11 15,000; GO12 10,500; GO13 15,000; GO14 9,750; GO15/16 8,250; each; GO17, 7,500; GO18/19 6,750 each; GO20 5,250; GO21 4,500.

1932 (June 30th) **-34 Nos. G56-68 overprinted with smaller "OS" ("S" is sans serif) in black.**

GO22	1d.	**green**	35	90
GO23	1½d.	**claret**	90	1·25
GO24	2d.	**vermilion** ..	90	1·25
GO25	2½d.	**green** (14/9/34)	1·50	1·75
GO26	3d.	**blue**	2·00	2·50
GO27	3½d.	**ani car** (14/9/34)	2·00	2·75
GO28	4d.	**olive-green** ..	2·00	2·50
GO29	5d.	**deep blue-green**	2·00	2·75
GO30	6d.	**bistre-browm** ..	2·75	4·00
GO31	9d.	**violet**	5·00	6·50
GO32	1/-	**pale blue-green** ..	7·00	8·50
GO33	2/-	**dull lake**	£14	£17
GO34	5/-	**olive-brown** ..	£45	£50
GO22/34		**set** (13v) ..	£75	£90

NEW HEBRIDES

Prior to August 1892 the stamps of New South Wales or of New Caledonia were used and were cancelled by an ink cross: from that month a "Vila, New Hebrides" cancellation was introduced, the earliest recorded use being December 30th 1892.

In 1897 a local issue was provided by the Australian New Hebrides Co. Ltd., and the stamps were valid for postage to Sydney and for inter-island mail.

The N.S.W. Postal Agency (opened August 1st 1891) and New Caledonia Postal Agencies (opened 1903 and 1905) were replaced by the Condominium Post Office on October 1st, 1908: and N.S.W. and New Caledonia stamps ceased to be valid from December 1st 1908.

. The first provisional issues consisted of overprints on Fiji for the British side of the P.O. and on New Caledonia for the French. All definitive issues from 1911 were issued concurrently with English and French inscriptions, but we only list the British issues.

1908 (Oct. 29th)-09 Stamps of Fiji (K.E. VII) overprinted "NEW HEBRIDES CONDOMIUM" in black (thin letters) at Fiji Government Printing Works, Suva.

(a) Wmk. Multiple Crown CA.

E1	½d.	grn and grey-grn ..	30	1·00
E2	1d.	red	45	1·00
		a overprint omitted in vert pair with normal ..	£3750	—
E3	1/–	grn and car (C) (1909)	£11	£14

(b) Wmk. Crown CA.

E4	½d.	grn and grey-grn (1909)	£20	£20
E5	2d.	dl purple and orange	90	1·25
E6	2½d.	dl pur and blu/blue..	90	1·25
E7	5d.	dl purple and green	3·25	3·75
E8	6d.	dl pur and car ..	3·25	3·75
E9	1/–	green and carmine ..	£125	£140
E1/9		set (9v).. ..	£150	£175

Only twelve vertical pairs of E2*a* exist.

Forgeries of E4 and E9 are recorded.

Numbers overprinted—E1, 40,920; E2, 73,200; E3, 14,640; E4, 2,280; E5, 39,360; E6, 30,000; E7/E8 19,200 each; E9, 1,440.

1910 (Dec. 15th) Stamps of Fiji specially printed and overprinted as before (thick letters) in black (1/– in red) by De La Rue. Wmk. Multiple Crown CA.

E10	½d.	green	2·00	2·50
E11	1d.	red	2·50	2·75
E12	2d.	grey	60	1·25
E13	2½d.	bright blue.. ..	70	1·75
E14	5d.	dl pur and ol-grn (C)	1·00	2·25
E15	6d.	dl pur and dp pur (C)	1·50	2·00
E16	1/–	black/green (C) ..	1·50	2·50
E10/16		set (7v)	9·00	£13
SP E10/16		specimen set ..	£140	‡

All values exist additionally overprinted "Specimen" 14½ x 2½mm.

Numbers overprinted—E10, 24,120; E11, 23,760; E12, 61,080; E14/E15, 18,240 each; E16, 17,880.

1911 (July 25th)-1921 (Oct.) (*Recess*) De La Rue. Perf. 14.
(a) Wmk. Multiple Crown CA, sideways – sheets 6 x 5 (from 1916 upright – sheets 6 x 10).

G1	½d.	green	75	75
G2	1d.	red	90	1·25
G3	2d.	grey	1·50	1·50
G4	2½d.	ultramarine ..	1·00	1·50
G5	5d.	sage-green	1·25	1·50
G6	6d.	purple	1·75	1·75
G7	1/–	black/green ..	2·00	3·00
G8	2/–	pur/blu (1912) ..	7·00	9·00
G9	5/–	grn/yel (1912) ..	£14	£16

(b) Wmk. Multiple Script CA (1921). Sheets 6 x 10.

G10	1d.	scarlet	1·50	2·00
G11	2d.	slate-grey ..	2·50	4·00
G12	6d.	purple	5·00	6·00
G1/12		set (12v)	£35	£45
SP G1/12		specimen set ..	£115	‡

All values exist overprinted "Specimen" 14¼ x 2¼mm.

1920 (June)-1921 (March) Provisional Issues: surcharged in black at Fiji Government Printing Works, Suva.

(I) On G5, G7, G8 and G9.

G13 1d. on 5d. **sage-green**

	(1921)	..	9·00	£10
	a surcharge			
	inverted	..	£375	—
G14	1d. on 1/– **blk/grn** (1920)		2·50	6·00
G15	1d. on 2/– **pur/blu** (1920)		2·50	6·00
G16	1d. on 5/– **grn/yel** (1920)		2·50	6·00

14 copies of G13*a* have been recorded.

Numbers Surcharged—G13, 9,900; G14, 15,000; G15/G16, 20,000 each.

(II) On stamps of equivalent French issue:
(a) Wmk. Multiple Crown CA.

G17 2d. on 40c. **red/yel** (1921)   2·50   6·00

(b) Wmk. "RF" in sheet.

G18 2d. on 40c. **red/yellow**
     (1921)   ..   £175   £185

Numbers Surcharged—G17, 19,800; G18, 1,200.

(c) Prepared for use but not issued.

G19 1d. on 5c. **green** ..   ..   —   —
G20 2d. on 40c. **green** (colour
     trial) ..   ..   —   —

None of G19 was issued in the islands, and only a few copies survived.

1924 Provisional Issue: surcharged in black at Fiji Government Printing Works, Suva on G1, G10 and G4.

G21	1d. on ½d.	**green**	..	1·00	4·50
G22	3d. on 1d.	**scarlet**	..	2·50	4·50
G23	5d. on 2½d.	**ultramarine**		4·50	6·00
		a surcharge			
		inverted	..	£400	—

Numbers Surcharged—G21, 26,910; G22, 44,940; G23, 20,820.

1925 (*Recess*) **De La Rue. As G1/9 but inscribed in Sterling and French currencies. Wmk. Multiple Script CA. Perf. 14. Sheets 6 x 10.**

G24	¼d.–5c.	**black**	..	35	65
G24	1d.–10c.	**green**	..	60	75
G26	2d.–20c.	**slate-grey**	..	60	75
G27	2½d.–25c.	**brown**	..	75	1·00
G28	5d.–50c.	**ultramarine**		1·00	1·00
G29	6d.–60c.	**purple**	..	2·25	2·75
G30	1/–1·25f.	**blk-emerald**		2·25	2·75
G31	2/–2·50f.	**purple/blue**	..	4·00	4·75
G32	5/–6·25f.	**green/yellow**		7·00	9·00
G24/32		**set** (9v)	..	£17	£21
SP G24/32		**specimen set**			
		(9v)	..	£90	‡

All values exist overprinted "Specimen' 15¾ x 1¾ mm.

3d.–30c. and 10d.–1f. values were also printed, but only issued with "Postage Due" overprinted (See GD3 and 5).

1938 (June 1st) -51 **Design, Island Scene, Designer, J. Kerhor. Printers, Bradbury, Wilkinson. Perf. 12 (L). Sheets 6 x 10.**

1	5c.	**bluish-green**	..	60	65
2	10c.	**dp orange**	..	90	80
3	15c.	**purple-violet**	..	90	90
4	25c.	**carmine-rose**		1·00	1·50
5	25c.	**chocolate-brown**	..	1·00	1·50
6	30c.	**dp blue**	..	1·25	1·50
7	40c.	**olive-green**	..	1·50	1·75
8	50c.	**lake-maroon**		1·50	1·25
9	1f.	**carmine/green**	..	5·50	5·50
		a dp car/blue-grn	..		
		(3/1/51)	..	4·50	4·50
10	2f.	**blue/green**	..	6·00	6·00
11	5f.	**red/yellow**	..	£14	£14
12	10f.	**purple/blue**	..	£25	£25
1/12		**set** (12)	..	£55	£58
SP1/12		**specimen set** perf.(12)	£75		‡

Whilst there are many shades of No. 4, originally the colour was carmine rose, and we were officially informed that there has only been one printing.

1953 (April 30th) **Designs, 5c.—20c.** (Canoes under sail); **25c.—50c.** (Native Carving, designed by Raoul Serres); **1f.—5f.** (Natives, designed by J. Hertenberger). **Printers** (*recess*) **Waterlow & Sons. Perf. 12½(L). Sheets 5 x 10.**

13	5c.	**green**	..	..	10	10
14	10c.	**scarlet**	..	..	15	15
15	15c.	**yellow-ochre**	..		15	15
16	20c.	**ultramarine**	..	..	15	20
17	25c.	**olive**	..	..	20	25
18	30c.	**brown**	..	..	25	25
19	40c.	**dark sepia**	..	..	30	35
20	50c.	**violet**	..	..	35	35
21	1f.	**orange**	..	..	70	75
22	2f.	**red-purple**	..	..	1·75	2·00
23	5f.	**scarlet**	..	..	5·00	6·00
13/23		**set** (11)	..	..	8·00	9·50

SPECIAL ISSUES

1949 (Oct. 10th) **U.P.U. Design, etc., as Aden, No. S11, but all** (*recess*) **by Waterlow & Sons.**

S1	10c.	**orange**	..	..	25	30
S2	15c.	**dull violet**	..	..	30	30
S3	30c.	**dull indigo-blue**	..	40	60
S4	50c.	**purple**	..	..	75	90
S1/4		**set** (4)	..	..	1·50	1·75

POSTAGE DUE STAMPS

1925 As G24 etc. but overprinted "POSTAGE DUE". Sheets 6 x 10.

GD1	1d.–10c. **green**	—	80
GD2	2d.–20c. **slate-grey** ..	—	80
GD3	3d.–30c. **red**	—	1·50
GD4	5d.–50c. **ultramarine** ..	—	2·00
GD5	10d.–1f. **carmine/blue**	—	3·00
GD1/5	**set** (5v) ..	£120	7·00
SP GD1/5	**specimen set** (5v) ..	£40	‡

All values exist overprinted "Specimen" in sans serif capitals 15¼ x 1¾mm.

1938 (June 1st) As No. 1, etc., but overprinted "POSTAGE DUE".

PD1	5c. **bluish-green** ..	1·50	1·75
PD2	10c. **dp orange** ..	1·75	2·25
PD3	20c. **carmine-rose** ..	2·50	3·50
PD4	40c. **olive-green** ..	3·50	5·00
PD5	1f. **carmine-green** ..	9·00	£12
PD1/5	**set** (5)	£17	£22

1953 (April 30th) As No. 13, etc., but overprinted "POSTAGE DUE".

PD6	5c. **green**	20	25
PD7	10c. **scarlet**	25	30
PD8	20c. **ultramarine**	45	60

PD9	40c. **dark sepia**	.. ..	1·00	1·50
PD10	1f. **orange**	.. ..	1·50	2·00
PD6/10	**set** (5)	.. ..	3·00	4·00

LOCAL ISSUES

Valid for postage to Sydney and for inter-island mail.

1897 (March 17th) (*litho*) **J. Sands and Co.,** Sydney **in sheets of 120 (10 x 12) on thick wove paper*** **No wmk. Rouletted 8½. Designer, A. F. Basset Hull.**

L1	1d. **black and lilac-rose**	1·00	—
L2	2d. **blue and red-brown**	1·50	—

*A few sheets of the 2d. were printed on toned paper.

Numbers Printed—L1, 240,000; L2, 120,000; Numbers Sold—L1, 100,000; L2, 26,000.

Remainders were sold to a Sydney stamp dealer in 1913.

NEW ZEALAND

All stamps were printed (*recess*) on "N.Z. Star" (*mult.*) wmk. paper unless otherwise mentioned. Various classes of paper have been used and designated "Esparto", "Woodpulp". These are listed as they are easily separated, "Esparto" being clear white wove paper. "Woodpulp" being yellowish with a criss-cross weave similar to linen. Stamp should be examined held against a light source.

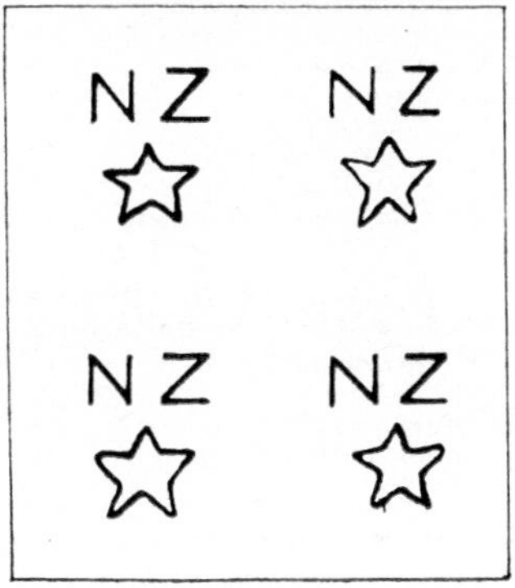

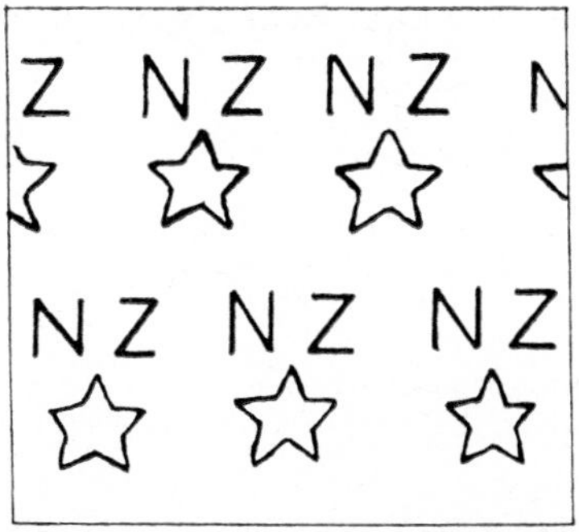

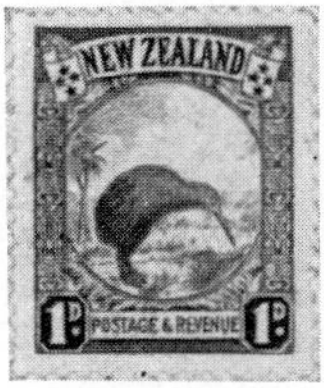

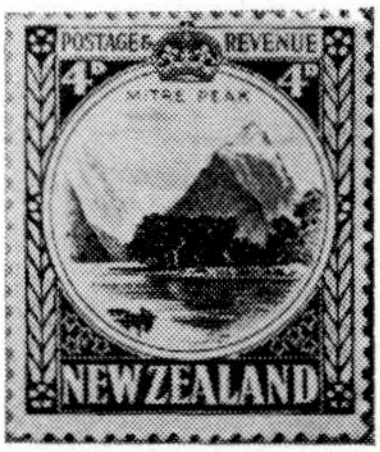

1935 Designs, ½d. (Pied Fantail); 1d. (Kiwi); 1½d. (Maori Woman); 2d. (Maori House); 2½d. (Mount Cook); 3d. (Maori Girl); 4d. (Mitre Peak); 5d. (Swordfish); 6d. (Harvesting); 8d. (Tuatara Lizard); 1/- (Tui Bird); 2/- (Capt. Cook at Poverty Bay); 3/- (Mount Egmont). Designers, J. Fitzgerald (½d., 4d.), C. H. and R. J. G. Collins (1d.), M. Matthews (1½d.), H. W. Young (2d.), L. C. Mitchell (2½d., 3d., 8d., 1/-, 3/-), W. J. Cooch and R. E. Tripe (5d.), T. I. Archer (6d.), T. H. Jenkins (2/-). Printers (*recess*) De La Rue, 2½d., 5d., 2/-, 3/-, Perf. 13—14 x 13½ (C); 2½d., Perf. 14 (L); Other values, Perf. 13¾ x 13½ (C). Designs, 2½d., 5d., 6d., 2/-, 3/-, H. All watermark single N.Z. Sheets Small format 24 x 10: 6d. and 8d. 16 x 10; 4d. 10 x 8; 5d. and 2/-, 12 x 10; 2½d. and 3/-, 6 x 10.

X1	½d.	**green**	20	10
X2	1d.	**scarlet**	20	10
X3	1d.	**Perf. 13½ x 14** ..	£10	8·00
		a booklet pane of 6	£10	£12
X4	1d.	**Die II**	80	50
X5	1½d.	**red-brown**	80	70
X6	1½d.	**Perf. 13½ x 14** ..	80	70
X7	2d.	**orange**	50	15
X8	2½d.	**Perf. 13—14 x 13½**	1·50	2·00
X9	2½d.	**Perf. 13½ x 14** ..	1·50	2·00
X10	3d.	**brown**	6·00	50
X11	4d.	**black-brown** ..	60	20
X12	5d.	**Perf. 13—14 x 13½** ..	7·00	1·25
X13	5d.	**Perf. 13½ x 14** ..	8·00	1·00
X14	6d.	**scarlet**	1·00	35
X15	8d.	**chocolate-brown** ..	1·00	70
X16	9d.	**scarlet and black** ..	1·75	1·00
X17	1/-	**green**	5·00	1·00
X18	2/-	**Perf. 13—14 x 13½** ..	6·50	2·50
		a COQK flaw	£20	£14
X19	2/—	**Perf. 13½ x 14** ..	£10	3·50
		a COQK flaw ..	£25	£12
X20	3/-	**Perf. 13—14 x 13½**	9·00	7·50
X21	3/-	**Perf. 13½ x 14** ..	9·00	7·50
X1/X21		**set** (cheapest perfs., 14 v)	£40	£16

Nos. X1—21 have been included for the convenience of those who collect all perforation varieties (both wmks.) of the pictorial set.

X4 The die used for this printing differs from that used previously by the heavy shading in the sky.

X18*a*/19*a* A short line on the second O of COOK transformed the letter to Q No. 1/4.

The horizontal perforation of stamps Perf. 13—14 x 13½ (C) goes half length 13 and the rest 14.

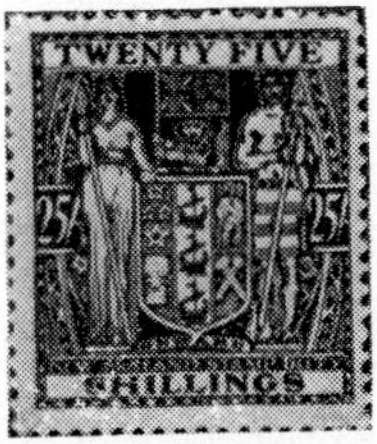

1931-9 Design, Arms of Dominion. Designer, H. L. Richardson. Printed (*typo*) on chalk-coated paper at the Govt. Printing Office, Wellington, from plates prepared at the Royal Mint, London. Wmk. "N.Z. Star" (single). Perf. (C). Sheets 10 x 8.

PF 1	1/3	**lemon**	5·00	5·00
PF 2	1/3	**orange-yellow** ..	5·00	2·00
PF 3	2/6	**brown**	6·00	1·00
PF 4	4/-	**red**	7·00	1·00
PF 5	5/-	**green**	8·00	2·00
PF 6	6/-	**carmine**	8·00	2·50

PF 7	7/–	**blue**	£12	3·00
PF 8	7/6	**green-grey** ..	£17	£15
PF 9	8/–	**slate-violet** ..	£10	3·00
PF10	9/–	**orange**	£15	£10
PF11	10/–	**carmine-lake** ..	£12	2·00
PF12	12/6	**purple**	£50	£30
PF13	15/–	**olive**	£30	£12
PF14	20/–	**pink**	£32	£12
PF15	25/–	**green-blue** ..	£80	£85
PF16	30/–	**brown**	£90	£65
PF17	35/–	**orange-yellow** ..	£850	£850
PF18	40/–	**violet**	£150	£25
PF19	50/–	**red**	£150	£140
PF20	60/–	**green**	£160	£40
PF21	70/–	**rose**	£450	£375
PF22	80/–	**light blue**	£200	£70
PF23	90/–	**green grey**	£275	£300
PF24	£5	**blue**	£225	£40
PF1/24		**set** (24)	£2500	£1850

Used price for set less 35/– £1000 (23).

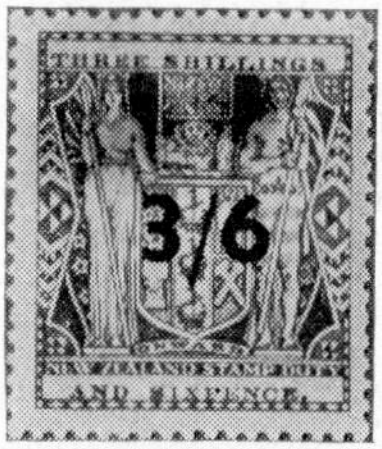

1938-40 Design as No. PF1, but surcharged so as to render stamps more readily distinguishable from other values of similar colour. Wmk. "N.Z. Star" (single).

PF25	3/6d./3/6d.	**green** (6/40)	7·00	2·50
PF26	5/6d./5/6d.	**mauve-lilac** (6/40) ..	£10	6·00
PF27	11s./11s.	**yellow** (6/40)	£28	£17
PF28	22s./22s.	**ver-red** (6/40)	£70	£65
PF29	35s./35s.	**or-yel** /39)	£65	£65
PF25/29		**set** (5) ..	£175	£155

Though described as postal-fiscals, Nos. PF1–29 are postage stamps in full sense. Values over £5 exist and sometimes these are found postally used. See also PF47–78 mult. wmk.

1936-43 Pictorial (*mult*) **N.Z. wmk. Printers, De La Rue. Perf. 13—14 x 13½.**

1	2½d.	**chocolate and slate**	90	1·00
2	5d.	**ultramarine**	4·00	50
3	2/–	**dp olive**	5·00	1·00
		a COQK flaw ..	£20	£10
4	4/–	**sepia and lt chestnut**	6·00	1·75

Perf. 14 x 13½.

5	½d.	**green**	10	10
6	1d.	**scarlet** (Die II) ..	10	10
		a booklet pane of 6 ..	£10	—
7	1½d.	**brown**	60	50
8	2d.	**orange**	10	10
9	3d.	**brown**	4·00	25
9a	4d.	**brown**	30	15
9b	6d.	**scarlet**	50	15
9c	8d.	**chocolate**	90	20
		d ditto wmk. sideways	1·75	60
9e	1/–	**green**	90	20
		f ditto Esparto ..	2·00	20

1939-43 Designs as No. X4, etc. (Pictorial Issue). Perf 13½ x 13¾. (C.) Printers De La Rue.

10	2/–	**dp olive** (3/39) ..	£28	1·50
		a COQK flaw ..	£50	£10

Perf. 12½ (L). Printers, Waterlow & Sons and De La Rue.

11	2d.	**dp orange** (6/41) ..	25	15
12	4d.	**blk and blk-sep** (8/41)	70	20
13	5d.	**dull ult** (7/41) ..	4·00	50
		a ditto Esparto paper	8·00	1·00
14	6d.	**red** (10/41)	40	15
15	8d.	**choc.-brown** (wmk. sideways) (7/41) ..	75	35
16	1/–	**dp green** (11/41) ..	5·00	1·75
17	2/–	**dp olive** (7/41) ..	5·00	75
		a COQK flaw ..	£15	£10
		d ditto Esparto paper ..	7·00	1·00
		c COQK flaw ..	£20	£12
18	3/–	**sepia and lt chestnut** (7/41)	8·00	5·00

Perf. 14 (L). Printers, 2d. (De La Rue), 4d. (Waterlow, and Perf. by De La Rue).

19	2d.	**dp orange** (6/41) ..	70	40
19a	2½d.	(line perf.)	75	90
19b	2½d.	(comb perf.)	75	90
20	4d.	**blk and blk-sepia** ..	£12	£10

Perf. 14 x 14¾ (L). Printers, De La Rue and Perf. by Harrison & Sons.

21	2d.	**dp orange** (6/41) ..	1·25	75

Perf. 14 x 14¼ (C). Printers, De La Rue.

22	4d.	**blk and sepia** (7/42)	30	20
23	6d.	**red** (6/42)	35	10
		a ditto Esparto paper ..	1·25	15
24	8d.	**choc** (wmk. sideways) (7/42)	75	20

Perf. 14 x 13½ (C) *. Printers, De La Rue.

25	2½d.	**choc and ind-slate** (11/42)	70	1·25
26	5d.	**dull ult** (11/42) ..	2·00	30
		a one albino	£80	—
27	2/–	**dp olive** (Plate I) (10/42)	4·00	1·00
		a COQK flaw ..	£15	£10
		b dp olive (Plate II) (7/42) ..	3·50	75
		c ditto (Plate III) (11/43)	4·50	1·50
28	3/–	**sep. and brn** (9/42) ..	3·75	1·00
		a ditto but perf. 13¾ x 13¾ ..	5·00	60
1/29		**set** (14) cheapest perfs	£20	£5

(*) This perforation is not constant, and a variation to the extent of almost ¼mm. can be found on stamps from the same sheet.

Nos. 3, 10, 17, 27—For note on Cook flaw see after X21.

11—This stamp was printed by De La Rue and perforated by Waterlow.

13, 17—The 5d. and 2/– exist printed and perf. by Waterlow, and printed by De La Rue and perf. by Waterlow. Remaining values in Perf. 12½ (L) were printed and perf. by Waterlow.

27—As can be seen from illustrations, the ratlines (horizontal lines) in the shrouds vary in the three plates (*see illustrations*). Plate III 27c also exist from very worn plate, with the "mushroom" designs at bottom frame line running into each other in almost solid colour.

27b—Stamps from the second plate were first to be placed on sale.

Plate I

Plate II   Plate III
(f)

1938-41 Design as No. X15 (Maori Panel) but from plate made by Coulls, Somerville & Wilkie, Wellington. Offset-litho.

Perf. 14 x 15 (C) (*Esparto paper*). Size 18 x 21 mm. (wmk. sideways).

28aa	9d.	**red and grey** (1/5/35)	2·00	50

Perf 13¾ x 14¼ (C) (*Esparto paper*). Size 18 x 21mm.

29	9d.	**red and grey-blk** (1/3/38)	2·00	40

Perf. 14 x 15 (C) (*Chalk-surfaced paper*). **Wmk. "N.Z. Star"** (*single*). *Typo*. Size 17½ x 20½mm.

30	9d.	**scarlet and blk** (5/41)	9·00	3·00

As before, but wmk. "N.Z. Star" (*mult*). (*Typo*).

31	9d.	**scar and blk** (29/9/41)	90	30

1938-52 Designer, W. J. Cooch. Printers (*recess*) **Bradbury, Wilkinson. Perf. 13¾ x 13½ (C). Sheets 24 x 10.**

32	½d.	**emerald-grn** (1/3/38)	20	10
		a booklet pane of 6	5·00	—
33	½d.	**or-brn** (10/7/41) E	10	5
		a buff-brown (/42) W	10	5
34	1d.	**rose-scar** (1/7/38)	40	10
		a booklet pane of 6	7·00	—
		b scarlet (/39)	40	10
35	1d.	**em-grn** (21/7/41) E	10	5
		a pale em (2/49) W	10	5
36	1½d.	**red-choc** (26/7/38)	2·75	75
		a booklet pane of 6	£15	—
37	1½d.	**scarlet** (1/2/44) E	10	10
		a rose-scar (1/2/44) W	10	10

38	2d.	**orange** (1/5/47)	10	10
		a orange-yel (5/48)	15	10
		b deep orange (4/49)	10	10
		c ditto (thin paper) (/50)	50	25
39	3d.	**dk grey-blue** (26/9/41) E..	15	10
		a dp blue (4/49) W	15	10
40	4d.	**pur-mauve** (1/5/47)	20	10
		a purple-lake (/50)	20	10
		b dp purple-lake (/52)	20	10
41	5d.	**slate-grey** (1/5/47)	50	15
42	6d.	**lake-car** (1/5/47)	25	10
		a rose-carmine (/50)	25	10
43	8d.	**violet** (1/5/47)	50	15
		a ditto (thin paper) (/50)	1·00	30
44	9d.	**lake-brown** (1/5/47)	50	15
		a dp grey-brown (2/49)	50	15
32-44		**set** (13)	6·00	2·00

Imperf. copies exist of stamps of King's head design. These it is alleged were illicitly obtained.

E—Esparto paper.
W—Woodpulp paper

1941 Nos. 32 and 36 surcharged.

45	1d./½d.	**emer-grn** (1/5/41)	10	10
46	2d./1½d.	**red-choc** (1/5/41)	10	10
		a inserted 2	£250	£200

46a—The 2 of the surcharge was inserted by a second overprinting operation. Traces of the first overprinting are generally visible, No. 10/10 (*certain sheets only*).

Coil Join Pairs

These exist numbered 1–19. On the margins between pairs numbers exist printed in type, and by rubber stamp.

Price for Mint Pairs

CJ 1	1d.	**green**		75
CJ 2	2d.	**orange**		1·00
CJ 3	3d.	**blue**		1·00
CJ 4	4d.	**purple lake**		1·50
CJ 4a	4d.	**deep purple**		1·50
CJ 5	5d.	**grey**		1·50
CJ 6	6d.	**lake-carmine**		2·00
CJ 7	8d.	**violet**		2·00
CJ 8	9d.	**lake-brown**		2·00
CJ 9	1/–	**wmk. sideways**		3·00
CJ10	1/–	**wmk. upright** (Die II)		3·50

CJ11	1/3	**brown-blue**	..	..	3·00
CJ12	1/3	**brown-blue** (Plate 2)		..	3·00
CJ1/12		**complete set** (12 pairs)		..	£20

All horizontal pairs (1d.–9d.) except 1/–, 1/3 vertical pairs.

1943-52 As Nos. PF1 etc. (Arms of Dominion type) but with wmk. "N.Z. Star" (*mult.*) **Perf. 14 (C).**

PF47	1/3	**yel-orange** (9/43)		2·00	20
PF48	2/6	**brown** (9/43)	..	3·00	20
		a wmk. inverted	..	4·00	1·00
PF49	4/–	**brownish-red**			
		(11/44)	..	3·00	50
		a wmk. inverted	..	4·00	60
PF50	5/–	**green** (9/43)	..	4·00	45
		a wmk. inverted	..	6·00	1·00
PF51	6/–	**rose-pink** (10/45)		6·00	1·00
		a wmk. inverted	..	7·00	2·00
PF52	7/–	**lt grey-blue** (7/44)		6·00	2·00
		a wmk. inverted	..	£10	2·00
PF53	7/6	**olive-gr** (21/12/50)		£10	£10
PF54	8/–	**dk vio-blue** (9/43)		6·00	3·00
		a wmk. inverted	..	£10	3·00
PF55	9/–	**brownish-orange**			
		(1/46)	..	8·00	4·00
		a wmk. inverted	..	£10	5·00
PF56	10/–	**carmine-red** (11/44)		6·00	1·00
		a wmk. inverted	..	8·00	2·00
PF58	15/–	**sage green** (10/45)		£10	6·00
		a wmk. inverted	..	£12	7·00
PF59	20/–	**dull pink** (10/45)	..	£10	2·00
		a wmk. inverted	..	£12	3·00
		b P14 x 13½ 20/10/58		£22	5·00
PF60	25/–	**blue** (11/44)	..	£80	£85
		a wmk. inverted	..	£90	£95
PF61	30/–	**brown** (11/44)	..	£80	£80
		a wmk. inverted	..	£90	£90
PF63	40/–	**pur-violet** (11/44)		£18	5·00
		a wmk. inverted	..	£20	7·00
PF64	50/–	**red** (9/8/51)	..	£90	£80
PF65	60/–	**green** (10/45)	..	£25	£10
		a wmk. inverted	..	£30	£12
PF66	70/–	**rose-red** (8/48)	..	£350	£300
		a wmk. inverted	..	£350	£300
PF67	80/–	**light blue** (12/2/52)		£30	£12
		a wmk. inverted	..	£40	£15
PF69	100/–	**blue-black** (10/45)		£60	£20
		a wmk. inverted	..	£65	£25
PF47/69a		**one of each** (20v)	..	£800	£550

1944-5 As Nos. PF25, etc. but wmk. "N.Z. Star" (*mult.*).

PF70	3/6d./3/6d.	**green** (11/44)	4·50	3·00
		a wmk. invtd.	5·00	3.50
		b sans serif caps	£18	£18
		c sans serif caps		
		wmk. invtd.	£20	£20
PF71	5/6d./5/6d.	**mauve-lilac**		
		(8/44) ..	6·00	4·00
		a wmk. invtd.	7·00	6·00
PF72	11s./11s.	**yellow** (/45)	£22	£15
		a wmk. invtd.	£25	£20
PF73	22s./22s.	**vermilion-red**		
		(/45) ..	£55	£50
		a wmk. invtd.	£60	£55
PF74	£6/£6	.. ..	£65	—
PF75	£7/£7	.. ..	£75	—
PF76	£8/£8	.. ..	£85	—
PF77	£10/£10	.. ..	£110	—

1947 (May 1st)-52 Design, Portrait of King. Printers (*recess*) **De La Rue. Perf. 14 x 14½ (C). Wmk. sideways unless otherwise mentioned. Sheets 10 x 16.**

75	1/–	**chestnut and claret**		50	20
		a ditto (wmk. uprt)	..	50	20
		b changed head die			
		(wmk. upright)			
		(3/50) ..	..	40	15
76	1/3	**chestnut and ult**			
		(F. Plate I)	..	60	20
		a (F. Plate II) (3/50)		80	20
		b ditto (wmk. upright)			
		(14/1/52)	..	60	30
77	2/–	**or-brn and dp grn**	..	75	20
		a ditto (wmk. uprt)	..	80	30
78	3/–	**dp chestnut and grey**	2·00	40
		a ditto (thin paper			
		(/51)	..	3·00	40
75/78		**set** (4) ..	..	..	3·50	90

Centre Plate I

Centre Plate II

Nos. 75, 75*a*, 77 and 77*a* were printed from Centre Plate I, remainder from Centre Plate II.

76/76*a* With Frame Plate I the scroll in the right hand side panel goes through to the inside vertical frame line without a break, but there is a break in the line in Frame Plate II (*see illustration*). This break was removed by retouching on No. 13/5.

Frame Plate I   Frame Plate II

1950 (July 29th) Design as No. PF1 (Arms of

79	1½d. **red**	20	15
	a wmk. inverted	15	10

Number Issued—14,543,360.

The majority had the wmk. inverted. The issue was withdrawn 28/11/50.

1952 (Dec. 12th) No. 35 surcharged 3d.

80	3d./1d. **emerald-green**	15	15

Number Issued — 18,626,640.

1953 (Sept. 11th) No. 33 surcharged 1d.

81	1d./½d. **orange-brown**	10	15

Number Issued — 7,291,440.

SPECIAL ISSUES

1937 (May 13th) Coronation. Printers (*recess*) Bradbury, Wilkinson. Perf. 14 x 13½ (C). Sheets 10 x 12.

S1	1d. **carmine**	..	15	10
S2	2½d. **dp blue**	..	30	30
S3	6d. **reddish-orange**	..	50	50

Number Issued—1d, 38,455,554; 2½d, 1,564,496; 6d. 2,079,611.

1940 (Jan. 2nd) Centenary of British Sover-

eignty. Designs, Views of New Zealand, etc. Designers, ½d., 3d and 4d. (L. C. Mitchell); Other Values (J. Berry). Printers (*recess*) Bradbury, Wilkinson. Perf. 14 x 13½ (C), 2½d. and 5d.; Perf. 13¼ x 13½ (C), Other Values. Designs, 2½d., 1/- V. Sheets 12 x 10 or 10 x 12 except 2½d, and 5d. which are 10 x 16.

S4	½d. **dp blue-green**	..	10	10
S5	1d. **purple-brn and red**		15	10
S6	1½d. **bl and mauve-purple**		30	20
S7	2d. **myrtle-grn and sepia**		15	10
S8	2½d. **myrtle-grn and dp bl**		20	25
S9	3d. **dp pur and crim-lake**		1·25	20
S10	4d. **choc and dp claret**		1·00	45
S11	5d. **light blue and brown**		1·00	1·00
S12	6d. **emer and pur-violet**		1·00	30
S13	7d. **black and vermilion**		2·00	3·25
S14	8d. **blk and ver** (8/3/40)		1·50	75
S15	9d. **sage-grn and dp or**		3·50	1·75
S16	1/- **sage-grn and dp mtle**		5·00	1·50
S4/16	**set** (13)	.. ..	£18	9·00

Numbers Issued—½d.36,957,240; 1d. 75,827,040; 1½d. 3,506,240; 2d. 110,219,640; 2½d. 2,038,400; 3d. 7,855,800; 4d. 3,358,800; 5d. 3,280,000; 6d. 5,818,800; 7d. 1,140,000; 8d. 3,359,160; 9d. 2,398,800; 1/- 3,605,520. (*A small quantity of the ½d. value were withdrawn.*)

1944 (May 1st) As No. S6 but surcharged TENPENCE at the Govt. Printing Office, Wellington.

S17	10d./1½d. **bl and mauve-pur**	20	20

Number Issued—3,842,280.

1946 (April 1st) Peace Designs, Views of New Zealand, Badges of Fighting Services, Portraits of Royal Family (2d.), H.M. N.Z.N. "Achilles" and "Dominion Monarch" (5d.). Designer, J. Berry. Printers, Harrison & Sons (*photo*) and Perf. 14 x 14¾ (C), 1½d. and 1/-, **Bradbury, Wilkinson** (*recess*) **and Perf. 13¼ x 13 (C). 1d. and 2d. Waterlow & Sons** (*recess*), Perf. 13¼ x 13½ (C), Other Values. Designs, 1½d., 8d., 1/- V. Sheets 1½d. 16 x 10; 1/-, 20 x 6; 1d. and 2d. 12 x 10. Others 8 x 15.

S18	½d. **dul mtle and dp brn**		5	5
	a T variety	..	2·00	2·00
	b dull myrtle and			
	chestnut brown	..	50	20
	c T variety	..	3·00	3·00
S19	1d. **emerald-green**	..	5	5
S20	1½d. **scarlet** (wmk. side-			
	ways)	.. ..	5	5
S21	2d. **purple**	.. ..	5	5

S22	3d. **ult and slate-green**	10	10
	a plane tail retouch ..	3·00	3·00
	b T variety	5·00	5·00
	c Aircraft (ult) omitted	£500	—
S23	4d. **olive and dp orange**	10	15
S24	5d. **grn and ultramarine**	15	15
	a "Trailing Aerial" from Foremast of "Dominion Monarch" (Row 8/1)	5·00	5·00
S25	6d. **choc and vermilion**	15	15
S26	8d. **black and lake** ..	20	20
S27	9d. **light blue and black**	40	40
S28	1/- **slate-black**	50	50
S18/28	**set** (11)	1·50	1·50

S18*a/c*, S22*b* A printer's guide in the form of T (*sideways*) is to be found on No. 12/3 of the ½d. A similar variety is to be found on the 3d. (Frame No. 42856) on left side above bottom corner wing Nos. 1/2, 2/2.

S22*a* Retouches are to be found on Nos. 2/4 and 3/2 (different plates) with tail on flying boat of the upper right corner lined in.

S22c One sheet was found with corner folded causing centre omitted.

Numbers Printed—½d. 9,499,960; 1d. 107,840,000; 1¼d. 4,500,000; 2d. 141,840,000; 3d. 12,499,000; 4d. 4,750,000; 5d. 7,999,920; 6d. 7,261,920; 8d. 5,559,960; 9d. 3,249, 960; 1/- 4,500,000.

1948 (Feb. 23rd) Otago Centennial. Designs, Views of Otago. Designer, J. Berry. Printers (*recess*) **Bradbury, Wilkinson. Perf. 13¼ x 13½ (C), 3d. Wmk. sideways. Design, 3d. V. Sheets 10 x 12 or 12 x 10.**

S29	1d. **jay-blue and green**..	10	10
	a missing hand var. ..	£200	—
S30	2d. **green and lt brown**	10	10
S31	3d. **purple-violet** ..	20	20
S32	6d. **grey-blk and car-lake**	30	30
S29/32	**set** (4)	70	70

S29*a* A lightening of pressure (*through a fault in the make-ready*) resulted in a gradual disappearance, as printing proceeded, of the Maori's left hand, and copies exist where the hand is completely missing.

Numbers Printed—1d. 5,000,000; 2d. 5,000,000; 3d. 2,500,000; 6d. 2,500,000; (*Not all were sold, but very few were destroyed.*)

1950 (Nov. 20th) Canterbury Centenary. Designs and Designers, 1d. (Anglican Cathedral, Christchurch, by J. Berry); 2d. (Symbolic design depicting arrival of pioneer woman, by L. C. Mitchell); 3d. (John R. Godley, Founder of Canterbury, by J. A. Johnstone); 6d. (Canterbury University College, by J. Berry); 1/- (Timaru, by J. Berry). Printers (*recess*) **Bradbury, Wilkinson. Perf. 13¼ x 13½ (C). Designs, 1d., 3d. V. Sheets 12 x 10 or 10 x 12.**

S33	1d. **lt blue and grey-grn**	10	10
	(wmk. sideways) ..	10	10
S34	2d. **brick-red and car** ..	10	10
S35	3d. **lt and dp blue** (wmk. sideways)	15	15
S36	6d. **lt blue and chocolate**	25	25
S37	1/- **lt blue and dp maroon**	50	50
S33/37	**set** (5)	1·00	1·00

Numbers Issued—1d. 5,000,000; 2d. 5,000,000; 3d. 2,500,000; 6d. 2,500,000; 1/- 2,500,000.

HEALTH (CHARITY) ISSUES

The charity surcharge goes to funds provided for children's homes and camps throughout New Zealand.

1929 (11th Dec.) Designer: Stanley Davis (from a photograph) (*Typo*) **Government Printing Office, Wellington. Wmk. "N.Z. Star". Perf. 14. Sheets 10 x 8.**

GH1 1d. +1d. **scarlet** £12   £12
     Number Issued—592,848

1930 (29th Oct.) (*Typo*) **Government Printing Office, Wellington. Wmk. "N.Z. Star". Perf. 14. Sheets as before.**

GH2 1d +.1d. **scarlet** £30   £30
     Number Issued—215,543.

1931 (31st Oct.) (*Typo*) **Government Printing Office, Wellington. Wmk. "N.Z. Star" Perf. 14½ x 14. Sheets 10 x 12.**

GH3 1d.+1d. **scarlet** £120 £120
GH4 2d.+1d. **blue** £100 £100

Numbers Issued—1d., 74,802; 2d., 111,929.

1932 (18th Nov) (*Recess*) **Government Printing Office, Wellington. Wmk. "N.Z. Star". Perf. 14. Sheets 10 x 6.**

GH5 1d.+1d. **carmine red** .. £24 £24

Number Issued—237,504.

1933 (8th Nov.) (*Recess*) **Government Printing Office, Wellington. Wmk. "N.Z. Star". Perf. 14. Sheets 10 x 6.**

GH6 1d.+1d. **carmine red** .. £12 £12

Number Issued—260,883.

1934 (26th Oct.) (*Recess*) **De La Rue. Wmk. "N.Z. Star". Perf. 14 x 13½. Sheets 10 x 8.**

GH7 1d.+1d. **carmine red** .. £11 £11

Number Issued—297,120.

1935 (30th Sept.) (*Recess*) **J. Ash, Melbourne. Printers. Wmk. "N.Z. Star". Perf. 11. Sheets 192—four panes, each 8 x 6.**

GH8 1d.+1d. **scarlet** .. .. 2·50 2·50

Number Issued—1,250,057

1936 (2nd Nov.) (*Recess*) **J. Ash, Melbourne. Wmk. "N.Z. Star". Perf. 11. Sheets 6 x 8.**

GH9 1d.+1d. **scarlet** .. 1·50 1·50

Number Issued—1,449,980.

1937 (Oct. 1st) Designers G. Bull and J.

M

Berry. Printers (*recess*) **Australian Note & Stamp Printers, Melbourne. Wmk. "N.Z. Star"** (*single*)**. Perf. 11¼ (C). Sheets 8 x 6**

H1 1d.+1d. **scarlet** .. .. 2·00 2·50

Number Issued—897,035.

1938 (Oct. 1st) Designer, J. Berry. Printers (*recess*) **Bradbury, Wilkinson, Wmk. "N.Z. Star"** (*mult*)**. Perf. 14 x 13½ (C). Sheets 10 x 8**

H2 1d.+1d. **scarlet** .. .. 2·50 2·75

Number Issued—1,234,720.

1939 (Oct. 16th) Designer, S. Hall. Printers (*recess*) **Australian Note & Stamp Printers. Wmk. "N.Z. Star"** (*single*)**. Perf. 11¼ (C). Surcharged** (*in black*) **at Govt. Printing Office, Wellington. Sheets 8 x 6.**

H3 1d./½d.+½d. **green** .. 3·00 3·50
H4 2d./1d.+1d. **scarlet** .. 3·50 3·00

Change of postal rates after printing was reason for surcharge.

Numbers Issued—1d., 482,746; 2d. 516,046.

1940 (Oct. 1st) As before, but without surcharge and values changed.

H5 1d.+½d. **green** .. .. 3·50 3·00
H6 2d.+1d. **light chestnut** .. 3·00 3·50

Numbers Issued—1d., 284,756; 2d., 359,972.

1941 (Oct. 4th) As before, but overprinted 1941 (*in black*) **at Govt. Printing Office, Wellington.**

H7 1d.+½d. **green** .. .. 2·60 2·75
H8 2d.+1d. **light chestnut** .. 2·75 3·00

Numbers Issued—1d., 349,543; 2d., 434,855.

1942 (Oct. 1st) Designer, etc., as Nos. H3—8. Sheets 8 x 6.

H9 1d.+½d. **green** 60 80
H10 2d.+1d. **light chestnut** 65 80

Numbers Issued—1d., 720,042; 2d. 942,425.

1943 (Oct. 1st) Designer, J. Berry. Printers (*recess*) **Bradbury, Wilkinson. Perf. 12 (L). Sheets 20 x 6.**

H11 1d.+½d. **green** 10 10
  a pair. imp. horiz. £2500 ‡
H12 2d.+1d. **reddish-brown** 10 10
  a pair imp. horiz. £2500 £2500

Each of the priced imperforate errors is unique.

Numbers Issued—1d., 3,133,111; 2d., 3,339,686.

1944 (Oct. 9th) Designed and Printed (*recess*) **Bradbury, Wilkinson. Perf. 13½ x 13¼ (C). Sheets 12 x 10.**

H13 1d.+½d. **dp green** .. 10 10
H14 2d.+1d. **dp blue** .. 15 15

Numbers Issued—1d 3,045,288; 2d. 3,405,260.

1945 (Oct. 1st) Designer, J. Berry. Printer, etc., as Nos. H13—4. Sheets 10 x 12.

H15 1d. +½d. **lt brn and olive-green**   ..   10   10
H16 2d. +1d. **bistre and car**   15   15

Numbers Issued—1d., 3,994,633; 2d. 3,994,855.

1946 (Oct. 24th) Designer, J. Berry. Printers (*recess*) **Waterlow & Sons. Perf. 13½ x 13¼ (C). Sheets 8 x 15.**

H17 1d. +½d. **ches and grn**   10   10
     a chestnut and yellow-grn   2·50   2·50
H18 2d. +1d. **ches and sepia-brown**   ..   10   10
     a reddish ches and sep-brn   1·00   1·00

Major Re-entries.—Doubling of inner vertical frame lines, under yacht, etc. (No. 8/8 in later printed sheets), 1d. +½d. (Nos. H17 and H17*a*). Partial doubling of soldier's profile and hat (in front) and child hanging leaves under Zealand, etc. (No. 14/1), 2d. +1d. (No H18) from £4 each.

Numbers Issued—1d. 4,500,000; 2d. 5,000,000.

1947 (Oct. 1st) Designer and Printer, etc., as

Nos. H17—18. Sheets 12 x 8.

H19 1d. +½d. **green**   ..   10   10
H20 2d. +1d. **crimson**   ..   10   10

Numbers Issued—1d. 5,500,000; 2d. 6,000,000.

1948 (Oct. 1st) Designer, E. Linzeil. Printers (*recess*) **Bradbury, Wilkinson. Perf. 13¼ x 13¼ (C). Sheets 12 x 10.**

H21 1d. +½d. **ult and dp green**   10   10
H22 2d. +1d. **brn-pur and red**   10   10

Numbers Issued—1d. 5,442,851; 2d. 5,903,958.

1949 (Oct. 3) Designer, J. Berry. Printers (*photo*) **Harrison & Sons. Perf. 14 x 14¾ (C). Sheets 20 x 6.**

H23 1d. +½d. **green**   10   10
H24 2d. +1d. **ultramarine**   10   10
     a "stop omitted"   8·00   9·00

H24*a* The stop normally under D of 1d. is missing on No. 1/2.

Numbers Issued—1d. 5,517,034; 2d. 5,999,109.

1950 (Oct. 2nd) Designers, R. S. Phillips and

J. Berry, from photo by Marcus Adams, Ltd. Printers (*photo*) **Harrison & Sons. Perf. 14 x 14¾ (C). Sheets 20 x 6.**

H25	1d.+½d. **bottle-green**	10	10
H26	2d.+1d. **dull maroon** ..	10	10

Numbers Issued—1d. 5,521,324; 2d. 6,816,448.

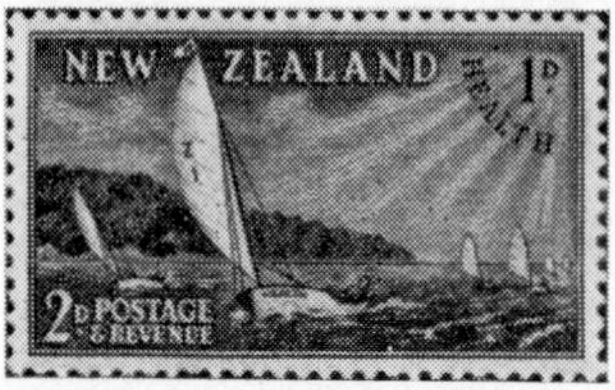

1951 (Nov. 1st) Design, Yachts of the "Takapuna" Class. Designers. Messrs. J. Berry and R. S. Phillips. Printers (*recess*) **Bradbury, Wilkinson. Perf. 13½ x 13¼ (C). Sheets 10 x 12.**

H27	1½d.+½d. **red and yellow**	10	10
H28	2d.+1d. **grey-grn and yel**	10	10

Numbers Issued—1½d. 5,100,013; 2d. 6,122,628.

OFFICIAL STAMPS

1936 As Nos. X2, etc. (Pictorial Issue), overprinted Official as No. O1. Wmk. single NZ.

XO1	1d. **scarlet** (11/36) Perf. 14 x 13½	15	10
	a perf. 13¾ x 14 ..	£10	£10
XO2	1½d. **red-brown** (7/36) .. perf. 13½ x 14 ..	85	85
	a perf. 14 x 13½ .. (only one block of four known to exist) from lower left corner of one sheet officially "stuck in" by N.Z. Post Office Staff.	£900	—
XO3	4d. **blk and dp sepia** (8/36)	75	75
XO4	1/– **green** Perf. 14 x 13½	3·00	4·00

1938 (July 4th) Design, Arms of Dominion. No. PF5 wmk "N.Z. Star" (*single*) **overprinted Official** (*ff's joined*). **Perf. 14 (C).**

O1	5/– **green**	£20	£10

1937-45 As No. 10, etc. (*Pictorial Issue*) **overprinted Official, as No. O1. Wmk. Mult. NZ. Perf. 13—14 x 13½ (C).**

O2	2½d. **choc and ind-slate** (26/7/38)	2·00	2·00
O3	2/– **dp olive** (5/37) ..	£10	4·00
	a COQK flaw ..	£22	£15

Perf. 14 x 13½ (C).

O4	½d. **green** (fantail) (7/37)	20	10
O4a	1d. **scarlet** Die II	20	10
O4b	1½d. **red-brown**	75	1·00
O5	2d. **dp orange** (1/38) ..	15	10
O6	3d. **brn** (Maori Girl) (1/3/38)	4·00	1·50
O7	6d. **red** (Perf. 13½ x 14 (C) (12/37)	1·00	50
O8	8d. **choc-brown** (1/45)	—	£475
O9	1/– **dp green** (2/37) ..	1·00	50
	a ditto Esparto ..	2·00	75
O10	2/– **dp olive** (Plate I) .. (/44)	8·00	2·50
	a COQK flaw ..	£20	£12
	b dp olive (Plate II)	6·60	4·50
	c ditto (Plate III) ..	6·50	4·50

Only a few used copies of O8 are known to exist. No mint example has been found.

Perf. 13½ x 13¾ (C)

O11	2/– **dp olive** (/39) ..	£20	3·00
	a COQK flaw ..	£35	£12

Perf. 14 (L) (2½d. **(L)** 1938 and **(C)** 1945).

O12	2d. **dp orange** (3/42) ..	1·00	1·00
O13	2½d. **choc. and ind-slate** (26/7/38)	1·50	2·00
O14	4d. **blk and blk-sepia** (8/41)	1·00	20

Perf. 14 x 14¼ (C).

O15	4d. **blk and sepia** (10/42)	1·00	25
O16	6d. **red** (7/42)	85	25
O17	8d. **choc** (wmk. sideways) (1/45)	1·10	2·00
O18	9d. **red and grey-black** (grn) (No. 29) (1/3/38)	8·00	9·00

Perf. 12½ (L).

O19	2d. **dp orange** (3/42) ..	£20	£12
O20	4d. **blk and blk-sepia** (12/41)	1·00	40
O21	6d. **red** overprint at bottom) (12/41) ..	1·25	50
	a ditto (overprint at top) (2/42) ..	1·25	50
O22	8d. **choc-brn** (wmk. sideways) (8/42) ..	1·50	1·00
O23	1/– **dp green** (4/42) ..	1·50	80
O24	2/– **dp olive** (4/42) ..	£10	3·00
	a COQK flaw ..	£25	£15
	b ditto Esparto ..	£12	3·00
	ba COQK flaw ..	£30	£18
O2/O24	**set** (12)	£22	£10

O3*a*/O10*a*/O11*a*/O24*a*,*ba* For Cook flaw see note after No. X21.

Perf. 14 x 15 (C).

O25	9d. **black and scar (blk)** (No. 31) (10/43) ..	5·00	5·00

1943 Design, Arms of Dominion type. No. PF50 overprinted Official.

O26	5/– **green** (/43)	8·00	2·50
	a yel grn P14 x 13½(61)	4·00	3·00

1940 (issued Jan. 2nd, except 8d., Mar. 8th) Nos. S4, etc. (Centenary Issue) overprinted Official (*tops of ff's not joined except on varieties*) **in black or red (½d. and 3d.).**

O27	½d. **dp blue-green** ..	10	5
O28	1d. **pur-brown and red**	30	5
O29	1½d. **blue and mauve-pur**	20	15
O30	2d. **myrtle-grn and sepia**	30	5
O31	2½d. **myr-grn and dp blue**	40	30
O32	3d. **dp pur and crim-lake**	1·20	30
O33	4d. **choc and dp claret**	2·00	50
O34	6d. **emer and pur-violet**	2·50	50
O35	8d. **black and vermilion**	2·50	1·80
O36	9d. **sage grn and dp or**	2·00	1·50
O37	1/– **sage-grn and dp myr**	6·00	2·00
O27/37	**set** (11)	£16	7·00

Numbers Printed—½d. 1,082,760; 1d. 3,452,880; 1½d. 361,200; 2d. 6,960,360; 2½d. 241,600; 3d. 904,200; 4d. 481,200; 6d. 661,200; 8d. 240,840; 9d. 241,200; 1/- 372,840. *(Small quantities of ½d., 1½d. and 2½d. stamps were withdrawn, but the rest were sold).*

As before, but ff's of overprint joined as on No. O1, etc.†

O38	½d. **dp blue-green** ..	6·00	6·00
O39	1d. **purple-brn and red**	8·00	8·00
O40	2d. **myrtle-grn and sepia**	6·00	6·00
O41	2½d. **myr-grn and dp blue**	6·00	6·00
O42	3d. **dp pur and crim-lake**	7·00	7·00
O43	4d. **choc and dp claret**	£20	£20
O44	6d. **emer and pur-violet**	£10	£10
O45	8d. **black and vermilion**	£10	£10
O38/45	**set** (8) joined pairs ..	£70	£70

(†) The variety "joined ff's" occurred once in a sheet on some values in one consignment only. (No. 4/3, 2½d.; No. 1/10, Other Values.)

1938-51 King's Head type *(Nos. 32, etc.)* **over-printed OFFICIAL, as No. O1, etc.**

O46	½d. **emer-green** (1/3/38)	15	15
O47	½d. **orange-brn** (1/6/46)	10	10
O48	1d. **rose-scarlet** (1/7/38)	20	10
O49	1d. **emer-grn** (10/7/41)	10	1p
O50	1½d. **red-choc** (26/7/38)	3·00	2·00
O51	1½d. **rose-scarlet** (2/4/51)	20	10
O52	2d. **orange** (1/5/47) ..	10	5
	a dp orange (/49) ..	15	10
O53	3d. **dp gr-blue** (16/10/41)	20	10
O54	4d. **pur-mauve** (1/5/47)	30	30
	a purple-lake (/50) ..	35	35
O55	6d. **lake-car** (1/5/47) ..	60	20
O56	8d. **violet** (1/5/47) ..	1·00	40
O57	9d. **reddish-brn** (1/5/47)	1·50	1·50
O58	1/- **chest and claret** (wmk. upright) (1/5/47) ..	1·50	50
	a ditto (wmk. side-ways) (1/5/47) ..	2·50	50
	b changed head die (wmk. upright) ..	3·00	1·50
O59	2/- **orange-brn and grn** (wmk. sideways) (1/5/47) ..	3·00	1·00
	a ditto (wmk. upright) (1/5/47) ..	3·00	1·00
O46/59	**set** (14)	£11	5·00

LIFE INSURANCE DEPARTMENT POSTAGE STAMPS

1937 Designers, W. B. Hudson and J. F. Rodgers. Printers *(typo)* **Govt. Printing Office, Wellington. Perf. 14 (C). Wmk. "N.Z. Star"** *(single)***. Chalk-coated paper. Sheets 120—two panes, each 6 x 10.**

L1	2d. **yellow**	1·50	1·50

A 2d. stamp, Perf. 14 x 15, and other stamps of same design Perf. 14 or Perf. 14 x 15 *(single wmk.)* were issued before 1937.

1944-7 As before, but wmk. "N.Z. Star" *(mult)* **and Perf. 14 x 15 (C).**

L2	½d. **yellow-green** (7/47)	1·00	1·00
L3	1d. **scarlet-red** (6/44) ..	40	20
L4	2d. **yellow** (5/46) ..	70	1·50
L5	3d. **chocolate** (10/46) ..	3·50	3·50
L6	6d. **rose-pink** (7/47) ..	6·00	5·00
L2/6	**set** (5)	£10	£10

Numbers Printed—½d. 28,920; 1d. 280,320; 2d. 166,440; 3d. 35,040; 6d. 29,400 (13,800 issued).

1947 (Aug. 1st) Designs, Lighthouses, ½d. (Castlepoint); 1d. (Taiarora); 2d. (Cape Palliser); 3d. (Eddystone); 4d. (Stephens Island); 6d. (The Brothers); 1/– (Cape Brett). Printers *(recess)* **Bradbury, Wilkinson. Wmk. N2 Star (mult) (sideways on 1d., 2d. and 2½d.) Perf. 13¼ x 13½ (C). Designs, 3d., 4d., 1/— V. Sheets 10 x 12 or 12 x 10.**

L7	½d. **orange-brn and myrt**	1·25	1·25
L8	1d. **pl blue and blk-olive**	20	20
L9	2d. **grey-blk and dk blue**	30	30
L9a	2½d. **blk and blue** (4/11/63)	2·50	3·00
L10	3d. **blue-grn and pur mauve**	40	40
L11	4d. **orange and brown**	50	50
	a wmk. sideways ..	80	60
L12	6d. **blue and dp brown**	70	70
L13	1/- **blue and chest-brn**	70	70
L7/13	**set** (8)	6·00	6·50

EXPRESS DELIVERY STAMPS

1903 Printers *(typo)* **Govt. Printing Office, Wellington. Wmk. "N.Z. Star"** *(single)***. Perf. 11. Sheets 6 x 10.**

ED1	6d. **red and violet** ..	£12	8·00

Fine Mint well centred copies are scarce.

1926/9 Perf. 14 x 14½

ED2	6d. **vermilion and mauve purple** (2/37) ..	6·00	7·00

Number Issued—60,000.

Perf. 14 x 15 (C).

ED3 6d. **car and bt-violet**
       (/26) £10   £11
ED4 6d. **ver and pur-vio**
       (12/38) £15   £18

Number Issued—12,000.

1939 (Aug. 16th) Designer, J. Berry. Printers (*recess*) **Govt. Printing Office, Wellington. Perf. 14 (L). Wmk. "N.Z. Star"** (*single*). **Sheets as before.**

ED5 6d. **violet** ..   ..   ..   1·00   1·00
       a bright violet   ..   1·00   1·00

Number Issued—240,000.

POSTAGE DUE STAMPS

1939 (Aug. 16th) Designer, J. Berry. Printers (*typo*) **Govt. Printing Office, Wellington. Perf. 15 x 14 (C). Wmk. "N.Z. Star"** (*single*) **sideways. Chalk-surfaced paper. Sheets 10 x 12.**

PD1 ½d. **turquoise-green**   ..   75   75
PD2 1d. **rose-carmine**   ..   40   20
PD3 2d. **blue**   ..   ..   ..   2·50   40
PD4 3d. **orange-brown**   ..   5·00   2·50

Numbers Printed—½d. 384,000; 1d. 1,440,000; 2d. 1,440,000; 3d. 456,000.

As before, but "N.Z. Star" (*mult*).

PD5 1d. **rose-carmine** (wmk.
       sideways) (4/49) ..   30   £10
PD6 2d. **blue** (wmk. sideways)
       (12/46)   50   40
PD7 3d. **orange-brown** (wmk.
       upright) (/43)   ..   6·00   6·00
       a ditto (wmk. side-
       ways) (6/45)   ..   3·50   1·00

PD7*a* In the first and second printings, the star of the wmk was to the left of NZ. It appears to the right on the printing released 28/11/49.

Price for PD5 used is for copies clearly dated prior to 1951 when Postage Due stamps officially ceased.

Number Issued—3d. 180,000.

NIGERIA

The Colony was formed on January 1, 1914 by the amalgamation of Northern Nigeria and Southern Nigeria (including Lagos); and in 1916 a part of the German Cameroons was also incorporated.

1914-26 *Typo* **Printers De La Rue & Co. Wmk. Mult. Crown C.A. perf. 14. Sheets 120— two panes, each 6 x 10 (except G1/2: 240— four panes, each 6 x 10).**

DIE I

G1	½d. **blue green** (O) ..	25	25
	a yellow green (O) ..	25	25
	b booklet pane of six..	£10	—
G2	1d. **carmine red** (O) ..	25	20
	a scarlet (O)	60	20
	b booklet pane of six..	£12	—
G3	2d. **grey** (O)	1·00	60
	a slate grey (O) ..	1·25	75
G4	2½d. **bright blue** (O) ..	70	40
G5	3d. **purple on yellow** (ch)	3·50	2·00
	a purple on white back (ch)	80	1·50
	b reddish purple, white back (ch)	80	1·50
	c purple on lemon (ch)	1·75	1·00
	d reddish purple on orange buff (ch)	2·00	1·25
	e purple on pale yellow (ch)	2·50	1·00
G6	4d. **black and red on yellow** (ch) ..	2·50	2·50
	a on white back (ch)	90	1·75
	b on lemon (ch) ..	1·75	2·00
	c grey black on orange buff (ch) ..	1·50	2·00
	d black on orange buff (ch)	1·75	2·00
	e black on pale yellow (ch)	3·50	5·00
G7	6d. **purple and violet** (ch)	1·50	1·50
	a dull purple and bright purple (ch) ..	1·50	1·50
G8	1/- **black on green** (ch)	2·50	1·75
	a on white back (ch)	1·25	1·50
	b blue green, olive back (ch)	4·00	3·50
	c on emerald olive back (ch)	3·75	3·50
	d on emerald back (ch)	1·25	3·50
G9	2/6 **black and red on blue** (ch)	3·50	4·50
G10	5/- **green and red on yellow** (ch) ..	9·00	£10
	a on white back (ch)	6·00	7·50
	b on lemon (ch) ..	9·00	9·00
	c on buff (ch) ..	9·00	£10
G11	10/- **green and red on green** (ch) ..	£21	£21
	a on white back (ch)	£21	£21
	b on blue green olive back (ch) ..	£450	£450
	c on emerald surface (ch)	£33	£33
	d on emerald back (ch)	£21	£19
G12	£1 **purple and black on red** (ch)	£80	£70

DIE II

G13	£1 **purple and black on red** (ch)	£80	£85
G1/13	**set** (12)	£110	£100
SPG1/12	**specimen set**(12)	£125	‡
SPG5/11	**specimen set** (5v on white backs) ..	£70	‡

1921-32 Wmk. Mult. Script C.A. Perf. 14.

DIE I

G14	½d. **deep green** (O) ..	25	20
	a green (O)	25	20
G15	1d. **bright aniline carmine** (O)	1·00	1·00
	a carmine (O) ..	20	20
	b rose scarlet (O) ..	25	25
	c booklet pane of six (O)	£12	—
G16	2d. **slate grey** (O) ..	1·50	40
	a grey (O)	1·75	60
G17	2d. **chocolate** (O) ..	1·50	80
	a booklet pane of six..	£15	—
G18	2½d. **ultramarine** (O) ..	60	65
G19	3d. **violet** (O)	1·50	1·50
G20	4d. **black and red/golden yellow** (ch) ..	8·50	6·00
G21	6d. **dull and bright purple** (ch)	1·75	1·75
G22	2/6 **black and scarlet on greenish blue** (ch)	8·00	6·50
G23	5/- **green and red/golden yellow** (ch) ..	£20	£22
G24	10/- **green and red on yellow green** (ch)	£50	£50
	a blue green and red/ blue green (ch)..	£50	£50
G14/24	**set** (11)	£90	£90

DIE II

G25	½d. **green** (O)	15	15
	a deep green (O) ..	15	15
G26	1d. **rose red** (O) ..	20	20
	a rose carmine ..	15	15
	b scarlet (O) ..	20	20
	c deep carmine (from booklets) ..	3·00	3·00
	d booklet pane of six..	£20	—
G27	1½d. **orange** (O) ..	50	25
G28	2d. **slate grey** (O) ..	60	25
	a booklet pane of six..	£20	—
	b grey (O)	75	30
G29	2d. **chestnut** (O) ..	1·00	1·25
	a booklet pane of six..	£20	—
G30	2d. **brown** (O)	25	25
	a booklet pane of six..	£20	—
G31	3d. **violet** (O)	1·50	1·50
	a mauve (O)	1·50	1·50
G32	3d. **bright blue** (O) ..	1·50	1·25
G33	4d. **grey black and red/ pale yellow** (ch) .	60	60
	a grey black and red/ lemon (ch) ..	50	50
	b black and red/yellow (ch)	75	75

G34	6d. **lilac and mauve** (*ch*)	95	1·20	
	a dp purple and purple (*ch*)	75	1·00	
	b purple and bt purple (*ch*)	80	1·00	
G35	1/- **jet black/bright green** (*ch*)	1·25	75	
	a black/bt green (*ch*)	1·25	75	
	b jet blk/emerald (*ch*)	1·25	75	
G36	2/6 **black and red/blue** (*ch*)	5·00	6·00	
	a black and lake/blue	5·50	6·50	
G37	5/- **yellow green and scarlet/lemon** (*ch*)	9·00	8·50	
	a blue green and red/lemon	9·00	8·50	
G38	10/- **bright green and red/yellow green** (*ch*)	£22	£25	
	a blue green and dull red/blue green (*ch*)	£22	£25	
G25/38	**set** (14)	£40	£42	
G14/38	**simple set** (15)	£40	£42	
SP G25/38	**specimen set** (14)	£135	‡	

1935 (May 6th) Silver Jubilee. Recess Printers Waterlow & Sons. Wmk. Mult. Script C.A. Perf. 11 x 12. Sheets 6 x 10.

G39	1½d. **ultramarine and grey**	25	25
G40	2d. **green and indigo**	30	30
G41	3d. **brown and dp blue**	75	80
G42	1/- **slate and purple**	2·00	2·50
G39/42	**set** (4)	3·00	3·50
SPG39/42	**specimen set** perf (4)	£22	‡

Numbers issued—G39, 2,466,840; G40, 1,070,820' G41, 384,480; G42, 626,220.

1936 (Feb. 1st) Various Pictorial Designs. Recess Printers, De La Rue. Wmk. Script C.A. Perf. 11½ x 13 or 12½ x 13½. Sheets 10 x 6 or 6 x 10.

G43	½d. **green**	25	20
G44	1d. **carmine**	25	20
G45	1½d. **brown**	30	20
	a 12½ x 13½	8·00	75
G46	2d. **black**	70	40
G47	3d. **blue**	1·00	75
	a perf 12½ x 13½	£22	£10

G48	4d. **red brown**	1·25	1·25	
G49	6d. **dull violet**	1·00	1·00	
G50	1/- **olive green**	4·00	3·75	

Perf. 14.

G51	2/6 **blk and ultramarine**	5·00	6·00	
G52	5/- **blk and sage green**	£11	£12	
G53	10/- **black and grey**	£27	£30	
G54	£1 **black and orange**	£50	£50	
G43/54	**set** (12)	£95	£100	
SPG43/54	**specimen set** (12)	£65	‡	

1938 (May 1st)-47 Designs, ½d.—1/3 (King's Head with Palms). Printers (*recess*) Bradbury, Wilkinson. Perf. 12 (L). Sheets 10 x 12.

1	½d. **green**	10	10
	a yellow-grn (15/11/46)	10	10
2	1d. **carmine-red**	4·00	1·25
	a rose-red (/41)	10	10
3	1d. **mauve-pur** (11/12/44)	10	10
4	1½d. **chestnut-brown**	10	10
	a chestnut (/44)	10	10
5	2d. **black**	10	15
6	2d. **rose-red** (11/12/44)	15	15
7	2½d. **orange** (28/4/41)	15	30
8	3d. **dark blue**	10	10
	a dp grey-blue (/44)	10	10
9	3d. **black** (11/12/44)	10	10
10	4d. **orange**	£16	5·00
11	4d. **dp blue** (11/12/44)	15	20
12	6d. **dp plum**	15	15
	a purple	15	15
13	1/- **sage-green**	50	20
	a olive-green (29/9/47)	50	20
14	1/3 **turquoise-blue** (13/2/40)	70	30
	a light blue (10/2/44)	60	25
	b wmk. sideways	—	£175

1938 (May 5th) Designs, 2/6 (Victoria-Buea); 5/-. (Niger at Jebba). Printers, (*recess*) De La Rue. Perf. 13 x 11¾ (C). Sheets 6 x 10.

15	2/6 **black and dp blue**	6·50	4·00
16	5/- **black and orange**	8·50	4·00

As Nos. 15—16, but Perf. 13½ (C).

17	2/6 **blk and dp blue** (6/42)	1·25	1·00
	a black and dark ult (15/11/46)	7·50	6·00
18	5/- **blk and orange** (8/42)	2·00	75

As Nos. 15—16, but Perf. 14 (L).

19	2/6	**blk and dp blue** (/42)	1·25	75
20	5/–	**black and orange**		
		(26/4/48)	2·00	1·25

As Nos. 15—16, but Perf. 12 (C).

21	2/6	**black and dp blue**		
		(15/8/51)	1·25	75
22	5/–	**black and orange**		
		(19/5/49)	2·00	1·25

As No. 1, etc., but Perf. 11¾ x 11½ (C).

23	½d.	**green** (15/2/50) ..	10	10
24	1d.	**mauve-pur** (15/2/50)	10	10
25	1½d.	**chestnut-brown**		
		(15/11/50)	10	10
26	2d.	**rose-red** (15/2/50) ..	10	10
29	6d.	**dp plum** (17/4/51) ..	15	10
30	1/–	**olive-green** (15/2/50)	25	10
31	1/3	**light blue** (14/6/50)..	35	25
23/31		**set** (7)	1·00	75
1/31		**set** (16) cheapest shade	£18	8·00
SP 1/16		**specimen set** perf (16)	£65	‡

SPECIAL ISSUES

1937 (May 12th) Coronation. As Aden, but Printers Bradbury, Wilkinson. Perf. 11 x 11¾ (C).

S1	1d.	**carmine-red** ..	10	10
S2	1½d.	**dp brown**	15	15
S3	3d.	**blue**	25	25
SP S1/3		**specimen set** perf (3)	£18	‡

1946 (Oct. 21st) Victory. As Aden.

S4	1½d.	**brown**	10	10
	a	reddish-brown ..	15	15
S5	4d.	**dp blue**	20	25
SP S4/5		**specimen set** perf (2)	£18	‡

1948 (Dec. 20th) Silver Wedding. As Aden.

S6	1d.	**magenta-purple** ..	10	10
S7	5/–	**orange-brown** ..	3·50	4·00

1949 (Oct. 10th) U.P.U. As Aden.

S8	1d.	**magenta**	20	20
S9	3d.	**indigo**	30	30
S10	6d.	**purple**	65	80
S11	1/–	**sage-green** ..	1·00	1·25
S8/11		**set** (4)	2·00	2·25

M*

NIUE

1932-38. As Cook Islands, Nos. X1—X6 and 1—3 but with frames altered to include NIUE. Sheets 8 x 10 or 10 x 8.

X1	½d. **black and green** ..	15	20
X2	1d. **black and scarlet** ..	15	20
X3	2d. **black and brown** ..	15	20
X4	2½d. **black and blue** ..	15	30
X5	4d. **blk and bright blue**	30	35
X6	6d. **black and orange** ..	50	50
1	1/- **black and pur-vio** ..	1·00	1·00
2	2/- **blk and dp chestnut**	1·25	1·25
3	3/- **gr-blue and em-grn**	2·00	2·00
X1/3	**set (9)**	5·00	5·50

Number Printed — 1/- 80,000; 2/- 40,000; 3/- 40,000.

1940 (Sept. 2nd) As Cook Islands No. 4, but with frame altered to include NIUE. Sheets 8 x 10.

4	3d./1½d. **blk and purple** ..	15	15

See note after Cook Islands No. 4.

Number Issued—295,360.

1941-2 Design, as No. PF3 New Zealand (*Arms of Dominion type*), **overprinted NIUE** (*thin type*) **in blue or red. Wmk. "N.Z. Star"** (*single*). **Perf. 14 (C).**

5	2/6 **brown** (4/41) ..	7·00	9·00
6	5/- **green-red** (4/41)	£45	£50
7	10/- **rose-car** (6/42) ..	£40	£45
8	20/- **dull pink** (6/42) ..	£50	£55
5/8	**set (4)**	£135	£150

The overprint in thicker type belongs to the 1931-2 issue.

Numbers Issued—5, 8,000; 6, 3,840; 7, 4,000; 8, 3,760.

1944-6 As Cook Islands Nos. 9—17, with frames altered to include NIUE. Sheets 8 x 10 or 10 x 8. Wmk. NZ star mult.

9	½d. **blk and grn** (9/44) ..	15	15
10	1d. **blk and dp scar** (12/44)	15	15
11	2d. **blk and chest-brn** (2/46)	15	15
12	2½d. **blk and slate-blue** (10/45)	15	15
13	4d. **blk and blue-grn** (3/44)	15	25
14	6d. **blk and red-orange** (9/44)	30	30
15	1/- **blk and pur-violet** (9/44)	50	75
16	2/- **blk and dp chestnut** (6/45)	1·00	1·25
17	3/- **dull blue and green** (8/45)	1·50	2·00
9/17	**set (9)**	3·50	4·75

Number Issued—½d. 383,840; 1d. 294,880; 2d. 110,240; 2½d. 89,680; 4d. 110 560; 6d. 108,400; 1/- 61,360; 2/- 73,760, 3/- 66,720.

1944-5 As Nos. 5—8 but wmk. "N.Z. Star" (*mult*).

18	2/6 **brown** (3/45) ..	1·50	1·75
	a wmk. inv.	2·00	2·00
19	5/- **green** (red) (11/44)	1·75	2·50
	a wmk. inv.	2·50	2·00
20	10/- **rose-car** (11/45) ..	6·00	7·50
	a wmk. inv. ..	7·00	9·00
21	20/- **pink** (11/45) ..	9·00	£12
	a wmk. inv. ..	£12	£14
18/21	**set (4)**	£17	£22

Numbers Issued—18, 11,920; 19, 19,920; 20, 7,600; 21, 12,000.

1950 (July 3rd) Designs ½d. (Map of Niue); 1d. (Capt. Cook's "Resolution"); 2d. (Alofi

Landing); **3d. (Native Hut)**; **4d. (Arch at Hikutavake)**; **6d. (Alofi Bay)**; **9d. (Fish Spearing)**; **1/– (Cave at Makefu)**; **2/– (Banana Palm)**; **3/– (Matapa Chasm). Designer, J. Berry. Printers** (*recess;* **Bradbury, Wilkinson Wmk. "N.Z. Star"** (*mult*) (*sideways on* 1d., 2d. 3d., 4d., 6d. *and* 1/–). **Perf. 14x13½ (C). Designs** ½d., 9d., 2/-, 3/- **V. Sheets 12 x 10 or 10 x 12.**

22	½d. **blue and red-orange**	10	10
23	1d. **sepia and green** ..	10	10
24	2d. **blk and rose-car** ..	10	10
25	3d. **blue and dull-violet**	15	15
26	4d. **olive-grn and choc**	15	20
27	6d. **emer and or-chest**	25	30
28	9d. **orange red and brn**..	40	40
29	1/– **dp purple and black**	50	50
30	2/– **or-brn and myr-grn**	1·00	1·00
31	3/– **dp blue and black** ..	1·25	1·50
22/31	**set** (10)	3·50	4·00

SPECIAL ISSUES

1937 (May 13th) Coronation. New Zealand Nos. S1—3, overprinted NIUE.

S1	1d. **carmine**	..	..	15	15
S2	2½d. **dp blue**			15	15
S3	6d. **reddish-orange**		..	25	35

Number Issued—1d. 730,429; 2½d. 575,288; 6d. 547,000.

1946 (June 1st) Peace. New Zealand No. S19, etc., overprinted NIUE in black or blue.

S4	1d. **emerald-green**	..	10	10
S5	2d. **purple (blue)**	..	10	10
S6	6d. **choc and vermilion**		20	20
S7	8d. **blk and lake (blue)** ..		20	20
S4/7	**set** (4)	.. ..	50	60

Number Printed—1d. 720,000; 2d. 720,000; 6d. 480,000; 8d. 480.000.

NORFOLK ISLAND

Previously used as a Convict Settlement, the island was incorporated in the State of New South Wales in 1896, and became a part of the Commonwealth of Australia in 1914.

From 1853, when administered by Tasmania, the stamps of that State were used and are believed to have been cancelled "102". Subsequently, the stamps of New South Wales and Australia were used and may be recognised by the datestamp.

All stamps were printed (*recess*) at the Australian Note and Stamp Printing Works on unwatermarked paper, unless otherwise mentioned.

1947 (June 10th) -1952 Design, as above, common to all values (Ball Bay). Perf. 14 (L). Toned paper. Sheets 5 x 8.

1	½d.	**orange**	15	15
	a	brown-orange (/49)	20	20
2	1d.	**purple-violet** ..	15	15
3	1½d.	**green**	25	25
4	2d.	**mauve-purple** ..	30	30
	a	mauve-violet (/52) .	45	45

5	2½d.	**bright scarlet** ..	35	35
	a	dp car-red (/52) ..	90	90
6	3d.	**beech-brown** ..	40	40
7	4d.	**claret**	50	50
8	5½d.	**deep slate**	60	60
9	6d.	**purple sepia** ..	75	75
	a	purple brown (/52) .	90	90
10	9d.	**magenta**	1·25	1·25
11	1/–	**grey olive**	1·25	1·25
12	2/–	**deep bistre** ..	5·00	4·00
1/12		**set (12)**	£10	9·00

No. 11 1/– (in grey olive and other colours) exists Perf. 11. These are essays or proofs and were never officially issued. (Price £25).

1956 (Nov.) -1959 As above but new printings and colours. Perf. 14 (L). White Paper.

13	½d.	**brown-orange** ..	1·50	1·50
	a	dp orange (thin paper)		
		(/58)	3·00	3·00
14	1d.	**dp violet**	3·00	3·00
	a	dark vio (thin paper)		
		(/58)	4·00	4·00
15	1½d.	**deep green** ..	3·00	3·00
	a	ditto (thin paper)		
		(26/9/58) ..	8·00	8·00
16	2d.	**reddish purple** ..	£90	£90
17	3d.	**green** (6/7/59) ..	2·50	2·50
18	2/–	**deep blue** (6/7/59) ..	£12	£12
1/18		**set** cheapest shade (14)	£24	£22

Nos. 13—18 were printed by Rotary Recess similar to contemporary Australian stamps.

NORTH BORNEO

1939 (Jan. 1st) Designs, 1c. (Buffalo Transport); 2c., 4c., 10c. (Indigenous Fauna); 3c., 6c., 12c., 15c. (Native Types of Inhabitants); 8c. (Map of Eastern Archipelago); 20c. (River Scene); 25c. (Native Craft); 50c. (Mount Kinabalu); $1—$5 (Arms of N.B. Co.). Printers (recess) Waterlow & Sons. No wmk. Perf. 12½ (L). Designs, 2c., 3c., 4c., 6c., 10c., 15c., $1, $2 V. Sheets 10 x 10.

1	1c.	grey-grn and chest-brn	25	30
2	2c.	pur and greenish-blue	25	25
3	3c.	blue-slate and green	25	30
4	4c.	olive and pur-vio	50	50
5	6c.	dp blue and claret	25	35
6	8c.	red	25	35
7	10c.	violet and dp olive	2·75	1·75
8	12c.	grn and ultramarine	40	1·50
9	15c.	dp emerald and lt brn	1·50	1·50
10	20c.	dp purple and slate	1·75	1·75
11	25c.	green and sepia	1·75	2·00
12	50c.	chocolate and violet	2·00	2·25
13	**$1**	**sep-brn and car-rose**	**3·50**	**5·50**
14	**$2**	**violet and ol-green**	**£15**	**£20**
15	**$5**	**blue-slate and blue**	**£35**	**£35**
1/15		set (15)	£60	£65
SP 1/15		specimen set perf (15)	£60	‡

Waterlow Archive Imperf. Plate Proofs (with security hole) complete sets exist 1c–$5 (15), Frames and complete design.

Waterlow printers samples o/printed "Specimen" —the following are known :- 3c, 4c, 10c, 12c, 20c, 50c all in unissued colours. Normally perf. stamps priced at £8 each.

1941 (Feb. 24th) Nos. 1 and 2 overprinted (in Sandakan) WAR TAX.

16	1c.	grey-grn and chest-brn	10	15
17	2c.	pur and greenish-blue	40	40

1945 (Dec. 17th) Nos. 1—15 overprinted BMA (British Military Administration).

18	1c.	grey-grn and chest-brn	40	30
19	2c.	pur and greenish-blue	40	30
20	3c.	blue-slate and grn	30	30
21	4c.	olive and pur-vio	3·00	3·00
22	6c.	dp blue and claret	35	40
23	8c.	red	60	1·00
24	10c.	violet and dp olive	1·00	1·25
25	12c.	grn and ultramarine	60	80
26	15c.	dp emerald and lt brn	60	80
27	20c.	dp purple and slate	80	1·00
28	25c.	green and sepia	1·25	1·25

29	50c.	chocolate and violet	1·50	2·00
30	$1	sepia-brn and car-rose	7·50	7·50
31	$2	violet and olive-grn	7·50	9·00
		a overprint double	£800	—
32	$5	blue-slate and blue	7·50	£10
18/32		set (15)	£30	£35

A rectangular boxed cancellation (22 x 19 mm) inscribed VICTORIA/DEC–/1846-1946/LABUAN was used at Victoria from December 24-31 1946 to commemorate the centenary of the cession of Labuan to Great Britain by the Sultan of Brunei. It may be found on all values of the above set and should not be mistaken to be an overprint.

Number issued—1c., 155,000; 2c., 149,991; 3c., 330,000; 4c., 80,000; 6c., 549,952; 8c., 265,000; 10c., 134,996; 12c., 230,000; 15c., 110,000; 20c., 104,996; 25c., 80,000; 50c., 45,000; $1, 20,000; $2, 20,000; $5, 22,500.

1947 (Dec. 22nd) Nos. 1—15 overprinted with Royal Cypher (in black or red) to denote change in status.

33	1c.	grey-grn and chest-brn (15/12/47)	25	25
34	2c.	pur and greenish-blue	25	30
35	3c.	blue-slate and grn (red)	25	30
36	4c.	olive and purple-vio (1/9/47)	15	15
		a short overprint bar	5·00	5·00
37	6c.	dp blue and claret (red	25	30
38	8c.	red (1/9/47)	15	20
39	10c.	violet and dp olive (15/12/47)	25	20
40	12c.	grn and ultramarine	25	30
41	15c.	dp emerald and lt brn	25	25
42	20c.	dp purple and slate	25	35
43	25c.	green and sepia	25	30
44	50c.	chocolate and violet	35	45
45	$1	sepia-brn and car-rose	50	60
46	$2	violet and olive-green	1·50	2·75
47	$5	blue-slate and blue (red)	5·00	7·00
33/47		set (15)	9·00	£13

36a The top bar, which is intended to block out THE STATE OF is about 1mm. shorter on No. 2/2 than on the other stamps of the sheet.

Number sold—1c., 906,522; 2c., 655,965; 3c., 395,883; 4c., 1,811,244; 6c., 351,954; 8c., 501,358; 10c., 483,227; 12c., 308,763; 15c., 278,554; 20c., 158,091; 25c., 263,610; 50c., 116,287; $1, 75,248; $2, 38,691; $5, 32,784.

1950 (July 1st) -52 Designs, 1c. (Mount Kinabalu); 2c. (Native Musical Instrument); 3c., 4c., 5c., 10c., $1, $5 (Native Industries

and Occupations); 8c. (Map); 15c., 30c. (Native Craft); 20c. (Bajau Chief); 50c. (Clock Tower, Jesselton); $2 (Murut with Blowpipe); $10 (Arms of N.B. Co.). Printers (*photo*) Harrison & Son. Wmk. "Script C.A." Perf. 14¾ x 13¾ (C). Chalk-surfaced paper. Designs, 3c., 4c., 5c., 30c., 50c., $1 V. Sheets 10 x 10.

48	1c.	lake-brown	10	15
49	2c.	grey-blue	10	15
50	3c.	green	10	15
51	4c.	purple-magenta	10	15
52	5c.	purple-violet	25	20
53	8c.	scarlet-red	25	25
54	10c.	purple-brown	20	25
55	15c.	bright ultramarine	30	25
	a	blue (1/5/52)	30	25
56	20c.	grey-brown	40	35
57	30c.	bistre-brown	45	30
58	50c.	car-lake (Jessleton)	60	1·00
	a	ditto (Jesselton)		
		(1/5/52)	60	1·00
59	$1	red-orange	1·00	1·25
60	$2	grey-green	2·00	2·75
61	$5	emerald-green	4·50	7·50
62	$10	mineral blue	9·00	£11
48/62		set (16)	£18	£25

58—An error in the spelling of Jesselton necessitated a correction in the design of the 50c. value.

SPECIAL ISSUES

1948 (Nov. 1st) Silver Wedding. As Aden.

S1	8c.	scarlet	20	25
S2	$10	dull purple	8·00	£12

1949 (Oct. 10th) U.P.U. As Aden.

S3	8c.	carmine-rose	30	25
S4	10c.	brown	35	35

S5	30c.	yellow-brown	75	1·00
S6	55c.	azure	1·00	1·25
S3/6		set (4)	2·25	2·75

POSTAGE DUE STAMPS

1939 (Jan. 1st) Design, Crest of North Borneo Coy. Printers (*recess*) Waterlow & Sons. Perf. 12½ (L). No wmk. Sheets 10 x 5.

PD1	2c.	chocolate-brown	1 25	9·00
PD2	4c.	carmine-red	1·50	£12
PD3	6c.	purple-violet	2·00	£17
PD4	8c.	green	3·00	£20
PD5	10c.	ultramarine	6·00	£25
PD1/5		set (5)	£13	£80

Waterlow Archive Imperf. Plate Proofs (punched with security hole). These are known 2c, 4c, 6c, 8c and 10c and they only seem to be in imperf. pairs complete design.

GERMAN PROPAGANDA LABELS

The 1944 German imitations of the G.B. 1937 Definitives ¼d to 3d (see after Great Britain for details) were also overprinted in black "LIQUIDA-TION/OF EMPIRE/BORNEO" within a vertical rectancular frame.

Prce (6v) unused or cancelled   £120

N. W. PACIFIC ISLANDS

These stamps were originally intended for use in the Caroline, Marianne and Marshall Islands which, together with New Guinea, Nauru and other territories in the area, were taken over from the Germans in 1914.

The three Island Groups were finally occupied by the Japanese instead of by the Australian Imperial Forces; and these overprinted stamps were, in the interests of economy, issued in New Guinea and Nauru. Certain of the higher denominations were also used at the Radio Station at Kulumadau in Papua.

Type I	Type II
Both 'S' in 'ISLANDS' normal.	First 'S' in 'ISLANDS' has short head and long tail.

Type III

Both 'S' in 'ISLANDS' have short head and long tail.

Type IV

As Type I, but 'ISLANDS' placed slightly right, so that stem of 'P' in 'PACIFIC' lies between 'I' and 'S' of 'ISLANDS' and second 'S' of 'ISLANDS' is to right of second 'C' in 'PACIFIC'.

There were five Settings, all 6 x 5.

Setting A Rows 1 and 2 Type I
(1d. and 2½d. Row 3 Type II
only)
1.1.15 Rows 4 and 5 Type III

Specialists recognise *five* different types, a different one on each horizontal row; but the differences between those on Rows 1 and 2, and on Rows 4 and 5, are very slight.

Setting B As Setting A.
(½d. only) except—Row 5 Types III,III.III.III.**II**.III.

Setting C As Setting A, except—
(All values
to 1/–)
15.3.15 Row 5 Types **I**.III.III.III.**II**.III.

Setting D As Setting A
(All values
to £1)
1.6.15

Setting E All values to £1 All Type IV
1919 (G39-G67)

Setting A was originally made from a 'Master' of five overprints, in a vertical row, from which six stereos were taken. Sheet margins were not removed. On the lower rows the overprint is placed higher on the stamps than is the case with the upper rows.

Setting B was made up from 30 separate electros, with the substitution of a new electro (Type II) in Row 5/5. Sheet margins were removed.

Setting C was as Setting B, but with further substitution (Type I) in Row 5/1. Sheet margins were removed.

Setting D was a new plate made from a fresh 'Master' showing slight differences in the letters, whilst preserving the pattern of Types I, II and III.

Setting E was a completely new plate, all Type IV.

Settings A-D were all by J. B. Cooke; Setting E was by T. S. Harrison.

1915-16 Stamps of Australia overprinted in black (sometimes with a purple tint) with Types I, II and III in a setting (A, B, C or D) 6 x 5 repeated four times to the sheet (120 – two panes, each 6 x 10).

(a) On K.G. V Typographed Definitives. Wmk. Second Single Crown over 'A'. Perf. 14. G4 1.1.15: remainder 15.3.15.

G1	½d. **bright green**	..	1·00	1·10
G2	½d. **green**	..	1·00	1·10
G3	½d. **dp bluish green**	..	1·00	1·10
	a overprint double	..	—	—
G4	1d. **pale rose** (Die I)	..	1·50	1·75
G5	1d. **dull red** (Die I)	..	1·50	1·75
	a overprint double	..	—	—
G6	1d. **car-red** (Die I)..	..	1·50	2·00
G7	1d. **car-red** (Die II)	..	£95	—
	a se-tenant pair (Dies I and II)	..	£120	—
G8	4d. **yellow-orange**	..	6·00	7·00
	a line through value	..	£100	£120
G9	4d. **lemon-yellow**	..	£120	£140
G10	5d. **brown**	..	4·00	4·50

G4/7—For details of Dies see Note after Australia No. G120.

G8a—A crack in the plate shows as a line through 'FOUR PENCE' on Row 2/6 (Right hand pane). Numbers printed—G4/7 (Setting A), 10,080.

(b) On Kangaroo Definitives. Perf. 12.

Die I　　　　　　　　　Die II

(i) Wmk. First Single Crown over 'A'. G12 1.1.15: G21/23 17.12.15: remainder 15.3.15.

G11	2d.	**grey** (Die I) ..	..	2·00	2·50
G12	2½d.	**indigo**		2·00	2·50
G13	3d.	**yel-olive** (Die I)	..	4·00	7·00
G14	3d.	**yel-olive** (Die II)	..	£90	£110
		a se-tenant pair (Dies I and II)	..	£150	£170
G15	3d.	**greenish olive** (Die I) ..	..	£90	£110
G16	3d.	**greenish olive** (Die II)	..	£475	—
		a se-tenant pair (Dies I and II)	..	£550	
G17	6d.	**dull blue**	..	8·00	9·00
G18	6d.	**bright blue** ..		9·00	£10
G19	9d.	**violet** ..	..	9·00	£14
G20	1/–	**green** ..	..	£12	£15
G21	5/–	**grey and yellow**	..	£500	£350
G22	10/–	**grey and pink**	..	£60	£60
G23	£1	**brn and ult** ..	..	£300	£200

Numbers printed—G12 (Setting A), 8,160; G21 120. (?)

(ii) Wmk. Second Single Crown over 'A'. G29 17.12.15: remainder Oct. 1915–March 1916(?)

G24	2d.	**grey** (Die I)	..	2·00	2·00
G25	2½d.	**indigo** ..	..	£1250	£1500
G26	6d.	**ultramarine** ..		4·00	4·00
G27	9d.	**violet** ..	..	4·00	4·00
G28	1/–	**emerald** ..	..	5·00	6·00
G29	2/–	**brown** ..	..	£45	£48
G30	5/–	**grey and yellow**	..	£45	£48
		a yellow printed double	..	£1750	—

G25—Although a large number of sheets was printed many were destroyed in a fire at the Rabaul Treasury; and only one pane is known.

Die IIA

Die IIB

(iii) Wmk. Third Single Crown over 'A'. Dec. 1915-Feb. 1918.

G31	2d.	**grey** (Die I) ..	..	3·00	3·00

G32	2d.	**grey** (Die IIA)	..	5·00	5·00
		a se-tenant pair (Dies I and IIA)	..	£65	—
G33	3d.	**yellow-olive** (Die I)	3·00	4·50
G34	3d.	**yel-olive** (Die IIB)	..	£30	£22
		a se-tenant pair (Dies I and IIB)	..	£50	—
G35	2/–	**brown** ..	..	£12	£15
G36	£1	**brn and ult** ..	..	£300	£300

G32*a* Die IIA cliché was substituted for Die I on Row 10/1 (upper left pane).

Numbers printed (Settings B, C and D – all watermarks)—½d., 159,240; 1d., 210,000; 2d., 55,800; 2½d., 42,000; 3d., 40,440; 4d., 42,000; 5d., 34,680; 6d., 36,360; 9d., 34,920; 1/–, 41,040; 2/–, 21,000; 5/–, 9,600; 10/–, 6,480; £1, 6,240.

1918 (May) Nos. G10 and G20 surcharged locally in black. Setting 6 x 5.

G37	1d. on 5d.	**brown** ..		£65	£55
G38	1d. on 1/–	**green** ..	..	£65	£55

Prices quoted for Nos. G1/38 are for Type I or III overprints on reasonably centred stamps. Type II overprints and well centred stamps are worth a premium.

Vertical strips of three from Rows 2-3-4 showing the three Types can occasionally be supplied at about five times the price of a single. The same applies to horizontal strips from Row 5 (Setting C).

Number surcharged—G37, 3,000.

1918-23 Stamps of Australia overprinted in black with Type IV. Setting E (6 x 5) repeated four times to the sheet.

(a) On K.G. V Typographed Definitives. Perf. 14.

(i) Wmk. Second Single Crown over 'A' (1918-22).

G39	½d.	**pale green** ..	..	60	80
G40	½d.	**blue-green** ..	..	80	90
G41	1d.	**carmine-red** (Die I)	1·50	1·00
G42	1d.	**carmine-red** (Die II)	£90	£90
		a se-tenant pair (Dies I and II) ..	..	£150	—
G43	1d.	**bright violet** ..	..	2·00	3·00
G44	2d.	**orange** (4/21)	..	5·00	6·00
G45	2d.	**scarlet** (7/22)	..	3·00	8·00
G46	4d.	**yellow-orange**	..	7·00	8·00
		a line through value..	£300	—
G47	4d.	**violet** (8/22) ..	..	£14	£15
		a thin letters ..	..	£275	—
G48	4d.	**ultramarine** ('22)	:	£10	£12
		a thin letters ..	..	£300	—
G49	5d.	**orange-brown** ..	..	4·00	6·00
G50	5d.	**chestnut** ..	..	5·00	7·00

G41/42—For details of Dies see Note after Australia No. G120.

G46a—See Note after No. G8a.

G47a/48a—'FOUR PENCE' is in thinner letters, the defective cliche (Row 2/6), which previously showed the 'line through value' variety, having been replaced.

(ii) Wmk. First Multiple (Crown over 'A') (1919).

G51	½d.	**green**	40	1·00

(b) On Kangaroo Definitives. Wmk. Third Single Crown over 'A'. Perf. 12. (1918-23).

G52	2d.	**grey** (Die I)	3·25	5·00
G53	2d.	**grey** (Die II).. ..	7·50	7·50
G.4	2½d.	**indigo**	4·00	6·00
		a missing fraction ..	£1250	£1250
G55	3d.	**greenish ol** (Die I)..	5·00	6·00
G56	3d.	**greenish ol** (Die II)	£15	£15
		a se-tenant pair (Dies I and II) ..	£100	—
G57	3d.	**lt olive** (Die II) ('23)	4·00	5·00
G58	6d.	**ultramarine**.. ..	5·00	6·00
G59	6d.	**blue-grey** ('21) ..	£20	£20
G60	9d.	**bt violet** ('19) ..	8·00	£12
G61	1/–	**emerald**	8·00	£11
G62	1/–	**blu-grn** (thin paper)	£10	£12
G63	2/–	**brown**	£14	£15
G64	5/–	**grey and yellow** ..	£22	£24
G65	10/–	**grey and pl pink** ..	£70	£65
G66	10/–	**grey and aniline carmine-pink** ..	£90	£65
G67	£1	**brn and ult**	£350	£350

G52/57—For details of Dies see Note before G11.

G54a—The '1' of '½' is missing (Row 1/3). Only 17 copies are known.

G62—The paper is very thin and the colour shows through clearly at the back.

G36 and G37 are known with the 'broken tail' variety, the Kangaroo's tail being broken off short and a small dot marking its normal tip. This variety must also have existed on 5/– and 10/– values.

Numbers printed—G65/66, 7,680; G67, 960 (mostly used at the Radio Station).

OFFICIAL STAMPS

1919-24 Nos. G41/67 (Type IV, Setting E) punctured 'OS'. The letter 'O' has twelve holes and the letter 'S' has eleven, the height varying between 8 and 9mm.

(a) K.G. V Typographed Definitives.

GO1	1d.	**carmine-red** (Die I)	—	—
GO2	1d.	**carmine-red** (Die II)	—	—
		a se-tenant pair (Dies I and II) ..	—	—
GO3	1d.	**violet** (9/24) ..	—	—
GO4	2d.	**orange**	—	—
GO5	2d.	**scarlet** (4/24) ..	—	—
GO6	4d.	**yellow-orange** ..	—	—
		a line through value	—	—

GO7	4d.	**violet**	—	—
		a thin letters	—	—
GO8	4d.	**ultramarine**.. ..	—	—
		a thin letters ..	—	—
GO9	5d.	**brown** ('24).. ..	—	—

(b) No. G117 of Australia (K.G. V Typographed Definitive on inferior rough unsurfaced paper, locally gummed) overprinted. Type IV, Setting E and punctured as before (Jan. 1925).

GO10	1d.	**rosine** (Die I) ..	—	£80
GO11	1d.	**rosine** (Die II) ..	—	£200
		a se-tenant pair (Dies I and II)	—	—

These overprinted stamps were not issued unpunctured.

(c) Kangaroo Definitives.

GO12	2½d.	**indigo**	—	—
GO13	3d.	**olive** ('21) ..	—	—
GO14	6d.	**blue-grey** ('21) ..	—	—
GO15	9d.	**bright violet** ('24)	—	—
GO16	1/–	**emerald** ('21) ..	—	—
GO17	2/–	**brown** ('22) ..	—	—
GO18	5/–	**grey and yel** ('22)	—	—
GO19	10/–	**grey and pink** ..	—	—
GO20	£1	**brn and ult** ..	—	—

The status of Nos. GO12/20 is uncertain.

For subsequent issues see Nauru (from 1916) and New Guinea (from 1925).

NORTHERN NIGERIA

All issues typographed by De La Rue & Co. 1900. Wmk. Crown C.A. Perf. 14. Sheets 120— two panes, each 6 x 10.

V1	½d. **dull mauve and green**		40	45
V2	1d. **dull mauve and car.** .		1·00	1·00
V3	2d. **dull mauve and yel-or**		2·00	2·50
V4	2½d. **dull mauve and ult** ..		4·50	4·50
V5	5d. **dull mauve and chest**		7·00	8·00
V6	6d. **dull mauve and violet**		7·00	8·00
V7	1/– **green and black**	..	£10	£10
V8	2/6 **grn and ultramarine**		£45	£50
V9	10/– **green and brown**	..	£125	£150
V1/9	**set (9)**	.. ..	£200	£220
SP V1/9	**specimen set**	..	£80	‡

Number issued—V1, 113,640; V2, 116,880; V3, 44,640; V4, 37,800; V5, 22,440; V6, 32,520; V7, 35,120; V8, 8,160; V9, 8,040.

1902 Wmk. Crown C.A. Perf.14. Sheets as before.

E1	½d. **purple and green** ..		20	30
E2	1d. **purple and carmine** .		40	30
E3	2d. **purple and yel-or** ..		75	1·00
E4	2½d. **pur and ultramarine**		50	75
E5	5d. **purple and chestnut**		1·25	2·50
E6	6d. **purple and dull violet**		4·00	4·00
E7	1/– **green and black**	..	3·00	3·00
E8	2/6 **grn and ultramarine**		6·00	9·00
E9	10/– **green and brown** ..		£35	£35
E1/9	**set (9)**	.. ..	£48	£52
SP E1/9	**specimen set (9)** ..		£85	‡

Number issued—E1, 270,720; E2, 289,080; E3/4, 96,000 each; E5, 41,880; E6, 64,320; E7, 97,200; E8, 18,360; E9, 17,640.

1904 Wmk. Mult. Crown C.A.

E10	£25 **green and carmine** (O) £16000		—
SP E10	**specimen**	£700	‡

This stamp was issued solely for fiscal purposes and very few fine mint copies are known, from 1,080 printed.

1905 Wmk. Mult. Crown C.A. Perf. 14.

E11	½d. **pur and green** (OC)		35	35
E12	1d. **pur and car** (OC) ..		45	25
E13	2d. **pur and orange** (OC)		75	1·00

E14	2½d. **pur and ult** (O)	..	2·00	2·50
E15	5d. **pur and chestnut**			
	(OC)	.. ..	4·00	5·00
E16	6d. **pur and violet** (OC)		4·00	4·00
E17	1/– **grn and black** (OC)..		6·00	7·50
E18	2/6 **grn and ult** (OC) ..		8·00	8·50
E11/18	**set (8)**	.. ..	£24	£28

Number issued—

		(O)	(C)
E11	..	61,200	278,280
E12	..	161,520	613,440
E13	..	20,640	158,160
E15	..	8,400	42,000
E16	..	19,920	127,560
E17	..	8,160	54,600
E18	..	8,160	24,360

1910/11 Wmk. Mult. Crown C.A. Perf. 14.

E19	½d. **blue green** (O)	..	15	15
E20	1d. **carmine red** (O)	..	15	15
E21	2d. **grey** (O)	.. ..	75	1·25
E22	2½d. **bright blue** (O)	..	75	1·25
E23	3d. **purple/yellow** (ch)..		60	40
E24	5d. **pur and ol-grn** (ch)..		1·25	1·75
E25	6d. **dull and dp pur** (ch)		1·50	2·00
	a dull and bt pur (ch)		75	1·50
E26	1/– **black/green** (ch)	..	1·25	1·00
E27	2/6 **blk and red blue** (ch)		9·00	6·00
E28	5/– **grn and red-yel** (ch)		£18	£15
E29	10/– **grn and red/grn** (ch)		£28	£28
E19/29	**set (11)**	.. ..	£58	£56
SP E19/29	**specimen set (11)** .		£80	‡

Number issued—E27, 36,480; E28, 177,120; E29, 36,360.

1912 Wmk. Mult. Crown CA. Sheets as before.

G1	½d. **blue green** (O)	..	15	15
G2	1d. **carmine red** (O)	..	15	15
G3	2d. **grey** (O)	.. ..	50	90
G4	3d. **purple/yellow** (ch)..		50	60
G5	4d. **blk and red/yel** (ch)		40	40
G6	5d. **pur and olive grn** (ch)		75	90
G7	6d. **pur and bt pur** (ch)..		90	1·25
G8	9d. **pur and car red** (ch)		1·00	1·50
G9	1/– **black on green** (ch) .		1·00	1·25
G10	2/6 **blk and red/blue** (ch)		6·00	6·00
G11	5/– **grn and red/yel** (ch)		£12	£14
G12	10/– **grn and red/grn** (ch)		£20	£21
G13	£1 **pur and blk/red** (ch)		£60	£50
G1/13	**set (13)**	.. ..	£100	£95
SP G1/13	**specimen set**	..	£110	‡

Number issued—G11, 121,800 G12, 60,600; G13, 60.720.

For later issues see NIGERIA.

NORTHERN RHODESIA

For details of Postal History and earlier issues see under RHODESIA.

1925 (Apr. 1st)-29 Printers (recess) **Waterlow & Sons. Designer, W. G. Fairweather. Sheets G1/9, 10 x 12; G10/19, 10 x 6.**

G1	½d.	**bright green**	15	15
	a	dull blue green	15	15
G2	1d.	**brown**	15	15
	a	deep brown	15	15
G3	1½d.	**deep carmine red**	15	15
	a	carmine red	15	15
G4	2d.	**yellow brown**	30	15
	a	orange brown	30	15
G5	3d.	**dull blue**	75	40
	a	ultramarine	75	40
G6	4d.	**dull violet**	90	40
	a	deep violet	90	40
	ab	imperf. between (vert. pair)	—	£2000
G7	6d.	**slate grey**	1·00	50
G8	8d.	**rose purple**	5·00	7·50
G9	10d.	**sage green**	5·00	7·50
	a	deep olive green	5·00	7·50
G10	1/–	**orange, brn and blk**	2·00	1·00
G11	2/–	**brn and ultramarine**	7·00	8·50
G12	2/6	**black and blue green**	6·00	6·00
G13	3/–	**violet and deep blue**	£10	9·00
G14	5/–	**grey and dull violet**	£10	8·00
G15	7/6	**rosy mauve and blk**	£42	£48
G16	10/–	**blue grn and black**	£26	£26
G17	£1	**car red and rose pur**	£110	£125
G1/17		**set** (17)	£200	£270
SP G1/17		**specimen set** perf	£400	‡

G6ab Only one used example is known with most of the lower stamp missing.

1935 (May 6th) Silver Jubilee. Printers (recess) **De La Rue Wmk. Script C.A. Perf. 13½ x 14. Sheets 6 x 10.**

G20	1d.	**light blue and ol-grn**	25	30

G21	2d.	**green and indigo**	60	60
G22	3d.	**brown and dp blue**	1·50	1·75
G23	6d.	**slate and purple**	2·00	2·50
	a	frame double. one alb.	£750	—
G20/23		**set** (4)	4·00	4·50
SPG20/23		**specimen set** perf.	£25	‡

Number issued—G20, 71,733; G21, 62,731; G22, 53,627; G23, 32,733.

1938 (Mar. 1st) -52 Design, King's Head and beneath river scene on the Zambezi, with dug-out canoe, as used by Ba-Lia tribe, with Giraffe and Elephants in the foreground. Printers (recess) **Waterlow & Sons. Perf. 12½ (L). Sheets 1—14, 12 x 20; 15—20, 10 x 6.**

1	½d.	**green**	10	10
2	½d.	**dp brown** (15/11/51)	20	25
3	1d.	**brown**	10	10
	a	dp brown (15/3/48)	15	15
4	1d.	**dp green** (15/11/51)	40	40
5	1½d.	**carmine-red**	1·50	40
	a	horiz. pr. imp. between	£4500	—
6	1½d.	**brownish-yellow** (10/1/41)	15	15
	a	buff-yellow (3/5/44)	15	15
7	2d.	**brownish-yellow**	£12	2·00
8	2d.	**car-red** (10/1/41)	25	25
	a	car-rose (15/3/48)	25	25
8b	2d.	**pur-claret** (1/12/5)	25	30
9	3d.	**ultramarine**	25	20
	a	bt ult (15/3/48)	25	20
10	3d.	**scarlet** (1/12/11)	35	35
11	4d.	**dull purple-violet**	30	15
12	4½d.	**ultramarine** (5/5/52)	1·00	1·50
13	6d.	**grey-black**	40	40
14	9d.	**violet** (5/5/52)	1·50	2·00
15	1/–	**dp orange and black**	60	20
16	2/6	**black and green**	1·50	1·00
	a	black, blue-green	1·50	1·00
17	3/–	**purple-vio and blue**	1·50	1·25
18	5/–	**grey and dull grey-purple**	3·00	3·25
	a	grey and dull purple (3/5/44)	3·00	3·25
19	10/–	**green and black**	4·00	5·00
20	£1	**rose-car and mauve-purple**	£14	£14
1/20		**set** (20)	£40	£40
SP 1/20		**specimen set** perf (13)	£75	‡

5a—Only 6 pairs are reported to exist.

1952 (Dec. 10th) As No. 2, but Perf. 12¼ x 13¾ (C).

21	½d.	**dp brown**	25	30

SPECIAL ISSUES

1937 (May 12th) Coronation. As Aden, but Printers, Bradbury, Wilkinson. Perf. 11 x 11¾ (C).

S1	1½d. **carmine-red**	..	15	15
S2	2d. **yellow-brown**	..	25	25
S3	3d. **blue**	..	35	40
SP S1/3	**specimen set** perf (3)		£15	‡

1946 (Nov. 26th) Victory. As Aden.

(a) **Perf. 13¾ x 14 (C).**

S4	1½d. **reddish-orange**	..	15	15
S5	2d. **carmine-red**	..	15	15
SP S4/5	**specimen set** perf (2)		£18	‡

(b) **Perf. 13¾ x 13¼ (C).**

S6	1½d. **reddish-orange**	..	35	40

1948 (Dec. 1st) Silver Wedding. As Aden.

S7	1½d. **orange**	.. ..	15	15
S8	20/– **maroon-lake** (*all* *recess*)	.. ..	9·50	£15

Number issued—1½d., 1,268,590; £1, 23,135.

1949 (Oct. 10th) U.P.U. As Aden.

S9	2d. **carmine-rose**	..	25	25
S10	3d. **indigo**	..	30	35
S11	6d. **grey** ..	.. ..	60	60
S12	1/– **orange**	.. .	1·00	1·00
S9/12	**set** (4)	.. ..	2·00	2·00

Number issued—2d., 306,280; 3d., 208,120; 6d., 239,042; 1/–, 167,602.

POSTAGE DUE STAMPS

1945 Printers (*typo*) De La Rue. Perf. 13¾ x 14 (C). Rough paper. Sheets 120—two panes, each 6 x 10.

PD1	1d. **black** ..	..	..	1·50	75
PD2	2d. **black** ..			90	90
PD3	3d. **black** ..	..	..	50	60
PD4	4d. **black** ..	..	..	2·00	2·25
PD1/4	**set** (4)	..	..	4·00	4·00

The 1945 printing can be distinguished from the original emission (in the same design) of 1929 by the paper on which they are printed. This being the rough paper brought into use during the war. The impression itself appears somewhat coarser.

1952 As before but printed on chalk-coated paper.

PD5	1d. **black** (23/1/52)	..	55	60
PD6	3d. **black** (23/1/52)	..	45	55

Watermark Varieties (Type A)

(See Introduction for details)

PD5b	1d. St. *Edward's* Crown..		£25	—
PD6a	3d. Missing crown	..	£30	—
PD6b	St. Edward's Crown..		£30	—

NYASALAND

The African Lakes Corporation opened a Trading Station at Mandala, then in N.E. Rhodesia but now in Nyasaland, in 1886; and mail was forwarded to the British Vice-Consul in Quillemaine. In 1889 N.E. Rhodesia came under the control of the British South Africa Company, whilst in the same year and in 1891 the British Government declared a Protectorate over the Shire District and South Nyasa.

The whole area, known as British Central Africa, became a Crown Colony in 1894; and in July 1907 the name was changed to Nyasaland Protectorate.

1892-93 Nos. V34 and V12 of Rhodesia overprinted 'B.C.A' and surcharged in black.

V19	3/- on 4/- **grey-black and ver** (10/93)..	£100	£100
V20	4/- on 5/- **or-yel** (8/92) ..	£30	£30

Number surcharged—V19, 1,380.

1895 No. V2 surcharged in black at Cape Town. 1st Setting—Horizontal row of 10: 2nd Setting—10 x 3, repeated twice.

V21	1d. on 2d. **sea-grn and ver**		6·00	£12
	a	dropped 'Y' ..	—	—
	b	dropped 'NY'..	—	—
	c	surcharge double ..	£800	£950

V21a—1st Setting only.
V21b—2nd Setting Rows 2/6 and 5/6.
V21c occurred on the third horizontal row in the 1st Setting. (3 sheets).

Stamps with double surcharge and without the stop after PENNY came from a trial printing made at Blantyre; they were not issued.

Number surcharged—5,940.

1891 (April)-95 Nos. V1/16 and V28/34 of Rhodesia overprinted 'B.C.A.' in black in complete sheets (10 x 6).

V1	1d.	**black**	1·00	1·00
	a	overprint double ..	—	—
V2	2d.	**sea-grn and ver** ..	80	2·00
	a	bisect diag. (1d.) on cover	—	£700
	b	bisect (horiz. or vert) (1d) on cover ..		
V3	4d.	**chestnut and black**	1·00	2·00
V4	6d.	**ultramarine**	£16	£11
V5	6d.	**deep blue**	3·50	3·50
V6	8d.	**rose-lake and ult** ..	5·00	£10
V7	8d.	**brn-red and ult** ..	8·00	£12
V8	1/-	**grey-brown**	5·50	5·00
V9	2/-	**vermilion**	£10	£11
V10	2/6	**grey-purple**	£14	£14
V11	3/-	**brn and grn** ('95) ..	£15	£15
V12	4/-	**grey and ver** ('93) ..	£19	£19
V13	5/-	**orange-yellow** ..	£19	£28
V14	10/-	**deep green**	£32	£55
V15	£1	**deep blue**	£200	£250
V16	£2	**rose-red**	£325	—
V17	£5	**sage-green**	£650	—
V18	£10	**brown**	£1600	—
V1/15		**set** (13v)	£300	£390
SPV1/18		**specimen set** (16v)..	—	—

V1a—The second overprint is fainter and to the left of normal.

V2a The bisect is known used at Blantyre on 28/10/95.

V2b The bisect is known used at Zomba 4-13/7/95.

V1/14—The overprinting plate was made up from three rows (10 x 3) duplicated for the lower three rows.

Collectors are warned of cleaned Fiscal stamps with forged postmarks. Genuinely used Rhodesian stamps are also known with forged overprints.

The B.C.A. stamps were also used in a number of places now within Rhodesian territory.

1895 Litho De La Rue. No Wmk. Perf. 14. Designer H. H. Johnston. Sheets V22/26. 120 – two panes, each 6 x 10: V27/32 12 x 5. Centres in black.

V22	1d.	**black**	..	1·75	2·25
V23	2d.	**green**	..	4·50	4·75
V24	4d.	**reddish buff** ..		7·50	7·50
V25	6d.	**blue**	..	£10	5·50
V26	1/-	**rose**	..	£11	9·00
V27	2/6	**magenta**		£60	£35
V28	3/-	**yellow**		£50	£16
V29	5/-	**olive**		£60	£35
V30	£1	**orange**		£575	£200
V31	£10	**vermilion**		£2000	—
V32	£25	**blue-green**		£3750	—
V22/29		**set** (8v) ..	..	£190	£100

SPV22/30 **specimen set** (9v) .. £175 ‡
SPV31 **specimen** (1v) .. £140 ‡
SPV32 **specimen** (1v) .. £375 ‡

Numbers printed—V22, 102,240; V23, 51,480;
V24, 101,160; V25, 199,560; V26, 100,320; V27,
97,080; V28, 99,600; V29, 49,200; V30, 49,040;
V31/32, 6,000 each.

Unsold remainders were destroyed early in 1896
when the following issue was received.

**1896 (July) As before but Wmk. Crown CA
(V33/37) or Crown CC (V38/43). Centres in
black.**

V33	1d. **black**	..	..	2·25	2·75
V34	2d. **green** ..		..	4·50	3·00
V35	4d. **orange-brown**		..	5·50	5·50
V36	6d. **blue** ..	..	..	4 50	3·75
V37	1/- **rose**	..	..	7·50	7·50
V38	2/6 **magenta**	..	..	£35	£35
V39	3/- **yellow** ..	..	..	£22	£14
V40	5/- **olive**	..	..	£40	£35
V41	£1 **blue** ..	..	..	£625	£375
V42	£10 **vermilion**	..	..	£2750	£1200
V43	£25 **green** ..	..	..	£5500	—
V33/40	**set** (8v)	..	..	£110	£90
SPV33/41	**specimen set** (9v) ..			£175	‡
SPV42	**specimen** (1v)	..	..	£100	‡
SPV43	**specimen** (1v)	..	..	£200	‡

In the foregoing two sets, on all except V22 and
V33, the horizontal background lines cross the
extremity of the helve of the pick held by the left
hand supporter.

**1897 (Aug.)-1901 Type De La Rue. Wmk.
Crown CA. (V44/51) or Crown CC (V52/57).
Perf. 14. Sheets V44/51 6 x 10: V52/57 12 x 5.**

V44	1d. **blk and ult** ..		80	40
V45	1d. **dl pur and car-rose**			
	('01)	..	60	80
V46	2d. **black and yellow** ..		50	90
V47	4d. **black and carmine**		2·75	2·75
V48	4d. **dl pur and ol-grn**			
	('01) ..	..	3·25	3·50
V49	6d. **black and green** ..		4·50	4·00
V50	6d. **dl pur and brn** ('01)		5·00	5·50
V51	1/- **blk and dl pur**	..	2·75	4·00
V52	2/6 **blk and ult** ..	..	£16	£15
V53	3/- **blk and sea-grn** ..		£100	£100
V54	4/- **black and carmine**		£22	£22
V55	10/- **blk and ol-grn** ('00)		£45	£55
V56	£1 **blk and dl purple** ..		£165	£110
V57	£10 **black and yellow** ..		£2500	£1200
V44/56	**set** (13v) ..	..	£325	£300
SPV44/56	**specimen set** (13v)		£130	‡
SPV57	**specimen** (1v) ..		£120	‡

Imperf. Colour Trials on unwatermarked paper
are known for the 1d. (V45) – various shades of

green and blue frames, with centres in black or
dark purple. Colour Trials of the 2/6 – frames in
purple or olive, and of the 10/- – frames in green
or yellow-green – also exist.

Numbers printed—V44, 36,000; V45, 291,660;
V46/47, 24,420 each; V48, 61,680; V49, 24,120;
V50, 61,200; V51, 12,120; V52 and V54, 6,000
each; V53, 36,120; V55, 18,000; V56/57, 3,120
each.

**1898 (Feb. 25th?) No. V53 locally surcharged
in red in complete sheets. Intended for
Fiscal use only (see Note after No. V62), but
also used for postage.**

V58	1d. on 3/- **blk and sea-grn**	4·50	5·50
	a 'PNNEY' ..	£575	—
	b 'Y' omitted ..	£300	—
	c 'ONE' omitted	—	—
	d surcharge		
	double ..	£300	£275

V58a—Row 4/11.

V58b—This variety is often found with albino
print of the 'Y'.

V58c—A sheet is known on which 'ONE' is only
partially printed on the last stamps in Rows
1, 2 and 5, is completely omitted on Row 3/12
and is normal on Row 4/12.

**1898 Embossed (centre) and Type-set
(frame and inscription) at Blantyre. No wmk.
Sheets 15 x 2. No gum. Intended for local
postal use.**

**1st Setting—Vertical frame lines contin-
uous across the two rows, Type-set printing
in two operations.**

**2nd Setting–Vertical frame lines broken
between the two rows. Type-set printing in
one operation.**

(a) 1st Setting. Imperf. (March 11th).

(i) Manuscript initials 'JTG' or 'JG' in black on reverse.

V59	1d. **ver and grey-blue** ..	—	£220
a	without initials ..	£500	—
b	centre inverted ..	£2500	—

V59b—Only 15 copies exist, from the top row of one sheet; they are without initials on reverse.

The initials are those of J. T. Gosling, the acting P.M.G. Examples are known on which his signature appears in full.

Number printed—480.

(ii) Albino printed Control Numbers (1-30) and letter or letters on reverse.

V60	1d. **ver and grey-blue** ..	—	£30

Number printed—4,320.

(b) 2nd Setting (with albino Control Numbers and letters as No. V60).

(i) Imperf. (March 11th).

V61	1d. **ver and ult**	—	9·00
a	without Control No...	£325	£25
b	Control doubly printed ..	—	—
c	Control (13D) on face	—	£1600
d	centre omitted ..	£2250	—
e	centre doubly embossed	—	—

V61d comes from the top row of the sheet.

(ii) Perf. 12 (June).

V62	1d. **ver and ult**	£250	5·00
a	without Control No..	£300	£15
b	two different Control Nos.	—	£200
c	Control printed in black	—	—

Numbers printed—V61/62, 24,000.

The provisionals V58–V62 resulted from a continued shortage of 1d. stamps between March and November 1898. A Post Office Notice of April 1898 stated "The penny surcharged stamps" (No. V58) "should only be used for revenue purposes, the public being requested to pay in money for the postage on all packets liable only to a charge of one penny. In the case of internal correspondence, tokens" (Nos. V59/62) "should be affixed in accordance with a recent instruction".

Covers are frequently found with a manuscript endorsement "Postage Paid" during this period.

1903-04 Typo De La Rue. Wmk. Crown CA

(E1/5) or Crown CC (E6/10). Perf. 14. Sheets E1/5 120 – two panes, each 6 x 10: E6/10 12 x 5

E1	1d.	**grey and carmine** ..	1·00	30
E2	2d.	**dl and bt purple** ..	2·75	2·25
E3	4d.	**grey-grn and blk** ..	3·25	3·25
E4	6d.	**grey and buff**	3·25	3·25
E5	1/–	**grey-blk and blue** ..	3·25	4·50
E6	2/6	**grey-grn and grn** ..	£12	£12
E7	4/–	**dl and bt purple** ..	£20	£20
E8	10/–	**grey-grn and blk** ..	£38	£50
E9	£1	**grey and carmine** ..	£130	£120
E10	£10	**grey and blue** ..	£2750	£2250
E1/9		**set** (9v)	£200	£200
SPE1/9		**specimen set** (9v) ..	£140	‡
SPE10		**specimen** (1v) ..	£210	‡

Imperf Colour Trials of No. E6 exist on Crown CA paper.

1907 As before but Wmk. Multiple Crown CA. Chalky paper.

E11	1d.	**grey and carmine** ..	75	65
E12	6d.	**grey and buff**	£16	£18

1907 Prepared for use, but not issued (Multi-Crown CA. Chalky paper).

E13	2d.	**dl and bt purple** ..	£7000	—
E14	4d.	**grey-grn and blk** ..	£7000	—

1908 (July 22nd) Typo De La Rue. Wmk. Multiple Crown CA (except No. E20 – Crown CA). Perf. 14. Sheets as before. E15/16 Ordinary: remainder Chalky.

E15	½d.	**green**	20	40
E16	1d.	**carmine**	10	15
E17	3d.	**purple/yellow** ..	1·25	1·50
E18	4d.	**blk and red/yel** ..	1·25	2·00
E19	6d.	**dl and bt purple** ..	2·00	2·75
E20	1/–	**black/green** ..	1·50	2·00
E21	2/6	**blk and red/blue** ..	£12	£15
E22	4/–	**car and blk** ..	£15	£18
E23	10/–	**grn and red/grn** ..	£40	£60
E24	£1	**pur and blk/red** ..	£175	£190
E25	£10	**pur and ult** ..	£3800	—
E15/24		**set** (10v)	£225	£275
SPE15/24		**specimen set** (10v)	£150	‡
SPE25		**specimen** (1v) ..	£160	‡

1913 (June 1st)-18 As before but Head of King George V. Wmk. Multiple Crown CA. G1/11 Ordinary: remainder Chalky.

G1	½d.	**green**	40	30
G2	½d.	**yellow-green** ..	60	30
G3	½d.	**blue-green/bluish** ('18)	40	30
G4	1d.	**red**	60	30
G5	1d.	**rose-red**	60	30
G6	1d.	**scarlet** ('16) ..	40	30
G7	2d.	**pale grey**	2·00	40
G8	2d.	**grey** ('16)	1·00	40

G9	2d.	**slate**	2·00	40	
G10	2½d.	**bright blue**	60	65	
G11	2½d.	**dull blue**	1·00	65	
G12	3d.	**purple/yellow** ('14)	1·25	1·50	
		a on pale yellow ..	1·75	1·75	
G13	4d.	**blk and red/yel** ..	1·50	1·50	
		a on lemon	2·25	2·25	
G14	4d.	**blk and scar/lemon**	3·00	2·00	
		a on pale yellow ..	4·00	2·00	
G15	6d.	**pur and bt violet** ..	3·50	4·50	
G16	6d.	**purple and lilac** ..	1·50	1·50	
G17	1/-	**black/green** ..	2·75	2·25	
		a on emerald ..	1·50	1·50	
		b on blu-grn, olive back	1·50	2·00	
G18	2/6	**blk and red/blue** ('14?)	5·50	6·50	
G19	4/-	**car and blk** ('18) ..	6·50	7·00	
G20	10/-	**grn and red/grn** ('18)	£23	£30	
G21	10/-	**pl grn and red/grn**	£30	£30	
G22	£1	**pur and blk/red** ('18)	£50	£50	
G23	£10	**pur and ult** ('18) ..	£2250	£1200	
G1/22		**set** (12v)	£85	£90	
SPG1/22		**specimen set** (12v)	£125	‡	
SPG23		**specimen** (1v) ..	£130	‡	

Numbers issued—G22, 21,300.

G18/22 for Damaged Scroll (Row 1/12) and Broken Crown (Row 2/12) varieties see after G39. N.B.—G23 may also show these flaws.

G1/17 overprinted N.F. in black seriffed letters were used by the Nyasa—Rhodesian Force in 1916 during the occupation of German East Africa (later Tanganyika).

1921-30 As before but Wmk. Multiple Script CA. G24/30 Ordinary: remainder Chalky.

G24	½d.	**yellow-green** ..	30	15
G25	½d.	**blue-green**	40	15
G26	1d.	**carmine**	30	20
G27	1d.	**scarlet**	40	20
G28	1½d.	**orange** (14/9/25) ..	7·50	7·50
G29	2d.	**pale grey**	45	40
G30	2d.	**slate**	60	40
G31	3d.	**purple/pale yellow**	1·50	1·25
G32	4d.	**blk and red/yellow** (2/10/26) ..	1·00	1·25
G33	6d.	**dul and bt purple**..	1·50	1·75
G34	1/-	**blk/emerald** (6/30)	4·00	3·75
G35	2/-	**pur and blue/blue** (10/12/26) ..	7·50	8·50
G36	2/6	**blk and red/blue** ..	8·50	9·50
G37	4/-	**carmine and black** (2/12/27) ..	6·50	5·50
G38	5/-	**grn and red/yel** (6/29) ..	£20	£22
G39	10/-	**grn and red/grn** ..	£50	£50
G24/39		**set** (13v)	£100	£105
SPG24/39		**specimen set** (13v)	£80	‡

Numbers issued—G35, 270,900; G36, 223,560; G38, 60,420; G39, 45,840.

G18/22 and G35/39 The Damaged Scroll (Row 1/12) and Broken Crown (Row 2/12) flaws are known—for details see notes after BERMUDA G55.

G18A	Damaged Scroll	£60	—
G18B	Broken Crown	£100	—
G19A	Damaged Scroll	£60	—
G19B	Broken Crown	£100	£120
G20A	Damaged Scroll	£130	—
G20B	Broken Crown	£175	—
G21A	Damaged Scroll	£120	—
G21B	Broken Crown	£175	—
G22A	Damaged Scroll	£250	—
G22B	Broken Crown	£300	—
G35A	Damaged Scroll	£50	—
G35B	Broken Crown	£100	—
G36A	Damaged Scroll	£60	—
G36B	Broken Crown	£100	—
G37A	Damaged Scroll	£50	—
G37B	Broken Crown	£80	—
G38A	Damaged Scroll	£150	—
G38B	Broken Crown	£250	—
G39A	Damaged Scroll	£400	—
G39B	Broken Crown	£500	—

1934 (June)-35 Recess Waterlow & Sons. Wmk. Multiple Script CA. Perf. 12¼. Designer Major H. E. Green. Sheets 6 x 10.

G40	½d.	**green**..	25	20
G41	1d.	**brown**	35	25
G42	1½d.	**carmine**	60	60
G43	2d.	**pale grey**	50	45
G44	3d.	**blue**	85	80
G45	4d.	**magenta** (20/5/35)	1·50	1·50
G46	6d.	**violet**	1·25	1·25
G47	9d.	**ol-bistre** (20/5/35)	2·25	4·50
G48	1/-	**black and orange**	2·25	4·00
G40/48		**set** (9v)	9·00	£12
SPG40/48		**specimen set** (9v)..	£40	‡

1935 (May 6th) Silver Jubilee. Recess Waterlow & Sons. Wmk. Multiple Script CA. Perf. 11 x 12.

G49	1d.	**ult and grey** ..	30	30
G50	2d.	**green and indigo** ..	80	80
G51	3d.	**brown and blue** ..	2·25	2·75
G52	1/-	**slate and purple** ..	5·00	5·50
G49/52		**set** (4v)	8·00	9·00
SPG49/52		**specimen set** (4v)	£22	‡

Numbers issued—G49, 484,615; G50, 302,781; G51, 53,074; G52, 42,480.

Remainders were withdrawn on December 31st, 1935.

1938 (Jan. 1st) -45 (recess) Waterlow & Sons. Perf. 12½) (L). Sheets 6 x 10.

1	½d. **green**	.. .. ..	40	15
2	½d. **brown** (15/12/42)	..	15	10
3	1d. **brown**	.. ..	35	15
4	1d. **green** (15/12/42)	..	15	10
5	1¼d. **carmine**	.. ..	65	75
6	1½d. **grey** (15/12/42)	..	25	30
	a imperf between stamp			
	and margin	..	£150	—
7	2d. **grey**	.. .. ..	65	35
8	2d. **carmine** (15/12/42)	..	15	15
	a imperf. between stamp			
	and margin	..	£250	—
9	3d. **dp blue**	..	15	10
10	4d. **magenta**	.. ..	25	45
11	6d. **purple-violet**	..	25	35
12	9d. **sage-green**	.. ..	35	1·00
13	1/– **black and dp orange**		40	60
1/13	**set** (13)	.. ..	4·00	4·00

6*a*—Sheet No. 0608 was imperforate between right vertical row of 10 and margin.

8*a*—A sheet exists with lower row imperforate between stamp and margin. A strip of three exists; three other copies at present not traced.

Typo De La Rue. Perf. 14 x 13¾ (C). Wmk. Multiple Script CA (except No. 18 — Multiple Crown CA). Sheets 12 x 5.

14	2/– **pur and bright blue/ grey-blue** (*ch*)	..	1·00	1·50
	a worn plate, background			
	criss-cross lines	..	1·50	1·50
	b scroll flaw	.. ..	£30	—
15	2/6 **black and carmine/ grey-blue** (*ch*)	..	1·25	1·75
	a scroll flaw	.. ..	£40	—
16	5/– **green and red/yellow** (*ch*)	..	6·50	9·00
	a dp grn and car/pale yel (*sub*) (6/3/44)		£11	£14
	b scroll flaw	.. ..	£60	—
17	10/– **grn and red/grn** (*ch*)		5·50	6·00
	a blue-grn and red/grn (*sub*) (/45)	..	£10	8·00
	b scroll flaw	.. ..	£60	—

18	£1 **pur and blk/salmon red** (*ch*)	.. ..	9·00	£10
	a scroll flaw	.. ..	£75	—
14/18	**set** (5)	.. ..	£20	£25
SP 1/18	**specimen set** perf (14)	£120	‡

16*a* Besides being on thinner paper this stamp has a lined appearance particularly noticeable on the centre design.

17*a* There is a distinct gloss on the surface of this stamp.

18 Copies exist in a brighter shade than normal and somewhat resembling first printings of £1 of Bermuda and Leeward Is., but we were officially advised that there was only one printing.

14*b*–18*a* See Bermuda for details of Scroll flaw Type A which occurred on Row 5/12 of certain printings.

1945 (Sept. 1st) -52 Designs, ½d., 9d. (Lake Nyasa); 1d. (K.A.R. Soldier); 1d. (Leopard, Territory's Badge); 1½d., 6d. (Tea Estate); 2d., 1/–, 10/– (Map of Nyasaland, etc.); 3d., 2/– (Fishing Village); 4d., 2/6 (Tobacco Plantation); 5/–, 20/– (Portrait of King George VI and Badge of Protectorate. (Recess) Bradbury, Wilkinson. Perf 12 (L). Designs, 1d. (both), 2/- V. Sheets 10 x 6 or 6 x 10.

19	½d. **black and chocolate**	..	10	10
20	1d. **black and deep green** (soldier)	.. ..	10	10
21	1d. **cinnamon & emerald** (leopard) (20/10/47)	15	15
22	1½d. **black and greenish-slate**		10	10
23	2d. **black and red**	..	15	10
24	3d. **black and blue**	..	15	10
25	4d. **black and claret**	..	15	30
26	6d. **black and violet**	..	20	10
27	9d. **black and olive-green**		25	60
28	1/– **indigo and myrtle-grn**		30	15
29	2/– **green and lake-brown**		80	1·00
30	2/6 **dp grn and grey-blue**		1·00	1·25
31	5/– **mauve and slate**	..	3·00	2·00
	a purple and dp slate (7/2/52)	..	1·50	1·75
32	10/– **dp red-claret and grn**		4·00	4·50
33	£1 **scarlet and grey-black**		£10	£12
19/33	**set** (15)	.. ..	£17	£20

SPECIAL ISSUES

1937 (May 12th) Coronation. As Aden, but Printers, Bradbury, Wilkinson. Perf. 11 x 11¾ (C).

S1	½d. **green**	..	..	10	10
S2	1d. **dp brown**	..	..	10	10
S3	2d. **grey-black**	..	..	35	35
SP S1/3	**specimen set** perf (3)		£15	‡

1946 (Dec. 16th) Victory. As Aden.

S4	1d. **pale green**	..	..	10	10
S5	2d. **reddish-orange**	..	10	10
SP S4/5	**specimen set** perf (2)	£20	‡

1948 (Dec. 15th) Silver Wedding. As Aden.

| S6 | 1d. **green** | .. | .. | 10 | 10 |
| S7 | 10/– **dull purple** | .. | .. | 6·00 | 8·00 |

1949 (Oct. 10th) U.P.U. As Aden.

S8	1d. **green**	..	..	20	20
S9	3d. **dp greenish-blue**	..	35	35
S10	6d. **purple**	..	..	50	50
S11	1/– **dull indigo**	..	..	75	75
S8/11	**set** (4)	..	..	1·75	1·75

1951 (May 15th) Diamond Jubilee. Design,

Arms of Territory and Original Arms of B.C.A. (Recess) Bradbury, Wilkinson. Perf. 11 x 11¾ (C).

S12	2d. **black and scar**	..	20	20
S13	3d. **black and grey-blue**	20	30
S14	6d. **black and violet**	..	35	55
S15	5/– **black and blue-slate**	2·75	3·25
S12/15	**set** (4)	..	..	3·25	4·00

Number issued—2d., 546,591; 3d. 108,211; 6d., 128,140; 5/–, 58,737.

Withdrawn August 14th, 1951.

POSTAGE DUE STAMPS

1950 (July 1st) (typo) De La Rue. Perf. 13¾ x 14 (C)

PD1	1d. **scarlet**	..	..	20	40
PD2	2d. **ultramarine**	..	40	80
PD3	3d. **green**	..	..	60	1·25
PD4	4d. **lake** ..	..	..	85	1·75
PD5	6d. **orange**	..	..	1·25	2·75
PD1/5	**set** (5)	..	..	3·00	6·00

PAKISTAN

All stamps without wmk. except overprinted issues of India.

1947 (Oct. 1st) Stamps of India (Nos. 20—32 and 13—19) overprinted PAKISTAN at Nasik.

1	3p.	slate	5	5
2	½a.	purple	5	5
3	9p.	green	5	5
4	1a.	rose-carmine	5	5
5	1½a.	slate-purple (typo)	5	5
6	2a.	vermilion	5	5
7	3a.	bright violet	5	5
8	3½a.	blue (typo)	10	20
9	4a.	brown	5	5
10	6a.	greenish-blue	15	10
11	8a.	violet-slate	15	5
12	12a.	dp crimson	25	10
13	14a.	purple	30	25
14	1r.	vio-grey and lt brown	30	20
15	2r.	vio-purple and brown	55	35
16	5r.	dp green and dp blue	1·00	55
17	10r.	vio-pur and red-claret	2·25	1·25
18	15r.	chocolate and dp grn	4·50	4·50
19	25r.	slate-vio and pur-vio	7·50	7·00
1/19		set (19)	£16	£14

1948 As before but overprinted at Karachi.

20	1a.3p.	bistre	60	75

Overprinting as on Nos. 1—19 was also officially done in the Government Printing Presses at Peshawar (less 14a. and Rs15) and at Karachi (less 14a.) from plates made in Lahore and, later, at Karachi.

The 1a.3p. value was additionally printed at Karachi; whilst, at Peshawar, the K.G. V 1a.3p., Rs15 and Rs25 were also overprinted.

Overprints of different type were also made at Dacca (Typeset 3p. to 8a.) and at Peshawar (Handstamp 2a.) under Provincial Government authority.

Innumerable varieties of metal and rubber handstamped, typed and MS overprints are also known on both Ordinary and Service stamps of KE VII, KG V and KG VI.

The strips of 1r. (No. 14) with and without overprint come from typo overprints made locally.

1948 (Aug. 14th) Designs, 3p., 6p., 9p. (Scales of Justice); 1a., 1½a., 2a. (Star and Moon to right); 2½a., 3½a., 4a. (Lloyd Barrage); 3a., 10a. (Karachi Airport); 6a., 8a., 12a. (Karachi Port Trust); 1r., 2r., 5r. (Salimulla Hostel, Dacca University); 10r., 15r., 25r. (Khyber Pass). Printers (recess) De La Rue, Rangoon. Designs, 3a., 10a., 1r., 2r., 5r. H. Sheets 21/25 160—two panes each 10 x 8; other Anna values (except 3a., 10a.) 10 x 8; 28, 33, 35-37, 5 x 16; 38-40, 10 x 6.

21	3p.	ver-red (12¼ x 12½ (C))	5	5
		a imperf (pair)	—	—
22	6p.	pur-vio (12¼ x 12½ (C))	5	5
23	9p.	myr-grn (12¼ x 12½ (C))	5	5
		a imperf (pair)	—	—
24	1a.	dk blue (12¼ x 12½ (C))	5	5
25	1½a.	dull myr (12¼ x 12½ (C))	5	5
26	2a.	ver-red (12¼ x 12½ (C))	5	5
27	2½a.	green (14 x 13½ (C))	5	5
28	3a.	green (13¾ x 14 (C))	5	5
		a imperf (pair)	—	—
29	3½a.	ult (14 x 13½ (C))	15	10
30	4a.	red-brn (12¼ x 12½ (C))	15	10
31	6a.	dp blue (14 x 13½ (C))	10	5
32	8a.	dk grey (12¼ x 12½ (C))	10	5
33	10a.	car-red (13¾ x 14 (C))	15	10
34	12a.	red (14 x 13½ (C))	15	10
35	1r.	bt ult (13¾ x 14 (C))	25	10
36	2r.	choc-brn (13¾ x 14 (C))	50	15
37	5r.	rose-crim (13¾ x 14 (C))	1·50	25
38	10r.	magenta (14 x 13¾ (C))	2·75	2·50
39	15r.	blue-grn (14 x 13¾ (C))	2·75	90
40	25r.	pur-vio (14 x 13¾ (C))	5·00	5·00
21/40		set (20)	£12	8·00

Perf. 11¾ (C).

41	10r.	magenta	4·50	80
42	15r.	blue-green	2·75	1·00
43	25r.	purple-violet	6·00	2·50

1949 As before but design altered (moon turned from right to left) to a waxing moon (3a. and 10a. centres re-drawn). Sheets as before.

44	1a.	dark blue	10	5
45	1½a.	dull myrtle	10	5
46	2a.	vermilion-red	10	5
47	3a.	green	15	10
48	6a.	dp blue	30	10
49	8a.	dark grey	30	10
50	10a.	carmine-red	30	25
51	12a.	red	40	25
44/51		set (8)	1·50	75

1951-7 Design, Khyber Pass. Printers (recess) Security Printing Cor., Karachi. Plates engraved by De La Rue. Perf. 13¼ x 13 (C).

52	10r.	magenta (/51)	4·50	90
53	15r.	blue-green (27/7/57)	4·50	5·00
54	25r.	purple-vio (1/11/54)	7·00	3·50

1952-4 Designs, 3p., 6p., 9p. (Scales of Justice); 1a., 1½a., 2a. (Star and Crescent); 1r., 2r., 5r. (Salimullah Hostel, Dacca University). Printers (recess) Security Printing Cor., Karachi. Plates engraved by De La Rue. Perf. 13¼ (C). Designs, 1r., 2r., 5r. Hor. Sheets as before.

55	3p.	vermilion-red (5/54) .	5	5
56	6p.	purple-violet (/54) ..	5	5
57	9p.	myrtle-green (/54) ..	10	5
58	1a.	dk blue (/52)	10	10
59	1½a.	dull myrtle (/53)	10	10
		a printed gummed side	£10	—
60	2a.	vermilion-red (/52) ..	10	10
61	1r.	ultramarine (/54) ..	65	35
62	2r.	choc brown (5/54) ..	1·25	55
63	5r.	rose-carmine (5/54) .	1·50	25
55/63		set (9)	3·50	1·50

SPECIAL ISSUES

1948 (July 9th) Independence. Designs, 1½a., (Constituent Assembly Building, Karachi); 2½a. (Karachi Airport Entrance); 3a. (Lahore Fort Gateway); 1r. (Crescent and Stars). All designs incorporating date 15 Aug., 1947. Designer, Ab. R. Chughtai. Printers (recess) De La Rue. Perf. 11¾ (C) (1r.) and Perf. 13¾ x 14 (C) Other Values. Design, 1r. V. Sheets—S1/3, 5 x 16; S4, 10 x 6.

S1	1½a.	dp ultramarine ..	5	5

S2	2½a.	green	5	5
S3	3a.	chocolate-brown ..	5	5
S4	1r.	dp scarlet	20	15
S1/4		set (4)	30	30

1948 (?) As No. S4 but Perf. 14 x 13¾ (C).

S4A	1r.	dp scarlet	2·50	2·50

1949 (Sept. 11th) 1st Anniversary Death of M. A. Jinnah. Design, Inscription in Arabic (1½a. and 3a.) and in English (10a.).Printers (recess) De La Rue. Perf. 13¾ x 14 (C). Sheets 5 x 16.

S5	1½a.	brown	25	20
S6	3a.	green	25	20
S7	10a.	black	1·00	85
S5/7		set (3)	1·40	1·00

Number issued—S5/6, 2,000,000 each; S7, 1,500,000.

1951 (Aug. 14th) 4th Ann. Pakistan Independence. Designs, 2½a. and 3½a. (Vase and Plate); 3a. and 12a. (Aeroplane and Hour-glass); 4a. and 6a. (Leaf Pattern in Saracenic style); 8a. and 10a. (Muslim Arch and Lamp). Designer, K. B. Abdur Rahman Chughtai. Printers (recess) De La Rue. Perf. 13 x 13¼ (C). Designs, 3a., 4a., 6a., 12a. V. Sheets 8 x 10.

S8	2½a.	red	5	5
S9	3a.	dp red	5	5
S10	3½a.	blue	15	15
S11	4a.	olive-green	10	5
S12	6a.	brown	10	5
S13	8a.	dp brown	15	5
S14	10a.	purple	15	10
S15	12a.	dp green-blue	20	10
S8/15		set (8)	90	50

OFFICIAL STAMPS

1947 (Oct. 1st) Official Stamps of India (No. O9, etc.) overprinted PAKISTAN at Nasik.

O1	3p.	slate	5	5
O2	½a.	dp purple	5	5
O3	9p.	green	5	5

O4	1a. rose-carmine	5	5	O19	2a. vermilion-red	5	5
O5	1½a. slate-purple	5	5	O20	3a. green	5	5
O6	2a. vermilion	5	5	O21	4a. red-brown	5	5
O7	2½a. purple-violet	5	5	O22	8a. dark grey (red)	15	5
O8	4a. dp brown	10	10	O23	1r. bt ultramarine	20	10
O9	8a. violet-slate	15	15	O24	2r. chocolate-brown	35	20
O10	1r. violet-grey and lt brn	20	15	O25	5r. rose-carmine	80	45
O11	2r. violet-purple and brn	40	35	O26	10r. mag (perf. 14 x 13¾ C)	2·00	1·25
O12	5r. dp grn and deep blue	1·25	1·00	O27	10r. mag (perf. 11¾ C)	2·75	1·50
O13	10r. vio-pur & red-claret	2·50	2·25	O14/26	set (13)	3·75	2·00
O1/13	set (13)	4·50	4·00				

1948 No. O14 of India overprinted PAKISTAN at Karachi.

O13a	1a.3p. bistre	1·25	1·50

Overprinting as on Nos. O1—O13 and, additionally on the 1a.3p. was also done in the Government Printing Press at Karachi.

Typeset overprints of different type were also made in the Government Printing Presses at Peshawar (including KG V 2½a., 12a., Rs2), Lahore (including KG V 1a.) and at Dacca.

See also under No. 20 for details of handstamped, typed and MS overprints.

1948 (Aug. 14th) No. 21, etc., overprinted SERVICE in black or red.

O14	3p. vermilion-red	5	5
O15	6p. purple-violet (red)	5	5
O16	9p. myrtle-green (red)	5	5
O17	1a. dar blue (red)	5	5
O18	1½a. dull myrtle (red)	5	5

1949 No. 44, etc., overprinted SERVICE in black or red.

O28	1a. dark blue (red)	5	5
O29	1½a. dull myrtle (red)	5	5
	a o'print inverted	—	£20
O30	2a. vermilion-red	5	5
O31	3a. yellow-green	5	5
O32	8a. dark grey (red)	15	10
O28/32	set (5)	25	20

Considerable care has to be exercised in buying copies of O29a. An Expert Committee certificate is advisable.

1951 (Aug. 14th) Stamps similar in design, etc., to Nos. S9, S11 and S13, but the word SERVICE substituted for PAKISTAN POSTAGE.

O33	3a. dp red	5	16
O34	4a. olive-green	10	10
O35	8a. dp brown	15	10
O33/35	set (3)	20	20

BAHAWALPUR

One of the Princely States within the Empire of India. Bahawalpur's Muslim Ruler acceded to Pakistan on October 3rd 1947. Since 1950 the stamps of Pakistan have been used exclusively within the former State.

Unless otherwise indicated all stamps are Recess. De La Rue on Multiple Star and Crescent wmk.

1933 (Feb. 3rd) Centenary of Alliance with Britain. No Wmk. Perf. 14.

1	1a. **black/green**	..	£30	£60

Die Proofs exist in black on thin paper (Price £120).

1947 (Aug.) Bahawalpur's independence from India (prior to accession to Pakistan). Stamps of India (CW 20–23, 25–32, 13–17 Wmk. Multiple Star) with the name "India" blocked out, and overprinted with a Star and Crescent and Persian one-line inscription ("The God-given Kingdom of Bahawalpur"). In red on Nos. 2, 4, 6, 8, 9, 11, 12, 16 and 17; remainder in black.

2	3p. **slate**	.. ..	—	—
3	½a. **purple**	.. ..	—	—
4	9p. **green**	.. ..	—	—
5	1a. **carmine**	.. ..	—	—
6	1½a. **dull violet**	..	—	—
7	2a. **vermilion**	..	—	—
	a overprint double		£50	—
8	3a. **bright violet**		—	—
9	3½a. **blue**	.. ..	—	—
10	4a. **brown**	..	—	—
11	6a. **greenish blue**	..	—	—
	a overprint double		£50	—
12	8a. **slate-violet**	..	—	—
13	12a. **lake**	..	—	—
14	14a. **purple**	.. ..	£40	—
15	R1 **grey and red-brn**		—	—
16	Rs2 **purple and brown**		—	—
17	Rs5 **green and blue** ..		—	—
18	Rs10 **purple and claret**		—	—
2/18	**set** (17v)		£300	—
2/13	**set** (12v) less 14a		£20	—

Number Issued – 2–14 240 each; 15–18 60 each.

This issue had a life of little over one month, and was withdrawn on October 3rd.

1974 (Dec. 1st) Bi-centenary of Abassi Dynasty. Wmk. sideways. Perf. 12½ x 11½. Sheets 5 x 10.

19	½a. **black and car.** ..	10	15

Number Issued – 500,000.

1948 (April 1st) Various Palaces and Portraits. Wmk. sideways on vertical designs. Perf. 12½ (Nos. 20–24) : 12½ x 11½ or 11½ x 12½ (Nos. 25–35) : 13½ x 14 (36/37). Sheets 5 x 10 or 10 x 5 (except 36/37 – 4 x 10).

20	3p. black and blue	5	10
21	¾a. black and claret	5	10
22	9p. black and green	5	10
23	1a. black and car	5	10
24	1¼a. black and violet	5	10
25	2a. green and car	5	10
26	4a. orange and brown	10	15
27	6a. violet and blue	10	15
28	8a. carmine and vio	10	15
29	12a. green and car	15	20
30	R1 violet and brown	20	30
31	R1 green and orange	15	25
32	Rs2 green and claret	35	50
33	Rs2 black and car	20	30
34	Rs5 black and violet	1·00	1·50
35	Rs5 choc and ultra	40	60
36	Rs10 scarlet and black	1·50	2·25
37	Rs10 brown and green	60	90
20/37	set (18v)	5·00	7·00

1948 (Oct. 3rd) First Anniversary of Union with Pakistan. Perf. 13. Sheets 5 x 10.
38   1¼a. carmine and grn   5   10
Number Issued – 500,000.

1948 (Oct. 15th) Centenary of Multan

Campaign (Sikh War). Perf. 11½. Sheets 10 x 5.
39   1½a. black and lake   10   15
Number Issued – 500,000.

1949 (Mar. 3rd) Silver Jubilee of Accession of H. H. The Amir. Various designs. Perf. 14. Sheets 5 x 10.

40	3p. black and ultra	5	10
	a imperf. (pair)	£20	—
41	¾a. black and orange	5	10
	a imperf. (pair)	£20	—
42	9p. black and green	5	10
	a imperf. (pair)	£20	—
43	1a. black and car	5	10
	a imperf. (pair	£20	—
40/33	set (4V.)	20	40
40a/43a	set imperf. (pairs) (4v)	£75	—

Number Issued – 500,000 each.

1949 (Oct. 10th) 75th Anniversary of U.P.U. Sheets 5 x 10.

(a) Perf. 13.
44	9p. black and green	5	10
	a imperf. (pair)	7·00	£10
45	1a. blk. and magenta	5	10
	a imperf. (pair)	7·00	£10
46	1½a. black and orange	5	10
	a imperf. (pair)	7·00	£10
47	2½a. black and blue	5	10
	a imperf. (pair)	7·00	£10
44/47	set (4V.)	20	40

(b) Perf. 17½ x 17.
48	9p. black and green	10	20
49	1a. blk and magenta	10	20
50	1½a. black and orange	10	20
51	2½a. black and blue	10	20
48/51	set (4v.)	40	80

OFFICIAL STAMPS

1933 (Feb. 3rd) No. 1 overprinted with one line Persian inscription "SARKARI" ('GOVERNMENT' or 'OFFICIAL') in black.
O1   1a. black/green   £35   —

1945 (Jan. 1st) Revenue stamps (various designs) converted for official postal use by means of a similar overprint in red. Perf. 14. Sheets 10 x 10.

O2	½a.	black and green	15	30
O3	1a.	black and carmine	25	50
O4	2a.	black and violet	25	50
	a	overprint "SAR-KARK" ..	£15	£25
O5	4a.	black and olive ..	30	60
O6	8a.	black and brown	35	70
	a	overprint "SAR-KARK" ..	£15	£15
O7	R1	black and orange	50	1·00
O2/7		set (6v)	1·75	3·50

O4a/O6a : The left up-stroke of the left hand Persian letter is missing on Row 6/3 giving the letter the shape of the Persian "K".

Numbers issued—90,000 each.

1945 (Mar. 10th) No. O3 re-drawn and similarly overprinted in red. No Wmk.

O8	1a.	black and brown	£15	£18

Nos. O2–O8 are known without the overprint, in which state they are purely Revenue stamps.

1945 (March) Nos. O6 (in changed colours), O7 and previously unoverprinted Rs2 Revenue stamp (in design of No. O2). Similarly overprinted and surcharged in Persian with Hijra date "1363" in black. No Wmk.

O9	½a. on 8a.	blk and purple	80	60
O10	1½a. on R1	blk and orange	1·75	1·50
O11	1½a. on Rs2	black and blue	2·50	2·25
O9/11		set (3v) ..	5·00	5·00

No. O9 is known without overprint and surcharge (see Note after O8).

1945 Nos. O2 and O4 (in changed colours) and O3 overprinted "SERVICE" in English and Persian (both reading upwards) in black. No Wmk.

O12	½a.	black and car ..	15	15
O13	1a.	black and car ..	25	30
O14	2a.	black and orange ..	30	35
	a	"SERVICE" omitted	£250	—
O12/14		set (3v)	70	70

O14a was caused by a paper fold, part of the overprint appearing on the reverse.

1945 No Wmk. Perf. 14. Sheets 10 x 10.

O15	3p.	black and blue ..	5	5
O16	1½a.	black and violet ..	10	10

1946 (May) Victory. Designer F. Meronti. Background Litho. No Wmk. Perf. 14. Sheets 5 x 10.

O17	1½a.	green and grey ..	25	30

Number Issued—100,000.

1948 Nos. 20, 23, 25, 26, 31, 33, 35, and 37 overprinted as Nos. O2/7 in red (O18, O22–25) or black (O19–21).

O18	3p.	black and blue ..	5	—
O19	1a.	black and carmine	5	—
O20	2a.	green and car ..	5	—
O21	4a.	orange and brown	5	—
O22	R1	green and orange	10	—
O23	Rs2	black and car ..	15	—
O24	Rs5	choc and ultra ..	25	—
O25	Rs10	brown and green	50	—
O18/25		set (8v)	1·00	—

1949 (Oct. 10th) 75th Anniversary of U.P.U. Nos. 44/51 similarly overprinted in red.

(a) Perf. 13.

O26	9p.	black and green ..	5	—
	a	imperf. (pair) ..	£10	£10
O27	1a.	blk and magenta ..	5	—
	a	imperf. (pair) ..	£10	£10
O28	1½a.	black and orange	5	—
	a	imperf. (pair) ..	£10	£10
O29	2½a.	black and blue	5	—
	a	imperf. (pair) ..	£10	£10
O26/29		set (4v) ..	20	—

(b) Perf. 17½ x 17.

O30	9p.	black and green ..	10	—
O31	1a.	blk and magenta ..	10	—
O32	1½a.	black and orange..	10	—
O33	2½a.	black and blue ..	10	—
O30/33		set (4v)	40	—

PAPUA

The territory was proclaimed a British Protectorate on November 6th, 1884, and became a British possession on September 4th 1888 under the name of BRITISH NEW GUINEA. The name was changed to Papua on September 1st 1906 when the territory came under Australian Federal control.

From August 1885 the stamps of Queensland were in use and were generally cancelled "N.G." (from 1888, "B.N.G.") in transverse ovals of horizontal bars.

Much of the territory was over-run by the Japanese in the Second World War and Civil Administration was suspended in 1942. Following the Japanese defeat in 1945, Australian stamps without overprint were used until the combined issue for Papua and New Guinea appeared in October 1952.

See also NEW GUINEA.

1901 (July 1st)-05 Recess De La Rue. Wmk. Multiple Rosettes. Perf. 14. Sheets 5 x 6. Centres in black.

I. Wmk. Horizontal.

(a) Thick paper.

E1	½d.	yellow-green	..	2·75	3·75
E2	1d.	carmine	..	1·75	2·75
E3	2d.	violet ..	..	3·25	3·25
E4	2½d.	ultramarine ..	..	5·50	5·70
E5	4d.	sepia ..	..	£12	£12
		a thin 'd'	..	£50	£50
E6	6d.	myrtle-green	..	£10	£12
E7	1/–	orange	..	£25	£28
E8	2/6	brown ('05) ..	..	£275	£250

(b) Thin paper.

E9	½d.	yellow-green	..	£40	£40
E10	2½d.	ultramarine ..	..	£48	£42
E11	2½d.	dull blue	..	£48	£42

II. Wmk. Vertical.

(a) Thick paper.

E12	½d.	yellow-green	..	1·75	2·00
E13	1d.	carmine	..	1·75	2·00
E14	2d.	violet ..	..	1·75	2·00
E15	2½d.	ultramarine ..	..	5·00	7·50
E16	4d.	sepia ..	..	£16	£19
		a thin 'd'	..	£60	£65
E17	6d.	myrtle-green	..	£20	£24
E18	1/–	orange	..	£20	£28
E19	2/6	brown ('05) ..	..	£350	£375

(b) Thin paper.

E20	½d.	yellow-green	..	4·00	5·00
E21	1d.	carmine	..	£17	£17

E22	2d.	violet ..	..	£14	8·00
E23	2½d.	ultramarine ..	..	£55	£50
E24	2½d.	dull blue	..	£55	£50
E25	4d.	sepia ..	..	£32	£37
		a thin 'd'	..	£90	£100
E26	6d.	myrtle-green	..	£100	£110
E27	1/–	orange	..	£100	£110
E28	2/6	brown ('05) ..	..	£250	£250
E1/28		set (8v)	..	£135	£150

E5a/16a/25a—The stem of 'd' in the left value tablet is thin: Row 4/3.

The 4d. value is known bisected vertically for use as 2d., and cancelled "B.N.G." at Kulamadau (Woodlarks) on September 20th, 1901.

Although a common Frame Plate was used, with inserted plugs for the different values, certain constant varieties occur only on the following :—

White Leaves above lower right value tablet: Row 4/5; ½d., 2d. (late printing only), 2½d.

White Leaves to right of lower left value tablet: Row 6/2; 2d. (very faint shading), 2½d. Row 6/3; ½d., 1/– (very faint shading on late printings).

E2 exists overprinted "CANCELLED".

Die Proofs of the Vignette and of the Frame (without value) exist in black on white card. Proofs of the issued stamp (without value) are known on unwatermarked paper with the vignette in black and the frame in various colours.

Colour Trials of the ½d. are known with frames in olive, dull blue, yellow, brown and black.

Numbers issued—2/6 (E8/19/28), 2,234.

1906 (Nov. 8th) Nos. E5/E22 overprinted in black by the Government Printer at Port Moresby. Setting 5 x 6.

I. Wmk. Horizontal (Thick paper).

E29	4d.	sepia ..	..	£75	£75
		a thin 'd'	..	£200	£200
E30	6d.	myrtle-green	..	£10	£12
E31	1/—	orange	..	8·00	£10
		a thick 'p'	..	£35	£40
E32	2/6	brown ..	..	£48	£50

II. Wmk. Vertical.

(a) Thin paper.

E33	½d.	yellow-green	..	3·00	4·00
		a thick 'p'	..	£18	£25

E34	1d.	**carmine**			4·50	4·00
E35	2d.	**violet**			2·50	2·75
		a thick 'p'			£12	£15

(b) Thick paper.

E36	2½d.	**ultramarine**		3·00	5·50
E37	4d.	**sepia**		£65	£65
		a thin 'd'		£175	£175
E38	6d.	**myrtle-green**		£10	£12
E39	1/–	**orange**		£85	£85
		a thick 'p'		£225	£225
E40	2/6	**brown**		£475	£550
E29/40		**set** (8v)		£140	£150

E29*a*/37*a*—See Note after No. E5*a* (Row 4/3).

E31*a*/33*a*/35*a*/39*a*—The vertical stroke of 'p' in 'Papua' is thickened: Row 1/4.

On all values a dot appears within the loop of 'p' in 'Papua': Row 2/3.

The 'White Leaf' varieties detailed after Nos. E1/28 are also found on this issue.

A Proof of the overprint is known in black on white card.

An Essay overprint 'PAPUA' is recorded (5 copies); and a single copy is known with both overprints ('PAPUA': 'Papua').

Numbers overprinted—E33, 11,040; E34, 12,960; E35, 29,610; E36, 12,000; E29/E37, 2,970; E30/E38, 6,300; E31/E39, 5,970; E32/E40, 2,730.

1907 (May) Nos. E1/E28 similarly overprinted in Brisbane. Setting 5 x 6.

I. Wmk. Horizontal.

(a) Thick paper.

E41	½d.	**yellow-green**		£12	£20
E42	2½d.	**dull blue**		£25	£28
E43	1/–	**orange**		£23	£29
E44	2/6	**brown**		£16	£20
		a overprint double		—	£300
		b overprint triple		—	£300
		c overprint vertical (downwards)		£300	—
		d overprint double (vertical)		£700	—

E44*b*—All three overprints are very close together, two being very faint.

E44*c* (12 copies) and E44*d* (3 copies) both come from the same sheet found in July 1908; the remaining 15 copies show parts of one or two overprints.

(b) Thin paper.

E45	½d.	**yellow-green**		£28	£28
E46	2½d.	**ultramarine**		6·00	£10
		a overprint double		—	—
E47	2½d.	**dull blue**		£24	£28
		a overprint double		—	—

II. Wmk. Vertical.

(a) Thick paper.

E48	2½d.	**ultramarine**		3·00	3·50
		a overprint double		—	—
E49	1/–	**orange**		£20	£22
E50	2/6	**brown**		£475	£600

(b) Thin paper.

E51	½d.	**yellow-green**		1·75	2·25
		a overprint double		£450	—
E52	1d.	**carmine**		2·00	2·50
		a overprint vertical (upwards) in par.		£200	£200
E53	2d.	**violet**		1·50	1·00
E54	2½d.	**ultramarine**		—	—
E55	4d.	**sepia**		£11	£13
		a thin 'd'		£45	£50
E56	6d.	**myrtle-green**		£10	£12
		a overprint double		£500	£500
E57	1/–	**orange**		£13	£14
		a overprint double		—	—
E58	2/6	**brown**		£11	£14
E41/58		**set** (8v)		£50	£60

E51*a*—The two overprints are almost coincidental.

E54—Only one copy is known.

E55*a*—See Note after No. E5*a* (Row 4/3).

E56*a*—The two overprints are well spaced, the first having been positioned too high.

Two constant varieties occur on all values— Broken 'p' in 'Papua': the lower left serif is missing from the vertical stroke – Rows 2/5, 4/1 and 5/1. (This variety is sometimes wrongly known as 'Inverted "d" ').

'Pa' raised in relation to 'pua'. Row 4/2.

The 'White Leaf' varieties detailed after Nos. E1/28 are also found on this issue.

A proof of the overprint setting is known on transparent paper.

Stamps from Rows 1/4 and 4/1 of all values are usually found with pin-holes through the white star ornament in the lower frame. These probably originated from the method employed to secure the sheets in position for overprinting.

Numbers overprinted—E41/E45/E51, 18,150; E52, 35,100; E53, 40,560; E42/E46/E47/E48/E54, 13,230; E55, 5,135; E56, 5,255; E43/E49/E57, 7,625; E44/E50/E58, 10,696.

Small PAPUA

Large PAPUA

1907-10 Litho, Commonwealth Stamp Printing Office Melbourne (J. B. Cooke), from transfers from the De La Rue recess plates. The new name was substituted by means of transfers from five engravings showing minor variations. Wmk. Crown over A (of Victoria). Sheets 5 x 6. Centres in black.

I. Small PAPUA.

(a) Wmk. Upright or Inverted.

(i) Perf. 11 (1907-08).

E59	1d.	**rose** (6/08)	1·40	1·75
E60	2d.	**purple** (10/08) ..	1·75	2·00
E61	2½d.	**bt ult** (7/08) ..	5·00	9·00
E62	2½d.	**pale ultramarine** ..	1·75	2·75
E63	4d.	**sepia** (20/11/07) ..	1·75	2·00
		a thin 'd'	£10	£12
E64	6d.	**myrtle-grn** (4/08) ..	4·50	6·00
E65	1/–	**orange** (10/08) ..	4·50	6·00
E59/65		**set** (6v)	£15	£18

E65 is known cancelled to order and with 'Specimen' overprint in black italics vertically upwards at left. This is believed to have been applied by an unknown Postal Administration on receipt of copies from the U.P.U.

E90 was also overprinted is similar circumstances.

(ii) Perf. 12½ (1907-09).

E66	2d.	**purple** (10/08) ..	2·00	2·00
E67	2½d.	**bt ult** (7/08)	7·50	£15
		a wmk. sideways ..	£16	£19
E68	2½d.	**pl ultramarine** ..	5·00	£10
E69	4d.	**sepia** (11/07) ..	3·00	3·00
		a thin 'd'	£15	£15
E70	1/–	**orange** (1/09) ..	£18	£23
E66/70		**set** (4v)	£25	£35

E67*a* was an error, and should not be confused with No. E83.

(b) Wmk. sideways (to left or right).

(i) Perf. 11 (1909-10).

E71	½d.	**yellow-grn** (12/09)	1·50	2·00
		a thick 'd'	6·00	8·00
E72	½d.	**deep green** ('10) ..	£12	£15
		a thick 'd'	£48	£50
E73	1d.	**carmine** (1/10) ..	4·25	4·00
E74	2d.	**purple** (2/10) ..	2·00	1·50
E75	2½d.	**dull blue** (1/10) ..	2·00	2·50
		a imperf between stamp and margin	—	—
E76	4d.	**sepia** (1/10)	2·25	2·75
		a thin 'd'	£12	£15
E77	6d.	**myrtle-grn** (12/09)	6·00	4·00
E78	1/–	**orange** (3/10) ..	£13	£16
E71/78		**set** (7v)	£30	£30

(ii) Perf. 12½ (1909-10).

E79	½d.	**yel-grn** (12/09) ..	75	1·25
		a thick 'd'	5·00	8·00
E80	½d.	**deep green** ('10) ..	£13	£15
		a thick 'd'	£50	£60

E81	1d.	**carmine** (12/09) ..	3·00	2·00
E82	2d.	**purple** (1/10) ..	1·50	1·25
E83	2½d.	**dull blue** (1/10) ..	4·00	5·00
E84	6d.	**myrtle-grn** (12/09)	£450	£425
E85	1/–	**orange** (3/10) ..	6·00	8·00

(iii) Perf. 11 x 12½.

E86	½d.	**yellow-green** ..	—	—
E87	2d.	**purple**	£250	—
E88	4d.	**sepia**	—	—
		a thin 'd'	—	—

E63*a*/69*a*/76*a*/88*a*—See Note after No. E5*a*. (Row 4/3)

E71*a*/72*a*/79*a*/80*a*—The 'd' in the right value tablet is thick: Row 5/1.

E75*a*—Although listed here it is believed that only one sheet existed with 'OS' puncture. (See No. EO 18*a*.)

E86 also exists perf. 12½ at right and perf. 11 on the other three sides.

E87 also exists perf. 12½ at left and perf. 11 on the other three sides and perf. 11 at bottom and perf. 12½ on the other three sides.

E88 also exists perf. 11, with additional perf. 12½ at top.

There are many constant varieties in the Vignette which appear on all values, the best known being the 'Rift in Clouds', (Row 5/3).

The 'White Leaf' varieties detailed after Nos. E1/28 are also found on this issue.

Numbers sold—E84, 60 copies (2 sheets); the major part of this printing was punctured 'OS'. (See No. EO27).

II. Large PAPUA. Perf. 11.

(a) Wmk. Upright or Inverted.

E89	½d.	**yel-grn** (6/11/07) ..	75	1·25

(b) Wmk. Sideways (to left or right).

E90	2/6	**chocolate** (12/09) ..	£16	£20

The 'White Leaf' varieties also occur on both values of this issue—Above lower right value tablet: Row 4/5; To right of lower left value tablet: Row 6/3.

E90—See Notes after Nos. E65 and E100.

Number printed—E90, 4,080.

Type I   Type II

III. Large PAPUA (New Plates from fresh transfers from the De La Rue recess plates: with PAPUA incorporated by transfers from five engravings showing minor variations). Wmk. Upright or Inverted. Perf. 12½. (1910).

E91	½d.	**dull green** (Dec.)	1·25	1·25
E92	½d.	**dull yellow-green**	1·25	1·25
E93	1d.	**carmine** (Sept.)	1·75	1·25
E94	2d.	**dl purple** (Nov.)	1·75	1·75
	a	'PCSTAGE'	£20	£23
E95	2½d.	**violet-blue** (Oct.)	2·50	3·50
E96	4d.	**sepia** (Oct.)	1·75	3·50
	a	thin 'd'	8·00	£12
E97	6d.	**myrtle-grn** (Sept.)	3·00	3·50
E98	1/–	**dp orange** (Nov.)	6·00	7·50
E99	2/6	**brn** (Type I) (Sept.)	£15	£20
E100	2/6	**brn** (Type II) (Sept.)	£15	£20
E91/100		**set** (8v)	£30	£40

E94*a*—Right hand label. Row 4/3.

E96*a*—See Note after No. E5*a*. (Row 4/3).

E94 is recorded with wmk. sideways.

E99 comes from a Frame Plate on which the value figures were transferred from three drawings each showing minor differences, but with a common thick diagonal stroke. (No. E90 also has this thick stroke, but the value figures differ from those on No. E99).

E100 comes from printings from a Frame Plate derived from transfers taken direct from the De La Rue recess plate (2/6 value); the diagonal stroke is thin.

E99/100 were printed from the same Vignette Plate, whereas No. E90 vignette shows a much darker impression and the edges of the sky are not graduated.

E90 also differs from E99/100 in wmk. and perf.

Numbers printed—E91/92, 20,040; E93, 39,990 (including a large number overprinted 'Stamp Duty'); E94, 39,870; E95, 15,060; E96, 24,840; E97, 20,010; E98, 19,950; E99/100, 40,000.

1911 (Feb. 6th)-16 Typo Commonwealth Stamp Printing Office, Melbourne (J. B. Cooke). Wmk. Crown over 'A' (of South Australia) sideways to left. Sheets 5 x 8.

(a) Perf. 12½ (1911-12).

G1	½d.	**yel-grn/yellowish**	50	50
G2	½d.	**green** (white paper)		
		(8/16)	40	40
G3	1d.	**rose-pink** (thick paper)	90	40
G4	1d.	**rose-red** (thin paper)	90	40
G5	2d.	**bt mauve/yellowish**	60	70
	a	on white paper	60	70
G6	2½d.	**bt ultramarine**	2·65	3·75
G7	2½d.	**dl ultramarine**	2·75	3·75
G8	4d.	**pale olive-green**	2·00	3·00
G9	6d.	**or-brn/yellowish**	1·75	3·25
	a	on white paper	1·75	3·25
G10	1/–	**yellow**	5·00	6·00
G11	2/6	**rose-carmine**	£12	£15
G1/11		**set** (8v)	£24	£30

(b) Perf. 14 (1915-16).

G12	1d.	**rose-pink** (6/15)	6·00	5·00
G13	1d.	**pl scarlet** ('16)	2·50	2·00

G1/2/5/8/9/12/13 all exist with wmk. inverted.

'CA' and 'JBC' monograms appear in the bottom margins below Rows 8/2 and 8/4.

Plate Proofs of No. G5 are known, perf. 14.

The Royal Collection contains 2d., 2½d. and 2/6d. stamps on thick unwatermarked paper and 6d. and 1/– stamps on thin unwatermarked paper. These possibly come from Proof Sheets.

Numbers printed—G3/4, 582,000; G12/13, 63,000.

Stamps of the preceeding issues are occasionally found apparently overprinted 'TAX' in large black sans-serif capitals. This was a handstamp normally struck on the cover to indicate deficient postage, but sometimes struck on the stamp.

1917 (Oct.) Nos. G1//5/6/8/9/11 surcharged 'ONE PENNY' in black serif capitals at Melbourne. Setting 5 x 8.

G14	1d. on ½d.	**yel-green**	50	50
G15	1d. on 2d.	**bt mauve**	3·50	3·50
G16	1d. on 2d.	**dp purple**	3·25	3·50
G17	1d. on 2½d.	**ultramarine**	1·25	1·50
G18	1d. on 2½d.	**dp ult**	1·25	1·50
G19	1d. on 4d.	**pl ol-green**	1·25	1·75
G20	1d. on 4d.	**dk olive**	1·25	1·75
G21	1d. on 6d.	**or-brown**	4·50	4·50
G22	1d. on 2/6	**rose-carmine**	1·75	3·50
G23	1d. on 2/6	**pl rose-car**	2·00	3·50
G14/23		**set** (6v)	£12	£14

G20—One sheet (40) is known on thick ungummed paper.

G14 exists with wmk. inverted.

1916 (Sept.)-31 As Nos. G1/11 but bicoloured and new values. Perf. 14.

The Printers at the Commonwealth Stamp Printing Office, Melbourne were:—

1916-18—J. B. Cooke (C)
1918-26—T. S. Harrison (H)
1926-27—A. J. Mullett (M)
1927-31—J. Ash (A)

G24	½d.	myrtle and pl ol ('19) (HA).. ..	20	15
G25	½d.	myrtle and pale apple-green ('27) (A)	15	30
G26	1d.	blk and car-red (9/16) (C) ..	70	30
G27	1d.	grey-blk and red ('19) (H)	90	20
G28	1d.	pur-blk and red (H)	90	20
G29	1d.	intense blk and red ('26) (H)	1·25	60
	a	ornament retouched	£12	—
G30	1½d.	pl ult and brn ('25) (H)	35	20
	a	'POSTACE' ..	£15	£10
G31	1½d.	ult and pl brn ('27) (M)	3·75	2·00
	a	'POSTACE' ..	£20	£15
G32	1½d.	bt blu and dp bt brn ('29) (A)	80	40
	a	'POSTACE' ..	£15	£10
G33	2d.	choc and pur ('19) (H)	1·25	70
G34	2d.	pur-brn and lk-red ('31) (A)	7·00	1·25
G35	2d.	choc and claret ('31) (A)	2·00	1·00
G36	2½d.	myrtle and ult ('19) (H)	1·75	3·75
G37	3d.	blk and bt blu-grn (12/16) (C) ..	1·00	1·00
G38	3d.	sepia-blk and bt blu-grn (H) ..	£10	7·00
G39	3d.	grey-blk and bt grn ('27) (A)	1·00	1·25
G40	4d.	brn and or ('19) (H)	2·75	3·00
G40A	4d.	light brown and or ('27) (A)	3·00	6·00
G41	5d.	sl and pl brn ('31) (A)	2·75	3·50
G42	6d.	dl and bt pur ('19) (H)	1·50	2·00
	a	'POSTACE' ..	£10	£15
G43	6d.	dl and reddish pur ('27) (A)	2·25	3·50
	a	'POSTACE' ..	£18	£24
G44	1/-	sepia and ol ('19) (H)	2·25	3·00
G45	1/-	sepia and pl olive ('27) (A)	2·00	3·00
G46	2/6	maroon and pink ('19) (H) ..	£10	£12
G47	2/6	maroon and bt pink ('27) (A)	£10	£12
G48	5/-	blk and ol-green (12/16) (C) ..	£18	£17
	a	on yel'ish paper (H)	£50	£50
G49	10/-	grn and ult ('25) (H)	£60	£65
G24/49		set (13v)	£95	£105

See also Nos. G65/66.

G29a—The white star ornament in the lower frame of Row 6/3 was retouched and the eight small dots greatly enlarged.

G30a/32a—Right hand label, Row 1/1.

G42a/43a—Left hand label, Row 6/2.

G34 was an error of colour, intended to match No. G33, and was quickly replaced by No. G35. Only 120 sheets (4,800 copies) were printed, including those punctured 'OS'. (See No. GO12).

G36—Stamps in green and grey were affected by the climate.

G37—Between one and five sheets (40-200 copies) printed in black and deep greenish blue were included in the third Cooke consignment. These are said to have been Colour Trials issued in error, but there is some doubt as to their status.

G29 and G42—The wmk. is normally inverted.

G40—The Ash printing is mostly with wmk. inverted.

G26/37/48 are the only Cooke printings and have the 'CA' and 'JBC' monograms below Rows 8/2 and 8/4. The other values all have the Printer's Imprint below Row 8/3.

Ash printings can usually be distinguished by the white paper.

Row 3/4 (G36 only)

Various varieties developed in the Harrison Vignette Plate, the most prominent being the 'lightning flash' which occurs only on the 2½d. (No. G36), Row 3/4.

Row 1/2 (1927-29 and 1932)

When Mullett and Ash subsequently used the Harrison Vignette Plate, certain values printed between 1927 and 1930 showed a different 'lightning flash' on Row 1/2. This variety has been seen on the 1½d. (G31/32 and overprints on these stamps) on the 3d. (G39 and overprints on this stamp) and on the 1/- (G45 and overprints on this stamp). It does not occur on the 2/6d. (G47) and may or may not occur on the ½d. (G25), and 6d. (G43).

Although not present on 1931 printings such as the 5d. (G41), the same variety re-appeared in 1932 on the 9d. and 1/3d. (G65/66).

1929 (Oct.)-30 (Sept.) Various stamps overprinted in black by the Government Printer at Port Moresby.

I. Setting 5 x 2 applied four times to the sheet.

(a) No. G37 on yellowish paper (Cooke).

G50	3d.	**blk and bt blue-grn** ..	1·75	2·50
		a overprint omitted in vertical pair with normal	£750	—

(b) No. G38 on yellowish paper (Harrison).

G51	3d.	**sepia-blk and bt blue-green**	£25	£28

II. Setting 5 x 8. (made up of four stereos) No. G39 (Ash).

G52	3d.	**grey-blk and bt-grn**	1·50	2·00
		a overprint double ..	£200	—
		b overprints tete beche (vertical pair) ..	£400	—
		c overprint omitted (in horizontal pair with normal)	£850	—
		d overprint omitted (in vertical pair with normal)	£850	—
		e overprint vertical (on back)	£850	—

G50a—At least three sheets were affected, on two of them the lower row lacked the overprint and on the other the overprint was omitted from Row 6.

G52b—The third and fourth rows of one sheet had the overprint inverted, thus providing ten tete beche vertical pairs.

G52c/d/e come from two sheets which received normal overprints on the top four rows, whereas the lower four rows were each overprinted on Nos. 5 only. This was caused by the lower left corner of the sheet being folded over, and several of the corner stamps received vertical overprints on the back.

G52c also comes from a single sheet on which the overprint was misplaced laterally; and G52d comes from a sheet on which the lower row missed the overprint, and also from a sheet on which the overprint was omitted from the third and fourth rows.

G52 The 'lightning flash' occurs on Row 1/2.

Numbers overprinted—G50, 30,000; G51, 6,000; G52, 36,000.

1930 (Sept. 13th) Various stamps overprinted in carmine by the Government Printer at Port Moresby. Setting 5 x 8.

(a) Nos. G38/G42/G44 (Harrison, on yellowish paper).

G53	3d.	**sepia-blk and bt blue-green**	£100	—
		a ovpt. double ..	£500	£550
G54	6d.	**dl and bt purple** ..	5·00	6·00
		a 'POSTACE'	£25	—
G55	1/–	**sepia and olive** ..	£10	£15
		a on white paper ..	£30	—
		b overprint inverted ..	£500	—

(b) Nos. G39/G43/G45. (Ash).

G56	3d.	**blk and blue-grn** ..	75	1·25
G57	6d.	**dl and reddish pur**	3·00	3·75
		a 'POSTACE'	£21	—
G58	1/–	**sepia and pl olive** ..	4·00	4·50

G54a/57a—See Note after Nos. G42a/43a (Row 6/2 – left hand labels).

G55b—One sheet recorded.

G55 with overprint in a much deeper shade is from a trial overprinting.

G56 and G58—The 'lightning flash' occurs on Row 1/2.

Numbers issued—G53, *480; G54, 20,000; G55, 18,400; G55a, 10,000; G56, 39,520; G57, 30,000; G58, 20,000.

*12 sheets were received, but it is believed that only 2 sheets (80 copies) were sold.

1931-32 Various stamps surcharged in black

by the Government Printer at Port Moresby. Setting 5 x 8.

(a) TWO PENCE (1.1.31) On Nos. G31/32.

G59 2d. on 1½d. **ult and pl brn**			
(M)		6·00	7·00
a 'POSTACE' ..		£28	—
G60 2d. on 1½d. **bt blue and dp**			
bt brn (A) ..		1·25	1·50
a 'POSTACE' ..		£15	—

G59a/60a—See Note after G30a/32a (Row 1/1 – right hand label).

The 'lightning flash' occurs on both stamps (Row 1/2).

Numbers surcharged—G59, 3,720; G60, 28,400.

(b) FIVE PENCE (26/7/31) On No. G45.

G61 5d. on 1/- **sepia and pl**			
olive (A) ..		80	1·50

The 'lightning flash' occurs on Row 1/2.
Number surcharged—30,000.

(c) NINE PENCE on Nos. G46/47.

G62 9d. on 2/6 **mar and pink**			
(12/31) (H)		75	1·25
G63 9d. on 2/6 **mar and bt**			
pink ('32) (A)		2·00	3·50

Numbers surcharged—G62, 20,000; G63, 12,000.

(d) FIFTEEN PENCE. On Nos. G48/48a.

G64 1/3 on 5/- **blk and ol-grn**			
(C)		2·00	2·75
a on yellowish			
paper (C)..		4·00	5·50

Number surcharged—20,000.

1932 As Nos. G24/49 but new values. Wmk. Third Multiple of Australia (C of A). Perf. 11.

G65 9d. **lilac and violet** (A)..		4·00	5·00
G66 1/3 **lilac and pl greenish**			
blue (A)		7·00	7·00
SPG65/66 **specimen** (pair) ..		£200	‡

The 'Lightning Flash' occurs on both values (Row 1/2).

All stamps from G67 are Recess John Ash on unwatermarked paper. Perf. 11, unless otherwise indicated.

1932 (Nov. 14th) Various frames. Designers, E. Whitehouse (2d., 4d., 6d., 1/-, 10/-): F.E. Williams (2/-, £1 and frames of other values): Williams and Gibson (photos for remaining vignettes). Sheets 8 x 5. Printers

J. Ash (all values): W. C. G. McCracken ½d. (G68), 1d., 2d., 4d.

G67	½d.	**black and orange**..	20	40
G68	½d.	**black and buff** ..	9·00	£10
G69	1d.	**black and green** ..	15	15
G70	1½d.	**black and lake** ..	75	1·75
G71	2d.	**scarlet**	1·75	50
G72	3d.	**black and blue** ..	1·75	3·00
G73	4d.	**olive-green**.. ..	2·00	3·25
G74	5d.	**blk and sl-green** ..	1·75	2·00
G75	6d.	**bistre-brown** ..	2·75	2·75
G76	9d.	**black and lilac** ..	6·00	7·00
G77	1/-	**blue-green**	3·50	6·00
G78	1/3	**blk and dl purple** ..	8·00	9·00
G79	2/-	**blk and sl-green** ..	8·00	£10
G80	2/6	**blk and maroon** ..	£15	£18
G81	5/-	**blk and ol-brown**..	£22	£22
G82	10/-	**lilac**	£40	£50
G83	£1	**blk and ol-grey** ..	£90	£80
G67/83		**set** (16v)	£200	£210

1934 (Nov. 6th) 50th Anniversary of Declaration of British Protectorate. Sheets 5 x 8.

G84 1d. **green**	..	.. ..	1·00	1·25
G85 2d. **scarlet**	..	.. ..	1·50	1·25
G86 3d. **blue**	..	.. ..	3·50	3·50
G87 5d. **purple**	..	.. ..	6·50	7·00
G84/87 **set** (4v) ..		.. ..	£10	£11

Proofs of G85 and G86 exist with transposed values.

Numbers printed—G84/85, 120,000 each; G86, 80,000; G87, 60,000.

1935 (July 9th) Silver Jubilee. Nos. G69/71/72/74 specially printed on highly chalk-surfaced paper and overprinted in black by Ash. Setting 8 x 5.

G88 1d. **black and green**		..	30	35
a acute accent ..		..	£12	—
G89 2d. **scarlet** ..		..	50	75
G90 3d. **black and blue**		..	1·25	1·75
a acute accent		..	£20	—
G91 5d. **blk and sl-grn**		..	5·00	5·50
a acute accent.		..	£35	—
G88/91 **set** (4v) ..		..	6·50	7·00

G88a/91a—An acute accent appears in place of the apostrophe in 'Majesty's', Row 5/4.

Numbers overprinted—G88/89, 120,000 each; G90, 60,000; G91, 40,000.

1937 (May 14th) Coronation. Highly chalk-surfaced paper. Sheets 5 x 8.

1	1d.	green	.. .. ..	10	10
	a	'halo'	.. .. ..	£25	—
2	2d.	scarlet	.. ..	10	10
3	3d.	blue	.. ..	10	10
4	5d.	lake-purple	.. ..	20	20
	a	re-entry	.. ..	£40	—
1/4		set (4v)	.. ..	50	50

1a—A crescent of lighter tone with thinner horizontal lines in the background, following the shape of the back of the head, gives the appearance of a halo. (Row 5/2, Plate 1a).

4a—There is doubling in the right lower corner. Row 2/5.

Numbers issued—1, 500,000; 2, 490,500; 3, 504,000; 4, 480,000.

Remainders were withdrawn December 31st, 1937.

1938 (Sept. 6th) 50th Anniversary of Declaration of British Possession. Highly chalk-surfaced paper. Sheets 5 x 8.

5	2d.	rose-red ..	.. ..	75	1·50
6	3d.	bright blue	.. ..	1·50	2·00
7	5d.	green	.. ..	2·50	3·00
8	8d.	brown-lake	.. ..	5·00	6·00
9	1/–	mauve	.. ..	£10	£10
5/9		set (5v)	.. ..	£18	£20

Remainders were withdrawn September 6th, 1939.

1939 (Sept. 6th)-41 Air Mail. Sheets 5 x 8.

(a) Printer J. Ash (6/9/39).

10	2d.	rose-red	.. ..	1·00	1·25
11	3d.	bright blue	.. ..	1·50	1·75
12	5d.	green	.. ..	2·00	1·50
13	8d.	brown-lake	.. ..	3·50	4·00
14	1/–	mauve	..	6·00	6·00

(b) Printer W. C. G. McCracken. Perf. 11½. (2/1/41).

15	1/6	dull olive	.. ..	£25	£30
10/15		set (6v) ..	.. ..	£37	£42

OFFICIAL STAMPS

Several values from EO1-GO17 exist in pairs, one stamp without the 'OS' puncture; the 'OS' puncture is also found double, misplaced or reading 'SO' (inverted or reversed).

Many of the stamps from EO1-GO8 may be found cancelled to order at Port Moresby.

1908 (Oct.) Nos. E44/50/58 punctured 'OS' at Port Moresby or Melbourne. Both letters have twelve holes and are 9mm in height.

EO1	2/6	black and brown	..	£20	£30

Number issued—500-600.

1909-10 Nos. E59/85 similarly punctured (Small PAPUA).

(a) Wmk. Upright or Inverted.

(i) Perf. 11.

EO2	1d.	rose ..	.. ..	1·50	2·00
EO3	2d.	purple	.. ..	2·00	2·25
EO4	2½d.	bt ultramarine	..	6·00	£10
EO5	2½d.	pale ultramarine	..	2·00	3·00
EO6	4d.	sepia ..	.. ..	2·00	2·25
	a	thin 'd'	.. ..	£10	£12
EO7	6d.	myrtle-green	..	5·00	7·00
EO8	1/–	orange	.. ..	5·00	7·00
EO2/8		set (6v)	.. ..	£15	£20

(ii) Perf. 12½.

EO9	2d.	purple	.. ..	2·00	2·00
EO10	2½d.	bt ultramarine	..	8·00	£16
EO11	2½d.	pl ultramarine	..	6·00	£12
EO12	4d.	sepia ..	.. ..	3·50	4·00
	a	thin 'd'	.. ..	£15	£20
EO13	1/–	orange	.. ..	£20	£25
EO9/13		set (4v)	.. ..	£30	£40

(b) Wmk. Sideways (to left or right).

(i) Perf. 11.

EO14	½d.	yellow-green	..	2·00	2·25
	a	thick 'd'	.. ..	£10	£12
EO15	½d.	deep green ..	..	£14	£18
	a	thick 'd'	.. ..	£50	£60
EO16	1d.	carmine	.. ..	4·50	5·00
EO17	2d.	purple	.. ..	2·50	2·00
EO18	2½d.	dull blue	.. ..	2·50	3·00
	a	imperf between stamp and margin		—	£75
EO19	4d.	sepia	.. ..	2·50	3·00
	a	thin 'd'	.. ..	£15	£18
EO20	6d.	myrtle-green	..	6·50	5·00
EO21	1/–	orange	.. ..	£14	£18
EO14/21		set (7v)	.. ..	£32	£35

(ii) Perf. 12½.

EO22	½d.	**yellow-green**	..	1·00	1·50
		a thick 'd'	.. ..	£10	£12
EO23	½d.	**deep green** ..		£14	£18
		a thick 'd'	..	£50	£60
EO24	1d.	**carmine**	.. ..	4·00	3·50
EO25	2d.	**purple**	.. ..	2·00	2·00
EO26	2½d.	**dull blue**	..	5·00	6·00
EO27	6d.	**myrtle green**	..	£35	£40
EO28	1/–	**orange**	.. ..	7·00	£10
EO22/28		**set** (6v)	.. ..	£50	£60

EO6*a*/12*a*/19*a*—See Note after No. E5*a*. (Row 4/3).

EO14*a*/15*a*/22*a*/23*a*—See Note after No. E71*a*. (Row 5/1).

EO18*a*—Six copies are known, all cancelled at Port Moresby on 21/8/12, from a sheet which was imperf between the right vertical column and the margin.

The 'Rift in Clouds' occurs on all values, (Row 5/3).

1910-11 Nos. E89/100 similarly punctured (Large PAPUA).

(a) Perf. 11. Wmk. Upright (EO29) or Sideways (EO30).

EO29	½d.	**yellow-green**	..	1·00	2·50
EO30	2/6	**chocolate** (6/10)	..	£50	£75

(b) Perf. 12½. Wmk. Upright or Inverted.

EO31	½d.	**dull green**	.. ..	1·50	1·75
EO32	½d.	**dl yellow-green**	..	1·50	1·75
EO33	1d.	**carmine**	.. ..	2·00	1·75
EO34	2d.	**dull purple**	..	2·00	2·00
		a 'PCSTAGE'	..	£15	£20
EO35	2½d.	**violet-blue** ..	..	3·00	4·00
EO36	4d.	**sepia** ..	.. ..	2·00	4·00
		a thin 'd'	..	£15	£25
EO37	6d.	**myrtle-green**	..	3·50	4·00
EO38	1/–	**deep orange**	..	7·00	9·00
EO39	2/6	**brown** (Type I)	..	£16	£24
EO40	2/6	**brown** (Type II)	..	£16	£24
EO31/40		**set** (8v)	.. ..	£50	£54

EO34*a*—See Note after No. E94. (Row 4/3).
EO36*a*—See Note after No. E5*a*. (Row 4/3).

EO30 exists punctured double, inverted and sideways.
Numbers punctured—EO30, 50.

1911-12 Nos. G1/11 similarly punctured. (Perf. 12½).

GO1	½d.	**yellow-green**	..	50	1·00
GO2	1d.	**rose-pink**	..	1·00	1·50
GO3	2d.	**bright mauve**	..	1·00	1·50
GO4	2½d.	**ultramarine** ..		3·00	4·00
GO5	4d.	**olive-green** ..		3·00	4·00
GO6	6d.	**orange-brown**	..	2·50	4·25
GO7	1/–	**yellow**	..	6·00	7·00
		a imperf.	.. ..	£60	—
GO8	2/6	**carmine**	.. ..	£15	£20
GO1/8		**set** (8v)	.. ..	£30	£40

1930 Nos. G24/47 similarly punctured.

GO9	½d.	**myrtle and pale apple-green** (A)		50	1·50

GO10	1d.	**purple-blk and red** (H)	..	1·00	1·50
		a ornament retouched	..	£12	—
GO11	1½d.	**bt blue and dp bt brown** (A)	..	1·00	2·50
		a 'POSTACE'	..	£10	£15
GO12	2d.	**pur-brn and lk-red** (A)	.. ..	7·00	2·50
GO13	3d.	**grey-blk and bt-green** (A)	..	1·50	4·00
GO14	4d.	**brn and or** (A)	..	2·25	4·50
GO15	6d.	**dl and bt pur** (H) ..		3·50	6·00
		a 'POSTACE'	..	£20	£30
GO16	1/–	**sepia and pl ol** (A)		5·00	8·00
GO17	2/6	**mar and pink** (H)	..	£14	£20
GO9/17		**set** (9v)	.. ..	£35	£48

GO10*a*—See Note after No. G29*a* (Row 6/3).

GO11*a*—See Note after No. G32*a* (Row 1/1).

GO15*a*—See Note after No. G42*a* (Row 6/2).

GO11/16—The 'Lightning Flash' occurs on Row 1/2.

1931 (July 29th) Nos. G24/47 overprinted in black by John Ash. Setting 5 x 8.

GO18	½d.	**myrtle and pale apple-grn** (A) ..		50	1·50
GO19	1d.	**intense blk and red** (H) ..	..	50	1·50
		a ornament retouched	..	£12	—
GO20	1½d.	**bt blu and dp bt brn** (A) ..	..	1·00	2·50
		a 'POSTACE'	..	8·00	£12
GO21	2d.	**choc and claret** (A)	.. ..	1·00	2·50
GO22	3d.	**grey-blk and bt green** (A) ..		1·00	4·00
GO23	4d.	**brn and or** (A) ..		1·50	4·00
GO24	5d.	**sl and pl brn** (A) ..		2·50	5·00
GO25	6d.	**dl and reddish purple** (A)	..	3·50	5·50
		a 'POSTACE'	..	£20	£30
GO26	1/–	**sepia and pl ol** (A)		5·00	7·50
GO27	2/6	**mar and pink** (H)	..	£12	£18
GO28	2/6	**mar and bt pink** (A) ..	..	£12	£18
GO18/28		**set** (10v) ..		£25	£50

G19—The wmk. is normally inverted.

GO19*a*—See Note after No. G29*a*. (Row 6/3).

GO20*a*—See Note after No. G32*a*. (Row 1/1).

GO25*a*—See Note after No. G42*a*. (Row 6/2).

GO20/26—The 'Lightning Flash' occurs on Row 1/2.

1932 Nos. G65/66 similarly overprinted.

GO29 9d. **lilac and vio** (A) ..   8·00   £14
GO30 1/3 **lilac and pl grn'ish**
        blue (A) £12   £18

The 'Lighting Flash' occurs on both values (Row 1/2).

POSTAL FISCALS

1912 (May) No. G3 overprinted in black at Port Moresby for Fiscal use (Setting 5 x 4 applied twice to the sheet). Authorised for postal use until mid 1913.

F1 1d. **rose-pink**   ..   ..   2·00   £10
    a overprint double   ..   —   —
    b overprint omitted in
       vertical pair with
       normal   ..   —   —

F1*a/b*—The overprint intended for the lower half of a sheet was placed one row high, resulting in a double overprint across Row 4 and overprint omitted across Row 8.

F1*b*—On another sheet the overprint intended for the lower half was placed one row low, resulting in the overprint being omitted across Row 5.

The use of this Fiscal Stamp was authorised in May 1912 during a shortage of 1d. stamps at Samarai and it was again used early in 1913 during a further shortage of 1d. stamps. The use of Fiscal Stamps for postal purposes was prohibited in the middle of 1913.

The original authority was only intended to cover the 1d. stamp, but it was ambiguously worded; and a number of other ½d., 1d., 6d. and 2/6 Fiscal Stamps (overprints also in serif or sans serif capitals) are known accepted used for postage.

PITCAIRN ISLANDS

In the latter part of the 19th century letters were occasionally despatched by hand of the masters of visiting ships to be posted on arrival at foreign ports. Such mail bore stamps of the country where it was posted, and may only be recognised by an impressed rubber stamp "PITCAIRN ISLAND" on the covers.

From 1921–26 letters were handstamped "POSTED AT PITCAIRN ISLAND—NO STAMPS AVAILABLE"; and in Great Britain and New Zealand were accepted for delivery at normal inland rates (collected "Postage Due").

From June 1927 until the Pitcairn Island stamps were issued, a New Zealand Postal Agency operated and contemporary stamps of New Zealand were used and cancelled with a named datestamp.

1940 (Oct. 15th) -52 Designs, ½d. (Oranges); 1d. (Christian on Bounty, and Pitcairn Is.); 1½d. (John Adams and his House); 2d. (Lieut. Bligh and Bounty); 3d. (Map); 4d. (Bounty Bible); 6d. (H.M. Bounty); 8d. (School, 1949); 1/- (Fletcher Christian and Pitcairn Is.); 2/6 (Christian on Bounty and Pitcairn Coast). Printers (recess) Bradbury, Wilkinson (1d., 3d., 4d., 8d., 2/6, Perf. 11½ x 11¼ (C), sheets

6 x 10; Waterlow & Sons (Other Values, Perf. 12½ (L), sheets 5 x 12.

1	½d.	**red-orange and green**	20	25
2	1d.	**purple and magenta**..	20	25
		a pur and lake-magenta		
		(4/12/52) ..	30	30
3	1½d.	**grey and carmine** ..	30	30
		a grey and rose-carmine		
		(13/11/44) ..	30	30
4	2d.	**green and red-brown**	60	75
5	3d.	**yel-grn and dp blue**..	75	90
6	4d.	**blk and grn** (1/9/51)..	6·00	6·00
7	6d.	**choc and greenish-slate**	1·00	1·25
		a brn and greenish-slate		
		(13/11/44) ..	80	1·00
8	8d.	**grn and pur** (1/9/51)..	6·00	6·00
9	1/-	**pur-vio and slate-grey**	1·50	2·00
10	2/6	**green and red-brown**	3·00	4·00
1/10		**set** (10)	£18	£20
SP 1/10		**specimen set** perf (8)	£70	‡

Booklets exist of Nos. 1/10 (less 4d. and 8d.), one of each denomination. Price for booklet— B1 £500.

SPECIAL ISSUES

1946 (Dec. 2nd) Victory. As Aden.

S1	2d.	**chocolate-brown** ..	25	25
S2	3d.	**dp blue**	50	50
SP S1/2		**specimen set** perf (2)	£30	‡

1949 (Aug. 1st) Silver Wedding. As Aden.

S3	1½d.	**scarlet**	40	50
S4	10/-	**slate-violet**	£30	£30

1949 (Oct. 10th) U.P.U. As Aden.

S5	2½d.	**beech-brown** ..	1·25	1·25
S6	3d.	**indigo**	1·00	2·00
S7	6d.	**green**	2·75	3·50
S8	1/-	**purple**	4 50	5·00
S5/8		**set** (4)	8·00	£10

Booklet B1

RHODESIA

The British South Africa Company was originally granted a Charter in 1889 covering Mashonaland; and Matabeleland was annexed in 1893. The area north of the Zambesi River also came under the control of the B.S.A. in 1899-1900, subsequently becoming the Colony of Northern Rhodesia in 1924.

The whole of the B.S.A. territories were named Rhodesia in 1895 in honour of Cecil John Rhodes; and the original Mashonaland and Matabeleland territories became Southern Rhodesia in 1924. The B.S.A. ceased to administer these territories after 1918.

Prior to the issue of B.S.A. stamps those of British Bechuanaland were used on the few established postal routes.

With the present currency restrictions in Rhodesia (Jan. 1979) many prices quoted below are well below the market in Rhodesia itself.

1891 (Jan. 2nd) *(recess)* **Bradbury, Wilkinson and Co. Thin Wove paper. No Wmk. Perf. 14-14½. Sheets V1/14 10 x 6; V15/18 6 x 10.**

V1	1d.	**charcoal black**	3·00	1·50
V2	1d.	**grey-black**	4·00	1·50
V3	6d.	**grey-blue**	6·00	3·00
V4	6d.	**steel-blue**	£20	8·00
V5	6d.	**pale dull blue**	8·00	3·00
V6	1/–	**blackish brown**	£15	£10
V7	1/–	**bistre brown**	£10	8·00
V8	2/–	**red**	£12	8·00
V9	2/–	**orange-red**	£10	7·00
V10	2/6	**slate purple**	£10	8·00
V11	2/6	**dull purple**	£10	8·00
V12	5/–	**orange-yellow**	£20	£11
V13	5/–	**yellow**	£20	£11
V14	10/–	**dull green**	£32	£35
V15	£1	**deep blue**	£95	£95
V16	£2	**dull brown-red**	£250	£95
V17	£5	**sage green**	£1150	£250
V18	£10	**brown**	£1600	£350
V1/15		**set (8)**	£200	£165
SPV1/15		**specimen set (8)**	£120	‡

V16—A later printing was made from the same plate by Waterlow. (See No. V85.)

Although these stamps are described as being without watermark, copies may be found showing portions of the papermakers' watermark.

The 1d., 6d. and 2/6d. values may also be found on a thicker paper without watermark.

These stamps were originally for use only within Rhodesia; but they were made internationally valid from 1.8.92.

Collectors are warned of the existence of cleaned and re-gummed copies of the high values, some with forged postmarks.

Proofs exist in the issued colours, but imperf. Colour Trials are known of the 1d. in brown and the £1 in grey blue, both overprinted "SPECIMEN" in blue or violet.

1891 (March) Nos. V3, V4 and V6 surcharged in black by Bradbury Wilkinson and Co. Setting 10 x 3, repeated twice.

V19	½d. on 6d.	**grey-blue**	£40	£45
V20	½d. on 6d.	**steel blue**	£55	£60
V21	2d. on 6d.	**grey-blue**	£40	£50
V22	4d. on 6d.	**grey blue**	£42	£55
V23	8d. on 1/–	**sepia**	£42	£55

These stamps were later made valid for international use.

1891 (April)-94 *(recess)* **(Value** *typo***) Bradbury, Wilkinson. Thin Wove paper. No wmk. Perf. 14-14½. Sheets 10 x 6.**

V24	½d.	**grey-blue and ver**	1·00	1·00
V25	½d.	**slate-blue and ver**	1·10	1·00
V26	½d.	**steel-blue and ver**	1·20	1·20
V27	½d.	**indigo and vermilion**	1·50	1·50
V28	2d.	**sage-grn and ver**	2·00	1·00
V29	3d.	**grey-black and green** (12/91)	2·00	1·50
V30	4d.	**lt chestnut and blk**	3·00	1·50
V31	8d.	**rose lake and blue** (12/91)	3·00	1·75
V32	8d.	**brn-red and blue**	3·00	1·75
V33	3/–	**yel-brn and green** (3/94)	£32	£32
V34	4/–	**grey-black and ver** (3/93)	£17	£17
V24/34		**set (7v)**	£60	£55

The Duty Plate was 10 x 3 thus necessitating two operations to complete the printing of the value on a sheet (10 x 6).

1895 (Nov.) As before but printed *(recess and typo)* **by Perkins Bacon from the same plates. Thick soft wove paper. No Wmk. Perf. 12¼. Sheets 10 x 6.**

V35	2d.	**yel-grn and red**	7·00	2·00
	a	"PENCF"	£35	—
	b	"PFNCE"	£35	—
V36	4d.	**cinnamon and black**	7·00	3·00
	a	"PENCF"	£35	—
	b	"PFNCE"	£35	—

Proofs exist in imperf. pairs with or without value.

Sheets still showed the Bradbury, Wilkinson imprint. The Duty Plate was 10 x 6.

Numbers printed—V35, 120,000; V36, 60,000.

THREE
PENCE

1896 Matabele Rebellion Provisionals, used at Bulawayo.

(a) April. Nos. V29, V34, V13 surcharged at The Bulawayo Chronicle Office.

V37	1d. on 3d.	grey-blk and green	£175	£200
		a "P" inverted	—	—
V38	1d. on 4/-	grey-blk and vermilion ..	£150	£150
		a "P" inverted	—	—
		b "y" inverted	—	—
		c single bar ..	—	—
V39	3d. on 5/-	yellow	£85	£95
		a "T" inverted	—	—
		b "R" inverted	—	—

V37a/V38a/V38b/V39a/V39b—These "errors" were all from clandestine printings; and V38c which has a single, instead of triple, bar cancelling the original value, is probably from the same source. Numbers issued—V37, 1,200; V38, 1,200; V39, 3,000.

(b) May 22nd. Cape of Good Hope stamps (Wmk. Anchor except V43 which is Crown CA) overprinted "BRITISH SOUTH AFRICA COMPANY" in black sans serif capitals in three lines by Argus Printing Co., Cape Town. The overprint setting was a horizontal row of six from which ten stereos were made to overprint a pane (6 x 10).

V40	½d.	grey-black	2·00	3·00
V41	1d.	rose-red	2·00	3·50
V42	2d.	brown ..	3·00	3·00
V43	3d.	pale claret ..	£12	£14
V44	4d.	blue	5·00	5·00
		a "COMPANY" omitted ..	£2250	—
V45	6d.	deep purple ..	£18	£19
V46	1/-	buff (July) ..	£35	£42
V40/46		set (7v) ..	£75	£85

Numbers printed—V40, 29,760; V41, 42,960; V42, 27,960; V43, 10,560; V44, 21,060; V45, 12,960; V46, 7,680.

Type I

Type II

1896 (Feb. 2nd)-97 (recess) (Value typo)

Perkins Bacon. Thick soft white wove paper. No Wmk. Perf. 14. Sheets 10 x 6. Type I (ends of scroll behind Springbok's legs).

(a) Die I (Plates 1 and 2) Body of lion only partly shaded: Small dot to right of tail of right hand supporter.

V47	1d.	car-red and em ..	2·00	1·00
V48	2d.	brown and mauve ..	2·00	1·00
V49	2d.	yel-brn and mauve..	2·00	1·00
V50	3d.	red-brown and blue	1·00	1·00
V51	4d.	blue and mauve ..	2·00	2·00
		a imperf between (pair)	—	—
V52	6d.	reddish pur and pink	£12	3·00
V53	8d.	grn and pur/buff ..	1·00	1·00
V54	8d.	grn and reddish lilac/ buff	1·20	1·00
		a imperf between (pair)	—	—
		b imperf (pair) ..	£500	—
V55	1/-	grn and vio-blue ..	3·00	2·00
V56	1/-	green and blue ..	3·50	2·00
V57	3/-	grn and pur/dl grn..	£14	£14
		a imperf (pair) ..		
V58	4/-	red and blue/em ..	£14	£14
V47/58		set (9v)	£45	£30
SPV47/58		specimen set (9v)..	£75	‡

(b) Die II (Plates 3 and 4) Body of lion heavily shaded all over. No dot to right of tail.

V59	½d.	ol-grey and reddish lilac	60	1·00
V60	½d.	ol-grey and reddish purple	70	1·00
V61	1d.	scarlet and emerald	50	1·00
V62	1d.	car-red and em ..	60	1·00
V63	2d.	brown and mauve	80	1·50
V64	4d.	sl-blue and reddish purple	£10	4·00
V65	4d.	dp blue and reddish purple	2·00	50
V66	6d.	dl purple and rose	4·00	1·50
V67	6d.	reddish purple and rose..	1·00	1·00
V68	2/-	indigo and grn/buff	6·00	1·50
V69	2/6	brn and reddish lilac/ol yel ..	7·00	6·50
V70	5/-	red-or and em ..	£12	£12
V71	10/-	sl and scar/rose ..	£24	£24
V59/71		set (9v)	£52	£45
SPV59/71		specimen set (9v)	£80	‡

1897 (Jan. 1st) As before but re-drawn. (recess) Waterlow and Sons Ltd. No Wmk. Perf. 13½-16. Sheets 10 x 6. Type II. (Ends of scroll between Springbok's legs).

V72	½d.	grey-blk and pur ..	80	1·00
V73	½d.	grey-blk and reddish purple	1·25	1·00
V74	1d.	red-orange and em..	1·50	1·10
V75	1d.	or-red and em ..	1·25	1·00
V76	2d.	sepia and mauve ..	1·25	1·00
V77	2d.	bistre-brown and mauve	1·10	1·00
V78	3d.	red-brn and lt blue..	1·25	1·00
V79	3d.	chest and lt blue ..	1·10	1 00
		a imperf between (pair)	£350	—
V80	4d.	sl-blue and reddish purple	1·20	1·10
V81	4d.	grey-blu and reddish purple	1·35	1·20
		a imperf between (pair)	£1250	—

V82	6d.	**dl purple and pink** ..	1·35	1·10
V83	8d.	**grn and pur/buff** ..	2·75	1·50
		a imperf between (pair)	—	—
V84	£1	**blk and red/pl grn** ..	£235	£110
V72/84		**set** (8v)	£240	£115

The following combinations of perforation exist:

13½ x 13½ x 13½ x 13½	1d. 3d. 6d. 8d.
13½ x 14 x 13½ x 13½	½d. 3d. 6d. 8d.
13½ x 14 x 13½ x 14	All values (except ½d. £1)
14 x 14 x 13½ x 14	All values (except 4d. £1)
14 x 14 x 14 x 14	All values (except 4d. £1)
14½ x 13½ x 14½ x 13½	2d.
14½ x 14½ x 14½ x 14½	All values (except £1)
14½ x 14½ x 15 x 14½	3d.
14½ x 15 x 14½ x 15	All values (except £1)
15 x 14½ x 14½ x 14½	3d.
15 x 14½ x 15 x 14½	All values (except 6d.)
15 x 14½ x 15 x 15	4d.
15 x 15 x 14½ x 15	1d. 4d.
15 x 15 x 15 x 15	All values (except ½d.)
15½ x 15½ x 15½ x 15½	½d. 4d. 6d.
15½ x 16 x 15½ x 16	1d. 3d. 4d. 6d.
16 x 15½ x 16 x 15½	6d.
16 x 16 x 16 x 16	½d. 1d. 3d. 4d. 6d.

(*Courtesy Mashonaland P.S.*)

1897 (Jan.) As No. V16 but printed (*recess*) **by Waterlow from the same B/W plate. Thick soft white wove paper. No Wmk. Perf. 15-16. Sheets 6 x 10.**

V85	£2	**rose-red**	£700	£150

This stamp served a postal use until April, 1897 only; thereafter, used copies are mainly cancelled remainders.

Colour Trials exist in lake, rose-lake and brown-lake.

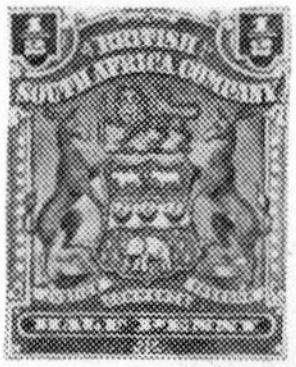

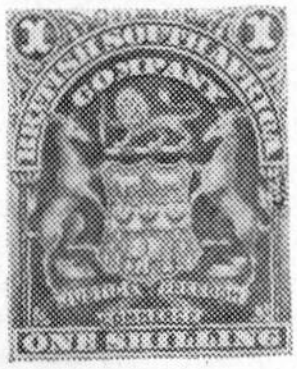

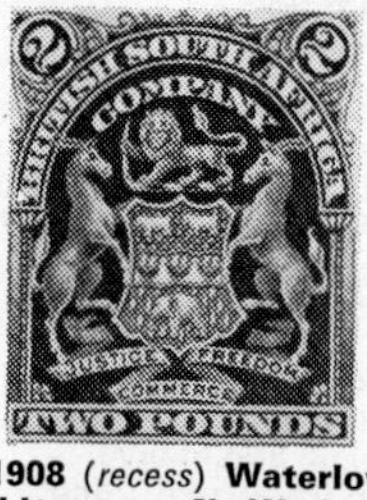

1898 (Oct.)-1908 (*recess*) **Waterlow and Sons. Thick soft white paper. No Wmk. Perf. 13½-16. Sheets 240 – four panes, each 6 x 10; except 7/6 and £1 (10 x 6).**

V86	½d.	**green** (9/99) ..	6·00	10
V87	½d.	**yellow-green** ..	25	10
		a imperf between (pair)	£175	—
		b imperf (pair) ..	£225	—
V83	1d.	**brown-red** ..	1·00	10
V89	1d.	**carmine-red** ..	1·10	10
		a imperf between (pair)	£100	—
		b imperf (pair) ..	£125	—
V90	1d.	**rose-red**	30	10
		a imperf between (pair)	£200	—
		b imperf (pair) ..	£225	—
V91	2d.	**brown** (8/99) ..	60	10
V92	2½d.	**lt blue** (11/02) ..	1·20	10
V93	2½d.	**pl tur blue** ('03) ..	1·00	10
		a imperf between (pair)	£150	—
V94	3d.	**claret** (5/08) ..	2·00	1·20
		a imperf between (pair)	£200	—
V95	4d.	**yel-olive** (8/00) ..	2·00	15
V96	4d.	**pl yellow-olive** ..	1·50	15
		a imperf between (pair)	£225	—
V97	6d.	**dl purple** (11/08)	3·25	2·50
V98	6d.	**reddish purple** ..	2·00	1·25
V99	1/–	**ochre** (11/08) ..	2·00	1·00
		a imperf between (pair)	£600	—
V100	1/–	**olive-bistre** ..	£70	£50
		a imperf between (pair)	£700	—
		b imperf (pair) ..	£650	—
		c bistre/brn ..	6·00	3·00
		d brn/yellow ..	3·00	2·00
V101	2/6	**grey** (4/06) ..	5·00	2·00
		a imperf between (pair)	£300	—
		b bluish violet ..	7·00	3·00
V102	3/–	**violet** (5/08) ..	5·00	3·00
V103	5/–	**orange-brn** (4/06)	7·00	3·00
V104	5/–	**yel-or** (4/06) ..	7·00	3·00
V105	7/6	**black** (11/01) ..	£15	£15
		a imperf between (pair)	—	—
V106	10/–	**grey-green** (5/08)	7·00	6·00
V107	£1	**grey-pur** (6/01) ..	£65	£12
V108	£2	**pur-brn** (5/08) ..	£40	£12
V109	£5	**dp blue** (8/01) ..	£1750	£1250
V110	£10	**lilac** (8/01).. ..	£2000	£1250
V110A	£20	**bistre**	—	—
V110B	£100	**cherry**	—	—
V86/107		**set** (14v)	£110	£30
SPV86/110		**specimen set** (17v)	£350	‡

V108-V110 served no postal purpose, but used copies with postal cancellations come from Game Licences.

The following combinations of perforation exist:—

13½ x 13½ x 13½ x 13½	1/–
13½ x 15 x 13½ x 15	1/–
14 x 14 x 14 x 14	½d. 1d. 2½d. 1/– 3/–
14½ x 14 x 14½ x 14	3/–
14½ x 14½ x 14½ x 14½	All values to £5.
14½ x 15 x 14½ x 15	All values to £5 (except 3/–)
14½ x 15 x 15 x 14½	½d.
14½ x 15 x 15 x 15	1d. £2
15 x 14½ x 14½ x 15	10/–
15 x 14½ x 15 x 14½	All values to £5 (except 7/6d.)
15 x 15 x 14½ x 15	£2
15 x 15 x 15 x 15	All values to £5.
15 x 15½ x 15 x 15½	1/–
15½ x 15 x 15½ x 15	1/–
16 x 16 x 16 x 16	£1

(*Courtesy Mashonaland P.S.*)

Colour Trials, perf. or imperf., exist — 1d. bright rose, deep green; 6d. red-lilac; 1/— black, bright rose, rose-lake; 10/— sage-green; £5 bright blue.

1905 (July 13th) Visit of British Association and opening of Victoria Falls Bridge. (Design from photo by P. M. Clark). *(recess)* **Waterlow and Sons. No Wmk. Perf. 14-15. Sheets 5 x 5.**

E1	1d.	**rose-red**	.. ..	1·50	1·50
E2	2½d.	**deep blue**	.. ..	3·50	3·50
E3	2½d.	**grey-blue**	.. ..	4·00	4·00
E4	5d.	**claret** ..	.. ..	7·00	9·00
E5	1/—	**dull green**	.. ..	£15	£18
	a	imperf between			
		(horiz pair)	..	£3500	—
	b	imperf (pair)	..	£2500	—
E6	2/6	**black**	.. ..	£60	£60
E7	5/—	**violet** ..	.. ..	£50	£50
E1/7		**set** (6v)	.. ..	£140	£150
SPE1/7		**specimen set** (6v) ..		£100	‡

E5*a*—Only five pairs exist.

E5*b*—One sheet of 25 is recorded.

All values exist perforated 14 and also 15. The 1d., 2½d., 5d. also exist perf. 14½ and perf. 15 x 14½. The 5d. also exists perf. 14½ x 15, and the 5/— perf. 14½.

1909 (April 15th) Nos. V86/V109 overprinted "RHODESIA" in black serif capitals by Waterlow and Sons. Perf. 13½-15.

E8	½d.	**yellow green**	..	£12	10
E9	½d.	**bright green**	..	20	10
	a	no "stop" ..		£10	£10
E10	1d.	**brown-red** ..	..	20	10
	a	no "stop" ..	..	£10	£10
	b	imperf between			
		(pair)	.. ..	£100	—
E11	1d.	**scarlet**	..	20	10
	a	no "stop" ..	..	£10	£10
	b	imperf between			
		(pair)	.. ..	£150	—
E12	2d.	**brown**	.. ..	1·00	60
E13	2d.	**pale brown** ..	..	1·10	60
	a	no "stop" ..		£12	£12
E14	2½d.	**pl turquoise blue** ..		20	20
E15	2½d.	**light blue** ..	..	40	25
E16	2½d.	**prussian blue**	..	50	35
	a	no "stop" ..	..	£10	£10
E17	3d.	**claret** ..	..	1·00	20
	a	no "stop" ..	..	£22	£16
E18	4d.	**yellow-olive**	..	1·50	45
E19	4d.	**pl yellow-olive**	..	1·20	40
	a	no "stop" ..	..	£12	£12
	b	overprint inverted..		—	—
E20	6d.	**reddish purple**	..	1·25	50
E21	6d.	**claret**	.. ..	4·00	2·00
	a	no "stop" ..	..	£15	£12
E22	1/—	**ochre** ..	.. ..	2·00	60

E23	1/—	**yellow-brown**	..	1·75	50
	a	no " stop" ..	..	£15	£12
E24	2/6	**grey** ..	..	5·00	3·00
	a	no "stop" ..	..	£20	£18
E25	3/—	**violet** ..	..	5·00	5·00
E26	5/—	**orange-brown**	..	8·00	7·00
	a	no "stop" ..	..	£20	£18
E27	7/6	**black** ..	..	£14	8·00
E28	10/—	**grey-green**	..	8·00	7·00
	a	no "stop" ..	..	£60	£65
E29	£1	**grey-purple**	..	£30	£20
	a	overprint omitted in			
		vertical pair with			
		normal ..	..	£3500	—
E30	£2	**purple-brown**			
		(bluish paper)	..	£1500	£95
	a	rose brn (1912)		£1750	£95
E31	£5	**deep blue**			
		(bluish paper)	..	£1850	£700
E8/29		**set** (14v)	..	£75	£50
SPE8/31		**specimen set** (16v)		£175	‡

E9*a*—The full stop after "Rhodesia" was omitted on most values in different positions.

E30/31 may be found both on bluish and white paper.

E30/31 served no postal purpose and their use was solely fiscal.

The following combinations of perforation exist:—

	14	14 x 14½	14½	14½ x 15	15 x 14½	15
½d.	X			X		
1d.	X					
2d.			X	X		X
2½d.	X	X	X	X		X
3d.			X	X	X	X
4d.			X	X	X	X
6d.	X		X	X	X	X
1/—	X		X			
2/6			X	X	X	X
3/—	X		X	X		X
5/—			X	X	X	X
7/6	X					
10/—			X			X
£1						X
£2						X
£5	X					X

(Courtesy Mashonaland P.S.)

Proofs of E29 are known with the overprint in various colours. This value is also recorded as having been overprinted in purple by E. Crowther at Fort Jamieson in 1911. (Perf. 13½ or 15). Price £80.

1909 (April)-11 Nos. V97/98/101/102/103 overprinted and surcharged in black by Waterlow and Sons.

E32	5d. on 6d.	**claret** ..		2·00	2·00
E33	5d. on 6d.	**reddish pur** ..		3·00	3·00
E34	5d. on 6d.	**red-brown** ..		4·00	4·00
E35	7½d. on 2/6	**grey** ..	..	2·00	1·75

E36	7½d. on 2/6 **slate**	2·00	1·75
E37	10d. on 3/– **violet**	4·00	4·00
E38	2/– on 5/– **orange** ..	6·00	6·00
E39	2/– on 5/– **yel-orange** ..	6·50	6·50
E32/39	**set** (4v)	£14	£13
SPE32/39	**specimen set** (4v)	£60	‡

All values exist perforated 14½, 14½ x 15, 15 x 14½ and 15. The 5d./6d. and 2/– on 5/– also exist perf. 14.

The so called violet surcharges (5d., 7½d. and 10d.) arise from inadequate mixing of violet ink, added to the black to improve its appearance. Price similar to normals.

1910 (Nov. 11th)-13 *(recess)* **Waterlow and Sons. Thick soft white wove paper. No wmk.** Portraits from photos by Downey. Issued to commemorate the visit of H.R.H. The Duke of Connaught and subsequently retained for definitive use.

I. Single Working Plates. Sheets 10 x 10 except 2½d. (5 x 10).

HALF PENNY

G1	**yellow-green** p.14 ..	2·00	40
	a imperf	£1800	—
	b imperf. between (vert. pair)	—	—
	c p.15	£90	8·00
	d p. 13½	£110	£10
	e p. 14 x 15.. ..	£1700	£1500
	f "double dot" below D in right value tablet	£300	£125
G1A	**bluish green** p.14 ..	4·00	40
	a p.15	£95	8·00
G2	**sage-green** p.14 ..	5·00	40
	a p.15	£200	8·00
G3	**olive-green** p.14 ..	£10	1·00
G4	**dull-green** p.14 ..	£30	£15
	a p.15	£90	6·00

ONE PENNY

G5	**carmine-red** p.14 ..	1·50	15
	a imperf	—	—
	b imperf between ..	£4000	—
	c p.15	£120	400
G6	**carmine** p. 13½	£900	£15
	a p.15	£110	4·00
G7	**rosine** p.14	3·50	10
G8	**scarlet** p.14	6·00	20
	a p.15	£125	4·00
G9	**brown-red** p.14 ..	9·00	20

TWO PENCE HALFPENNY

G10	**blue** p.14	7·00	4·00
	a p.15	£45	£30
G11	**steel blue** p. 14 ..	7·00	4·00
G12	**chalky blue** p.14 ..	7·00	4·00
G13	**dull ultramarine** p.14	8·00	5·00
G14	**prussian blue** p.13½ ..	£14	£14

G1a—One sheet was found at Umtali.

G5a—One sheet was found at Bulawayo.

Numbers printed—G1/4, 7,885,100; G5/9, 14,100,100; G10/14, 189,050.

II. Double Working Plates. Sheets 5 x 10.

TWO PENCE

G15	**blk and grey-blk** p. 14..	8·00	3·00
	a p.15	£200	£12
G16	**black and grey** p. 14 ..	8·00	3·00
	a p.15	£200	£12
G17	**blk and sl-grey** p.14 ..	7·00	3·00
G18	**black and slate** p. 14 ..	8·00	2·00
	a p.15	£200	£12
G19	**blk-pur and sl-grey** p. 14	£80	£80

THREE PENCE

G20	**magenta and yel-bist** p. 14	£35	£30
	a p.15	£400	£35
G21	**dl pur and yel-ochre** p. 14	8·00	3·00
	a p.15.	£400	£35
G22	**brn-pur and yel-ochre** p. 14	£38	£30
G23	**pur and ochre** p. 14 ..	£38	£30
	a p. 14 x 15 ..	£900	£175

FOUR PENCE

G24	**black and orange** p. 14	6·00	6·00
	a p.15	£24	£30
	b p. 15 x 14 ..	£175	—
	c p. 14 x 15 ..	£175	—
G25	**grn-blk and yel-or** p. 14	£40	£25
	a p.15	£24	£30
G26	**pur brn and brn-or** p. 14	£30	£15

FIVE PENCE

G27	**lake-brn and yellow-olive** p. 14	£60	£30
	a p.15	£350	£35
G28	**red-brown and yellow-olive** p. 14 ..	£12	£10
G29	**lake-brown and olive-green** p. 14 ..	£12	£10
G29A	**pur-brn and ochre** p. 14	£225	£125

SIX PENCE

G30	**red-brn and reddish-purple** p. 14 ..	8·00	5·00
	a p.15	£400	£40
G31	**red-brown and purple-brown** p. 14 ..	8·00	4·00
G32	**red-brown and brown-purple** p. 14 ..	8·00	4·00
G33	**chestnut & mauve** p.14	£250	£25

EIGHT PENCE

G34	**blk and dl pur** p. 14 ..	£400	—
	a p. 13½	£50	£90
G35	**dl pur and dl pur** p. 14..	£70	£20
	a p. 13½	£90	£90
G36	**blackish grn and dl pur** p. 14	£45	£18

TEN PENCE

G37	**scar and dl pur** p. 14 ..	£20	£25
G38	**rosine and plum** p. 14..	£220	£30

ONE SHILLING

G39	**blk and blue-grn** p. 14	£15	£10
	a p. 14 x 15	£2250	£900
G40	**intense blk and tur-grn**		
	p. 14	£12	5·00
G41	**intense black and blue-**		
	green p. 15	£300	£20
G41A	**pur-blk and bl-grn** p. 15	£110	£15

TWO SHILLINGS

G42	**blk and ult mar** p. 14 ..	£25	£20
G42A	**blk and bl-grn** p. 15 ..	£350	£35
G43	**blk and steel blue** p. 14	£135	£22
G44	**pur-blk and steel-blue**		
	p. 14	£1250	£120

TWO SHILLINGS AND SIXPENCE

G45	**blk and lake** p. 14 ..	£260	£200
G46	**blk and car-red** p. 14 ..	£260	£200
G47	**bistre-brn and car** p. 14	£425	£300
G47A	**blk and rose carmine** p. 14	£300	£150
G47B	**sepia and crimson** p. 14	£300	£175

THREE SHILLINGS

G48	**slate-green and dl pur**		
	p. 14	£90	£70
G49	**bright green and red-**		
	ish magenta p. 14 ..	£400	£250

FIVE SHILLINGS

G50	**scarlet and yellow**		
	green p. 14	£225	£110
G51	**ver and deep grn** p. 14	£185	£110
G52	**crimson and apple grn**		
	p. 14	£185	£110

SEVEN SHILLINGS AND SIXPENCE

G53	**car and bright bl** p. 14	£400	£400
G54	**car and pl blue** p. 14 ..	£400	£400
G55	**car-red and Reckitts**		
	blue p. 14	£600	£475

TEN SHILLINGS

G56	**myrtle and or** p. 14 ..	£300	£200
G57	**blue-grn and red-or** p. 14	£300	£200

ONE POUND

G58	**crim and sl-blk** p. 14 ..	£500	£350
G59	**rosine and grey-blue**		
	p. 14	£500	£300
G60	**car-red and bluish blk**		
	p. 14	£500	£250
G60A	**deep carmine and slate**		
	p. 14	£600	£350
G60B	**carmine and pale blue**		
	slate p. 14	£600	£300
G61	**red and black** p. 15 ..	£2750	£850
G1/61	**set** (18v)	£1000	£1250
SPG1/61	**specimen set** (18v)	£3500	‡

G19—The black-purple is a most distinctive colour and shows through on the back of the stamp.

G44 Although so-called purple-black' the vignette is actually black; but it has a pinkish wash behind the Heads which was probably caused by printing from an imperfectly cleaned plate. The 'purple' colour shows through on the back of used copies.

All values printed from Double Plates (G15/61) have a constant variety known as "Gash in Ear" at Row 1/2. This variety consists of a short horizontal line immediately above the lobe of Queen Mary's right ear. Price about six times normal.

The vast range of shades in all values of the "Double Head" issues was a result of uncertain supplies of printing inks during the war years.

Numbers printed—G15/19, 551,950; G20/23, 269.050; G24/26, 169,050; G27/29, 96,050; G30/33, 590,050; G34/36, 58,050; G37/38, 42,050; G39/41, 885,050; G42/44, 235,050; G45/47, 17,050; G48/49, 13,050; G50/52 13,050; G53/55, 10,550; G56/57, 9,550; G58/61, 43,030.

1910 (Oct.) Prepared for use, but not issued. As G58/61.

G62	£1	**brn-red and pur-brn**	£4250	—

This stamp became, in fact, a Colour Trial of which 100 sheets had been printed in response to a request for brighter colours for the £1 value. It was not issued on account of its close similarity to the 10d. stamp, and the whole stock was subsequently destroyed with the exception of 100 copies which were sold with other remainders in 1924. (Sheet serial numbers 1 and 2) top right corner.

1913 (Sept. 1st)-24 (*recess*) **Waterlow and Sons. No Wmk.**

I. Single Working Plates. Sheets 240 – four panes, each 10 x 6 or 6 x 10.

A. Toned Wove paper with yellowish gum (1913-22).

HALF PENNY

G63	**blue-green** p. 14 ..	1·00	20
	a imperf between (pair)		
	p. 14	£200	—
	b p. 15	1·50	1·00
G64	**yellow-green** p. 14 ..	1·25	20
	a imperf between (pair)		
	p. 14	£200	—
	b p. 15	2·00	1·00
G65	**myrtle-green** p. 14 ..	1·50	20
	a p. 15	2·00	1·25
G66	**green** p. 14	1·00	10
	a p. 14½ x 15	—	—
	b p. 14 x 15	£400	£60
	c p. 15 x 14	£400	£60

ONE PENNY

G67	**carmine** p. 14	50	10
	a imperf between (pair)		
	p. 14	£200	—

	b p. 15	£150	—
	c imperf between (pair)	£1000	—
G68	**crimson** p. 14	£150	—
	a imperf between (pair)		
	p. 14	£100	£10
G69	**brown-red** p. 14 ..	60	10
	a p. 15	60	10
G70	**rose-red** p. 14	50	10
G71	**venetian red** p. 14 ..	50	10
G72	**red** p. 14	50	10
	a p. 13½	—	£250

THREE HALF PENCE

G73	**bistre brown** p. 14 ..	60	10
	a imperf between (pair)		
	p.14	£185	—
	b p. 15	2·00	2·00
G74	**yellow ochre** p. 14 ..	50	10
	a imperf between (pair)		
	p. 14	£185	—
G75	**drab-brown** p. 14 ..	80	10
	a imperf between (pair)		
	p. 14	£185	—
	b p. 15	2·00	2·00
	c p. 15 x 14	—	—

TWO PENCE HALF PENNY

G76	**deep blue** p. 14	1·50	1·25
	a p. 15	5·00	5·00
G77	**blue** p. 14	1·50	1·25
	a p. 15	5·00	5·00
G78	**steel blue** p. 14	2·00	3·00

B. White wove paper with clear white gum (1922-24).

HALF PENNY

G79	**dull green** p. 14 ..	1·00	10
	a imperf between (pair)		
	p. 14	£350	—
	b p. 15	6·00	3·00
G80	**myrtle-green** p. 14 ..	1·00	50
G81	**green** p. 14	60	40

ONE PENNY

G82	**carmine-red** p. 14 ..	1·00	75
	a imperf between (pair)		
	p. 14	£300	—
G83	**rose-red** p. 14	1·00	75
	a imperf between (pair)		
	p. 14	£300	—
	b p. 15	£10	£10
G84	**red** p. 14	1·00	60
	a p. 15	9·00	8·00
G85	**rosine** p. 14	1·00	50
G86	**vermilion** p. 14 ..	1·50	75
G87	**aniline red** (8/24) p. 14	£10	2·00

THREE HALF PENCE

G88	**bistre** p. 14	80	20
	a imperf between (pair)		
	p. 14	£400	—
G89	**bistre-brown** p. 14 ..	5·00	4·00
G90	**ochre** p. 15	8·00	4·00

See after G149 for set price.

This series (G79/90) came from separate printings made in 1922 and in 1923: all the Perf. 15 stamps are from the 1923 printing.

The wove mesh of the paper shows clearly through the gum on the 1922 printings, but is not so clearly seen on the 1923 printings.

Numbers printed (all printings on both papers)—½d., 24,038,000; 1d., 41,118,100; 1½d., 23,369,240; 2½d., 147,000.

Half Penny
Type I

Half-Penny.
Type II

1917 Nos. G67 and G70 (Toned paper. Perf. 14) surcharged in panes of 60 at the Northern Rhodesia Administration Press, Livingstone. Setting 10 x 2, repeated three times.

(a) With Type I in blue-black to purple aniline (August 15th).

G91	½d. on 1d. **rosine**	1·00	1·50
G92	½d. on 1d. **carmine-red** ..	1·00	1·50
	a surcharge inverted ..	£1750	£1750
	b wide spaced "n n" ..	3·00	4·50
	c wide spaced "n y" ..	2·00	3·00

G92*a*—Two sheets (120 copies) were found in October, 1917.

One sheet, from which used copies come, was carmine; whilst the other sheet from which unused copies come, tended towards a vermilion shade.

G92*b*—The letters are spaced 1½mm instead of ¾mm on Rows 2/5, 4/5 and 6/5.

G92*c*—The letters are wider spaced on Nos. 1, 8 and 9 in rows 2, 4 and 6.

"Half" is set slightly to the right on Rows 1, 3 and 5.

Both shades of the surcharge appear in the same sheet, arising from inadequate mixing of the ink.

Number printed—60,000.

(b) With Type II in deep to aniline violet (September 22nd).

G93	½d. on 1d. **rosine**	50	85
G94	½d. on 1d. **carmine-red** ..	50	85

Both shades of the surcharge appear in the same sheet.

Number printed—60,000.

The provisional surcharges G91/94 were intended for use only in Northern Rhodesia where an increase in postal rates to 1½d. caused a shortage of ½d. stamps pending receipt of the new 1½d. value. There was no such shortage of ½d. stamps in Southern Rhodesia.

(1913-24)

II. Double Working Plates. Sheets 6 x 10.
Although only one Master Die was used for the Head Plates either it, or its secondary dies, were retouched three or more times, resulting in four distinct states.

State IIIA

Uneven outline to top of cap.
Anchor shank in cap badge broken by lower cross lines.
Left ear shaded and outlined (as State IIIB).
White patch above left shoulder (as State II).

State I

No outline to top of cap.
Anchor shank in cap badge unbroken.
Left ear unshaded and without outline.
White patch above left shoulder.

State IIIB

Firm outline to top of cap.
Anchor shank in cap badge broken by lower cross lines.
Left ear shaded and outlined.
Background lines above left shoulder touch jacket, collar, beard and moustache.

State II

Faint broken outline to top of cap.
Anchor shank in cap badge unbroken.
Left ear shaded but without outline.
White patch above left shoulder.

STATE I

TWO PENCE

G95	**black and grey** p. 14 ..	2·00	1·50
C96	**black and grey-brown**		
	p. 14	2·50	2·00

THREE PENCE

G97	**black and yellow** p. 14	6·00	2·00
	a p. 15	2·00	2·00
G98	**blk and or-yel** p. 14 ..	4·00	3·00

FOUR PENCE

G99	**blk and red-or** p. 14 ..	2·00	2·00
	a p. 15	£30	£10
G100	**black and orange** p. 14	3·00	2·50

FIVE PENCE

G101	**black and green** p. 14	2·00	2·50
G102	**blk and yel-grn** p. 14 ..	2·00	2·50

SIX PENCE

G103	**black and lilac** p. 14 ..	£30	£10
	a p. 15	2·00	1·50
G104	**black and reddish-lilac** p. 14	£34	£12

TWO SHILLINGS

G105	**black and brown** p. 14	£10	9·00
	a p. 15	5·00	5·00

The EIGHT PENCE has also been recorded in State I, about eight copies p.14 and a single copy p.15 – all mint.

STATE II
TWO PENCE

G106	**black and grey** p. 14 ..		
	a p. 14/15 (compound)	2·00	1·50
G107	**blk and brownish-grey** p. 14	4·00	2·00
G108	**blk and grey-blk** p. 15..	1·50	2·00

THREE PENCE

G109	**blk and deep yellow** p. 14 ..	4·00	1·0C
G110	**blk and pl yellow** p.14..	8·00	1·00
G111	**blk and yel-buff** p. 14..	1·50	80

FOUR PENCE

G112	**blk and red-or** p. 14 ..	2 00	1 00
G113	**blk and or-red** p. 14 ..	2·00	1·00
G114	**blk and or-ver** p. 15 ..	£185	£90

FIVE PENCE

G115	**black and green** p. 14	2·00	3·00
G116	**black and dl green** p. 14	2 00	3 00

SIX PENCE

G117	**black and mauve** p. 14		
G118	**blk and dl pur** p. 14 ..	3·00	1·00
G119	**blk and reddish pur** p. 14	5·00	1·00
		5·00	1·00

EIGHT PENCE

G120	**violet and green** p. 14..	5·00	4·00
G121	**reddish vio and grn** p. 14	6·00	4·50
G122	**reddish lilac and green** p. 14	7·00	5·00
G123	**vio and dl grn** p. 15 ..	£50	£50

TEN PENCE

G124	**blue and red** p. 14 ..	4·00	4·00
G125	**blue and car-red** p. 14..	5·00	4·00
G126	**dp blue and rose-red** p. 15	3·00	4·00

ONE SHILLING

G127	**blk and grey-blue** p. 14	5·00	4·00
G128	**blk and tur-blue** p. 14..	2·50	3·00
G129	**blk and dl grn** p. 14 ..	3·00	3·50
G130	**blk and greenish blue** p. 15	3·00	2 00

TWO SHILLINGS

G131	**black and brown** p. 14	9·00	4·00
G132	**blk and bistre-brn** p. 14	£16	7·00

TWO SHILLINGS AND SIX PENCE

G133	**indigo and drab** p. 14..	7·00	4·00
	a p. 15	8·00	8·00
G134	**steel blue and drab** p. 14	£15	6·00
G135	**steel blue and ol-grey** p. 14	£15	6·00

THREE SHILLINGS

G136	**pur-brn and lt blue** p. 14	£16	£21
	a p. 15	£300	£125
G137	**red-brn and lt blue** p. 14	£16	£21
G138	**brn and lt blue** p. 14 ..	£15	£21

FIVE SHILLINGS

G139	**indigo and myrtle-grn** p. 14	£30	£12
G140	**dp blue and dl grn** p. 14	£15	£12
G141	**blue and yel-grn** p. 15..	£22	£15
G142	**blue and blue-grn** p. 15	£150	—

SEVEN SHILLINGS AND SIX PENCE

G143	**mauve and grey-black** p. 14	£70	£75
G144	**sl-lilac and sl-black** p. 15	£30	£35

TEN SHILLINGS

G145	**crim and yel-grn** p. 14..	£55	£60
G146	**red and green** p. 15 ..	£100	£120

ONE POUND

G147	**black and violet** p. 14	£350	£375
G148	**black and plum** p. 14 ..	£375	£400
G148A	**black and purple** p.15..	£425	£450
G149	**blk and reddish pur** p. 15	£425	£450
G63/90 and G95/149 **set** (19v)		£450	£450
SPG63/90 and G95/149			
	specimen set (19v) ..	£400	‡

STATE IIIA.

All values except 10d. were recorded on toned paper by C.P. Rang in 1933. We have seen 2d, 8d and 10/– and would welcome confirmation before considering a complete listing of State IIIA.

STATE IIIB.

A. Toned Wove paper with yellowish gum (1913-22).

TWO PENCE

G150	blk and brownish-grey p. 14	3·00	2·00
	a imperf between (pair) p. 14	£1200	—
	b p. 15	£1200	£400
G151	blk and grey-blk p. 14..	2·00	2·00
G152	blk and sl-violet p. 14..	1·00	1·00
G153	black and sepia p. 14..	2·00	1·00

THREE PENCE

G154	black and yellow p. 14	1·50	1·09
G155	blk and or-yel p. 14	1·50	1·00

FOUR PENCE

G156	black and red p. 14	4·00	1·00
G157	blk and or-red p. 14	4·00	1·00
G158	black and salmon p. 14	3·00	1·00

FIVE PENCE

G159	blk and dl grn p. 14	2·00	2·50
	a imperf between (pair) p. 14	£1250	—
G160	blk and pl sage-grn p. 14	2·00	2·00
G161	blk and apple-grn p. 14	2·00	2·00
G162	black and green p. 14..	1·75	2·00

SIX PENCE

G163	blk and reddish pur p. 14	2·00	1·50
	a imperf between (pair) p. 14	—	—
G164	blk and reddish lilac p. 14	3·00	2·00
G165	blk and sl lilac p. 14	2·50	1·50
G166	black and lilac p. 14	2·50	1·50

EIGHT PENCE

G167	reddish vio and grey-green p. 14	7·00	5·00
G168	bluish vio and dl grn p. 14	7·00	5·00
	a imperf. vert. (hor. pair)	—	—
G169	bluish vio and pl tur green p. 14	£450	—

TEN PENCE

G170	dp blue and car p. 14..	4·00	4·00
	a p. 14/15 (compound)	—	—
G171	steel blue and red p. 14	4·00	4·00
G172	royal blue and brn-red p. 14	6·00	6·00

ONE SHILLING

G173	blk and lt blue p. 14	2·50	2·00
G174	blk and blue-grn p. 14	2·00	1·50
G175	black and dl green p. 14	5·00	5·00
G176	blk and grn p. 14	£14	7·00

TWO SHILLINGS

G177	black and brown p. 14	5·00	40·0
	a imperf between (pair) p. 14	—	£3500
G178	blk and yel-brn p. 14..	£20	£10

TWO SHILLINGS AND SIX PENCE

G179	greenish blue and drab p. 14	£25	6·00
G180	steel blue and ol-brn p. 14	£12	£12
G181	dp blue and bistre-brn p. 14	£20	£10

THREE SHILLINGS

G182	choc and lt blue p. 14..	£50	£16
G183	brn-pur and greenish blue p. 14	£45	£16

FIVE SHILLINGS

G184	blue and blue-grn p. 14	£18	£10
G185	steel blue and dl green p. 14	£18	£10

SEVEN SHILLINGS AND SIX PENCE

G186	plum and grey-black p. 14	£250	£275

TEN SHILLINGS

G187	car-red and yel-grn p. 14	£95	£80

ONE POUND

G188	black and violet p. 14	£300	£190
G188A	black and dp violet p. 14	£325	£200
G189	black and purple p. 14	£300	£190
G190	black and sl lilac p. 14	£300	£190
G150/190	set (15v)	£650	£575

B. White Wove paper with clear white gum (1922-23).

TWO PENCE

G191	blk and grey-blk p. 14..	80	40
G192	blk and sl-pur p. 14	1·20	50
G193	black and agate p. 15..	£10	—

THREE PENCE

G194	black and yellow p. 14	2·00	3·00
G195	blk and pl or-yel p. 14..	2·00	3·00

FOUR PENCE

G196	blk and red-or p. 14	3·00	2·00
	a p. 15	£10	—
G197	black and orange p. 14	3·00	2·00
G198	blk and or-red p. 15	£10	—

SIX PENCE

G199	blk and sl vio p. 14	1·00	40
G200	blk and reddish lilac p. 14	1·50	50
G201	black and lilac p. 15	£12	—

EIGHT PENCE

G202	sl-vio and pl blue-grn p. 14	7·00	6·00
G203	sl-pur and pl grey-grn p. 14	7·00	6·00
G204	bluish vio and dl grn p. 15	£12	—

TEN PENCE

G205	royal blue and red p. 14	3·00	4·00
G206	royal blue and car-red p. 14	3·00	4·00
G207	royal blue and rose-red p. 15	£18	—

ONE SHILLING

G208	blk and tur grn p. 14 ..	1·25	£150
	a imperf between (pair) p. 14	£1250	—
G209	blk and pl tur-blue p. 15	£18	—

TWO SHILLINGS

G210	black and brown p. 14	4·00	5·00
	a p. 15	£30	—

TWO SHILLINGS AND SIX PENCE

G211	lt blue and red-brn p. 14	9·00	5·00
G212	sl-blue and pur-brn p. 14	9·00	4·00
G213	greenish blue and pur-brown p. 14	8·00	5·00
G214	dp blue and ol-brn p. 15	£30	—

THREE SHILLINGS

G215	red-brn and tur-blue p. 14	£10	£10
G216	red-brn and grey-blue p. 14	£14	£10
G217	pur-brn and lt blue p. 15	£40	—

FIVE SHILLINGS

G218	steel blue and blue-grn p. 14	£22	£12
G219	steel blue and dp bluish green p. 14	£22	£12
G220	dp blue and bt grn p. 15	£45	—

SEVEN SHILLINGS AND SIX PENCE

G221	plum and blue-blk p. 14	£50	£60
G222	plum and grey-blk p. 14	£50	£60

TEN SHILLINGS

G223	car and bt grn p. 14 ..	£40	£35
G224	car and pl grn p. 14 ..	£40	£35

ONE POUND

G225	black and purple p. 14	£275	£220
	a p. 15	£300	—
G226	blk and reddish pur p. 14	£275	£220
G191-G225	p. 14 set (14v)	£400	£335
G193-G225a	p. 15 set (11v)	£450	—

Nos. G210a/214/217/220/225a were not sent out to Rhodesia and used copies consequently performed no postal service.

This series (G191/226) came from separate printings made in 1922 and in 1923, some values having been included in both printings. All the Perf. 15 stamps are from the 1923 printing.

The wove mesh of the paper shows clearly through the gum on the 1922 printings but is not so clearly seen on the 1923 printings.

The vast range of shades in all values of the "Admiral" issues was a result of uncertain supplies of printing inks during and immediately after the war, and of a shortage of skilled printers.

Various values of these issues may be found with a colour wash applied by hand to unprinted areas where the head had not been printed centrally within the frame.

Numbers printed (all printings)—2d., 11,300,400; 3d., 1,868,000; 4d., 744,000; 5d., 256,000; 6d., 2,988,000; 8d., 197,000; 10d., 178,000; 1/–, 2,293,500; 2/–, 1,084,000; 2/6, 402,200; 3/—, 92,800; 5/—, 165,100; 7/6, 30,080; 10/–, 79,000; £1, 102,201.

For subsequent issues see Southern Rhodesia (from 1924) and Northern Rhodesia (from 1925).

St. CHRISTOPHER

St. Christopher was the first British possession in the West Indies to be colonized, in 1623.

From May, 1858 to March, 1860 contemporary G.B. stamps were in use and were cancelled with "A12" in a transverse oval of horizontal bars.

An Uncrowned Circle PAID Frank was struck in red to indicate prepayment of postage on overseas letters from 1866 until the first St. Christopher stamps were issued. (See Introduction).

See also Leeward Islands.

1866-70. PAID Frank. *On Cover*

VF1 .. — £500

1858-60 Stamps of Great Britain identified by their Catalogue Nos. after prefix 'SC'.

Used at Basse-Terre : 'A12'

SC V39	1d. **rose-red** ..	..	
SC V51	2d. **blue** ..	..	..
SC V44	4d. **rose** ..	..	..
SC V45	6d. **lilac** ..	..	..
SC V47	1/– **green**	..	..

1870 (April 1st)-79. (*typo*). **De La Rue. Wmk. Crown CC. Sheets 5 x 4.**

(a) Perf. 12½.

V1	1d.	**dull rose** ..	£23	£21
	a wmk. sideways	..	£120	£100
V2	1d.	**magenta** ..	£17	£17
V3	1d.	**pale magenta** ..	£17	£17
V4	6d.	**green**	£40	£12
	a value doubly printed	—	—
V5	6d.	**yellow-green** ..	£40	£16

(b) Perf. 14. (1875-79).

V6	1d.	**magenta** ..	£30	£10
	a bisect vert or diag (½d.) on cover..	‡	£450
V7	1d.	**pale magenta** ..	£25	8 00
V8	2½d.	**red-brown** (11/79)..	£70	£55
V9	4d.	**blue** (11/79) ..	£70	£18
	a wmk. sideways ..	—	—
V10	6d.	**green**	£17	9·00
	a wmk. sideways ..	£90	—
	b imperf between (pair)	—	—

Die Proofs exist in black on white glazed card with blank value tablets, and in the colours of the 1d. and 6d.

1882-90. As before, but Wmk. Crown CA. (Perf. 14.).

V11	½d.	**dull green**	90	1 00
	a wmk. sideways ..	—	—
V12	1d.	**dull magenta** ..	£160	£50
	a bisect diag (½d.) on cover	‡	—

V13	1d.	**carmine-rose** ..	70	90
	a bisect diag (½d.) on cover	‡	—
V14	2½d.	**pale red-brown** ..	£80	£40
V15	2½d.	**deep red-brown** ..	£90	£45
V16	2½d.	**ultramarine** ..	2·20	2·50
V17	4d.	**blue**	£225	£30
V18	4d.	**grey**	1·75	2·00
V19	6d.	**olive-brown** ('90) ..	£90	£90
V20	1/–	**mauve** ('86) ..	£90	£85
V21	1/–	**bright mauve** ..	£95	£90
SPV19/20	**specimen set** (2v)	£60	‡

V13*a*—Three copies of this bisect, used with No. 13 on piece dated 4.1.87, are in the Royal Collection.

V13/16/18/19/20—Imperforate stamps are believed to have come from Proof sheets.

1885 (March). No. V13 surcharged "Half-penny" twice (diagonally in black serif letters) prior to bisection.

(a) Reading upwards.

V22	½d.	**on half 1d. car-rose**	£13	£22
	a surcharge double ..	—	—
	b surcharge inverted..	£200	£160
	c unsevered stamp ..	£60	£70

(b) Reading downwards.

V23	½d.	**on half 1d. car-rose**	—	—
	a surcharge double ..	—	—
	b surcharge inverted..	—	—
	c unsevered stamp ..	—	—

Type I   Type II

1885-86. No. V10 surcharged locally in black.

(a) Type I (March, 1885)

V24	4d.	**on 6d. green**	£25	£30
	a surcharge double ..	£750	—
	b stop after 'PENCE'..	£45	£50

(b) Type II. (June, 1886)

V25	4d.	**on 6d. green**	£30	£50
	a surcharge double ..	£750	£850
	b no stop after 'd' ..	£90	£100

Type I

ONE
PENNY.

Type II

1886-88. Nos. V10, V11 and V16 surcharged locally in black.

(a) Type I (V28 has no bar through original value).

V26	1d.	on 6d. **green** (6/86)	£11	£17
	a	surcharge double ..	—	£600
	b	surcharge inverted..	£2750	—
V27	1d.	on ½d. **dl grn** (5/87)..	£22	£25
V28	1d.	on 2½d. **ult** (5/88) ..	£5000	£5000

(b) Type II.

V29	1d.	on 2½d. **ult** (5/88) ..	£22	£27
	a	surcharge inverted..	£4000	£2750

V26*a* is only known used with violet or pen cancellation.

1890 (Feb.). No. V19/V20 of Antigua used provisionally at St. Christopher (Cancellation is 'A12' instead of 'AO2').

V30	1d.	**car-red or rose** ..	‡	£100
	a	on cover ..	‡	£350

POSTAL FISCALS

1883. Nos. V25, F6, F8 and F9 of Nevis overprinted 'Saint Christopher' in two lines diagonally in violet locally. On F4 the overprint is in smaller letters horizontally.

F1	1d.	**lilac**	..	..	£95	—
F2	4d.	**orange**..	..	..	£10	—
F3	6d.	**green** ..	..	..	£17	£22
F4	1/–	**mauve** ..	..	..	£20	—

1885. As Nos. V11/21 but in changed colours, and additional value, overprinted "SAINT KITTS/NEVIS/REVENUE" by De La Rue.

F5	1d.	**rose**	..	..	1·00	2·50
F6	3d.	**mauve** ..	..	..	2·50	7·50
F7	6d.	**orange-brown**	..	1·25	7·50
F8	1/–	**olive**	..	..	1·00	7·50
F9	5/–	**bistre** ..	..	..	£10	—

Numbers printed—F5, 35,640: F6, 10,000:
F7, 5,000: F8, 15,220.

F4 and F9 were probably not issued for postal use.

From November, 1890 until 1903 only the stamps of Leeward Islands were used in St. Christopher.

From 1903 the stamps of St. Kitts-Nevis were in concurrent use with those of Leeward Islands until June, 1956.

ST. HELENA

The island was discovered by the Portuguese in 1502 and was finally settled by the East India Company in 1659. Between 1815 and 1821 it was under military occupation during the exile of Napoleon; and it was ceded to the Crown in 1834.

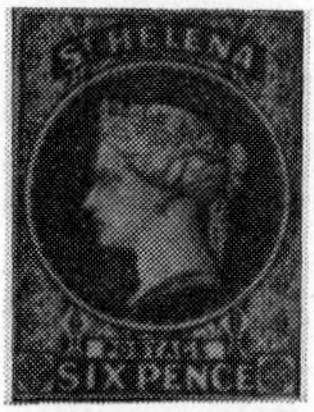

1856 (Jan.)-64 Recess Perkins, Bacon & Co. Wmk. Large Star. Sheets 12 x 20.

(a) Imperf.

V1	6d. **blue**	£250	£110

(b) Perf. 14-16 (Clean cut). 1861.

V2	6d. **blue**	£300	£100

(c) Perf. 14-16 (Rough). 1862-64.

V3	6d. **blue**	£175	£90

V1—Copies used prior to 1861 are normally cancelled in red.
Die Proofs exist in black on soft white card.
Plate Proofs exist in black.

Numbers printed—V1, 6,500; V2, 6,000; V3 46,080.

See also Nos. V21/22/28/32.

The Die, Transfer Roller and Plate were handed to the Agent General for Crown Colonies on January 28th, 1862, together with 456 sheets of imperforate stamps. Of this stock, 350 sheets were returned to Perkins Bacon for perforating in November 1863 and some of these stamps are No. V3.

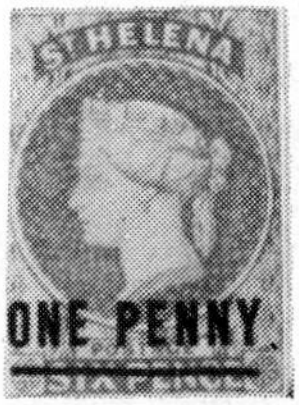

1863-80 Recess De La Rue (from the Perkins Bacon Plate). Wmk. Crown CC (rarely well centred: and known inverted, reversed, and inverted and reversed).

With the exception of the 6d. denomination (Nos. V21/22/28/32) these issues consist of 6d. stamps printed in different colours for each value and then surcharged in black sans serif capitals over a bar obliterating the 'SIX PENCE' (setting 12 x 5, applied four times to the sheet).

A. Imperf. (July 1863). Thin bar

1d. Type I	**Words**	**17 x $2\frac{3}{4}$mm.**	**Bar $16\frac{1}{2}$mm.**
Type II		**$18\frac{1}{2}$ x $2\frac{3}{4}$mm.**	**$18\frac{1}{2}$mm.**
4d.		**$16\frac{3}{4}$ x 3mm.**	**16mm.**

V4	1d. **lake** (Type I)	£55	£70
	a surcharge double ..	£1500	£800
	b surcharge omitted ..	—	—
V5	1d. **lake** (Type II)	£55	£45
	a se-tenant with Type I..	£500	—
V6	4d. **carmine**	£275	£100
	a surcharge double ..	£4000	£4000

V4*b* (12 copies) came from the bottom row of the same sheet on which V4*a* (12 copies) occurred.

It is likely that the carmine 6d. also existed without surcharge.

Die Proofs of the basic stamp exist in dark blue on unwatermarked paper and on glazed card.

Plate Proofs of V4/5 exist with the basic stamp in brown-red.

Numbers printed—V4/5, 16,560; V6, 10,800.

The dates given in the following Sections B, C, and D are those on which supplies were invoiced by De La Rue.

B. Perf. $12\frac{1}{2}$. (January 1864-July 1873).

(i) Thin Bar $16\frac{1}{2}$-17mm.

1d.	**Words**	**17-$17\frac{1}{2}$ x $2\frac{3}{4}$mm.**	**(1/64).**
3d.		**$17\frac{1}{2}$-18 x 3mm.**	**(12/67).**
4d.		**$16\frac{1}{2}$-17 x 3mm.**	**(1/64)**
1/–		**$17\frac{1}{2}$-18 x 3mm.**	**(1/64)**

V7	1d. **lake**	£12	£15
	a surcharge double ..	—	£800
V8	3d. **purple**	£25	£22
V9	4d. **carmine**	£25	£20
	a surcharge double ..	—	£2750
V10	1/– **dp yel-grn**	£40	£30
	a surcharge double ..	—	—

V7/9/10 are known with the bar omitted or misplaced to the top of the stamp.
Numbers printed—V7, 51,360; V8, 26,880; V9, 30,240; V10, 12,720.

(ii) Thick Bar 14-$14\frac{1}{2}$mm. (14-15mm. on No. V11).

1d.	**Words**	**$16\frac{1}{2}$-$17\frac{1}{2}$ x $2\frac{3}{4}$**	**(6/68)**
2d.		**15 x 3**	**(12/67)**
3d.		**$17\frac{1}{2}$-18 x 3**	**(7/73)**
4d. Type I		**$17\frac{3}{4}$-$18\frac{1}{4}$ x 3**	**(12/67)**
Type II		**$18\frac{3}{4}$-19 x 3**	**(12/67)**
1/–		**$16\frac{1}{2}$-17 x $2\frac{3}{4}$**	**(5/65)**
5/–		**18-$18\frac{1}{4}$ x $2\frac{3}{4}$**	**(12/67)**

V11	1d. **lake**	£22	£20
	a surcharge double ..	—	—
V12	2d. **yellow**	£30	£35
V13	3d. **purple**	£40	£40
	a surcharge double ..	—	£2500
V14	4d. **carmine** (Type I) ..	£22	£20
	a surcharge double ..	—	£2200
	b surcharge omitted ..	—	—
V15	4d. **carmine** (Type II) ..	£45	£40
	a surcharge double ..	—	—
	b surcharge double (Types I and II) ..	£6000	£6000
	c se-tenant with Type I	—	—
V16	1/– **deep yellow-green**	£100	£50
	a surcharge double ..	£5000	—
	b surcharge omitted ..	—	—
V17	5/– **dp orange-yellow** ..	£90	£90

V14*b*/16*b*—(12 copies each). These errors arose from the method of surcharging the sheet four times (each 12 x 5): in the case of V16*b* the double surcharge occurred across Row 5 and the omission of surcharge on Row 10. There are also 12 copies each of V14*a* and V16*a*.

V11/V16 are all known imperf. It is believed these varieties came from Proof sheets, but a used copy of No. V11 is reputed to exist.

Numbers printed—V11, 48,000; V12, 27,360; V13, 11,520; V14/15, 50,880; V16, 48,852; V17, 12,960.

Net sales of V17 were 7,632, the balance of 5,328 being sold as remainders (cancelled with violet diamond shaped mark in the centre of each block of four) in 1898.
See Note after No. V44.

(iii) Thin Bar 18mm. (16½-17mm on No. V18).

1d. Words 17-17½ x 3mm. (taller, thinner letters than No. V7) (3/71).

2d.		**18**	x 3mm.	**(7/73)**
1/-		**17½-17¾** x 3mm.		**(3/71)**

V18	1d.	**lake**		8·00	8·00
		a surcharge in blue-black		£300	£230
		b blue-black surcharge double		—	—
V19	2d.	**yellow**		£27	£10
		a surcharge in blue-black		£2750	£1800
V20	1/-	**deep green**		£90	9·00
		a surcharge in blue-black		—	—
		b short topped 'E'		£200	£30

V20*b*—The 'E' in 'ONE' has a short top (Row 7/6).

Numbers printed—V18, 96,730; V19, 10,320; V20, 49,920.

(IV) Without surcharge.

V21	6d. **dull blue** (3/71)		£150	£50
V22	6d. **ultramarine** (7/73)		£120	£40

Numbers printed—V21, 12,480; V22, 24,960.

C. Perf. 14 x 12½. (July 1876).

(i) Thick Bars as B(ii) (V11/17) except words on No. V26 measure 16½mm.

V23	1d.	**lake**	£14	9·00
V24	2d.	**yellow**	£25	£20
V25	3d.	**purple**	£75	£30
V26	4d.	**carmine**	£75	£30

Numbers printed—V3, 66,000; V24, 24,000; V25, 12,240; V26, 12,960.

(ii) Thin Bars as B(iii) (V18/20).

V27	1/- **deep green**	£90	£15

Number printed—34,080.

(iii) Without surcharge.

V28	6d. **milky blue**	£55	£15

Number printed—47,520.

D. Perf. 14. (January 1880).

(i) Thick Bars as B(ii) (V11/17).

V29	1d.	**lake**	£15	9·00
		a bisect vert (½d.) on piece	‡	—

V30	2d.	**yellow**	£35	£15
V31	1/-	**yellow-green**	£18	£10

Numbers printed—V29, 75,120; V30, 24,000; V31, 48,000.

(ii) Without surcharge.

V32	6d. **milky blue**	£55	£15

Number printed—24.960.

1884-94 As before but Wmk. Crown CA (rarely well centred: and known inverted, reversed and inverted and reversed). Perf. 14.

With the exception of the 6d. denomination (No. V43) this issue also consists of 6d. stamps printed in different colours for each value and then surcharged in black sans serif capitals over a bar obliterating the 'SIX PENCE' (except No. V38 which is surcharged in large figures). Setting ½d., 12 x 20: 2½d. 6 x 10 and other values 12 x 5, applied four times to the sheet.

Thick Bars as B(ii) (V11/17).

½d.	Type I	Words	17-17½ x 3mm.
	Type II		14-14½ x 3mm.
2½d.		Bar	13-14mm.
4d.	Type I	Words	16½ x 3mm.
	Type II		17 x 3mm.

Thin Bars as B(iii) (V18/20).

1/-		Bar	17½mm.

V33	½d.	**emerald** (Type I)	3·25	4·00
		a spaced 'NY'	4·00	—
		b surcharge double	5·00	—
		c surcharge double and spaced 'NY'	1·25	1·75
V34	½d.	**green** (Type I)	—	—
		a spaced 'NY'	1·00	1·25
V35	½d.	**dp green** (Type II) ('93)	1·00	1·50
V36	1d.	**red** (11/87)	3·00	4·00
V37	2d.	**yellow** ('94)	1·50	2·00
V38	2½d.	**ultramarine** (9/93)		
		a stamp doubly printed	£2000	—
		b surcharge double	£3000	—
V39	3d.	**mauve** (5/87)	2·00	2·50
		a surcharge double	—	—
V40	3d.	**violet** (5/87)	4·00	5·00
		a surcharge double	—	—
V41	4d.	**pl brown** (Type I) (4/90)	5·00	6·50
		a additional bar	£120	—
V42	4d.	**sepia** (Type II)	6·00	5·50
		a additional bar	£120	—
V43	6d.	**grey** (5/87)	6·00	5·50
V44	1/-	**yellow-green** ('94)	£18	£20
		a surcharge double	—	—
		b short topped 'E'	£140	—
V33/44		**set** (8v)	£30	£32
SPV33/44		**specimen set** (6v)	£35	‡

V33*a*/34*a*—The 'N' and 'Y' in PENNY are spaced 1¼mm. (Row 18/12).

V38*a*—The top row only (12 copies) of one sheet was double printed.

V38*b*—Row 10/1–6 were doubly surcharged on one sheet only. The Royal Collection contains a block of six (Row 9–11/6–7) in which the double surcharge is included se-tenant horizontally with normal.

V41*a*42/*a*—An additional long thin bar occurs on Row 7/4.

V44*b*—The 'E' in 'ONE' has a short top. (Row 7/6).

V44*a*—The last seven stamps in the first row and all stamps in Rows 2, 3 and 4 were doubly surcharged on one sheet (the fifth row being normal).

V38—The surcharges in the 3rd and 9th vertical rows are larger or more heavily printed, than in other rows.

V33/44 may all be found without watermark (from Row 12) and with bars omitted or misplaced.

Stamps of this issue are known with Trial Perforation 12. Similarly perforated stamps without surcharge are Colour Trials.

Numbers issued—V33/34, 324,480; V35, 144,000; V36, 261,600; V37, 84,000; V38, 142,560; V39/40, 131,520; V41/42, 108,000; V43, 166,560; V44, 24,480.

The following Remainders of this issue (together with Remainders of No. V17 and Nos. V45/51) were sold in 1898.

½d., 208,320; 1d., 142,560; 2d., 32,080; 2½d., 104,400; 3d., 75,840; 4d., 82,800; 6d., 58,400; 1/–, 18,120.

The majority were cancelled with a special diamond-shaped postmark in violet, impressed at the centre of each block of four. The violet postmark can be removed, and Collectors are warned of cleaned unused stamps, and also of cleaned and bogus-postmarked stamps.

See Introduction for details of Dies I and II.

1890 (March)-97 Typo De La Rue. Wmk. Crown CA. Perf. 14. Sheets 240 – four panes, each 6 x 10. 1½d.—Die I: other values—Die II. (Plates 2 and 3).

V45	½d. **green** (1/97) ..	1·20	1·50
V46	1d. **carmine** (10/96) ..	2·25	2·50
V47	1½d. **red-brn and grn** (3/90)	2·50	2·50
V48	2d. **or-yel** (10/96) ..	2·50	3·75
V49	2½d. **ultramarine** (10/96)	4·00	5·00
V50	5d. **violet** (10/96) ..	7·00	£11
V51	10d. **brown** (10/96) ..	£11	£15
V45/51	**set** (7v)	£30	£40
SPV45/51	**specimen set** (7v)..	£75	‡

Numbers printed—V45, 102,000 (Plate 2); V46, 101,400 (Plate 2); 47, 120,000; V48, 100,800; V49, 101,400; V50, 60,600; V51, 60,600.

Remainders of this issue (including 72,960 copies of V47) were sold in 1898. See Note after No. V44.

1902 (Feb.–24th)-11 Typo De La Rue. Perf 14. Sheets 120 two panes, each. 6 x 10.

(a) Wmk. Crown CA.

E1	½d. **green** (3/02)	50	75
E2	1d. **carmine**	1·50	2·00
E3	10/– **green and red/green** (5/08) (C)	£200	£250

(b) Wmk. Multiple Crown CA.

E4	2½d. **blue** (5/08)	1·50	2·50
E5	4d. **blk and red/yel** (OC)	1·75	3·00
	a on straw coloured	1·75	3·00
E6	6d. **dl and dp pur** (OC)..	2·50	5·00
SPE1/6	**specimen set** (6v) ..	£135	‡

E5/6—Chalky paper May 1908; Ordinary paper 1911.

1903 (June) Typo De La Rue. Wmk. Crown CC. Perf. 14. Sheets 12 x 5.

E7	½d. **brn and grey-grn** ..	1·00	1·50
	a on bluish paper ..	£55	£40
E8	1d. **black and carmine** ..	1·25	1·75
	a on bluish paper ..	£55	£40
E9	2d. **blk and sage-green** ..	6·00	6·00
	a on bluish paper ..	£55	£40
E10	8d. **black and brown** ..	£11	£13
E11	1/– **brn and brn-orange**..	£17	£20
E12	2/– **black and violet** ..	£20	£25
E7/12	**set** (6v)	£55	£65
SPE7/12	**specimen set** (6v) ..	£75	‡

Die Proofs of the vignettes and of the frames exist in black on glazed card.

There were 19 different Colour Trials of No. E8, all imperf on Wmk. Crown CA paper.

1911 Prepared for use but not issued. As No. E8 but Wmk. Multiple Crown CA.

E13	1d. **red**	—	—
SPE13	**specimen** (1v) ..	£170	‡

These stamps were supplied in error against a repeat order for No. E2. With the exception of a very small number of copies, the whole supply was destroyed.

1912-13 As Nos. E1/6 but Head of King George V. Wmk. Multiple Crown CA.

(a) Inscribed "Postage & Revenue" (1912).

G1	4d. blk and red/yellow (C)	2·00	8·50
G2	6d. dl and dp purple (C) ..	2·50	8·50

(b) Inscribed "Postage Postage" (1913).

G3	4d. blk and red/yellow (O)	2·50	5·00
	a split 'A'	£24	—
G4	6d. dl and dp purple (O) ..	5·00	£11
	a split 'A'	£40	—
SPG1/4 specimen set (4v) ..		£60	‡

G3a/4a The apex of 'A' in POSTAGE is split in the right hand panel (No. 45 : left pane).

1912-22 As Nos. E7/12 but Head of King George V.

(a) Wmk. Multiple Crown CA. (1912-16).

G5	½d. black and green	..	40	50
	a "thick paper"		£30	£16
G6	1d. blk and car-red	..	50	70
G7	1d. blk and scar ('16)	..	£20	£16
G8	1½d. black and orange	..	1·50	2·00
G9	2d. blk and greyish-sl	..	1·50	2·00
G10	2½d. black and bt blue	..	1·50	3·00
G11	3d. blk and pur/yel	..	2·00	3·00
G12	8d. blk and dl purple	..	6·00	9·00
G13	1/– black/green ..	..	9·00	£13
G14	2/– black and blue/blue	..	£18	£22
G15	3/– black and violet	..	£25	£30
G5/15	set (10v)	..	£60	£80
SPG5/15 specimen set (10v)		£100	‡

(b) Wmk. Multiple Script CA. (January 1922).

G16	1d. green ..	..	60	2·00
G17	1½d. rose-scarlet	..	4·00	6·50
G18	3d. bright blue ..	..	8·00	£11
G16/18	set (3v)	..	£12	£18
SPG16/18 specimen set (3v)		£35	‡

G5 may be found on both thick and thin papers.

G7 was a war-time printing as was G5a on paper much thicker than No. G6.

Die Proofs exist in black on glazed card and of all values in the issued colours.

Type I	Type II

1916-19 War Tax. No. G6/7 overprinted and surcharged in black by De La Rue.

(a) Type I on thin paper. (Sept. 1916).

G19	1d. + 1d. blk and scar ..	30	60

	a surcharge double ..	—	—
SPG19	specimen (1v)	£20	‡

(b) Type II on thick or thin paper. (1919).

G20	1d. + 1d. blk and car-red	30	40
SPG20	specimen (1v)	£20	‡

1922-27 Typo De La Rue. Designer T. Bruce. Perf. 14. Sheets 12 x 5.

(a) Wmk. Multiple Crown CA. (Chalky paper).

G21	4d. grey and blk/yel		2·00	4·50
	a cleft rock ..	..	£80	—
	b torn flag ..	..	£70	—
	c split mast ..	..	£80	—
G22	1/6 grey and grn/blu-green	..	£25	£35
	a torn flag ..	..	£250	—
G23	2/6 grey and red/yel	..	£30	£40
	a torn flag ..	..	£350	—
G24	5/– grey and grn/yel	..	£40	£50
	a torn flag ..	..	£325	—
G25	£1 grey and pur/red	..	£200	£275
	a torn flag ..	..	£900	—
G21/25	set (5v)	..	£290	£400
SPG21/25 specimen set (5v)		£220	‡

Numbers printed : G21, 120,720 ; G22, 10,080 ; G23, 9,120 ; G24, 7,620 ; G25, 5,880.

(b) Wmk. Multiple Script CA. (Chalky paper except Nos. G40/42/43).

G26	½d. grey and black	..	30	30
	a wmk inverted..		£80	—
G27	1d. grey and green	..	40	40
G28	1d. grey and blue-grn	..	30	30
G29	1½d. rose ..	..	2·00	2·50
G30	1½d. rose-carmine	..	£10	8·00
G31	1½d. dp carmine-red	..	£65	£100
G32	2d. grey and slate	..	80	80
G33	2d. grey and grey-grn	..	1·50	2·00
G34	3d. bright blue ..	..	1·00	1·50
G35	3d. pale blue ..	..	60	1·00
	a wmk reversed	..	£55	—
G36	5d. grn and car/grn ('27)	..	3·00	4·00
G37	6d. grey and bt purple	..	3·50	6·00
G38	8d. grey and bt violet..	..	3·00	8·00
G39	1/– grey and brown	..	6·00	£12
G40	1/6 grey and grn/grn..	..	8·50	£12
G41	2/– pur and blu/blu ('27)	..	8·50	£12
G42	2/6 grey and red/yel	..	£10	£15
G43	5/– grey and grn/yel	..	£20	£25
G44	7/6 grey and yel-or	..	£35	£45
G45	10/– grey and ol-grn	..	£80	£85

G46 15/- **grey and pur/blue** £600 £650
G26/46 **set** (16v) £800 £850
SPG26/46 **specimen set** (16v) £350 ‡

G28 may be found with thin white or thick yellow gum.

G31 is on thick paper with dark brown gum.

G34/35 exist with watermark reversed.

The grey vignettes vary in shade on most values from a brownish-grey to almost black.

Varieties (a) Cleft rock Row 5/1.

(b) Torn flag, Row 4/6.

(c) Split mast, Row 2/1.

		(a)	(b)	(c)
G26	½d.'	£20	£50	£20
G27/28	1d.	£30	£35	£30
G29	1¼d.	£60	£60	£50
G30	1½d.	£220	‡	£220
G31	1½d.	£300	‡	£300
G32/33	2d.	£40	£40	£40
G34/35	3d.	£45	£60	£50
G36	5d.	£50	‡	£75
G37	6d.	£100	£80	£60
G38	8d.	£120	£90	£90
G39	1/-	£120	£150	£60
G40	1/6	£220	‡	£220
G41	2/-	£220	‡	£200
G42	2/6	£180	‡	£180
G43	5/-	£250	‡	£250
G44	7/6	£400	£300	£400
G45	10/-	‡	£350	‡
G46	15/-	‡	£1350	‡

Prices are for unused copies. Fine used examples are less frequently found and command a substantial premium over these prices.

The 'Cleft Rock' and 'Split Mast' varieties did not occur on the first printing (G22-G25, G45/46 and numbers as shown of G27/28-23,880; G37-15,900; G39-13,920; G44-6,480).

The 'Torn Flag' variety occured on the first and second (Feb. 1923) printings, but was repaired in 1926 and did not occur on susequent printings.

Numbers printed (All printings): G26, 391,920; G27/28, 357,600; G29, 118,440; G30/G31, 44,160; G32/33, 332,040; G34/35, 120,540; G36, 63,390; G37, 78,300; G38, 131,160; G39, 49,920; G40, 20,220; G41, 20,760; G42, 20,460; G43, 21,240; G44, 11,820; G45, 6,720; G46, 6,460.

G43-G46 were mainly required for Stamp Duty use vide Ordinance No. 3 of March 30 1922, and the majority of those used were for this purpose.

Imperf. Colour Trials of G27/28 exist on un-watermarked paper in mauve and green, orange and green, green and brown.

1934 (April 23rd) Centenary of British Sovereignty. Recess Bradbury Wilkinson. Wmk. Multiple Script CA. Perf. 12. Sheets 6 x 10 (except No. G54 – 10 x 6).

G47	½d. **black and purple** ..	50	70
G48	1d. **black and green** ..	1·00	1·20
G49	1½d. **black and scarlet**..	1·75	2·00
G50	2d. **black and orange** ..	2·25	2·50
G51	3d. **black and blue** ..	3·50	4·50
G52	6d. **black and lt blue** ..	6·00	7·00
G53	1/- **black and sepia** ..	£12	£17
G54	2/6 **black and crimson**	£27	£35
G55	5/- **blk and choc** ..	£50	£65
G56	10/- **black and purple** ..	£185	£200
G47/56	**set** (10v)	£275	£325
SPG47/56	**specimen set** (10v)	£125	‡

1935 (May 6th) Silver Jubilee. Recess De La Rue. Wmk. Multiple Script CA. Perf. 13½ x 14. Sheets 6 x 10.

G57	1½d. **indigo and red** ..	30	40
G58	2d. **ult and grey** ..	60	70
G59	6d. **green and indigo** ..	3·00	3·50
G60	1/- **slate and purple** ..	7·50	8·00
G57/60	**set** (4v)	£11	£12
SPG57/60	**specimen set** (4v)	£20	‡

Remainders were withdrawn on December 31st 1935.

1938 (May 12th) -51 Design (Badge of Colony, Three-masted sailing vessel, flying St. George's Cross, off Headlands, King and

Queen Rocks). (Recess) Waterlow & Sons. Perf. 12½ (L). Sheets 6 x 10.

1	½d. **violet**	10	10
2	1d. **green**	5·00	5·00
3	1d. **orange-yel** (8/7/40) ..	10	15
	a dp yellow (/45) ..	3·00	3·00
4	1d. **blk and grn** (1/11/49)	30	40
5	1½d. **scarlet**	15	15
	a carmine-red (24/5/44)	20	20
6	1½d. **blk and carmine-rose**		
	(1/11/49)	40	60
7	2d. **orange**	20	20
	a pale red-orange		
	(24/5/44)	15	15
8	2d. **blk and car** (1/11/49)	40	60
9	3d. **ultramarine**	£20	£12
10	3d. **grey** (8/7/40)	30	30
	a slate (24/5/44) ..	25	25
11	4d. **ultramarine** (8/7/40) .	25	30
	a bt ult (24/5/44) ..	30	30
12	6d. **dull light blue** ..	30	35
	a sky-blue (24/5/44) .	20	30
13	8d. **sage-green** (8/7/40) .	60	60
	a olive-green (24/5/44)	1·25	2·00
	b dp olive-grn (8/11/51)	50	60
14	1/- **sepia**	60	70
	a dp sepia (4/6/50) ..	50	40
15	2/6 **claret**	2·00	2·00
	a. bright claret ..	1·50	1·75
16	5/- **light choc-brown** ..	3·50	3·50

17	10/- **dp purple**	7·00	8·00
1/17	**set** (17)	£38	£34
SP 1/17	**specimen set** perf (12)	£70	‡

Nos. 1, 3, 5, 7 and 10 are known overprinted "ROYAL VISIT/29th. APRIL,/1947", but the status of the overprint is uncertain (set price £90).

SPECIAL ISSUES

1937 (May 19th) Coronation. As Aden.

S1	1d. **green**	15	20
S2	2d. **orange**	40	30
S3	3d. **blue**	50	50
SP S1/3	**specimen set** perf (3)	£14	‡

1946 (Oct. 21st) Victory. As Aden.

S4	2d. **reddish-orange** ..	20	20
S5	4d. **grey-blue**	20	20
SP S4/5	**specimen set** perf (2)	£14	‡

1948 (Oct. 20th) Silver Wedding. As Aden.

S6	3d. **black**	20	25
S7	10/- **slate-violet**	6·00	7·00

1949 (Oct. 10th) U.P.U. As Aden.

S8	3d. **carmine-rose** ..	15	30
S9	4d. **indigo**	40	50
S10	6d. **dull olive**	1·00	1·25
S11	1/- **slate-black**	1·50	1·60
S8/11	**set** (4)	3·00	3·50

St. KITTS-NEVIS

See under NEVIS and ST. CHRISTOPHER for details of the early Postal History and previous issues.

1903 Printers (typo) De La Rue & Co. Wmk. Crown CA. Perf. 14.

E1	½d. purple and dp green	2·00	1·50
E2	1d. grey-blk and carmine	2·50	75
E3	2d. purple and brown ..	3·00	£10
E4	2½d. grey-blk and blue ..	£12	8·00
E5	3d. grn and orange ..	5·00	7·50
E6	6d. grey-blk and purple	6·50	8·50
E7	1/– grn and brn orange	7·00	9·00
E8	2/– green and black ..	£15	£12
E9	2/6 grey-blk and violet	£22	£30
E10	5/– dull pur and sage grn	£40	£45
E1/10	set (10)	£110	£130
SP E1/10	specimen set (10) ..	£85	‡

1905-9 Wmk. Mult Crown CA. Perf. 14.

E11	½d. pur and dp grn (O)..	4·50	5·00
E12	1d. grey-blk and car (C)	1·00	1·00
E13	2d. reddish pur and pale brn (C)	1·20	2·00
	a dull pur and dp brn (OC)	1·20	2·00
E14	2½d. grey-blk and blue (O)	£12	7·00
E15	3d. grn and orange (OC)	2·00	2·50
E16	6d. grey-blk and vio (O)	7·00	£12
	a grey-blk and dp pur (C)	4·75	9·00
E17	1/– grey-green and brn-orange (O) ..	3·00	80
	a grn and yel-or (C)	2·75	80
E11/17	set (7)	£27	£27

1907-18 Wmk. Mult Crown CA. Perf. 14.

E18/20 O; E21/22 C.

E18	½d. grey-green	70	90
	a green	60	50
	b dull blue green ..	30	1·00
	c deep blue green ..	40	70
E19	1d. carmine	1·00	40
	a rose-red	60	40
	b scarlet	50	35
E20	2½d. ultramarine	1·00	1·25
	a bright blue	1·00	1·20
E21	6d. grey-blk and bt pur	4·75	9·00
E22	5/– dl purple and sage-green	£35	£40
E18/22	set (5)	£40	£50
SPE18/20	specimen set (3)	£35	‡

1916 (Oct.). No. E18 overprinted in black.

G1	½d. dull blue-green ..	15	20
	a deep green	20	25
	b wmk. reversed ..	—	—
SPG1	specimen set (1) ..	£25	‡

1918 (Aug.). Special printing. (Wmk. Mult. Crown CA.) overprinted in black.

G2	1½d. orange	20	25
SPG2	specimen (1) ..	£25	‡

1920-22 Printers (typo) De La Rue & Co. Wmk. Mult. Crown CA. (sideways) Perf. 14. Sheets 5 x 12.

G3/7 O; G8/15 C.

G3	½d. blue-green	50	30
G4	1d. carmine	50	50
G5	1½d. dull orange	60	1·00
	a yellow orange ..	50	1·00
G6	2d. slate grey	2·50	3·50
	a deep slate	2·25	3·00
G7	2½d. ultramarine	1·00	1·50
G8	3d. purple/yellow ..	1·00	2·50
G9	6d. dl and bt mauve ..	2·50	5·00
G10	1/– grey and black/blue-green	1·50	4·00
	a brn-grey and blk on grn	2·00	4·00
G11	2/– pur and blue/blue ..	9·00	£10
G12	2/6 grey and red/blue ..	9·00	£15
G13	5/– grn and red/yellow	£12	£22
G14	10/– grn and red/grn ..	£28	£35
G15	£1 pur and blk/red ..	£225	£285
G3/15	set (13)	£290	£385
SP G3/15	specimen set (15)..	£195	‡

1921/9 Wmk. Mult. Script CA. (sideways). Perf. 14. G16/24 O; G25/30 C.

G16	½d.	**deep green** ..	20	25
	a	deep blue green ..	20	25
	b	dull blue green ..	20	25
	c	yellow green ..	2·00	1·25
G17	1d.	**rose carmine**	30	35
	a	rose red	30	35
G18	1d.	**deep violet**	1·25	40
	a	dull violet	30	30
	b	bright mauve ..	30	30
G19	1½d.	**rose red**	90	1·25
	a	carmine red ..	1·00	1·50
G20	1½d.	**red brown**	35	40
G21	2d.	**grey**	35	40
	a	slate grey ..	35	40
G22	2½d.	**pale bright blue** ..	1·25	4·25
	a	ultramarine ..	1·75	1·00
	b	ultramarine (**C**) ..	80	2·50
G23	2½d.	**brown**	1·00	2·75
G24	3d.	**dull ultramarine**	80	1·50
	a	bright ultramarine ..	1·00	1·70
G25	3d.	**dp pur/golden yel** ..	1·00	1·50
	a	pur/yel	1·00	1·50
	b	pur/pale yel ..	1·00	1·50
G26	6d.	**dull and bt pur** ..	1·50	2·75
G27	1/-	**blk/emerald** ..	5·50	7·00
G28	2/-	**pur and blue/blue** ..	5·50	8·00
G29	2/6	**blk and red/blue** ..	£11	£14
G30	5/-	**grn and red/lemon**	£20	£27
	a	grn and red/pale yellow ..	£15	£18
G16/30		**set** (15)	£47	£66

SP G16/30 **specimen set** (15) overprinted or perforated .. ..   £175   ‡

1923. Tercentenary of Colony. (*Typo*) **De La Rue & Co. Wmk. Mult. Script CA (sideways). Perf. 14. Chalk-surfaced paper. Sheets 5 x 12.**

G31	½d.	**black and green** ..	1·50	1·50
G32	1d.	**black and bt violet** ..	1·50	1·50
G33	1½d.	**black and red** ..	2·00	3·00
G34	2d.	**black and slate grey**	2·00	3·00
G35	2½d.	**black and brown** ..	3·50	4·00
G36	3d.	**black and ult** ..	4·00	7·00
G37	6d.	**black and bt purple** .	8·00	£11
G38	1/-	**black and olive grn** .	£11	£15
G39	2/-	**black and blue/blue** .	£16	£25
G40	2/6	**black and red/blue** .	£30	£35
G41	10/-	**black and red/em** ..	£225	£375

Wmk. Mult. Crown CA. (sideways).

G42	5/-	**blk and red/yellow** ..	£120	£200
G43	£1	**blk and purple/red** ..	£1100	£1250
G31/43		**set** (13)	£1500	£1750

SPG 31/43 **specimen set** (13) £600   ‡

1935 (May 6th) Silver Jubilee. (*Recess*) **Waterlow & Sons. Wmk. Script CA. Perf. 11 x 12. Sheets 6 x 10.**

G44	1d.	**indigo and red** ..	30	50
G45	1½d.	**ult and grey** ..	50	80
G46	2½d.	**brn and deep blue** ..	80	1·50
G47	1/-	**slate and deep pur** .	4·00	6·00
G44/47		**set** (4)	5·00	7·50

SP G44/47 **specimen set** perf (4) .. .. .. £20   ‡

Number issued—G44, 71,380; G45, 60,300; G46, 52,380; G47, 41,690.

1938 (Aug. 15th) -50 Designs, ½d., 1d., 1½d. 2½d. (**King's Head**) (*small format*), **Perf. 13¾ x 14** (**C**), sheets 120—two panes, each 6 x 10. 2d., 3d., 1/-, 2/6 (**King's Head and Seal of Nevis, Hygeia administering Stream of Life**); 6d., 5/- (**King's Head and Seal of St. Kitts, Columbus sighting Island of St. Christopher**) (*large format*), **Perf. 13 x 11¾** (**C**). **Printers** (*typo*) **De La Rue. Designs,** ½d., 1d., 1½d., 2½d. V, **Others H. Sheets 5 x 12.**

1	½d.	**green**	10	10
	a	blue-green (4/5/43) .	10	10
2	1d.	**scarlet-rose** ..	20	20
	a	carmine (4/5/43) ..	15	15
	b	rose-pink (23/4/47)	£10	£10
	c	rose-red (29/7/47) ..	15	15
3	1½d.	**orange**	10	10
	a	pale orange(27/3/44)	10	10
4	2d.	**scarlet and grey** (thin paper)	5·00	2·00
	a	scar and slate (*ch*) (/40)	4·00	2·50
5	2½d.	**dull ultramarine** ..	60	60
	a	bt ultramarine (4/5/43)	15	15
6	3d.	**dull lilac and scarlet** (thin paper) ..	1·00	1·00
	a	dull lilac and scarlet (ch) (/40)	80	80
7	6d.	**dull grn and dp pur** ..	1·00	1·00

8	1/– **greyish-blk and grn**..	1·50	1·50
9	2/6 **greyish-blk and red**..	6·00	7·50
10	5/– **dull green and red** ..	£12	£14
SP 1/10 **specimen set** perf (10)		£48	‡

With the exception of Nos. 5a and 6a all the above are on thin paper.

No. 2b is considerably paler than other printings and care in purchasing should be exercised.

As Nos. 5—10, but Perf. 14 (L).

11	2d. **scarlet and grey** (thin paper) (/41)	35	35
	a scarlet and slate (thin paper) (/41) ..	5·00	3·50
	b scarlet and grey (ch) (28/7/49) ..	20	20
12	3d. **dull pur and scarlet** (ch) (/42) ..	4·00	3·00
	aa dull purple and bt scar (sub) (/42) ..	£17	8·00
	aaa deep violet and purple (ch) (/47) ..	£18	9·00
	a dull pur and scar (sub) (4/5/43) ..	50	50
	b pale pur and ver-red (ch) (7/6/50) ..	15	15
13	6d. **dull grn and dp purple** (ch) (/42) ..	9·00	8·50
	aa dull green and purple (sub) (/43) ..	1·50	1·25
	a dull green and red-pur (sub) (/43) ..	1·00	1·00
	b dull grn and light red-pur (ch) (29/7/47)	40	30
14	1/– **black and green** (sub) (4/5/43) ..	2·00	1·50
	aa blk, dp grn (sub) (/45)	1·00	1·50
	a black and green (ch) (28/7/49) ..	50	50
15	2/6 **blk and red** (ch) (/42)	£10	£12
	a black and red (sub) (4/5/43) ..	2·00	2·50
	b black and red (ch) thicker paper than 15 (/49) ..	1·75	2·00
16	5/– **dull green and scarlet** (ch) (/42) ..	£15	£15
	a grey-grn and scarlet (sub) (4/5/43) ..	4·00	5·50
	b grey-grn and dp scarlet (ch) (7/6/50) ..	4·00	5·00

1948 (Sept. 1st) Design, Map of Islands. Perf. 13¾ x 14 (C). Chalk-surfaced paper. Sheets 6 x 10.

17	10/– **black and dp blue** ..	9·00	£12
18	£1 **black and choc-brn** ..	£16	£20
1/18	**set** (12) cheaper perf ..	£34	£40

Supplies of Nos. 12, 12aa, 13, 15 and 16 were sent to the Colony November 12th, 1941, but not put on sale until several months later.

1952 (June 14th) Designs, 1c. (Bath House,

Nevis); 2c. (Warner Park, St. Kitts); 3c. (Map of Islands); 4c. (Brimstone Hill, St. Kitts); 5c. (Nevis from Sea); 6c. (Pinney's Beach) Nevis); 12c. (Sir T. Warner's Tomb, St. Kitts); 24c. (Old Road Bay, St. Kitts); 48c. (Cotton Plantation, Nevis); 60c. (Treasury, St. Kitts); $1.20 (Salt Pond, Anguilla); $4.80 (Sugar Factory, St. Kitts). Printers (recess) Waterlow & Sons. Perf. 12½ (L). Designs, 1c., 2c., 4c., 5c., 6c., 24c. to $4.80 H. Sheets 5 x 10 or 10 x 5.

19	1c. **olive-grn and orange-buff**	15	15
20	2c. **emerald-green** ..	20	15
21	3c. **red and violet** ..	20	20
22	4c. **red**	25	20
23	5c. **blue and grey** ..	30	30
24	6c. **ultramarine** ..	40	40
25	12c. **blue and brown** ..	50	50
26	24c. **black and dp red** ..	65	65
27	48c. **olive-grn and choc**	1·50	1·25
28	60c. **orange and dp green**	1·50	2·50
29	$1.20 **green and ult** ..	5·00	4·00
30	$4.80 **emerald and carmine**	£10	£14
19/30	**set** (12)	£20	£24

SPECIAL ISSUES

1937 (May 12th) Coronation. As Aden.

S1	1d. **scarlet**	15	10
S2	1½d. **light brown** ..	15	15
S3	2½d. **blue**	30	35
SPS1/3	**specimen set** perf (3)	£14	‡

1946 (Nov. 1st) Victory. As Aden.

S4	1½d. **orange**	10	10
S5	3d. **carmine-red** ..	15	15
SPS4/5	**specimen set** perf (2)	£14	‡

1949 (Jan. 3rd) Silver Wedding As Aden.

S6	2½d. **ultramarine** ..	10	10
S7	5/– **rose-carmine** ..	3·50	4·50

1949 (Oct. 10th) U.P.U. As Aden.

S8	2½d. **dull violet-blue** ..	20	40
S9	3d. **carmine** ..	30	50
S10	6d. **reddish-mauve** ..	80	1·00
S11	1/– **quartz-green** ..	1·25	1·50
S8/11	**set** (4) ..	2·50	3·00

1950 (Nov. 10th) Tercentenary of British Settlement in Anguilla. As Nos. 2—8, but Nos. S15—7 Perf. 13 x 12½ (C) overprinted by De La Rue in black or red.

S12	1d. **rose-red** ..	10	15
S13	1½d. **orange**	10	15
S14	2½d. **blue**	15	15
S15	3d. **dull purple and red**..	10	15
S16	6d. **dull grn and red-pur**	40	80
S17	1/– **black and green** (red)	50	1·00
S12/17	**set** (6) ..	1·25	2·25

Watermark Varieties (Type B)

(See Introduction for details).

S13a	1½d. Crown Missing ..	£360	—
S13b	St. Edward's Crown	£250	—

1951 (Feb. 16th) West Indies University College. (See Antigua.)

S18	3c. **black and orange** ..	25	40
S19	12c. **grn and lake-magenta**	40	70

O

St. LUCIA

The island changed hands many times from 1790, but was finally ceded to Great Britain by the Congress of Vienna in 1814. It now forms part of the Windward Islands.

Following the use of hand-stamps or other manuscript marks, a Crowned Circle PAID Frank was registered at the G.P.O. in London on May 1st, 1844; and was thereafter struck in red to indicate prepayment of postage on overseas letters. (See Introduction).

From May, 1858 to April,1860 contemporary G.B. stamps were in use and were cancelled with "A11" in a transverse oval of horizontal bars.

The Crowned Circle Frank was again used from May 1st, 1860 until the first St. Lucia stamps were issued. The Frank was also used in black as late as May 9th, 1904 during a shortage of 1d. stamps.

1844-60 PAID Frank   *On Cover*
VF1   ..   £700

1858-60 Stamps of Great Britain identified by their Catalogue Nos. after prefix 'SL'

Used at Castries : 'A11'

SL V39	1d.	**rose-red**	.. ..
SL V36A	2d.	**blue** ..	.. ..
SL V44	4d.	**rose** ..	.. ..
SL V45	6d.	**lilac** ..	.. ..
SL V47	1/–	**green**	.. ..

1860 (Dec. 18th) *(recess)* **Perkins, Bacon and Co. Wmk. Small Star. Perf. 14-16. Sheets 12 x 20.**

V1	1d.	**rose-red**	.. ..	£125	£40
	a	imperf between			
		(horiz pair)	..	—	—
	b	double print	..	£800	—
	c	deep rose	..	£125	£40
V2	4d.	**blue**	.. ..	£200	£175
	a	imperf between			
		(horiz pair)	..	—	—
	b	deep blue	..	£225	£185
	c	greenish blue	..	£225	£185
V3	6d.	**green**	.. ..	£175	£125
	a	imperf between			
		(horiz. pair)	..	—	—
	b	deep green	..	£200	£175
	c	pale green	..	£200	£175

This, and succeeding issues to No. V32 were undenominated and identified only by the colour.

Numbers printed—V1, 8,640; V2, 3,120; V3, 4,080; plus, in each case, 240 stamps (being a sample sheet of each discovered in London at the end of the century).

Perkins, Bacon made only one printing of each value; and in January 1862 the Die, Roller and Plate were handed to De La Rue.

1863 As before but printed *(recess)* **by De La Rue from the same Plate. Wmk. Crown CC. Perf 12½.**

V4	1d.	**lake**	.. ..	£40	£30
	a	imperf (pair)	..	£950	—
	a	brown lake	..	£50	£40
V5	4d.	**indigo**	..	£60	£50
	a	imperf (pair)	..	£500	—
	b	deep indigo	..	£70	£50
V6	6d.	**emerald green**	..	£150	£120
	a	imperf. (pair)	..	£600	—
	b	pale emerald	..	£160	£130
SPV4*a*, V5*a*	**ovp specimen** (2)			£1800	‡

Numbers printed—V4, 10,050; V5, 3,120; V6, 5,520.

1863 (?) Prepared but not issued. Nos. V6 and V5 surcharged in words.

V7	½d. on 6d.	**emerald grn**		£40	—
V8	6d. on 4d.	**indigo**		£750	—

1864 (Nov. 19th) As before. Wmk. Crown CC. (a) Perf. 12½.

V9	1d.	**black** ..	.. ..	£18	£14
	a	imperf (pair)	..	£220	—
V10	4d.	**yellow**	..	£55	£20
	a	imperf (pair)	..	£400	—
V11	4d.	**lemon-yellow**	..	£220	—
V12	4d.	**chrome-yellow**	..	£70	£25
V13	4d.	**olive-yellow**	..	£90	£25
V14	6d.	**violet** ..	.. ..		
V15	6d.	**mauve**	..	£40	£25
	a	imperf (pair)	..	£325	—
V16	6d.	**deep mauve**	..	£50	£25
	a	imperf (pair)	..	£325	—
V17	1/–	**brown-orange**	..	£150	£25
	a	imperf (pair)	..	£325	—
V18	1/–	**yellow-orange**	..	£150	£25
	a	imperf between			
		(horiz. pair)	..	—	—
SPV9*a*		**ovp specimen** (1v)	..	£450	‡
V10, V14, V17		**ovp "Cancelled"** (3)		£2500	‡

(b) Perf 13.

V19	1d.	**black** ..	.. ..	—	—
V20	4d.	**yellow**	..	—	—
V21	4d.	**chrome-yellow**	..	—	—
V22	6d.	**mauve**	..	—	—
V23	6d.	**violet** ..	.. ..	—	—
V24	1/	**orange-red** ..	..	—	—
V25	1/	**orange**	.. ..	—	—

The records regarding the actual existence of this perforation are somewhat obscure.

(c) Perf 14.

V26	1d.	**black** ..	.. ..	£14	£10
	a	imperf between			
		(horiz. pair)	..	—	—
V27	4d.	**yellow**	..	£45	£20
V28	4d.	**olive-yellow**	..	£50	£22
V29	6d.	**mauve**	..	£45	£17
V30	6d.	**pale lilac**	..	£50	£17
V31	6d.	**violet** ..	.. ..	£75	£25
V32	1/–	**orange**	..	—	—
	a	imperf (pair)	..	£250	—

2½ PENCE

FOUR PENCE

1881 (Sept.) Special printings in new colours, surcharged in black by De La Rue.

V33	½d. **green**	.. .. ..	£20	£22
V34	2½d. **brown-red**	.. ..	£14	£16

Numbers printed—V33, 12,720; V34, 13,200.

1882-84 As before, but Wmk Crown CA, surcharged in black by De La Rue. (V37 in red).

(a) Perf. 12.

V35	4d. **yellow** ..	.. ..	£175	£25

A Colour Trial is known in deep brown, without surcharge.

(b) Perf. 14.

V36	½d. **green**	.. .. ..	£10	£12
V37	1d. **black**	.. .. ..	£10	£10
	a bisect (½d.) on cover		‡	£850
V38	4d. **yellow** ..	.. ..	£80	£20
V39	6d. **violet** ..	.. ..	£30	£20
V40	1/- **orange**	.. ..	£160	£75
SPV40	**ovpt. specimen** (1)		£300	‡

V37*a* may be found bisected diagonally or vertically.

Stamps in light blue overprinted "TWO PENCE/ REVENUE" in black and stamps in dark blue overprinted "THREE PENCE/REVENUE" in red were fiscals which were *not* authorised for postal use (see F12/15/16). Copies are known from which either the whole overprint or only the word "REVENUE" has been fraudulently removed.

Numbers printed—V37, 22,320; V38, 10,080; V39, 9,600; V40, 2,640.

All stamps to G54 are (*typo*) De La Rue. Perf. 14, unless otherwise indicated.

See Introduction for details of Dies I and II.

1883 (July 6th)-86. Wmk Crown CA. Die I. Sheets 6 x 10.

V41	½d. **dull green**	.. ..	1·75	1·75
V42	1d. **carmine**	.. ..	9·00	9·00
V43	2½d. **blue** ..	.. ..	6·00	1·50
V44	4d. **brown** ('85) ..	..	8·00	1·75
	a imperf (pair)	..	£300	—
V45	6d. **lilac** ('86)	.. ..	£125	£140
	a imperf (pair)	..	£350	—
V46	1/- **orange-brown** ('85)		£185	£75

Numbers printed—V44, 12,000; V45/46, 2,400 each.

1886-98 As before.

(a) Die I. (1886-87).

V47	1d. **mauve** ..	.. ..	2·50	4·00
	a imperf (pair)	..	£200	—
V48	1d. **dl mauve and purple** ('87) ..	..	2·50	4·00
V49	3d. **dl mauve and green**		£16	£13
V50	6d. **dl mauve and blue** ('87) ..	..	6·00	9·00
V51	1/- **dl mauve and red** ('87) ..	..	£20	£18
V47/51	**set** (4v)	.. ..	£40	£45
SPV48/51	**specimen set** (4v) ..		£55	‡

V48 represents the change in printing from single to doubly fugitive ink.

Number printed—V47, 43,600.

(b) Die II. (1891-98).

V52	½d. **dull green** ..	..	15	20
V53	1d. **dl mauve and pur** ..		50	20
V54	2d. **ult and orange** ('98)		1·50	1·00
V55	2½d. **ultramarine**	..	1·25	40
V56	3d. **dl mauve and green**		2·50	2·75
V57	4d. **brown** ..	..	2·50	2·75
V58	6d. **dl mauve and blue**		3·50	7·00
V59	1/- **dl mauve and red**		3·00	5·50
V60	5/- **dl mauve and or** ..		£17	£23
V61	10/- **dl mauve and black**		£35	£35
V52/61	**set** (10v)	.. ..	£65	£75
SPV54/60/61	**specimen** (3v) ..		£60	‡

Type I

Type II

Type III

1891-92 Nos. V49, V56, V44 and V50 surcharged locally in black (Die I except No. V63).

(a) With Type I or II.

V62	½d. on 3d. **dl mauve and grn**		£30	£30
	a small "O" in "ONE" ..		£40	£40
	b small "A" in "HALF" ..		£40	£40
V63	½d. on 3d. **dl mauve and grn (Die II)**		£24	£20
	a small "O" in "ONE" ..		£80	£80

b small "A" in
"HALF" .. £80 £80
c surcharge
double .. £400 £375
d surcharge
inverted .. £800 £400
e surcharge
double–one
inverted .. £350 £350
V64 1d. on 4d. **brown** (12/91) £14 £14
a surcharge
double .. £80 —
b surcharge
inverted .. — £350
c thick first "N" £16 £16
d surcharge
double .. £80 —
e surcharge
inverted .. — £325
f thick second
"N" .. £17 £17

V64*c/d/e*—The first "N" in "PENNY" has a very thick diagonal stroke.

V64*f*—The second "N" in 'PENNY" has a very thick diagonal stroke.

(b) With Type III twice, prior to bisection.

V65 ½d. **on half 6d.**
dl mauve and
blue £10 £10
a surcharge side-
ways .. £175 —
b surcharge
double .. £200 £225
c surcharge
triple .. £290 —
d thick "1" .. £80 £80
e "2" omitted .. £175 —
f fraction bar
omitted .. £80 £80
g "1" for fraction
bar £140 £140

V65*d*—The "1" in the fraction is thick and has a sloping serif.

V65*e*—There are also examples of the "2" partially omitted.

V65*g*—A small thin figure "1" was used in place of the fraction bar.

1902 (Dec. 15th) 400th Anniversary of discovery of the island by Columbus. (*Recess*) **De La Rue. Wmk. Crown CC (sideways). Perf. 14.**

E1 2d. **green and brown** .. 5·00 6·00
SPE1 **specimen** (1v) .. £45 ‡

Number printed—250,000.

Imperforate Colour Trials exist in blue and red on unwatermarked paper. Price £120.

1902-03 Wmk. Crown CA. Sheets 120 – two panes, each 6 x 10.

E2 ½d. **dl purple and green** 60 50
E3 1d. **dl pur and carmine** 70 60
E4 2½d. **dl pur and ult** 5·50 6·00
E5 3d. **dl purple and yellow** 5·00 5·50
E6 1/– **green and black** .. 7·50 8·50
E2/6 **set** (5v) £18 £20
SPE2/6 **specimen set** (5v) .. £55 ‡

1904-11 Wmk. Multiple Crown CA. Sheets as before.

E7 ½d. **dl pur and grn (OC)** .. 40 45
E8 ½d. **green** ('07) 30 20
E9 1d. **dl pur and car (OC)** .. 40 15
E10 1d. **carmine** ('07) .. 45 15
E11 2½d. **dl pur and ult (OC)** .. 2·50 3·75
E12 2½d. **blue** ('07) .. .. 2·00 2·75
E13 3d. **dl purple and yellow** 3·00 5·00
E14 3d. **pur/yel C** ('09) .. 1·25 3·25
E15 6d. **dl pur and vio (OC)**
('05) .. 5·00 6·50
E16 6d. **dl and bt pur C** ('07) 5·00 7·50
E17 6d. **dull purple C** ('10) .. 9·00 £10
E18 1/– **grn and blk C** ('05) .. £10 £12
E19 1/– **black/green C** ('09) 7·50 9·00
E20 5/– **green and car** ('05) .. £22 £25
E21 5/– **grn and red/yel C**
('11) £25 £30
E7/21 **set** (14v) £85 £110
SPE7/21 **specimen set** (14v) £90 ‡

1912-20 Various Frames Wmk Multiple Crown CA. Sheets as before.

G1/10 O; G11/21 C.

G1 ½d. **deep green** 20 20
G2 ½d. **pale green** 20 20
G3 ½d. **yellow green** ('16) .. 25 20
a on bluish paper 2·00 —
G4 1d. **carmine-red** .. 1·25 10
G5 1d. **rose-red** 80 30
G6 1d. **scarlet** ('16) .. 95 10
a on bluish paper
(7/19) .. .. 2·00
G7 2d. **grey** .. .. 2·00 3·00
G8 2d. **slate-grey** ('16) 4·25 4·75
G9 2½d. **ultramarine** .. 1·50 2·00
G10 2½d. **bright blue** ('18) 1·50 2·00
G11 3d. **purple/yellow** .. 75 1·50
a on pale yellow (Die I) 3·75 4·25

	b on pale ye! (Die II) ..	3·75	5·50
G12	4d. **blk and red/yellow**	95	2·50
	a white back	95	2·50
G13	4d. **grey and car/or yel**		
	(white back) ..	1·50	3·00
G14	4d. **grey and pl or/yel**		
	(white back) ..	1·75	3·00
G15	6d. **dl and bt purple** ..	2·00	4·00
G16	6d. **purple and mauve** ..	2·00	4·00
G17	6d. **grey-pur and pur**		
	('18)	4·00	5·50
G18	1/– **black/green** ..	2·75	4·00
	a on blue-green (olive		
	back)	3·75	4·50
G19	1/– **orange-brown** ('20)	1·25	3·00
G20	2/6 **black and red/blue** ..	£12	£15
G21	5/– **green and red/yellow**	£21	£25
G1/21	**set** (11v)	£40	£55
SPG1/21	**specimen set** (11v)	£80	‡

G11*a*/*b* See Introduction for details of Dies I and II.

1916-19 War Tax. Nos. G4 and G6 overprinted WAR TAX in black sans serif capitals.

(a) Locally in two lines. Setting 6 x 5 applied twice to panes 6 x 10. (June).

G22	1d. **scarlet**	2·00	3·50
	a overprint double ..	£200	£185
G23	1d. **carmine**	£14	£15

G22 represents the normal supply overprinted on stamps from Plate 3.

G23 is on stamps from Plate 1, and it is believed that only one sheet from this Plate was overprinted (120 copies).

The upper margins were folded under before panes were overprinted; and, when folded out, show an inverted and reversed albino overprint.

(b) By De La Rue, in one line (Sept.).

G24	1d. **scarlet**	10	10
G25	1d. **dp scarlet** (thick		
	paper) (6/19) ..	20	20
SPG24	**specimen** (1v) ..	£20	‡

1921-26 As Nos. G1/21 but Wmk. Multiple Script CA.

G26/42 O; G43/54 C.

G26	½d. **pale green**	10	10
G27	½d. **dull green**	10	10
G28	½d. **bright green** ..	10	10
G29	1d. **rose-red**	1·00	3·00
G30	1d. **bright rose** ..	1·00	3·00
G31	1d. **brown** ('22) ..	25	15
G32	1d. **deep brown** ..	25	15
G33	1d. **black-brown** ..	25	15
G34	1½d. **carmine** ('22) ..	30	55
G35	2d. **grey**	25	20
G36	2d. **slate-grey**	25	20
G37	2½d. **bright blue**	1·25	1·50
G38	2½d. **orange** ('25) ..	5·00	5·50
G39	2½d. **dull blue** ('26) ..	1·25	1·50
G40	3d. **bright blue** ('22) ..	3·00	4·50
G41	3d. **deep blue**	2·50	1·75
G42	3d. **dull blue** ('26) ..	1·25	1·75
G43	3d. **purple/yellow** ('26)	50	1·50
	a on buff	50	1·50
G44	3d. **plum/yellow** ..	1·75	2·50
	a on buff	1·75	2·50
G45	4d. **blk and scar/yel** ('24)	65	2·50
G46	4d. **grey and car/yellow**	65	2·50
G47	6d. **dl purple and purple**	1·50	2·35

G48	6d. **bt purple and mauve**	1·50	3·25
G49	6d. **brn-pur and mauve**	1·50	3·25
G50	6d. **pl lilac and mauve** ..	1·50	3·25
G51	1/– **orange-brown** ..	1·75	3·75
G52	1/– **bright chestnut** ..	1·75	3·75
G53	2/6 **blk and red/blue**		
	('24)	8·00	£13
G54	5/– **grn and red/pl yel**		
	('23)	£16	£26
G26/54	**set** (14v)	£35	£55
SPG26/54	**specimen set** (14v)	£110	‡

Stamps of this issue may be found cancelled "CASTRIES ST. LUCIA" in single circle with "1st/AIR MAIL" in place of the date. This was used on September 25th, 1929 on the occasion of the first air mail despatch by Charles Lindbergh's Pan American flight to Trinidad. It was again used, with "1st" removed, on the return flight to Antigua on October 5th, 1929. On both occasions the normal date stamp was applied to the cover, alongside the cancelled stamp. Various low values on cover price from £30.

1935 (May 6th) **Silver Jubilee.** (*recess*) **De La Rue. Wmk. Multiple Script CA. Perf 13½ x 14. Sheets 6 x 10.**

G55	½d. **black and green** ..	20	30
G56	2d. **ultramarine and grey**	50	80
G57	2½d. **brown and blue** ..	1·00	1·50
G58	1/– **slate and purple** ..	3·50	4·50
G55/58	**set** (4v)	5·00	6·50
SPG55/58	**specimen set** (4v)	£22	‡

Remainders were withdrawn on December 31st, 1935.

1936 (March 1st) (*recess*) **De La Rue. Wmk.**

**Multiple Script CA. Perf. 14 (G67/G70 13 x 12).
Sheets 6 x 10 or 10 x 6.**

G59	½d.	**black and green**	20	15
G60	1d.	**black and brown**	15	15
G61	1½d.	**black and scarlet**	20	25
	a	perf. 12 x 13	5·50	1·75
G62	2d.	**black and grey**	20	30
G63	2½d.	**black and blue**	30	35
G64	3d.	**black and green**	75	85
G65	4d.	**black and red-brown**	50	80
G66	6d.	**black and orange**	75	1·00
G67	1/–	**black and light blue**	1·25	2·50
G68	2/6	**black and ult.**	6.00	7·50
G69	5/–	**black and violet**	7·50	£10
G70	10/–	**black and carmine**	£35	£40
G59/70		**set** (12v)	£50	£60
SPG59/70		**specimen set** (12v)	£60	‡

**1936 (April 8th) As Nos. G59/60 but Perf.
13 x 12 for use in Stamp Vending Machines.**

G71	½d.	**black and green**	15	40
G72	1d.	**black and brown**	1·00	1·00

**1938 (Sept. 22nd) -48 Designs, ½d.–3d. (King's
Head), Printers Waterlow & Sons, Perf.
14¾ x 14 (C); 6d. (Columbus Sq., Castries);
1/- (Govt. House, Morne Belle Vue), Printers
De La Rue, Perf. 13½ (C); 2/- (Petit Piton and
Gros Piton); 10/- (Device of Colony), Printers
Bradbury, Wilkinson, Perf. 12 (L); 5/- (Load-
ing Bananas on "C.N.S." Liner), Printer
Waterlow & Sons, Perf. 12½ (L). Designs, ½d.
to 3d. and 10/- V, Others H. (recess). Sheets—
Small Format 15 x 8; Large 6 x 10.**

1	½d.	**green**	15	10
2	1d.	**violet**	75	15
3	1d.	**scarlet** (20/9/48)	10	10
4	1½d.	**scarlet**	15	10
5	2d.	**grey**	10	20
6	2½d.	**ultramarine**	10	10
7	3d.	**orange**	15	10
8	6d.	**claret**	50	50
	a	bt claret (22/5/43)	1·75	1·25
	b	lake-claret (30/7/45)	50	50
9	1'-	**brown**	60	60
	a	light brown (22/5/43)	60	60
10	2/–	**blue-blk and dp claret**	1·25	1·28
11	5/–	**black and dp purple**	2·50	3·50
12	10/–	**black/yellow**	4·00	5·50

**Design as No. 1, but new values, and Perf.
12½ (L).**

13	½d.	**green** (22/5/43)	10	10
	a	blue-green (8/2/46)	10	10
14	1d.	**violet** (22/9/38)	10	15

15	1d.	**scarlet** (8/4/47)	10	10
16	1½d.	**scarlet** (22/5/43)	15	20
17	2d.	**grey** (22/5/43)	10	10
18	2½d.	**ultramarine** (22/5/43)	10	10
	a	dull blue	10	10
19	2½d.	**violet** (8/4/47)	10	10
20	3d.	**orange** (22/5/43)	15	10
21	3½d.	**ultramarine** (8/4/47)	15	20
22	8d.	**chestnut-brn** (8/2/46)	30	40
	a	chocolate-brown	30	40
23	3/–	**magenta** (8/2/46)	3·00	3·25
24	£1	**sepia** (8/2/46)	£10	£14
1/24		**set** (17) cheapest perfs	£20	£28
SP1/24		**specimen set** perf (17)	£110	‡

As Nos. 8—9, but Perf. 12 (C).

25	6d.	**lake-claret** (23/2/48)	1·25	1·25
26	1/-	**lt-brown** (23/2/48)	1·25	1·25

**1949 (Oct. 1st) Designs, 1c.—16c., as No. 13,
but currency changed. (recess) Waterlow.
Perf. 12½ (L); Other Values, as No. 12 but
currency changed and name of country below
Device of Colony. (recess) Bradbury Wilkinson. Perf. 11½ x 11½. (C). Sheets as before.**

27	1c.	**green**	10	10
28	2c.	**dp magenta**	10	10
29	3c.	**scarlet**	10	15
30	4c.	**slate-grey**	10	10
31	5c.	**violet**	10	10
32	6c.	**orange**	10	10
	a	pair imp. left margin	—	£400
33	7c.	**ultramarine**	10	10
34	12c.	**brown-lake**	25	35
35	16c.	**dp chocolate**	25	20
36	24c.	**dp and pale blue**	30	30
37	48c.	**dp and pale olive**	1·00	80
38	·1.20	**dp and pale pur-vio**	1·25	2·00
39	·2.40	**dp and pale green**	3·50	8·50
40	$4.80	**dp and pale car-red**	7·00	£11
27/40		**set** (14)	£13	£22

**1949 (Nov. 19th) -52 As Nos. 27, 28 and 34,
but 1c. Perf. 14 (L); Others, Perf. 14¾ x 14 (C).**

41	1c.	**green**	25	35
		a block four	£30	—
42	2c.	**dp magenta**	50	60
		a block four	£30	—
43	4c.	**grey** (/52?)	‡	£2000
44	12c.	**brown-lake** (/52)	£200	£100

32a—A sheet was discovered imperf. between left
margin and first vertical row of stamps. Separated
into two singles and three pairs (eight copies
in total), they were placed on five covers and

postmarked SOUFRIERE 1 Oct., 49. One pair is damaged.

43—Forgeries of this variety exist in mint condition. Most of the used are cancelled in "PATIENCE". About 10 copies in total are known.

A few 1c. and 2c. (Nos. 41, 42) were issued in sheet form—most being from coils.

SPECIAL ISSUES

1937 (May 12th) Coronation. As Aden, but Printers Bradbury, Wilkinson. Perf. 11 x 11¾ (C).

S1	1d. **violet**	10	10
S2	1½d. **carmine-red** ..	10	10
S3	2½d. **dp blue**	10	10
SP	S1/3 **specimen set** perf (3)	£15	‡

1946 (Oct. 8th) Victory. As Aden.

S4	1d. **lilac**	10	10
S5	3½d. **dull blue**	15	10
SP	S4/5 **specimen set** perf (2)	£17	‡

1948 (Nov. 26th) Silver Wedding. As Aden.

S6	1d. **scarlet**	10	10
S7	£1 **brownish-purple** ..	£10	£12

Number issued (Colony only)—1d., 93,437; £1, 3,202.

1949 (Oct. 10th) U.P.U. As Aden.

S8	5c. **dull violet**	20	25
S9	6c. **dp orange**	20	25
S10	12c. **reddish-mauve** ..	25	40
S11	24c. **quartz-green** ..	45	75
S8/11	**set** (4)	1·00	1·50

Number issued (Colony only)—5c., 38,519; 6c., 31,194; 12c., 7,610; 24c., 7,104.

1951 (Feb. 16th) West Indies University College. (See Antigua.)

S12	3c. **black and red** ..	10	10
S13	12c. **black and claret-red**	20	20

Number issued (Colony only)—3c., 49,972; 12c., 45,500.

1951 (June 19th) Castries Reconstruction. Design, Phoenix rising from the flames of burning Castries. Printers (*flames typo, frame recess*) **Bradbury, Wilkinson. Perf. 13½ x 13 (C). Sheets 6 x 10.**

S14	12c. **scarlet and dp blue**	40	45

Issued to commemorate the reconstruction of Castries after its destruction by fire in June, 1948.

Number issued—137,343.

1951 (Sept. 25th) New Constitution 1951. Nos. 28, 30, 31, 34 overprinted in black.

S15	2c. **dp magenta** ..	10	10
S16	4c. **slate-grey**	10	10
S17	5c. **violet**	15	50
S18	12c. **brown-lake**	25	40
S15/18	**set** (4)	50	1·00

Number issued—2c., 146,000; 4c., 107,420; 5c., 114,011; 12c., 90,918.

POSTAGE DUE STAMPS

1931-32. Type-set by "The Voice" Printing Company, Castries. Perf. 12 (Rough). Sheets 6 x 10; the top, right and lower margins being imperforate. No gum.

(a) Pale bluish grey horizontally laid paper with watermark in the centre of the sheet, Large Crown under "KINGSCLERE" in double lined capitals, covering not more than nine stamps.

GD1	1d. **black**	60	60
	a round "o" in "No."	2·00	2·00

(b) Bright blue horizontally laid paper without watermark (Jan. 1932).

GD2	1d. **black**	2·00	2·00
	a round "o" in "No."	5·00	5·00
	b no stop after		
	"LUCIA"	8·00	8·00

(c) Wove paper without watermark.

GD3	2d. **blk/orange-buff** ..	1·00	1·00
	a round "o" in "No."	4·00	4·00
GD4	2d. **black/yellow** ..	1·00	1·00
	a round "o" in "No."	4·00	4·00
	b no stop after		
	"LUCIA"	£10	£10
	c imperf between (vert pair)	£1000	—

GD1*a*/2*a*/3*a*/4*a*—The "o" in "No." on Row 10 came from a wrong fount.

GD2*b*/4*b*—Row 9/2.

GD4*c*—Six pairs are known from a sheet which was not perforated horizontally between Rows 9 and 10 (Numbered 6903/4, 6913/4, 6923/4, 6933/4, 6943/4, 6953/4).

Other varieties are known, including no stop after "St." in varying positions.

All stamps were serially numbered by the G.P.O. at Castries. The numbers progress in each sheet from the top right downwards and to the left; and there are many instances of wrongly placed or inadequately inked numbers. Incorrect numbers were also overstamped with the correct number.

1933-47 Printers (*typo*) **De La Rue. Perf. 13¾ x 14 (C). Sheets 6 x 10.**

PD1	1d.	**black**	40	25
PD2	2d.	**black**	50	35
PD3	4d.	**black** (25/6/47)	60	60
PD4	8d.	**black** (25/6/47)	1·00	1·00
SPPD1/4		**specimen**	£60	‡

1949 (Oct. 1st) As before, but currency changed. Uncoated paper.

PD5	2c.	**black**	15	15
PD6	4c.	**black**	30	30
PD7	8c.	**black**	40	40
PD8	16c.	**black**	75	75

1952 (Nov. 27th) Chalk-surfaced paper.

PD9	2c.	**black**	10	10
PD10	4c.	**black**	20	20
PD11	8c.	**black**	30	30
PD12	16c.	**black**	60	60

Watermark Varieties (Type A)

(See Introduction for details)

PD9a	2c.	Crown missing	£20	—
PD9b		St. Edward's Crown	£15	—
PD10a	4c.	Crown missing	£20	—
PD10b		St. Edward's Crown	£15	—
PD11b	8c.	St. Edward's Crown	£30	—
PD12b	16c.	St. Edward's Crown	£30	—

POSTAL FISCALS

1881 Nos. V26/32 (Wmk. Crown CC. Perf. 14) surcharged in two lines in black or in red (F1 and F5).

(a) In small serif capitals.

F1	One Penny Stamp	**black**	£15	£15
	a	surcharge inverted	£300	£300
	b	surcharge double	£300	£300
F2	Four Penny Stamp	**yellow**	£300	£300
	a	bisect (2d.) on cover	‡	—
F3	Six Pence Stamp	**mauve**	£40	£50
	a	surcharge double	—	—
F4	Shilling Stamp	**orange**	£30	£30
	a	"SHILEING"	£275	£200
	b	"SHILDING"	£275	£200

(b) In large lower-case serif type.

F5	One Penny Stamp	**black**	£15	£15
	a	surcharge double	£250	—
F6	Four Penny Stamp	**yellow**	£20	£22
F7	Six Pence Stamp	**mauve**	£20	£22
F8	Shilling Stamp	**orange**	£20	£22

1881 Nos. V33 (Wmk. Crown CC) and V40 (Wmk. Crown CA) overprinted "Stamp".

F9	½d.	**green**	£15	£15
	a	"Stamp" double	£175	£175
F10	1/–	**orange**	£25	£25
	a	"Stamp" double	£175	£175

1882 As Nos. V35/40 (Wmk. Crown CA) surcharged and overprinted "REVENUE" in two lines in large sans serif capitals in black (F13/15/17/18) or in carmine (F11/12/14/16).

(a) Perf. 12.

F11	1d.	**black**	8·00	£10
	a	bisect (½d.) diag on cover with two whole stamps	‡	—
F12	3d.	**deep blue**	£10	£10
F13	1/–	**orange**	£10	£10

(b) Perf 14.

F14	1d.	**black**	7·00	7·00
	a	imperf (pair)	£250	—
F15	2d.	**pale blue**	4·00	5·00
	a	imperf (pair)	£300	—
F16	3d.	**deep blue**	£12	£12
F17	4d.	**yellow**	4·00	4·00
F18	6d.	**mauve**	£10	£10

1883 Nos. V36/37/42/35 locally overprinted "Revenue" in black or in carmine (F19/20/22) lower-case serif letters.

(a) Overprint measures 11mm.

F19	1d.	**black**	6·00	—
	a	surcharge and overprint inverted	—	—
	b	surcharge and overprint double	£90	£100

(b) Overprint measures 13 mm.

F20	1d.	**black**	£10	£12
	a	surcharge and overprint double	—	—

(c) Overprint measures 15¼mm.

F21	½d.	**green**	£10	£12
	a	"REVENUE" double	—	£70
F22	1d.	**black**	5·00	6·00
	a	"REVENUE" double	£60	—
	b	"REVENUE" double, one inverted	£75	—
	c	"REVENUE" triple	£80	—
F23	1d.	**rose** (Die I)	—	£12
F24	4d.	**yellow**	—	£15

1884 No. V47 overprinted "REVENUE" in sans serif capitals in London (F26 in carmine).

F25	1d.	**dl mauve** (Die I)	4·00	5·00
	a	imperf (pair)	—	—
F26	1d.	**slate**	4·00	5·00
	a	imperf (pair)	—	—

LOCAL ISSUES

Issued by Messrs. Duboulay, Minvielle and Co. (the managers of the St. Lucia Steam Conveyance Company Limited) to cover local postal charges on letters carried between Castries and other towns on the island. Their use is believed to have ceased in 1890.

1871 (?) **Top part of double circle inscribed "St. Lucia Steam Conveyance" struck in black or blue on white gummed label with or without blue frame.**

LI	No value (1d.?).	..	—	£2000
	a with frame ..	..	—	£2000

This provisional stamp was pen-cancelled.

1873 (?) (*litho*) **in Paris. No Wmk. Imperf. Sheets 6 x 12.**

L2	1d.	**blue**	..	..	—	—
L3	3d.	**carmine**	..	..	—	—
L4	6d.	**violet** ..	..	..	—	—
L2/4		**set** (3v)	..	..	5·00	—

There were two printings, the first being on unsurfaced paper with dark brown gum and the second on chalk-surfaced paper with yellow or pale brown gum. Stamps from the second printing are not known used and it is possible that they were never actually issued.

Forgeries exist in the following colours on unsurfaced paper with clear shiny gum.

1d.	Scarlet	Deep blue
3d.	Rose	Green
6d.	Mauve	Yellow

GERMAN PROPAGANDA LABELS

The 1944 German imitations of the G.B. 1937 Definitives ½d to 3d (see after Great Britain for details) were also overprinted in black "LIQUIDA-TION/OF EMPIRE/Sta. LUCIA" within a vertical rectangular frame.

Price (6v) unused or cancelled £120.

St. VINCENT

The island was originally granted to the Earl of Carlisle by King Charles I in 1627. It subsequently passed into French hands, but was ceded to Great Britain by the Treaty of Paris in 1763 and is now one of the Windward Islands.

Following the use of other handstamps or manuscript marks, a Crowned Circle PAID Frank was registered at the G.P.O. in London on January 30th, 1852; and was thereafter struck in red to indicate prepayment of postage on overseas letters. (See Introduction).

From May, 1858 to April, 1860 contemporary G.B. stamps were in use and were cancelled with "A10" in a transverse oval of horizontal bars.

The Crowned Circle Frank was again used from May 1st, 1860 until the first St. Vincent stamps were issued.

1852-61 PAID Frank.   *On Cover*

VF1   ..   £300

1858-60 Stamps of Great Britain identified by their Catalogue Nos. after prefix 'SV'.

Used at Kingstown : 'A10'

SV V39	1d.	rose-red	..	
SV V36A	2d.	blue	..	..
SV V44	4d.	rose	..	..
SV V45	6d.	lilac	..	..
SV V47	1/-	green	..	..

All stamps to V39 are (*recess*) **Perkins, Bacon and Co. Sheets 10 x 6, unless otherwise indicated.**

1861 (May 8th)-68. No wmk.

(a) Perf. 14-16. (Intermediate).

V1	1d.	rose-red	..	..	—	£300
	a	imperf between				
		(horiz pair)		£600	—	
V2	6d.	deep yellow-green	..	£2500	£250	

(b) Perf 14-16. (Rough).

V3	1d.	rose-red	..	..	£25	£15
	a	imperf between				
		(horiz. pair)	..	£300	—	
	b	imperf (pair)	..	£240	—	
V4	6d.	deep green (9/62)	..	£45	£15
	a	imperf between				
		(horiz. pair)	..	£600	—	
	b	imperf (pair)	..	£250	—	

(c) Perf. 11-12¼.

| V5 | 1d. | rose red ('63?) | .. | £25 | £15 |
| V6 | 6d. | deep green (7/68) | .. | £150 | £40 |

(d) Perf. 11-12¼ x 14-16.

| V7 | 1d. | rose-red | .. | .. | £1500 | £750 |

Die Proofs on India paper and Plate Proofs on white wove paper of both values are known in black and in the issued colours.

Total printings—1d., 195,000; 6d., 118,140.

1866 (Aug.) No wmk. Sheets 10 x 3.

(a) Perf. 14-16.

| V8 | 1/- | slate-grey | .. | .. | £150 | £50 |

(b) Perf. 11-12¼.

V9	4d.	deep blue	..	..	£150	£50
	a	imperf between				
		(horiz. pair)	..	—	—	
V10	1/-	slate-grey	..	..	£100	£600

(c) Perf. 11-12¼ x 14-16.

| V11 | 1/- | slate-grey | .. | .. | £150 | £70 |

Die Proofs on India paper and Plate Proofs on white wove paper of both values are known in black and of the 4d. in blue.

Numbers printed—V8/10/11, 15,000; V9, 15,000.

1869 As before, but new colours. Perf. 11-12¼.

V12	4d.	yellow (Oct. ?)	..	£225	£110
V13	1/-	indigo (June ?)	..	£225	£75
V14	1/-	brown (Oct. ?)	..	£250	£110

Numbers printed—V12/13/14, 9,000 each.

1871 (April)-75 As before but wmk. Small Star (upright or sideways).

(a) Perf. 14-16. (Rough).

V15	1d.	black	..	..	£25	£10
	a	imperf between				
		(vert pair)	..	£2500	—	
V16	6d.	deep-green	..	..	£150	£50

(b) Perf. 11-12¼.

| V17 | 1/- | lilac-red (5/72) | .. | £450 | £100 |

(c) Perf. 15 (approx.)

V18	1d.	black ('72)	..	..	£15	8·00
V19	6d.	dull green ('73)	..	£300	£20
V20	6d.	bt blue green ('75)	..	£400	£25

(d) Perf. 11-12¼ x 15.

| V21 | 1/- | lilac-rose ('73) | .. | £2500 | £400 |

Plate Proofs of V17 exist in deep lilac red on white wove paper.

V20 is only known with watermark sideways.

Total printings—1d., 144,000; 6d., 54,000.

Numbers printed—V17/V21, 9,000 each.

1875 (April ?) As before but new colour. Perf. 11-12¼.

| V22 | 1/- | claret | .. | .. | .. | £350 | £150 |

Number printed—9,000.

1876-78 As before but new colours (except V23).

(a) Perf. 11–12¼ x 15 (1876).

V23	1d.	**black**	£25	5·00
		a imperf between		
		(horiz. pair) ..	—	—
V24	6d.	**pale yellow-green** ..	£200	£35
		a imperf (pair) ..	—	—
V25	1/–	**vermilion**	£200	£60
		a imperf between		
		(horiz. pair) ..	—	—

(b) Perf. 11–12½. (July 1877).

V26	4d.	**deep blue**	£150	£50

(c) Perf. 15 (approx.) (1878).

V27	6d.	**pale yellow-green** ..	£200	£25
V28	1/–	**vermilion**	—	£2500
		a imperf (pair) ..	—	£1000

V24*a*—A copy in the Royal Collection shows parts of the stamps above and on both sides and has a reasonable bottom margin.

Total printings—1d., 180,000; 6d., 36,000; 1/–. 18,000.

Number printed—V26. 6,000.

1880 (May) No. V20 locally surcharged in red twice and perforated 12 vertically down the centre.

V29	1d.	**on half 6d. bt blu-grn**	£175	£125
		a unsevered pair ..	£400	£300

Number surcharged—1,800.

1880 (June) As before, but new colours and new value. (V33 – Sheets 5 x 4). Perf. 11–12½.

V30	1d.	**olive-green**	£50	£10
V31	6d.	**bright green** ..	£200	£45
V32	1/–	**bright red**	£250	£45
		a imperf between		
		(horiz. pair) ..	—	—
V33	5/–	**rose-red**	£450	£350
		a imperf	£1000	—

V33 appears to be on multi-star paper, but this is on account of the Small Star watermark having been laid out to match smaller size stamps.

Die Proofs are known in black on India paper.

Numbers printed—V30, 60,000; V31, 18,000; V32, 9,000; V33, 2,000.

V33 is even scarcer than the printing indicates, as a considerable number were fiscally used – some with a "Fifty Pounds Revenue" overprint authorised by official notification on September 15th, 1882.

V33 is also known perf. 14 and wmk. Crown CA. This is believed to have been from a trial printing made by De La Rue after they took over the Plates in February 1882.

(See also the Note after Nos. V61/62).

1881 Nos. V31/32 locally surcharged.

(a) In red twice (as No. V29) and perforated 12 vertically down the centre. (September 1st.)

V34	½d.	**on half 6d. bt. green**	£90	£90
		a unsevered pair ..	£200	£200
		b fraction bar omitted		
		in pair with normal	£2000	£250

(b) "ONE PENNY" in black sans serif capitals with bar obliterating original value (December 1st).

V35	1d.	**on 6d. bt green** ..	£200	£150

(c) "4d." in bold black type with bar obliterating original value (November).

V36	4d.	**on 1/– bt vermilion** ..	£600	£450

V35 is also known surcharged in red twice and perforated 12 vertically down the centre (as V34). It is believed that this may have been a trial surcharge, rejected in favour of the issued provisional.

Numbers surcharged—V34, 1,440; V35, 1,620; V36, 630.

1881 (Dec.) As before but new colours and new value (V37 – Sheets 10 x 6). Perf. 11–12¼.

V37	½d.	**orange**	4·00	2·00
V38	1d.	**drab**	£400	5·00
V39	4d.	**bright blue**	£500	£50
		a imperf between		
		(horiz. pair) ..	—	—

Numbers printed—V37/38, 60,000 each; V39, 15,000.

Die Proofs on India paper and Plate Proofs on white wove paper of V37 exist, both in black.

The Perkins Bacon Dies, Rollers and Plates were handed to the Crown Agents on February 25th, 1882.

1882 (Nov.)-84 As before but printed (*recess*) by De La Rue from the same plates. Wmk. Crown CA*.

(a) Perf. 14.

V40	1d.	**drab** ..	£10	5·00
V41	2½d.	on 1d. **lake ('83)** ..	5·00	2·00
V42	4d.	**bt blue**	£100	£25
V43	4d.	**dull blue** ..	£200	£100

(b) Perf. 12.

V44	½d.	**green ('84)**	£20	£15
V45	4d.	**bright blue**	£100	£20
V46	4d.	**dull blue**	£400	£120

V47	6d.	**bright green** ('83) ..	£150	£150
V48	1/-	**or-vermilion** ('83) ..	£25	£20

V41 was not a provisional, but was a surcharge "2½ PENCE" in black over a bar obliterating the original value of a special printing of the 1d. stamp, done to save the cost of making a plate for the new value (See No. V74).

Numbers printed—V40, 60,000; V41, 124,400; V42/43/45/46, 14,790; V44, 18,000; V47, 6,120; V48, 9,300.

The following stamps (Perf. 12) are believed to have been Colour Trials.

½d.	**orange**	£750	—
1d.	**rose-red, grn, milky blue, yellow-brown, lake-brown, violet**..	£750	—
5/-	**carmine lake** ..	£1500	—

*De La Rue Crown CA watermarks were laid out for sheets of 240 stamps (four panes, each 6 x 10). This paper did not match the Perkins Bacon plates, and the "Crown CA" is consequently not in register with the stamps. All stamps except the 4d. and 1/- values may be found with the watermark "CROWN AGENTS", normally intended to fall in gutter margins.

1885 (March) No. V41 locally surcharged in black.

V49	1d. on 2½d. on 1d. **lake** ..	6·00	7·00
	a three bars	—	—

V49*a*—The original surcharge "2½ PENCE" is obliterated by three, instead of the normal two bars (Possibly a proof).

1885 (April)-93 As before but new colours (except V50). Perf. 14.

V50	½d.	**green**	50	20
V51	½d.	**deep green** ..	2·00	50
V52	1d.	**rose-red** ..	1·00	75
V53	1d.	**rose** ('86) ..	4·00	1·50
V54	1d.	**red** ('87) ..	80	30
V55	1d.	**car-red** ('89)	£15	3·00
V56	2½d. on 1d.	**milky-blue** (8/89) ..	£10	4·00
V57	4d.	**red-brown** ..	£150	£15
V58	4d.	**pur-brn** (6/86)	£10	4·00
V59	4d.	**choc** ('87) ..	8·00	3·00
V60	6d.	**violet** (10/88)	£50	£50
V61	5/-	**lake** (10/88)..	£13	£14
V62	5/-	**brn-lake** ('93)	£15	£10

V56—See note below V41.

V61/62—Stamps with this perforation but in the colour of No. V33 are believed to have been Proofs from an early De La Rue attempt to match the Perkins Bacon colour.

Numbers printed—V56, 30,480; V57, 9,720; V60, 3,300.

1890-92 No. V59 locally surcharged.

(a) "2½d." in black with bar obliterating original value (Aug. 1890).

V63	2½d. on 4d. **chocolate** ..	£30	£30
	a fraction bar omitted ..	£150	£150

(b) "5 PENCE" in purple in two lines with bar obliterating original value (November 1892).

V64	5d. on 4d. **chocolate** ..	4·00	5·00

V63*a*—Row 1/7 and Row 2/14.

1890-94 As before but new colours and new value (V68/70 – Sheets 10 x 6).

V65	2½d. on 1d.	**grey-blue** ..	6·00	1·00
V66	2½d. on 1d.	**blue** ('93) ..	75	25
	a surcharge double ..	—	—
V67	4d.	**yellow** (3/93) ..	1·00	2·00
V68	5d. on 6d.	**carmine lake** (3/93) ..	4·00	5·00
V69	5d. on 6d.	**dp lake** ('93) ..	75	1·00
V70	5d. on 6d.	**lake** ('94) ..	1·50	2·00
	a surcharge double ..	—	£2000
V71	6d.	**dl pur** ('91) ..	1·50	2·00
V72	1/-	**orange** ('91) ..	4·00	5·00
V73	1/-	**red-or** ('92) ..	5·00	6·00

V65/66—See note below V41.

V68/70—Not provisionals but surcharged "FIVE PENCE" in black sans serif capitals on special printings of the 6d. stamps to save the cost of making a new plate (see No. V75).

1897 As before but new values. Wmk. Crown CA. Perf. 14.

(a) July 13th. Printed (recess) from plates laid down by De La Rue from the Perkins Bacon Die. Sheets 6 x 10.

V74	2½d.	**blue**	1·50	3·00
V75	5d.	**sepia**	5·00	6·00

(b) Oct. 6th; Surcharged "THREE PENCE" in black sans serif capitals on a special printing of the 1d. stamp.

V76	3d. on 1d.	**mauve**	3·00	3·50
V77	3d. on 1d.	**red-mauve** ..	4·00	4·50

Numbers printed—V74, 121,200; V75, 116,520; V76/77, 120,000.

1899 (typo) De La Rue. Wmk. Crown CA. Perf 14. Sheets 120 – two panes each 6 x 10.

V78	½d.	**dl mauve and grn**..	35	40
V79	1d.	**dl mauve and car**	1·75	60
V80	2½d.	**dl mauve and blue**	2·25	4·00
V81	3d.	**dl mauve and ol** ..	3·00	4·50
V82	4d.	**dl mauve and or** ..	2·25	5·50
V83	5d.	**dl mauve and blk**	4·75	7·00
V84	6d.	**dl mauve and brn**	6·50	9·00
V85	1/-	**grn and car** ..	£12	£16
V86	5/-	**grn and blue** ..	£35	£45
V78/86		**set** (9v)	£60	£85
SPV78/86		**specimen set** (9v)	£85	‡

1902 As before, but Head of King Edward VII.

E1	½d.	**dl purple and green**	30	35
E2	1d.	**dl purple and car** ..	35	15

E3	2d.	**dl purple and black**	2·00	2·50
E4	2½d.	**dl purple and blue** ..	3·00	3·50
E5	3d.	**dl purple and olive**..	4·00	4·00
E6	6d.	**dl purple and brown**	5·50	6·50
E7	1/–	**green and carmine**..	£10	£15
E8	2/–	**green and violet**	£15	£22
E9	5/–	**green and blue** ..	£30	£35
E1/9		**set** (9v)	£65	£85
SPE1/9		**specimen set** (9v) ..	£85	‡

1904-11 As before but wmk Multiple Crown CA. Chalky paper.

E10	½d.	**dl pur and grn OC** ('05)	20	30
E11	1d.	**dl pur and car OC**	1·50	70
E12	2½d.	**dl pur and blue** ('06) ..	3·75	5·00
E13	6d.	**dl pur and brn** ('05)	7·50	8·50
E14	1/–	**grn and car OC** ('06)	7·50	8·50
E15	2/–	**pur and bt blue/blue** ('09) ..	£18	£23
E16	5/–	**grn and red/yel** ('00)	£25	£30
E17	£1	**pur and blk/red** ('11)	£325	£450
E10/17		**set** (8v)	£375	£500
SPE15/17		**specimen set** (3v)	£140	‡

Type I

Type II

1907-11 (recess) **De La Rue. Wmk. Multiple Crown CA. Perf. 14. Sheets 6 x 10.**

(a) Type I (1907).

E18	½d.	**green**	30	30
E19	1d.	**carmine**	1·00	60
E20	2d.	**orange**	1·50	2·50
E21	2½d.	**blue**	4·50	4·50
E22	3d.	**violet**	6·00	9·00
E18/22		**set** (5v)	£12	£15
SPE18/22		**specimen set** (5v)	£50	‡

(b) Type II (Jan. 8th, 1909) Redrawn (without dot under 'd').

E23	1d.	**carmine**	60	60
E24	6d.	**dull purple** ..	5·00	£10
E25	1/–	**black/green**.. ..	5·50	6·00
E23/25		**set** (3v)	£10	£16
SPE23/25		**specimen set** (3v)	£35	‡

(c) Type II again redrawn with dot under 'd' (1909-11).

E26	½d.	**green** ('10)	40	50
E27	1d.	**carmine**	25	25
E28	2d.	**grey** (8/11)	1·00	1·25
E29	2½d.	**ultramarine** (7/10) ..	1·00	2·50
E30	3d.	**purple/yellow** ..	1·50	2·00
E31	6d.	**dull purple**	2·25	4·50
E26/31		**set** (6v)	6·00	£10
SPE26/31		**specimen set** (6v)	£45	‡

1913-17 (recess) **De La Rue. Wmk. Multiple Crown CA. Perf. 14 (C or L). Shets 12 x 10.**

G1	½d.	**green**	10	10
G2	1d.	**red**	30	15
G3	1d.	**rose-red**	45	15
G4	1d.	**scarlet** (1/17) ..	1·00	1·25
G5	2d.	**grey**	2·50	3·75
G6	2d.	**slate**	1·00	2·00
G7	2½d.	**ultramarine** ..	60	70
G8	3d.	**purple/yellow** ..	1·00	2·00
		a on lemon ..	2·00	3·50
		b on pale yellow ..	1·50	2·50
G9	4d.	**red/yellow**	60	1·50
G10	5d.	**olive-green**	1·50	5·50
G11	6d.	**claret**	1·50	2·00
G12	1/–	**black/green**.. ..	2·50	3·00
G13	1/–	**bistre** ('14)	3·00	5·00
G14	2/–	**blue and purple** ..	6·00	£10
G15	5/–	**car and myrtle** ..	£12	—
G16	£1	**mauve and black** ..	£95	£100
G1/16		**set** (13v)	£115	£130
SPG1/16		**specimen set** (13v)	£120	‡

G8a and 15 are known with watermark reversed.

G14/15/16 were printed from new dies similar to Type II (See E26/31). The motto "PAX ET JUSTITIA" is slightly shorter than before, being a little over 7mm as compared with just over 8mm. previously.

1915 (Jan. 30th) No. G12 surcharged locally in red.

G17	1d. on 1/–	**black/green** ..	1·50	6·00
		a "ONE" omitted	£400	—
		b "ONE" double	£400	—
		c "PENNY."	£375	—
		double ..	—	—

Prices for G17b and c are for clear double impressions.

The surcharge was handstamped on two stamps at a time in two operations. The first operation applied the PENNY. overprint throughout the sheet, and "ONE" was added at the second operation. This method of surcharging accounts for the differing spacing between the two lines, which varies between 6½mm. and 10 mm.

4,440 stamps were surcharged between January 28th and 30th and sold out on the day of issue. A further 11,150 were surcharged between February 1st and 6th and were placed on sale on February 8th.

Total number issued—15,590.

WAR STAMP.
Type I

WAR STAMP.
Type II

WAR STAMP
Type III

1916 (June)-18 War Tax. Nos. G2/4 overprinted in black.

(a) Locally with first setting Type I. 2-2½mm. between lines.

G18	1d.	**red**	4·00	—
	a	overprint double ..	£60	£60

(b) Locally with second setting Type I. 2-2½ mm. between lines.

G19	1d.	**red**	1·00	1·25

The overprints on G18/19 were handstamped on two stamps at a time. In the first setting the left hand overprint was followed by a comma and the right hand overprint by a full stop: thus, all the stamps in vertical columns 1 3, 5, 7, 9 and 11 have commas whilst those in columns 2, 4, 6, 8, 10 and 12 have full stops.

In the second setting both overprints were followed by full stops and the two settings can therefore only be identified in pairs.

(c) Locally with third setting. Type I. 1½mm. between lines.

G20	1d.	**red**	£50	—

(d) Locally with Type II. 3¼mm. between lines (May 1917).

G21	1d.	**carmine-red**	80	1·00
	a	overprint double ..	£85	—

Number printed—G21, 15,000.

(e) In London with Type III on seven special printings 1916 (Aug. 28th)-18.

G22	1d.	**carmine-red**	25	25
G23	1d.	**pale rose-red** ..	15	20
G24	1d.	**deep rose-red** ..	15	20
G25	1d.	**pl scarlet** ('18) ..	15	20
SPG22		**specimen** (1v) ..	£25	‡

1921-32 As Nos. G1/16 but wmk. Multiple Script CA.

G26	½d.	**green**	10	10
G27	1d.	**carmine** ..	15	15
G28	1d.	**red**	10	10
G29	1½d.	**brown** ('32) ..	25	25
G30	2d.	**grey**	20	25
G31	2½d.	**bt blue** ('26) ..	30	35
G32	3d.	**bright blue** ..	2·00	2·75
G33	3d.	**pur/yel** ('26) ..	1·00	1·25
G34	4d.	**red/yellow** ('30) ..	1·25	2·50
G35	5d.	**sage-green** ..	1·25	2·50
G36	6d.	**claret** (11/27) ..	1·50	2·50
G37	1/–	**bistre-brown** ..	1·50	2·50
G38	1/–	**ochre** ('27).. ..	3·00	5·00
G39	2/–	**blue and purple** ..	6·00	£10
G40	5/–	**car and myrtle** ..	£12	£20
G41	£1	**mauve and black** ('28)	£85	£95
G26/41		**set** (14v) ..	£110	£140
SPG26/41		**specimen set** (14v)	£100	‡

G39/40/41—See note under G14/15/16.

1935 (May 6th) Silver Jubilee. (recess) Waterlow and Sons. Wmk. Multiple Script CA. Perf. 11 x 12. Sheets 6 x 10.

G42	1d.	**blue and scarlet** ..	30	30
G43	1½d.	**ult and grey** ..	35	40
G44	2½d.	**brown and blue** ..	1·00	1·50
G45	1/–	**slate and purple**	3·00	4·50
G42/45		**set** (4v)	4·50	6·00
SPG42/45		**specimen set** (4v)	£25	‡

Numbers printed—G42, 72,000; G43, 60,000; G44, 52,000; G45, 48,000.

Remainders were withdrawn on December 31st, 1935.

1938 (Mar. 11th) -47 Designs, ½d., 2d., 3d., 6d., 2/- to £1 (Badge of Colony; 1d. (Young's Island and Fort Duvernette); 1½d. (Kingstown and Fort Charlotte); 2½d., 3½d. (Bathing Beach, Villa); 1/- (Victoria Park, Kingstown). Printers (recess) Bradbury, Wilkinson. Perf. 12 (L). Designs, 1d, 1½d., 2½d. (both), 3½d., 1/- H. Sheets 6 x 10 or 10 x 6.

1	½d.	**blue and green** ..	5	5
	a	blue, blue-green ..	10	5
2	1d.	**dp blue and lake-brn**	15	10
	a	dp blue and red-choc (25/9/44) ..	10	5
3	1½d.	**grn and rose-scar**	20	10
	a	green and scarlet (/43)	10	10
4	2d.	**yellow-grn and black**	20	20
	a	green and black (/43)	15	15
5	2½d.	**blue-blk and blue-grn**	10	15
	a	indi-blk and greenish-blue (/43)	50	50
	b	slate-blk and blue-grn (6/5/46) ..	30	30
6	2½d.	**green and grey-brown** (14/1/47)	15	15
7	3d.	**orange and dp purple**	10	10
	a	orange and purple ..	20	20
8	3½d.	**blue-blk and blue-grn** (1/4/47)	20	20
9	6d.	**black and dp lake**	20	20
	a	black, pale purple ..	30	30
	b	black, bright purple .	30	30
10	1/–	**purple and green** ..	40	15
	a	pur-vio and yel-grn (/43)	50	20

11	2/–	**blue and dp purple** ..	1·25	70
	a	ultra and purple ..	1·25	80
12	2/6	**red-brn and steel-blue** (14/1/47)	1·25	1·40
13	5/–	**dp crim and myrtle-grn**	2·25	2·50
	a	crimson and green ..	2·25	2·50
14	10/–	**violet and sepia-brn** (14/1/47)	4·00	4·00
15	£1	**purple-violet and blk**	£10	£12
	a	bright purple, black ..	£10	£12
1/15		**set (15)**	£20	£21
SP 1/15		**specimen set** perf (11)	£85	‡

Copies of No. 3 with vermilion frames are changelings.

1949 (Mar. 26th) **As No. 1, etc., but currency changed. Sheets 6 x 10.**

16	1c.	**blue and green** ..	10	10
17	2c.	**dp blue and lake-brn**	10	10
18	3c.	**green and scarlet** ..	15	15
19	4c.	**green and black** ..	10	10
20	5c.	**green and grey-brown**	10	10
21	6c.	**orange and dp purple**	15	15
22	7c.	**blue-blk and greenish-blue**	15	15
23	12c.	**black and dp lake** ..	15	15
24	24c.	**purple and green** ..	40	20
25	48c.	**blue and dp purple** ..	80	80
26	60c.	**red-brn and steel-blue**	1·00	1·00
27	$1.20	**dp crim and myrtle-grn**	3·00	3·50
28	$2.40	**violet and sepia-brn**	5·00	6·00
29	$4.80	**pur-violet and black**	£10	£11
16/29		**set (14)**	£20	£22

1952 (June 10th) **As No. 16, etc., but colours changed, and new value. (Nos. 31 and 33 have designs interchanged in relation to Nos. 18 and 21). Designs, 1c., 3c., 4c., V; Others H.**

30	1c.	**green and black** ..	10	10
31	3c.	**orange and dp purple**	10	10
32	4c.	**blue and green** ..	10	10
33	6c.	**grn and scarlet-rose**	10	15
34	10c.	**blue-blk and greenish-blue**	20	20
30/34		**set (5)**	60	65

SPECIAL ISSUES

1937 (May 12th) **Coronation. As Aden, but Printers, Bradbury, Wilkinson. Perf. 11 x 11¾ (C).**

S1	1d.	**violet**	10	10
S2	1½d.	**carmine-red**	10	10
S3	2½d.	**dp blue**	20	20
SP S1/3		**specimen set** perf (3)	£13	‡

1946 (Oct. 15th) **Victory. As Aden.**

S4	1½d.	**carmine-red**	10	10
S5	3½d.	**dp blue**	10	10
SP S4/5		**specimen set** perf (2)	£14	‡

1948 (Nov. 30th) **Silver Wedding. As Aden.**

S6	1½d.	**scarlet**	10	10
S7	£1	**red-purple**	£10	£12

The £1 "Wedding" stamp was originally printed in black, but as the colony's supply was stolen in transit, another printing in red-purple was made. In the Royal Collection there is a block of four of the black variety.

1949 (Oct. 10th) **U.P.U. As Aden.**

S8	5c.	**dull ultramarine** ..	10	10
S9	6c.	**purple-violet** ..	10	10
S10	12c.	**reddish-mauve** ..	20	20
S11	24c.	**quartz-green** ..	50	60
S8/11		**set (4)**	90	1·00

1951 (Feb. 16th) **West Indies University. (See Antigua.)**

S12	3c.	**green and red** ..	10	10
S13	12c.	**black and claret** ..	20	20

1951 (Sept. 21st) **New Constitution 1951. No. 18, etc., overprinted in black.**

S14	3c.	**grn and scarlet-rose**	15	15
S15	4c.	**green and black** ..	15	15
S16	5c.	**green and grey-brn**	20	25
S17	12c.	**black and dp lake** ..	25	35
S14/17		**set (4)**	75	90

Number issued—3c., 91,098; 4c., 138,992; 5c., 117,329; 12c., 97,204.

SAMOA

Samoa, discovered in 1722, consists of four main islands, SAVAI'I, UPOLU, TUTUILA and MANU'A. Early correspondence was from Missionary Workers, the earliest recorded dated 11th July 1836. The first postal service was established when the first stamps of Samoa were issued on 1st October 1877. This service, not very successful, closed at the end of 1881.

John Davis was appointed Postmaster in April 1885 and until he issued his "Palm Trees" stamps on 20th December 1886 used American stamps. These were cancelled with a cork cancellor, the Apia date-stamp applied alongside. Only five such covers have been recorded the earliest dated 2nd May 1885. John Davis' Post Office closed on 28th February 1900 when the islands were partitioned, Germany taking the Western Islands (Savai'i and Upolu) and America taking the Eastern Islands (Tutuila and Manu'a). American stamps are still used in Eastern Samoa.

German stamps overprinted "SAMOA" were issued in March 1900 being replaced at the end of that year by German Colonial Stamps inscribed "SAMOA". After the outbreak of World War I, the New Zealand Expeditionary Force landed at Upolu on 29th August 1914 and took control of the Post Office. Stamps were overprinted G.R.I. and surcharged. They were replaced with New Zealand stamps overprinted "SAMOA" at the end of September 1914. Samoa re-commenced issuing their own stamps with the "Huts" issue in 1921, although the higher value stamps of New Zealand overprinted "SAMOA" continued in use until Samoa became independent in 1962.

The title of the territory was later changed as is reflected in the issues from 1935 onwards, to Western Samoa; this was done in order to differentiate it from Eastern Samoa under U.S. administration.

1877-81. Designed by Mr. Boney. Printers (*litho*) **S. T. Leigh and Co., Sydney. Outer edges of all sheets imperf.**

State I

Line above 'X' of 'EXPRESS' complete or showing signs of wear. Perf. 12¼. Sheets 4 x 5. (1/10/77).

V1	1d.	**ultramarine** ..	£20	£30
V2	3d.	**deep scarlet** ..	£25	£30
V3	6d.	**bright violet**..	£25	£30
		a pale lilac ..	£25	£30

From October 1877–March 1878 stamps were cancelled by writing the date across them in ink as there was no cancelling device.

State II

Line above 'X' of 'EXPRESS' completely broken. Sheets 2 x 5.

(a) Perf. 12¼. (1878).

V4	1d.	**ultramarine** ..	£20	£30
V5	3d.	**vermilion** ..	£22	£35
V6	6d.	**bright violet**..	£20	£30
		a pale lilac ..	£20	£30
V7	1/–	**dull yellow** ..	£30	£45
		a orange-yellow ..	£30	£45
V8	2/–	**chocolate** ..	£50	£75
		a brown ..	£50	£75
V9	5/–	**green** ..	£200	£300

(b) Perf. 12. (1879).

V10	1/–	**dull yellow** ..	£75	£100

State III

Line above 'X' of 'EXPRESS' repaired. 1d. sheets 4 x 5, others sheets 2 x 5.

(a) Perf. 12¼. (1879).

V11	1d.	**ultramarine** ..	£20	£30
V12	3d.	**vermilion** ..	£25	£30
V13	6d.	**lilac** ..	£25	£30
V14	2/–	**chocolate** ..	£50	£75
		a brown ..	£50	£75
V15	5/–	**green** ..	£175	£250

(b) Perf. 12. (1879).

V16	1d.	**ultramarine** ..	£12	£15
		a blue ..	£12	£15
		b deep blue ..	£12	£15
V17	3d.	**vermilion** ..	£18	£25
		a carmine-vermilion..	£18	£25
V18	6d.	**bright violet**..	£15	£20
		a deep violet ..	£15	£20
V19	2/–	**chocolate** ..	£50	£75
V20	5/–	**green** ..	£150	£225

State IV

As State III but with addition of a spot of colour under 'M' of 'SAMOA' on the coloured curve. Perf. 12. Sheets 2 x 5. (1880).

V21	9d.	**orange-brown** ..	£18	£25

(I) REMAINDERS (Prepared for issue but not issued). In 1881 all values including a new 2d. were printed in State IV arriving after the Post Office closed and never placed on sale. The 1d., 2d. and 6d. values were printed in sheets of 21 (3 x 7) and the 3d., 9d., 1/–, 2/– and 5/– in sheets of 12 (3 x 4). The 2d. value was printed in rose and the other values in the same colours as the issued stamps. All were Perf. 12. Being printed in very small quantities they are much rarer than the original stamps. Complete sheets have been recorded on only the 1d., 2d., 3d and 6d. values.

(II) REPRINTS. Between 1884 and 1892, three reprints of the stamps, including a 2d. value, were produced in State IV in sheets of 40 (5 x 8). The first printing in 1884 were Perf. 12 (clean cut) with sheet margins, the second in 1892 were Perf. 12 (rough) without sheet margins the outer edges being imperf. and the third, also in 1892, were Perf. 12¼ (clean cut) without sheet margins. All were printed on whiter paper than the originals and are very common. Complete sheets exist but are scarce.

(III) FORGERIES. These are known, by Yardley and Fournier, the latter being the most dangerous, and may be identified by the following. Yardley (type I) curl on top loop of 'S' in SAMOA and white flaw in lower right coloured triangle (four examples of 1d. value in blue only are recorded); Yardley (type II) pearls in upper band regularly spaced only one appearing below 'M' of SAMOA (known in all values including 2d. rose) singles are common complete sheets of 40 (5 x 8) are rare; a third type is also known in 1d. brown (two recorded). Fournier—pearl below Ex of Express merges with solid colour above. Types exist with small and larger letters in value panel. Single stamps are common; complete sheets with small letters are known and are scarce.

1886-1900. Palm Trees Issue. Dies engraved by Bock and Cousins. Printers (*typo*) **Government Printing Office, Wellington. Wmk NZ and Star. Sheets 10 x 6—2 panes.**

(a) Perf. 12½. (20/12/86).

V22	½d.	**purple-brown**	2·00	75
V23	1d.	**yellow-green**	2·50	2·00
V24	2d.	**brown-orange**	3·00	1·50
		a orange	3·00	1·50
V25	4d.	**deep blue**	5·00	3·00
		a blue	5·00	3·00
V26	6d.	**brown-lake** (1891)	—	£250
V27	1/-	**rose-carmine**	£10	5·00
		a bisected, used on cover (1895)	‡	£100
V28	2/6	**violet**	£20	£10

Numbers printed—V22, 13,080; V23, 13,080; V24, 13,080; V25, 12,840; V26, 360; V27, 12,720; V28, 12,600.

(b) Perf. 12 x 11½. (1887-90).

V29	½d.	**purple-brown** (1887)	75	15
		a dp purple-brn (1890)	75	15
		b purple-black (1890)	75	15
V30	1d.	**yellow-green** (1887)	1·50	20
		a green (1890)	1·50	20
		b blue-green (1890)	1·50	20
V31	2d.	**brown-orange** (1887)	2·50	25
		a dull orange (1890)	2·50	25
		b yellow-orange (1890)	2·50	25
		c wmk. reversed	—	—
V32	4d.	**blue** (1887)	4·00	30
		a deep blue (1890)	4·00	30
		b wmk. reversed	—	—
V33	6d.	**brown-lake** (1887)	5·00	50
		a maroon (1890)	5·00	50
V34	1/-	**rose** (1890)	£10	1·50
		a wmk. reversed	—	—
V35	2/6	**violet** (1887)	£20	2·50
		a bright violet (1890)	£20	2·50
V29/35		**set** (7v)	£40	5·00

Numbers printed—V29, 174,000; V30, 175,200; V31, 173,040; V32, 47,400; V33, 62,040; V34, 47,280; V35, 83,040.

(c) Perf. 11.

(i) White Paper (1895-1900).

V36	½d.	**purple-brown** (1895)	15	10
		a dp purple-brn (1895)	15	10
		b purple-black (1900)	25	1·50
V37	1d.	**green** (1895)	15	10
		a pl blue-green (1897)	15	10
		b blue-green (1897)	25	10
		c deep green (1900)	25	1·50
		d dp blue-green (1900)	20	1·50
		e gummed on both sides	2·50	—
V38	2d.	**yellow** (1895)	2·50	1·75
		a orange-yellow (1896)	50	15
		b bright-yellow (1897)	1·50	75
		c orchre (1897)	50	15
		d pale ochre (1897)	50	50
		e brown-ochre (1900)	75	1·75
V39	4d.	**blue** (1895)	1·00	1·25
		a deep blue (1900)	75	1·25
V40	6d.	**brown-lake** (1895)	75	1·00
		a deep brown-lake (1900)	1·00	1·00
		b maroon (1900)	1·50	2·50
V41	1/-	**rose** (1895)	2·00	75
		a bisected, used on cover (1895)	‡	£200
		b rose-pink (1895)	1·00	1·25
		c carmine (1900)	1·25	1·50
V42	2/6	**violet** (wmk inverted (1895)	4·50	3·50
V43	2/6	**deep mauve** (wmk. upright) (189?)	—	£15

Numbers printed—V36, 256,920; V37, 256,080; V38, 339,240; V39, 90,120; V40, 77,760; V41, 89,400; V42/43, 18,360.

(ii) Toned Paper (1898).

V44	1/-	**dl rose-carmine**	75	75
		a rose-carmine	75	75
V45	2/6	**dp purple** (wmk. reversed)	2·50	3·00
		a imperf. between vert. pair	£150	—

Numbers printed—V44, 70,680; V45, 71,880.

(d) Perf. 11 colour changes. (1899).

V46	½d.	**dl blue green**	25	35
		a deep green	25	35
V47	1d.	**red-brown**	25	35
		a dp red-brown	25	35
V36/47		**set** (9v)	6·00	7·00

Numbers printed—V46, 199,160; V47, 119,280.

In this issue three different types of watermark exist, the main differences being the distance between NZ and the Star (6mm, 7mm or 4mm) and the width of NZ and the Star which also varies in each type.

V27*a*, V41*a* On 1st April, 1895 the Apia post office was destroyed by fire and all stamps lost. The only stamps available were a few 1/- stamps Perf. 12½ kept in the Customs House. These were bisected diagonally and used to show that postage had been paid. On 22nd May, 1895 a new supply of the Perf. 11 1/- stamps arrived from Wellington. A few of these are known to have been bisected and genuinely used until the end of May, 1895. As a result of philatelic demand, 1/—

stamps Perf. 11 were bisected, usually vertically or with a slight slant, by the Postmaster in September, 1895 and attached to envelopes or sheets of paper and cancelled with a date-stamp showing dates in September, 1895. The Postmaster, realising this date was too late adjusted his date-stamp to show dates in April, May and June when the provisional bisects were in genuine use. These cancelled to order bisects are common and worth about £1.50 on piece.

1892-1900. King Malietoa. Die engraved by A. E. Cousins. Printers *(typo)* **Goverment Printing Office, Wellington. Wmk. NZ and Star. Sheets 10 x 6—2 panes.**

(a) Perf. 12½. (1892).

V48	2½d.	**rose**	.. .. ..	1·00	25

Number printed—24,600.

(b) Perf. 12 x 11½. (1892).

V49	2½d.	**rose**	.. .. ..	50	15
	a	pale rose	.. ..	50	15

Number printed—59,880.

(c) Perf. 11. (1895).

V50	2½d.	**rose**	.. ..	15	10
	a	rose-carmine (1897)		15	10
	b	dp rose-carmine (1900)		30	1·50
	c	dl rose-carmine (1900)		30	1·50

Number printed—209,520.

(d) Perf. 10 x 11. (1896).

V51	2½d.	**black** (error of colour)		50	75
	a	perf. 11	.. ..	£30	£25

Number printed—118,080.

1893 (Nov.) Provisional Issues. Numbers V32 and V32a surcharged with letters or figures.

V52	5d./4d.	**dp blue** (type I) ..		£45	£40
	a	blue	.. ..	£45	£40
V53	5d./4d.	**dp blue** (type II)		£15	£12
	a	blue	.. ..	£15	£12
	b	bars omitted	..	—	—

V54	5d./4d.	**dp blue** (type III) (12/93)	..	£15	£10
V55	5d./4d.	**dp blue** (type IV) (12/93)	..	2·50	1·00
	a	blue	.. ..	2·50	1·00
	b	bars omitted	..	—	£60

Type I	Small lettering.
Type II	Larger lettering.
Type III	No stop after '5d'.
Type IV	Stop after '5d'.

Types I, II and IV exist with part of the overprint double. Various sub-types of Types I and II exist.

Forgeries are known of Type I with slightly larger lettering, the distance between 'Five' and 'PENCE' being 2¾mm. There is only one short thick obliterating bar instead of long thick and thin bars.

1894-1900. Flag of Samoa. Die engraved by A. E. Cousins. Printers *(typo)* **Government Printing Office, Wellington. Wmk. NZ and Star (sideways pointing to left as viewed from back). Sheets 6 x 10—2 panes.**

(a) Perf. 11½ x 12. (1894).

V56	5d.	**red**	.. .. ..	1·00	75
	a	dull red	.. ..	1·00	75

Number printed—60,720.

(b) Perf. 11. (1895).

V57	5d.	**red**	.. .. ..	2·00	1·00

Number printed—18,480.

(c) Perf. 11. Wmk. sideways-inverted. (1900).

V58	5d.	**red**	.. .. ..	25	35
	a	deep scarlet..	..	25	35
	b	scarlet	.. ..	25	35

Number printed—119,400.

Type I — '2' without serif

Type II — '2' with serif

Type I — wide 'R'
Type II — narrow 'R'
Type III — wide '3'

1895-1900. Provisional Issues. Numbers V31a, V38 and V38a surcharged in blue (1½/2d.) or black (3d./2.).

(a) Perf. 12 x 11½. (26/1/95).

V59	1½d./2d.	**dull orange**	
		(type I)	1·75	1·00
V60	3d./2d.	**dull orange**	
		(type I)	1·75	1·00
		a surcharge double	—	—

(b) Perf. 11.

(i) Original Stereos. (6/95).

V61	1½d./2d.	**orange-yellow**		
		(type I) ..	1·00	75
		a yellow	£15	£10
		b surcharge double	—	—
		c surcharge omitted in pair with normal ..	—	—
V62	3d./2d.	**orange-yellow**		
		(type I)	1·25	1·00
		a yellow	£15	£10
		b surcharge double	—	—

(ii) New Stereos. (1896).

V63	1½d./2d.	**yellow** (type II) ..	£20	£15
		a surcharge double	—	—
V64	3d./2d.	**yellow** (type II) ..	1·25	1·00
		a surcharge double	—	—
		b imperf. between vertical pair ..	£200	—
		c surcharge omitted in pair with normal ..	—	—

(iii) Green surcharge on a special printing of the 2d. value. (Feb. 1900).

V65	3d./2d.	**red-orange** (type III) ..	£15	—

Number printed—71,640.

1898-99. Provisional Issues. Number V37a, V37b, V44, V44a, and V45 surcharged (typo) in black or red at Wellington.

V66	2½d./1d.	**blue-green (R)**		
		(1899)	25	30
		a pl blue-green ..	25	30
		b surcharged inv.	—	£75
V67	2½d./1/—	**dl rose-carmine**		
		(10/98) ..	1·50	1·75
		a rose-carmine ..	1·50	1·75
		b surcharge double	—	—
V68	2½d./1/—	**rose-carmine (R)**		
		(1899)	1·50	1·75
		a surcharge double	—	—
V69	2½d./2/6	**deep purple**		
		(1899)	1·50	1·75
V66/69		**set** (4)	4·50	5·25

V67 was handstamped locally before sheets arrived from Wellington.

1899-1900. Provisional Government Issue. Two special printings of the Perf. 11 issues overprinted 'PROVISIONAL GOVT.' in black or red. Wmk. NZ and Star (sideways-inverted on 5d.).

V70	½d.	**dl blue-green (R)** ..	20	15
		a dp yellow-green (1900)	10	25
V71	1d.	**red-brown**	20	15
		a dp red-brown (1900)	10	25
V72	2d.	**orange (R)**	25	20
		a deep ochre (1900)	15	25
V73	4d.	**deep blue (R)** ..	40	30
		a blue (1900) ..	20	50
V74	5d.	**deep scarlet**.. ..	70	50
		a dull red (1900) ..	35	75
V75	6d.	**brown-lake**	1·50	1·00
		a maroon (1900) ..	75	1·00
V76	1/—	**dp rose-carmine** ..	2·00	2·50
		a rose-carmine (1900)	1·25	3·50
V77	2/6	**mauve (R)**	2·00	4·00
		a deep mauve (1900)	2·25	7·50
V70/77		**set** (8v)	4·75	8·50

Numbers printed—V70, 48,000; V70a, 94,800; V71, 47,520; V71a, 94,560; V72, 48,120; V72a, 94,200; V73, 48,480; V73a, 94,680; V74, 48,480; V74a, 94,440; V75, 48,000; V75a, 71,400; V76, 47,640; V76a, 71,400; V77, 48,120; V77a, 47,160.

1900 (March) Stamps of Germany overprinted "SAMOA" diagonally reading upwards in black at the Imperial Printing Office, Berlin. Perf. 13½ x 14½. No watermark.

E1	3pf	**brown**	2·00	3·00
		a yellow-brown ..	2·00	3·00
E2	5pf	**green**	3·00	4·50
		a deep green	3·00	4·50
E3	10pf	**carmine**	5·00	7·50
		a rose-carmine ..	5·00	7·50
E4	20pf	**ultramarine**	£20	£30
		a Prussian blue ..	£20	£30

E5	25pf	**orange**	..	..	£25	£40
E6	50pf	**chocolate**	..	..	£30	£60
		a red-brown	..	..	£30	£60

1900 (Dec.) 1919. Design, Ex-Kaiser's Yacht 'Hohenzollern'. Printers (*typo*) Imperial Printing Office, Berlin. 30pf-80pf Perf. 14; others Perf. 14¼.

(a) No watermark.

E7	3pf	**brown**	..	..	50	1·00
E8	5pf	**green** ..	..	..	75	1·00
E9	10pf	**carmine**	..	..	75	1·00
E10	20pf	**ultramarine**	..		75	2·50
		a blue ..	..	..	75	2·50
E11	25pf	**black and red/yellow**		1·00	£10
E12	30pf	**black and orange/buff**		1·25	£10
E13	40pf	**black and carmine**		1·50	£15
E14	50pf	**black and purple/buff**		1·75	£20
E15	80pf	**black and carmine/ rose** ..	..	..	2·00	£25
E16	1m	**carmine**	..	..	3·00	£50
E17	2m	**blue**	..	..	5·00	£75
E18	3m	**violet-black**		7·50	£100
E19	5m	**carmine and dk green**	£100	£300
		a wrong centre plate..		—	—

E19*a* The wrong centre plate has the shading of the sky extending across the folds of the scroll containing the colony name. The normal centre plate has breaks in the shading of the sky to fit the scroll folds.

3pf, 5pf, 10pf, 5m stamps with Lozenges wmk. were prepared but due to the outbraek of World War I, were not placed on sale in Samoa, only being sold in Berlin.

1914 (Sept 3) German Samoa stamps overprinted G.R.I. in black and surcharged at Apia. Pfennig values vertical setting of 10, mark values horizontal setting of 4.

G1	½d./3pf	**brown**	..	..	£10	5·00
		a surcharge double	£300	£250
		b no fraction bar in '½'..	..	£25	£15
		c '1' to left of '2' in '½'..	..	£25	£15
		d comma after 'I'	£200	£125
G2	½d./5pf	**green**	..	..	£10	5·00
		a surcharge double	£300	£250
		b no fraction bar in '½'..	..	£25	£15
		c '1' to left of '2' in '½'..	..	£25	£15
		d comma after 'I'	£200	£125
G3	1d./10pf	**carmine** ..		£20	£10
		a surcharge double	£300	£250
G4	2½d./20pf	**ultramarine**	..	£10	5·00
		a surcharge double	£300	£250
		b no faction bar in '½'..	..	£25	£15

		c '1' to left of '2' in '½'..	..	£25	£15
		d comma after 'I'	£200	£125
		e surcharge inverted	£300	£250
G5	3d./25pf	**black and red/ yellow**	..	£40	£20
		a surcharge double	£300	£250
		b comma after 'I'	£200	£125
G6	4d./30pf	**black and orange/ buff**	..	..	£75	£40
		a surcharge double	£300	£250
G7	5d./40pf	**black and carmine**	£75	£40
G8	6d./50pf	**black and purple/ buff**	..	..	£20	£10
		a surcharge double	£300	£250
		b inverted '9' for '6'	..	..	£50	£30
G9	9d./80pf	**black and carmine/rose**	..	£75	£40
G10	1/–/1m	**carmine** (type I)	£1000	£750
G11	1/–/1m	**carmine** (type II)	£3000	£2000
G12	2/–/2m	**blue**	..	..	£750	£500
G13	3/–/3m	**violet-black**	..	£500	£400
		a surcharge double	£2000	£1500
G14	5/–/5m	**carmine and black**	£400	£325

G1*b*, G2*b*, G4*b* The missing fraction bar variety is from Row 6.

G1*c*, G2*c*, G4*c* The '1' to left of '2' in '½' variety is from Row 1.

G1*d*, G2*d*, G4*d*, G5*b* A comma was used in place of a stop after 'G.R.I.' Row 10, second printing only.

G8*b* An inverted '9' was used for a '6' on Row 9. This has the top of the figure turned down more than the normal and the '*d*' is positioned higher.

G10 Surchage on the first printing of 5m value was '1 Shillings'.

G11 Surcharge corrected to '1 Shilling' for second and third printings.

Numbers surcharged—G1, 16,700; G2, 14,700; G3, 7,000; G4, 19,700; G5, 3,800; G6, 1,600; G7, 1,400; G8, 6,000; G9, 1,700; G10, 100; G11, 35; G12, 126; G13, 458; G14, 534.

1914 (Sept. 29)-16. Stamps of New Zealand overprinted SAMOA in black or red. Designs, ½d., 2d., 6d. and 1/– King Edward VII; 1d. Dominion type; 2½d. Lake Wakatipu. Printers (*recess*) Government Printing Office, Wellington. ½d., 1d., Perf. 14 x 15; 2d., 6d., 1/– Perf. 14 x 14½; 2½d. Perf. 14. Wmk. 'single' NZ and Star. ½d. and 1d. sheets 10 x 24; others 10 x 12.

G15	½d.	**green (R)**	..	..	10	10
		a yellow-green	..	10	10
		b damaged 'M'	..	5·00	2·50

G16	1d.	**carmine**	10	10
		a deep carmine ..	10	10
		b overprint omitted in vert. pair with normal	—	—
		c damaged 'M' ..	5·00	2·50
G17	2d.	**mauve (R)** (10/14) ..	50	50
		a reddish-mauve ..	60	60
G18	2½d.	**dark blue (R)** (10/14)	1·00	1·00
		a deep blue	1·00	1·00
		b wmk. inverted ..	—	—
G19	6d.	**pale carmine** (10/14)	7·50	7·00
		a carmine (P.14 x 14½)	1·25	1·00
		aa Perf. 14 x 13½ (1916)	£10	£10
		ab se-tenant pair (G19*a*/G19*aa*)	£15	£15
G20	1/–	**vermilion**	2·50	2·50
G15/20		**set** (6v)	5·25	5·00

G15*b*, G16*c* The 'M' of 'SAMOA' is damaged on Row 4/11.

G16*b* One sheet was issued in error with the overprint misplaced downwards to such an extent that the top row of stamps were without overprint and the overprint appeared in the bottom sheet margin.

Numbers printed—G15, 281,760; G16, 741,360; G17, 71,160; G18, 53,880; G19, 44,760; G20, 31,680.

1914-29. Postal Fiscal stamps of New Zealand overprinted SAMOA in black or red. Printers (*typo*) **Government Printing Office, Wellington. Wmk. 'single' NZ and Star (sideways). Sheets 6 x 10.**

(a) Chalk surfaced De La Rue paper.
(i) Perf. 14 (rough).

G21	2/–	**blue (R)** (9/17) ..	£50	£75
G22	2/6	**grey-brown** (9/17)	3·00	4·50
G23	5/–	**yellow-green (R)** (11/14)	8·00	£13
G24	10/–	**maroon** (11/14) ..	£15	£20
G25	£1	**rose-carmine** (11/14)	£35	£55

Numbers overprinted—G21, 1,400; G22, 14,820; G23, 9,960; G24, 9,060; G25, 5,700.

(ii) Perf. 14½ x 14 (clean cut).

G26	2/–	**deep blue (R)** (3/18)	3·00	4·50
G27	2/6	**grey-brown** (10/24)	£40	£60
G28	3/–	**purple (R)** (6/23) ..	£10	£15
G29	5/–	**yellow green (R)** (9/17)	6·00	7·50
G30	10/–	**maroon** (3/18) ..	£15	£20
G31	£1	**rose-carmine** (3/18)	£30	£45
G32	£2	**mauve (R)** (5/29) ..	£60	—

Numbers overprinted—G26, 41,340; G27, 6,000; G28, 10,320; G29, 24,600; G30, 15,480; G31, 6,540; G32, 3,000.

(b) Chalk surfaced Cowan paper. Perf. 14 x 14½.

G33	2/–	**blue (R)** (12/25) ..	£60	£90
G34	2/6	**dp grey-brown** (10/28)	£50	£75
G35	3/–	**mauve (R)** (9/25) ..	£30	£45
G36	5/–	**yellow-green (R)** (11/26)	£10	£15
		a overprint at top of stamp	—	—
G37	10/–	**brown-red** (12/25)	£75	£100
G38	£1	**rose-pink** (11/26) ..	£40	£60
G21/31, 33/38		**set** (6v)	£60	£90

Postally used examples of G32 have been seen, the value mainly being used for fiscal purposes.

G36*a* One sheet was purchased locally with the overprint at the top of the stamp (over 'FIVE') instead of across the middle of the stamp.

Numbers sold—G33, 600; G34, 1,384; G35, 2,040; G36, 13,560; G37, 12,060; G38, 3,360.

1916-19. King George V stamps of New Zealand overprinted SAMOA in black or red. Designed by H. L. Richardson. Wmk. 'single' NZ and Star.

(a) Typograph printed. Perf. 14 x 15. Sheets 10 x 24.

G39	½d.	**green (R)** (1916) ..	10	10
		a damaged 'M' ..	5·00	2·50
G40	1½d.	**grey-black (R)** (1917)	15	15
		a black	15	15
		b damaged 'M' ..	5·00	2·50
G41	1½d.	**orange-brown (R)** (1919)	15	15
		a damaged 'M' ..	5·00	2·50
G42	2d.	**yellow (R)** (1916) ..	15	15
		a orange-yellow ..	15	15
		b damaged 'M' ..	5·00	2·50
G43	3d.	**dp chocolate** (1917)	50	50
		a damaged 'M' ..	£10	5·00

Numbers sold—G39, 267,120; G40, 133,680; G41, 228,960; G42, 223,440; G43, 53,280.

(b) Recess printed. Sheets 10 x 12. Top four rows Perf. 14 x 13½; Bottom six rows Perf. 14 x 14½.

G44	2½d.	**deep blue (R)** (1916)	35	50
		a perf. 14 x 14½ ..	50	75
		b se-tenant pair (G44/*a*)	3·00	4·50
G45	3d.	**dp chocolate** (1919)	50	75
		a perf. 14 x 14½ ..	75	1·25
		b se-tenant pair (G45/*a*)	4·50	7·00
G46	6d.	**carmine** (1917) ..	1·00	1·50
		a perf. 14 x 14½ ..	1·50	2·25
		b se-tenant pair (G46/*a*)	£10	£15
G47	1/–	**vermilion** (1916) ..	75	1·25
		a perf. 14 x 14½ ..	1·25	2·00
		b se-tenant pair (G47/*a*)	7·50	£12
G39/47		**set** (8v)	3·00	4·00

Numbers sold—G44, 83,040; G45, 65,760; G46, 47,520; G47, 57,600.

1920 (July) Victory Issue of New Zealand overprinted SAMOA in black or red. Printers (*typo*) **De La Rue. Perf. 14. Wmk. 'single' NZ and Star (sideways on ½d., 1½d., 3d. and 1/–). ½d., 3d. and 1/– sheets 20 x 7; 1d. sheets 8 x 20; 1½d. sheets 20 x 8; 6d. sheets 7 x 20.**

G48	½d.	**green (R)**	20	30
G49	1d.	**carmine**	25	40
		a broken 'A'	£35	£15
G50	1½d.	**brown-orange (R)** ..	75	1·00
		a broken 'A'	£40	£20
G51	3d.	**chocolate**	1·00	1·50
G52	6d.	**violet (R)**	2·00	3·00
G53	1/–	**orange-red**	2·50	4·00
G48/53		**set** (6v)	6·00	9·00

G49a On Row 2/19 of the second setting only, the second 'A' of 'SAMOA' has no bar, and both legs show nicks where the bar should be.

G50a On Row 4/1 of the first setting the bar of the second 'A' of 'SAMOA' is missing and appears as an inverted 'V'.

Numbers sold—G48, 98,000; G49, 76,180; G50, 59,537; G51, 36,114; G52, 31,301; G53, 30,426.

1921 (Dec. 23)-22 Designed by Bradbury, Wilkinson. Printers (*recess*) Government Printing Office, Wellington. Wmk. 'single' NZ and Star. Sheets 10 x 12.

(a) Perf. 14 x 14½.

G54	½d.	**green**	50	75
G55	1d.	**lake**	30	45
G56	1½d.	**chestnut**	30	45
	a	doubling of 'REVEN'	7·50	5·00
	b	doubling of 'REVE'	5·00	3·50
G57	2d.	**yellow**	50	75

(b) Perf. 14 x 13½.

G58	½d.	**green** (1922) ..	20	30
G59	1d.	**lake** (1922) ..	15	20
	a	carmine-lake ..	10	15
G60	1½d.	**chestnut** (1922) ..	1·00	1·50
	a	doubling of 'REVEN'	£15	£10
	b	doubling of 'REVE'	£10	7·50
G61	2d.	**yellow** (1922) ..	80	1·25
G62	2½d.	**deep blue**	75	1·25
	a	slate-blue	50	75
G63	3d.	**deep chocolate** ..	75	1·00
G64	4d.	**bright violet** ..	1·00	2·00
G65	5d.	**light blue**	1·00	2·00
G66	6d.	**carmine**	80	1·25
	a	bright carmine ..	75	1·25
G67	8d.	**dp red-brown** ..	1·75	3·50
G68	9d.	**sage-green**	1·75	3·50
G69	1/–	**orange-vermilion** ..	1·25	2·50
G54/69		**set** (12v)	9·00	£17

G56a/G60a On Row 6/9 'REVEN' of 'REVENUE' is double due to accidental pressure of the transfer roller whilst making the printing plate.

G56b/G60b A similar accidental entry exists on Row 1/8 where 'REVE' of REVENUE' is double.

Numbers sold—G54/G58, 341,458; G55/G59, 1,062,178; G56/G60, 102,638; G57/G61, 372,858; G62, 51,978; G63, 55,338; G64, 45,138; G65, 40,338; G66, 65,058; G67, 27,498; G68, 27,858; G69, 75,978.

1926-28. 'Admiral· issue of New Zealand overprinted SAMOA in red. Designed by H. L. Richardson. Printers (*typo*) Government Printing Office, Wellington. Perf. 14. Wmk. 'single' NZ and Star. Sheets 8 x 10.

(a) Jones Paper.

G70	2/–	**deep blue** (11/26)	..	3·00	4·50
G71	3/–	**mauve** (10/26)	..	3·00	4·50

Numbers overprinted—G70, 24,000; G71, 23,920.

(b) Cowan Paper (10/11/27).

G72	2/–	**light blue**	..	..	6·00	9·00
G73	3/–	**pale mauve**	..	..	£15	£25

Numbers sold—G72, 12,520; G73, 5,280.

1932 (Aug.) Arms Fiscal Stamps of New Zealand overprinted SAMOA in black or red. Designed by H. L. Richardson. Printers (*typo*) Government Printing Office, Wellington. Perf. 14. Wmk. 'single' NZ and Star. Sheets 8 x 10.

G74	2/6	**deep brown** (**R**)	..	£10	£15
G75	5/–	**green** (**R**)	..	£15	£25
G76	10/–	**carmine-lake**	..	£30	£45
G77	£1	**pink** ..	..	£35	£50
G78	£2	**bright purple**	..	£150	—
G79	£5	**indigo-blue** (**R**)	..	£500	—

G78/G79 Used examples have been seen. These values were mainly used for fiscal purposes.

Numbers sold—G74, 4,720; G75, 5,520; G76, 5,120; G77, 5,680.

1935 (May 7) Silver Jubilee of King George V. Numbers G55, G62 and G66a on thick paper, and a special printing of G59a, G62a and G66 on thin paper overprinted in black SILVER JUBILEE OF KING GEORGE V 1910-1935.

(a) Perf. 14 x 14½.

G80	1d.	**lake** ..	..	..	£25	£35

(b) Perf. 14 x 13½.

G81	1d.	**lake** ..	..	..	25	35
	a	carmine-lake	..	25	35
G82	2½d.	**deep blue**	..	..	75	1·00
	a	slate-blue ..	..	75	1·00
G83	6d.	**carmine** ..	..	1·50	2·25
	a	bright carmine	..	1·50	2·25
G81/83		**set** (3v) ..	..	2·50	3·50

Numbers sold—G80, 960; G81, 110,923; G82, 60,982; G83, 50,878.

WESTERN SAMOA

1935 (Aug. 7) Designs ½d. (Samoan Girl and Kava Bowl); 1d. (Apia); 2d. (River Scene); 2½d. (Samoan Chief and Wife); 4d. (Samoan Canoe and House); 6d. (Valima); 1/– (R. L. Stevenson's Tomb); 2/– (Lake Lanuto'o); 3/– (Falefa Falls). Designers, ½d. L. C. Mitchell; 2½d. centre L. C. Mitchell, frame J. Berry; 6d. W. J. Cooch; others J. Berry. Printers (*recess*) **De La Rue. 2d. Perf. 14; others Perf. 13½ x 14 (hor. design) or Perf. 14 x 13½ (vert. designs). Wmk. 'single' NZ and Star. Sheets 10 x 8 (hor. designs) or 8 x 10 (vert. designs).**

G84	½d.	**yellow-green** ..	10	5
G85	1d.	**black and carmine**..	10	5
G86	2d.	**grey-black and orange**	10	5
		a wmk. inverted ..	—	—
		b perf. 13½ x 14 ..	1·00	1·00
G87	2½d.	**black and deep blue**	10	5
G88	4d.	**black and sepia** ..	20	15
		a grey and sepia ..	30	25
G89	6d.	**bright magenta** ..	20	15
		a magenta	30	25
G90	1/–	**violet and grey-brown**	50	40
G91	2/–	**dp green and dp brown**	75	60
G92	3/–	**grey-blue and orange-brown**	1·00	75
G84/92		**set** (9v)	3·00	2·25

Numbers printed—G84, 480,000; G85, 720,000; G86, 240,000; G87, 120,000; G88, 200,000; G89, 156,000; G90, 120,000; G91, 60,000; G92, 60,000.

1935 (Aug. 7) -42 As numbers G74-G79 but overprinted in WESTERN SAMOA in black or red.

(a) Cowan Paper.

G93	2/6	**deep brown**	5·00	7·50
G94	5/–	**green**	7·50	£10
G95	10/–	**carmine-lake** ..	£15	£20
G96	£1	**pink**	£25	£35
G97	£2	**bright violet** (R) ..	£50	£75
G98	£5	**indigo-blue** (R) ..	£125	£175

Numbers overprinted—G93, 7,840; G94, 7,920; G95, 7,760; G96, 7,840.

(b) Wiggins Teape Paper.

G99	5/–	**green** (1942) ..	£10	£15
G100	10/–	**pl carmine-lake** (1941)	£15	£20
G101	£2	**bright purple** (R) (1942)	£75	£100
G102	£5	**indigo-blue** (R) (1942)	£125	£175

Numbers overprinted—G99, 3,840; G100, 4,000.

1940 (Sept. 2nd) Design, Samoan Chief. Printers (*recess*) **Bradbury, Wilkinson. Perf. 14 x 13½ (C). Sheets 10 x 8.**

1	3d./1½d.	**brown**	10	10

See notes after Cook Islands No. 4.

Number printed—400,000.

1942-9 Designs, ½d. (Samoan Girl with Kava Bowl); 2d. (River); 2½d. (Samoan Chief and Wife); 5d. (Post Office, Apia). Printers (*recess*) **Bradbury, Wilkinson (5d.), De La Rue (Other Values). Designs, 2d., 5d. H. Sheets as before.**

(a) Perf. 14 x 14½ (C) (2d. C and L).

2	½d.	**yellow-green** (5/47) .	20	40
3	2d.	**black and red-orange** (5/42)	60	50
4	2½d.	**blk and dp blue** (2/49)	1·00	1·00

(b) Perf. 13½ x 14 (C).

5	5d.	**blk and blue** (8/6/49)	40	50

3—this value changed from line to comb perforation 8/45.

Numbers issued—2/3, 400,000 each.
4/5, 1,000,000 each.

1945-50 Design as New Zealand No. PF48, etc., overprinted WESTERN SAMOA in red or blue. Perf. 14 (C). Wmk NZ over star.

6	2/6 **brown** (6/45)	..	1·50	2·50
	a wmk. inv.		2·00	3·50
7	5/- **green** (5/45)	..	3·00	5·00
	a wmk. inv. ..	..	4·00	7·00
8	10/- **rose-carmine** (4/46)		9·00	9·00
	a wmk. inv. ..	..	£12	£12
9	20/- **dull pink** (6/48)		£28	£28
	a wmk. inv.		—	—
10	30/- **brown** (8/48)		£60	£85
	a wmk inverted	..	£75	£100
11	40/- **violet (red)** (11/47) .		£70	£90
	a wmk. inv. ..	..	£85	£100
12	60/- **green** (8/48)		£85	£135
	a wmk. inv. ..	..	£95	£150
13	100/- **blue-black (red)**			
	(31/1/50)	..	£190	£275
	a wmk. inv. ..	..	£200	£300
6/13	**set** (8)	..	£375	£600

Numbers issued—6, 44,400; 7, 35,840; 8, 19,520; 9, 8,000; 10, 7,440.

SPECIAL ISSUES

1939 (Aug. 29th) 25th Anniversary of New Zealand Control. Designs, 1d. (Coastal Scene); 1½d. (Map of Western Samoa, etc.);

2½d. (**Samoan Dancing Party**); 7d. (**Robert Louis Stevenson**), Designer, J. Berry (1d. and 1½d.), L. C. Mitchell (**Other Values**). Printers (*recess*) Bradbury, Wilkinson. Perf. 14 x 13½ (C). Design, 7d. V. Sheets 8 x 10 or 10 x 8.

S1	1d. sage and scarlet	..	30	40
S2	1½d. lt blue and chestnut..		50	60
S3	2½d. red-brn and dp blue..		1·50	1·75
S4	7d. vio and greenish-slate		3·50	3·75
S1/4	**set** (4)		5·50	6·00

Numbers printed—S1, 240,000; S2, 160,000; S3, 120,000; S4, 120,000.

1946 (June 1st) Peace. New Zealand No. S19, etc., overprinted WESTERN SAMOA in black or blue.

S5	1d. **emerald-green**	..	10	10
S6	2d. **purple (blue)**	..	10	10
S7	6d. **choc and vermilion** ..		15	20
S8	8d. **blk and lake (blue)** ..		15	30
S5/8	**set** (4)	..	45	65

Numbers printed—S5, 720,000; S6, 720,000; S7, 528,000; S8, 480,000.

SARAWAK

The origin of Sarawak lies in the appointment in 1841 of James (later Sir James) Brooke by the Sultan of Brunei as Governor of the province. The State, which was successively governed by Sir James Brooke's nephew (Sir Charles) and great-nephew (Sir Charles Vyner) was later considerably enlarged and was recognised as independent in 1863. It became a British Protectorate in 1888 and a Crown Colony on July 1st 1946.

Following the use of various Franks, principally on Government mail, East India stamps were used on foreign mail from 1859 and were cancelled B.172, or 'D14' in a vertical oval of horizontal bars, at Singapore.

From 1869 until Sarawak joined the U.P.U. in 1897 the stamps of Sarawak were valid only within the State or as far as Singapore. Letters to addresses beyond Singapore were required to bear, in addition, Straits Settlements stamps to cover the international postage, for which purpose the Kuching Post Office also sold Straits Settlements stamps.

1869 (March 1st) Local Stamp. Litho Maclure, Macdonald and Macgregor. No wmk. Perf. 11. Sheets 200 – two panes, each 10 x 10.

V1 3c. **brown/yellow** £25 £80

Original engraved Die Proofs are known in orange-brown on yellow surfaced white paper, perf. 12. Finished Die Proofs exist in black on India paper.

Plate Proofs exist in black/yellow, dull purple, black, and brown/yellow; also in the issued colour but imperforate.

This issue was, in fact, posthumous as Sir James Brooke had died in 1868; and it was demonetized on March 31st 1871.

1871 (Jan.) Local Stamp. Litho Maclure, Macdonald and Macgregor. No wmk. Perf. 11. Sheets 200 – two panes, each 10 x 10.

V2 3c. **brown/yellow** .. .. 1·00 1·50

a imperf. between (vert. pair)	£150	—
b imperf. between (horiz. pair)	£150	—

Although unwatermarked, copies may be found showing portions of the papermaker's watermark 'LNL' in double lined capitals.

Original engraved Die Proofs are known in orange-brown on yellow surfaced white paper, perf. 12. Finished Die Proofs exist in black on India paper.

Imperforate Plate Proofs exist in the issued colour.

Numbers sold—50,000 (the total printing was 250,000, of which 200,000 were used for subsequent provisionals. See Nos. V36 and V44.)

1874 No. V2 locally handstamped in black "TWO CENTS", in sans serif capitals (14¼mm x 2¼mm).

V3 2c. on 3c. **brown/yellow** .. — —

Forged surcharges (15–15½mm x 3mm) without the stop after 'CENTS' are known on genuine stamps, both unused and used.

A manuscript surcharge '2' is known on two unused copies.

1875 (Jan. 1st). Local stamps. As before but new values. Perf. 11½.

V4 2c.	**mauve/lilac**	..	1·50	2·50
	a strip of five	..	£12	£20
	b imperf. (pair) ..	..	—	—
V5 4c.	**red-brown/yellow**	..	1·50	1·50
	a strip of five	..	£12	£12
	b imperf. (pair) ..	..	—	—
	c imperf. between (vert. pair)		—	—
V6 6c.	**green/green**	..	1·50	1·50
	a strip of five	..	£12	£12
	b imperf. (pair) ..	..	—	—
V7 8c.	**blue/blue**	..	2·00	2·50
	a strip of five	..	£16	£20
	b imperf. (pair) ..	..	—	—
V8 12c.	**red/rose** ..	..	3·00	3·00
	a strip of five	..	£25	£25
	b imperf. (pair) ..	..	—	—
V4/8	**set (5v)**	..	9·00	£10

V4*a*/8*a* A strip of five transfers was laid down horizontally from No. V2 for each value, and the original THREE CENTS erased. The new values were then inserted by hand five times for each value, giving five different types. The new strips of five transfers were then each repeated twenty times to create each pane of 100.

Although unwatermarked, all values may be found showing portions of the papermakers' watermark (LNT on No. V6, and LNL on the other values).

Copies of Nos. V5/6/7 rouletted or perf. 6½ or pin perf. come from Proof sheets, stolen from the printers and unofficially perforated.

Imperf. litho proofs of all values exist in deeper shades than those of the issued stamps.

This issue was demonetized in June 1897.

1888 (Nov. 10th) - 97. Typo De la Rue. No. Wmk. Perf. 14. Sheets 6 x 10.

V9	1c.	purple and black (6/6/92)	60	80
V10	2c.	purple and carmine (11/11/88)	1·25	90
V11	2c.	purple and aniline -rose ('97)	2·50	1·50
V12	3c.	purple and ultra-marine (11/11/88)	60	80
V13	3c.	purple and dull blue ('89)	75	95
V14	4c.	purple and yellow	3·75	5·00
V15	5c.	purple and green (12/6/91)	3·00	1·50
V16	6c.	purple and brown (11/11/88) ..	3·50	5 00
V17	8c.	green and carmine (11/11/88)	1·50	1·75
V18	8c.	green and aniline-rose ('97)	3·00	4·00
V19	10c.	green and purple (12/6/91)	6·00	5·50
V20	12c.	green and ultra-marine (11/11/88)	1·00	2·50
V21	12c.	green and dull blue ('89)	1·00	2·00
V22	16c.	green and orange (28/12/97)	7·50	8·00
V23	25c.	green and brown (19/11/88) ..	8·00	7·50
V24	32c.	green and black (28/12/97)	8·50	8·00
V25	50c.	green (26/7/97) ..	£10	£12
V26	$1	green and black (2/11/97) ..	£16	£16
V9/26		set (14v).	£65	£68

V9/13 are recorded overprinted 'SPECIMEN' vertically in red serif capitals 23mm x 5½mm.

V10 also exists overprinted 'Specimen.' in black italic script 20mm x 3mm/2mm.

V25/26 are known with similar italic script overprint, and it is believed that this overprint was applied to waste sheets for experimental work in connection with a proposed issue for Rhodesia (See also Note after Nos. V37/41).

Die Proofs of the key plate design and of the duty plate design exist on white glazed card in black, green and lilac.

Plate Proofs exist perf. 14 and imperf. in the adopted and other combinations of colour

Numbers printed – V9, 181,080; V10/11, 216,300; V12/13, 176,700; V14, 52,620; V15, 61,560; V16, 12,840; V17/18, 104,100; V19, 31,200; V20/21, 55,500; V22, 10,440; V23, 14,640; V24, 10,440; V25, 13,320; V26, 12,120.

1897 Prepared for use but not issued. Design and other details as before.

V27	$2	green and blue ..	£320	—
V28	$5	green and violet ..	£320	—
V29	$10	green and carmine..	£320	—

Although inscribed 'Postage and Revenue' these stamps were never taken into postal use. In company with Nos. V12/13, V15, V19, V25 and V26 they were fiscally used after being overprinted in black either 'R' or 'R. Revenue only.'; nevertheless copies of Nos. V27/29 are known without this fiscal overprint.

1889-92 Various stamps surcharged in black at the Government Printing Office at Kuching.

(a) No. 17 handstamped (Aug. 3rd. 1889).

V30	2c. on 8c.	green and carmine surcharge ..	1·50	3·00
	b	surcharge double ..	£100	—
		surcharge inverted	£400	—
	c	surcharge omitted in pair with normal. ..	£325	—

Type I

Type II   Type III

(b) Nos. V20/21 handstamped (Feb. 17th 1891).

V31	5c. on 12c.	Type I ..	£20	£22
	a	surcharge double ..	£275	£300
	b	surcharge inverted ..	—	—
	c	surcharge sideways ..	—	—
	d	surcharge double, one sideways ..	—	—
	e	surcharge treble, one inverted ..	—	—
	f	surcharge omitted in pair with normal	—	—

g stop omitted in pair with normal	£50	£50
V32 5c. on 12c. **Type II** ..	£40	£45
a surcharge double	—	—
b stop omitted in pair with normal ..	£275	£300
V33 5c. on 12c. **Type III** ..	£110	£110
a surcharge double ..	£275	£300

Type I   **Type II**

(c) Nos. V12/13. Setting 6 x 10.

V34 1c. on 3c. **Type I** (12/1/92)	£15	£15
a surcharge double ..	£190	£200
V35 1c. on 3c. **Type II** (2/92)	2 00	3·50
a stop omitted	£40	—

V34*a*—Only one sheet of sixty was twice surcharged.

V35*a* Row 2/6 and 7/6 (not constant throughout the printing).

Numbers surcharged—V34, 12,000; V35, 36,000.

Type III

(d) No. V2. Type III. Setting 10 x 10 (May 1892).

V36 1c. on 3c. **brown/yellow**	80	80
a bar double ..	—	—
b bar omitted ..	—	—
c ONE CENT double ..	—	—
d surcharge double ..	£70	—
e surcharge albino in pair with normal ..	—	—
f surcharge in manuscript	—	—
g imperf. between (vert. pair). ..	£200	—

There were two settings for this surcharge. The first consisted of the words 'ONE CENT', the cancelling bar being added across the pane row by row at a subsequent operation; whereas the second setting printed the words and bar in one operation.

Nos. V36*a/b/c* generally come from the first setting, but many of the defective, omitted and albino varieties of this surcharge resulted from the presence, before printing, of gum on the face of the sheets and its subsequent removal. The presence of gum over the face of the stamps arose from the original consignment having been stored without interleaving, with the consequent transference of gum from the back of one sheet to the face of the next.

Numbers surcharged—100,000.

1895 Recess, Various Frames, Perkins Bacon and Co. No Wmk. Sheets 10 x 6.

(a) Perf. 11½–12 (Jan. 1st).

V37 2c. **brown-red**	2·50	3 75
a imperf between (horiz. pair) ..	£80	—
b imperf between (vert. pair). .	£80	—
V38 4c. **black**	2·00	1·50
a imperf. between (horiz. pair) ..	£80	—
V39 6c. **violet**	3·00	4·00
V40 8c. **green**	4·50	5·00
V37/40 **set** (4v.)	£10	£12

(b) Perf. 12½ (September).

V41 2c. **brown-red**	1·50	2·50
a imperf. between (horiz. pair) ..	£90	—

V37 is recorded overprinted 'Specimen' diagonally upwards in black 15½mm x 2/1¼mm.

Die Proofs of all values exist in black on thin card, and in blue, vermilion-red, plum and green on thick card.

Die Proofs of an unissued 1c. (in the design of the issued 4c.) are known in black or violet on card, and in several colours on paper.

Plate Proofs of all values exist in black on India paper.

Colour Trials of all values, including the unissued 1c., are known in various colours.

The 2c. may be found surcharged '2', '3', '4', '5', or '6' PENCE: this was applied to waste sheets, in various colours, for experimental work in connection with a proposed issue for Rhodesia.

(See also Note after Nos. V25/26).

The origin of this issue lay in the erroneous despatch on March 1st 1894 to Perkins Bacon, instead of De la Rue, of a requisition for a further supply of 60,000 copies of No. V9.

Numbers printed—V37/38, 40,000 each; V39/40, 30,000 each; V41, 60,000.

1899 Various stamps surcharged at the Government Printing Office at Kuching. Setting 10 x 10.

(a) Nos. V8 (in black) and V7 (in red) June 29th.

V42 2c. on 12c.	**red/pale rose**		75	1·25
	a strip of five ..		£12	—
	b small 's' ..		8 00	£10
	c surcharge inverted		£200	—
	d surcharge inverted (small 's')..		£350	—
V43 4c. on 8c.	**blue/blue** ..			
	a strip of five ..		1 75	2·50
	b small 's' ..		£30	—
	c albino overprint ..		£14	£20

(b) No. V2 (in black) September 19th.

V44 2c. on 3c.	**brown/yellow**			

Number surcharged—100,000.   80   1·75

(c) No. V6 (in red). November 16th.

V45 4c. on 6c.	**green/green** ..		8·00	9·00
	a strip of five ..		£90	—
	b raised stop ..		£40	—

V42*a*/43*a*/45*a* See Note after Nos. V4*a*/8*a*.
V42*b*/43*b* occurs on Rows 1/2, 1/8 and 4/1.
V42*c* only occurred on one pane (100 copies).
V42*d* occurs on Rows 7/10, 10/3 and 10/9.
V45*b* Row 1/5.

V43 may be found with defective or albino surcharge, arising from the same causes referred to in the note after No. V36.

Imperforate copies of V42/43/44 are believed to have come from Proof sheets held in Sarawak and possibly used as Proofs of the surcharges.

It is doubtful if No. V45 was ever commercially used as it was placed on sale six days after the issue of the new 4c. (No. V52).

1899 (Nov. 10th)–1908. As Nos. V9/26 but inscribed 'POSTAGE POSTAGE' Typo De la Rue.

V46	1c.	**bright blue and rosine** (1/1/01)	30	25
V47	1c.	**blue and rosine** ..	30	10
V48	1c.	**ult marine and car**..	1·50	30
V49	1c.	**dl blue and carmine**	2·50	2·50
V50	2c.	**green** (16/12) ..	25	15
V51	3c.	**dull purple** (1/2/08)	50	15

V52	4c.	**rose-car** (10/11) ..	1·00	75
V53	4c.	**aniline carmine** ..	2·00	15
V54	4c.	**scarlet-vermilion** ..	1·75	1·50
V55	4c.	**pale scarlet**	2·00	1·50
V56	8c.	**yel and black** (6/12)	1·50	1 25
V57	10c.	**ultramarine** (10/11)	1·50	25
V58	12c.	**mauve** (16/12) ..	2·50	2·00
V59	12c.	**dp aniline mauve** ..	7·50	5·00
V60	16c.	**chestnut and green** (16/12) ..	2·00	1·50
V61	20c.	**bistre and mauve** (4/00) ..	2 75	3·50
V62	25c.	**brown and bl** (16/12)	3·00	3·50
V63	50c.	**sage-grn and rosine** (16/12)	8·00	£10
V64	$1	**carmine and green** (16/12)	£15	£18
V65	$1	**aniline car and grn**	£20	£22
V46/65		**set** (12v)	£36	£38

On certain stamps an additional line of shading is apparent on the Rajah's collar. There is no constant position for this 'Collar Flaw'.

Die Proofs of the Key Plate design exist in black on thick card; and a similar proof is recorded in green on gummed paper.

Imperforate Plate Proofs exist for all values except No. V61.

Colour trials of V51 and V57 exist in various colour combinations.

No. V51 is known overprinted 'Specimen' In black Italic script 18½mm x 4/3mm; and No. V62 exists overprinted 'CANCELLED' (14¾mm x 2mm).

1899 Prepared for use but not issued.

V66	5c.	**olive-grey and grn**	8·00	—

30,600 copies were despatched to Sarawak, and a number of sheets was subsequently sold as remainders.

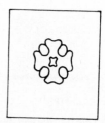

1902 (Jan. 7th). As No. V50 but Wmk. Rosette.

E1	2c.	**green**	4·50	1·00

The printing of a repeat order for No. V50 was by mistake on the part of De la Rue, made on paper normally used at that time for the stamps of Johore, and Zanzibar.

Numbers issued—61,200.

Between January 18th and 24th 1918, during a shortage of stamps at Miri, the Resident authorised a manuscript franking "Postage Paid 4 (or 7) cts." A facsimile of his signature (R. S. Douglas) was impressed alongside the Frank, and the Miri datestamp applied.

1918-23 Type De La Rue. No Wmk. Chalky paper. Perf. 14. Sheets 6 x 10.

G1	1c.	**slate blue and car** ..	15	20
G2	1c.	**dp blue and carmine**	25	20
G3	1c.	**dull blue and rose** ..	25	20
G4	2c.	**green**	30	25
G5	2c.	**dull green**	35	30
G6	2c.	**purple** (3/23) ..	20	45
G7	3c.	**brown-purple** ..	75	75
G8	3c.	**dull brown-purple**..	75	90
G9	3c.	**dull green** (3/22) ..	20	20
G10	4c.	**rose-carmine** ..	75	60
G11	4c.	**rose-red**	60	1·00
G12	4c.	**brown-purple** (4/23)	20	40
G13	5c.	**yellow-orange** ('22)	45	50
G14	6c.	**dull claret** (1/22) ..	45	50
G15	6c.	**bright claret** ..	1·00	2·50
G16	8c.	**yellow and black** ..	75	1·20
G17	8c.	**carmine** ('22) ..	80	2·00
G18	10c.	**dull blue**	75	1·75
G19	10c.	**bright blue**	90	2·25
G20	10c.	**ultramarine**		
		a double strike ..	—	—
G21	10c.	**black** ('23)	1·00	1·25
G22	12c.	**bright purple** ..	1·10	2·25
G23	12c.	**dull purple**	1·25	2·30
G24	12c.	**blue** (/22)	3·00	4·50
G25	12c.	**cobalt**	2·50	4·00
G26	16c.	**chestnut and green**	1·50	2·00
G27	20c.	**bistre and mauve** ..	1·00	1·50
G28	20c.	**olive and violet** ..	1·50	2·00
G29	25c.	**brown and blue** ..	1·50	2·00
G30	30c.	**ochre-brn and slate** ('21)	1·25	2 50
G31	30c.	**pale ochre-brn and slate**	1 40	3·00
G32	50c.	**olive-grn and rose** ..	1·75	3·00
G33	50c.	**sage-grn and car** ..	2·00	3·00
G34	$1	**carmine and green**	5·00	7·00
G1/34		**set** (21v)	£20	£32
SPG 1/34		**specimen set** (21v)	£80	‡

G20*a* shows as a doubling of the right hand 'POSTAGE' tablet and occurred only on the right hand vertical column of sheets from the last printing.

Numbers printed—G1/3, 576,300; G4/5, 440,220; G6, 381,660; G7/8, 139,700; G9, 249,780; G10/11, 529,860; G12, 969,480; G13, 635,100; G14/15, 301,140; G16, 9,240; G17, 24,780; G18/20, 97,680*; G21, 44,700; G22/23, 41,580*; G24/25, 170,520; G26, 28,500; G27/28, 36,960; G29, 20,640; G30/31, 34,560; G32/33, 28,200; G34, 17,100.

* *Less* 13,841 and 13,587 respectively used for subsequent surcharges (Nos G37-G41).

1918 Prepared for use but not issued.

G35	1c.	**slate-blue and slate**	£80	—

Further supplies of No. G1 were ordered in early 1918 and, at the time, De La Rue were asked to supply stamped 1c. postcards in blue. The colours were transposed by error, and the stamps were not consequently issued; a small number of sheets was retained in Sarawak, and the balance (approx. 7,000 copies) were sold as remainders.

1918 Red Cross Essay. No. G35 overprinted 'RED CROSS' and surcharged 'Three Cents' in red or black. Setting 6 x 10.

G36	3c. on 1c	**slate-blue and slate (red)** ..	£50	—
		a ovpt in black	£70	—

1923 Nos G18/19/22/23 locally surcharged in black at the Government Printing Office at Kuching. Setting 6 x 10.

(a) First Printing. Bars 1¼mm apart.

G37	1c. on 10c.	**ultramarine** (12/1) ..	7·00	8·00
		a double strike of stamp ..	£20	£22
		b "cnet" ..	£90	£100
G38	2c. on 12c.	**purple** (8/3) ..	2·00	4·00
		a narrow 'W' ..	6·00	8·00
SPG 37/38		**specimen** (pair)	£50	‡

G37*a* See Note after No. G20*a*.

G37*b* Row 9/5 (217 copies of which 7 were sent to U.P.U. as Specimens).

G38*a* The 'W' in 'TWO' is 3½mm wide instead of the normal 4½mm wide, on all the stamps in Rows 9 and 10 (2,484 copies, of which about 77 were sent to U.P.U. as specimens).

G37/38 All sheets have margins at left and bottom only.

Numbers surcharged—G37, 13,020; G38, 12,420.

(b) Second Printing. Bars ¾mm apart.

G39	1c. on 10c.	**pl ultramarine**	£80	—
G40	1c. on 10c.	**bright blue** ..	£30	—
		a "cnet" ..	£600	—
G41	2c. on 12c.	**purple**	£16	—
		a narrow 'W' ..	£30	—

G39 It is believed that only one sheet in this shade was included in the second printing, and that 'cent' was correctly spelled on Row 9/5.

G40*a* The type was re-set for the second printing and the previous error 'cnet' did not appear on Row 9/5. However, the printer had been instructed to make the second overprinting identical to the first and, after printing 13 sheets of this value, he realised that the correct spelling on Row 9/5 did not represent a 'true copy'. Accordingly, he scratched out 'en' on this position and re-overprinted 'ne'.

G41*a* The 'W' in 'TWO' is only 3½mm wide (as on No. G38a) but the variety occurs on the two right hand vertical columns in this printing (448 copies).

This second printing was made solely to satisfy demands from Stamp Dealers and none were placed on sale in Sarawak. The small number of stamps was obtained in London, sent out to Kuching on January 24th 1923 to be surcharged, and returned to London on March 6th; being London stocks, the colours are much fresher than those of the first printing which was made on stocks of stamps which had been tropically affected.

Numbers surcharged—G39, 60; G40, 761; G41, 1,347.

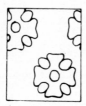

1928 (April 4th)-29. As Nos G1/34 but Wmk. Multiple Rosettes. Chalky paper. Sheets 10 x 10.

G42	1c.	slate-blue and car ..	25	30
G43	2c.	bright purple ..	25	15
G44	3c.	green	25	50
G45	4c.	brown-purple ..	80	15
G46	5c.	yel-orange (5/8/29)	50	1·50
G47	6c.	claret	50	20
G48	8c.	rose-red	1·00	1·50
G49	8c.	rosine	1·25	1·50
G50	10c.	black	75	1·25
G51	12c.	deep blue	1·00	1·25
G52	12c.	cobalt	90	1·00
G53	16c.	chestnut and green	1·00	1·25
G54	20c.	ol-bistre and violet	1·00	1·50
G55	25c.	brn and bright blue	1·10	1·50
G56	30c.	bistre and slate ..	3·00	2·50
G57	50c.	ol-grn and carmine	1 50	3·00
G58	$1	bright rose and grn	5·00	7·00
G42/58		set (15v).	£16	£22
SPG42/58		specimen set (15v)	£90	‡

The key plate showed a small white flaw across the right frame lines, giving the appearance of an 'apostrophe' between the 'O' and 'S' of 'POSTAGE' —Row 3/8 (all values).

Numbers printed—G42, 150,000; G43, 200,000; G44/47, 120,000 each; G45, 600,000; G48/49,.

15,000; G50, 25,000; G51/52, 10,000; G53/54/57, 15,000 each; G55/58, 10,000 each; G56, 20,000,

1932 (Jan. 1st). Recess Waterlow. Wmk Coronet. Perf. 12¼. Sheets 10 x 10.

G59	1c.	indigo	30	20
G60	2c.	green	30	20
G61	3c.	violet	40	20
G62	4c.	red-orange	20	10
G63	5c.	deep lake	40	10
G64	6c.	scarlet	1 50	2·50
G65	8c.	orange-yellow ..	80	1·00
G66	10c.	black	80	2·00
G67	12c.	dp ultramarine ..	1·00	2·00
G68	15c.	chestnut	1·25	3·00
G69	20c.	red-or and violet ..	1·25	3·00
G70	25c.	or-yel and chnut ..	2·25	4·00
G71	30c.	sepia and vermilion	2·50	4·00
G72	50c.	carmine and olive..	3·00	4·00
G73	$1	green and carmine	6·00	8·00
G59/73		set (15v.)	£20	£32
SPG59/73		specimen set (15v)	£60	‡

Plate Proofs—one ungummed imperforate sheet of each value in the issued colours.

Numbers printed—G59, 1,000,000; G60/64/67 1,200,000 each; G61, 700,000; G62, 5,000,000; G63/68, 500,000 each; G65/66/71, 200,000 each; G69/70/72/73, 100,000 each.

Large quantities were withdrawn on August 30th 1934 and were subsequently destroyed.

G59 in sepia and G69 in mauve and black on unwatermarked paper, overprinted in black WATERLOW & SONS LTD./SPECIMEN and with a 2mm diameter hole punched out at lower left, are Sample stamps produced by the Printers as examples of their work. Price (Pr) — £25.

1934 (May 1st). Recess Bradbury Wilkinson. No Wmk. Perf 12. Sheets 10 x 10.

G74	1c.	purple	10	10
G75	2c.	green	10	10
G76	3c.	black	15	10
G77	4c.	bright purple ..	10	10
G78	5c.	violet	10	20

		a imperf. between stamp and margin	£50	—
G79	6c.	**carmine**	10	10
G80	8c.	**red-brown**	40	45
G81	10c.	**scarlet**	20	30
G82	12c.	**blue**	20	1·50
G83	15c.	**orange**	20	1·00
G84	20c.	**olive-grn and car**	50	50
G85	25c.	**violet and orange**	25	50
G86	30c.	**red-brn and violet**	50	75
G87	50c.	**violet and scarlet**	1·50	1·00
G88	$1	**scarlet and sepia**	1·50	1 00
G89	$2	**bt pur and violet**	3 00	4·00
G90	$3	**carmine and green**	5·00	5·00
G91	$4	**blue and scarlet**	6·00	7·00
G92	$5	**scarlet and red-brn**	£10	£12
G93	$10	**black and yellow**	£16	£18
G74/93		**set** (20v)	£45	£50
SPG74/93	SP1/6	**spec. set** (26v)	£150	‡

G78*a*—One sheet was imperf. between left hand margin and first vertical row.

Die Proofs of G80, with bottom tablet inscribed 'Postage', are known in black on glazed card.

Plate Proofs—One ungummed imperforate sheet of each value in the issued colours.

1941 (Mar. 1st). As before, but new colours.

1	2c.	**black**	25	50
2	3c.	**deep green**	15	30
3	6c.	**maroon-brown**	20	50
4	8c.	**carmine**	20	20
5	12c.	**deep orange**	25	1·50
6	15c.	**deep blue**	25	1·50
1/6		**set** (6v)	1·25	4·00
SP1/6		**specimen set** (6v) (see SPG74/93)	—	‡

No. 2 on Multiple Script CA paper: see No. 29*a*.

Sarawak was occupied by the Japanese from December 17th 1941 to September 9th 1945. Nos. G74/93 and 1/6 remained in use until they were replaced by unoverprinted Japanese stamps on October 1st 1942.

During the occupation, Sarawak, North Borneo and Brunei were administered as a single territory (North Borneo), and the stamps of all three States were later overprinted and used throughout the whole area.

Immediately following the re-occupation by Australian Forces, internal mail was carried free and bore neither stamps nor postmarks; but, from October 29th 1945, Australian stamps (1d, 3d, 6d, 1/-) were used on external mail.

At Baram (alternative name MARUDI), Australian stamps were not available, and the Civil Affairs Officer (C. B. Murray) produced a provisional stamp, typed on paper cut from a ruled accounts book. The typed inscription was in lines "Postage Paid/16 cents/ C.A.O./MARUDI" and each copy was initialled by Mr. Murray and cancelled with the District Office mark and the Baram c.d.s.

1945 (Dec. 17th) British Military Administration. Nos. G74/93 and 1/6 overprinted BMA in black sans serif letters (in red on Nos. 8, 11, 18, and 26). Setting 10 x 10.

7	1c.	**dp purple**	10	10
8	2c.	**black**	10	10
		a overprint double	—	£425
9	3c.	**dp green**	10	10
10	4c.	**purple-magenta**	10	10
11	5c.	**violet**	15	30
12	6c.	**maroon-brown**	25	50
13	8c.	**carmine**	1·50	2·50
14	10c.	**red**	25	40
15	12c.	**dp orange**	35	1·00
16	15c.	**dp blue**	35	15
17	20c.	**olive-grn and dp car**	50	1·25
18	25c.	**pur-vio and orange**	50	1·50
19	30c.	**red-brown and violet**	50	1·75
20	50c.	**violet and deep red**	50	30
21	$1	**scarlet and sepia**	75	1·00
22	$2	**dp magenta and violet**	2·00	3·00
23	$3	**carmine and green**	2·50	3·50
24	$4	**blue and red**	3·00	4·00
25	$5	**scarlet and chocolate**	£20	£25
26	$10	**black and deep yellow**	£18	£22
7/26		**set** (20)	£50	£65

8*a* One example so far recorded, used at Jesselton in North Borneo.

During the period of Military Administration the area continued to be administered as a single territory, and the North Borneo BMA stamps were also sold in Sarawak. These BMA issues were withdrawn from sale in Sarawak on April 25th 1946, although they remained valid for use until July 31st 1946; and they continued in use in North Borneo and Brunei until 1947.

Numbers issued—7, 65,000; 8, 80,000; 9/10, 50,000 each; 11, 60,000; 12, 55,000; 13/14/16, 45,000 each; 15, 30,000; 17/18/20, 20,000 each; 19, 15,000; 21, 14,000; 22, 5,000, 23/24/25, 3,000 each; 26, 2,500.

1946 (April 26th). Nos. G74/93 and 1/6 reissued when Civil administration was resumed, and remained in use until Sarawak became a Crown Colony.

1947 (April 16th). Crown Colony status. Nos. G74/92 and 1/6 reprinted on Wmk. Multiple Script CA paper, and overprinted in black or red (Nos. 28, 29 and 35-38)

27	1c.	dp purple	10	10
28	2c.	black	10	10
29	3c.	dp green	10	10
		a albino overprint ..	£500	—
30	4c.	purple-magenta ..	10	10
31	6c.	maroon-brown ..	10	10
32	8c.	carmine	10	10
33	10c.	red	10	10
34	12c.	dp orange	10	10
35	15c.	dp blue	10	10
36	20c.	olive-green and dp carmine	15	20
37	25c.	pur-vio and orange	10	10
38	50c.	vio and dp red ..	10	10
39	$1	scarlet and sepia ..	50	75
40	$2	dp magenta and violet	1·00	2·25
41	$5	scarlet and chocolate	2·00	2·50
27/41		set (15)	4·00	6·00
SP27/41		specimen set (15v)	£100	‡

29a A mint block of twelve was found in Singapore in 1949.

Numbers issued—27, 1,500,000; 28, 850,000; 29, 1,300,000; 30, 420,000; 31, 440,000; 32, 780,000; 33, 210,000; 34/35/38, 330,000 each; 36, 170,000; 37, 220,000; 39, 160,000, 40, 130,000; 41, 75,000.

1950 (Jan. 3rd) -52 Designs, 1c. (Troides Brookiana Butterfly); 2c. (Tarsier); 3c. (Kayan Tomb); 4c., 8c., 12c., 50c. (Native Types of Inhabitants); 6c., 15c., $1 (Native Occupations); 10c. (Scaly Ant Eater); 10c., $2 (Map of Sarawak); 20c. (Rice Barn); 25c. (Pepper Vines); $5 (Arms of Sarawak). Recess ($5 Arms typo) Bradbury Wilkinson. Perf. 11¼ x 11½ (C). Wmk. Multiple Script CA. Designs, 2c., 3c., 4c., 6c., 50c., V. Sheets 10 x 10

42	1c.	greenish-grey-black .	10	10
		a black (20/11/52) ..	15	15
43	2c.	orange-vermilion ..	15	15
44	3c.	green	15	15

45	4c.	sepia-brown ..	15	15
46	6c.	dp turquoise-blue ..	15	15
47	8c.	carmine-red	35	50
48	10c.	orange (ant eater) ..	35	50
49	10c.	orange (map) (1/2/52)	10	10
50	12c.	purple-violet ..	40	30
51	15c.	blue	30	15
52	20c.	choc and vermilion ..	15	15
53	25c.	green and carmine ..	30	15
54	50c.	choc and pur-vio ..	35	30
55	$1	myrtle and sepia ..	1·50	1·25
56	$2	blue and dp carmine	2·00	3·50
57	$5	yellow, black, red and dp purple	6·00	4·50
42/57		set (16)	£10	£11

48a An error in the drawing of the ant eater necessitated replacement.

SPECIAL ISSUES

1946 (May 18th) Centenary of Rulership of Brooke Dynasty. Design, Portraits of Sir James Brooke, Sir Charles Vyner Brooke and Sir Charles Brooke in three panels. Recess, Bradbury Wilkinson. Perf. 12 (L). No wmk. Sheets 10 x 10.

S1	8c.	lake-carmine ..	15	30
S2	15c.	dp blue	40	50
S3	50c.	black and red ..	75	1·25
S4	$1	black and sepia ..	3·50	5·50
S1/4		set (4)	4·50	6·50
SPS1/4		specimen set (4v.) ..	£35	‡

Plate Proofs—One imperforate sheet of each value in the issued colours.

Japanese occupation of the territory prevented issue in 1941 as intended.

Numbers issued—S1, 295,200; S2, 111,750; S3, 80,350; S4, 46,500.

1948 (Oct. 25th) Silver Wedding. As Aden.

S5	8c.	scarlet	15	15
S6	$5	chocolate	5·50	9·00

1949 (Oct. 10th) U.P.U. As Aden.

S7	8c.	carmine-rose ..	25	30
S8	15c.	indigo	35	40
S9	25c.	green	60	80
S10	50c.	dull violet ..	1·50	1·75
S7/10		set (4)	2·50	3·00

SEYCHELLES

France held the islands until they were captured by Great Britain in 1794 and incorporated as a dependency of Mauritius in 1810. They were later separated from Mauritius, and became a Crown Colony in 1903.

The first Post Office was opened at Victoria on December 11th, 1861 ; and from then until April 5th, 1890 the stamps of Mauritius were used and were cancelled 'B64' in a transverse oval of horizontal bars. The cancellation was normally struck in black, but is known also in blue. The G.B. 6d. of 1862 is also reported bearing the 'B64' cancellation.

All stamps to G81 are Typo De la Rue. Perf.14. Sheets 120-two panes, each 6 x 10.

See Introduction for details of Dies I and II.

1890 (April 5th)-92 Wmk. Crown CA.

(a) Die I (Plate 1) 1890.

V1	2c.	**green and carmine** ..	90	3·00
V2	4c.	**carmine and green** ..	3·50	4·50
V3	8c.	**purple-brown and blue**	1·50	2·75
V4	10c.	**ultramarine and brown**	2·25	4·25
V5	13c.	**grey and black** ..	1·50	4·25
V6	16c.	**chestnut and blue** ..	2·25	2·25
V7	48c.	**ochre and green** ..	7·50	8·00
V8	96c.	**mauve and carmine**	£13	£15
V1/8		**set** (8v)	£30	£40
SPV1/8		**specimen set** (8v) ..	£90	‡

(b) Die II (Plate 2) 1892.

V9	2c.	**green and carmine** ..	65	70
V10	4c.	**carmine and green**	70	70
V11	8c.	**purple-brown and blue**	1·25	1·50
V12	10c.	**ultramarine and brown**	1·50	1·50
V13	13c.	**grey and black** ..	1·50	1·50
V14	16c.	**chestnut and blue**	6·00	5·50
V9/14		**set** (6v) ..	£10	£10
SPV9/13		**specimen set** (5v) ..	—	‡

Die Proofs of both Dies exist in black on glazed card.

Imperforate Colour Trials of the 4c. are known on unwatermarked paper.

Die I   Carmine
Die II   Grey and blue

Numbers issued—V1/9 250,440 ; V2/10, 127,680 ;*
(Both Dies)   V3/11 174,680 *; V4/12 154,520 *
                 V5/13. 43,800 ; V6/14, 94,240 *;
                 V7 18,060 *; V8 9,840 *.

*Net figures after deduction of quantities later surcharged (see Nos. V15/21, V37/38, V40/41).

1893 (Jan. 1st) Nos. V6/7/8/10/14 locally surcharged in black. Setting 6 x 5, applied four times to the sheet. There were three different settings used for No. V15.

V15 3c. on 4c.	(Die II)	..	50	80
	a surcharge inverted	..	£130	£140
	b surcharge double	..	£150	£160
	c surcharge double in pair with normal	..	—	—
	d surcharge omitted in pair with normal	..	£1400	£1500
V16 12c. on 16c.	(Die I)		1·25	1·50
	a surcharge inverted	..	£200	£250
	b surcharge double	..	£850	£1000
V17 12c. on 16c.	(Die II)		1·25	1·50
	a wide spacing	..	£50	£60
V18 15c. on 16c.	(Die I)		4·50	5·50
	a surcharge inverted	..	£120	£130
	b surcharge double	..	£225	£240
V19 15c. on 16c.	(Die II)		3·00	1·50
	a surcharge inverted	..	£240	£240
	b surcharge double	..	£350	£250
V20 45c. on 48c.		..	3·75	3·00
V21 90c. on 96c.	..	..	£11	£12
	a broad 'O'	..	£60	£60

V15c/d—These two varieties were caused by the misplacement to the left of the surcharge intended for the upper half of the right hand pane on one sheet. V15c occurs on the right vertical column of the left hand pane and V15d on the same column of the right hand pane.

V16a—The surcharge was inverted on one sheet and the stamps were defaced by means of vertical strokes in red ink. This sheet was not sold at the Post Office but was included amongst remainders later sold. The red ink has been chemically removed from a number of copies.

V17a—The vertical spacing between '12' and 'cents' is 6mm. instead of the normal 2½mm. Position not known.

V19a—The surcharge was inverted on one sheet and the original value was obliterated on some copies by means of a horizontal bar in red ink. This red ink has also been chemically removed.

V21a—The 'O' in '90' is ½mm. wider than normal. Position not known.

Nos. V15/16/18/20 may be found with 'cents' either above the value, or omitted, due to misplacement of the surcharge.

Numbers issued—V15, 90,480; V16/17, 23,760; V18/19, 24,000; V20, 13,200; V21, 8,160.

1893 (Nov.) As Nos. V9/14 (Die II), but new values.

V22	3c.	**dull purple and or**	30	40
V23	12c.	**sepia and green**	65	1·00
V24	15c.	**sage-green and lilac**	1·50	1·50
V25	45c.	**brown and carmine**	8·00	8·50
V22/25		**set** (4v)	£10	£11
SPV22/25		**specimen set** (4v)	£35	‡

Imperforate Colour Trials of V22 and V23 are known on unwatermarked paper, both bi-coloured and mono-colour.

Numbers issued—V22, 131,880; V23, 107,880; V24, 100,860; V25, 28,560 *.

* Net figure after deduction of quantities later surcharged (See V26/27).

1896 (Aug. 1st) No. V25 locally surcharged in black. Setting 6 x 5, applied four times to the sheet.

V26	18c. on 45c.	**brn and car** ..	2·50	2·75
	a surcharge double	..	£350	£350
	b sucharge treble	..	£275	£325
V27	36c. on 45c.	**brn and car** ..	5·50	8·00
	a surcharge double	..	£425	£500

Constant varieties occur in the overprint 'CENTS' on both values—

c—Short stemmed 'T' — Row 1/3 of the Setting
d—Short first upright to 'N' — Row 1/5 of the Setting
e—Raised 'S' — Row 2/6 of the Setting
f—Broken 'C' — Row 5/1 of the Setting
g—Short limbed 'E' — Row 5/3 of the Setting

	V26	V27
c	£30	£50
d	£20	£30
e	£25	£35
f	£30	£40
g	£30	£40

Both values may be found with the surcharge misplaced either vertically or horizontally, resulting in part of the surcharge falling on the adjoining stamp

Numbers issued—V26, 12,600; V27, 6,000.

1897-1900 As Nos. V22/25 (Die II), but new values and colours.

V28	2c.	**or-brn and grn** ('00)	35	80
V29	6c.	**carmine** ('00) ..	80	1·25

V30	15c.	**ultramarine** ('00) ..	2·75	2·50
V31	18c.	**ultramarine**.. ..	1·50	2·50
V32	36c.	**brown and carmine**	8·00	7·50
V33	75c.	**yel and violet** ('00)	£12	£14
V34	R1	**purple and red** ('00)	7·00	6·00
V35	R1.50	**grey and car** ('00) ..	£18	£20
V36	R2.25	**mauve and grn** ('00)	£18	£20
V28/36		**set** (9v)	£65	£70
SPV28/36		**specimen set** (9v) ..	£90	‡

Imperforate Colour Trials of V34 exist in several colours on unwatermarked paper.

1901 (June 21st–Oct.) Nos. V11/12/14/32 locally surcharged in black. Setting 6 x 5, applied four times to the sheet.

V37	3c. on 10c.	(Die II) (Oct.) ..	65	1·50
	a surcharge double	..	£250	£300
V38	3c. on 16c.	(Die II) (Aug.)..	65	1·50
	a surcharge double	..	£250	£300
	b surcharge inverted	..	£250	£250
	c '3 Cents' omitted	..	£250	£300
V39	3c. on 36c.	(June 21st) ..	65	1·50
	a surcharge double	..	£325	£325
	b '3 Cents' omitted	..	£250	£300
	c large '3' inserted	..	—	—
V40	6c. on 8c.	(Die II) (Aug.) ..	65	1·50
	a surcharge inverted	..	£250	£250
SPV37/40		**specimen set** (4v)	£50	‡

V38*c*/39*b*—These varieties occurred because the type failed to take up the ink, although faint traces occasionally show.

V39*c*—The normal '3' having failed to print on Row 2/2 of the setting, a much larger figure was subsequently printed at a second operation.

Numbers issued—V37, 42,000; V38, 31,200; V39, 60,000; V40, 40,000.

1902 (June) Nos. V10/33/34/36 locally surcharged in black. Setting 6 x 5, applied four times to the sheet.

V41	2c. on 4c.	(Die II) ..	1·50	3·00
V42	30c. on 75c.	.. ..	2·75	6·50
	a narrow 'O' ..		£11	£22
V43	30c. on R1	.. ..	2·75	6·50
	a narrow 'O' ..		£11	£22
V44	45c. on R1	.. ..	4·00	8·00
V45	45c. on R2.25	.. ..	6·50	8·50
	a narrow '5' ..		£40	£45
SPV41/45		**specimen set** (5v) ..	£60	‡

V42a/43a—The '0' in '30' is narrow in four positions in the Setting. Rows 3/6 and 5/2-4.

V45a—The '5' in '45' is narrow. Row 4/1 of the Setting.

Nos. V37/45, although issued during the reign of King Edward VII, are listed with the issues of Queen Victoria as a matter of convenience.

Numbers issued—V41, 18,000; V42/43/44, 9,000 each; V45, 6,000.

1903 (May 26) Wmk. Crown CA.

E1	2c.	**or-brn and grn** ..	40	60
E2	2c.	**chnt and grn** ('04)	25	35
E3	3c.	**dull green**.. ..	55	60
E4	6c.	**carmine**	40	15
E5	12c.	**ol-brn and grn** ..	90	40
E6	15c.	**ultramarine** ..	1·00	1·75
E7	18c.	**sage-grn and car**	2·50	3·75
E8	30c.	**violet and green**	3·25	3·75
E9	45c.	**brown and car** ..	3·25	4·50
E10	75c.	**yel and violet** ..	4·50	6·00
E11	R1.50	**black and car** ..	£12	£12
E12	R2.25	**mauve and green**	9·00	£12
E1/12		**set** (11v) ..	£35	£40
SPE1/12		**specimen set** (11v)	£95	‡

E9 exists with watermark inverted.

Numbers issued—E5, 60,000; E6, 28,000*; E7, 18,000*; E8, 30,000; E9, 6,000*; E10, 12,000; E11/12, 6,000 each.

* Net figures after deduction of quantities later surcharged (See E13/15).

1903 (July 3rd–Sept. 2nd) Nos. E6/7/9 locally surcharged in black. Setting 6 x5, applied four times to the sheet.

E13	3c. on 15c.	**ultramarine** ..	1·50	2·00
		a short 'C' ..	£20	£11
E14	3c. on 18c.	**sa-grn and car** ..	3·75	4·25
		a short 'C' ..	£20	£11
E15	3c. on 45c.	**brn and car** ..	1·25	3·25
		a short 'C' ..	£20	£11
SPE13/15		**specimen set** (3v) ..	£50	‡

E13a/15a—The lower loop of the 'c' in 'cents' is shortened on Row 2/6 of the Setting.

Numbers issued—E13, 32,000; E14, 12,000; E15, 24,000.

1906 As Nos.E1/12 but Wmk.Multiple Crown CA.

E16	2c.	**chestnut and grn** ..	25	30
E17	3c.	**dull green**	40	30
E18	6c.	**carmine**	35	15
E19	12c.	**olive-brn and grn** ..	1·25	25
E20	15c.	**ultramarine**.. ..	75	2·00
E21	18c.	**sage-grn and car** ..	1·50	2·50
E22	18c.	**pale sage-green and carmine** ..	1·5C	2·50
E23	30c.	**violet and green** ..	3·25	3·25
E24	45c.	**brown and carmine**	2·50	4·25
E25	75c.	**yellow and violet** ..	6·00	7·50
E26	R1.50	**black and carmine**	8·50	9·00
E27	R2.25	**mauve and green** ..	£12	£13
E16/27		**set** (11v)	£35	£40

Numbers issued—E16/17/18, 120,000 each, E19/20, 54,000 each; E21/22, 36,000; E23/24; 12,000 each; E25/26/27, 6,000 each.

1912 (Apr.)-13 As before but Head of King George V.Wmk.Multiple Crown CA. Inscription POSTAGE–POSTAGE

G1	2c.	**chestnut and green**	20	45
G2	3c.	**green**	25	10
G3	3c.	**dull green**	40	20
G4	6c.	**carmine** (6/13) ..	1·25	10
G5	6c.	**aniline car** ('16) ..	4·50	3·00
G6	12c.	**ol-brown and green** (1/13)	70	2·25
G7	12c.	**drab and green** ..	1·25	3·00
G8	15c.	**bright blue**	1·00	70
G9	15c.	**cobalt**	1·50	1·00
G10	18c.	**sage-grn and car** (1/13)	60	2·75
G11	18c.	**pl sage-grn and car**	1·00	3·00
G12	30c.	**vlt and grn** (1/13) ..	2·75	1·00
G13	45c.	**brn and car** (1/13)..	1·50	3·25
G14	75c.	**yel and vio** (1/13) ..	3·75	2·75
G15	R1.50	**black and car** (1/13)	2·50	1·50
G16	R2.25	**mve and grn** (1/13)	£13	£15
G17	R2.25	**br pur and grn** ('15)	£11	7·00
G1/17		**set** (11v)	£22	£20
SPG1/17		**specimen set** (11v)	£90	‡

A constant variety occurred on the earliest printings of all values, where the 'A' in 'POSTAGE' in the right hand panel is split at the top on Row 8/3 (left pane only). Price 10 to 15 times normal.

See Introduction for details of Dies I and II.

1917-22 Wmk.Multiple Crown CA. G18/27-O: G28/43 -C. Inscription POSTAGE & REVENUE.

(a) Die I (1917-20).

G18	2c.	**or-brn and grn** ..	15	25
G19	3c.	**green**	15	10

G20	3c.	**dull green**	25	15
G21	5c.	**brown** ('20).. ..	30	40
G22	5c.	**deep brown**.. ..	15	35
G23	6c.	**carmine**	20	10
G24	6c.	**rose-red** ('19) ..	1·75	35
G25	12c.	**greenish slate** ('19)	30	90
G26	12c.	**pl grey** (worn plate)	1·00	2·00
G27	15c.	**ultramarine**.. ..	20	1·25
G28	18c.	**pur/yel** ('19) ..	1·00	2·00
		a on orange-buff('20)	5·00	5·50
G29	25c.	**blk and red/yel** ('20)	1·75	2·50
		a on orange-buff('20)	£13	£15
G30	30c.	**dull purple and olive**	2·75	3·75
G31	30c.	**pl dl pur and olive**		
		(worn plate)	4·00	5·00
G32	45c.	**dl pur and or** ('19)..	1·75	3·25
G33	50c.	**dl pur and blk** ('20)	2·25	3·25
G34	50c.	**reddish lilac and blk**	3·00	4·00
G35	75c.	**black/blue-green**		
		(olive back) ..	2·25	3·25
G36	R1	**dl pur and red** ('20)	7·00	8·00
G37	R1.50	**slate-purple and**		
		blue/blue.. ..	9·00	£10
G38	R2.25	**yel-grn and violet**..	£13	£16
G39	R5	**grn and blue** ('20) ..	£20	£25
G18/39		**set** (16v)	£55	£70
SPG18/39		**specimen set** (16v)	£140	‡

G18/19/23/27/30/38 may be found on bluish paper (Plate 5).

G26/31 the impression of the key Plate is very light and gives a whitish appearance especially on the King's forehead.

(b) Die II (1922).

G40	18c.	**purple/pale yellow**	1·50	3·50
G41	25c.	**blk and red/pale yel**	2·00	2·00
G42	75c.	**blk/blue-green**		
		(emerald back) ..	3·00	4·50
G43	R1.50	**slate-lilac and blue/**		
		blue	6·00	9·00

1921 As before but Wmk Multiple Script CA (Die II) G44/63 and G65/66 -O: G64 and G67/78 C.

G44	2c.	**chestnut and green**	15	15
G45	2c.	**or-brn and green** ..	20	15
G46	2c.	**light brown and grn**	25	20
G47	3c.	**green**..	15	15
G48	3c.	**dull green**	20	15
G49	3c.	**black** ('22)	20	15
G50	4c.	**green** ('22)	20	25
G51	4c.	**dull green**	30	25
G52	4c.	**sage-grn and car**		
		('28)	1·50	3·50
G53	5c.	**deep brown**.. ..	1·25	1·50
G54	6c.	**carmine**	35	80
G55	6c.	**purple** ('22).. ..	15	10
G56	6c.	**slate-lilac**	20	10
G57	6c.	**reddish violet** ..	30	15
G58	9c.	**red** ('27)	60	1·50
G59	12c.	**grey**	65	35
G60	12c.	**carmine** ('22) ..	25	15
G61	12c.	**scarlet** ('25).. ..	35	20
G62	15c.	**bright blue**	2·50	3·25
G63	15c.	**yellow** ('22).. ..	60	2·50
G64	18c.	**pur/pale yel** ('25) ..	1·50	3·25
G65	20c.	**bright blue** ('22) ..	90	1·50
G66	20c.	**dull blue** ('36) ..	2·25	1·50
G67	25c.	**blk and red/pale yel**		
		('25)	1·25	2·50
G68	30c.	**pl dl pur and olive**..	90	2·50
G69	30c.	**dl purple and olive**		
		(worn plate) ..	1·25	2·50

G70	45c.	**pl dl purple and or**..	90	2·50
G71	45c.	**dp dl purple and o**e	1·25	3·00
G72	50c.	**dl purple and blk** ..	1·25	2·50
G73	75c.	**blk/emerald** ('24) ..	5·00	5·50
G74	R1	**dl purple and red** ..	6·00	7·00
G75	R1	**dp dl pur and red** ..	7·00	7·00
G76	R1.50	**pur and blue/blue**..	5·50	7·00
G77	R2.25	**yel-grn and vlo** ..	6·50	8·00
G78	R5	**yel-grn and blue** ..	£22	£24
G44/78		**set** (24v)	£55	£75
SPG44/78		**specimen set** (24v)	£200	‡

G69 See note after Nos. G26/31.

Nos. G47/48 and G59 were re-issued in 1926.

1932 As before, but reversion to Die I.

G79	12c.	**grey** (O)	1·50	1·50
G80	R1	**dl pur and red** (C) ..	6·00	8·50
G81	R1	**rdish lil and red** (C)	8·00	9·00

1935 (May 6th) Silver Jubilee. Recess Bradbury Wilkinson. Wmk. Multiple Script CA. Perf. 11 x 12. Sheets 6 x 10.

G82	6c.	**ultramarine and gr**	15	20
		a extra flagstaff ..	£55	—
G83	12c.	**green and indigo** ..	30	25
		a extra flagstaff ..	£775	—
G84	20c.	**brown and blue** ..	35	60
		a extra flagstaff ..	£55	—
G85	R1	**slate and purple** ..	1·00	2·50
		a extra flagstaff ..	£45	—
G82/85		**set** (4v)	1·75	3·50
SPG82/85		**specimen set** (4v)	£22	‡

G82a/G85a—Extra flagstaff occurs on No 49. (Row 9/1).

Remainders were withdrawn on December 31st 1935.

1938-49 Designs, 2c., 9c., 18c., 25c., 50c.,

1r.50 (Coco-de-mer Palm); 3c., 12c., 15c., 30c., 75c., 2r.25 (Tortoise); Other Values (Fishing Pirogue). Printers photo Harrison & Sons. Perf. 14¾ x 13¾ (C). Chalk-surfaced paper unless otherwise indicated. Designs, 2c., 3c., 9c., 12c., 15c., 18c., 25c., 30c., 50c 75c., 1r.50, 2r.25 V. Sheets 8 x 15 or 15 x 8.

1	2c.	**pur-brown** (10/2/38)	10	10
		a purple-chocolate (sub) (18/11/42)	10	10
2	3c.	**green** (1/1/38) ..	55	30
3	6c.	**dp orange** (1/1/38)..	55	30
4	9c.	**scarlet-red** (10/2/38)	80	1·25
5	12c.	**mauve-pur** (1/1/38)	2·75	1·00
6	20c.	**blue** (1/1/38) ..	2·50	4·50
7	25c.	**yel-bistre** (1/1/38) ..	7·00	6·50
8	30c.	**lake-claret** (10/2/38)	4·00	5·00
9	45c.	**brown-pur** (10/2/38)	10	15
		a brown-purple (sub) (18/11/42) ..	15	15
10	50c.	**grey-violet** (10/2/38)	30	15
		a grey-violet (sub) (18/11/42) ..	20	15
11	75c.	**grey-blue** (10/2/38)	£12	£17
12	1r.	**yellow-grn** (10/2/38)	£20	£22
13	1r.50	**ultramarine** (10/2/38)	80	1·00
		a ult (sub) (18/11/42)	60	90
14	2r.25	**olive** (10/2/38) ..	80	1·00
		a olive (sub) (18/11/42)	60	90
15	5r.	**brownish-red** (10/2/38) ..	3·00	3·00
		a brownish-red (sub) (18/11/42) ..	4·00	4·00
SP 1/15		**specimen set** perf (15)	£100	‡

As before but colours changed, and new values. Sheets 6 x 10 or 10 x 6 (A 1949 printing of No. 25 was released in sheets 8 x 6 the last two vertical rows having been removed).

16	3c.	**orange** (8/8/41) ..	15	15
		a orange (sub) (18/11/42) ..	20	15
17	6c.	**dull grey-grn** (8/8/41)	30	20
		a wmk. inverted ..	£50	—
		b grn (sub) (18/11/42)	15	10
		c green (5/4/49) ..	10	10
18	9c.	**dull grey-blue** (8/8/41)	15	15
		a dull grey-blue (sub) (18/11/42) ..	10	15
		b dull blue (sub) (19/11/45) ..	50	25
		c dull blue (5/4/49) .	30	25
19	15c.	**brownish-carmine** (8/8/41)	50	40
		a brownish-red (sub) (18/11/42) ..	25	25
20	18c.	**mauve-mag** (8/8/41)	30	15
		a mauve-magenta (sub) (18/11/42) ..	15	10
		b rose-magenta (F.A.) (5/4/49) ..	15	10
21	20c.	**yellow-bistre** (8/8/41)	40	25
		yellow-bistre (sub) (18/11/42) ..	10	15
22	30c.	**blue** (8/8/41) ..	20	15
		a blue (sub) (18/11/42)	10	15
23	50c.	**bt violet** (13/6/49)..	15	15
24	75c.	**grey-lilac** (8/8/41)..	40	40
		a grey-lilac (sub) (18/11/42) ..	25	25
25	1r.	**grey-black** (8/8/41)	25	30

		a grey-black (sub) (18/11/42) ..	50	35
1/25		**set** (25) all colours ..	£55	£60

17a Only very few copies are reported, possibly two or three sheets.

1952 (Mar. 3rd) Designs, 2c., 40c., 10r. (Sail Fish); 3c., 25c., 2r.25 (Tortoise); 9c., 50c., 1r.50 (Coco-de-mer Palm); 18c., 20c., 45c. (Pirogue); 18c., 1r., 5r. (Map). Printers (photo) Harrison & Sons. Perf. 14¾ x 13¾ (C). Chalk-surfaced paper. Designs, 2c., 3c., 9c., 25c., 40c., 50c., 1r.50, 2r.25, 10r. V. Sheets 10 x 5 or 5 x 10.

26	2c.	**lilac**	..	..	10	10
27	3c.	**red-orange**	..	..	10	10
28	9c.	**grey-blue**	..		15	10
29	15c.	**dp yellow-green**		..	15	10
30	18c.	**terracotta-pink**		..	15	10
31	20c.	**orange-yellow**		..	15	10
32	25c.	**vermilion-pink**		..	20	15
33	40c.	**dull ultramarine**		..	25	30
34	45c.	**lake-brown**	..		25	30
35	50c.	**violet-magenta**		..	25	25
36	1r.	**grey-black**	..		40	50
37	1r.50	**brilliant blue**		..	70	1·75
38	2r.25	**olive**	..	..	1·25	2·00
39	5r.	**dull red**	..		3·00	4·00
40	10r.	**green**	..	..	5·50	8·00
26/40		**set** (15)	..	..	£11	£16

Watermark Varieties (Type A)
(See Introduction for details)

26a	2c.	Crown missing
26b		St. Edward's Crown
27a	3c.	Crown missing
27b		St. Edward's Crown
28a	9c.	Crown missing
28b		St. Edward's Crown
29a	15c.	Crown missing
29b		St. Edward's Crown
30a	18c.	Crown missing
30b		St. Edward's Crown
31a	20c.	Crown missing
31b		St. Edward's Crown
32a	25c.	Crown missing
32b		St. Edward's Crown
33a	40c.	Crown missing
33b		St. Edward's Crown
34a	45c.	Crown missing
34b		St. Edward's Crown
35a	50c.	Crown missing
35b		St. Edward's Crown
36b	1r.	St. Edward's Crown
37b	1r.50	St. Edward's Crown
38b	2r.25	St. Edward's Crown
39b	5r.	St. Edward's Crown

Prices : 2c—18c from £25
20c—50c from £75
1R—5R from £150

SPECIAL ISSUES

1937 (May 12th) Coronation. As Aden, but Printers Bradbury, Wilkinson. Perf. 11 x 11¾ (C).

S1	6c.	sage-green	.. ..	10	10
S2	12c.	orange	.. ..	10	10
S3	20c.	dp blue	.. ..	30	30
SP S1/3	specimen set perf (3)			£15	‡

1946 (Sept. 23rd) Victory. As Aden.

S4	9c.	light blue	.. ..	10	10
S5	30c.	dp blue	.. ..	10	10
SP S4/5	specimen set perf (2)			£17	‡

1948 (Nov. 11th) Silver Wedding. As Aden.

S6	9c.	ultramarine	..	10	30
S7	5r.	rose-carmine	..	3·50	5·00

1949 (Oct. 10th) U.P.U. As Aden but all recess.

S8	18c.	magenta	.. ..	10	15
S9	50c.	purple-violet	..	35	35
S10	1r.	grey	.. ..	35	50
S11	2.25c.	sage-green	..	1·25	1·25
S8/11	set (4)		.. ..	2·00	2·00

POSTAGE DUE STAMPS

1951 (Mar. 1st) Design adapted from that of Australia. Recess (border) and Typo (centre) Bradbury, Wilkinson. Perf. 11¾ x 11½ (C). Thick rough paper. Centre scarlet. Sheets 6 x 10.

PD1	2c.	scarlet	.. ..	45	50
PD2	3c.	green	.. ..	45	50
PD3	6c.	ochre	.. ..	10	10
PD4	9c.	red-orange	..	10	10
PD5	15c.	purple	.. ..	10	10
PD6	18c.	dp blue	.. ..	10	10
PD7	20c.	dp brown	.. ..	10	10
PD8	30c.	lake-brown	.. ..	10	10
PD1/8	set (8)		.. ..	1·25	2·00

SIERRA LEONE

1938-51 Designs, ½d., 1d., 3d., 4d., 1/-, 2/- and £1 (View of Freetown); Other Values (Rice Harvesting). Printers (*recess*) Waterlow & Sons. Perf. 12½ (L). Wmk. sideways. Sheets 6 x 10 and 5 x 12 (1941).

1	½d.	**blk and grn** (1/5/38)	10	10
	a	black and emerald-green (13/11/44)	15	10
2	1d.	**black and brown-lake** (1/5/38)	10	10
	a	imperf. between, vertical pair	—	£600
3	1½d.	**scarlet** (1/5/38)	2·50	20
4	1½d.	**pur-mauve** (1/2/41)	15	10
	a	mauve (13/11/44)	10	10
5	2d.	**pur-mauve** (1/5/38)	5·00	1·50
6	2d.	**scarlet** (1/2/41)	10	10
	a	bright scarlet	15	10
7	3d.	**blk and ult** (1/5/38)	10	10
	a	bright ultramarine	20	10
8	4d.	**black and chocolate** (20/6/38)	35	30
	a	black and red-brown (23/5/50)	25	30
9	5d.	**sage-green** (20/6/38)	40	90
	a	olive-green (6/3/44)	35	80
10	6d.	**grey** (20/6/38)	15	10
11	1/-	**black and sage-green** (20/6/38)	40	25
	a	black and olive-green (5/5/49)	25	20
12	1/3	**orange-yel** (1/7/44)	35	20
13	2/-	**blk and sepia** (20/6/38)	60	65
	a	black and dp sepia (23/5/50)	50	60

14	5/-	**choc-brn** (20/6/38)	1·50	1·25
	a	reddish-brn (19/3/45)	1·50	1·24
15	10/-	**emerald** (20/6/38)	4·00	3·00
	a	pale emerald (13/10/48)	4·50	3·50
16	£1	**indigo** (20/6/38)	7·00	6·50
	a	dk blue (11/12/47)	6·00	5·50
	b	dk steel blue (19/12/51)	6·00	5·50
1/16		**set** (16)	£19	£12
SP 1/16		**specimen set** perf (16)	£75	‡

2a Forged pairs exist mint. Only one pair is reported to exist in used condition, which is cancelled, April 18th, 1940, Freetown.

Minor frame re-entries exist on ½d., 4d. and 1/– values each being worth about 5 times normal. Positions are :—

Nos. 1, 1*a*—Rows 5/2, 6/2 and 7/2
Nos. 8, 8*a*—Rows 1/1, 1/4, 2/2, 3/1 and 7/2
Nos. 11, 11*a*—Rows 1/4, 8/4 and 9/4

SPECIAL ISSUES

1937 (May 12th) Coronation. As Aden but Printers Bradbury, Wilkinson. Perf. 11 x 11¾ (C).

S1	1d.	**orange**	20	15
S2	2d.	**dp purple**	20	15
S3	3d.	**dp blue**	30	35
SP S1/3		**specimen set** perf (3)	£14	‡

1946 (Oct. 1st) Victory. As Aden.

S4	1½d.	**lilac**	10	10
S5	3d.	**ultramarine**	10	10
SP S4/5		**specimen set** perf (2)	£16	‡

1948 (Dec. 1st) Silver Wedding. As Aden.

S6	1½d.	**magenta-purple**	10	10
S7	£1	**bluish-slate**	6·00	7·50

1949 (Oct. 10th) U.P.U. As Aden.

S8	1½d.	**dull purple**	15	15
S9	3d.	**indigo**	20	20
S10	6d.	**grey**	40	40
S11	1/-	**sage-green**	70	70
S8/11		**set** (4)	1·25	1·25

SOMALILAND PROTECTORATE

Egyptian influence ceased with the withdrawal of the Khedival garrisons in 1884, and agreed areas of Somaliland came under British, French and Italian control. The British area was administered by the Resident in Aden under the authority of the Government of India.

The country was officially called Somaliland Coast Protectorate but it was usually referred to as British Somaliland to distinguish it from the French and Italian areas. In 1898 control passed to the Foreign Office and the official title became British Somaliland. In 1903 the title was changed to Somaliland Protectorate.

Egyptian stamps were used until 1884 and unoverprinted Indian stamps came into use from 1887. They continued to be used at the Military Post Offices after the introduction of the overprinted stamps in the civilian Post Offices on June 1st, 1903

1903 (June 1st.) Stamps of India (Typo. De La Rue) overprinted in black sans serif capitals at the Government Printing Office Calcutta. (a) Overprint at top (Stamps of Queen Victoria).

V1	½a.	**yellow green**	..	40	1·25
		a 'BRIT SH' ..	..	£55	—
V2	1a.	**carmine**	..	50	1·25
		a 'BRIT SH' ..	..	£55	—
V3	2a.	**pale violet**	..	45	45
		a 'BRIT SH' ..	..	₺90	—
		b overprint double ..		£200	—
V4	2½a.	**ultramarine..**	..	80	2·25
		a 'BRIT SH ..	..	£140	—
V5	3a.	**brown-orange**	..	90	2·00
		a 'BRIT SH'	..	£125	—
V6	4a.	**slate-green**	..	1·00	2·25
V7	6a.	**olive-bistre..**	..	1·40	3·00
V8	8a.	**dull-mauve**	..	1·50	3·50
V9	12a.	**purple/red** ..	..	2·50	4·00
V10	R1	**green and carmine**		6·50	6·00
V11	Rs2	**car and yellow-brn**		8·00	£12
		a curved overprint ..		£50	—
V12	Rs3	**brown and green** ..		9·00	£12
		a curved overprint ..		₹60	—
V13	Rs5	**ultra and violet** ..		£10	£15
		a curved overprint ..		£70	—
V1/13		**set (13v.)** ..	..	£38	£12

V1a/5a—Prices are for stamps with the letter completely omitted. Examples may also be found showing progressive shortening of the letter. Row 2/6 (No. 18) and Row 15/1 (No. 169) except V4a (Row 15/1 only).

V11a/12a/13a The overprint is curved (convex, both lines) on Row 3/4 of the top right pane (Sheets—96 : eight panes (2 x 4), each 4 x 3).

Numbers sold—V1/2, 48,000 each; V3, 22,342; V4, 19,902; V5, 15,796; V6, 14,092; V7, 11,855; V8, 11,635; V9, 10,762; V10, 8,446; V11, 4,191; V12, 3,954; V13, 3,828.

Remainders were destroyed 30.4.06.

(b) Overprint at bottom

(i) Stamps of Queen Victoria (2.11.03)

V14	2½a.	**ultramarine** ..	..	1·25	3·00
		a 'SUMALILAND'	..	£45	—
		b 'SOMAL.LAND'	..	£45	—
		c 'BRIT SH'	..	£45	—
V15	6a.	**olive-bistre**	..	£30	—
		a 'SOMAL.LAND'	..	1·50	2·25
V16	12a.	**purple/red**	..	3·50	5·00
		a 'SUMALILAND'	..	£60	—
		b 'SOMAL.LAND'	..	£60	—
V17	R1	**green and carmine**	..	5·00	6·00
		a 'SUMALILAND'	..	£100	—
		b 'SOMAL.LAND'	..	£100	—
V18	Rs2	**car and yellow-brn**		£18	£22
		a 'SUMALILAND'	..	£110	—
		b 'SOMAL.LAND'	—	£110	—
		c curved overprint	..	£110	—
V19	Rs3	**brown and green**	..	£20	£25
		a 'SUMALILAND'	..	£120	—
		b 'SOMAL.LAND'	..	£120	—
		c curved overprint	..	£120	—
		d overprint double (one albino), both inverted		£230	—
V20	Rs5	**ultra and violet**	..	£20	£25
		a 'SUMALILAND'	..	£100	—
		b 'SOMAL.LAND'	..	£100	—
		c curved overprint	..	£100	—
V14/20		**set (7v.)** ..	..	£65	£85

V14a/16a/17a Row 2/9 (No. 21).

V18a-20a Row 1/3 of top left pane.

V14b/16b/17b Row 17/5 (No. 197).

V15a Row 17/5 (No. 133 of the setting which was repeated twice over the sheet, four vertical rows of type having been removed from the setting used for the other Anna values).

V14c See Note after V5a. Row 7/12 (No. 84).

V18b-20b Row 3/4 of third pane on right. The variety usually appears as a very short letter 'I'.

V18c-20c See Note after V13a. Row 3/4 of top right pane.

Numbers sold—V14, 12,140; V15, 10,994; V16, 8,199; V17, 5,249; V18, 1,700; V19, 1,644 (of which 96 were V19d) ; V20, 2,216.

Remainders were destroyed 30.4.06.

(ii) Stamps of King Edward VII (See India Nos. E4/17). (Sept. 1-Nov. 2, 1903).

E1	½a.	**green** (1.9.03)	..	40	50
		a 'SUMALILAND'	..	£25	—
		b 'SOMAL.LAND'	..	£12	—
		c 'BRIT SH' ..	..	£90	—
E2	1a.	**carmine** (8.10.03)..		50	50
		a 'SUMALILAND'	..	£30	—
		b 'SOMAL.LAND'	..	£15	—
		c 'BRIT SH' ..	..	£85	—
E3	2a.	**violet** ..	..	1·00	2·25
		a SUMALILAND	..	£45	—
		b 'SOMAL.LAND'	..	£45	—
		c 'BRIT SH' ..	..	£325	—

E4	3a.	**orange-brown** ..	1·25	2·25
		a 'SUMALILAND' ..	£50	—
		b 'SOMAL.LAND' ..	£50	—
E5	4a.	**olive**	1·25	2·00
		a 'SUMALILAND' ..	£50	—
		b 'SOMAL.LAND' ..	£50	—
E6	8a.	**mauve**	2·00	2·25
		a 'SUMALILAND' ..	£60	—
		b 'SOMAL.LAND' ..	£60	—
		c dropped 'D' ..	£90	—
E1/6		**set (6v.)**	6·00	9·50

E1a-6a Row 2/9 (No. 21).

E1b-6b Row 16/7 (No. 187) when 'B' of 'BRITISH' is over 'OM' of 'SOMALILAND'; also on Row 17/5 (No. 197) when 'B' is over 'M'.

E1c See Note after V5a. Row 11/5 (No. 125).

E2c/3c See Note after V5a. Row 7/12 (No. 84).

E6c Row 10/12 (No. 120). The 'D' in 'SOMALI-LAND' is dropped 5 mm., usually appearing half on the stamp and half in the interpanneau margin (Sheets 240 : two panes, each 12 x 10, one above the other).

Numbers sold—E1, 96,000; E2, 82,198; E3, 16,241 ; E4, 14,173; E5, 13, 594; E6, 11,902.

Remainders were destroyed 30.4.06.

Nos. V1 to E6 may all be found with a great variety of broken, thick, short and spaced letters.

1904 (Feb.-Sept. 3rd) Typo De La Rue. Perf 14.
(a) Wmk Crown CA. Sheets 120-two panes, each 6 x 10.

E7	½a.	**dl green and green** (15/2)	30	1·75
E8	1a.	**grey-black and red**	30	2·00
E9	2a.	**dl and bt purple** ..	1·00	1·50
E10	2½a.	**bright blue** ..	1·50	3·25
E11	3a.	**chocolate and grn**	1·50	3·25
E12	4a.	**green and black** ..	2·00	3·25
E13	6a.	**green and violet** ..	3·50	5·50
E14	8a.	**grey-blk and pl blue**	3·50	7·00
E15	12a.	**grey-blk and or-buff**..	6·00	9·00

(b) Wmk. Crown C.C. Sheets 5 x 12.

E16	R1	**green**	7·50	£10
E17	Rs3	**dull and bright pur**	£15	£18
E18	Rs3	**green and black** ..	£20	£24
E19	Rs5	**grey-blk and car**	£20	£24
E7/19		**set (13v.)**	£75	£100
SPE 7/19		**specimen set (13v.)**	£90	‡

Numbers printed—(Approx.) E7/8, 84,000 each; E9, 14,400; E10/11, 12,000 each; E12, 10,800;

E13, 7,200; E14, 7,440; E15, 5,760; E16, 4,320; E17, 2,160; E18/19, 1,440 each.

1905-11. As before but Wmк. Multiple Crown CA.

E20	½a.	**dl green and green**	40	1·50
E21	½a.	**bluish green** ('09)	2·25	3·25
E22	1a.	**grey-black and car OC**	40	1·40
			1·75	2·00
E23	1a.	**red** ('09)	1·75	2·50
E24	2a.	**dl and bt purple OC**	3·00	3·50
E25	2½a.	**bright blue O** ..	2·00	4·00
E26	3a.	**choc and grn OC**	2·00	4·90
E27	4a.	**green and black OC**	2·00	4·00
E28	6a.	**green and violet OC**	2·50	5·00
E29	8a.	**grey-black and pale blue O**	9·00	£15
E30	8a.	**black and blue C** ..	2·50	£15
E31	12a.	**grey-black and or-buff O**	2·50	6·50
E32	12a.	**blk and or-brn C** ..	£10	£15
E20/32		**set (11v.)**	£19	£35
SPE23		**specimen (1v)** ..	£10	‡

Numbers printed—E20, 60,000; E21, 24,000; E22, 60,000 (O), 300,000 (C): E23, 120,000; E24, 8,400 (O), 18,000 (C), E25, 16,800; E26, 8,400 (O), 1,800 (C) ; E27, 8,400 (O), 1,800 (C); E28, 8,400 (O), 1,200 (C) ; E29, 8,400; E30, 1,200; E31, 8,400; E32, 3,600.

1912 (Nov.) 19 Typo De La Rue. Wmk. Multiple Crown CA. Perf. 14. Sheets G1/16 120 – two panes, each 6 x 10: G17/20 5 x 12: G1/5 and G9 – 0: G6/8 and G10/20 C.

G1	½a.	**green** . ..	20	50
G2	½a.	**dull green**	20	45
G3	½a.	**blue-green** ..	30	30
G4	1a.	**carmine** (11/'12) ..	50	75
G5	1a.	**scarlet** ('17) ..	1·00	1·50
G6	2a.	**lilac and magenta**	2·00	2·50
G7	2a.	**dl and bt purple** ..	3·00	3·50
G8	2a.	**dl and bright violet -purple** ('19) ..	3·00	3·75
G9	2½a.	**blue**	60	1·50
G10	3a.	**choc and blue-grn**	60	1·75
G11	3a.	**choc and yel-grn**	60	1·50
G12	4a.	**grn and blk** (12/'12)	90	2·50
G13	6a.	**green and violet** ..	90	2·00
G14	8a.	**grey-blk and pl blue**	1·50	3·50
G15	8a.	**black and blue** ..	1·75	4·00
		a 'PROTECTRATE'	£35	—
G16	12a.	**grey-black and or-buff**	1·75	4·25
G17	R1	**green** (11/'12) ..	2·50	4·50
G18	Rs2	**dl pur and pur** ('19)	8·00	£12
G19	Rs3	**grn and black** ('19)	£10	£16
G20	Rs5	**black and scar** ('19)	£18	£25

G1/20	**set** (13v.)	..	..	£45	£75
SPG1/20	**specimen set** (13v.)			£95	‡

G15*a*. Row 5/2 left hand pane.

G1/3 and 10/11 exist with watermark inverted.

Numbers printed—G1/3, 132,000; G4, 372,000; G5, 240,000; G6/8, 33,000; G9, 30,000; G10/11, 30,000; G12, 30,000; G13, 28,800; G14/15, 24,000; G16, 24,000; G17, 18,600; G18, 6,000; G19, 6,000; G20, 6,000.

1921. As before but Wmk. Multiple Script CA. G21/25 and G28/29—O : G26/27 and G30/39 —C.

G21	½a.	**dull green**	..	..	10	60
G22	½a.	**blue-green**	..		10	70
G23	1a.	**red**	..	..	10	50
G24	1a.	**rosine**	..	..	10	55
G25	1a.	**scarlet**	..	..	10	45
G26	2a.	**dl and bt purple**	..		50	80
G27	2a.	**purple-brn and pur**			70	1·25
G28	2½a.	**bright blue**	..		70	1·75
G29	2½a.	**dull blue**			80	2·25
G30	3a.	**chocolate and grn**			1·00	2·25
G31	4a.	**green and black**	..		90	2·75
G32	6a.	**green and violet**	..		1·00	3·00
G33	6a.	**grn and bluish vio**			1·25	2·50
G34	8a.	**grey-blk and pl blue**			1·50	3·00
G35	12a.	**grey-blk and or-**				
		buff		..	4·00	8·00
G36	R1	**dull green**	..	..	5·00	8·00
G37	Rs2	**dull pur and pur**	..		£12	£20
G38	Rs3	**dl green and black**			£24	£35
G39	Rs5	**black and scarlet**	..		—	—
G21/39	**set** (13v.)		..	..	£50	£85
SPG21/39	**specimen set** (13v.)			£90	‡

Numbers printed—G21/22, 126,000; G23/25, 924,000; G26/27, 294,000; G28/29, 90,000; G.30, 90,000, G31, 63,000; G32/33, 66,000; G34, 48,000, G35, 36,000, G36, 54,000; G37, 33,000; G38, 18,000; G39, 27,000.

1935 (May 6th.) Silver Jubilee. Recess Waterlow and Sons. Wmk Multiple Script CA. Perf. 11 x 12. Sheets 6 x 10.

G40	1a.	**blue and scarlet**	..	90	1·25
G41	2a.	**ultmar and grey**	..	1·25	2·25
G42	3a.	**brown and blue**	..	1·75	3·50
G43	R1	**slate and purple**	..	3·50	6·25
G40/43	**set** (4v.)		..	7·00	£13
SPG40/43	**specimen set** (4v.)		£24	‡

Numbers printed—G40, 81,200; G41, 70,300; G42, 62,700; G43, 50,900.

Remainders were withdrawn on December 31st 1935.

1938 (May 10th) Designs, ½a.—3a. (Black-headed Sheep); 4a.—12a. (Greater Kudu Antelope); 1r.—5r. (Map of Territory). All with Head of King (*facing left*). **Printers recess Waterlow & Sons. Perf. 12½ (L). Designs, 1r. to 5r. H. Sheets—Anna values 12 x 10; Rupee values 6 x 10.**

1	½a.	**green**	..	..	20	50
2	1a.	**scarlet-red**	..	..	20	50
3	2a.	**lake**	..	..	15	50
4	3a.	**blue**	..	..	1·00	1·50
5	4a.	**dp brown**	..	..	1·00	1·50
6	6a.	**violet**	..	..	70	1·00
7	8a.	**grey**	..	..	1·00	2·50
8	12a.	**reddish-orange**	..	1·25	2·50
9	1r.	**green**	..	..	7·00	£10
10	2r.	**purple**	..	..	3·50	7·00
11	3r.	**blue**	..	..	3·00	6·00
12	5r.	**black**	..	..	4·00	7·00
	a	horiz. pr. imp. between		£1500	—
1/12	**set** (12)		..	..	£23	£40
SP 1/12	**specimen set** perf (12)		£40	‡

12*a* Only 6 pairs are reported to exist.

Used prices are for copies with postmarks dated prior to August 19th 1940 when the territory was occupied by Italian Forces; and quantities of this issue were looted.

The Italian occupation ended on March 16th 1941; and from July 1st 1941 the contemporary stamps of Aden continued in use in British Somaliland until the new definitive set was issued on April 27th 1942.

1942 (April 27th) As No. 1, etc., but portrait changed to full face. Sheets—Anna values 8 x 15; Rupee values 10 x 6.

13	½a.	**green**	..	..	5	10
14	1a.	**scarlet-red**	..		5	10
15	2a.	**lake**	..	..	30	30
16	3a.	**blue**	..	..	5	20
17	4a.	**dp brown**	..	..	5	20
18	6a.	**violet**	..	..	15	20
19	8a.	**grey**	..	..	15	20
20	12a.	**reddish-orange**	..	25	40

21	1r.	**green**	..	..	70	80
22	2r.	**purple**	..	..	1·25	1·75
23	3r.	**blue**	..	..	1·50	2·25
24	5r.	**black**	..	..	3·00	2·50
13/24		**set** (12)			7·50	9·00
SP13/24		**specimen set** (12)	..		£50	‡

1951 (April 2nd) No. 13, etc., surcharged in black or red, to bring in line with changed currency (100 Cents= 1 Shilling).

25	5c./½a.	**green**	..	..	10	10
27	10c./2a.	**lake**	..	..	10	10
28	15c./3a.	**blue**	..	..	10	15
29	20c./4a.	**dp brown**	..	..	10	15
		a sepia-brown	..		35	40
30	30c./6a.	**violet**	..	..	15	20
31	50c./8a.	**grey**	..	..	15	20
32	70c./12a.	**red-orange**	..	..	20	30
		a vermilion	..		25	35
33	1s./1r.	**green**	..	..	25	40
34	2s./2r.	**purple**	..	..	60	90
35	2s./3r.	**blue**	..	..	80	1·00
36	5s./5r.	**black** (red)	..		1·50	2·00
25/36		**set** (11)	..		4·00	5·50

SPECIAL ISSUES

1937 (May 13th) Coronation. As Aden.

S1	1a.	**scarlet** ..	..	..	5	25
S2	2a.	**grey-black**	..	..	10	30
S3	3a.	**blue**	..	..	30	90
SP S1/3		**specimen set** perf (3)		£15	‡

Numbers printed—S1, 490,000, S2, 394,000, S3, 390,000.

1946 (Oct. 15th) Victory. As Aden.

(a) Perf. 13¾ x 14 (C).

S4	1a.	**carmine-red**	..	..	5	5
S5	3a.	**dp blue**	..	..	5	5
SP S4/5		**specimen set** perf (2)		£12	‡

(b) Perf. 13¾ x 13¼ (C).

S6	1a.	**carmine-red**	..	..	30	2·50

1949 (Jan. 28th) Silver Wedding. As Aden.

S7	1a.	**scarlet** ..	..	..	5	5
S8	5r.	**grey-black**	..	..	3·00	3·00

1949 (Oct. 10th) U.P.U. As Aden, but surcharged in black or red.

S9	1a./10c.	**carmine-rose** ..		10	10
S10	3a./30c.	**indigo** (red)	..	15	20
S11	6a./50c.	**purple**	..	25	35
S12	12a./1/–	**orange**	..	50	60
S9/12		**set** (4)	..	1·00	1·25

OFFICIAL STAMPS.

1903 (June 1st). Service stamps of India (Queen Victoria) overprinted in black sans serif capitals.

VO1	½a.	**yellow-green**	..	4·00	£15
		a misplaced overprint reading 'On S.H.M.'		£30	—
VO2	1a.	**carmine**	..	6·00	7·50
		a 'BRIT SH' ..		—	—
VO3	2a.	**pale violet** ..	..	7·50	£17·50
VO4	8a.	**dull mauve** ..	..	£14	£160
		a stop omitted	..	—	—
VO5	R1	**green and carmine**		£15	£125
VO1/5		**set** (5v.)	..	£45	£320

VO1a Examples from the left vertical row have the 'S' omitted, so that the overprint reads 'On H.M.', It is thought that the six top rows of one sheet missed the overprint, and that the misplaced overprint was the result of an attempt to correct the omission.

VO2a Recorded on Row 7/12 (No. 84) and usually appearing as 'BRIT.SH'.

VO4a Row 20/12 (No. 240) The stop after 'M' of 'On H.M.S.' was removed in an attempt to correct the 'joined M and full stop' variety which occurred on the Indian stamps.

Nos. VO1 to VO5 may all be found with a variety of broken, dropped and spaced letters.

Numbers sold—(Numbers printed shown in brackets, the balances having been sold as remainders) VO1, 760 (7,200); VO2, 2,143 (7,200); VO3, 614 (4,800); VO4, 145 (2,400); VO5, 321 (2,400).

1903 Prepared for use but not issued. Stamps of India overprinted in black sans serif capitals.

(a) Stamp of Queen Victoria.

VO6	R1	**green and carmine**		£15	—
		a dropped 'E'	..	£600	—
		b 'SUMALILAND'	..	£600	—
		c 'BRIT SH'	..	£600	—
		d 'SERVICE' different fount	..	£600	—
		e 'SOMAL.LAND'	..	£600	—

(b) Stamps of King Edward VII (See India Nos. E4/17).

EO1 ½a.	**green**	75	—
	a dropped 'E' ..	£40	—
	b 'SUMALILAND ..	£40	—
	c 'BRIT SH'	£40	—
	d 'SERVICE' different		
	fount	£40	—
	e 'SOMAL.LAND' ..	£40	—
EO2 1a.	**carmine**	75	—
	a dropped 'E' ..	£40	—
	b 'SUMALILAND' ..	£40	—
	c 'BRIT SH'	£40	—
	d 'SERVICE' different		
	fount	£40	—
	e 'SOMAL.LAND' ..	£40	—
EO3 2a.	**violet**	1·50	—
	a dropped 'E' ..	£60	—
	b 'SUMALILAND' ..	£60	—
	c 'BRIT SH'	£60	—
	d 'SERVICE' different		
	fount	£60	—
	e 'SOMAL.LAND' ..	£60	—
EO4 8a.	**mauve**	£15	—
	a dropped 'E' ..	£600	—
	b 'SUMALILAND' ..	£600	—
	c 'BRIT SH'	£600	—
	d 'SERVICE' different		
	fount	£600	—
	e 'SOMAL.LAND'	£600	—

VO6*a*, EO1*a*-4*a* Row 1/6 (top pane). The second 'E' in SERVICE is dropped as much as 3½mm. EO2*a* also exists with the variety corrected.

VO6*b*, EO1*b*-4*b* Row 2/9 (No. 21).

VO6*c*, EO1*c*-4*c* Row 7/12 (No. 84).

VO6*d*, EO1*d*-4*d* Row 1/7 (bottom pane). SERVICE measures 11½mm instead of the normal 11mm. and the letters, other than 'S' are all smaller.

VO6*e*, EO1*a*-4*e* Row 16/7 (bottom pane : No. 187) This variety shows very clearly on VO6*e* and EO2*e*; on the other three values it usually appears as a short letter 'I'.

Nos. VO6 to EO4 may all be found with a great variety of broken and spaced letters.

A very few examples of this issue are known genuinely postmarked; but, as they are dated after the Officials were withdrawn from use at the end of August 1905, they were probably cancelled by favour.

Numbers sold—numbers printed shown in brackets, the balance having been sold as Remainders. VO6, 21 (2,400); EO1, 976 (36,000); EO2. 496 (36,000); EO3, 17 (24,000); EO4, 16 (2,400),

1904 (Sept. 1st)-05 Nos. E7/8/9/14/24/16 overprinted in black sans serif capitals by De La Rue.

(a) Wmk Crown CA.

EO5 ½a.	**dull green and grn**		3·00	£25
	a stop omitted	..	£190	—
EO6 1a.	**grey-blk and red**	..	5·00	7·50
	a stop omitted	..	£175	—
EO7 2a.	**dull and bright pur**		£65	£35
	a stop omitted	..	£600	£325
EO8 8a.	**grey-blk and pl blue**		£45	£75
	a stop omitted	..	£190	—

(b) Wmk. Multiple Crown CA (7/05)

EO9 2a.	**dl and bt purple O**		£45	£250
	a stop omitted	..	£475	—

(c) Wmk. Crown CC

EO10 R1	**green** ..	..	£80	£225
SPEO5-8				
and 10	**specimen set** (5v.)	£100	‡

EO5*a*-9*a* These varieties come from the fifth vertical row of either pane where the stop after 'M' of the overprint shows small, as a trace or omitted entirely.

The prices are for the latter which is usually found on Row 2/5 of each pane, except in the case of EO9 where it is found on Row 1/5 of the right pane under the Plate Number.

These varieties are also found on the Anna stamps overprinted 'Specimen'.

Numbers sold—numbers printed shown in brackets, the balance having been sold as Remainders. EO5, 679 (5,160); EO6, 2,323 (4,800); EO7, 764 (960); EO8, 164 (1,080); EO9, 31 (960); EO10, 554 (960).

Few of the 554 copies of EO10 sold in the Protectorate were postally used on official mail.

All Official stamps were withdrawn on August 31st, 1905.

SOUTH AFRICA

All stamps were printed (*roto*) at the Govt. Printing Works, Pretoria, on paper with "Springbok's Head" wmk. and printed alternately in English and Afrikaans, unless otherwise mentioned. (*Numerous flaws are to be found on South African stamps, but as these are usual with the form of printing used, only the most outstanding can be considered worthy of catalogue rank.*)

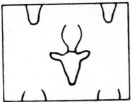

1938-49 SUIDAFRIKA (*Without Hyphen*). **Designs, 2d. (Union Buildings); 4d. (Kraal); 2/6 (Ox Wagon). Perf. 14 (C). Wmk. upright. (Other Values with Suidafrika unhyphenated were issued before 1937.)** (*Stamps as No. 1, but of slate and violet shades are from earlier printings.*) **Sheets 120—two panes, each 6 x 10 (except X1—12 x 10).**

			Pr. M.	Pr. U.
1	2d.	**dk blue and violet** (/38)	£40	£20
2	4d.	**dp brown** (/41)	£12	7·00
	a	lt chestnut (/47)	£15	7·00
	b	dp chestnut (/47)	4·50	3·00
	c	dp red-brown (/49)	4 00	2 50
3	2/6	**blue and brn** (/45)	£20	£10
X1	½d.	**grey-green** (/36)	2 00	1 00
	a	perf. 13½ x 14	£10	£12

(As C.W. 41 but hyphenated)

No. 1—This re-drawn design shows War Memorial to the left of value.

No. 2—The scroll at the base of the stamps (2–2*c*) resemble chain links (*see illustration*). Stamps of a light yellow-brown shade in this re-drawn design were first issued in 1936.

No. 2*b*—In this printing the curved upper outer line is broken in the centre on all stamps.

No. 3—Stamps of the same design (*with centres in green*) were first issued in 1932.

1937-54 SUID-AFRIKA (*With Hyphen*). **Designs ½d. (Springbok's Head); 1d. (Van Riebeck's Ship "Dromedaris"); 1½d. (Gold Mine); 2d. (Union Buildings); 3d. (Groote Schuur); 6d. (Orange Tree); 1/- (Gnus); 2/6 and 5/- (Ox Wagon); 10/- (Groot Constantia). Perf. 14¾ x 14 (C)** (½d., 1d. and 6d.). **Perf. 14 (C) (Other Values). Designs, ½d., 1d., 6d. V.** (*The coarser screen can be detected with the aid of a magnifying glass through the design being made up of a series of small regular or irregular dots in some instances lines appear to have saw-like edges.*) **Sheets— Small Format 12 x 20; Large Format 6 x 20.**

Unscreened.

4	½d.	**grey and green** (4/37)	2·00	50
	a	grey and dp grn (/37)	3·00	60
	b	grey and dp blue-grn (/40)	2·00	06
	c	sepia blk and myrtle-green (/41)	2·00	60
	d	sepia-grey and bright green (/45)	2·00	60
	e	sepia-brown and grn (/47)	2·00	60
	f	grey-blk and greenish-blue (/47)	2·50	60

g dp grey and blue-grn (8/47) ..	2·50	60
h dp grey and dull blue-green (cross hatch) (11/47)	£20	£15
5 1d. grey and carmine-red (/38)	80	10
aa perf. 13½ x 14 ..	£10	£12
ab frame omitted	£225	—
a grey and red-car (5/40)	2·00	20
b sepia-grey and rose-carmine (/47) ..	1·50	15
c sepia-grey and mag-rose (/48)	2·00	20
d grey and car (blurred frame) (/48) ..	1·50	15
e grey and rose-magenta (/48)	1·25	15
f grey and rose (/49)..	1·00	10
7 2d. blue and violet (11/38)	£32	£17
8 2d. grey and purple-lilac (5/41)	3·00	3·00
10 6d. grn and ver (Type 1) (10/37) ..	£28	7·00
aa falling ladder ..	£35	£30
a green and vermilion (Type 2) (6/38) ..	5·00	2·50
b green and brownish-orange (Type 2) (/42)	5·00	2·50
c green and vermilion (Type 3) (/46) ..	3·00	1·75
d grey-grn and red-orange (Type 3) (10/46)	3·00	1·75
11 1/- sepia-brn and chalky-blue (2/39) ..	6·00	1·25
a frame omitted	£500	—
b dp sepia and grey-blue (/46)	5·00	1·25
c choc and blue-slate (/47)	6·00	1·25
d brown and slate-blue (/48)	6·00	1·25
13 5/- black and light green (12/41) ..	£35	£15
a black and blue (9/44)	£18	8·00
b black and green (/46)	£18	8·00

Frame Coarser Screened.

14 ½d. grey and green (1/48)	1·50	20
a grey and dull blue-green (/48) ..	1·25	15
b grey and dp blue-grn (/48)	1·25	15
c sepia-grey and pale green (/48) ..	1·50	15

Centre Coarser Screened.

20 2d. slate and pur-vio (re-drawn (1st State) (3/45) ..	2·00	1·50
a slate and vio (2nd State) (5/46) ..	2·00	1·50
b slate and bt vio (2nd State) (/47) ..	1·50	1·25
21 3d. dull ult (2/40) ..	2·00	60
b ult (/40) ..	1·50	50
c light ult and blue (/47)	6·00	2·00
22 3d. blue (/47) ..	3·50	1·00
23 10/- blue and sepia (8/39)	£35	£15

a blue and sepia black (/44)	£35	£15
b vio-blue and black (/47)	£24	8·00
c vio-blue and sepia (/49)	£24	7·00

All Coarser Screened.

25 ½d. sepia-grey and green (2/49)	50	25
a sepia-grey and bt grn (/49)	40	20
b sepia-grey and dp grey-green (/49) ..	35	20
c black and dp blue-green (/50) ..	30	20
d jet-black and dp blue-green (4/51) ..	20	10
26 1d. sepia-grey and mag-rose (9/50) ..	1·00	15
a sepia-blk and dp mag-rose (11/50) ..	20	15
b blue-blk and mag-rose (4/51) ..	20	10
27 1d. grey-blk and car-mag (re-drawn) (22/2/51)	70	10
a grey-black and rose-scarlet (5/53) ..	50	10
b slate-black and mag-rose (/53) ..	50	10
28 1½d. gold and blue-green (/37) ..	3·00	1·25
a dull gold and slate-green (/40) ..	3·00	1·25
29 2d. slate-blue and purple (3/50) ..	30	25
30 3d. dull blue (re-drawn) (4/49) ..	50	30
31 3d. blue (3/51) ..	50	30
a dp blue (/50) ..	£20	£12
32 6d. green and red-orange (1/50) ..	60	40
a grn and brn-orange (/51)	75	40
33 1/- sepia and slate-blue (1/50)	1·50	1·00
a sepia-blk and dp violet-blue (4/52) ..	£10	6·00
34 2/6 grey-green and brown (8/49) ..	7·00	4·50
a green and chestnut-brown (4/52) ..	6·00	4·50
35 5/- black and grey-green (9/49)	£14	7·00

1

2

3

4*g*—For this printing, design was reduced ¼mm. each way from 18½ x 22½mm. No. 4*h*, and subsequently was reduced a further ¼mm.

4*h*—Panels running along top and bottom of stamps have crossed lines.

5, 5*a*—Design of No. 5 measures 18½mm. x 22½mm. Nos. 5*a*–5*f* and 26–26*b* measure 18¼ x 22¼mm.

10—**Type 1**—These stamps are not only paler in shade, but the inscription SUID-AFRIKA is only 16½mm. long.
Type 2—The same inscription is 17mm. long, which results in the S being perceptibly nearer to the left side of the containing panel.

Type 3—The design is only 18 x 22mm. (Type 1 and 2 18½ x 22½) and the top scrolls are closed (*see illustrations*). On stamps printed in English shading of leaves and background of tree is faint in Type 1 and much deeper in Type 2.

10*aa*—A very obvious plate flaw No. 5/10 (*see illustration*).

13—Stamps of the same design but with frames of a deep myrtle-green shade belong to earlier printings.

20, 20*a*—Not only do the shades differ from Nos. 7 or 8, but the Union Buildings are taken from another angle, and in the 1*st State* (No. 20) the 2 of the value touches the surrounding circle (*see illustration at head of set*), but in the 2*nd State* (Nos. 20*a*–*b*) the 2 is cut clear. Centres only are screened.

21-22—Apart from centre only being screened the scrolls each side above 3d. are shaded unevenly (*see illustration*).

26*b*—From booklets only.

27—The design has been reduced to 17½ x 21½mm. and re-drawn with the horizon well defined; the sun's rays are bolder and the number of shaded lines in the border reduced from 69 to 53.

28—Stamps of a middle green shade (*as distinct from the later blue-green*) are from the Nov. 1936 printing.

30—Not only are both centres and frames screened (irreg.) but scrolls above 3d. are evenly lined with variation in shading.

(30)   (21/22)

31—Now printed in one operation (previously two) the centre and frame screens are of a regular pattern. The stamp is much deeper in shade than No. 30, and the most notable difference is in the clouds, these being well defined.

1941-51 As Nos. 28 and 29, but reduced in size. Perf. 14 x 14¾ (C). Wmk. sideways.

36	1½d. **buff and slate-green** (8/41)	50	10
	aa "waffle" print (8/41)	6·00	—
	a buff and slate-blue (/47)	30	10
	b buff and grey-blue (/48)	20	10
	c yellow background omitted	£325	—
37	2d. **blue-slate and purple** (4/50)	40	15
	a dp blue-slate and dp purple (7/50)	40	15
	b slate-blue and bt purple (4/51)	20	10

36*aa*—The very coarse screen used resulted in the variety.

1943-52 Coils. Designs as Nos. 4 and 5, but re-drawn and printed monocolour. Perf. 14¾ x 14 (C).

38	½d. **blue-green** (18/2/43)	30	30
	a grn (clear impression) (/49)	20	20
39	1d. **car-mag** (9/43)	45	35
	a carmine (/47)	40	35
	b coloured blotch	3·50	2·50
	cc white corner	3·00	2·00
	d carmine-red (clear impression (/49)	30	35
	e missing sun	3·00	3·00
	f dp mag-car (/52)	30	35

Horizontal pairs of both ½d. and 1d. of this coil printing are known. Price from £400 —

39*cc*   39*b*

39*b*—A large blotch appears at the right side.

39cc—Near the left bottom corner of the design a white patch has the appearance of a worn plate.

39e—The sun at the right side is missing.

1948 (April 1st) Design as No. 36, but format altered and Perf. 14 and Roul. 6½ horizontally (*alternately*). **Wmk. sideways.**

40	1½d. **buff and slate-blue-green**	15	15
	a buff and grey-green .	25	25

1948 Design as No. 4, but printed from plates of 1926 issue (*typo*). (*Suidafrika no hyphen*). **Perf. 14¾ x 14 (C).**

41	¼d. **grey and dull-grey-green** (July) ..	35	40

Special printing made to use up a stock of paper already cut.

1952-4 Designs, 4d. (Native Kraal); 5/- (Ox Wagon, inscription South Africa redrawn (*see illustrations*). **Stamps printed alternately in English and Afrikaans. Inscription Suid-Afrika with hyphen. Perf. 14 (C). Screened.**

46	4d. **dk brown** (22/8/52)..	30	30
	a reddish-choc (4/53)	50	35
47	5/- **blk and dp yel-grn** (1/54)	£14	9·00
	a grey-blk and yel-grn (5/54)	£14	£10
	Cyl. 4d., 103; 5/-, 72/8.		
1/47	**set** ¼d.–10/- cheapest type (11 pairs) ..	£45	£20

47—In the redrawing of the inscription South Africa the serif at the top of the A and the projections each side at bottom of the U have been removed. (*See illustrations*).

SPECIAL ISSUES

1937 (May 12th) Coronation. Perf. 14 (C). Wmk. sideways (*found also facing left or right in all values*). **Sheets 6 x 20.**

S1	½d. **dk grey and green** ..		15	15
S2	1d. **grey-blk and car** (Cyl. 55)		1·00	45
	a ditto (Cyl. 30a) ..		15	15
S3	1½d. **orange and greenish-grey**		15	25
S4	3d. **ultramarine**		25	30
S5	1/- **red-brn and turquoise-blue**		1·00	1·00
	a missing hyphen ..		7·00	6·00
S1/5	**set** (5)		1·70	1·85

Number printed (pairs—½d., 13,018,500; 1d., 21,156,000; 1½d., 2,392,500; 3d., 1,970,100; 1/-, 1,477,500.

S2—Cyl. 55. Relatively clear impression. Greyish shading around head. Front lobe and back of ear clearly outlined. Face and neck entirely shaded (*wmk. facing right only*). Cyl. 30a (as used for centres of all other values in set). Inferior impression. Deeper shading around head, except behind. Ear not outlined. Shading of face and neck patchy (*wmk. facing right or left*).

S5a—The hyphen is missing between SUID AFRIKA, No. 2/13.

1938 (Dec. 14th) Voortrekker Centenary Memorial Fund. Designs, ½d. (Ploughing); 1d. (Wagon); 1½d. (Signing Treaty); 3d. (Memorial). Perf. 14 (C) (½d. and 1d.). Perf.

14¾ x 14 (C) (1½d. and 3d.). *(Surcharge for Memorial Fund).* **Sheets 6 x 20.**

S6	½d.+½d. **slate-blue and grn**	1·50	1·50
S7	1d.+1d. **dp blue and car**	2·00	2·00
S8	1½d.+1½d. **choc. and dp grn**	6·00	6·00
S9	3d.+3d. **dull blue**	6·00	6·50
S6/9	**set** (4)	£15	£16

Number printed (pairs)—½d., 6,144,000; 1d., 11,560,000; 1½d., 3,564,000; 3d. 2,100,000.

1938 (Dec. 14th) **Great Trek** *(Voortrekker).* **Designs, 1d.** (Wagon Wheel); **1½d.** (Voortrekker Family). **Designer, W. H. Coetzer. Perf. 14¾ x 14 (C). Sheets 6 x 20.**

S10	1d. **slate-blue and car**..	1·40	1·60
S11	1½d. **dull grn and chestnut**	1·60	1·60
S10/11	**set** (2)	3·00	3·20

Number printed (pairs)—1d., 4,380,000; 1½d., 5,244,000.

1939 (July 17th) **250th Anniversary of Landing of the Huguenots. Designs, ½d.** (Old Vicarage Paarl); **1d.** (Dawning Light); **1½d.** (Huguenot Dwelling). **Perf. 14 (C)** (½d. and 1d.). **Perf. 14¾ x 14 (C)** (1½d.). *(Surcharge for Commemoration Fund).* **Sheets 6 x 20.**

S12	½d.+½d. **sepia and dp green** ..	2·00	2·00
S13	1d.+1d. **dp grn and car**	2·50	3·50
S14	1½d.+1½d. **dull grn and dp purple** ..	4·00	6·00
S12/14	**set** (3)	8·00	£11

Number printed (pairs)—½d., 2,490,000; 1d., 1,344,000; 1½d., 1,290,000 (includes quantities overprinted S.W.A.).

1941-42 War Effort *(large size).* **Designs, Members of Forces, War Weapons, etc. Perf.**

14 (C) (2d., 4d. and 6d.) and wmk. sideways. Perf. 14¾ x 14 (C) (Other Values) and wmk. upright. 2d. and 1/- (Bi-Lingual); Other Values in English and Afrikaans alternately. Designs 3d., 1/- H. Sheets—S15/17m 12 x 20; others 20 x 6 or 6 x 20.

S15	½d. **green** (19/11/41) ..	30	25
	a blue-green (7/42)..	65	75
S16	1d. **carmine** (3/10/41) ..	15	10
	a dull carmine (/42)..	15	10
S17	1½d. **dp myrtle** (12/1/42)	15	10
	a myrtle-green (/42) .	15	10
S18	2d. **violet** (single) (15/9/41)	30	10
	a pale vio (single) (/42)	40	15
S19	3d. **blue** (1/8/41) ..	75	1·00
	a prussian blue (/42)	50	50
S20	4d. **chestnut** (20/8/41)..	1·75	1·50
	a red-brown (6/42) ..	8·00	7·00
S21	6d. **dp orange** (3/9/41)..	1·50	2·00
S22	1/– **chocolate** (single) (27/10/41)	2·00	1·00
	a reddish-choc (single) (/42)	1·75	1·00
S15/22	**set** (8)	6·50	5·50

1942-5 War Effort *("Bantams").* **Designs as No. S15, etc., but reduced in size. ½d., 1d., 3d. and 4d. in Units of Three. Other Values in Pairs and Perf. and Roul. alternately** *(vertically)* *(Prices for units or pairs),* **wmk. sideways** (3d., 4d., 1/-). **Sheets S24/25/28/29, 20 x 18 or 18 x 20; others, 20 x 12 or 12 x 20. Perf. 14** *(three sides)* **and Roul. 13** *(vertically)* **Other Values.**

S23	1½d. **reddish-brown** (8/42)	15	15
	a right side background missing	60	60
	b roul. 13 and 6½ (se tenant)	1·50	1·50

Perf. 14¾ x 14 *(all round)* **and Sub-Divided Roul 6½** (½d., 1d., 3d., 4d.); **Perf. 14** *(three sides)* **Roul 6½ Other Side. 4d and 1/- Bilingual.**

S24	½d. **blue-green** (10/42)..	30	15
	a upper background missing	4·00	4·00
	b background added	4·00	4·00
	c roul. missing between	£90	—
	d dp green (3/43) ..	1·20	1·00
	e upper background missing	4·00	4·00
	dp greenish-blue (7/44)	70	60
	g upper background missing	4·00	4·00
	h background added	4·00	4·00
S25	1d. **carmine** (1/43) ..	30	15

	a roul. missing be-			
	tween	£90	—
	b bt carmine (3/44)..	30	15
S26	1½d. **reddish-brown** (3/43)	30	15
	a right side background		
	missing ..	4·00	4·00
	b roul. missing be-		
	tween	£60	—
S27	2d. **pur-vio** (2/43) ..	50	40
	a roul. missing be-		
	tween	£140	—
	b violet (1/45) ..	25	30
	c bt violet (4/45) ..	25	30
S28	3d. **blue** (10/42) ..	80	90
	a dull blue (/44) ..	1·00	90
S29	4d. **slate-green** (single)		
	(10/42)	70	70
	a blue-green (8/44) .	50	60
S30	6d. **dp orange** (10/42) ..	80	80
	a dull orange (3/45)..	80	80
S31	1/- **chocolate** (single)		
	(11/42)	1·25	1·25
	a bursting shell ..	5·00	5·00
	b upper background		
	missing	5·00	5·00
S24/31	**set** (8)	4·50	4·25

Early printings bore "war savings" slogans in self colours on margins, but in 1944 these were printed in violet on the ½d., 1d. and 4d. values. In 1945 these slogans were replaced by lines and figures (240 *and* 360 *according to numbers of stamps in the sheets*) in ½d. (green), 1d. (both violet and carmine), 2d. and 6d. (violet). All values except the 6d. are known with misplaced slogans (*printed on the stamps themselves*).

S24*a, e, g,* S31*b*—The shading of background on the upper part of the stamps on first row is absent, and extensive retouching on the ½d. value S24*h* repaired the omission.

S31*a*—Above the right armoured car a number of dots give the appearance of a bursting shell, No. 11/20.

1943-6 War Effort. Design, Signaller. Perf. 14¾ x 14 (C). Sheets 20 x 12.

S32	1/3 **olive-brown** (2/1/43)	2·00	3·00
	a dp sepia (5/46) ..	1·75	1·75

1945 (Dec. 3rd) Victory. Designs, 1d. (Soldier

with Flag); 2d. (Ploughing); 3d. (Star Gazing). Perf. 14 (C). Sheets 6 x 20.

S33	1d. **bp brown and car** ..	10	10
	a aniline centre ..	—	—
	b barbed wire Row 9/6	1·50	—
S34	2d. **slate-blue and pur-**		
	vio	15	15
S35	3d. **dp blue and blue** ..	20	40
S33/35	**set** (3)	45	65

Number printed (pairs)—1d., 14,117,880; 2d., 19,441,920; 3d., 4,367,640 (includes quantities overprinted S.W.A.).

1947 (Feb. 17th) Royal Visit. Designs, Portraits of Royal Family. Perf. 14¾ x 14 (C). Sheets—S36, 12 x 20; others, 6 x 20.

S36	1d. **dp slate and carmine**	10	10
S37	2d. **purple-violet** (Cyl.		
	6912)	1·00	—
	a ditto (Cyl. 39) ..	10	10
S38	3d. **dp blue**	10	10
	a blinded princess ..	1·50	1·50
S36/38	**set** (3)	30	30

Number printed (pairs)—1d., 18,572,400; 2d., 22,392,120; 3d., 4,317,900 (includes quantities overprinted S.W.A.).

S37—The scroll is shaded above and below the words SOUTH AFRICA, giving a bevelled appearance. There is no break in the small scroll at the bottom left corner on stamps with Afrikaans inscription. Also there are 9 dots in the centre of the flower at the left hand side on all stamps (Cyl. 6912).

S37*a*—The scroll is plain and unshaded. There is a break in the small scroll near the join to the large scroll at the left bottom corner on Afrikaans stamps. There are only 8 dots in the centre of the left-hand flower (Cyl. 389).

S38*a*—A smudge (*constant*) is to be found on No. 19/2 across the eyes of Princess Elizabeth.

1948 (April 26th) Silver Wedding. Design, Portrait of King and Queen (*from photographs by Dorothy Wilding*) framed by Silver Leaves (*Leucadendron Argenteum*). Perf. 14 (C). Sheets 6 x 20.

S39   3d. **silver and dp blue** ..   10   10

Number printed (pairs)—5,070,000 (includes quantities overprinted S.W.A.).

1949 (May 2nd) Centenary of Arrival in Natal of British Settlers. Design, "Wanderer" lying off Durban. Perf. 14¾ x 14 (C). Sheets 6 x 20.

Sheets of No. S40 bear Cyl. No. 29, but those of S40*a* (stamp deeper in shade) have no cyl. number.

S40	1½d. **reddish-choc** ..	15	15
	a brown-claret ..	20	20

Number issued (pairs)—24,976,740.

1949 (Oct. 1st) U.P.U. Perf. 14 x 14¾ (C). Wmk. sideways. Sheets 6 x 20.

S41	½d. **dp blue-grn** (Cyl. 60)	10	10
	a dk blue-grn (Cyl. 31)	30	25
S42	1½d. **brownish-lake** ..	15	10
S43	3d. **bt ultramarine** ..	15	15
	a C variety	1·50	1·50
S41/43	**set** (3)	40	35

S43*a*—The C on No. 1/1 resembles G through a marked flaw.

Number printed (pairs)—½d., 12,101,580; 1½d., 17,244,300; 3d., 2,413,620.

1949 (Dec. 1st) -50 Inauguration of Voortrekker Monument. Designs (*bi-lingual in-*

scriptions); **1d. (Voortrekkers on way to Natal); 1½d. (Monument); 3d. (Triptych). Perf. 14¾ x 14 (C). Sheets 6 x 20.**

S44	1d. **lake-magenta** ..	10	10
	a claret (1/50) ..	20	10
S45	1½d. **dull green**	10	10
	a dull blue-green ..	15	10
S46	3d. **dp slate-blue** ..	10	10
S44/46	**set** (3)	30	30

Number printed—
1d., 21,585,480; 1½d., 32,205,720; 3d., 3,187,680

OFFICIAL STAMPS

1938-49 Designs, 2d. (as No. 1); 1/- (as No. 11 but SUIDAFRIKA unhyphenated); 2/6 (as No. 3), overprinted OFFICIAL (*at right*) and OFFISIEEL (*reading downwards*).

O1	2d. **dark blue and violet** (No. 1) (/39) ..	8·00	9·00
O2	1/- **brown and dp blue** (/38) ..	6·00	5·00
O3	2/6 **grey-green and brn** (/39) ..	£10	£10
O4	2/6 **blue and brown** (No. 3) (/46) ..	8·00	6·00

O2—The overprint measures 21mm. between lines. Stamps with overprint measuring 19mm. were issued in 1932.

O3—The overprint measures about 21mm. Stamps with overprint measuring 17½-18mm. belong to the 1933 issue.

1937-51 As No. 4, etc., overprinted as before with OFFISIEEL to left.

O5	½d. **grey and green** (No. 4) (7/38) ..	80	40
	aa wmk inverted ..	80	50
	a grey and dp blue-grn (No. 4*b*) (/46) ..	60	30
	aa sepia-blk and myrtle-grn (No. 4*c*) (/47)	60	30
	b dp grey and blue-grn (No. 4*g*) (/49) ..	40	20
	c grey and dull blue-grn (No. 14*a*) (/49)	30	20

O6 1d. **grey and car-red**
     (No. 5) (/37) ..   1·00   40
   a grey and red-car
     (No. 5a) (/45) ..   60   20
   b sepia-grey and rose
     car (No. 5b) (/49)   60   20
   c grey and car (blurred
     frame) (No. 5d)
     (/49)   60   20
   d grey and rose (No. 5f)
     (/50) ..   40   20
O7 1½d. **gold and blue-green**
     (No. 28) (9/37) ..   1·25   75
   a dull gold and slate-grn
     (No. 28a) (/42) ..   1·00   75
O8 1½d. **buff and slate-green**
     (reduced) (No. 36)
     (/47)   75   25
   a buff and grey-blue
     (No. 36b) (/49)..   75   25
   b buff and slate-green
     (wide overprint)
     (No. 36) (/50) ..   30   20
O9 2d. **blue and violet**
     (No. 7) (/38) ..   4·50   4·50
O10 2d. **slate and vio** (No. 20a)
     (/47)   60   75
   a slate and bt violet
     (No. 20b) (/49)..   60   75
O11 6d. **green and ver** (1)
     (No. 10) (/38) ..   £18   £14
   a green and ver (2)
     (No. 10a) (/40)..   2·00   1·50
   b green and brownish-
     orange (2) (No.
     10b) (/43) ..   3·00   1·50
   c green and ver (3)
     (No. 10c) (/48)..   2·00   1·50
   d grey-green and red-
     orange (3) (No.
     10d) (/49) ..   1·00   75
O12 1/- **sepia-brn and chalky-
     blue** (No. 11) (3/40)   1·50   1·00
   aa strip of 6 across
     sheet, first stamp
     printed "Official"
     twice both left
     and right, last
     stamp printed
     "Offisieel" twice
     both left and right £175 —
   a dp sepia and grey-blue
     (No. 11b) (/48)..   1·00   80
   b choc and blue-slate
     (No. 11c) (/49)..   1·00   80
   c brn and slate-blue
     (No. 11d) (/50)..   1·50   80
   d sepia and slate-blue
     (No. 33) (6/50)   1·00   80
O13 5/- **black and green**
     (No. 13b) (/51) ..   £10   £10
O14 10/- **violet-blue and sepia**
     (No. 23c) (7/50) ..   £20   £15
O5/O14 **set in pairs** ½d.–10/-
     (8) £35   £30

O8b The width between lines of overprint is
    approximately 16½mm. instead of 15mm. as
    in O8. The lettering is bolder and more widely
    spaced.

O10 Stamps exist with overprint in two different
    founts. One larger, with the letters more widely
    spaced than the other, and se tenant.

1940 Designs as before but with **OFFICIAL**
(*overprint*) **at left.**

O15 5/- **black and green**
      (No. 13a) (/40) ..   £10   £10
O16 10/- **blue and sepia**
      (No. 23) (3/40) ..   £15   £12

1944 - 48 As No. O5a, etc., second **E** of
OFFISIEEL with diaeresis.

O17   ½d. **grey and dp blue-
      green** (No. 4b)
      (10/44) ..   25   30
O17a 1½d. **buff and slate-grn**
      (No. 36) (/46) ..   £18   £18
O17b 2d. **slate and violet**
      (No. 20a) ..   £45   £40
O17c 1/- **dp sepia and grey-
      blue** (No. 11b) ..   —   —
O17d 2/6 **blue and brown**
      (No. 3) ..   £250   £300

No O17 OFFICIAL of overprint is at left and reads
upwards.

1944 No. 36a, etc., overprinted as before,
but with overprint reading upwards No. O19
OFFICIAL at right, Nos. O18-19a at left.

O18 1½d. **buff and slate-blue**
      (No. 36a) (/49) ..   75   60
O19 2d. **grey and purple-lilac**
      (No. 8) (3/44) ..   60   75
O19a 2d. **blue-slate and pur**
      (No. 37) (/50) ..   £120   —
     a used single ..   ‡   £50

1950 No. 36a overprinted sideways **OFFICIAL**
at top **OFFISIEEL** at bottom.

O19b 1½d. **buff and slate blue** —   —

It is reported that one sheet was sold at post office counter, Pretoria. Information seems to indicate this ovpt was not issued by the post office.

1950-3 No. 25c, etc., overprinted with new fount (*OFFICIAL at right, reading downwards*).

O20	½d. **black and dp blue-green** (No. 25c) ..	5	5
O21	1d. **grey and rose-mag** (No. 5e) (9/50) ..	15	20
O22	1d. **sepia-grey and mag-rose** (No. 26) (6/51)	15	20
	a sepia-blk and dp magenta-rose (No. 26a) (6/51)	15	10
O23	1d. **grey-black and mag-carmine** (No. 27) (1/52)	15	10
	a grey-blk and rose-scar (No. 27a) ..	10	10
O24	1½d. **buff and grey-blue** (No. 36b) (2/51) ..	15	15
O25	2d. **blue-slate and pur** (No. 37) /8/50) ..	15	10
	a dp blue-slate and dp pur. (No. 37a) (10/50) ..	15	10
O26	6d. **grn and red-orange** (No. 32) (11/50) ..	30	20
	a grn and brn-orange (No. 32a) (1/51)	50	20
O27	1/- **sepia and slate-blue** (No. 33) (9/50) ..	50	50
	a sepia-blk and dp vio-blue (No. 34a) ..	£50	£20
O28	2/6 **grey-grn and brn** (No. 34) (11/50) ..	3·00	2·50
	a green and chestnut-brown (No. 34a)	3·00	2·50
O29	5/- **black and green** (No. 13a) (7/51) ..	8·00	7·00
	a black and grey-green (No. 35) (2/2/53) ..	8·00	7·00
O30	10/- **violet-blue and blk** (No. 23b) (11/50)..	£12	£10
O20/O30	**set in pairs** (9) ..	£24	£20

POSTAGE DUE STAMPS

1937-38 Design, Value on White Background (small "d" after figure), Bi-lingual Frame.

Perf. 14¾ x 14 (C). Sheets 120—two panes, each 6 x 10.

PD1	2d. **blk and dp pur** (/37)	40	40
	a 2d. doubled ..	£10	£10
PD2	6d. **dp grn and dp orange** (/38)	2·50	1·00

PD1—This stamp replaced one which had value (*typo*) and frame (*roto*), and can be distinguished by the screened appearance of the value, which thus differs from the solid appearance of the previous issue. The digit is also thicker.

PD1a—See note after PD17.

1943-47 Design, Value in Colour on White Background. Bi-lingual Frame. Units of Three, Perf. 14¾ x 14 (C) (all round) and Sub-divided by Roul. 6½. Sheets 360 – six panes, each 6 x 10.

PD3	½d. **dp green** (9/47) ..	25	30
PD4	1d. **carmine** (20/4/43) ..	10	30
	a bt carmine (/46) ..	20	30
PD5	2d. **dp violet** (/43) ..	10	35
	a bt violet (/46) ..	30	90
PD6	3d. **dp blue** (/45) ..	25	60

1948-9 As Nos. PD1–2 but with Capital D after Figure. Bi-lingual Frame. Perf. 14¾ x 14 (C).

PD7	½d. **blk and dp grn** (/48)	5	15
PD8	1d. **blk and mag-red** (/48)	10	15
PD9	2d. **blk and vio** (/49) ..	10	15
	a 2d. doubled ..	£10	8·00
PD10	3d. **blue-blk and grey-blue** (/48) ..	25	25
PD11	6d. **dp grn and dp orange** (/48)	30	30

PD9a—See note after PD17.

1950-8 Design as 1948 issue, but hyphenated SUID-AFRICA. Perf. 14¾ x 14 (C).

PD13	1d.	**blk and mag-red**			
		(3/50)		10	10
PD14	2d.	**blk and pur-vio**			
		(4/51)		10	10
		a 2d. doubled ..		£10	8·00
		b blk and bt vio			
		(10/57) ..		10	10
		c 2d. doubled ..		£10	8·00
		d centre omitted ..		—	—
PD15	3d.	**sl-blk and sl-blue**			
		(3/50)		40	10
PD16	4d.	**dk grn and lt em**			
		(2/58)		30	15
		a major retouch ..		£10	£10
PD17	6d.	**dp grn and dp or**			
		(12/51)		80	40
PD18	1/–	**dk brn and red-brn**			
		(2/58)		1·50	1·50

PD1*a*/9*a*/14*a*, *c*—The value on Rows 15/5, 15/6, 16/5 and 16/6 (20 x 12) is thicker than normal and the centre of D narrower. This is caused by a double image being reproduced during the preparation of the diapositive.

PD16*a*—A flaw on the 4 was partially covered by a crude retouch Row 1/1.

PD14*d*—Is recorded in a pane of sixty. Purchasers are warned that the item was stolen in February, 1964 from our premises.

MINIATURE SHEETS
(Unused)

Panes of stamps from booklets.

1934-41.

MS1	½d.	booklet pane of 6	..	2·50	—
MS2	1d.	booklet pane of 6	..	3·50	—
MS3	1½d.	booklet pane of 4	..	3·50	—
MS4	2d.	booklet pane of 4	..	4·00	—

Razor Type Booklet

MS5	½d.	pair	..	..	..	50	—
MS6	1d.	pair	..	..	..	60	—

1948 (Aug.) Designs, ½d. (Springbok's Head); 1d. (Ship); 1½d. (Gold Mine). Perf. 14¾ x 14 (C). (1½d. Wmk. sideways). Panes surrounded by selvedge, with slogans. Panes of 6.

Pane M

MS7	½d.	**grey and dl gren** (No. 14)	1·00
MS8	1d.	**sepia-blk and rose-car** (No. 56)	1·50
MS9	1½d.	**buff and grey-blue** (No. 36*b*)	2·00

1951 (April) Designs, ½d. and 1d. as before; 2d. as No. 37. Screened Panes with selvedge (plain) on two sides. Panes of 6.

MS10	½d.	**jet black and dp blue-grn** (No. 25*d*)	1·00
MS11	1d.	**blue-sl and mag-car** (No. 26*b*)	1·50
MS12	2d.	**sl-blue and bt pur** (No. 37*a*)..	2·00

SOUTH WEST AFRICA

All stamps were printed in Afrikaans and English (*alternately*) on paper with same wmk. unless otherwise indicated.

1931-54. Perf. 14 x 13½. Wmk. Springbok's Head. Sheets 6 x 10.

		Unused Pair	Used Pair
X1	½d. **black and emerald**	(30	30
X2	1d. **indigo and red** ..	30	30
X3	2d. **blue and brown** ..	30	30
X4	3d. **pl blue and blue** ..	40	40
X5	4d. **green and purple** ..	50	65
X6	6d. **blue and brown** ..	70	1·25
X7	1/– **chocolate and blue**	1·75	1·50
X8	1/3 **violet and yellow** ..	2·75	3·75
X9	2/6 **carmine and grey** ..	6·00	7·00
X10	5/– **green and brown** ..	£12	£14
X11	10/– **brown and emerald**	£22	£30
X12	£1 **lake-deep green** ..	£45	£60
X1/11	**set (12)**	£90	£115

1937 (Mar. 1st)-52 Design, Train, Plane and R.M.S. "Capetown Castle" exemplifying Transport of Mail. Printers (*recess*) Bradbury, Wilkinson. Perf. 13¾ x 13½ (C). Sheets as before.

1	1½d. **purple-brown**	50	40
	a dp pur-brn (/52) ..	40	30

SPECIAL ISSUES

See South Africa for details of special issues common to both countries. The overprints are (*typo*).

1937 (May 12th) Coronation. Printers (*recess*)

Bradbury, Wilkinson. Perf. 13½ x 13¾ (C). Wmk. sideways. Centres black. Sheets 120 – two panes, each 10 x 6.

S1	½d. **emerald-green**	..		15	25
S2	1d. **red**	..	.. ..	15	25
S3	1½d. **orange**	..	..	15	25
S4	2d. **brown**	..	.. ..	20	35
S5	3d. **blue**	..	.. ..	30	35
S6	4d. **deep purple**	..	..	40	50
	a re-entry		.. ..	£30	£30
S7	6d. **yellow** ..	..	..	50	60
S8	1/– **grey** ..	..	..	1·00	1·25
S1/8	**set (8)** ..	..	..	2·50	3·50

S6*a* Doubling of leaves and frame at lower left. No. 3 in bottom row of lower pane (Afrikaans inscription).

1938 (Dec. 14th) Voortrekker Centenary Memorial. Nos. 6–9 of South Africa, overprinted SWA.

S9	½d.+½d. **sl-blue and grn**		25	35
S10	1d.+1d. **dp blue and carmine** ..		35	45
S11	1½d.+1½d. **choc and dp green** ..		90	1·25
S12	3d.+3d. **dull blue** ..		2·00	2·50
S9/12	**set (4)**		3·00	4·00

Number Overprinted (pairs)—10,000 each value.

1938 (Dec. 14th) Great Trek (Voortrekker). Nos. S10–S11 of South Africa, overprinted SWA.

S13	1d. **sl-blue and carmine**		30	35
S14	1½d. **dl grn and chestnut**		75	1·00
S13/14	**set (2)**		1·00	1·25

Number Overprinted (pairs)—1d., 240,000; 1½d., 120,000.

1939 (July 17th) 250th Anniversary of Landing of the Huguenots. Nos. S12–4 of South Africa, overprinted SWA.

S15	½d.+½d. **sepia and dp green** ..		30	60
S16	1d.+1d. **dp green and carmine** ..		60	90
S17	1½d.+1½d. **dl green and dp purple** ..		1·50	2·50
S15/17	**set (3)**		2·25	3·75

1941-2 War Effort (large size). Nos. S15–22 of South Africa, overprinted SWA.

S18	½d. **green** (19/11/41) ..		5	10
	a blue-green (/42) ..		5	10
S19	1d. **carmine** (3/10/41) ..		5	10
	a dl carmine (/42) ..		5	10
S20	1½d. **dp myrtle** (1/42) ..		10	20
	a myrtle-grn (/42) ..		10	20
S21	2d. **vio** (single) (15/9/41)		10	10
	a pl vio (single) (/42) ..		10	10
S22	3d. **blue** (8/41) ..		20	30
	a pruss-blue (/42) ..		20	30
S23	4d. **chestnut** (20/8/41)		35	50
	a red-brown (/42) ..		2·00	3·00
S24	6d. **dp orange** (9/41) ..		40	60
S25	1/– **choc** (single) (27/10/41)		45	35
	a reddish-choc (single) (/42)		45	35
S18/25	**set (8)**		1·50	2·00

The overprint on the 3d. and 1/– values is larger than that used for the others.

1942-5 War Effort ("Bantams"). Nos. S24–31 of South Africa, overprinted SWA. (Prices for units or pairs).

S26	½d. **blue-grn** (10/42) ..		10	10
	a upper background missing		2·00	2·50
	b background added		2·00	2·50
	c deep green		10	10
	d upper background missing		2·00	3 00
	e deep greenish-blue (44)		10	10
	f upper background missing		2 25	3·00
	g background added		2·50	3·00
S27	1d. **carmine** (1/43) ..		10	10
	a bt carmine (/45) ..		10	20
S28	1½d. **reddish-brn** (8/42)..		10	10
	a right side background missing ..		3·50	4·00
S29	2d. **pur-vio** (/43).. ..		25	25
	a violet (/45)		15	25
	b bt violet (/45) ..		20	25
	c overprint middle of stamp		3·00	3·00
S30	3d. **blue** (10/42)		20	30
	a dull blue (/44) ..		20	30
S31	4d. **sl-grn** (11/42) ..		30	35
	a overprint inverted ..		£125	—
	b blue-green (/44) ..		30	35
S32	6d. **dp or** (10/42) ..		35	50
	a o'print inverted ..		£200	—
	b dl orange (/45) ..		35	50
S33	1/– **choc** (large o'print) (12/42)		85	1·25
	a bursting shell ..		3·00	3·50
	b upper background missing		2·00	2·00
	c choc (small o'print) (/44)		70	65
	d bursting shell ..		3·00	3·50
	e upper background missing		2·00	2·00
	f o'print inverted ..		£200	£120
S26/33	**set** (8)		2·00	2·25

S32—Whilst somewhat similar the overprint on this stamp differs from S32*b* inasmuch as the S of the latter overprint is slightly broader than before and the W a fraction narrower. (*For details of varieties see corresponding set of South Africa*).

The overprint on the 1½d. and 1/– is in larger type (as used for S34).

1943-6 War Effort. No. S32 of South Africa, overprinted SWA.

S34	1/3 **ol-brn** (2/1/43) ..	1·00	1·00
	a dp ol-brn (/46) ..	1·00	1·00

1945 (Dec. 3rd) Victory. Nos. S33–5 of South Africa, overprinted SWA.

S35	1d. **dp brn and car** ..		5	10
	a o'print inverted ..		£85	—
	b aniline centre.. ..		—	—
	c barbed wire Row 9/6		—	—
S36	2d. **sl-blue and pur-vio** ..		5	10
S37	3d. **dp blue and blue** ..		10	15
S35/37	**set** (3)		20	35

1947 (Feb. 17th) Royal Visit. Nos. S36–38 of South Africa, overprinted SWA.

S38	1d. **dp slate and carmine**	5	5
S39	2d. **pur-vio** (Cyl. 6912) ..	5	5
S40	3d. **deep blue**	10	10
	a blinded princess ..	2·00	2·00
S38/40	**set** (3)	20	20

S39—See South Africa No. S37 for details.

1948 (April 26th) Silver Wedding. No S39 of South Africa, overprinted SWA.

S41	3d. **silver and dk blue** ..	5	5

1949 (Oct. 1st) U.P.U. Nos. S41-3 of South Africa, overprinted SWA.

S42	½d. **dp blue-grn** (Cyl. 60)	10	10
S43	1½d. **brownish-lake** ..	10	10
S44	3d. **bt ultramarine** ..	15	15
	a C var	2·50	2·50
S42/44	**set** (3)	30	30

S44*a*—See South Africa S43*a*.

Number overprinted (pairs)—½d., 847,440; 1½d., 847,380; 3d., 607,980.

1949 (Dec. 1st) Inauguration of Voortrekker Monument. Nos. S44–46 of South Africa, overprinted (*roto*) SWA (printed bi-lingually).

S45	1d. **lake-magenta** ..	5	10
S46	1½d. **dull green**	5	10
S47	3d. **dp slate-blue** ..	5	10
S45/47	**set** (3)	15	25

Number overprinted—1d., 924,240; 1½d., 850,000; 3d., 865,630.

OFFICIAL STAMPS

1938 (July 1st) No. 1 overprinted OFFICIAL and OFFISIEEL in red.

O1	1½d. **purple-brown** ..	1·00	1·50

Stamps with forged double overprint exist.

1945-50 Pictorial Issue of 1931, overprinted in red as No. O1 but in a smaller and thicker type

Printers *(recess)* **Bradbury, Wilkinson. Perf. 13¾ x 13½ (C).**

O2	½d. **blk and emer** (/45) ..	20	20
	a overprint deep red ..	2·00	2·00
O3	1d. **dk bl and scar** (/50)	20	20
O4	1½d. **pur-brown** (/45) ..	30	30
	a overprint double ..	£80	—
	b o'print dk red (/50)	2·00	2·00
O5	2d. **blue-blk and sepia brn** (/47)	£220	£220
O6	6d. **blue and ol-brown** (/45)	80	60
	a o'print dk red (/50)	3·00	3·00
O2/O6	**set** (5 pairs)	£220	£220

1951 (Nov. 15th) **As No. O3, etc., but overprint in changed fount.**

O8	1d. **dk blue and scar** ..	20	40
	a overprint transposed	5·00	5·00
	b block four, one pair normal one pair transposed ..	£15	£20
O9	1½d. **purple-brown** ..	40	50
	a overprint transposed	4·00	5·00
	b block of four, one pair normal one pair transposed ..	£20	£24

O10	2d. **blue-blk and sepia-brown**	75	1·00
	a overprint transposed	4·00	5·00
	b block of four, one pair normal one pair transposed ..	£12	£15
O11	6d. **dk blue and ol-brn**..	75	1·00
	a overprint transposed	5·00	5·00
	b block of four, one pair normal, one pair transposed	£15	£12
O8/O11	**set** (4) pairs	2·00	3·00

O8*a*, O9*a*, O10*a*, O11*a*—The overprint in English appears on stamps printed in Afrikaans and vice versa.

O8*b*, O9*b*, O10*b*, O11*b*—The transposed overprint occurs in two forms :—

(1) Each vertical row of 10 overprinted OFFICIAL or OFFISIEEL right down the row, i.e. column setting, this caused every alternate stamp to be transposed (values existing thus 1½d. and 6d.).

(2) Top half of sheet set correctly but row 6 across set as row above it. This caused the lower 5 rows of sheet to be set all transposed (values existing thus 1d., 1½d., 2d., and 6d.).

1952 As O8/O11 but overprint in thicker type in deep vermilion ink.

O12	½d. **black and green** ..	20	40
O13	1d. **blue and scarlet** ..	30	50
O14	1½d. **brown**	40	60
O15	2d. **blue and brown** ..	40	60
O16	6d. **blue and ol-brown**..	1·00	1·15
O12/16	**set** (5)	2·25	3·52

SOUTHERN NIGERIA

All issues *Typo.* **Printers, De La Rue & Co.**

1901/2 Wmk. Crown CA. Perf. 14. Sheets 120 – two panes, each 6 x 10.

V1	½d.	**brn, grey and pl grn** ..	25	25
	a	blk and pl green ..	20	20
V2	1d.	**brn, grey and rosine** ..	25	30
	a	blk and rosine ..	20	25
V3	2d.	**blk and chestnut** ..	1·20	1·00
V4	4d.	**blk and sage-grn** ..	1·50	1·75
V5	6d.	**black and purple** ..	1·50	1·75
V6	1/–	**green and black** ..	3·50	3·50
V7	2/6	**black and brown** ..	8·50	£10
V8	5/–	**black and yellow** ..	£25	£35
V9	10/–	**black and pur/yel** ..	£65	£70
V1/9		**set** (9)	£90	£100
SP V1/9		**specimen set** (9) ..	£60	‡

Numbers issued—V1, 202,560; V2, 204,480; V3, 25,440; V4, 20,880; V5, 20,640; V6/7, 10,560 each; V8, 5,520; V9, 2,880.

1903/4 Wmk. Crown CA. Perf. 14. Sheets as before.

E1	½d.	**grey, blk and pl grn**	25	20
E2	1d.	**grey, blk and rosine**	40	20
E3	2d.	**grey, blk and chest**	50	65
E4	2½d.	**grey, blk and br blue**	2·00	1·20
E5	4d.	**grey, blk and ol-grn**	1·00	1·25
E6	6d.	**grey, blk and dl pur**	4·00	5·50
E7	1/–	**grey, grn and blk** ..	4·50	4·00
E8	2/6	**grey, blk and brn** ..	5·50	7·00
	a	grey, blk and yel-brn	£40	£50
E9	5/–	**grey, blk and yellow**	£25	£28
E10	10/–	**grey, blk and pur/yel**	£25	£25
E11	£1	**green and violet** ..	£200	£250
E1/11		**set**	£250	£300
SP E1/11		**specimen set** (11) ..	£90	‡

Numbers issued—E1, 198,240; E2, 214,800; E3, 30,120; E4,20,160; E5, 24,840; E6, 19,680; E7, 9,840; E8, 10,080; E9, 5,040; E10, 11,040; E11, 1,080.

1904/8 Wmk. Mult. Crown CA. Perf. 14. Sheets as before.

E12	½d.	**grey and br grn** (O)	10	10
	a	grey, blk and yel-grn		
		(*ch*)	10	10

E13	1d.	**grey, blk and car**		
		(OC)	15	15
	a	booklet pane ..	£15	—
E14	2d.	**grey, blk and chest**		
		(O)	50	50
	a	grey and chest (O) ..	65	65
E15	2½d.	**grey, blk and bt blue**		
		(O)	60	65
E16	3d.	**or-brn and bt-pur**		
		(*ch*)	3·00	1·50
E17	4d.	**grey, blk and ol-grn**		
		(OC)	3·00	1·75
	a	grey, blk and pl ol-grn (*ch*)	2·00	4·00
E18	6d.	**grey, blk and bt pur**		
		(OC)	1·25	1·25
E19	1/–	**grey, grn and blk** (O)	1 00	1 00
	a	grey, grn and jet blk (*ch*)	1·50	1·50
E20	2/6	**grey, blk and brn**		
		(OC)	7·00	6·00
E21	5/–	**grey, blk and yel** (OC)	£11	£10
E22	10/–	**grey, blk and pur/yel**		
		(*ch*)	£60	£70
E23	£1	**grn and vio** (OC) ..	£65	£80
E12/23		**set** (12)	£130	£150
SP E 16		**specimen**	£10	‡

Numbers issued :—

	O	C
E12,	403,920	404,760
E13	427,560	465,840
E14,	189,000	—
E15,	66,480	—
E16,	—	101,760
E17,	6,360	60,840
E18,	16,680	127,920
E19,	65,100	121,920
E20,	6,360	39,720
E21,	6,240	18,720
E22,	—	12,480
E23,	1,200	5,280

62,400 (O) and 65,040 (C) of E13 were made up in Booklets.

I—Thick 1 and small d.

II—Thinner 1 and larger d.

1907/11 Wmk. Mult. Crown CA. Perf. 14. Sheets as before (except E26/26a – 12 x 20).

E24	½d.	**grey-green** (O) ..	35	15
	a	blue-green (O) ..	15	15
	b	booklet pane ..	£12	—
E25	1d.	**rose-car** (I) (O) ..	50	25
	a	booklet pane of 6 ..	£12	—
E26	1d.	**rose-car** (II) (O) ..	15	15
	a	car-red (II) (O) ..	15	15

E27	2d. **grey** (O)	70	50	
E28	2½d. **ultramarine** (O) ..	70	1·50	
E29	3d. **dl pur/yel** (*ch*) ..	60	45	
	a **dp pur/yel** (*ch*) ..	60	45	
E30	4d. **brn-grey on yel** (*ch*)	70	70	
E31	6d. **dl pur and pur** (*ch*)	2·00	1·25	
	a **dl and bt pur** (*ch*) ..	2·75	1·25	
E32	1/– **blk on grn** (*ch*) ..	2·25	85	
E33	2/6 **blk and red/blue** (*ch*)	3·00	1·25	
E34	5/– **grn and red/yel** (*ch*)	£17	£18	
E35	10/– **grn and red/grn** (*ch*)	£23	£25	
E36	£1 **pur and blk/red** (*ch*)	£60	£70	
E24/36	**set** (13)	£90	£100	
SP E24/36 **specimen set** (12)..		£110	‡	

Numbers issued—E24, 1,328,280; E25, 2,729,400; E26, 3,815,940; E27, 239,280; E28, 143,400; E29, 240,000; E30, 151,800; E31, 361,440; E32, 365,520; E33, 151,440; E34, 79,920; E35, 32,160; E36, 20,520.

61,080 of E24 and 912,600 of E25 were made up in Booklets.

1912 Wmk. Mult. CA. Perf. 14. Sheets as before.

G1	½d. **green**	20	20	
	a booklet pane of 6 ..	£10	—	
G2	1d. **red**	40	15	
	a booklet pane of 6 ..	£15	—	
G3	2d. **grey**	55	60	
G4	2½d. **bright blue** ..	75	1·00	
G5	3d. **dp purple/yellow** ..	50	40	
	a purple/orange, buff	50	40	
G6	4d. **blk and red/yel** ..	1·00	1·25	
G7	6d. **dl and bt purple** ..	1·25	60	
G8	1/– **black on green** ..	1·50	75	
G9	2/6 **blk and red/blue** ..	5·00	5·50	
G10	5/– **grn and red/yel** ..	£11	£12	
G11	10/– **grn and red/grn** ..	£27	£30	
G12	£1 **pur and blk/red** ..	£60	£75	
G1/12	**set** (12)	£105	£120	
SP G1/12 **specimen set** (12)..		£120	‡	

Numbers issued—G1, 797,160; G2, 1,893,660; G3,151,800; G4, 112,080; G5, 183,960; G6, 90,960; G7, 224,160; G8, 242,880; G9, 30,480; G10, 30,120; G11, 18,000; G12, 12,600.

For later issues see NIGERIA.

SOUTHERN RHODESIA

For details of the early Postal History and previous stamp issues see under RHODESIA.

All stamps were printed (*recess*) by Waterlow & Sons on unwatermarked paper unless otherwise mentioned.

1924 (April 1st)-1930. Perf. 14 (line). No wmk. Sheets 240 – 4 panes 10 x 6 (G1–G3); G4/G14 10 x 6.

G1	½d.	**deep blue-green** ..	15	10
	a	green	15	10
	b	horizontal pair imperf between ..	£250	—
	c	vertical pair imperf between..	£300	—
	d	tete beche strip of six	—	‡
G2	1d.	**rose-carmine** ..	15	10
	aa	pale rose ..	20	10
	a	coil perf 12½ ..	6·00	£10
	b	scarlet ..	20	10
	ba	imperf pair.. ..	£350	—
	c	coil perf 12½ ..	6·00	£10
	d	horizontal pair imperf between ..	£250	—
	e	vertical pair imperf between.. ..	£300	—
	f	tete beche strip of six	—	‡
G3	1½d.	**bistre-brown** ..	30	15
	a	dp bistre-brown ..	30	15
	b	horizontal pair imperf between ..	£850	—
	c	vertical pair imperf between.. ..	£850	—
	d	double impression on reverse ..	—	—
G4	2d.	**blk and pur-grey** ..	50	25
	a	blk and sl-pur ..	60	25
	b	horizontal pair imperf between ..	£1250	—
G5	3d.	**blue**	1·00	60
	a	indigo blue ..	1·50	60
	aa	pale blue ..	1·50	60
	b	imperf pair.. ..	£650	—
G6	4d.	**black and orange** ..	1·25	1·25
	a	black, red orange ..	1·25	1·25
G7	6d.	**black and mauve** ..	1·50	80
	a	blk, bt mauve ..	1·50	70
	ab	blk, violet mauve ..	2·00	1·00
	b	horizontal pair imperf between ..	£1250	—
G8	8d.	**purple and green** ..	4·00	4·50
	a	pale pur and grn ..	4·50	4·50
G9	10d.	**blue, rose** ..	4·50	4·50
	a	bt blue, pl rose ..	5·00	4·50
G10	1/-	**black, turquoise** ..	3·50	2·00
	a	blk, greenish blue..	4·00	2·00

	b	black, pale blue ..	3·50	2·00
	c	black, deep blue ..	3·50	2·00
G11	1/6	**black, yellow** ..	6·00	8·00
	a	blk, or-yel ..	6·00	8·00
	b	horizontal pair imperf between ..	—	—
G12	2/-	**black and brown**	£10	£10
	a	black, deep brown	£12	£10
G13	2/6	**blue and blk-brn** ..	£18	£20
	aa	blue, slate brn ..	£20	£20
	a	horizontal pair imperf between ..	—	—
G14	5/-	**blue and blue-green**	£35	£40
	a	blue and pale green	£35	£40
	b	deep blue and deep blue-green ('28)	£1750	—
G1–14		**set ½d.–5/– (14v)** ..	£75	£85

Imperforate marginal copies of the ½d., 1d., 1½d. exist from normal sheets which have not been perforated on the wing margins. These varieties are worth three or four times normal, but should not be confused with the rare imperforate between errors.

G1d, G2f—Booklet (tete beche) printings of G1 (600,000) and G2 (1,200,000) were made in 1927; sheets, two panes each 6 x 10 (horizontal rows – 3 normal, 3 inverted).

Numbers printed (all printings): the number of printings is shown in brackets—G1 (7), 28,000,000; G2 (7), 41,905, 080; G3 (3), 15,615,000; G4 (6), 2,621,980; G5 (6), 1,421,020; G6 (4), 550,000; G7 (5), 1,780,000 (plus 1927 printing); G8 (3), 248,000; G9 (3), 248,000; G10 (7), 1,839,020; G11 (3), 728,000; G12 (5), 815,000; G13 (5), 390,240; G14 (1), 33,000; G14b (1), 240.

Ex The Waterlow Archive.

1. Sold by De La Rue, 1971/73. The Archive consists of imperf. proof sheets (with Security Hole in each stamp) in issued colours ½d.–5/– complete Head and Frame, and K.G.V Head only values 2d.–5/– (perf.). Price complete set in pairs ½d.–5/– (20 pairs) £400—Individual pairs from £25 each.

2. Trial Printings also exist:— ½d., 1d., G1d., G2f—Tete Beche (imperf. and perf.). 1d., 3d., G2ba, G5b Imperf. pairs no security hole. Also imperf. between ½d., 1d., 1½d. in both vertical and horizontal pairs from £50 each. G14b 5/– Deep blue and deep blue green.

3. Waterlow perforated printers samples o/printed "Specimen" ½d. brown, 2d. black and red, 2d. black and lilac—set of 3—£45.

K.G. V Admiral Large Type Revenue Design.
3/–. 7/6d., 10/–, £1, £5, £10, £20 Cw GR1/7— Price £50; Waterlow Archive imperf. plate proofs in issued colours in pairs Head and Head & Frame (14 pairs)—£250; Normally perf. stamps (with security hole) 3/– – £30 (7)—£45.

1931-1937 Printed (*recess*) by Bradbury Wilkinson. Line perf. 12. Sheets 6 x 10 (except

G15/16/17 – 240 – four panes, each 10 x 6).

G15	½d.	**green**	10	05
		a booklet pane of six	£12	—
G16	1d.	**red**	15	10
		a booklet pane of six	£15	—
G17	1½d.	**deep brown**	£20	£22
		a booklet pane of six	£100	—
G18	4d.	**black, orange-red** ..	1·20	25
		a black, bt orange ..	1·35	25
G19	6d.	**black, rose-lilac** ..	1·50	15
		a black, purple-lilac..	1·75	15
G20	8d.	**violet and dp green**	2·50	2·00
		a purple. olive-green	3·00	2·00
G21	9d.	**vermilion and olive**	5·50	5·00
G22	10d.	**bt blue and lake** ..	3·50	2·50
		a blue, scarlet-lake ..	4·00	2·50
G23	1/–	**black, greenish-blue**	3·50	60
		a black, slate-green..	4·00	60
G24	1/6	**blk and or-yel** ..	6·50	8·00
		a blk, chrome-yellow	7·50	8·00
G25	2/–	**black and brown** ..	5·00	5·00
G26	2/6	**blue, grey-brown** ..	£10	£10
G27	5/–	**blue, blue-green** ..	£22	£20
		a printed on gummed side	£1100	—

G27*a* A complete sheet of sixty is reported to exist.

1933 Perf. 11½ (comb).

G28	½d.	**green**	10	05
		a yellow-green ..	20	05
G29	1d.	**red**	30	05
G30	1½d.	**deep brown**	35	15
		a yellow brown ..	40	15
G31	4d.	**black, br orange** ..	6·00	1·50
G32	6d.	**black, purple-lilac**..	4·50	30
G33	6d.	**purple, olive-green**	8·00	8·00
G34	10d.	**blue and scar-lake**	4·00	4·00
G35	1/–	**blk and slate green**	6·50	4·50
G36	1/6	**blk and chrome yel**	£20	£20
G37	2/–	**black and brown** ..	£20	£14
G38	2/6	**blue and sepia-grey brown**	£20	£12

1935-37 Perf. 14 line.

G39	½d.	**green**	15	10
		a blue-green	20	10
G40	1d.	**red**	20	10
G41	4d.	**blk and bt orange** ..	£10	£12
G42	6d.	**blk and pur-lilac** ..	7·00	1·00
		a black and rose-lilac	8·00	1·00
G43	1/–	**blk and slate-green**	£75	£60

1931 (April 1st) Victoria Falls. Perf. 15 x 14 (comb). (*Typo*) **Waterlow. Sheets 6 x 10.**

G44	2d.	**grey and grey brown**	2·00	1·75
G45	3d.	**bright blue**	4·50	5·00
G15/45		**set** ½d.–5/– (15 val cheapest perf) ..	£65	£60

1932 (May 2nd) Victoria Falls. Perf. 12½ (L). Sheets 6 x 10.

G46	2d.	**green and chocolate**	40	15
G47	3d.	**deep bright blue** ..	2·00	75
		a vertical pair imperf between	£1800	£2250

G47*a* One sheet of 30 pairs is known, some stamps damaged. Two used pairs are reported.

Numbers printed—G46, 5,000,000; G47, 3,000,000·

Falls Waterlow Archive imperf. proofs.

2d. Frame, Vignette, complete design (3 singles)— £40; 3d. complete (1 stamp)—£20.

Waterlow perforated printers samples o/printed "Specimen" 2d. Grey-green and purple, 2d. Crystal and mauve, 3d. black and slate.

1935 (May 6th) Silver Jubilee. Perf. 11 x 12. Sheets 6 x 10.

G48	1d.	**olive and carmine** ..	15	15
G49	2d.	**em-green and sepia**	50	70
G50	3d.	**violet and dark blue**	1·75	2·25
G51	6d.	**black and purple** ..	2·50	2·50
G48/51		**set** (4)..	4·50	5·00

Numbers issued—G48, 6,822,000; G49, 520,440; G50, 235,440; G51, 549,540.

Withdrawn 31/12/35.

1935 Jubilee Waterlow Archive imperf. proofs.

1. 1d, 2d, 3d, 6d. Vignette singles (Victoria Falls) (4)—£200; 1d., 2d., 3d., 6d. Combined Vignette & Frame (8 pairs)—£500.

2. Waterlow perforated printers samples o/printed "Specimen" 1d. Purple, 1d. Purple-brown and blue, 2d. Grey-green and purple, 3d. Purple and brown (4)—£40.

1937 (Nov. 25th)-50. Perf. 14 (L). Sheets

10 x 6 (except Nos. 1–3; 340 – four panes, each 10 x 6).

1	½d.	**yellow-green**	05	05
	a	green (/50)..	05	05
	aa	booklet pane of 6 ..	—	—
2	1d.	**red**	05	05
	a	booklet pane of 6 ..	£12	—
	aa	pair imperf at right between stamp and margin	£125	—
3	1½d.	**reddish-brown** ..	05	10
	a	dp red-brn (/45) ..	05	10
4	4d.	**deep orange**	10	10
5	6d.	**dark grey**	15	10
6	8d.	**turquoise-green** ..	40	20
7	9d.	**light blue**	25	15
8	10d.	**purple**	35	1·00
9	1/–	**black and green** ..	20	10
	a	double print of frame	£100	—
10	1/6	**black and dp orange**	70	60
11	2/–	**black and dp brown**..	75	25
12	2/6	**dp ult and purple** ..	1·25	50
13	5/–	**dp blue and green** ..	2·50	75
1/13		**set (13)**	6·00	3·50

Later printings of all values exist on a much thinner paper than original 1937 printings.

Withdrawn June, 30th 1954.

1937 K.G. VI Waterlow Archive imperf. proofs.

1/–, 1/6d., 2/–, 2/6d., 5/– (Frame only) (5 pairs)— £120; ½d.–5/– Combined designs (13 pairs)—£300.

1937 K.G. VI Waterlow Archive imperf. proofs Revenue Type.

1. Large Portrait 3/–, 7/6d., 10/–, £1, £2, £5, £10, £20, £50, (18 pairs)—£100;

   3/– to £50 normally perforated Cw R8/R16— Price £50.

2. Waterlow printers sample o/printed "Specimen" Small design—6d. Sepia; Large (Revenue) design—7/6d. Magenta and 10/– Brown—set (3)—£8.

1935-41 Design, View of Victoria Falls (with Inscription Postage and Revenue). Perf. 14 (I).

14	2d.	**dp grn and choc** (/41)	10	10
	a	(/35) dp grn and choc P.12½	1·00	1·00
15	3d.	**dark blue** (1/38) ..	25	15

1950 As No. 14 but Perf. 14 x 13¾ (C).

16	2d.	**dp green and lt choc**	15	15

SPECIAL ISSUES

1937 (May 12th) Coronation. Design, Victoria Falls with Train in Foreground. Perf. 12½ (L). Sheets 6 x 10.

S1	1d.	**olive-grn and rose-car**	15	15
S2	2d.	**emerald and sepia** ..	15	15
	a	imperf (pair)	£400	—
S3	3d.	**pur-violet and blue** ..	90	1·25
	a	imperf. (top margin)	—	—
S4	6d.	**black and purple** ..	60	60
S1/4		**set (4)**	1·50	2·00

S2a is from a single sheet from Waterlow Archives.

Number issued—1d., 3,587,294; 2d., 932,710; 3d., 370,440; 6d., 480,588. Withdrawn August 31st, 1937.

Coronation Waterlow Archive imperf. proofs.

1d., 2d., 3d. Vignette singles (Railway Train) (3)— £120; 1d., 2d., 3d. Vignette, 1d., 2d., 6d. Combined vignette & frame (6 pairs)—£400; (6d. Vignette, 3d. combined may not exist).

Waterlow perforated printers samples o/printed "Specimen" 1d. Brown and violet, 1d. Orange and black, 1d. Bl-green and black, 4d. Black and blue-green. Price £40.

1940 (June 3rd) B.S.A. Company's Golden Jubilee. Designs, ½d. (Arms of Company); 1½d. (Cecil Rhodes); other values (Views and Scenes in Territory). Designers, Mrs. L. E. Curtis (½d., 1d., 1½d., 3d.), Mrs. I. Mount (other values); Rhode's portrait, S. P. Kendrick. Perf. 14 (L). Designs, 1½d., 4d., 6d. V. Sheets 10 x 6 or 6 x 10.

S5	½d.	**grey-vio and grn** ..	10	05
S6	1d.	**vio-slate and red** ..	10	05
S7	1½d.	**blk and choc-brn** ..	10	05
	a	shaded collar ..	£10	£10
S8	2d.	**green and violet** ..	10	10
S9	3d.	**black and dp blue** ..	15	15
S10	4d.	**green and lt brown** ..	25	40
S11	6d.	**grey-green and sepia**	35	55
S12	1/–	**grn and dp steel-blue**	45	70
S5/12		**set (8)**	1·50	1·75

S7a Shading lines on left collar Row 6/1.

Numbers printed—S5, 7,012,000; S6, 9,734,000; S7 3,239,000; S8, 168,000; S9, 363,000;

S10, 200,000; S11, 350,000; S12, 282,000. Withdrawn Oct. 31st, 1944.

1940 B.S.A. Jubilee Waterlow Archive imperf. proofs.

½d., 1d., 1½d., 2d., 3d., 4d., 6d., 1/– Vignette or frame (8 singles)—£125; ½d., 1d., 1½d., 2d., 3d., 4d., 6d., 1/– Complete design in pairs (8 pairs)—£300.

1943 (Nov. 1st) 50th Anniversary of Occupation of Matabeleland. Printers (roto) Govt. Stamp Printers, Pretoria. Wmk. "Springbok's Head" sideways. Perf 14 (C). Sheets 10 x 6.

S13	2d.	**brown and dp green**	10	10
	a	sepia-brn and dp grn	10	10

The 8th stamp in each of the six rows is narrower (1mm.) than other stamps on most sheets, as occurs also with stamps of South Africa which were similarly perforated.

Withdrawn Oct. 31st, 1944.

1947 (April 1st) Royal Visit. Designs, Portraits of Royal Family. Perf. 14 (L). Sheets 6 x 10.

S14	½d.	**black and green**	..	10	10
S15	1d.	**black and car-red**	..	10	10

Withdrawn April 30th, 1947.

1947 Royal Visit Waterlow Archive imperf. proofs.

½d. & 1d. Frame only pairs—£80; ½d. & 1d. Combined centre and frame (pairs)£80; Waterlow printers sample o/printed "Specimen" ½d. Black and ochre, 1d. Black and blue (2)—£18.

1947 (May 8th) Victory. Design, Portraits of

Royal Family. Perf. 14 (L). Sheets S16, 240 – four panes, each 10 x 6; S17/19, 10 x 6.

S16	1d.	**carmine-red**	..	..	10	10
S17	2d.	**slate**	..	..	10	10
	a	frame double print, one albino	..	..	—	—
	b	part double print	..	£225	—
S18	3d.	**deep blue**	..	..	15	15
S19	6d.	**orange**	..	..	15	15
S16/19	**set** (4)	..	..	..	50	50

S17*b* The top and right hand side of the Head, frame at right and part of top lettering are doubled.

Withdrawn Nov. 8th, 1947

1947 Victory Waterlow Archive imperf. proofs.

1d., 2d., 3d., 6d (4 pairs)—£100; Waterlow printers sample o/printed "Specimen' 1d. Blue-green, 2d. Brown, 3d. Brown, 6d. Olive (4)—£30.

1949 (Oct. 10th) U.P.U. As Aden No. S9–10, but inscribed Southern Rhodesia. Sheets 5 x 12.

S20	2d.	**green-slate**	..	..	10	10
S21	3d.	**slate-blue**	..	..	30	35

Withdrawn Jan. 10th, 1950.

1950 (Sept. 12th) Diamond Jubilee of Colony. Perf. 14 (L). Sheets 5 x 12.

S22	2d.	**em and grey-sepia**	..	15	10

Number issued—2,819,032. (Printed—4,650,000)

Withdrawn Dec. 31st, 1950.

1950 Diamond Jubilee Waterlow Archive imperf. proofs.

2d. Frame only single—£25; 2d. Complete design pair—£40.

POSTAGE DUE STAMPS

1951 (Oct. 1st) Postage Due Stamps of Great Britain, overprinted Southern Rhodesia.

PD1	½d.	**emerald-green**	..		10	15
PD2	1d.	**cobalt**	..	..	20	25
PD3	2d.	**agate** ..		..	20	30
PD4	3d.	**violet** ..		..	25	40
PD5	4d.	**grey-green**	..	..	£48	£55
PD6	4d.	**light blue**	..	..	30	40
PD7	1/–	**blue**	..	..	60	75
PD1/7	**set** (7)	..	..	..	£48	£55

Number overprinted—½d., 222,720; 1d., 671,040; 2d., 229,120; 3d., 922,880; 4d. PD5, 109,680; PD6, 1,839,360; 1/–, 672,240.

SUDAN

The territory was originally acquired by Egypt, and Egyptian stamps without overprint were used from 1874.

Following the revolt led by the Mahdi in 1882 the garrisons were withdrawn, until the territory was reoccupied from March 1897. An Anglo-Egyptian Condominium was proclaimed in 1899.

Although the overprinted stamps were issued in March 1897, Egyptian stamps without overprint are known used as late as October 23rd, 1899.

1897 (March 1st) Stamps of Egypt (1884 1888 and 1893 Sphinx and Pyramid). Wmk. Star and Crescent, overprinted "SOUDAN" in Arabic and French at Imprimerie Nationale Bulaq, Cairo in panes of 60 (10 x 6).

V1	1m.	**yellow-brown** ..	75	1·00
		a strip of six ..	£20	—
		b overprint inverted	£180	—
V2	1m.	**deep-brown** ..	1·00	1·00
		a strip of six	£20	—
V3	2m.	**yellow-green** ..	1·20	1·30
		a strip of six ..	£25	—
V4	2m.	**blue-green** ..	1·50	1·80
		a strip of six ..	£25	—
V5	3m.	**yellow**	1·20	1·30
		a strip of six	£25	—
V6	3m.	**orange-yellow** ..	1·50	1·80
		a strip of six ..	£25	—
V7	5m.	**carmine-rose** ..	2·00	2·00
		a strip of six ..	£30	—
		b overprint inverted	£180	—
V8	1p.	**ultramarine** ..	3·50	4·00
		a strip of six ..	£60	—
V9	1p.	**pale ultramarine** ..	·4·00	4·00
		a strip of six	£60	—
V10	2p.	**orange-brown** ..	£17	£12
		a strip of six ..	£220	—
V11	2p.	**dp orange-brown** ..	£17	£12
		a strip of six ..	£220	—
V12	5p.	**slate**	£18	£12
		a strip of six ..	£225	—
		b overprint double ..	—	—
V13	10p.	**mauve**	£20	£25
		a strip of six ..	£250	—
V1/13		**set** (8v)	£60	£57

(a) Six varieties of type are found in each vertical strip of six.

Type:

i. Right hand Arabic letter short and placed high.

ii. The same letter is lower. 3rd from right lower than 4th.

iii. Right hand Arabic letter lower still and closer to next.

iv. Right hand Arabic letter spaced further away.

v. The same letter is lower still but closer.

vi. Third letter from right is broken off short.

(b) A number of minor varieties, caused by broken type, exist on all values.

(c) Only one used copy of V12b is known, in the Royal Collection.

(d) The 1m, 5m. and 5p. are known with overprint omitted in pair with normal.

(c) Part of the stock of unsold remainders was overprinted 'TEL' and used as Telegraph stamps.

All stamps of Sudan, except where otherwise stated, were printed by De La Rue and Co.

 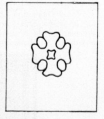

1898 (March 1st) (*Typo*). Wmk. Rosette. Perf. 14. Designer Co. E. A. Stanton. Sheets 120 — two panes, each 12 x 5.

V14	1m.	**brown and pink** ..	30	25
V15	2m.	**green and brown**	75	1·00

V16	3m.	mauve and green	75	1·00
V17	5m.	carmine and blk	40	25
V18	1p.	blue and brown	2·00	1·50
V19	2p.	black and blue ..	4·50	2·00
V20	5p.	brown and green	6·00	4·50
V21	10p.	black and mauve	8·00	4·50
V14/21		set (8v)	£22	£10

The 2p. is recorded bisected and used as 1p.

1902-21 (Typo). Wmk. Multiple Star and Crescent. Perf. 14. Sheets as before.

E1	1m.	brown and car ..	10	10
E2	2m.	green and brown	20	15
E3	3m.	mauve and green	50	20
E4	4m.	blu and bistre (1/07)	40	1·00
E5	4m.	ver and brn (10/07)	1·00	1·00
E6	5m.	scarlet and black..	70	10
E7	1p.	blue and brown ..	1·20	20
E8	2p.	blk and blue	5·00	1·50
E9	2p.	pur and or-yel (12/21) ..	1·00	1·00
E10	5p.	brown and green ..	3·00	75
E11	10p.	black and mauve ..	7·50	1·25
E1/11		set (11v)	£20	7·00

E9 is known only on Chalky paper. E10 and E11 exist on both ordinary and Chalky paper.

1903 (Sept.) V20 surcharged "5 Milliemes" in blocks of 30 stamps at Khartoum.

E12	5m./5p.	brn and grn ..	1·50	2·50
		a surcharge inverted ..	£125	£200

60,000 copies were surcharged, of which 180 copies (six blocks of 30) had the surcharge inverted.

1921-22 (Typo). Chalk surfaced paper. Wmk. Multiple Star and Crescent. Perf. 14. Sheets 240 – four panes, each 6 x 10.

G1	1m.	black and orange	30	40
G2	2m.	yel-or and choc ..	2·00	1·50
G3	3m.	mauve and green	1·00	1·00
G4	4m.	green and choc ..	1·00	1·00
G5	5m.	ol-brn and blk	70	10
G6	10m.	carmine and black	1·00	15
G7	15m.	br blu and chestnut (12/21)	1·50	1·00
G1/7		set (7v)	7·50	5·00

1927-40 (Typo). Wmk. Multiple "SG". Perf. 14. Small format 1m.–15m., large format 2p.–20p.

G8	1m.	black and orange..	10	10
G9	2m.	orange and choc ..	10	10
G10	3m.	mauve and green	10	10
G11	4m.	green and choc ..	10	10
G12	5m.	brown and black ..	10	10
G13	10m.	red and black	15	10
G14	15m.	blue and chestnut	15	10
G15	2p.	purple and yellow	30	20
		a (sub)	15	10
G16	3p.	red-brn and blue ..	50	25
		a (sub)	25	15
G17	4p.	ult and grey ..	25	10
G18	5p.	chest and green ..	60	10
		a (sub)	30	10
G19	6p.	grn-blue and blk ..	60	15
		a (sub)	80	20
G20	8p.	emerald and black	1·00	40
		a (sub)	—	—
G21	10p.	black and violet ..	80	30
		a (sub)	—	—
G22	20p.	pl blue and blue ..	2·40	40
		a (sub)	1·20	40
G8/22		set (15)	5·00	2·40

G8/14 exist on sub and chalky paper, price same either way.

1931 Air Stamps. G12, G13 and G15 overprinted "AIR MAIL".

G23	5m.	brn and blk (March 1st)	1·00	1·50
G24	10m.	red and blk (Feb. 15th)	1·25	1·75
G25	2p.	pur and yel (Feb 15th)	1·50	2·50
		a raised "R" ..	4·00	5·00

G25a The raised "R" in "AIR" is constant on Nos. 3, 6, 9, 12, 30, 33, 36, 51, 54, 57 and 60 in the sheet.

Numbers Sold—G23, 70,193; G24, 56,822; G25, 55,908.

1931 (Aug. 22nd)-1935 Air Stamps. (Recess)

Wmk. Multiple "SG". Perf. 14. Designers, Lady Rugman and Mr. Hulbert. Sheets 5 x 10.

G26	3m.	grn and brn (1/1/33)	2·50	3·00
G27	5m.	black and green ..	1·00	1·00
G28	10m.	black and red	1·50	1·50
G29	15m.	brown and sepia ..	80	70
		a wmk. inverted ..	—	—
G30	2p.	black and orange	50	50
G31	2½p.	magenta and blue (1/1/33)	1·50	80
G32	3p.	black and grey ..	1·00	1·00
G33	3½p.	black and violet ..	1·75	2·00
G34	4½p.	brown and grey ..	8·00	9·00
G35	5p.	black and ult ..	2·50	2·50
G36	7½p.	myr-grn and tur-grn (17/10/35) ..	3·50	4·00
G37	10p.	dp sepia and grnish-blue (17/10/35)	6·00	3·00
G26/37		set (12)	£30	£29

Numbers Printed—3m., 46,606; 5m., 134,717; 10m., 109,477; 15m. and 2½p., 380,000 each; 2p. 140,000; 3p., 120,000; 3½p., 45,000; 4½p., 21,295; 5p., 60,000; 7½p. and 10p., 35,000 each.

1932 (July 18th) Air Stamp. G15 surcharged "2¼" in English and Arabic and overprinted "AIR MAIL".

G38	2½p./2p.	pur and yel ..	5·00	6·00

Numbers Sold—30,465.

1935 (Jan. 1st) 50th Anniversary of General Gordon's death. (Recess). Wmk. Multiple "SG". Perf. 14. Sheets 10 x 5 or 5 x 10.

G39	5m.	green	50	40
G40	10m.	yellow-brown ..	60	60
G41	13m.	ultramarine ..	1·50	2·75
G42	15m.	scarlet	1·00	1·00
G43	2p.	blue	1·00	1·00
G44	5p.	orange-ver ..	1·75	1·75
G45	10p.	purple	4·25	4·00
G46	20p.	black	£20	£22
G47	50p.	red-brown ..	£50	£55
G39/47		set (9v)	£80	£85

Numbers Sold—5m., 821,095; 10m., 78,678; 13m., 25,210; 15m., 70,856; 2p., 55,829; 5p., 21,087; 10p., 13,821; 20p., 7,225; 50p., 5,501.

1935 (March-April) Air Stamps. G28, G26, G27 and G34 surcharged in English and Arabic at Khartoum.

G48	15m./10m.	blk and red	80	1·00
		a surcharge double ..	£450	£475
G49	2½p./3m.	grn and brn	1·75	3·00
		a penultimate Arabic letter omitted ..	£45	£45
		b small "½"	6·00	8·00
G50	2½p./5m.	blk and grn	1·00	1·50
		a penultimate Arabic letter omitted ..	£45	£45
		b small "½"	5·00	6·00
		c surcharge inverted	£450	£475
		d surcharge inverted with variety "a"	—	—
		e surcharge inverted with variety "b"	—	—
G51	3p./4½p.	brn and grey	3·00	5·00
G52	7½p./4½p.	brn and grey	6·00	7·00
G53	10p./4½p.	brn and grey	5·00	7·00
G48/53		set (6v) ..	£17	£24

One sheet (50) each of G48a and G50c were printed and a number of copies sold.

G49a and G50a occur on No. 49 only.

G49b and G50b are constant on Nos. 17, 27, 32 36, 41, 42 and 46.

NORMAL

LETTER OMITTED

SMALL ½

Numbers Sold—15m., 58,300; 2½p. (on 3m.) 24,050; 2½p. (on 5m.), 47,750; 3p., 16,000; 7½p. and 10p., 10,000 each.

1937 Air Stamps. As G29–G33 and G35–G37 but Perf. 11¾ x 12½.

G54	15m.	chocolate and b/n (4/3/37)	1·00	60
G55	2p.	blk and dp orange	7·50	9·00
G56	2½p.	mag and blue (/36)	1·00	1·00

G57	3p.	**black and grey** (4/3/37)	3·00	2·50
G58	3½p.	**blk and dl violet** ..	6·00	7·00
G59	5p.	**blk and ult** (4/3/37)	2·00	2·00
G60	7½p.	**myr-grn and tur-grn**	3·50	3·50
G61	10p.	**deep sepia and greenish-blue** ..	4·00	4·50
G54/61		**set (8)**	£28	£30

Numbers Sold—15m., 90,000; 2p., 3½p., 7½p., 10p., 15,000 each. 2½p., 175,000; 3p., 120,000; 5p., 48,000.

1938 (July 1st) Air Stamps. G31, 33, 36, 37 and G58, G60 and G61 surcharged in English and Arabic by De La Rue.

(a) Perf. 14 (L).

G62	3p./3½p.	**blk and dl vio** ..	5·00	6·00
G63	3p./7½p.	**myr-grn and tur-grn**	1·00	1·50
G64	5p./10p.	**deep sepia and greenish-blue**	1·50	2·00

(b) Perf. 11¾ + 12½ (C).

G65	5m./2½p.	**mag and blue** ..	40	50
G66	3p./3½p.	**blk and dl vio** ..	£200	£200
G67	3p./7½p.	**myr-grn and tur-grn**	£200	£200
G68	5p./2½p.	**mag and blue**	£175	—
G69	5p./10p.	**deep sepia and greenish-blue**	£200	£220

One sheet of G68 was surcharged, in error, "5 Piastres".

Numbers Sold—P14, 3p. (on 3½p.), 17,650; 3p. (on 7½p.) 37,750; 5p., 32,400.

P11¾ x 12½, 5m., 171,350; 3p. (on 3½p.); 3p. (on 7½p.), 5p., 100 each.

1940-41 Forces Mail Provisionals. G13, G12 and G20 surcharged in English and Arabic (4½p. on 5m. in English only) at Khartoum.

2	5m./10m.	**red and blk (C)** (25/2/40)	15	30
		a extra Arabic "M"	7·00	8·00

		b missing dots ..	7·00	8·00
		c missing Arabic "L"	7·00	8·00
		d inserted "5" ..	£40	—
3	4½p./5m.	**brn and black (sub)** (9/2/41)	6·00	4·00
4	4½p./8p.	**em and blk (sub)** (12/12/40) ..	6·00	4·00

NORMAL   EXTRA "M"   MISSING "L"

2*a* An extra "M" makes the Arabic read "MIL-MEEM (Row 5/1, upper left pane of 60).

2*b* The two diamond-shaped dots below the Arabic are missing (Row 8/6., upper right pane of 60).

2*c* The up-stroke of the Arabic "L" is missing (Row 10/1 upper right pane of 60).

2*d* The "5" of the surcharge was inserted by a second operation on a small number of sheets (Row 4/5, lower right pane of 60).

Numbers Sold—No. 2, 191,040; No. 3, 60,000; No. 4, 119,700.

1941 (Mar.-Aug.) Design, Nile Scene near Khartoum. Designer, Miss H. M. Hebbert. Printers (*litho*) **Security Press, Nasik, India. Perf. 14 x 13¾ (C)** (*small format*)**. Perf. 13¾ x 14 (C)** (*large format*)**. No wmk.** (*An emergency issue made necessary by difficulty of obtaining supplies of normal issue from Great Britain owing to the war*)**. Sheets, small format, 120 – six panes, each 4 x 5; large format 10 x 8.**

5	1m.	**slate and orange** ..	10	40
6	2m.	**or and choc-brn** ..	25	40
7	3m.	**mauve and green**..	20	15
8	4m.	**sl-green and choc-brown**	10	25
9	5m.	**ol-brn and blk** ..	10	10
10	10m.	**crim-rose and blk**	2·50	2·00
11	15m.	**ult and chestnut** (25/3/41)	10	10
12	2p.	**pur-mar and or** ..	3·00	2·00
13	3p.	**red-brn and dk blue** (25/3/41)	75	20
14	4p.	**ultramarine and blk** (23/3/41)	50	30
15	5p.	**red-chest and dp grn**	3·50	3·50
16	6p.	**grn-blue and blk** ..	5·00	2·00
17	8p.	**dl em-grn and blk**	5·00	2·50
18	10p.	**dp slate and pur** ..	£14	5·00
19	20p.	**dl blue and dk blue**	£16	£15
5/19		**set (15)**	£45	£33

The 4p. value has been seen with frame double; and other values are reported to exist in similar state. Such double prints frequently appear on stamps printed offset-litho at Nasik.

Numbers Sold—(Issue date 25/3/41) 15m., 422,400; 3p., 306,800; 4p., 115,580.

(Issue date 10/8/41) 1m., 2m., 52,680 each; 3m., 51,480; 4m., 51,120; 5m., 2,051,520; 10m., 31,680; 2p., 52,080; 5p., 10p., 21,600 each; 6p., 21,840; 8p., 22,000; 20p., 10,960.

1948 (Jan. 1st) Design, as No. G8, etc., but with Inscription on Bottom Panel corrected to read "BARIID AL SUDAN" instead of "BOSTA SUDANIYA" (Sudan Postage). Sheets, small format, 10 x 10; large format, 10 x 5.

20	1m.	black and orange	10	10
21	2m.	orange and choc	10	10
22	3m.	mauve and dp grn	10	10
23	4m.	grn and choc-brn	10	10
24	5m.	ol-brn and blk ..	10	10
25	10m.	dl rose and blk ..	10	10
		a centre inverted	—	—
26	15m.	ult and red-chest	15	10
27	2p.	pur mar and or ..	30	15
28	3p.	red-brn and dk blue ..	30	15
29	4p.	ult and black ..	40	30
30	5p.	dl or and grey-grn	60	40
31	6p.	tur-blue and blk..	50	50
32	8p.	tur-grn and blk (sub) ..	60	80
33	10p.	grey-blk and pur-mauve (sub) ..	80	80
		a blk and red-mauve (*ch*) (6/48) ..	—	—
34	20p.	blue and dp blue (sub) ..	2·00	1·00
35	50p.	car-red and ult ..	3·00	2·25
20/35		set (16)	9·00	7·00

25*a* One used damaged copy is known to exist.

1948 (June) As No. 34 but Perf. 13¼ x 13 (C) and printed on chalk paper.

35A	20p.	blue and dp blue ..	£13	—

1951 (Sept. 1st) Designs, Scenes, Customs, and Fauna of Sudan. Designers, Col. W. L. Atkinson (1m., 2m., 4m., 5m., 10m., 3p., 3½p., 20p.); Col. E. A. Stanton (50p.); Other Values from photographs. Printers (*typo*) De La Rue. 1m. to 15m., Perf. 13¾ x 14 (C). Other Values. Perf. 13¼ x 13 (C). Chalk-coated paper. Designs, 2p., 3p., 3½p., 4p., 5p., 6p., 8p., 10p., 20p. H. Sheets, small format, 10 x 10; large format, 5 x 10 or 10 x 5.

36	1m.	black and orange	10	10
37	2m.	black and blue ..	10	10
38	3m.	black and green..	20	25
39	4m.	black and lt green	10	10
40	5m.	black and purple	10	10
41	10m.	black and azure	10	10
42	15m.	black and lt red ..	10	10
43	2p.	dk blue and lt blue	15	10
44	3p.	brown and blue ..	15	10
45	3½p.	emerald and brn	15	10
46	4p.	blue and black ..	15	10
47	5p.	brn and emerald	15	10
48	6p.	lt blue and black	15	10
49	8p.	blue and lt brown	40	20
50	10p.	black and dp grn	40	20
51	20p.	green and black..	50	40
52	50p.	carmine and black	1·50	1·25
36/52		set (17)	4·00	3·00

AIR STAMPS

1950 (July 1st)-51 Design, Views and Scenes in Territory. Printers (*recess*) De La Rue. Perf. 12 (C). Sheets 5 x 10.

A16	2p.	blk and grey-grn	30	15
A17	2½p.	blue and red-or	30	25
A18	3p.	lake and dp blue	30	20
A19	3½p.	dp choc and lt brn	40	50
A20	4p.	lt brn and lt blue	40	50
A21	4½p.	black and ult	50	50
		a blk and dl blue (6/51) ..	—	—
A22	6p.	blk and car-red	50	50
A23	20p.	blk and pur-lake	1·50	1·50
A16/23		set (8)	4·00	4·00

SPECIAL ISSUES

1948 (Oct. 1st) Sudan Stamp Jubilee. Perf. 12¾ x 13 (C). Chalk-surfaced paper. Sheets 10 x 5.

S1	2p.	blk and grey blue			
		(Type i)	50	50
		a ditto (Type II) ..	75	75

(*Type I*) Behind camel's neck a circular unshaded portion has the appearance of a setting sun and the white patch on the ground is entirely irregular in shape. (*Illustration is of Type I*).

(*Type II*) The sky is entirely shaded in, and on the ground the top of the white patch behind the front legs of the camel finishes in a straight line.

Both types are to be found on sheets of either Plates I or II centre.

1948 (Dec. 23rd) Opening of Legislative Assembly. Perf. 12¾ x 13 (C). Chalk-surfaced paper. Sheets 10 x 5.

S2	10m.	car-rose and blk ..	20	10
S3	5p.	dl or and dp grn ..	50	30

POSTAGE DUE STAMPS

1897 (March 1st) Postage Due Stamps of

Egypt (1889). Wmk. Star and Crescent, over-printed "SOUDAN" in Arabic and French at Imprimerie Nationale, Bulaq, Cairo. In panes of 60 (10 x 6). Perf. 14.

VPD1	2m.	green	70	60
		a strip of six	7·00	8·00
VPD2	4m.	maroon	70	70
		a strip of six	7·00	8·00
VPD3	1p.	ultramarine ..	1·25	1·50
		a strip of six	£12	£15
VPD4	2p.	orange	2·50	3·00
		a strip of six	£18	£22
VPD1/4		set (4v)	5·00	5·50

Six varieties of type are found in each vertical strip of six (See illustration following V1-V13).

A number of minor varieties, caused by broken type, exist on all values.

The 2m. exists in a horizontal strip of seven with overprint omitted on right hand stamp.

The 4m. and 2p. values were authorised to be used bisected in 1901-2 to represent 2m. and 1p. (generally bisected diagonally).

1901 (Jan. 1st) (*Typo*) Wmk. Multiple Star and Crescent. Perf. 14. Designer, Col. E. A. Stanton. Sheets 120 (12 x 10): later printings 2 panes, each 6 x 10.

VPD5	2m.	black and brown	15	15
VPD6	4m.	brn and grn ..	15	15
VDP7	10m.	grn and mauve	30	30
VPD8	20m.	ult and car ..	1·00	70
VPD5/8		set (4v)	1·50	1·25

Originally on Ordinary paper, all values were re-printed on Chalky paper in 1911-12.

The 2m. and 4m. values are known bisected, but such was not officially authorised.

1927-30 (*Typo*). Wmk. Multiple "SG". Perf. 14. Sheets as before.

GPD1	2m.	blk and brn (C)		
		('30)	10	10
GPD2	4m.	brn and grn (C)	15	15
GPD3	10m.	grn and mauve		
		(CO)	20	20
GPD1/3		set (3v)	45	45

1948 (Jan. 1st) Design, Gunboat "Zafir." Perf 14 x 13¾ (C). Chalk-surfaced paper (*altered Arabic inscription*). **Sheets 10 x 10.**

PD1	2m.	blk and dk orange	20	20

PD2	4m.	**choc and green**	25	25
PD3	10m.	**green and mauve**	25	25
PD4	20m.	**ult and carmine**	30	30
PD1/4		**set** (4)	1·00	1·00

OFFICIAL STAMPS

1900 (Feb. 8th)-**1901** (Jan.) **V7** and **V14** punctured "SG" by hand at Khartoum and Wadi Halfa. The "S" has 14 holes and the "G" 12 holes, the letters being 10 mm. in height.

VO1	5m.	**rose-car** (8/2/00)	£25	£13
VO2	1m.	**brn and pink** (1/01)	£20	£17

The letters are found normal, reversed, inverted and inverted and reversed.

1903 V14 overprinted "O.S.G.S." in blocks of 30 stamps at Khartoum.

EO1	1m.	**brown and pink** ..	1·50	1·50
	a	overprint at top ..	—	—
	b	oval "o" ..	£45	—
	c	round stops ..	6·00	7·00
	d	overprint inverted	£150	—
	e	overprint inverted with variety (a) ..	—	—
	f	overprint inverted with variety (b) ..	£1250	—
	g	overprint inverted with variety (c) ..	£300	—
	h	overprint double	£180	—
	i	overprint double with variety	—	—
	j	overprint double with variety	£450	—

EO1*a* The overprint was normally done at the bottom of the stamp.

EO1*b* An oval "O" was used in the overprint on No. 19.

EO1*c* Square stops were generally used but the stops on the bottom horizontal row (Nos. 25-30) are round.

Dangerous forgeries have been made of all these errors.

1903 (Jan. 1st)-12 **V21, E1, E3, E6, E7, E8, E10** and **E11** overprinted "O.S.G.S." in sheets of 120 by De La Rue.

(i) Wmk. Rosette.

EO2	10p.	**blk and mauve** (3/06)	3·00	3·00

(ii) Wmk. Multiple Star and Crescent.

EO3	1m.	**brn and car** (9/04)	25	20
	a	overprint double	—	—
EO4	3m.	**mauve and grn** (2/04)	40	25
	a	overprint double	—	—
EO5	5m.	**scar and blk** ..	40	10
EO6	1p.	**blue and brn** ..	80	20
EO7	2p.	**blk and blue** ..	1·50	40
EO8	5p.	**brn and grn** ..	1·00	50
EO9	10p.	**blk and mauve** (9/12)	2·00	3·00
EO2/09		**set** (8v)	9·00	7·00

A mis-shaped "O" occurs on No. 7 of the lower pane on all values.

1912-22 E1–E11 (Wmk. Multiple Star and Crescent) punctured "SG" by De La Rue. The "S" has 12 holes and the "G" 13 holes,

the letters being 6 mm. in height.

GO1	1m.	**brown and car**	35	20
GO2	2m.	**green and brown**	35	20
GO3	3m.	**mauve and green**	60	20
GO4	5m.	**scarlet and black**	70	15
GO5	1p.	**blue and brown**	80	20
GO6	2p.	**black and blue** ..	2·50	80
GO7	2p.	**pur and or-yel** ..	80	50
GO8	5p.	**brown and green**	1·75	50
GO9	10p.	**black and mauve**	3·25	80
GO1/09		**set** (9v)	£10	3·00

1922 G3–G6 (Wmk. Multiple Star and Crescent) punctured "SG" by De La Rue. The "S" has 9 holes and the "G" 10 holes, letters being 5 mm. in height.

GO10	3m.	**mauve and grn**	15	15
GO11	4m.	**grn and choc** ..	70	25
GO12	5m.	**olive and blk** ..	45	15
GO13	10m.	**car and blk** ..	70	15
GO10/013		**set** (4v)	2·00	80

1927 G10–G21 (Wmk. Multiple SG) punctured "SG" by De La Rue. Small letters on Millieme values and large letters on Piastre values.

GO14	3m.	**mauve and grn**	20	10
GO15	4m.	**grn and choc** ..	80	80
GO16	5m.	**brn and blk** ..	20	10
GO17	10m.	**red and blk** ..	20	10
GO18	2p.	**pur and yel** ..	20	10
GO19	5p.	**chestnut and green** ..	1·50	35
GO20	10p.	**blk and vio** ..	2·00	30
GO14/O20		**set** (7v) ..	5·00	1·75

1936-46 G8–G22 (Wmk. Multiple SG) overprinted "SG" in black by De La Rue. The letters are 2mm. and 2½mm. in height on Millieme and Piastre values respectively.

O1	1m.	**blk and or** (sub) (22/11/46)	10	10
O2	2m.	**or and choc** (sub) (1/3/45) ..	10	10
O3	3m.	**mauve and dp grn** (ch) (28/1/37)..	10	10
O3A	4m.	**green and choc** ..	10	10
O4	5m.	**ol-brn and blk** (ch) (5/3/40) ..	10	10
O5	10m.	**car-red and blk** (ch) (1/6/46) ..	20	10
O6	15m.	**blue and chest-brn** (ch) (12/6/37)	20	15
O7	2p.	**pur-mar and or** (ch) (30/3/37)..	25	20
	a	ditto (sub) ..	—	—
O8	3p.	**red-brn and dk blu** (sub) (1/4/46)	35	40
O9	4p.	**ult and blk** (ch) (1/4/46)	35	30
	a	ditto (sub) ..	—	—
O9B	5p.	**dl or and grey-grn** (sub) ..	35	30
O10	6p.	**tur-blue and blk** (sub) (1/4/46) ..	1·00	50
O11	8p.	**emer-grn and blk** (sub) (1/4/46) ..	1·00	80
O12	10p.	**grey-black and purple** (ch) (1/9/37) ..	1·00	1·00
	a	ditto (sub) ..	1·50	1·00
O13	20p.	**blue and dp blue** (sub) (29/6/46)	2·50	3·00

| O1/13 | | **set** (15) | .. | .. | 7·00 | 7·00 |

1948 (**Jan. 1st**) **No. 20, etc., overprinted "S.G." in black.**

O14	1m.	**blk and orange**	10	10
O15	2m.	**orange and choc**	10	10
O16	3m.	**mauve and dp green**	10	10
O17	4m.	**green and choc-brown**	10	10
O18	5m.	**ol-brn and blk** ..	10	10
O19	10m.	**dl rose and blk**	10	10
O20	15m.	**ult and red-chest**	15	15
O21	2p.	**pur-mar and or**	15	15
O22	3p.	**red-brn and dk blue**	15	15
O23	4p.	**ult and blk**	25	15
O24	5p.	**dl or and grey-green**	30	20
O25	6p.	**tur-blue and blk**	35	20
O26	8p.	**tur-grn and blk**	40	20
O27	10p.	**grey black and pur-mauve** ..	60	40
O28	20p.	**blue and dp blue** (*sub*)	1·50	70
O29	50p.	**car-red and ult**	4·00	3·00
O14/29		**set** (16) ..	8·00	5·50

As Nos. O23 and O28 but Perf. 13¼ x 13 (C)

| O29a | 4p. | **ult and black** .. | 5·00 | 6·00 |
| O29b | 20p. | **blue and dp blue** | — | — |

We have never seen a copy of O29b, but it is reported to exist.

1950 (**July 1st**)**-51 Nos. A16–A23 overprinted "S.G." in black or red.**

OA30	2p.	**blk and grey-grn** (**red**)	25	20
OA31	2½p.	**blue and red-or**	25	25
OA32	3p.	**lake and dp blue**	25	20
OA33	3½p.	**dp choc and lt brn**	30	30
OA34	4p.	**lt brn and lt blue**	35	40
OA35	4½p.	**blk and ult** (**red**)	50	60
	a	blk and dl blue (red) (4/51) ..	1·50	1·25
OA36	6p.	**blk and car-red** (**red**)	40	60
OA37	20p.	**blk and pur-lake** (**red**)	1·50	1·75
OA30/37		**set** (8)	3·50	4·00

1951 (**Sept. 1st**)**-58 Nos. 36–52, overprinted "S.G." in black or red.**

O38	1m.	**blk and or** (**red**)	10	10
O39	2m.	**black and blue** (**red**)	10	10
O40	3m.	**black and green** (**red**)	20	25
O41	4m.	**black and lt grn** (**red**)	10	10
O42	5m.	**black and purple** (**red**)	10	10
O43	10m.	**blk and azure** (**red**)	10	10
O44	15m.	**black and lt red** (**red**)	10	10
O45	2p.	**dk blue and lt blue**	10	10
	a	overprint inv ..	£350	—
O46	3p.	**brown and blue**	15	10
O47	3½p.	**emer and brown**	20	15
O48	4p.	**blue and black** ..	20	15

O49	5p.	**brown and emer**	20	10
O50	6p.	**lt blue and blk** ..	25	15
O51	8p.	**blue and lt brn**	30	15
O52	10p.	**blk and dp green** (**red**)	50	20
	a	blk and dp grn (black) ('58)	50	20
O53	20p.	**green and black**	1·00	30
	a	overprint invtd	—	£300
O54	50p.	**car and black** ..	3·00	1·00
O38/54		**set** (18) ..	6·50	2·50

ARMY OFFICIAL STAMPS

1905 Jan. 1st) **E1** (**Wmk. Multiple Star and Crescent**) **overprinted "ARMY OFFICIAL" in blocks of 30 stamps (half panes 6 x 5) at Khartoum.**

(i) "ARMY" reading up and "OFFICIAL' reading down.

EA1	1m.	**brown and carmine**	1·50	80
	a	" !" for "I"	£11	7·00
	b	small overprint ..	9·00	5·00

(ii) "OFFICIAL" reading up and "ARMY" reading down.

EA2	1m.	**brown and carmine**	£15	£15
	a	" !" for "I"	£275	£275
	b	small overprint ..	£200	£200

(iii) Horizontally, "OFFICIAL" being inverted.

EA3	1m.	**brown and carmine**	£140	—
	a	" !" for "I"	£1750	—
	b	small overprint ..	£1000	—

(iv) Horizontally, "ARMY" being inverted.

EA4	1m.	**brown and carmine**	£140	—
	a	" !" for "I"	£1750	—
	b	small overprint ..	£1000	—

1905 (**Nov.**) **V14** (**Wmk. Rosette**) **overprinted as before, "ARMY" reading up and "OFFICIAL" reading down.**

EA5	1m.	**brown and pink** ..	£60	£50
	a	" !" for "I"		—
	b	small overprint ..	£700	—

An exclamation mark (!) was used in lieu of the first "I" in "OFFICIAL" on No. 29.

The normal overprint measures—ARMY 9¼mm. OFFICIAL 16 mm. but on Nos. 6 and 12 (the right hand stamps of the first two horizontal rows) a smaller fount was used, measuring — ARMY 8¼ mm, OFFICIAL 13½ mm.

A single copy, used on piece at Khartoum North, has both "ARMY" and "OFFICIAL" reading down.

A total of 60,000 stamps was overprinted of which about half were destroyed in October, 1906. They were in use at 18 Post Offices between January and December 1905 and the sale to the public was at first strictly prohibited.

ARMY SERVICE STAMPS

1906 (Jan. 1st)-1911. E1–E11 (Wmk. Multiple Star and Crescent) overprinted "ARMY SERVICE" in panes of 60 at Cairo.

(i) First Printing, lines spaced 14 mm.

ES1	1m.	**brown and carmine**	£90	£80
	a	overprint double		
		one albino ..	—	—

(ii) Later Printings, lines spaced 12 mm.

(a) Earlier Printings: Broad "A" in "Army".
(b) 1908 Printings: Narrow "A" in "Army".
(c) 1911 Printings: Short tail to "y" in "Army".

ES2	1m.	**brown and carmine**	1·50	35
	a	overprint double, one oblique ..	—	£300
	b	overprint inverted	£200	£200
	c	"Servic" for "Service" ..	—	—
	d	"Army" omitted ..	—	—
ES3	2m.	**green and brown** ..	3·00	1·25
	a	overprint omitted in pair with normal	£1000	—
	b	"Army" omitted ..	£1200	—
ES4	3m.	**mauve and green** ..	2·50	60
	a	overprint inverted	£1200	—
ES5	5m.	**scarlet and black** ..	1·00	20
	a	overprint double ..	£150	£150
	b	overprint inverted	—	£120
	c	overprint double ' one inverted ..	£400	£170
	d	"Servi" for "Service"	—	—
	e	"Amry" for "Army"	—	£1300
	f	"Armv" for "Army"	—	—
ES6	1p.	**blue and brown** ..	1·50	25
	a	"Army" omitted ..	£1200	£1200
ES7	2p.	**blk and blu** (1/09)	5·50	4·00
	a	overprint double ..	—	—
ES8	5p.	**brn and grn** (5/08)	£25	£10
ES9	10p.	**blk and mauve** (5/11)	£450	£600
ES1/9		**set** (9v)	£575	£690
SPES2/6		**specimen set** (5v)	£175	‡

ES1 is said to have been a trial printing of one sheet (120 copies) which was issued in error. It was only used at Halfa in December, 1906.

Number Recorded—ES2a, 1; ES2b, 60; ES4a, 4; ES5e, 4 (all used); ES7a, 2; ES9, 120.

1908-11 V19–V21 (Wmk. Rosette) overprinted as before.

ES10	2p.	**black and blue**	8·00	4·00
ES11	5p.	**brown and grn**	£30	£30
ES12	10p.	**blk and mauve**	£40	£40
ES10/12		**set** (3v)	£75	£70
SPES10/11		**specimen** (3v) ..	£175	‡

1912-22 V17 and E1–E11 punctured "AS" by De La Rue. The "A" has 12 holes and the "S" 11 holes, the letters being 6 mm. in height.

(i) Wmk. Rosette.

ES13	5m.	**carmine and blk**	£175	—

(ii) Wmk. Multiple Star and Crescent.

ES14	1m.	**brown and car**	30	10
ES15	2m.	**green and brown**	30	10
ES16	3m.	**mauve and grn** ..	40	10
ES17	5m.	**scarlet and blk**	40	10
ES18	1p.	**blue and brown**	60	15
ES19	2p.	**black and blue**	2·00	35
ES20	2p.	**pur and or, yel**	1·50	30
ES21	5p.	**brown and green**	3·00	25
ES22	10p.	**blk and mauve**	£12	3·00
ES14/22		**set** (9v)	£20	4·00

Only one used example of ES13 is known.

1922-25 G2–G6 (Wmk. Multiple Star and Crescent) punctured "AS" by De La Rue.

ES23	2m.	**or and choc** ..	60	45
ES24	5m.	**ol-brn and blk** ..	30	15
ES25	10m.	**car and blk** ..	40	15
ES23/25		**set** (3v)	1·25	75

MILITARY TELEGRAPH STAMPS

1897 Nos. V7/13 overprinted "TEL" in sans serif capitals within an oval frame.

		In black		In blue	
VMT1	5m. ..	30	25	2·50	2·00
VMT2	1p. ..	30	25	8·00	2·50
VMT3	2p. ..	2·50	40	—	—
VMT4	5p. ..	6·00	1·00	£20	5·00
VMT5	10p. ..	£10	4·50	£50	£12

1898 (March 1st) (*typo*)**. Wmk. Rosette. Perf. 14. Sheets of 72 (6 x 12), the stamps being additionally perforated vertically down the centres.**

VMT6	5m.	**brn-lake and vio**	60	30
VMT7	1p.	**black and red** ..	1·25	50
VMT8	2p.	**grn and brn-lake**	1·25	75
VMT9	5p.	**vio and blk** ..	40	30
VMT6/9		**set** (4v)	3·50	2·00

1899-1901 (*Typo*) **Wmk. Multiple Star and Crescent. Perf. 14.**

VMT10	5m.	**brn-lake and vio**	20	20
VMT11	5m.	**yel-brn and ult**	20	20
VMT12	1p.	**blk and red** ..	20	20
VMT13	2p.	**grn and brn-lilac**	£15	£15
VMT14	5p.	**vio and blk** ..	20	20
VMT15	10p.	**rose and grn** ..	20	20
VMT16	25p.	**ult and brn** ..	20	20
VMT10/16		**set** (7v)	£16	£16

Prices are for complete stamps mint and for half stamps (left or right same price) used. Whole used stamps are occasionally found (same price as mint).

The Military Telegraph Stamps were demonetised on December 31st, 1914.

SWAZILAND

From 1890 whilst administered jointly by Great Britain and South Africa the stamps of the latter were overprinted for use in the territory. Following the Boer War, Swaziland came, successively, under the jurisdiction of Transvaal and the Union of South Africa whose stamps it used until it became a British Protectorate in 1933.

1933 (Jan. 2nd). Printers De La Rue & Co. Wmk. Mult. Script CA. Perf. 14. Designer, C. C. Tugman. Sheets 6 x 10.

G1	½d. **green**	..	..	10	20
G2	1d. **carmine**	..	..	15	10
G3	2d. **brown** ..	..	..	20	20
G4	3d. **blue**	..	..	20	40
G5	4d. **orange**		..	40	90
G6	6d. **bright purple**		..	70	1·25
G7	1/- **olive**	..	..	1·25	2·75
G8	2/6 **bright violet** ..		..	4·50	8·00
G9	5/- **grey**	..	..	£15	£18
G10	10/- **sepia**	..	..	£65	£70
G1/10	**set** (10)	..		£85	£100
SP G1/10	**perf specimen**		..	£50	‡

1934 Overprinted OFFICIAL (prepared for use but not issued).

GO1 to GO4.

½d., **green**; 1d., **carmine**; 2d., **brown**; 6d., **bright purple**. Mint sets fetch about £2750 when offered.

1935 (4th May) Silver Jubilee (*recess*) **Printers**

Bradbury, Wilkinson & Co. Wmk. Script CA. Perf. 11 x 12. Sheets 6 x 10.

G11	1d.	**dp blue and scar**		15	20
		a extra flagstaff	..	£30	£35
G12	2d.	**ult and grey-blk**		25	50
		a extra flagstaff	..	£40	£45
G13	3d.	**brn and dp blue**	..	65	80
		a extra flagstaff	..	£25	£30
G14	6d.	**slate and purple**	..	80	1·25
		a extra flagstaff	..	£40	£45
G11/14		**set** (4)	.. ..	1·75	2·50
SPG11/14		**perf specimen** (4)	£18		‡

Numbers issued—G11,90,800; G12, 62,780; G13, 59,800; G14, 49,000.

Extra flagstaff variety. Row 9/1

1938 (April 1st)-42 Design, King's Head framed by Native Shields, Spears, etc. Printers (*recess*) **De La Rue. Perf. 13¼ x 13 (C). Sheets as before.**

1	½d.	**green**	..	..	5	10
2	1d.	**scarlet**	..	..	10	10
3	1½d.	**light blue**	..	..	25	20
4	2d.	**yellow-brown**		..	20	25
5	3d.	**ultramarine**	..	..	25	35
		a deep blue (/42)		..	20	25
		b dp ult (/42) ..		..	10	20
6	4d.	**orange**	..	..	25	35
7	6d.	**purple**	..	..	30	30
8	1/-	**olive**	..	..	80	40
9	2/6	**violet**	..	..	1·25	1·50
10	5/-	**grey**	..	..	2·75	2·75
11	10/-	**sepia**	..	..	5·00	4·00
1/11		**set** (11) ..		..	£10	£10
SP1/11		**specimen set** perf (11)			£35	‡

As No. 3 but Perf. 14 (L).

12	1½d.	**light blue** (/42)	..	10	25

1943-50 As No. 1, etc., but Perf. 13¼ x 13¾ (C).

13	½d.	**green** ..	.. ..	10	15
		a ol-grn (15/2/50) ..		10	10
14	1d.	**scarlet** (11/1/43) ..		10	10
		a rose-scar (22/10/47)		10	10

15 1½d. **lt blue** (11/1/43) .. 10 25
   a blue (19/8/48) .. 10 25
   b jay blue (15/2/50) .. 10 25
16 2d. **yel-brn** (11/1/43) .. 10 10
   a fawn (26/11/45) .. 40 40
17 3d. **ult** (11/1/43) .. 20 25
   a lt ult (1/10/46) .. 20 25
   b dp blue (22/10/47) 10 20
18 4d. **orange** (11/1/43) .. 15 25
19 6d. **mauve** (11/1/43) .. 20 70
   a purple (5/7/44) .. 10 15
   b mauve-red (30/7/45) 10 15
   c mauve-purple
      (22/10/47) .. 15 35
20 1/- **olive** (11/1/43) .. 25 15
   a brn-ol (15/2/50) .. 25 15
21 2/6 **violet** (11/1/43) .. 50 60
   a pur-vio (22/10/47).. 1·25 1·25
   b reddish-vio (15/2/50) 50 60
22 5/- **grey** (11/1/43) .. 2·00 3·00
   a dk slate (17/5/44) .. 7·00 9·00
23 10/- **sepia** (11/1/43) .. 3·00 3·50
13/23 **set** (11) .. .. .. 5·50 6·00

SPECIAL ISSUES

**1937 (May 12th) Coronation. As Aden, but
printers, Bradbury, Wilkinson. Perf. 11 x 11¾
(C).**

S1 1d. **carmine-red** 10 10
S2 2d. **brown** 10 10
S3 3d. **blue** 15 15
SP S1/3 **perf specimen set** (3) £10 ‡

**1945 (Dec. 3rd) Victory. Nos. S33–5 of South
Africa, overprinted SWAZILAND.**

                      Pr. M   *Pr. U*

S4 1d. **dp brn and carmine** .. 10 15
   a aniline centre .. .. 1·00 1·00
   b barbed wire variety
      Row 9/6 .. .. 4·00 5·00
S5 2d. **sl-blue and vio** .. 15 15
S6 3d. **dp blue and blue** .. 15 20
SP S4/6 **perf specimen** (3 pairs) — ‡

**1947 (Feb. 17th) Royal Visit. As Basutoland,
Nos. S7–10.**

S7 1d. **scarlet** 5 5
S8 2d. **green** 5 5
S9 3d. **ultramarine** 15 10
S10 1/- **dull mauve** 20 20
S7/10 **set** (4) 40 35
SPS7/10 **perf specimen set** (4) £15 ‡

1948 (Dec. 1st) Silver Wedding. As Aden.

S11 1½d. **ultramarine** 10 10
S12 10/- **brownish-purple** .. 4·00 4·00

1949 (Oct. 10th) U.P.U. As Aden.

S13 1½d. **dull ultramarine** .. 10 10
S14 3d. **indigo** 15 20
S15 6d. **reddish-mauve** .. 20 30
S16 1/- **sage-green** 40 45
S13/16 **set** (4) .. .. .. 75 1·00

POSTAGE DUE STAMPS

1933-57 Printers (*typo*) **De La Rue. Perf. 13¾ x
14 (C). Sheets 6 x 10.**

PD1 1d. **carmine** 20 25
   a deep carmine .. 20 25
PD2 2d. **purple, pl purple** .. 1·00 1·00
   a pur and pur-vio .. 80 80
   b dull violet (2/48) .. 60 60

Whilst the designs of the 1947 printing were
similar to those originally issued in 1933, they
were not only printed on rough paper but the
1d. was a deeper shade of carmine (the 1d. is
also thicker and the stop under d larger), and the
2d. is also of a darker shade, particularly the 2d.
in the centre.

**1951 As before but printed on chalk-coated
paper.**

PD3 1d. **dp car** (24/10/51) .. 10 15
PD4 2d. **pur-vio** (22/5/52) .. 15 20

Watermark Variety (Type A)

See Introduction for details.

PD3b 1d. St. Edward's Crown £30 —

TOBAGO

Tobago was ceded to Great Britain in 1814, and was amalgamated with Trinidad in 1888.

Following the use of other handstamps or manuscript marks, a Crowned Circle PAID Frank was registered at the G.P.O. in London on October 31st, 1851; and was thereafter struck in red to indicate prepayment of postage on overseas letters (See Introduction).

From May 1858 to March 1860 contemporary G.B. stamps were in use and were cancelled with "A14" in a transverse oval of horizontal bars.

The Crowned Circle Frank was again used from April 1st, 1860 until the first Tobago stamps were issued.

1851-1879 PAID Frank   *On Cover*
VF1   ..   £850

1858-60 Stamps of Great Britain identified by their Catalogue Nos. after prefix 'TO'

Used at Scarborough : 'A14'

TO V39	1d.	**rose-red**	..	..
TO V44	4d.	**rose** ..	..	..
TO V45	6d.	**lilac** ..	..	..
TO V47	1/-	**green**	..	..

All stamps are (*typo*) **De La Rue. Perf. 14. Sheets 6 x 10.**

1879 (Aug. 1st) Fiscal stamps issued for postal use pending receipt of "Postage" stamps. Wmk. Crown CC.

F1	1d.	**rose**	..	..	£12	£13
F2	3d.	**blue**	..	..	£18	£13
F3	6d.	**orange** ..	..	..	£15	£14
F4	1/-	**green**	..	..	£160	£22
	a bisect (6d.) on cover			‡	—	
F5	5/-	**slate**	..	..	£300	£250
F6	£1	**mauve** ..	..	..	£3000	—

Similar stamps, but wmk. Crown CA, are Fiscals which were not authorised for postal use.

1880 (Nov.) No. F3 bisected vertically and surcharged (manuscript).

F7	1d. **on half 6d. orange**	..	— £300

1880 (Dec. 20th) Wmk. Crown CC.

V1	½d.	**purple-brown**	..	£10	£10
V2	1d.	**venetian red** ..	..	£14	8·00
	a bisect (½d.) on cover			‡	—
V3	4d.	**yellow-green**	..	£70	£10
	a malformed "CE"	..		£300	£180
	b bisect (2d.) on cover			‡	—
V4	6d.	**stone** ..	..	..	£100 £45
V5	1/-	**yellow-ochre**	..	£14	£12

V3a—The "C" in "PENCE' is smaller than the other letters; and the second "E" has weak middle and lower horizontal strokes, and is slightly squat (Row 10/6 – Plate 1).

1883 (April) No. V4 locally surcharged in black "2½ PENCE".

V6	2½d. on 6d.	**stone** ..	..	5·00	3·00
	a surcharge	..		—	—
	double	..		—	—
	b large "2"	..		£40	£30

V6b—The figure "2" is larger and has a long tail.

1882-84 As before but wmk. Crown CA.

V7	½d.	**purple-brown** ('83)		2·00	8·00
V8	1d.	**venetian red** ..	..	2·00	3·00
	a bisect diag. (½d.) on cover ('83)			‡	—
V9	2½d.	**dull blue** ('83)	..	2·00	2·00
V10	2½d.	**bright blue** ..	..	1·00	1·50
V11	2½d.	**ultramarine** ..	..	1·00	1·00
V12	4d.	**yellow-green** ('84) ..		£90	£70
	a malformed "CE"	..		£325	—
V13	6d.	**stone** ('84)	..	..	£275 £200

V12a—See Note below V3a.

1885-96 As before but new colours.

V14	½d.	**dull green** ('86)	..	10	20
V15	1d.	**carmine** ('89)	..	20	20
	a large "O" in "ONE"	..		£25	—
V16	4d.	**grey** ('85)	..	50	50
	a malformed "CE" ..	..		£30	£30
	b imperf (pair)	..		£700	—
V17	6d.	**orange-brown** ('86)	..	2·00	3·00
V18	6d.	**or-brn and dp brn** ..		2·00	3·00
V19	1/-	**olive-yellow** ('94)..		3·00	4·00
V20	1/-	**pl olive-yellow**	..	£10	—
V21	1/-	**or-brn** (9/96)	..	5·00	—
V14/21		**set** (6v)	..	£10	—
SPV14/20		**specimen set** (5v)		£65	‡

V16a—See Note below V3a.

V18—The value is printed in deep brown, compared with the orange-brown Key Plate printing.

V21—6,000 copies of this stamp were inadvertently printed in the colour of the 6d. stamp in August, 1896. The error of colour was brought to the notice of De La Rue by J. Tilleard, then Honorary Secretary of the London (now Royal) Philatelic Society; and was subsequently the subject of a complaint by the Colonial Postmaster.

Although De La Rue immediately supplied a replacement printing in the correct colour, large numbers of the error had already been bought by dealers before instructions were received in the Colony to withdraw the stamps from sale.

1886-92 Nos. V9/13/16/17 locally surcharged in black. Two settings, each 6 x 2 (repeated five times on the sheet).

Setting I: Nos. 3 and 10: Wide space between figure and "PENNY".

Setting II: No. 10 only with wide space; Nos. 7, 9 and 10: Raised "P" in "PENNY".

(a) ½ PENNY. Setting II, except V24 which also exists with Setting I.

V22 ½d. on 2½d.	**dl blue** (4/86).	2·00	3·00
	a wide spaced surcharge	£10	£12
	b surcharge double ..	—	—
	c surcharge omitted (in pair with V22) ..	—	—
	d surcharge omitted (in pair with V22*a*) ..	—	—
V23 ½d. on 4d.	**grey** ('91-'92)	6·00	£10
	a malformed "CE" ..	£150	—
	b surcharge double ..	—	—
V24 ½d. on 6d.	**stone** (1/86)..	3·00	4·00
	a wide spaced surcharge	£18	£20
	b surcharge double ..	—	—
	c surcharge inverted ..	—	—
	d surcharge inverted (wide spaced) ..	—	—

V25 ½d. on 6d.	**or-brn** (10/89)	£15	£20
	a wide spaced surcharge	£80	£90
	b surcharge double ..	—	—

(b) 1 PENNY. Setting II.

V26 1d. on 2½d.	**dl blue** (7/89)	5·00	7·00
	a wide spaced surcharge	£25	£30
	b surcharge omitted (in pair with normal) ..	—	—
	bisect (½d.) on cover..	‡	—

(c) 2½ PENCE.

V27 2½d. on 4d.	**grey** ('91-'92)	3·00	5·00
	a malformed "CE" ..	£120	—
	b surcharge double ..	—	—

V23*a*/27*a*—See Note below V3*a*.

V26*c*—The bisect is se-tenant with two whole surcharged stamps to give the 2½d. rate.

1896 Fiscal stamp, as Nos. F1/6 but wmk. Crown CA, surcharged locally in black "½d. POSTAGE" (in two lines). Two settings, each 6 x 2 (repeated five times on the sheet).

V28 ½d. on 4d.	**lilac and car**..	3·00	4·00
	a wide spaced surcharge ..	7·00	£10

V28*a* occurs on only one of the settings.

The stamps of Trinidad were used in Tobago from 1896 to 1913; and thereafter the joint issues for Trinidad and Tobago.

TOKELAU ISLANDS

The islands were administered by, and used the stamps of, Western Samoa from 1925 until they became a Dependency of New Zealand.

1948 (June 22nd) Designs, ½d. (Atafu Village, flanked by Maps); 1d. (Nukunono Hut and Map); 2d. (Fakaofo Village and Map). Designer, J. Berry. Printers (*recess*) Bradbury, Wilkinson. Wmk. "N.Z. Star" (*mult*). Perf. 13½ x 13¼ (C). Sheets 12 x 10.

1	½d. **lilac and dp cinnamon**	10	15
2	1d. **chest and myr-grn**	15	15
3	2d. **dp em and dp blue** ..	15	25
1/3	**set** (3)	40	50

Numbers printed: 1-1,100,000 (of which 887,520 were surcharged in 1956 and 1967). 2 and 3 – 2m each.

TONGA

All stamps were printed (*recess*) by De La Rue.

(Die I)

**1943 (Jan.) Wmk. Tortoises. Perf. 14 (L).
Sheets 10 x 6.**

1	1½d. **grey-black**	.. ..	25	65

The design of this stamp is slightly larger than that of the 1935 printing, also the perforation was previously 14 x 13¾ (C).

Other values, with wmk. tortoises, were issued before 1937.

(Die II)

1942 (Sept. 18th)-49 Designs, ½d. (Arms of Tonga); 1d. (Ovava Tree); 2d., 2½d. and 1/– (Queen Salote); 3d. (Prehistoric Trilith, Haamonga); 6d. (Coral); 2/6 (Parrot); 5/– (Vavau). Designs, 1d., 3d., 5/– H. Wmk. Mult. Script CA. (Sideways on 5/–). Sheets 10 x 6 or 6 x 10.

(a) Perf. 13¾ x 14 (C).

2	½d. **green**	.. .. ..	10	15
3	1d. **black and carmine-red**			
	(1/10/46)		35	30
	a black and dp scarlet			
	(30/3/49)	.. ..	15	30

(b) Perf. 14 (L).

4	1d. **blk and car-red**	..	15	20
5	2d. **blk and pur-vio** (Die II)		10	20
6	2½d. **ultramarine**	.. ..	15	20
	a wide D variety	..	£25	£25
	b value recut	.. ..	£25	£25
7	3d. **blk and yel-grn**	..	15	20
8	6d. **red-scarlet**	.. ..	30	50
9	1/– **sl-blk and chest**	..	30	65
	a grey-black and chest..			
	(30/3/49)	.. ..	40	65
10	2/6 **dp purple** (30/1/43)	..	4·00	5·00
11	5/– **special and brn-orng**		1·50	3·00
	(30/1/43)	..		
1/11	**set** (11)	.. ..	6·50	£10
SP1/11	**specimen set** perf (9)		£45	‡

(Die III)

(c) Perf. 13¾ (C).

12	2d. **grey-blk and pur-vio**			
	(Die III) (30/3/49) ..		2·00	2·25
13	1/– **sl-grey and chest**			
	(23/4/47)	.. ..	30	65

5—The ball of the 2 is larger and the word PENI-E-UA is shorter than in Die I. There is a spur at left side of U. Stamps of Die 1 were issued before 1937.

Normal D   Wide D

6*a*—The D in the value panel is broader in No. 4/10 (*see illustration*).

6*b*—The 2½-in. value tablet has been re-cut (No. 1/1).

9, 13—The 1 in the value panel is made up of a number of lines, but in the case of No. 9*a* these lines have been partly blocked out separately on each stamp in the sheet.

12—The letters below the bottom frame (PEN-E-UA) are taller in Die III, and the 2 of the value is altered in shape (*see illustrations*).

SPECIAL ISSUES

1938 (Oct. 12th) 20th Anniversary of Queen Salote's Accession. Design, Full length Portrait of Queen Salote (lower panel dated 1918-38). Perf. 13¾ (L). Wmk. Tortoises. Sheets 10 x 6.

S1	1d.	**blk and car-red**	30	70
S2	2d.	**blk and pur-vio**	1·50	1·50
S3	2½d.	**blk and ult**	1·50	2·25
S1/3		**set (3)**	3·00	4·00
SPS1/3		**specimen set** perf (3)	£35	‡

1944 (Jan. 25th) Silver Jubilee of Queen Salote's Accession. Design, as No. S1, etc. but date on lower panel altered to 1918-43. Perf. 13¾ (L). Sheets 10 x 6.

S4	1d.	**black and carmine**	10	15
	a	blk and dp carmine (5/7/44)		
S5	2d.	**blk and pur-vio**	15	20
S6	3d.	**blk and dp green**	15	25
S7	6d.	**black and orange**	25	35
S8	1/–	**blk and chocolate**	30	45
S4/8		**set (5)**	80	1·25
SPS4/8		**specimen set** perf (5)	£35	‡

S5: Copies with frames of blue have appeared on the market which do not conform with any known printing.

Number issued—1d., 245,180; 177,560; 3d., 101,160; 6d., 76,684; 1/–, 82,147.

1949 (Oct. 10th) U.P.U. (See Aden for details).

S9	2½d.	**dull violet-blue**	15	10
S10	3d.	**deep olive**	20	25
S11	6d.	**carmine-red**	25	25
S12	1/–	**beech-brown**	30	35
S9/12		**set (4)**	80	90

Number issued—2½d., 141,790; 3d., 116,240; 6d., 114,500; 1/–, 100,340.

1950 (Nov. 1st) Queen Salote's 50th Birthday. Designs, Portraits of Queen Salote. Printers (*photo*) Waterlow & Sons. Perf. 12½ (L). Wmk. "Script C.A." Chalk-surfaced paper. Designs, 1d., 1/– V. Sheets 12 x 5 or 5 x 12.

S13	1d.	**rose-red**	15	25
S14	5d.	**green**	40	45
S15	1/–	**purple-violet**	50	60
S13/15		**set (3)**	1·00	1·25

Number issued—1d., 107,510; 5d., 74,850; 1/–, 72,230.

1951 (July 2nd) 50th Anniversary Treaty of Friendship. Designs, ½d. (Map of Islands); 1d. (Palace, Nuku'alofa); 2½d. (Beach View); 3d. ("Bellona"); 5d. (Tonga Flag); 1/– (Arms of G.B. and Tonga). Printers (*recess*) Waterlow & Sons. Perf. 12½ (L) (3d.). Perf. 13¼ x 13½ (C); (Other Values). Designs, 1d., 2½d., 5d., 1/– H. Sheets 12 x 5 or 5 x 12.

S16	½d.	**green**	20	25
S17	1d.	**black and carmine**	30	30
S18	2½d.	**olive-green and brn**	40	50
S19	3d.	**yellow and blue**	70	75
S20	5d.	**carmine and green**	70	90
S21	1/–	**orange and violet**	1·25	1·50
S16/21		**set (6)**	3·25	4·00

TRANSJORDAN (Jordan)

1939 Design, Portrait of Emir Abdullah. Printers, Perkins, Bacon. Perf. 13¼ x 13 (C). Sheets 10 x 10.

1	1m.	chestnut	.. ..	50	20
2	2m.	slate-green	.. ..	40	20
3	3m.	yellow-green	..	70	40
4	4m.	rose-carmine	..	2·00	60
5	5m.	orange	.. ..	3·50	70
6	10m.	red	.. ..	8·00	2·00
7	15m.	ultramarine	..	1·50	50
8	20m.	olive-green	..	4·00	2·00
1/8		set (8)	.. ..	£20	6·00

An unheralded printing shown, by postmarked copies, to have been placed on sale in 1939, with mint copies turning up from time to time in post-office stocks proving that there had been no general release. Similar stamps Perf. 14 were issued in 1929.

1942 Design as No. 1, etc., but with Arabic Inscriptions altered. Printers (litho) Survey Dept., Cairo. Perf. 13¼ x 13½. (C). No wmk. This printing was rendered necessary owing to destruction by enemy action in London of Perkins Bacons plates. Sheets 10 x 10.

9	1m.	chocolate-brown	..	10	15
10	2m.	grey-green	.. ..	10	15
11	3m.	green	.. ..	10	15
12	4m.	rose-carmine	..	15	15
13	5m.	orange	.. ..	15	15
14	10m.	scarlet	.. ..	50	45
15	15m.	dp ultramarine	..	40	35
16	20m.	olive-green	..	50	45
9/16		set (8)	.. ..	2·00	2·00

Numbers issued—9, 122,500; 10, 155,000; 11/12, 100,000 each; 13, 218,000; 14, 107,500; 15, 68,000; 16, 43,000.

1943-7 Design as No. 1, etc., but printed by Bradbury, Wilkinson and Perf. 12 (L).

17	1m.	red-brown (2/1/43)		5	5
18	2m.	blue-grn (2/1/43)	..	5	5
	a	grey-grn (/43)	..	10	10
19	3m.	green (2/1/43)	..	5	5
	a	yel-grn (/43)	..	10	10

20	3m.	rose-car (12/5/47)		5	5
21	4m.	rose-car (2/1/43)	..	5	5
	a	dp rose-carmine (30/4/45)	..	15	15
22	4m.	green (12/5/47)	..	10	5
23	5m.	orange (2/1/43)	..	10	5
	a	yel-or (3/4/44)	..	10	5
24	10m.	ver-red (2/1/43)	..	15	5
25	10m.	pl violet (12/5/47)	..	10	5
26	12m.	scarlet (12/5/47)	..	15	5
27	15m.	blue (2/1/43)	..	20	10
28	15m.	olive-grn (12/5/47)		10	10
20	20m.	sage-grn (3/4/44)	..	20	10
	a	dp ol-grn (30/4/45)		20	10
30	20m.	blue (12/5/47)	..	15	20
31	50m.	lake (3/4/44)	..	35	20
32	90m.	bistre (3/4/44)		50	50
33	100m.	blue (3/4/44)	..	45	45
34	200m.	violet (3/4/44)		80	60
35	500m.	grey-brn (3/4/44)	..	2·25	2·25
36	£1	grey-blk (3/4/44)	..	4·50	4·50
17/36		set (20)	.. ..	£10	9·50
SP20, 22, 25, 26, 28, 30		perf.			
		spec. (6v).	£20		‡

POSTAGE DUE STAMPS

1939. Printers, Perkins Bacon. Perf. 13¼ x 13 (C). Sheets 10 x 10.

PD1	1m.	chestnut	.. ..	£20	£10

Similar stamps, but Perf. 14, were issued in 1929.

1942 (Dec. 22nd) Design as PD1 but Arabic inscription altered. Printers (litho) Survey Dept., Cairo. Perf. 13¼ x 13½ (C). No wmk. Sheets as before.

PD3	1m.	chestnut	.. ..	30	40
PD4	2m.	orange	.. ..	30	50
PD5	10m.	red	.. ..	50	60

1944 Design as PD1. Printers, Bradbury, Wilkinson. Perf. 12 (L). Sheets as before.

PD6	1m.	light brown	..	15	15
PD7	2m.	orange	.. ..	20	20
PD8	4m.	yellow-green	..	25	20
PD9	10m.	carmine-red	..	40	40
PD10	20m.	olive-green	..	50	60
PD6/10		set (5)	.. ..	1·50	1·50

TRINIDAD

Trinidad was colonized by Spain in 1532 and following capture in 1797, was ceded to Great Britain under the Treaty of Amiens in 1802.

Following the use of other handstamps or manuscript marks, a Crowned Circle PAID Frank was registered at the G.P.O. in London on March 21st, 1852 and was thereafter struck in red to indicate prepayment of the additional postage for overseas. This was normal until 1867 and commands no premium. Its use without adhesives to indicate prepayment of full rate in cash is rare.

1852-59 PAID Frank. *On Cover*

VF1 (No adhesive stamps) £850

All stamps from V1 to V43 are (*recess*) **Perkins Bacon and Co.**

1851 (Aug. 14)-57 No wmk. Imperf. Sheets 10 x 11.

(a) Blued Paper.

V1	1d.	**purple-brown** ..	5·00	£25
V2	1d.	**blue** (12/51)	4·00	£20
V3	1d.	**deep blue** (8/53) ..	£70	£45
V4	1d.	**grey** (12/51)	£18	£20
V5	1d.	**brn'ish-grey** (3/53) ..	£13	£22
V6	1d.	**brown** (2/53) ..		
V7	1d.	**brn'ish red** (5/54) ..	£150	£30
V8	1d.	**brick red** ('55) ..	£55	£30

(b) White Paper (1854-57).

V9	1d.	**purple-grey** (8/54) ..	8·00	£25
V10	1d.	**dark grey** (8/54) ..	£13	£33
V11	1d.	**rose-red** ('57) ..	£575	£35

V1/11 and all stamps of this denomination issued up to No. V82 bear no indication of value.

The first printing was received in the Colony in January 1849 but was not issued on account of delay in establishing a Post Office under control of the Colony. This printing (25,000 blue and 25,000 dark grey) had greatly deteriorated from long storage in Trinidad, but some were salvaged and later issued.

V3 is a very bright deep blue shade from a later printing (8/53).

A second printing was received in the Colony in December, 1850 and consisted of Nos. V1 and V2.

Numbers printed—V1/V2, 5,500 each; V9/10, 50,000.

1859 (May 9th) No wmk. Imperf. Sheets, 12 x 20.

V12	4d.	**grey-lilac**	£35	£130
V13	6d.	**green (shades)** ..	—	£250
V14	1/-	**indigo**	£35	£150

The 4d. in deep purple (with or without CANCELLED in bars) and the 1/- in purple-slate were Colour Trials which were not accepted. The 6d. also exists with CANCELLED in bars.

Die Proofs of all three values exist in black on card and India paper on card.

Numbers printed—V12, 4,000; V13, 9,000; V14 7,000.

1859-60 As before but Pin Perf.

(a) Perf. 12½.

V15	1d.	**carmine-lake**	£225	£20
V16	1d.	**rose-red**	£225	£20
V17	4d.	**dull purple**	—	£300
V18	4d.	**dull lilac**	—	£300
V19	6d.	**deep bluish green** ..	£850	£80
V20	6d.	**yellow-green** ..	£850	£80
V21	1/-	**purple-slate** ..	£1500	£450

(b) Perf. 13½-14.

V22	1d.	**carmine-lake**	£65	9·00
V23	1d.	**rose-red**	£40	£10
V24	4d.	**dull purple**	—	£100
V25	4d.	**dull lilac**	£325	—
V26	4d.	**brownish purple** ..	£35	£50
V27	6d.	**deep bluish green** ..	£125	£35
V28	6d.	**yellow-green** ..	£150	£35
V29	6d.	**bright yellow-green**	£35	£45
		a imperf between (vert. pair)	£1600	—
V30	1/-	**purple-slate**	—	£250

V29*a*—Twelve pairs are known, including four pairs in the Royal Collection.

(c) Compound perf. 13½-14 x 12½.

V31	1d.	**carmine-lake**	—	—

Numbers printed—1d., 170,000; 4d., 21,000; 6d., 38,000; 1/-, 3,000.

1860 (Aug.) As before but Perf. 14-16½.

(a) Clean Cut Perf.

V32	1d.	**rose-red**	£40	£15
		a imperf between (horiz. pair)	—	—
		b as *a* but also imperf between stamp and margin ..	—	—
V33	4d.	**brownish purple** ..	£50	£30
V34	4d.	**lilac**	—	£100
V35	6d.	**bt yellow-green** ..	£65	£45
V36	6d.	**deep bluish-green** ..	£85	£75

V32*b* is known imperf between stamp and right margin, also top margin.

Numbers printed—V32, 89,000; V33/34, 9,000; V35/36, 14,000.

(b) Rough Perf.

V37	1d.	**rose-red**	..	..	£30	9·00
V38	1d.	**rose**	..	..	£30	9·00
V39	4d.	**lilac**	..	..	£165	£15
V40	4d.	**dull sepia**	..	..	£75	£15
V41	6d.	**deep blue-green**	..	£160	£20
		a yellow green	..	£350	£25
V42	1/–	**deep bluish purple**	..	£375	£130
V43	1/–	**indigo**	..	..	£325	£70

V37 and 42 exist with CANCELLED between bars.

V43 with "intermediate" perfs is now considered to be "rough" perf.

Numbers printed—V37/38, 180,070; V39/40, 30,240; V41, 26,160; V42/43, 9,120.

Many of the stamps listed above come from Remainders found in Perkins Bacon's premises in 1887 and amongst the papers of a one-time Crown Agent for the Colonies in 1896. The imperf between varieties (V29*a*, V32*a/b*) came from these sources.

The Perkins, Bacon Dies, Rollers and Plates were handed to the Crown Agents on January 28th, 1862. Later printings from the same plates were made by De La Rue. (See V52 etc.).

1852–60 PROVISIONAL LITHOGRAPHS

During the following five periods various circumstances led to shortages of stamps, and locally lithographed stamps were in temporary use:

Sept., 1852–May, 1853.
March, 1855–June, 1855.
Dec., 1856–Jan., 1857.
Oct., 1858–Jan., 1859.
March, 1860–June, 1860.

(*Litho*) **from die engraved by Charles Petit. No wmk. Imperf. Sheets 9 x 6.**

(a) 1852 (Sept. 25th)-53.

V44	1d.	**blue** (thick yellowish paper)	..	..	—	£800
V45	1d.	**blue** (bluish cartridge paper) (2/53)	..	—	£850

(b) 1855 (March 25th) Impression less sharp.

V46	1d.	**pl to greenish blue** (thinner paper)	..	—	£500

(c) 1856 (Dec. 13th) Background lines often over-inked.

V47	1d.	**bt to prussian blue** (creamy paper)	..	—	£475

(d) 1858 (Oct. 25th) Background lines barely visible.

V48	1d.	**dp greenish blue**	..	—	£275
V49	1d.	**slate-blue**	..	..	—	£275

(e) 1860 (March 12th) Background lines absent.

V50	1d.	**grey to bluish grey**	..	—	£185
V51	1d.	**red** (shades)	..	£10	£180

Like the Perkins, Bacon 1d. stamps, these lithographed copies bear no indication of value.

Remainders of V51 were found in the Colonial Secretary's Office in 1882, and complete sheets are known.

Prices for V44/51 are for average copies and a substantial premium may be expected for copies in fine condition.

Dates given are earliest recorded for each printing.

1862-63 As Nos. V37/43 but printed (*recess*) by De La Rue from the Perkins Bacon plates. Thick paper. No wmk.

(a) Perf. 11½-12.

V52	1d.	**crimson-lake**	..	£30	7·50
V53	4d.	**deep purple**	..	£30	£16
V54	6d.	**deep green**	..	£225	£16
V55	1/–	**bluish-slate**	..	£275	£45

(b) Compound Perf. 11½-12 x 11.

V56	1d.	**crimson-lake**	..	—	£180
V57	6d.	**deep green**	..	—	£2000

(c) Perf. 13 (1863).

V58	1d.	**lake**	..	..	£11	£10
V59	6d.	**emerald-green**	..	£140	£25
V60	1/–	**bright mauve**	..	£1200	£125

(d) Perf. 12¼ (1863).

V61	1d.	**lake**	..	..	7·00	7·00

V52—Imperf Colour Trials by De La Rue exist on unwatermarked paper in pale lilac, deep lilac purple and orange-red.

1863-76 As before but Wmk. Crown CC.

(a) Perf. 12¼.

V62	1d.	**lake**	..	..	8·00	2·50
		a wmk sideways	..	£35	5·00
V63	1d.	**rose**	..	..	8·00	1·25
		a imperf (pair)	..	—	—
V64	1d.	**scarlet**	..	..	7·00	1·00
V65	1d.	**carmine**	..	..	8·00	1·25
V66	4d.	**bright violet**	..	£25	4·50
		a imperf (pair)	..	—	—
V67	4d.	**pale mauve**	..	£60	4·50
V68	4d.	**dull lilac**	..	£10	5·00
V69	4d.	**grey** ('72)	..	£20	2·50
V70	4d.	**bluish-grey** ('72)	..	£20	3·00
V71	6d.	**emerald green**	..	£15	6·00
V72	6d.	**deep green**	..	£100	6·00
V73	6d.	**yellow-green**	..	£11	3·00
		a imperf (pair)	..	—	—
V74	6d.	**apple-green**	..	£10	3·50
V75	6d.	**blue-green**	..	£16	3·00
V76	1/–	**bright deep mauve**	..	£55	4·00
V77	1/–	**lilac-rose**	..	..	£34	4·00
V78	1/–	**aniline mauve**	..	£27	4·00
V79	1/–	**chrome-yellow** ('72)	..	£33	2·00

(b) Perf. 14 (1876).

V80	1d.	**lake**	..	..	1·75	60
		a bisect (½d.) on cover	..	—	£150

V81	1d.	**rose-carmine** ..	2·50	75
V82	1d.	**scarlet**	£12	1·00
V83	4d.	**bluish grey**	£14	1·50
V84	6d.	**bright yellow-green**	£14	1·50
V85	6d.	**dp yellow-green** ..	£15	1·25
V86	1/–	**chrome-yellow** ..	£15	3·50

(c) Perf. 14 x 12½ (1876).

V87	6d.	**yellow-green** ..	—	£2000

V80*a* can exist stuck on to stationery by the Post Office.

1869 (*typo*) **De La Rue. Wmk. Crown CC. Perf. 12¾. Sheets 12 x 20.**

V88	5/–	**rose-lake**	£25	£22

Die Proofs exist in black and in deep pinkish mauve on white glazed card.

Number printed—10,020.
(See also No. V110).

1879-82 Undenominated (1d.) stamps surcharged HALFPENNY or ONE PENNY in black sans serif capitals by De La Rue. Perf. 14.

(a) Wmk. Crown CC. (6/79).

V89	½d.	**lilac**	4·00	4·50
V90	½d.	**mauve**	4·50	5·00
		a wmk. sideways ..	£10	£10

(b) Wmk. Crown CA ('82).

V91	½d.	**lilac**	£120	£20
V92	1d.	**rose-carmine** ..	6·00	75
		a bisect diag. or vert (½d.) on cover ('82-'83)	‡	£130

V89/92—These stamps were not issued with these watermarks without the surcharge.

Numbers printed—V89/90, 49,630; V91, 11,000; V92, 216,150.

1882 As Nos. V83 but Wmk. Crown CA. Perf. 14.

V93	4d.	**bluish grey**	£28	4·50

Number printed—70,320.

1882 (May 9th-Dec. 27th) Nos. V84/85 locally surcharged "1d." (in various styles) and the original value deleted in manuscript.

(a) In black.

V94	1d. on 6d.	**bt yel-grn** ..	—	£375

(b) In red.

V95	1d. on 6d.	**bt yel-grn** ..	3·00	2·00
V96	1d. on 6d.	**dp yel-grn** ..	3·00	2·50
		a bisect vert (½d.) on cover (12/82) ..	‡	£120

1883 (Jan.)-84 (*typo*) **De La Rue. Wmk. Crown CA. Perf. 14. Sheets 120 – two panes, each 6 x 10.**

V97	½d.	**dull green**	30	20
V98	1d.	**carmine**	50	20
		a bisect diag (½d.) on cover	‡	£300
V99	2½d.	**bright blue**	1·50	25
V100	4d.	**grey**	1·50	50
V101	6d.	**olive-black** ('84) ..	1·75	2·00
V102	1/–	**orange-brown** ('84)	3·25	2·25
V97/102		**set** (6v)	8·00	5·00

1891 (Feb. 23rd) Visit of Duke of York (later King George V) Nos. V97/102 and V88 locally surcharged "9d." in black.

V103	9d. on ½d.	**dull green** ..	—	—
V104	9d. on 1d.	**carmine** ..	—	—
V105	9d. on 2½d.	**bright blue**	—	—
V106	9d. on 4d.	**grey**	—	—
V107	9d. on 6d.	**olive-black**	—	—
V108	9d. on 1/–	**orange-brn**	—	—
V109	9d. on 5/–	**rose-lake** ..	—	—
V103/109		**set**	£2500	—

Five sets of V103/109 were surcharged, one of which was also date stamped, and three of which were given to be sold for charity. Various items of Postal Stationery were similarly surcharged.

1894 As No. V88 but new colour. Perf. 14.

V110	5/–	**marone**	6·00	9·00

See also No. V88.

1896 (Aug. 17th)-1900 (*typo*) **De La Rue. Perf. 14. Sheets V111/119 120 – two panes, each 6 x 10; V120/122, 12 x 5.**

(a) Wmk. Crown CA.

V111	½d.	**dl pur and grn** ..	15	15
V112	½d.	**pl dl pur and bt grn**	15	15
V113	1d.	**dl pur and rose** (Type I)	25	15
V114	1d.	**dl pur and rose** (Type II)	£35	1·25

V115 2½d. **dl purple and blue** 50 40
V116 4d. **dl pur and orange** .. 1·50 2·50
V117 5d. **dl pur and mauve** 1·75 3·00
V118 6d. **dl pur and black** .. 1·75 2·00
V119 1/– **grn and brown** .. 3·00 4·00

(b) Wmk. CA over Crown.

V120 5/– **green and brown** .. £18 £22
V121 10/–**green and ult** .. £175 £145
V122 £1 **grn and car OC** .. £110 £100
V111/122 **set** (10v excluding
V114) £310 £275

SPV111/122 **specimen set**
(10v) .. .. £85 ‡

V113/114—Type I—Centre of "O" in "ONE" is
round; Type II—Centre of "O" in "ONE" is oval
vertically (1900).

V111—Colour trials exist on unwatermarked paper
in green and purple combined with varous colours
for the denomination.

V120/V121/V122—Imperf. colour trials exist in the
issued colours.

**1899 (Dec.) Prepared for use but not issued.
No. V117 surcharged in black by De La Rue.
"3d." with bar obliterating FIVE PENCE.**

V123 3d. on 5d. **dull purple** .. £4000 ‡
SPV123 **specimen (1)** .. £65 ‡
Number printed—6,240.

**1898 (July 31st) 400th Anniversary of
Discovery by Columbus.** (recess) **De La Rue.
Wmk. Crown CC. Perf. 14. Sheets 12 x 5.**

V124 2d. **brn and dl violet** .. 1·50 75
SPV124 **specimen (1)**.. .. £35 ‡
Number printed—539,400.

Colour Trials, imperf and on unwatermarked paper,
are known in a large variety of colour combinations.
Price from £95 each.

1901-06 As Nos. V111/120 but new colours.

E1 ½d. **grey-green** ('02) .. 20 15
E2 1d. **brn and blk/red** (Type
II) 25 10
a value omitted .. £6000 —
E3 2½d. **pur and blue/blue**
('02) .. .. 1·25 60
E4 4d. **green and blue/buff
OC** ('03) .. .. 1·00 1·25
E5 1/– **blk and blue/yel** ('03)
E6 5/– **lilac and mauve** 3·00 2·75
E7 5/– **dp pur and mauve
OC** ('06) .. £12 £13
.. £12 £13
E1/7 **set** (6v) £17 £17
SPE1/7 **specimen set** (6v) .. £60 ‡
E2—See Note after V114.

E2a—One pane of 60 was found in Trinidad. At
most nine were sold the remainder being returned
to London and destroyed. Of those sold some
were used and lost and only two unused (possibly
three) survived.

E2—Colour trials both on unwatermarked and
Crown CA paper exist in a large variety of
colour combinations on various coloured papers.

**1904-09 As before but Wmk. Multiple Crown
CA.**

E8 ½d. **grey-green OC** .. 40 25
E9 ½d. **blue-green** ('06) .. 1·00 50
E10 1d. **black/red OC** (Type
II) 35 15
E11 1d. **rose-red** ('07) .. 30 15
E12 2½d. **purple and blue/blue
C** .. .. .. 5·00 2·00
E13 2½d. **blue** ('06) 50 25
E14 4d. **grey and red/yel C**
('06) .. .. 1·50 2·75
E15 4d. **black and red/yel C** 4·50 4·50
E16 6d. **dl pur and blk C** ('05) 4·50 3·25
E17 6d. **dl and bt pur C** ('06) 2·50 2·75
E18 1/– **blk and blue/yel C**.. 4·50 5·00
E19 1/– **pur and blue/golden
yellow C** .. .. 5·50 6·00
E20 1/– **black/green C** ('06) 1·50 2·00
a on emerald .. 1·75 2·50
E21 5/– **dp pur and mauve C**
('07) £17 £20
E22 5/– **dk lilac and violet C**
(11/09) £17 £20
E23 £1 **grn and car C** ('06).. £90 £75
E8/23 **set** (14v) £130 £125
SPE11/20 **specimen set** (6v) £45 ‡

E11 was printed from a new Die on which the
letters of value are short and thick, and the top of
Britannia's spear cuts the top line of shading.

E14/E15—Imperforate colour trials exist in the
issued colours of 4d., 6d. and 1/– values (E15,
E17, E20).

1909 (typo) **De La Rue. Wmk. Multiple Crown
CA. Perf. 14. Sheets 120 – two panes, each
6 x 10.**

E24 ½d. **green** 15 10
E25 1d. **rose-red** 15 10
E26 2½d. **blue** .. .. 1·25 1·50
E24/26 **set** (3v) .. .. 1·50 1·60
SPE24/26 **specimen set** (3v) £32 ‡

From 1913 the joint Trinidad and Tobago issues
came into use.

POSTAGE DUE STAMPS

1885 (Jan.1st) *(typo)* **De La Rue. Wmk. Crown CA. Perf. 14. Sheets 6 x 10.**

VD1	½d.	**slate-black**	7·50	1·50
VD2	1d.	**slate-black**	30	30
VD3	2d.	**slate-black**	2·50	40
		a value in blue-black	—	—
VD4	3d.	**slate-black**	3·25	75
VD5	4d.	**slate-black**	4·25	2·50
VD6	5d.	**slate-black**	4·25	1·00
VD7	6d.	**slate-black**	6·00	4·00
VD8	8d.	**slate-black**	6·00	4·00
		a double print	—	—
VD9	1/–	**slate-black**	6·00	7·00
		a upright diagonal ..	£20	—
VD1/9		**set** (9v)	£35	£20

VD8*a*—Both frame and value are doubled.

VD9*a*—The diagonal bar is more upright on No. 5 of all rows.

All values are known overprinted specimen.

1905-06 As before but Wmk. Multiple Crown CA.

ED1	1d.	**slate-black**	20	20
ED2	2d.	**slate-black**	30	25
ED3	3d.	**slate-black**	30	25
ED4	4d.	**slate-black**	50	60
ED5	5d.	**slate-black**	1·25	1·00
ED6	6d.	**slate-black**	2·00	1·50
ED7	8d.	**slate-black**	2·00	1·50
ED8	1/–	**slate-black**	4·50	3·50
		a upright diagonal	£20	—
ED1/8		**set** (8v)	£10	8·00

ED8*a*—See Note after VD9*a*.

OFFICIAL STAMPS

1894 Nos. V97/102 and V88 locally overprinted "O S" in black.

VO1	½d.	**dull green**	9·00	9·00
VO2	1d.	**carmine**	£11	£11
VO3	2½d.	**ultramarine**	£12	£12
VO4	4d.	**grey**	£14	£14
VO5	6d.	**olive-black**	£14	£14
VO6	1/–	**orange-brown**	£22	£22
VO7	5/–	**rose-lake**	£40	£42

1909 Nos. E8 and E11 locally overprinted "OFFICIAL" in black sans serif capitals.

EO1	½d.	**green**	30	30
EO2	1d.	**rose-red**	15	15
		a overprint double ..	—	£65
		b overprint inverted ..	—	£60
		c overprint vertical ..	£15	—

1910 (April) No. E24 similarly overprinted.

EO3	½d.	**green**	15	15
		a spaced "OF" ..	—	—

EO3*a*—The "O" and first "F" of "OFFICIAL" are wide spaced.

LOCAL ISSUE

Issued by David Bryce (the owner of the S.S. Lady McLeod) to cover local postal charges on letters carried by his vessel between Port of Spain and San Fernando.

1847 (April 11th) *(litho)* **(In Trinidad by Charles Petit?). Thick yellowish paper. No Wmk. Imperf. Sheets 10 x 10.**

L1	5c.	**deep blue**..	£8500	£4250

Although the stamps bear no indication of value, they were sold at 5c. (or $4 per 100). Used copies are usually cancelled with a pen mark in the form of a cross or a series of diagonal lines which do not normally tie the stamp to the cover.

The majority of surviving copies are used on entire or on cover.

It is said that the Die from which the lithographic stone was prepared was destroyed in 1895.

TRINIDAD & TOBAGO

See under TOBAGO and TRINIDAD for details of the early Postal History, and previous issues.

All stamps to G95 are (*typo*) **De La Rue. Perf. 14.**

1913-23 Wmk. Multiple Crown CA. Sheets G1/19 240 – four panes, each 6 x 10.

G1	½d.	**green**	15	15
G2	½d.	**yellow-green** ('15) ..	35	30
G3	½d.	**dark green**	35	30
G4	½d.	**blu grn/bluish** (3/18)	4·50	4·50
		a on thick bluish paper		
		('17)	30	25
G5	1d.	**bright red**	30	25
G6	1d.	**scarlet** (5/16) ..	15	10
G7	1d.	**pink** (thick paper)		
		('18)	2·25	50
G8	1d.	**rose-carmine/bluish**		
		(7/18)	15	10
		a on thick bluish paper		
		(7/18)	15	10
G9	2½d.	**ultramarine** ..	1·25	50
G10	2½d.	**deep blue** (9/16) ..	1·00	75
G11	2½d.	**bt blue/bluish** ('18)	2.00	1·00
		a on thick bluish paper		
		('18)	2·00	1·00
G12	4d.	**grey and red/yellow OC**	80	1·25
		a on pl yellow ('23) ..	2·50	3·50
		b on buff (thick paper)	7·00	—
G13	4d.	**blk and bt red/lemon** ('17)	9·00	—
		a on yellow	2·50	2·50
		b white back ('13) ..	2·50	2·50
G14	4d.	**blk and dl red/yel** ..	2·50	2·50
G15	6d.	**dl and reddish purple C**	3·25	2·00
G16	6d.	**dl and dp purple** ('18)	1·75	1·75
G17	6d.	**dl purple and violet**	2·00	2·50
G18	6d.	**dl purple and mauve** ('18)	2·00	2·50
G19	1/-	**black/green** ..	1·75	2·00
		a white back	1·00	2·00
		b on blue-green (olive back)	1·75	2·00
		c on emerald	1·75	1·50
G20	5/-	**pur and bt pur C** ('14)	9·00	£10
G21	5/-	**brn-pur and dp pur** ('18)	£10	£11
G22	5/-	**pl pur and mauve** ('19)	£13	£14
G23	5/-	**dl and dp violet** ('20)	£16	£18

G24	5/-	**dp pur and bt violet** ('20)	£12	£15
G25	£1	**grn and car C** ('14) ..	£75	£65
G26	£1	**dp yel-grn and pink** ('18)	£70	£70
G27	£1	**pl yel-grn and crim** ('19)	£70	£70
G28	£1	**grey-grn and rose-pink** ('20)	£70	£70
G29	£1	**dp grn and rose-pink** ('20)	£65	£75
G1/29		**set** (8v)	£78	£80
SPG1/29		**specimen set** (12v)	£120	‡

1915-16 Red Cross. Nos. G5/6 locally overprinted in red (Cross) and black (Outline to cross, and date) in sheets of 120 (two panes, each 6 x 10).

(a) October 21st, 1915.

G30	1d.	**bright red**	25	35
		a cross to right ..	£10	—
		b forked "1" ..	£10	—
		c thick "5"	£10	—
		d narrow "2"	£10	—
		e antique "2"	£10	—
		f broken "2"	£10	—
		g broken "O"	£10	—

G30*a*—The Cross is 2mm. to the right. Right hand pane Row 2/5.

G30*b*—The "1" in "21" has a forked foot. Right hand pane. Row 7/6.

G30*c*—The "5" in "15" is thick. Right hand pane, Row 8/1.

G30*d*—The "2" in "21" is narrow. Right hand pane, Row 10/3.

G30*e*—The "2" in "21" is antique type. Left hand pane, Row 5/5.

G30*f*—The "2" in "21" is broken, and "1" and "5" in "15" joined. Left hand pane, Row 7/2.

G30*g*—The "0" in "10" is broken. Left hand pane, Row 8/3.

(b) October 19th, 1916.

G31	1d.	**scarlet**	15	30
		a no stop after "16" ..	3·00	3·75
		b "19.10.16" omitted	—	—

The lateral position of the Cross in relation to the date varies considerably.

G31*a*—The stop after "16" is omitted. Right hand pane, Row 1/4 and 5/2.

These stamps were issued on and near the anniversary of Trafalgar Day (October 21st, 1805). They were valid for 1d. postage, of which ½d. was made over to Red Cross Funds.

Numbers printed—G30, 100,000; G31, 250,000.

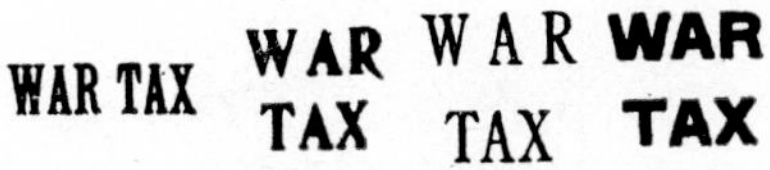

WAR TAX **WAR** W A R **WAR**
TAX TAX **TAX**

Type I   Type II   Type III   Type IV

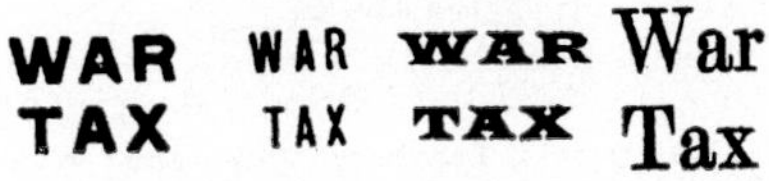

WAR WAR **WAR** War
TAX TAX **TAX** Tax

Type V   Type VI   Type VII   Type VIII

1917-18 War Tax. Nos. G1/8 locally over-printed in black in sheets of 120 (two panes, each 6 x 10).

(a) Type I. April 2nd 1917.

G32	1d.	**scarlet** (thin paper: yellow gum).. ..	15	20
G33	1d.	**dp red** (thick paper: clear gum)	35	35
		a overprint inverted ..	£65	—

Numbers printed—G32, 210,000; G33, 30,000.

(b) Type II. May 7th, 1917.

G34	½d.	**dp green** (thin paper)	10	10
		a on thick bluish paper	15	15
		b overprint omitted (in pair with normal)	£65	—
G35	1d.	**red** (thin paper) ..	10	15
		a on thick bluish paper	15	20
		b overprint omitted (in pair with normal)	£65	—
G36	1d.	**scarlet**	15	15
		a overprint double ..	£40	—

Numbers printed—G34, 240,000; G35/36, 240,000.

(c) Type III. June 21st, 1917.

G37	½d.	**yel-grn** (thin paper)..	35	30
G38	½d.	**dp green** (medium paper)	35	35
		a on thick bluish paper	40	45
G39	1d.	**bright red** (25/6) ..	10	10
		a on thick bluish paper	15	15
		b overprint omitted (in pair with normal)	£65	—

Numbers printed—G37, 12,000; G38, 96,000; G39, 240,000.

G34b/35b/39b—These varieties were caused by a shift of the overprint to the left, so that the right hand vertical column lacked the overprint and an overprint appeared on the left margin.

(d) Type IV. July-September, 1917.

G40	½d.	**yel-grn** (thin paper) (21/7)	75	1·00
G41	½d.	**dp grn** (thick bluish paper)	15	20
G42	1d.	**bt scarlet** (thick bluish paper) (6/9) ..	10	10

Numbers printed—G40, 12,000; G41, 228,000; G42, 240,000.

(e) Type V. September 7th, 1917.

G43	½d.	**dl green** (thin paper)	15	15
G44	½d.	**dp grn** (thick bluish paper)	15	15
G45	1d.	**red** (thick bluish paper)	4·00	5·00

Numbers printed—G43/44, 240,000; G45, 6,000.

(f) Type VI. October 31st, 1917.

G46	1d.	**bt red** (thick paper)..	15	15
		a overprint inverted ..	£35	—

(g) Type VII. January 7th, 1918.

G47	1d.	**dl scarlet** (thin paper: clear gum)	15	15
		a overprint inverted ..	£35	—
G48	1d.	**bt red** (thick paper: yellow gum).. ..	20	20
		a overprint inverted ..	£35	—
		b overprint double ..	£55	—

Number printed—G47/48, 240,000.

(h) Type VIII. February-November, 1918.

G49	½d.	**dl grn/bluish** (13/2)	15	15
G50	½d.	**dp grn** (thick bluish grey paper) (6/18)..	20	20
G51	½d.	**dp yel-grn** (thick bluish grey (9/18) ..	15	15
		a on thin bluish-grey paper	15	15
		b overprint omitted (in pair with normal)	£125	—
		c "Tax" omitted ..	£150	—
G52	1d.	**scarlet** (thin paper) (13/2)	15	15
		a overprint double ..	£35	—
G53	1d.	**dl car** (thick bluish grey paper) (6/18)..	15	15
		a "Tax" spaced (14/9)	50	50
		b overprint double (G53*a*)	£60	—
		c on thin bluish grey paper (G53) (9/18)	50	50
G54	1d.	**rose-red** (thin paper) (11/18)	25	25
		a on thick paper ..	30	30

G51*c*—A complete sheet is known on which Row 10/1 of the left hand pane shows the overprint "War" only, and the word "Tax" appears on the reverse of the stamp (the corner of the sheet having been folded over).

G53*a* came from a later printing in which 19 stamps in the sheet had "Tax" wider spaced, so that the "x" of "Tax" fell to the right of the "r" of "War" instead of slightly to the left. "Tax" is spaced in the following positions:—

Left Pane: Row 3/2 and 4; Row 5/2, 4 and 6; Row 6/3; Row 7/6; Row 8/1 and 5; Row 10/3.

Right pane: Row 1/3; Row 2/2; Row 5/3 and 5; Row 6/6; Row 7/3; Row 8/6; Row 9/3 and 4.

In G54 this irregular spacing was corrected.

1921-22 As Nos. G1/29 but Wmk. Multiple Script CA. G55/64 O; G65/67 C.

G55	½d.	**green**	20	15
G56	½d.	**yellow-green** ..	20	15
G57	1d.	**scarlet**	15	15
G58	1d.	**brown** ('22) ..	15	15
G59	2d.	**grey** ('22)	1·25	1·25
G60	2½d.	**bright blue**	60	1·25
G61	3d.	**bright blue** ('22) ..	1·25	1·25
G62	6d.	**dl and bt purple** ..	1·25	1·25
G63	6d.	**dl pur and mauve**..	1·25	1,25

G64	6d.	**brn-pur and mag** ..	1·25	1·25
G65	5/–	**dl pur and pur** ('21)	£15	£17
G66	5/–	**dp pur and pur** ('22)	£15	£17
G67	£1	**green and carmine**	£70	£75
G55/67		**set** (9v)	£87	£95
SPG55/67		**specimen set** (9v)	£85	‡

1922-28 Sheets 160 – two panes, each 8 x 10.

(a) Wmk. Multiple Crown CA. C.

G68	4d.	**blk and red/pl yellow**	50	60
G69	1/–	**black/emerald** ..	1·75	2·50
G70	1/–	**grey and blk/em** ..	1·75	2·50

(b) Wmk. Multiple Script CA. G71/84 O; G85/95 C.

G71	½d.	**green**	10	10
G72	½d.	**bright green**	10	10
G73	½d.	**yellow-green**	10	10
G74	1d.	**brown**	15	10
G75	1d.	**dark brown**	15	10
	a	wmk inverted ..	£10	—
G76	1½d.	**rose**	35	15
G77	1½d.	**rose-red**	35	15
G78	1½d.	**scarlet**	20	15
G79	2d.	**grey**	30	20
G80	2d.	**deep grey**	30	20
G81	2d.	**pale grey**	30	20
G82	3d.	**blue**	75	35
G83	3d.	**royal blue**	75	35
G84	3d.	**pale blue**	75	35
G85	4d.	**grey and car/yel** ('28)	1·50	1·75
G86	4d.	**jet blk and car/pl yellow**	1·50	1·75
G87	4d.	**grey and scar/pl yel**	1·50	1·75
G88	6d.	**dl pur and pur** ..	3·75	6·50
G89	6d.	**dl pur and bt pur** ..	3·75	6.50
G90	6d.	**grn and red/em** ('24)	1·50	75
G91	6d.	**grn and brick red/ emerald**	1·50	75
G92	1/–	**black/emerald** ..	1·50	1·00
G93	5/–	**dl pur and mauve**..	£10	£11
G94	5/–	**dl pur and pur** ..	£10	£11
G95	£1	**green and bt rose**	£80	£90
G71/95		**set** (11v)	£95	£100
SPG68/95		**specimen set** (13v)	£95	‡

1935-37 (*recess*) **Bradbury, Wilkinson. Wmk. Multiple Script CA (sideways). Sheets 6 x 10.**

(a) Perf. 12. February 1st, 1935.

G96	1c.	**blue and green** ..	35	15
G97	2c.	**ult and yel-brn** ..	45	25
G98	3c.	**black and scarlet**	15	15
G99	6c.	**sepia and blue** ..	25	25
G100	8c.	**sage-grn and ver** ..	40	35
G101	12c.	**black and violet** ..	35	50
G102	24c.	**blk and ol-grn** ..	1·00	1·00
G103	48c.	**deep green**	4·50	5·50
G104	72c.	**myrtle-grn and car**	£10	£12
G96/104		**set** (9v)	£16	£19
SPG96/104		**specimen set** (9v)	£40	‡

(b) Perf. 12¾. 1936-37.

G105	1c.	**blue and green** ..	10	10
G106	2c.	**ult and yel-brn** ..	10	10
G107	3c.	**black and scarlet**	15	15
G108	6c.	**sepia and blue** ..	25	35
G109	12c.	**black and violet** ..	50	1·00
G110	24c.	**blk and ol-grn** ..	1·50	1·75
G105/110		**set** (6v)	2·50	3·25

1935 (May 6th) **Silver Jubilee.** (*recess*) **Bradbury Wilkinson. Wmk. Multiple Script CA. Perf. 11 x 12. Sheets 6 x 10.**

G111	2c.	**ult and grey-blk** ..	10	10
	a	extra flagstaff ..	£20	—
G112	3c.	**dp blue and scar** ..	15	15
	a	extra flagstaff ..	£30	—
G113	6c.	**brn and dp blue** ..	45	65
	a	extra flagstaff ..	£40	—
G114	24c.	**slate and purple**..	1·75	2·25
	a	extra flagstaff ..	£45	—
G111/114		**set** (4v)	2·25	3·00
SPG111/114		**specimen set** (4v)	£17	‡

G111*a*/114*a*—Extra flagstaff occurs on No. 49 (Row 9/1).

Number printed—G111, 1,300,000 ; G112, 502,000 ;
G113, 151,600 ; G114, 90,800.
Remainders were withdrawn on December 31st,
1935.

**1938 (May 2nd)-50 Designs, 1c. (First Boca);
2c. (Imperial College of Tropical Agriculture);
3c. (Mount Irvine Bay, Tobago); 4c. (War
Memorial, Memorial Park); 5c. (G.P.O. and
Treasury); 6c. (Raleigh discovering Lake
Asphalt); 8c. (Queen's Park, Savannah); 12c.
Town Hall, San Fernando); 24c. (Gov. House);
60c. (Blue Basin Waterfall). Printers** (recess)
**Bradbury, Wilkinson. Perf. 11½ x 11¼ (C).
Sheets 5 x 12.**

1	1c.	**dp blue and pl grn** ..	5	5
	a	vio-blue and pl green		
		(21/6/50)	5	5
2	2c.	**dk blue and lt brn** ..	5	5
	a	indigo and chest-brn		
		(12/11/45)	5	5
3	3c.	**black and red**	4·00	60
4	3c.	**green and choc-brn**		
		(1/4/41)	5	5
	a	green and pur-brn		
		(18/9/44)	5	5
	b	grn and dp pur-brn		
		(16/3/49)	5	5
5	4c.	**brown**	1·75	90
6	4c.	**scarlet** (1/4/41) ..	15	15
	a	scar-rose (6/42) ..	15	15
	b	dp scar-rose (16/3/49)	20	15
7	5c.	**dp claret** (1/5/41) ..	10	5
	a	magenta (22/9/47)	15	5
8	6c.	**sepia-brn and blue** ..	10	5
	a	sepia-brn and dl blue		
		(10/43)	20	5
	b	sepia-brn and grey-		
		blue (22/9/47) ..	30	10
	c	sepia-brn and br blue		
		(16/3/49)	15	5
9	8c.	**sage-grn and dp or** ..	10	10
	a	sage-grn and red-or		
		(10/43)	10	10
10	12c.	**blk and pur-vio** ..	1·25	75
	aa	blk and dp vio (/41)	2·50	1·00
	a	blk and dp pur-vio		
		(18/9/44) ..	50	10
11	24c.	**blk and ol-grn** ..	40	15
	a	blk and dp ol (6/42)	40	15
12	60c.	**myrtle-grn and car** ..	1·25	75
	a	dk myrtle and carmine		
		(10/43)	1·00	60

**1940-2 Design (small format) Portrait of King
with Palms left side. Perf. 12 (L). Printers as
before. Sheets 12 x 10.**

13	$1.20	**bluish-grn** (2/1/40)	1·25	50
	a	green (6/42) ..	1·25	50
14	$4.80	**car-rose** (2/1/40) ..	£10	5·00
	a	bt car-rose	£10	5·00
1/14		**set** (14)	£18	8·00
SP1/14		**specimen set** perf		
		(13)	£50	‡

SPECIAL ISSUES

1937 (May 12th) Coronation. As Aden.

S1	1c.	**green**	10	10
S2	2c.	**yellow-brown** ..	15	15
S3	8c.	**orange**	30	30
SP S1/3		**specimen set** perf (3)	£14	‡

1946 (Oct. 1st) Victory. As Aden.

S4	3c.	**brown**	10	10
S5	6c.	**dp blue**	10	10
SP S4/5		**specimen set** perf (2)	£13	‡

1948 (Nov. 22nd) Silver Wedding. As Aden.

S6	3c.	**chestnut-brown** ..	10	10
S7	$4.80	**rose-car** (all recess)	8·00	9·50

1949 (Oct. 10th) U.P.U. As Aden.

S8	5c.	**magenta**	10	10
S9	6c.	**indigo**	15	25
S10	12c.	**purple**	30	30
S11	24c.	**sage-green**	50	50
S8/11		**set** (4)	1·00	1·00

**1951 (Feb. 16th) West Indies University
College. (See Antigua). Inscribed "TRINI-
DAD" only.**

S12	3c.	**green and brown** ..	15	10
S13	12c.	**blk and pur-vio** ..	40	35

POSTAGE DUE STAMPS

(Inscribed "TRINIDAD")

1923-45 (typo) **De La Rue. Wmk. Multiple
Script CA. Perf. 13¾ x 14. Sheets 6 x 10.**

GD1	1d.	**black**	30	40
GD2	2d.	**black**	30	40
GD3	3d.	**black** ('25) ..	35	40
GD4	4d.	**black** ('29) ..	1·25	1·50
GD5	5d.	**black** ('44) ..	1·25	1·50
GD6	6d.	**black** ('45) ..	1·50	2·50
GD7	8d.	**black** ('45) ..	2·00	3·50
GD8	1/–	**black** ('45) ..	7·50	8·00
	a	upright diagonal	£15	£12
GD1/8		**set** (8v)	£13	£16
SPGD1/8		**specimen set** (8v)	£65	‡

GD8*a*—The diagonal bar is more upright on No. 5 of all rows (See Trinidad Nos. VD9a and ED8a).

GD2/4—Early printings were on smooth paper, whereas the 1940 printings were on rough paper.

1947 (Sept. 1st) Design, etc., as before, but currency changed. Sheets 6 x 10.

PD7	2c. **black** ..	..	..	15	15
PD8	4c. **black** ..	..	..	10	15
PD9	6c. **black** ..	..	..	15	15
PD10	8c. **black** ..	..	..	15	25
PD11	10c. **black** ..	..	..	30	45
PD12	12c. **black** ..	..	..	30	45
PD13	16c. **black** ..	..	..	40	75
PD14	24c. **black** ..	..	..	50	75
PD7/14	**set** (8)	..	..	2·00	3·00
SPPD7/PD14	**specimen set** (8v)	£70			‡

1953-61 Printers (*typo*) **De La Rue. Perf 13¾ x 14 (C). Chalk-surfaced paper. Sheets 6 x 10.**

PD15	2c. **black** (20/1/53)	..	15	15
PD16	4c. **black** (10/8/55)	..	15	15
PD17	6c. **black** (20/1/53)	..	15	15
PD18	8c. **black** (10/9/58)	..	15	20
PD19	10c. **black** (10/8/55)	..	20	20
PD20	12c. **black** (20/1/53)	..	40	50
PD21	16c. **black** (22/8/61)	..	25	30
PD22	24c. **black** (10/9/55)	..	40	40
PD15/22	**set** (8)	..	..	1·50	2·00

Watermark Varieties (Type A)

(See Introduction for details).

PD15a	2c. Crown missing	..	£25	—
PD15b	St. Edward's Crown		£12	—
PD17a	6c. Crown missing	..	£30	—
PD17b	St. Edward's Crown		£18	—
PD20a	12c. Crown missing	..	£35	—
PD20b	St. Edward's Crown		£20	—

OFFICIAL STAMPS

Type I

Type II

Type III

Type IV

1913-17 Nos. G1/4 locally overprinted in black in sheets of 120 (two panes, each 6 x 10).

(a) Type I (1913).

GO1	½d. **green** ..	..	..	20	20
	a overprint vertical ..			—	—

(b) Type II (1914).

GO2	½d. **green** ..	..	..	60	75

(c) Type III (with stop) August 1916.

GO3	½d. **yellow-green**	..	25	25
	a overprint double ..		9·00	—

(d) Type III (without stop) July 1917.

GO4	½d. **dp grn** (thick paper)	30	30
GO5	½d. **green** (thin paper) ..	30	30
GO6	½d. **yel-grn** (thin paper)	30	30

Number printed—GO4/6, 12,000.

(e) Type IV. August 22nd, 1917.

GO7	½d. **yel-grn** (thin paper)	30	50
GO8	½d. **blue-grn** (thick paper)	15	15
GO9	½d. **green** (thin paper)	20	20

SEMI POSTAL ISSUES

1914 (September 18th) Red Cross Fund. Locally type-set. Perf. 11. Sheets 4 x 5.

GSP1	1 **fraction red** ..	..	30	5·00

These labels were issued by the local Red Cross Society and sold at ½d. for the benefit of their funds.

They were also officially authorised for use on correspondence, franked by certain members of the Red Cross Committee, which was entitled to carriage postage free.

On September 18th, 1914, before instructions had been given to outlying Post Offices, 900 letters bearing these labels in the handwriting of Mrs. E. M. Phillips were presented at the G.P.O. for despatch and some signed later by her to authenticate them. On this occasion only the Red Cross labels were postmarked (G.P.O. Port of Spain, Trinidad, 3 p.m.) ; thereafter, strict instructions were given that the labels should not be postmarked. (Price used on cover £75).

GERMAN PROPAGANDA LABELS

The 1944 German imitations of the G.B. 1937 Definitives ½d. to 3d. (see after Great Britain for details) were also overprinted in black "LIQUIDA-TION/OF EMPIRE/TRINIDAD" within a vertical rectangular frame.

Price (6v) unused or cancelled £120.

TRISTAN DA CUNHA

Originally occupied by Great Britain in 1816 to prevent its possible use as a base to rescue Napolean from St. Helena, the island was declared a dependency of St. Helena on January 3rd, 1938.

There was no Post Office until stamps were issued in 1952; and mail was despatched by visiting ships either without stamps or with G.B. (or other Commonwealth issues) often cancelled with an undated circular postmark in black, blue or red. (See illustration below).

These are a number of types of circular, oval and rectangular cancellations and collectors should refer to the handbook "Tristan da Cunha" by J. Mackey & G. Crabb published 1965.

During the 1939-45 War the island was known as H.M.S. Atlantic Isle and there was a certain volume of mail from Services personnel.

1952 (Jan. 1st) No. 1, etc., of St. Helena, overprinted TRISTAN DA CUNHA, for use in the Island Dependency. Sheets 6 x 10 (overprint setting 3 x 5).

1	½d.	**violet**	25	40
2	1d.	**black and green**	25	50
3	1½d.	**blk and car-rose**	25	80
4	2d.	**black and carmine**	25	90
5	3d.	**slate**	50	1·00
6	4d.	**ultramarine**	60	1·25
7	6d.	**sky-blue**	1·00	1·25
8	8d.	**dp olive-green**	1·25	2·50
9	1/–	**deep sepia**	1·25	3·50
10	2/6	**claret**	7·50	8·50
11	5/–	**lt choc-brn**	£18	£22
12	10/–	**deep purple**	£45	£55
1/12		**set (12)**	£75	£95

Inverted overprints on 1d. CW2, are bogus.

TURKS ISLANDS

The islands were settled from and administered by Bermuda until 1799, when they came under Bahamas until 1848. In 1873 they were transferred as a dependency of Jamaica, and became a Crown Colony on August 6th, 1962.

A Crowned Circle PAID Frank was registered at the G.P.O. in London for use (in red) to indicate prepayment of postage on overseas letters (See Introduction).

? PAID FRANK		On cover
VF1		£750

1867 (April 4th) *(recess)* **Perkins Bacon. No Wmk. Perf. 11-12. Sheets 10 x 3.**

V1	1d.	**dull rose**	..	..	£15	£18
		a neck flaw	..	..	£75	—
V2	6d.	**black**	..	..	£25	£25
V3	1/-	**dull blue**	..	..	£25	£25

V1*a*—A flaw appears on the Queen's neck. Row 3/4.

Die Proofs of all three values exist in black on white card, and of the 1d. and 6d. in black on India paper.

Plate Proofs of all three values exist in black on white wove paper.

Numbers printed—V1, 60,010; V2/V3, 12,000 each.

1873-79 As before but Wmk. Small Star.

(a) Perf. 11-12 x 14½-15½.

V5	1d.	**dl rose-lake** (7/73)	..		£18	£18
V4	1d.	**dull red** (1/79)	..		£25	£25
		a imperf. between				
		(pair)	..	..	£2000	—
V6	1/-	**lilac** ('79)	..	..	£2000	£750

(b) Perf. 11-12.

V7	1d.	**dull red**	..	..	£25	£25

V6 was intended to have been the same colour as V3.

Numbers printed—V4, 40,000; V5/V7, 20,000; V6, 5,000.

1881 (Jan. 1st) **Nos. V2/3** and **V5/6 locally surcharged in black.**

(a) ½.

V8	½d. on 1d.	**dull red**	..		£15	£15
		a surcharge double	..		—	—
V9	½d. on 6d.	**black**	..	..	£22	£25
V10	½d. on 1/-	**dull blue**	..		£25	£30
		a surcharge double	..		£800	—
V11	½d. on 1/-	**lilac**	..	..	£30	£30
		a surcharge double	..		£800	—

(b) 2½.

V12	2½d. on 1d.	**dull red**		£90	—
V13	2½d. on 6d.	**black**	..	£75	£75
		a surcharge double	..	—	—
		b imperf between (pair)	..	—	—
V14	2½d. on 1/-	**dull blue**	..	£175	—
V15	2½d. on 1/-	**lilac**	..	£250	£250
		a fraction double	..	£800	—

(c) 4.

V16	4d. on 1d.	**dull red**	..	£175	£175
		a surcharge inverted	..	—	—
V17	4d. on 6d.	**black**	..	£20	£80
V18	4d. on 1/-	**lilac**	..	£180	—

The above represents a completely simplified listing of a very complicated series of provisional surcharges.

½d. Twelve different settings employing 13 different types of fraction.

2½d. Nine different settings employing 13 different types of numerals.

4d. Six different settings employing 3 different types of numerals.

Prices quoted for V8 to V18 are, in each case, for the cheapest variety.

The Perkins Bacon Dies, Rollers and Plates were handed to the Crown Agents on March 18th, 1881.

See Introduction for details of Dies I and II.

1881 (Aug.-Oct.) **As before but printed** *(recess)* **by De La Rue from the same plates; and new value (4d.)** *(typo).* **Wmk. Crown CC (sideways on 1d., 6d. and 1/-). Perf. 14.**

V19	1d.	**brown-red** (Oct.)	..	£14	£14
V20	4d.	**ultramarine** (Die I)	..	£24	£24
V21	6d.	**olive-black** (Oct.)	..	£40	£40
V22	1/-	**slate-green** (Oct.)	..	£45	£45

Numbers printed—V19, 6,000; V20, 20,220; V21, 2,010; V22, 2,100.

1882-89 As before but Wmk. Crown CA. ½d., 2½d. and 4d. *(typo)*; **1d., 6d. and 1/- (recess).**

(a) Perf. 14.

V23	½d.	**blue-green** (Die I) (2/82)	..	4·50	8·00
V24	½d.	**pale green** (Die I) ('86)	..	1·00	1·75
V25	1d.	**orange-brn** (10/84)		£14	£20
		a bisect vert or diag (½d.) on cover	..	‡	£450
V26	1d.	**crimson-lake** (7/89)		1·25	2·50

V27	1d.	**lake**	1·00	2·25
V28	1d.	**pale rosy lake** ..	1·00	3·00
V29	2½d.	**red-brown** (Die I)		
		(10/84)	8·00	£11
V30	4d.	**grey** (Die 1) (10/84)..	3·50	4·50
		a bisect (2d.) on cover	‡	£400
V31	6d.	**yellow-brown** ('89)	4·50	4·50
V32	1/–	**sepia** ('86)	2·25	3·50

(b) Perf. 12.

V33	1d.	**crimson-lake** (7/87)	4·00	4·75
		a imperf between (pair)	—	—
SPV30/31	**specimen set** (2v)	£35	‡

1889 (May). No. V26 surcharged "One Penny" in black at Grand Turk.

V34	1d. on 2½d.	**red-brown** ..	3·50	4·00
		a surcharge		
		diagonal	—	—

See Introduction for details of Dies I and II.

1893 (April)-95 (*typo*) **De La Rue. Wmk. Crown CA. Perf. 14. Sheets 120 – two panes, each 6 x 10.**

V35	½d.	**dl green** (Die II) ('94)	35	40
V36	2½d.	**ult** (Die II) (4/93) ..	1·50	1·25
V37	4d.	**dl pur and ult** (Die II)		
		(5/95)	1·50	4·50

V38	5d.	**ol-grn and car** (6/95)	1·50	4·50
		a bisect diag (2½d.) on		
		cover	‡	£800
SPV36/38	**specimen set** (3v)	£45	‡

1893 (June). No. V30 surcharged ½d. in a horizontal setting of six in black at Grand Turk: a thick line obliterates the original value.

(a) 1st Setting. Fraction bar separate on each stamp.

V39	½d. on 4d.	**grey**	£85	£60

(b) 2nd Setting. Fraction bar continuous across the sheet. Thin and thick bars 10¾mm. apart. "2" directly under "1".

V40	½d. on 4d.	**grey**	£40	£37

(c) 3rd Setting. As 2nd Setting but bars 11¾ mm. apart.

V41	½d. on 4d.	**grey**	£40	£40

(d) 4th Setting. As 2nd Setting but bars 11mm. apart. On five of the six varieties in the strip the "2" is below the space between "1" and "d".

V42	½d. on 4d.	**grey**	£40	—

A 5th Setting shows very minor variations.

From 1900 the joint Turks and Caicos issues came into use.

TURKS & CAICOS ISLANDS

See under TURKS ISLANDS for previous issues. The title of the dependency changed in 1900.
All stamps to G57 (*recess*) **De La Rue & Co. Perf. 14.**

1900 Wmk. Crown CA.

E1	½d.	**yellow-green**	1·50	2·50
		a no wmk	£20	—
E2	1d.	**red**	1·50	1·50
		a no wmk	£20	—
E3	2d.	**sepia**	1·75	1·75
		a no wmk	£20	—
E4	2½d.	**blue**	3·25	5·75
		a grey blue	1·75	2·50
		b no wmk	£24	—
		c wmk inverted ..	£40	—
E5	4d.	**orange**	3·00	4·00
E6	6d.	**dull mauve**	2·25	4·00
		a no wmk	£20	—
E7	1/–	**brown**	2·00	4·00
		a red- brown	1·75	3·50
E1/7a		**set** (7)	£12	£18

All values occur with watermark letters of marginal inscription.

1900 Wmk. Crown C.C.

E8	2/– **purple**	£40	£45
E9	3/– **red**	£55	£60
SP E1/E9 **specimen set** (9) ..	£125	‡

1905/8 Wmk. Mult. Crown C.A., design as E1/7.

E10	½d.	**yellow-green**	60	60
E11	1d.	**red**	4·00	2·00
E12	3d.	**purple/yellow** ..	2·00	4·00

1909 Wmk. Mult. Crown C.A.

E13	½d.	**green**	15	15
		a wmk reversed ..	£20	—
E14	1d.	**red**	20	25
E15	2d.	**grey**	2·50	3·25
E16	2½d.	**ultramarine**	1·50	2·50
		a wmk reversed ..	£30	—
E17	3d.	**reddish-pur/yel** ..	2·00	3·00
		a dp pur/pl yel ..	2·00	3·00
E18	4d.	**red/yellow** ..	3·25	3·25
E19	6d.	**purple**	5·50	5·00
E20	1/–	**black/green**	4·00	4·75
		a black/blue-green ..	4·00	4·75
E21	2/–	**red/green**	£20	£24
E22	3/–	**black/red**	£25	£28
E13/22		**set** (10)	£60	£70
SP E13/22 **specimen set** (10)	£120	‡

1910 Wmk. Mult. Crown C.A.

E23	¼d.	**rosy-mauve**	30	30
E24	¼d.	**red**	20	20
		a rose-scarlet	20	20
		b salmon-pink (thick paper)	50	50
SPE23/24 **specimen set** (2)	£15	‡

1913-1918 Wmk. Mult. Crown C.A.

G1	½d.	**green**	20	30
G2	1d.	**deep red**	1·00	90
		a bt rose-scarlet ..	90	90
		aa wmk reversed ..	£20	—
		b crimson	90	90
		c carmine-red (thick greyish paper) ..	90	90
		d rose-pink (thick greyish paper) ..	90	90
		e rose-red (thick greyish paper) ..	90	90
G3	2d.	**slate-grey**	60	80
G4	2½d.	**ultramarine**	2·50	2·75
		a bright blue	2·50	3·00
G5	3d.	**purple / yellow** (thick paper) ..	2·00	3·50
		a purple/lemon ..	8·00	—
		b reddish-pur/or buff	2·50	2·75
		ba wmk reversed ..	£40	—
		c sl-pu /or buff ..	2·00	2·75
		d reddish-pur/buff ..	2·00	1·75
		e pur/pl yel ..	2·75	2·00
G6	4d.	**red/yellow** ..	2·75	3·50
		a red/yel-buff ..	2·00	3·50
		b car/pl yellow ..	2·00	3·50
		c lk- red/pl yellow ..	2·00	3·50

G7	5d. **pl olive-green** ..	3·25	5·50	
G8	6d. **dull purple**	4·00	5·50	
G9	1/– **brown-orange** ..	2·00	3·50	
G10	2/– **dp red/blue-green** ..	7·00	8·00	
	a dp red/greenish white	£20	£28	
	b rose-car/emer ..	8·00	£10	
	ba wmk reversed ..	£50	—	
	c lake-red/green ..	8·00	£10	
G11	3/– **jet-blk/bt red** ..	£15	£22	
	a black/dull red ..	£14	£20	
	b sl-black/red ..	£18	£25	
G1/11	**set (11)**	£40	£50	
SPG1/11	**specimen set (11)** ..	£100	‡	

WAR TAX

1917 (Jan.) Overprinted in black at bottom of stamp.

G12	1d. **red**	15	40	
	a overprint double ..	£70	—	
	b TAX omitted ..	—	—	
	c WAR TAX omitted in vert pair with normal	—	—	
	d invert ovpt at top ..	£50	—	
	e ovpt double one invert	£50	—	
	f ovpt double (one invert) in pair with one stamp ovpt inverted ..	£200	—	
G13	3d. **purple/pl yellow** ..	30	50	
	a overprint double ..	£20	—	
	aa ovpt double one invert	—	—	
	b purple/lemon ..	30	50	

Varieties *e* and *f* come from the same sheet where stamps 1 to 5 of all rows are variety *e* and stamp 6 of all rows variety *f*.

1917 (Oct.) Overprint in black at top or middle of stamp.

G14	1d. **red**	15	25	
	a invert ovpt at bottom or centre	£12	—	
	b ovpt omitted in pair with normal ..	£65	—	
	c double ovpt, one at top, one at bottom	£17	—	
	d as 14c but additional ovpt in top margin	£45	—	
	e 14c in vertical pair with normal ..	£85	—	
	ovpt invtd in pair with normal	£110	—	
	g double ovpt at top in pair with normal ..	£85	—	
	h ovpt double	£18	£20	
G15	3d. **purple/lemon** ..	30	50	
	a ovpt double ..	£10	—	
	b ovpt double, one invtd	£15	—	

1918 Overprinted in red at bottom of stamp.

G16	3d. **pur/yel** (ovpt bt red) ..	1·50	2·00	
	a ditto ovpt brn-red ..	1·75	2·25	
	aa ovpt double ..	—	—	

1919 Overprinted in violet at bottom of stamp.

G17	1d. **bt-rose-scarlet** ..	25	30	
	a wmk inverted ..	—	—	
	aa carmine ..	1·25	1·50	
	b WAR omitted ..	£45	—	
	bb crimson	3·00	—	

	c overprint double ..	8·00	—	
	d ovpt double in pair with normal ..	£45	—	
	e triple overprint ..	—	—	

WAR

TAX

1918 Overprinted in black.

G18	1d. **bt rose-scarlet** ..	35	60	
	a wmk inverted ..	—	—	
	b bright carmine ..	15	25	
G19	3d. **purple/yellow** ..	20	35	
SPG18/19	**specimen set (2)** ..	£40	‡	

1919 Overprinted in red.

G20	3d. **sl-pur/or-buff** ..	30	35	
	a bt reddish brn/or-buff	3·00	—	
SPG20	**specimen (1)**	£25	‡	

W A R
T A X

1919 Overprinted in black.

G21	1d. **bt rose-red** (thick greyish paper) ..	15	25	
	a rose-pink (thick greyish paper) ..	20	25	
G22	3d. **sl-pur/or-buff** ..	70	90	
	a ditto wmk inverted ..	£10	—	
	b ditto wmk reversed ..	£10	—	

W A R

T A X

G23	1d. **red**	20	25	
	a scarlet	20	25	
	b rose-red	20	25	
	c overprint inverted ..	—	—	
G24	3d. **reddish-pur/or-buff** ..	20	30	
	a ditto wmk reversed	5·00	—	
	aa wmk invert and rever	8·00	—	
	b sl-pur/or-buff ..	20	30	
	c ditto wmk inverted	5·00	—	
	d wmk invert and rever	8·00	—	

The bottom two rows of this setting have WAR and TAX approx. 1 mm further apart.

G12/24	**set (13)**	3·50	—	

1921 Wmk. Mult. Script C.A.

G25	¼d. **rose red** (Cactus) ..	15	30	
G26	½d. **green**	45	60	
G27	1d. **carmine red** ..	45	60	
G28	2d. **grey**	75	1·50	
	a slate grey ..	75	1·50	
G29	2½d. **blue**	1·25	3·00	
	a bright blue ..	1·25	2·75	
G30	5d. **bright olive green** ..	3·00	4·75	
G31	6d. **purple**	4·50	7·50	
G32	1/– **orange brown** ..	9·00	£16	
	a dull orange brown ..	9·00	£16	
	b bright orange ..	9·00	£16	
G25/32*a*	**set (8)**	£18	£32	
SP G25/32	**specimen set (8)** ..	£100	‡	

1922/6 Wmk. Mult. Script C.A.

G33	¼d.	**black** (Cactus)	15	20
G34	½d.	**yellow green**	20	30
	a	green	35	45
	b	bright apple green..	90	1·00
G35	1d.	**brown**	70	90
	a	dull brown	60	80
G36	1½d.	**scarlet**	1·00	1·25
	a	dull scarlet	1·00	1·25
G37	2d.	**slate grey**	90	1·25
	a	deep slate ..	90	1·25
G38	2½d.	**dull pur/pale yellow**	25	50
	a	reddish pur/lemon..	35	60
	b	deep purple/lemon	40	70
G39	3d.	**ultramarine**	1·00	1·25
	b	bright blue	1·00	1·25
G40	4d.	**red/yellow** ..	1·25	1·50
	a	wmk. reversed	—	—
	b	carmine/pale yellow	2·00	3·00
	c	dp car/pale yellow..	2·00	3·00
G41	5d.	**sage green** ..	1·25	2·00
	a	wmk.invert and rever	—	—
	b	lime green	£12	—
G42	6d.	**purple**	1·50	2·00
	a	wmk. reversed	—	—
G43	1/–	**chestnut brown**	1·50	3·00
	a	orange brown	1·50	3·00
G44	2/–	**deep red/emerald** ..	5.00	6·00
	a	dull red/emerald	5·00	6·00
G33/44a	**set** (12)		£12	£18
SP G33/44	**specimen set** (12)		£90	‡

Wmk. Mult. Crown C.A.

G45	2/–	**red/emerald**	£10	£11
	a	dull lake red/bluish green	£20	—
G46	3/–	**jet black/red**	6·00	8·00
	a	black/red	6·00	8·00
G33/46	**set** (14)		£27	£36
SP G45/46	**specimen set** (2)		£30	‡

1928 Inscribed Postage and Revenue. Wmk. Mult. Script C.A.

G47	½d.	**yellow green**	15	15
	a	green	15	15
G48	1d.	**bistre brown**	15	25
	a	sepia brown	15	25
	b	brown	15	25
G49	1½d.	**scarlet**	25	50
G50	2d.	**deep slate grey**	30	25
	a	slate grey	30	25
G51	2½d.	**purple/lemon yellow**	50	70
	a	reddish pur/lemon yel	50	70
	b	dp pur/pale yellow	1·00	60

G52	3d.	**dull blue**	70	1·00
	a	bright blue ..	50	90
G53	6d.	**purple**	75	1·00
	a	reddish purple ..	90	1·25
G54	1/–	**brown orange** ..	1·50	2·00
G55	2/–	**red/emerald** ..	6·00	8·00
G56	5/–	**dp grn/yellow buff**	£22	£28
	a	bt green/lemon yel	£20	£26
G57	10/–	**slate purple/blue** ..	£30	£35
G47/57	**set** (11)		£55	£70
SP G47/57	**specimen set** (11)	£110	‡

Imperforate Plate Proofs exist in deep blue o n thin card (except 6d. 1/–, 10/–).

1935 (May 6th) Silver Jubilee. Recess. Printers, Waterlow & Son. Wmk. Mult. Script C.A. Perf. 11 x 12. Sheets 6 x 10.

G58	½d.	**black and green** ..	15	20
G59	3d.	**brown and dp blue**..	75	90
G60	6d.	**light blue and olive green**	1·00	1·25
G61	1/–	**slate and purple** ..	3·00	4·00
G58/61	**set** (4)		4·50	6·00
SP G58/61	**specimen set** perf (4)	£23	‡

Number issued—G58, 191,935; G59, 49,697; G60, 47,101 ; G61, 45,831.

1938 (June 18th) -45 Designs, ¼d. to 1/- (Salt Raking); Other Values (Salt Industry). (*recess*) Waterlow and Sons. Perf. 12½ (L). Designs, 2/–, 5/–, 10/– V. Sheets 10 x 6.

1	¼d.	**black**	10	10
2	½d.	**yellow-green** ..	15	15
	a	green (6/11/44) ..	10	10
3	1d.	**chocolate-brown** ..	10	10
	a	red-brown (12/11/45)	10	10
4	1½d.	**scarlet**	10	15
	a	car-red (12/11/45) .	10	15
5	2d.	**grey**	10	10
	a	slate-grey (6/11/44)	10	10
6	2½d.	**orange**	20	20
	a	dp orange (6/11/44)	20	20
7	3d.	**blue**	15	15
	a	bright ult (6/11/44)..	10	10
8	6d.	**dull mauve** ..	1·75	2·00
9	6d.	**sepia** (9/2/45) ..	25	40
10	1/–	**dp bistre** ..	1·25	3·00
11	1/–	**olive-grey** (9/2/45) ..	50	60
12	2/–	**dp rose-carmine** ..	1·25	1·75
	a	bright rose-carmine..	1·00	1·25
13	5/–	**green**	3·50	3·75
	a	blue-green (6/11/44)	3·50	4·00

14 10/– **bright violet** .. 4·00 4·00
    a violet .. .. 4·00 4·00
1/14 **set** (12) £12 £13
SP 1/14 **specimen set** perf (14) £75 ‡

1950 (Aug. 2nd) Designs, ½d., ., 5/–1d (Salt Industry); 1½d. (Caicos Mail); 2d. (Grand Turk); 2½d. (Sponge Diving); 3d. (South Creek); 4d. (Map of Islands); 6d. (Grand Turk Lighthouse); 1/– (Gov. House); 1/6 (Cockburn Harbour); 2/– (Gov. Offices); 10/– (Badge of Dependency). (*recess*) **Waterlow and Sons. Perf. 12¼ (L). Sheets 6 x 10.**

15 ½d. **green** 10 10
16 1d. **red-brown** 15 30
17 1½d. **carmine** 15 25
18 2d. **red-orange** 15 25
19 2½d. **olive-grey** 15 35
20 3d. **bright blue** 15 35
21 4d. **black and rose-red** .. 50 60
22 6d. **black and blue** .. 70 75
23 1/– **black and slate-green** 60 75
24 1/6 **black and scarlet-red** 1·00 1·25
25 2/– **emerald and ult** .. 1·50 2·50
26 5/– **blue and black** .. 3·50 4·00
27 10/– **black and deep lilac** .. 8·00 9·00
15/27 **set** (13) £15 £18

SPECIAL ISSUES

1937 (May 12th) Coronation. As Aden.
S1 ½d. **green** 10 10
S2 2d. **slate** 15 20

S3 3d. **blue** 25 30
SP S1/3 **specimen set** perf (3) £13 ‡

1946 (Nov. 4th) Victory. As Aden.
S4 2d. **black** 10 10
S5 3d. **dp blue** 15 15
SP S4/5 **specimen set** perf (2) £18 ‡

1948 (Sept. 13th) Silver Wedding. As Aden.
S6 1d. **chestnut-brown** .. 10 10
S7 10/– **dull purple** .. .. 4·50 8·00

1948 (Dec. 14th) 100th Anniversary of Separation from Bahamas. Designs, ½d., 2d. (Badge of Colony); 3d. (Blue Ensign); 6d. (Map of Islands); Other Values (Portraits of Victoria and George VI). (*recess*) **Waterlow and Sons. Perf. 12¼ (L). Designs, ½d., 2d. V. Sheets 10 x 6 or 6 x 10.**

S8 ½d. **grey-green** 10 15
S9 2d. **carmine-red** .. 25 25
S10 3d. **dull blue** 30 40
S11 6d. **purple-violet** .. 40 50
S12 2/– **black and blue** .. 75 1·00
S13 5/– **blk and dp emerald** 3·00 3·50
S14 10/– **blk and choc-brown** 5·00 7·00
S8/14 **set** (7) .. .. 9·00 £12

1949 (Oct. 10th) U.P.U. As Aden.
S15 2½d. **red-orange** 10 20
S16 3d. **indigo** 25 35
S17 6d. **dull brown** 40 50
S18 1/– **sage-green** 65 80
S15/18 **set** (4) .. .. 1·25 1·75

R

VIRGIN ISLANDS

The islands, including St. Thomas and St. John which later passed into Danish possession, were originally settled by Great Britain in 1666.

Following the use of other handstamps or manuscript marks, Crowned Circle PAID Franks were registered at the G.P.O. in London on December 15th, 1842 and on June 21st, 1854 and were thereafter struck in red to indicate prepayment of postage on overseas letters (See Introduction).

From May, 1858 to March 1860 contemporary G.B. stamps were in use and were cancelled with "A 13" in a transverse oval of horizontal bars.

The Crowned Circle Franks were again used from April 1st, 1860 until the first Virgin Islands stamps were issued.

See also under Leeward Islands.

1842-66 PAID Franks.   *On Cover*
VF1 **(1842)**	..	£1250
VF2 **(1854)**	..	£1500

1858-60 Stamps of Great Britain identified by their Catalogue Nos. after prefix 'VI'

Used at Tortola: 'A13'
VI V39	1d. **rose-red**	..	..
VI V44	4d. **rose** ..	..	..
VI V45	6d. **lilac** ..	..	..
VI V47	1/– **green**	..	..

1866-68 (*litho*) **Waterlow and Son (per Nissen and Parker) No Wmk. Sheets 5 x 5.**

(a) Perf. 12 (1866).
V1	1d.	**green** (white wove) ..	£22	£25
V2	1d.	**dp green** (white wove)	£22	£25
V3	1d.	**green** (toned)..	.. £20	£25
V4	1d.	**dp green** (toned)	£30	£35
V5	6d.	**rose** (white wove) ..	£45	£50
		a large "V" ..	.. £220	£240
V6	6d.	**dp rose** (white wove)	£50	£65
		a large "V" ..	.. £220	£240
V7	6d.	**rose** (toned) ..	.. £30	£40
		a large "V" ..	.. £200	£220

(b) Perf. 15 x 12 (1868).
V8	1d.	**green** (toned)..	.. —	—

V5*a*/6*a*/7*a*—The "V" is taller than the other letters in "VIRGIN" and has a serif at the top of the right stroke (Row 2/1).

Stamps of this and subsequent unwatermarked issues may be found showing portions of the papermakers watermark.

Engraved Die Proofs exist in several colours on hard white wove paper and on white card.

Proofs from the Litho stone of the 6d. value exist in blue, orange-red and deep rose.

1867-68 As before but Perf. 15. Sheets V9/10 3 x 4 (wide space setting): V11 20 (narrow spaced setting): V12/16 5 x 5: V17/19 5 x 4.
V9	1d.	**yel-grn** (white wove)	£28	£28
V10	1d.	**green** (white wove) ..	£32	£34
V11	1d.	**yellow-green** (toned)	£30	£34
V12	4d.	**lake-red/pale rose** ..	£22	£28
V13	4d.	**lake-red/buff**	£20	£24
V14	4d.	**lake-brown/buff** ..	£20	£24
V15	6d.	**pl rose** (white wove)	£140	£150
V16	6d.	**dull rose** (toned) ..	£90	£95

Die Proofs of the 4d. stamp exist in various colours.

An imperforate Plate Proof exists in the issued colour.

Type I   Type II

There are two types of the 1/– stamp:

Type I has a single outer frame line;

Type II has an outer frame of two thin lines close together.

		Type I		Type II	
1/–	**blk and rose-car**				
V17	on white wove paper	£60	£80	£95	£110
	a long tailed "S" ..	£125	£145	£200	£225
V18	on toned paper ..	£60	£80	£95	£110
	a long tailed "S" ..	£125	£145	£200	£225
V19	on blued paper ..	—	—	£120	£180
	a long tailed "S" ..	—	—	£275	£300

(See also Nos. V45/46.)

Type III   Type IV

1867-68 As Nos. V17/19 but with coloured bands along the perforation gutters, frequently obscuring the outer frame lines. Marginal stamps may be found with the perforations outside the coloured band.

(a) Type III (two outer frame lines).

V20	1/– **blk and crim** (white wove)	£28	£34
	a long tailed "S"	£75	£85
	b centre omitted .. £20000		—
V21	1/– **blk and crim** (toned)	£28	£34
	a long tailed 'S'	£75	£85
V22	1/– **blk and crim** (blued)	£250	£300
	a long tailed "S"	£450	£500

(b) Type IV (two outer frame lines, and additional intermediate frame).

V23	1/– **blk and rose-car** (white wove)	£30	£35
V24	1/– **blk and rose-car** (toned)	£30	£35

V17a/22a—The second "S" in "ISLANDS" has an elongated lower loop (Row 3/1).

V20b—Only seven copies of this error are known, and it is uncertain whether it was actually issued or came from a proof sheet.

1879 (litho) **De La Rue (from the Waterlow Die). Wmk. Crown CC (sideways). Perf. 14. Sheets 6 x 4.**

V25	1d.	**green**	£30	£30
		a no wmk.	—	—
V26	1d.	**yellow-green** ..	£55	£55
		a wmk. upright ..	£28	£32

Imperf Plate Proofs are known on white glazed paper. The stamps were actually supplied in February, 1877.

Number printed—6,504.

See Introduction for details of Dies I and II.

1879-84 (Typo) **De La Rue (Die I). Perf. 14. Sheets 6 x 10.**

(a) Wmk. Crown CC.

V27	1d.	**emerald-green** ('80)	£20	£22
V28	2½d.	**red-brown** ('79) ..	£30	£34
		a imperf (pair) ..	—	—

(b) Wmk. Crown CA (1883).

V29	½d.	**yellow-buff**	£28	£32
V30	½d.	**yellow-green** ..	3·00	5·00
		a imperf (pair) ..	—	—
V31	½d.	**dull blue-green** ..	5·00	8·00
V32	1d.	**pale rose** ..	9·00	9·00
V33	1d.	**deep rose**	£20	£21
V34	2½d.	**ultramarine** ('84) ..	3·00	5·00
		a imperf (pair) ..	—	—

Numbers printed—V29, 5,000; V30/31, 24,610; V32/33, 19,860; V34, 5,040 (?)

1887-89 (litho) **De La Rue (from the Waterlow Die). Wmk. Crown CA. Perf. 14. Sheets 1d. and 6d. – 6 x 4; 4d. and 1/– – 8 x 3.**

V35	1d.	**red** ('89)	4·00	3·50
V36	1d.	**rose-red** ('89) ..	4·00	3·50
V37	1d.	**rose** ('89)	4·00	6·00
V38	4d.	**chestnut** ..	£12	£12
V39	4d.	**pale chestnut** ..	£12	£12
V40	4d.	**bright chestnut** ..	£14	£14
V41	4d.	**brown-red**	£16	£18
V42	6d.	**lilac** ('88)	£12	£15
V43	6d.	**dull violet** ('88) ..	£12	£15
V44	6d.	**deep violet** ('88) ..	£14	£18
		a long "I"	£50	—
V45	1/–	**sepia** ('89) Type I ..	£24	£26
V46	1/–	**brown** ('89) Type I ..	£240	—
SPV35/46		**specimen set** (4v)	£95	‡

V44a—The "I" is taller than the other letters in "ISLANDS" (Row 1/3).

V46 in light brown is believed to be a colour changeling, not issued in this shade.

V45/46 have the single lined outer frame (See Note above No. V17).

Proofs of the 1/– stamp exist in the issued colour and also in carmine.

Numbers printed—V35/37, 9,840; V38/41, 1,200; V42/44, 4,800; V45/46, 1,200.

1888 (July) Nos. V20/21 handstamped locally "4D" in violet. Sheets 5 x 4.

V47	4d. on 1/–	**blk and crim** (white wove)	£55	£68
		a long tailed "S"	£120	£140
		b surcharge double ..	—	—
		c surcharge inverted ..	—	—
V48	4d. on 1/–	**blk and crim** (toned) ..	£55	£68
		a long tailed "S"	£120	£140

V47a/48a—See Note after No. V24.

Number issued—2,500.

From November, 1890 until 1899 only the stamps of Leeward Islands were used in Virgin Islands. During this period a barred "A 91" canceller was in use at Tortola; but it should be noted that a similar numbered canceller was in use at Southsea (Hampshire) from 21.10.81 to 20.9.93.

The following issues were in concurrent use with Leeward Island stamps until June, 1956.

1899 (recess) **De La Rue. Wmk. Crown CA.
Perf. 14. Sheets 120 – two panes, each 6 x 10.**

V49	½d.	**yellow-green**	40	80
	a	"HALFPFNNY"	£40	£45
	b	"HALFPENNY"	£40	£45
	c	imperf between		
		horizontal pair	—	—
V50	1d.	**dull brick red**	3·00	3·00
V51	1d.	**deep brick red**	3·50	3·50
	a	imperf between		
		stamp and margin	£80	—
V52	2½d.	**ultramarine**	6·00	8·00
V53	4d.	**brown**	6·00	8·00
	a	"FOUR PENCF"	£500	£550
V54	6d.	**dull violet**	4·50	6·00
V55	7d.	**deep green**	6·00	7·00
V56	1/–	**brown-yellow**	£12	£14
V57	5/–	**indigo**	£40	£50
V49/57		**set (8v)**	£75	£90
SPV49/57		**specimen set (8v)**	£80	‡

V49a (Row 10/1), V49b (Row 8/2) (1,006 of each) and V53a (298)—These varieties were confined to the first printing; and were corrected in April 1899 after the Crown Agents' attention had been drawn to them by Whitfield King & Co. of Ipswich.

Although printed mono-colour the denominations of this issue were added at a second operation.

Colour Trials of the ½d. exist in a variety of colours.

All stamps from E1 to G58 are (typo) **De La Rue. Perf. 14 unless otherwise indicated.**

**1904 (June 1) Wmk. Multiple Crown CA.
Sheets 120 – two panes, each 6 x 10.**

E1	½d.	**dl purple and green**	30	40
E2	1d.	**dl purple and scarlet**	60	80
E3	2d.	**dl purple and ochre**	4·00	6·00
E4	2½d.	**dl purple and ult**	3·00	4·00
E5	3d.	**dl purple and black**	3·50	5·00
E6	6d.	**dl purple and brown**	4·00	6·00
E7	1/–	**green and scarlet**	6·00	8·00
E8	2/6	**green and black**	£20	£22
E9	5/–	**green and blue**	£40	£50
E1/9		**set (9v)**	£75	£95
SPE1/9		**specimen set (9v)**	£90	‡

**1913-21 As before but Head of King George V.
G1-10 O; G11-15 C.**

(a) Wmk. Multiple Crown CA.

G1	½d.	**green**	30	50
G2	½d.	**blue-green** ('16)	60	80
	a	thin "1" in fraction	£25	—
G3	½d.	**blue-grn and dp grn**		
		('19)	40	70
G4	1d.	**deep red**	3·00	4·00
G5	1d.	**dp red and carmine**	3·00	4·00
G6	1d.	**scarlet** ('17)	2·00	3·00
G7	1d.	**rose-carmine** ('19)	£14	5·00
G8	2d.	**grey**	2·00	4·00
G9	2d.	**slate-grey** ('19)	3·00	4·00
G10	2½d.	**bright blue**	2·00	3·50
G11	3d.	**purple/yellow**	2·00	3·00
G12	6d.	**dl and bt purple**	1·50	3·50
G13	1/–	**black/green**	2·75	4·00
G14	2/6	**black and red/blue**	£12	£16
G15	5/–	**grn and red/yel**	£32	£38
G1/15		**set (9v)**	£52	£70
SPG1/15		**specimen set (9v)**	£85	‡

(b) Wmk. Multiple Script CA (1921).

G16	½d.	**green**	25	50
G17	½d.	**myrtle green**	30	60
G18	1d.	**scar and dp car**	75	1·10
G19	1d.	**rosine and dp car**	85	1·50
G16/19		**set (2v)**	1·00	2·00
SPG16/19		**specimen set (2v)**	£30	‡

G2a—The "1" in the fraction is very thin on Row 1/3 (that on Row 1/4 is somewhat thicker than normal).

1917 (Oct. 26th)-19 War Tax Nos. G4/7 and G11 overprinted "WAR   STAMP" in black sans serif letters in London.

G20	1d.	**carmine**	85	2·00
G21	1d.	**pale red/bluish**	25	35
G22	1d.	**scarlet**	25	80
G23	3d.	**purple/yellow**	25	1·00
	a	on lemon	1·75	3·00
	b	on pale yellow	1·20	2·00
	c	wmk inverted	£25	—
SPG20/23		**specimen set (2v)**	£35	‡

**1922-28 G24-30 and G49-G58 C; G31-48 O.
Sheets 120 – two panes, each 6 x 10.**

(a) Wmk. Multiple Crown CA.

G24	3d.	**pl dl pur/pl yel**	25	70
G25	3d.	**purple/buff**	30	75
G26	3d.	**dl purple/yellow**	35	80
G27	1/–	**grey-blk/bt grn**	85	2·50
	a	on emerald	1·25	2·75
G28	1/–	**black/green**	1·50	3·00
G29	2/6	**black and red/blue**	3·00	4·50
G30	5/–	**grn and red/pl yel**	£20	£28
G24/30		**set (4v)**	£24	£34
SPG24/30		**specimen set (4v)**	£40	‡

(b) Wmk. Multiple Script CA.

G31	½d.	**dull green**	10	20
G32	½d.	**blue-green** ..	15	25
G33	1d.	**rose-red**	15	35
G34	1d.	**rose-carmine** ..	20	45
G35	1d.	**reddish violet** ('27)	75	1·50
G36	1d.	**reddish lilac** ..	1·00	1·75
G37	1d.	**scarlet** ('29) ..	75	1·00
G38	1½d.	**rose-red** ('27) ..	1·50	2·50
G39	1½d.	**rosine**	2·00	3·00
G40	1½d.	**brown** ('28) ..	1·50	2·00
G41	2d.	**grey**	50	75
G42	2d.	**slate-grey** ..	75	1·00
G43	2d.	**deep slate** ..	75	1·00
G44	2d.	**brownish grey** ..	1·00	1·25
G45	2½d.	**pale bright blue** ..	1·50	3·00
G46	2½d.	**dull orange** ('23) ..	1·00	1·00
G47	2½d.	**dull blue** ('27) ..	1·50	3·00
G48	3d.	**purple/pl yellow** ..	60	1·00
		a on golden yellow	1·25	1·50
		b on yellow buff ..	1·50	2·00
G49	5d.	**dl purple and olive**	3·50	8·00
G50	5d.	**pl dl purple and ol**	4·00	8·00
G51	6d.	**dl and bt purple** ..	75	2·00
G52	6d.	**reddish pur and pur**	1·00	2·00
G53	1/–	**grey-black/emerald**	1·50	2·00
		a on green	2·00	2·25
G54	1/–	**black/emerald** ..	1·50	2·00
G55	2/6	**black and red/blue**	4·50	8·00
G56	5/–	**dp grn and red/lem**	£12	£16
G57	5/–	**pl grn and red/lem yellow**	£14	£18
G58	5/–	**grn and red/pl yel**..	£14	£18
G31/58		**set** (15v)	£28	£45
SPG31/58		**specimen set** (15v)	£95	‡

1935 (May 6th) **Silver Jubilee** (*recess*) **Waterlow and Sons. Wmk. Multiple Script CA. Perf. 11 x 12. Sheets 6 x 10.**

G59	1d.	**blue and scarlet** ..	10	20
G60	1½d.	**ult and grey** ..	15	30
G61	2½d.	**brown and blue** ..	45	50
G62	1/–	**slate and purple** ..	1·50	2·25
G59/62		**set** (4v)	2·00	3·00
SPG59/62		**specimen set** (4v)	£26	‡

Remainders were withdrawn on December 31st., 1935.

1938-47 (Issued 1/8/38 unless indicated other-

wise). Design, Head of King with Badge of Colony in bottom right corner. Printers (*photo*) **Harrison & Sons. Perf. 14 (C). Sheets 8 x 15.**

1	½d.	**green** (*ch*)	5	5
		a green (sub) (2/10/43)	5	5
2	1d.	**scarlet** (*ch*)	5	5
		a scarlet (sub) (2/10/43)	5	5
3	1½d.	**red-chocolate** (*ch*) ..	10	10
		a red-chocolate (sub) (2/10/43) ..	5	5
4	2d.	**pale grey** (*ch*) ..	20	20
		a pale grey (sub) (2/10/43) ..	10	10
5	2½d.	**ultramarine** (*ch*) ..	15	15
		a ult (sub) (2/10/43)..	10	10
6	3d.	**orange** (*ch*)	15	15
		a orange (sub) (2/10/43)	12	15
7	6d.	**purple-violet** (*ch*) ..	25	25
		a purple-violet (sub) (2/10/43) ..	20	20
8	1/–	**brown-olive** (*ch*) ..	40	40
		a brown-olive (sub) (2/8/42) ..	40	40
9	2/6	**sepia** (*ch*)	1·25	1·25
		a sepia (sub) (2/8/42)	1·25	1·50
10	5/–	**dull claret** (*ch*) ..	1·75	2·00
		a dull lake (sub) (2/8/42) ..	2·00	2·00
11	10/–	**blue** (*ch*) (1/12/47) ..	5·00	6·00
12	£1	**black** (*ch*) (1/12/47)..	£12	£16
1/12		**set** (12)	£19	£25
SP 1/12		**specimen set** perf (12)	£70	‡

1952 (April 15th) **Designs, 1c.** (Sombrero Lighthouse) ; **2c., 4c., 8c., 12c.,** $4.80(Maps of Various Islands) ; **3c., 5c.** (Sheep and Cattle Scenes) ; **24c.** (Presidency Badge) ; **60c.,** $1.20, $2.40 (Seascapes). **Printers** (*recess*) **De La Rue. Perf.** 12½ x 13 (C). **Designs, 1c., 24c. V. Sheets 10 x 5 or 5 x 10.**

13	1c.	**black**	5	5
		a re-entry	5·00	5·00
14	2c.	**dp green**	10	10
15	3c.	**blk and sepia-brn** ..	5	5
16	4c.	**carmine-red** ..	10	10
17	5c.	**claret and black** ..	10	10
18	8c.	**blue**	15	15
19	12c.	**violet**	20	25
20	24c.	**sepia**	30	40
21	60c.	**sage-green and blue**	75	1·25
22	$1.20	**black and blue** ..	2·50	3·00
23	$2.40	**dp grn and red-brn**	4·00	5·00
24	$4.80	**dp blue and rose-car**	8·00	£11
13/24		**set** (12)	£14	£21

No. 13*a* The re-entry consists of a doubling of the lines and lettering below lighthouse on Row 5/5

SPECIAL ISSUES

1937 (May 12th) Coronation. As Aden, but Printers, Bradbury, Wilkinson. Perf. 11 x 11¾

S1	1d.	carmine-red	5	5
S2	1½d.	light brown	15	15
S3	2½d.	dp ultramarine	40	50
SP S1/3		specimen set perf (3)	£12	‡

1946 (Nov. 1st) Victory. As Aden.

S4	1½d.	chestnut-brown	5	5
S5	3d.	yellow-orange	10	10
SP S4/5		specimen set perf (2)	£14	‡

1949 (Jan. 3rd) Silver Wedding. As Aden.

S6	2½d.	ultramarine	10	10
S7	£1	grey-black	7·00	£10

1949 (Oct. 10th) U.P.U. As Aden.

S8	2½d.	dull violet-blue	10	10
S9	3d.	orange-yellow	20	20
S10	6d.	reddish-mauve	35	35
S11	1/–	sage-green	70	80
S8/11		set (4)	1·25	1·40

1951 (Feb. 16th) West Indies University College. (See Antigua).

S12	3c.	black and red-brown	10	20
S13	12c.	black and violet	40	80

1951 (April 2nd) Restoration of Legislative Council, 1950. Design, Map of Islands. Printers (recess) Waterlow & Sons. Perf. 14¾ x 14 (C). Sheets 6 x 10.

S14	6c.	orange	10	15
S15	12c.	purple-violet	20	30
S16	24c.	brown-olive	40	45
S17	$1.20	claret	1·85	2·25
S14/17		set (4)	2·50	3·00

ZANZIBAR

1936-52 Perf. 14. Wmk. Mult. Script CA. Sheets—10 x 10 (Small); 12 x 5 or 5 x 12 (Large).

X1	5c. green	5	5
X2	10c. black	5	5
X3	15c. red	5	5
X4	20c. brown-orange ..	5	5
X5	25c. purple/yellow ..	5	10
X6	30c. deep ultramarine ..	5	5
X7	40c. sepia-brown ..	10	5
X8	50c. lake	10	5
X9	1/– green	15	10
X10	2/– slate	30	30
X11	5/– scarlet	1·75	1·50
X12	7/6 blue	3·25	3·00
X13	10/– green and brown ..	2·30	2·00
X1/13	set (13)	—	—
	perf. spec. set ..	£25	‡

1946-51 Design, Portrait of Sultan Kalif bin Harub. Printers (recess) De La Rue. Perf. 14 x 13½ (C). Sheets 10 x 10.

1	5c. green (19/6/47) ..	10	10
2	10c. black (19/6/47) ..	10	10
3	15c. car-red (24/5/51) ..	15	15
4	20c. brn-orange (15/11/46)	15	15
5	25c. pur/yel (22/3/48) ..	20	20
6	30c. dp ult (19/6/47) ..	20	20
7	40c. sepia-brn (24/5/51)..	20	20
8	50c. lake (15/11/46) ..	25	25

SPECIAL ISSUES

1944 (Nov. 20th) Bicentenary of Al-Busaid

Dynasty. Printers (recess) De La Rue. Perf. 14 (L). Sheets 10 x 10.

S1	10c. ultramarine	..	10	10
S2	20c. brick-red	.. ..	10	10
S3	50c. grey-green	.. ..	10	10
S4	1/– dp purple-slate	..	10	10
S1/4	set (4)	.. ..	35	35
SPS1/4	spec. set (perf.) (5v)	£40	‡

1946 (Nov. 11th) Victory. Nos. 2 and 6 overprinted in red. Perf. 14 x 13½ (C).

S5	10c. black	5	10
S6	30c. ultramarine ..	5	10
SPS5/6	specimen pair ..	£25	‡

1949 (Jan. 10th) Silver Wedding. As Aden.

S7	20c. orange	10	10
S8	10/– chocolate	2·50	3·00

1949 (Oct. 10th) U.P.U. As Aden.

S9	20c. red-orange	10	15
S10	30c. indigo	10	20
S11	50c. reddish-mauve ..	15	25
S12	1/– quartz-green ..	20	30
S9/12	set (4)	50	85

POSTAGE DUE STAMPS

1946-7 Design, Value on Unshaded Background. Printers (typo) De La Rue. Perf. 13¾ x 14 (C). Sheets 10 x 10.

PD1	5c. purple-violet (/46)..	10	10
PD2	10c. crimson-red ..	10	15
PD3	20c. myrtle-green ..	15	20
PD4	30c. chocolate-brown ..	15	20
PD5	40c. dull ultramarine ..	15	20
PD6	1/– slate-green ..	40	50
PD1/6	set (6)	1·00	1·25
SPPD1/6	spec. set (perf.) (5v)	£22	—

Apart from shade differences (which are considerable) these stamps can be distinguished from those issued in 1936 (except 40c., which differs in shade only) by the rough paper on which they are printed.

ZULULAND

The Zulus had established a powerful kingdom before Natal became a British Colony in 1843. Subsequent border disputes culminated in the Zulu War of 1879, and the proclamation of British possession on May 19th 1887. Zululand was later annexed to Natal on December 30th 1897, and from July 1st 1898 used the stamps of that Province.

Type I

1888 (May 1st) – 93 Stamps of Great Britain (Nos. V176/153/180 - 195/169) overprinted in black by De La Rue (Type I).

V1	½d.	vermilion	1·50	2·00
V2	1d.	deep purple (Die II)	4·50	4·50
V3	2d.	green and carmine	6·50	7·50
V4	2½d.	purple/blue	7·50	8·50
V5	3d.	purple/yellow	9·50	£11·50
V6	4d.	green and brown	£10·50	£12·50
V7	5d.	dull purple and blue (Die II) ('93)	£24·50	£24·50
V8	6d.	purple/red	3·50	£13·50
V9	9d.	dull pur and blue	£34	£34
V10	1/-	green	£50	£54
V11	5/-	rose	£140	£150
V1/11		set (11v.)	£275	£300
SPV1/11		specimen set (10v) (No V2)	£275	‡

V1 and V3 are known with forged inverted, overprints and forged postmarks.

Numbers sold—V1, 268,224; V2, 459,776; V3, 31,987; V4, 28,544 V5, 11,949; V6, 20,250; V7, 6,428; V8, 11,405; V9, 3,701; V10, 4,654; V11. 998 (including sales for fiscal use).

Type I　　　　　　Type II

1889-94 Stamps of Natal (Wmk Crown CA Perf. 14) overprinted in black.

(a) With Type II.

V12	½d.	green	£10	£10
	a	overprint double	£425	—
	b	overprint inverted	£475	—
	c	overprint omitted in pair with normal	£1200	£1200
	d	stop omitted	£24	£28

(b) With Type I (Jan. 1894).

V13	6d.	mauve	£21	£21
SPV13		specimen	£20	‡

Numbers sold—V12, 11,245; V13, 6,325.

1894 (Mar.)-96. Typo De La Rue. Wmk Crown CA. Perf. 14. Sheets 120 – two panes, each 6 x 10.

V14	½d.	mauve and green (7/94)	1·00	1·00
V15	1d.	mauve and carmine	3·00	1·00
V16	2½d.	mauve and ultra ('95)	5·00	5·00
V17	3d.	mauve and olive-brn ('95)	7·00	3·00
V18	6d.	mauve and black ('95)	7·00	8·00
V19	1/-	green ('95)	£10	£12
V20	2/6	green and black (2/96)	£29	£29
V21	4/-	green and carmine ('95)	£38	£48
V22	£1	purple/red ('95)	£200	£210
V23	£5	purple and black/red (7/94)	£1400	£500
V14/22		set (9v.)	£275	£300
SPV14/23		specimen set (10v.)	£275	‡

Numbers printed—V14, 424,800; V15, 524,000; V16/18, 100,800 each; V17/19, 50,400 each; V20/21, 12,000 each; V22, 4,200; V23, 1,200.

POSTAL FISCALS

1894-96 Fiscal stamps of Natal (Typo De La Rue. Wmk. Crown CA. Perf. 14. Sheets 240 – four panes, each 6 x 10) overprinted in black (Type I).

F1	1d.	dull mauve	1·50	2·50
F2	1/-	mauve and carmine	£75	£95
F3	5/-	mauve and carmine	£130	£160
F4	9/-	mauve and carmine	£180	£240
F5	£1	green	£380	£350
F6	£5	green and red	£375	£350
F7	£20	green and black	—	—
SPF1		specimen (1d. only)	£20	‡

Only No. F1 was authorised for postal use, but the other values are known postally used.

Numbers sold—F1, 120,224.

Part imperf. varieties exist F1/F7 possibly from proof sheets.

Omnibus Issues

		No. of Stamps	Mint	Used
1935 **Silver Jubilee**		250	£400	£450
1937 **Coronation** ...	...Colonies only ...	135	£12	£13
	Complete	202	£25	£30
1946 **Victory**	...Colonies only ...	90	£5	£6
	Complete	164	£10	£12
1947 **Royal Visit**		26	£1	£1
1948 **Silver Wedding**	...Low values only ...	71	£5	£6
	Complete	138	£400	£425
1948 **Olympic Games**		24	£3	£3
1949 **U.P.U.**	...Colonies only ...	256	£55	£60
	Complete	330	£100	£110
1951 **B.W.I. University**	...Low values only ...	14	£3	£3
	Complete	28	£5	£6
1951 **B.W.I. Constitution**		16	£3	£3
1953 **Coronation** ...	...Colonies only ...	62	£20	£22
	Complete	106	£35	£40
1954 **Royal Visit**		13	£3	£3
1957 **Scout Jamboree**		12	£5	£6
1958 **B.W.I. Federation**		30	£5	£6
1963 **Freedom from Hunger** Colonies only ...		37	£40	£42
1963 **Red Cross** ...	...Colonies only ...	70	£65	£70
1964 **Shakespeare** ...	...Colonies only ...	12	£3	£3
	F.D.C.s	12	—	£5
1965 **I.T.U.**	...Colonies only ...	64	£30	£30
	F.D.C.s	64	—	£35
1965 **I.C.Y.**	...Colonies only ...	62	£15	£18
1966 **Churchill**	...Colonies only ...	132	£50	£50
	F.D.C.s	132	—	£50
1966 **Royal Visit** ...	...Colonies only ...	26	£6	£7
1966 **World Cup** ...	...Colonies only ...	40	£10	£12
1966 **W.H.O.**	...Colonies only ...	44	£12	£13
1967 **UNESCO** ...	...Colonies only ...	81	£25	£30
1968 **Human Rights** ...	..33 Territories ...		£35	£40

We can usually supply from stock at the above prices.

Omnibus Issues—Crown Colonies

Issuing Territories	1935 Silver Jubilee (44)	1937 Coronation (45)	1946 Victory (45)	1948 Silver Wedding (61)	1949 U.P.U. (64)	1951 B.W.I. University (14)	1951 B.W.I. Const. (4)	1953 Coronation (62)	1958 B.W.I. Fed. (10)	1963 F.F.H. (37)	1963 Red Cross (35)	1964 Shakespeare (12)	1965 I.T.U. (32)	1965 I.C.Y. (31)	1966 Churchill (33)	1966 Royal Visit (13)	1966 World Cup (20)	1966 W.H.O. (22)	1967 UNESCO (27)
Aden		×	×	×	×			×		×					×				
Kathiri			×	×	×			×							×				
Qu'aiti			×	×	×			×							×				
S. Arab Fed.										×	×		×	×	×		×	×	×
Antigua	×	×	×	×	×	×		×		×	×	×	×	×	×	×	×	×	×
Ascension	×	×	×	×	×			×	×	×	×		×	×	×	×	×	×	×
Bahamas	×	×	×	×	×	×		×		×	×	×	×	×	×	×	×	×	×
Barbados	×	×	×	×	×	×	×	×	×	×	×	×	×	×	×	×	×	×	×
Basutoland	×	×	×	×	×			×		×	×		×	×	×				
Bechuanaland	×	×	×	×	×			×		×	×		×	×	×				
Bermuda	×	×	×	×	×			×		×	×	×	×	×	×		×	×	×
Br. Ant. Terr.					×			×		×	×		×	×	×				
Br. Guiana	×	×	×	×	×	×	×	×	×	×	×		×	×	×	×	×	×	×
Br. Honduras	×	×	×	×	×	×		×	×	×	×		×	×	×	×	×	×	×
Br. Solomons	×	×	×	×	×			×		×	×		×	×	×				
Brunei	×	×	×	×	×			×		×	×		×	×	×				
Cayman Is.	×	×	×	×	×			×		×	×		×	×	×	×	×	×	×
Ceylon	×	×	×	×	×			×		×	×		×	×	×				
Cyprus	×	×	×	×	×			×		×	×	×	×	×	×	×	×	×	×
Dominica	×	×	×	×	×	×		×		×	×		×	×	×	×	×	×	×
Falkland Is.	×	×	×	×	×			×		×	×	×	×	×	×		×	×	×
Falkland Deps.	×	×	×	×	×			×		×	×		×	×	×		×	×	×
Fiji	×	×	×	×	×			×		×	×		×	×	×				
Gambia	×	×	×	×	×			×		×	×		×	×	×				
Gibraltar	×	×	×	×	×			×		×	×	×	×	×	×		×	×	×
Gilbert/Ellice	×	×	×	×	×			×		×	×	×	×	×	×	×	×	×	×
Gold Coast	×	×	×	×	×			×											
Grenada	×	×	×	×	×	×		×		×	×		×	×	×	×	×	×	×
Hong Kong	×	×	×	×	×			×		×	×	×	×	×	×			×	×
Jamaica	×	×	×	×	×			×		×	×		×	×	×		×	×	×
K.U.T.	×	×	×	×	×			×		×	×		×	×	×				
Leeward Is.	×	×	×	×	×			×		×	×		×	×	×				

Malaya																			
Johore				×	×			×											
Kedah				×	×			×											
Kelantan				×	×			×											
Malacca				×	×			×											
Negri				×	×			×											
Pahang				×	×			×											
Penang				×	×			×											
Perak				×	×			×											
Perlis				×	×			×											
Selangor				×	×			×											
Singapore				×	×			×											
Straits	×	×																	
Trengganu				×	×			×											
Malta	×	×	×	×	×			×		×	×								
Mauritius	×	×	×	×	×			×		×	×		×	×	×				×
Montserrat	×	×	×	×	×	×		×	×	×	×	×	×	×	×	×		×	×
Newfoundland	×	×																	
New Hebrides					×			×		×	×		×	×	×		×	×	×
Nigeria	×	×	×	×	×			×											
N. Borneo				×	×			×		×									
N. Rhodesia	×	×	×	×	×			×											
Nyasaland	×	×	×	×	×			×											
Pitcairn Is.			×	×	×			×		×	×		×	×	×		×	×	×
St. Christopher	×	×	×	×	×	×		×	×		×		×	×	×	×	×	×	×
St. Helena	×	×	×	×	×			×		×	×		×	×	×		×	×	×
St. Lucia	×	×	×	×	×	×	×	×	×	×	×	×	×	×	×	×	×	×	×
St. Vincent	×	×	×	×	×	×	×	×	×	×	×		×		×	×		×	×
Sarawak				×	×			×		×									
Seychelles	×	×	×	×	×			×		×	×		×	×	×		×	×	×
Sierra Leone	×	×	×	×	×			×											
Somaliland	×	×	×	×	×			×											
Swaziland	×	×		×	×			×		×	×		×	×	×				×
Tonga					×					×	×								
Trinidad/Tobago	×	×	×	×	×	×		×	×										
Tristan Da Cunha								×		×	×		×	×	×		×	×	×
Turks/Caicos	×	×	×	×	×			×		×	×	×	×	×	×	×			×
Virgin Is.	×	×	×	×	×	×		×		×	×	×	×	×	×	×			×
Zanzibar			×	×	×					×									
Total Number	4 vals each =176	3 vals each =135	2 vals each =90	2 vals each =122	4 vals each =256	2 vals each =28	4 vals each =16	1 val each =62	3 vals each =30	1 val each =37	2 vals each =70	1 val each =12	2 vals each =64	2 vals each =62	4 vals each =132	2 vals each =26	2 vals each =40	2 vals each =44	3 vals each =81
						*	*		*										

* No Dominion Issues

Omnibus Issues—Dominions and other Commonwealth Territories

Issuing Territories	UNESCO 1967	W.H.O. 1966	1966 World Cup	1966 Royal Visit	Churchill 1966	I.C.Y. 1965	I.T.U. 1965	Shakespeare 1964	Red Cross 1963	F.F.H. 1963	1957 Scout Jamboree	1954 Royal Visit	Coronation 1953	U.P.U. 1949	1948 Olympic Games	1948 Silver Wedding	1947 Royal Visit	Victory 1946	Coronation 1937	1935 Silver Jubilee
(total)	6	3	4	2	11	13	18	2	16	14	4	10	16	16	6	8	6	17	15	19
G.B.			3+3		2+2	2+2	2+2	5+4	3+3	2+2	3		4	4	4	2		2	1	4
Morocco Ag.													4	4	4	2			1	4
Morocco (Sp.)														4	4			2	1	4
Morocco (Fr.)													4	4	4	2			1	4
Tangier											3		4	4	4	2				3
Bahrain														4		2				
Kuwait														4		2				
Muscat														4						
Qatar														4		2				
Aden													1							
Kathiri														4						
Qu'aiti														4						
Australia					3	8	7		1		3	3	3	3				3		3
Bahawalpur														4+4				1 / 3×2		
" Service														4+4				3×2		
Basutoland																	4	4		
Bechuanaland																	4			
Bermuda																				
Br. Guiana																				
Canada																				6
Ceylon																			1	3
Cook Is.																				
Cyprus					3														3	
Fiji																				
Gambia																				
Gibraltar	2	2	5		2	2	2	4	2	2										6
Ghana		4			6	4	4		4	3										
Hyderabad																				
India	5				3	2	2		2	2				4				4		7
Ireland																				

Jamaica									1		2			1		2	4			
K.U.T.									1		4	2		4	4					4
Lesotho																				4
Maldive Is.											7	5								
Malayan Fed.											3									
Malaysia														3						
Malta									1							4				
Nauru	4	4																		
Newfoundland		11																		
New Guinea	2	4																		
New Zealand	3	3	11					5	2			1		1	1	1				
Nigeria											2	3		3	3					3
Niue	3	3	4					2												
Pakistan											2	1		1	2					1
Papua	4	4										1								
Samoa	3		4					2											4	
Sierra Leone											2	3				11				
S. Africa	4×2	5×2	3×2	3×2	1×2		3×2	1				2		2						
S. W. Africa	4	8×2	3×2	3×2	1×2		3×2	5				2								
S. Rhodesia	4	4	4	2			2	1				1		3						
Swaziland			3×2	4												1				
Tokelau Is.								1												
Trinidad-Tobago ...											2				1		4			
Zambia														2	2				2	
Burma			4				6													
Egypt	1																			
Jordan							5													
Palestine							5													
Total Number	74	67	74	26	16	24	74	44	13	12	39	37	13	46	38	40	8	26	12	20
Add Crown Col.	176	135	90	—	122	—	256	62	—	—	37	70	12	64	62	132	26	40	44	81
Grand Total	250	202	164	26	138	24	330	106	13	12	76	107	25	110	100	172	34	66	56	101
				*		*			*	*										

* No Colonial Issues

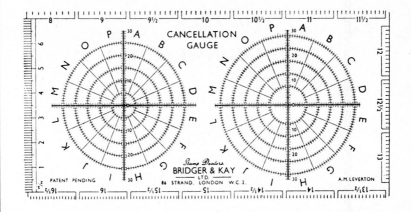

BRIDGER & KAY.

24 PALL MALL LONDON SW1Y SLP

Please complete if you wish

to receive **ALL DETAILS**

regarding **SUPPLEMENTS**

to this 14th Edition

"COMMONWEALTH FIVE REIGNS"

Name...

....

....

....

ORIGINAL ORDER
No.

Registration Fee 50p (Stamps)

**Telephone:
01 839 2153**